Basic College
MATHEMATICS

BASIC COLLEGE MATHEMATICS WITH P.O.W.E.R. LEARNING

ISBN 978–0–07–340624–4
MHID 0–07–340624–4

ISBN 978–0–07–748336–4 (Annotated Instructor's Edition)
MHID 0–07–748336–7

Senior Vice President, Products & Markets: *Kurt L. Strand*
Vice President, General Manager, Products & Markets: *Marty Lange*
Vice President, Content Production & Technology Services: *Kimberly Meriwether David*
Director, Developmental Mathematics: *Dawn R. Bercier*
Director of Development: *Rose Koos*
Director of Digital Content Development: *Nicole Lloyd*
Development Editor: *Liz Recker / Elizabeth O'Brien*
Market Development Manager: *Kim M. Leistner*
Lead Project Manager: *Peggy J. Selle*
Buyer: *Nicole Baumgartner*
Senior Media Project Manager: *Sandra M. Schnee*
Senior Designer: *David W. Hash*
Cover/Interior Designer: *Rokusek Design, Inc.*
Cover Image: *Power button icon © tkemot*
Lead Content Licensing Specialist: *Carrie K. Burger*
Compositor: *Aptara®, Inc.*
Typeface: *10/13 Times New Roman MT Std*
Printer: *R. R. Donnelley*

Library of Congress Cataloging-in-Publication Data

Messersmith, Sherri.
   Basic college mathematics with P.O.W.E.R. learning / Sherri Messersmith, Lawrence Perez, Robert S. Feldman.—1st ed.
      p. cm.
   Includes index.
      ISBN 978–0–07–340624–4 — ISBN 0–07–340624–4 (hard copy : alk. paper) 1. Mathematics–Textbooks. 2. Study skills. I. Perez, Lawrence. II. Feldman, Robert S. (Robert Stephen), 1947- III. Title.

QA37.3.M47 2014
510–dc23
                    2012018150

www.mhhe.com

Basic College
MATHEMATICS

SHERRI MESSERSMITH
College of DuPage

LAWRENCE PEREZ
Saddleback College

ROBERT S. FELDMAN
University of Massachusetts Amherst

With contributions from William C. Mulford, *The McGraw-Hill Companies*

About the Authors

Sherri Messersmith
Professor of Mathematics, College of DuPage

Sherri Messersmith began teaching at the College of DuPage in Glen Ellyn, Illinois in 1994 and has over 25 years of experience teaching many different courses from developmental mathematics through calculus. She earned a Bachelor of Science degree in the Teaching of Mathematics at the University of Illinois at Urbana-Champaign and taught at the high school level for two years. Sherri returned to UIUC and earned a Master of Science in Applied Mathematics and stayed on at the university to teach and coordinate large sections of undergraduate math courses as well as teach in the Summer Bridge program for at-risk students. In addition to the P.O.W.E.R. Math Series, she is the author of a hardcover series of textbooks and has also appeared in videos accompanying several McGraw-Hill texts.

Sherri and her husband are recent empty-nesters and live in suburban Chicago. In her precious free time, she likes to read, cook, and travel; the manuscripts for her books have accompanied her from Spain to Greece and many points in between.

Lawrence Perez
Professor of Mathematics, Saddleback College

Larry Perez has fifteen years of classroom experience teaching math and was the recipient of the 2010 Community College Professor of the Year Award in Orange County, California. He realized early on that students bring to the classroom different levels of attitude, aptitude, and motivation sometimes accompanied by a tremendous fear of taking math. Confronted by this, he developed a passion for engaging students, demanding him to innovate traditional and online pedagogical techniques using architecture created with student feedback as the mechanism of design. He is the creator of the award-winning online learning environment Algebra2go® and has presented his work and methodology at conferences around the country.

Larry is a Veteran of the United States Navy Submarine Force and is a graduate of California State University Fullerton earning degrees in Electrical Engineering and Applied Mathematics. In his spare time he enjoys mountain biking and the great outdoors.

Robert S. Feldman
Dean and Professor of Psychology, University of Massachusetts Amherst

Bob Feldman still remembers those moments of being overwhelmed when he started college at Wesleyan University. "I wondered whether I was up to the challenges that faced me," he recalls, "and although I never would have admitted it then, I really had no idea what it took to be successful at college."

That experience, along with his encounters with many students during his own teaching career, led to a life-long interest in helping students navigate the critical transition that they face at the start of their own college careers. Bob, who went on to receive a doctorate in psychology from the University of Wisconsin-Madison, teaches at the University of Massachusetts Amherst, where he is the Dean of the College of Social and Behavioral Sciences and Professor of Psychology. He also directs a first-year experience course for incoming students.

Bob is a Fellow of both the American Psychological Association and the Association for Psychological Science. He has written more than 200 scientific articles, book chapters, and books, including P.O.W.E.R. Learning: *Strategies for Success in College and Life,* 6e and *Understanding Psychology,* 11e. He is president-elect of the FABBS Foundation, an umbrella group of societies promoting the behavioral and brain sciences.

Bob loves travel, music, and cooking. He and his wife live near the Holyoke mountain range in western Massachusetts.

Table of Contents

This chapter is available online at:
www.connectmath.com and www.mcgrawhillcreate.com

Consistent Integration of Study Skills

In *Basic College Mathematics,* strategies for learning are presented alongside the math content, making it easy for students to learn math *and* study skills at the same time. The P.O.W.E.R. framework aligns with the math learning objectives, providing instructors with a resource that has been consistently integrated throughout the text.

A **STUDY STRATEGIES** feature begins each chapter. Utilizing the P.O.W.E.R. framework, these boxes present steps for mastering the different skills students will use to succeed in their developmental math course. For example, these boxes will contain strategies on time management, taking good notes and, as seen in the sample below, taking a math test.

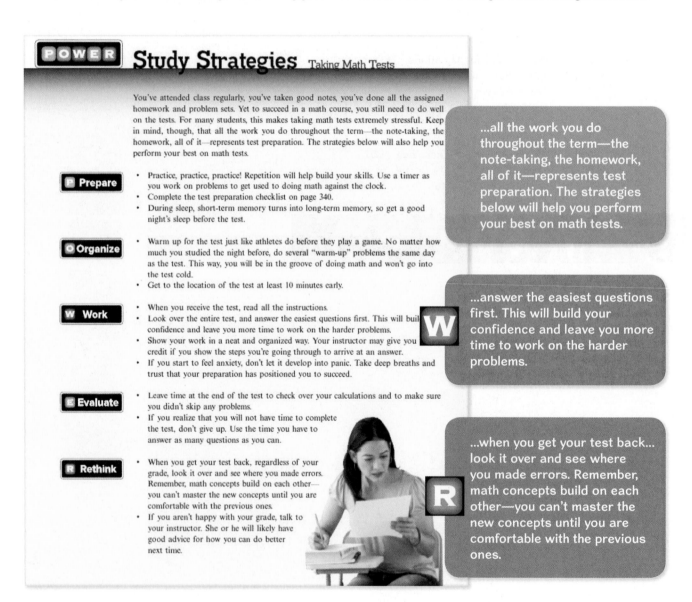

POWER

Study Strategies — Taking Math Tests

You've attended class regularly, you've taken good notes, you've done all the assigned homework and problem sets. Yet to succeed in a math course, you still need to do well on the tests. For many students, this makes taking math tests extremely stressful. Keep in mind, though, that all the work you do throughout the term—the note-taking, the homework, all of it—represents test preparation. The strategies below will also help you perform your best on math tests.

P Prepare
- Practice, practice, practice! Repetition will help build your skills. Use a timer as you work on problems to get used to doing math against the clock.
- Complete the test preparation checklist on page 340.
- During sleep, short-term memory turns into long-term memory, so get a good night's sleep before the test.

O Organize
- Warm up for the test just like athletes do before they play a game. No matter how much you studied the night before, do several "warm-up" problems the same day as the test. This way, you will be in the groove of doing math and won't go into the test cold.
- Get to the location of the test at least 10 minutes early.

W Work
- When you receive the test, read all the instructions.
- Look over the entire test, and answer the easiest questions first. This will build confidence and leave you more time to work on the harder problems.
- Show your work in a neat and organized way. Your instructor may give you credit if you show the steps you're going through to arrive at an answer.
- If you start to feel anxiety, don't let it develop into panic. Take deep breaths and trust that your preparation has positioned you to succeed.

E Evaluate
- Leave time at the end of the test to check over your calculations and to make sure you didn't skip any problems.
- If you realize that you will not have time to complete the test, don't give up. Use the time you have to answer as many questions as you can.

R Rethink
- When you get your test back, regardless of your grade, look it over and see where you made errors. Remember, math concepts build on each other—you can't master the new concepts until you are comfortable with the previous ones.
- If you aren't happy with your grade, talk to your instructor. She or he will likely have good advice for how you can do better next time.

...all the work you do throughout the term—the note-taking, the homework, all of it—represents test preparation. The strategies below will help you perform your best on math tests.

W ...answer the easiest questions first. This will build your confidence and leave you more time to work on the harder problems.

R ...when you get your test back... look it over and see where you made errors. Remember, math concepts build on each other—you can't master the new concepts until you are comfortable with the previous ones.

Chapter 5 POWER Plan

P Prepare

What are your goals for Chapter 5?	How can you accomplish each goal?
1 Be prepared before and during class.	• Don't stay out late the night before, and be sure to set your alarm clock! • Bring a pencil, notebook paper, and textbook to class. • Avoid distractions by turning off your cell phone during class. • Pay attention, take good notes, and ask questions. • Complete your homework on time, and ask questions on problems you do not understand.
2 Understand the homework to the point where you could do it without needing any help or hints.	• Read the directions, and show all of your steps. • Go to the professor's office for help. • Rework homework and quiz problems, and find similar problems for practice.
3 Use the P.O.W.E.R. framework to learn ways to improve the way you take math tests: *Is Anxiety the Hardest Problem on the Test?*	• Read the Study Strategy as it is outlined in the P.O.W.E.R. framework. • Decide which steps you might need to improve. • Complete the emPOWERme that appears before the Chapter Summary.
4 Write your own goal. _____ _____	•_____ _____

What are your objectives for Chapter 5?	How can you accomplish each objective?
1 Learn to read, write, and round decimals.	• Use place value, number lines, and writing a decimal as a fraction or mixed number to help understand what a decimal represents. • The same rounding principles you learned previously still apply to decimals.
2 Learn how to perform basic operations on decimals.	• Write the procedures for adding, subtracting, multiplying, and dividing with decimals in your own words. • Know how to multiply or divide by a power of 10. • Be able to solve applied problems using decimals.
3 Learn to write a fraction as a decimal.	• Understand the two ways to write a fraction as a decimal. One way is to use division, and the other is to write an equivalent fraction with a denominator that is a power of 10. • Know how to compare a decimal and a fraction.
4 Understand how to use measures of central tendency.	• Be able to find a mean, weighted mean, median, and mode. • Know what the different measures represent.
5 Write your own goal. _____ _____	•_____ _____

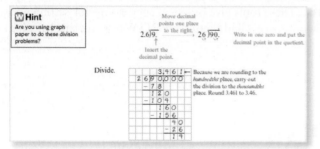

Hint
Are you using graph paper to do these division problems?

Move decimal points one place to the right.

$2.6\overline{)9.}$ → $26\overline{)90.}$

Write in one zero and put the decimal point in the quotient.

Insert the decimal point.

Divide.

```
        3.461
26)90.000
  -78
   120
  -104
    160
   -156
      40
     -26
      14
```

Because we are rounding to the *hundredths* place, carry out the division to the *thousandths* place. Round 3.461 to 3.46.

WORK HINTS provide additional explanation and point out common places where students might go wrong when solving a problem. Along with the ***Be Careful*** boxes, these tools act as a built-in tutor, helping students navigate the material and learn concepts even outside of class.

IN-CLASS EXAMPLES are available only in the Annotated Instructor Edition. These examples offer instructors additional problems to work through in class. In-class example problems align with the Guided Student Notes resource available with this package.

EXAMPLE 3

In-Class Example 3

Write each fraction as a decimal.

a) $\dfrac{3}{100}$ b) $\dfrac{859}{1000}$ c) $\dfrac{273}{10,000}$

Answer: a) 0.03 b) 0.859 c) 0.0273

Write each fraction as a decimal.

a) $\dfrac{9}{100}$ b) $\dfrac{137}{1000}$ c) $\dfrac{421}{10,000}$

Solution

a) Reading the fraction to ourselves will help us determine how to correctly write the decimal.

$\dfrac{9}{100}$ is read as "nine hundredths."

PUTTING IT ALL TOGETHER One of the challenges students struggle with is putting all of the steps they've learned together and *applying* that knowledge to a problem. **Putting It All Together** sections will help students understand the big picture and work through the toughest challenge when solving applications—*problem recognition,* or knowing *when* to use *what* method or thought process. These sections include a summary and several problems that help students reason through a problem using conversational, yet mathematically correct, language.

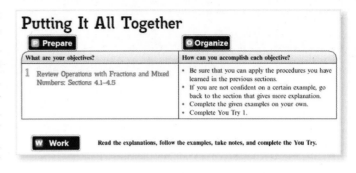

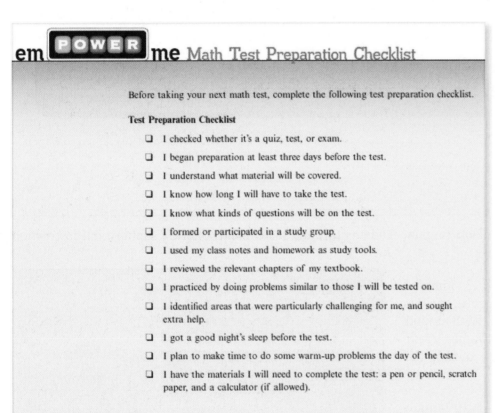

em**POWER**me boxes circle back to the opening **Study Strategies** and give students a checklist to evaluate how well they followed through on all of the positive habits recommended to successfully master a skill.

Instructor POWER Tool Kit

The Messersmith/Perez/Feldman Series offers instructors a robust digital resources package to help you with all of your teaching needs.

Resources in your P.O.W.E.R. tool kit include:

- Connect Hosted by Aleks*
- ALEKS 360*
- Instructor Solutions Manual
- Student Solutions Manual
- Guided Student Notes*
- Classroom Worksheets*

- Instructor Resource Manual
- Test Bank Files
- Computerized Test Bank
- Faculty Development and Digital Training*
- PowerPoint Presentations
- Extensive Video Package*

*Details of these resources are included in the following pages!

Videos

Hundreds of videos are available to guide students through the content, offering support and instruction even outside your classroom.

Exercise Videos – These 3–5-minute clips show students how to solve various exercises from the textbook. With around thirty videos for every chapter, your students are supported even outside the classroom.

Lecture Videos – These 5–10-minute videos walk students through key learning objectives and problems from the textbook.

P.O.W.E.R. Videos – These engaging segments guide students through the P.O.W.E.R. framework and the study skills for each chapter.

Faculty Development and Digital Training

McGraw-Hill is excited to partner with our customers to ensure success in the classroom with our course solutions.

Looking for ways to be more effective in the classroom? Interested in learning how to integrate student success skills in your developmental math courses?

Workshops are available on these topics for anyone using or considering the Messersmith/Perez/Feldman P.O.W.E.R. Math Series. Led by the authors, contributors, and McGraw-Hill P.O.W.E.R. Learning consultants, each workshop is tailored to the needs of individual campuses or programs.

New to McGraw-Hill Digital Solutions? Need help setting up your course, using reports, and building assignments?

No need to wait for that big group training session during faculty development week. The McGraw-Hill Digital Implementation Team is a select group of advisors and experts in Connect Hosted by ALEKS™. The Digital Implementation Team will work one-on-one with each instructor to make sure you are trained on the program and have everything you need to ensure a good experience for you and your students.

Are you redesigning a course or expanding your use of technology? Are you interested in getting ideas from other instructors who have used ALEKS™ or Connect Hosted by ALEKS in their courses?

Digital Faculty Consultants (DFCs) are instructors who have effectively incorporated technology such as ALEKS and Connect Hosted by ALEKS Corp. in their courses. Discuss goals and best practices and improve outcomes in your course through peer-to-peer interaction and idea sharing.

Contact your local representative for more information about any of the faculty development, training, and support opportunities through McGraw-Hill. http://catalogs.mhhe.com/mhhe/findRep.do

Need a tool to help your students take better notes?

GUIDED STUDENT NOTES

By taking advantage of Guided Student Notes, your students will have more time to learn the material and participate in solving in-class problems while, at the same time, becoming better note takers. Ample examples are included for appropriate coverage of a topic that will not overwhelm students. Use them as they are or download and edit the Guided Student Notes according to your teaching style.

Guided Student Notes
Messersmith – Introductory Algebra

Name:_____

5.1a Basic Rules of Exponents
Product Rule and Power Rule

Base   **Exponent**

Identify the base and the exponent in each expression and evaluate.

1) 3^4 5) $(-5)^3$

2) $(-3)^4$ 6) $2(5)^2$

3) -3^4 7) $4a(-3)^2$

4) -5^2 8) $-(2)^4$

Product Rule   **Power Rule**

Find each product.   *Simplify using the power*

9) $5^2 \cdot 5$ 13) $\left(4^8\right)^3$

10) $y^4 y^9$ 14) $\left(m^2\right)^5$

11) $-4x^5 \cdot \left(-10x^8\right)$ 15) $\left(q^8\right)^7$

12) $d \cdot d^7 \cdot d^4$ 16) $\left(df^2\right)^3$

1

Guided Student Notes
Messersmith – Introductory Algebra

Name:_____

5.1b Basic Rules of Exponents
Combining the Rules

How to Solve Exponent Problems That Require Several Rules

Simplify each expression. Some problems may require a combination of both product and power rules.

1) $(4f)^2 (2f)^3$ 4) $-3\left(4a^2b^3\right)^2$

2) $(2x)^3 (2x)^2$ 5) $\left(\dfrac{3d^2}{6}\right)^3$

3) $2x\left(4x^2t^4\right)^2$ 6) $\dfrac{\left(12y^3\right)^2}{\left(4z^{10}\right)^3}$

1

Develop your students' basic skills with a ready-made resource.

WORKSHEETS FOR STUDENT AND INSTRUCTOR USE

Worksheets for every section are available as an instructor supplement. These author-created worksheets provide a quick, engaging way for students to work on key concepts. They save instructors from having to create their own supplemental material and address potential stumbling blocks in student understanding. Classroom tested and easy to implement, they are also a great resource for standardizing instruction across a mathematics department.

The worksheets fall into three categories: Worksheets to Improve Basic Skills; Worksheets to Help Teach New Concepts; and Worksheets to Tie Concepts Together.

The worksheets are available in an instructor edition, with answers, and in a student edition, without answers.

Worksheet 5E
Messersmith – Introductory Algebra

Perform the indicated operations and simplify.

1) $\frac{1}{3} + \frac{2}{5}$

3) $\frac{4}{7} + \left(-\frac{7}{8}\right)$

5) $-\frac{5}{9} + \left(-\frac{1}{3}\right)$

7) $\frac{3}{4} + \frac{1}{6}$

Worksheet 3C
Messersmith – Beginning Algebra

Name: Answer Key

Find 2 numbers that...

MULTIPLY TO	and ADD TO	ANSWER
27	6	9 and 3
72	18	12 and 6
24	11	8 and 3
4	3	1 and 4
10	7	5 and 2
121	22	11 and 11
54	3	9 and 6
54	29	27 and 2
16	10	8 and 2
30	17	15 and 2
9	6	3 and 3
8	2	4 and 2
21	10	7 and 3
60	19	15 and 4
56	15	8 and 7
28	3	4 and 7
72	6	12 and 6
100	25	20 and 5
40	6	4 and 10
11	12	11 and 1
20	12	10 and 2
35	2	7 and 5
77	18	11 and 7
108	21	12 and 9
3	2	3 and 1

Connect Math Hosted by ALEKS Corp.

Built By Today's Educators, For Today's Students

Fewer clicks means more time for you…

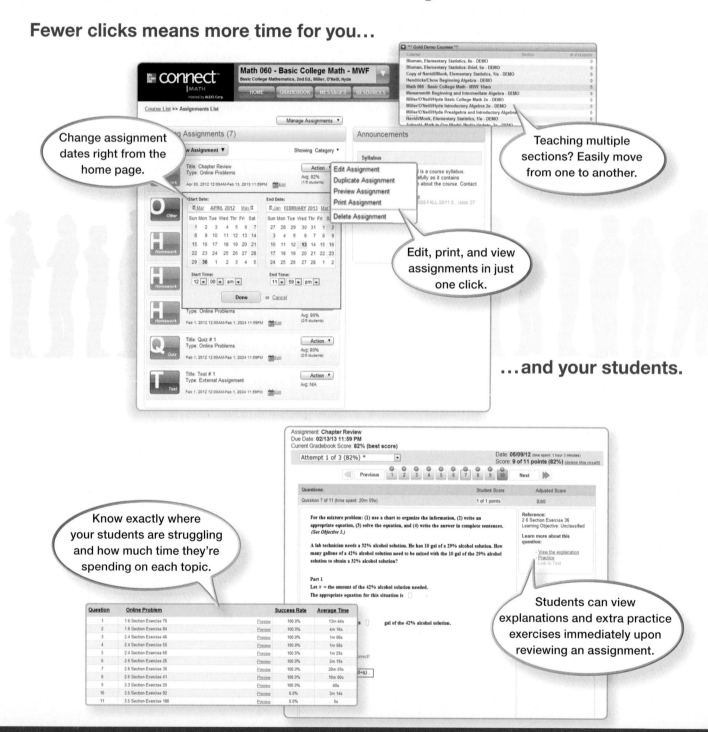

Change assignment dates right from the home page.

Teaching multiple sections? Easily move from one to another.

Edit, print, and view assignments in just one click.

…and your students.

Know exactly where your students are struggling and how much time they're spending on each topic.

Students can view explanations and extra practice exercises immediately upon reviewing an assignment.

Quality Content For Today's Online Learners

Online Exercises were carefully selected and developed to provide a seamless transition from textbook to technology.

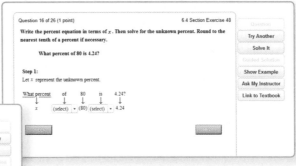

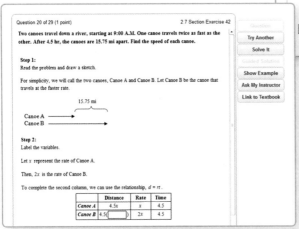

For consistency, the guided solutions match the style and voice of the original text as though the author is guiding the students through the problems.

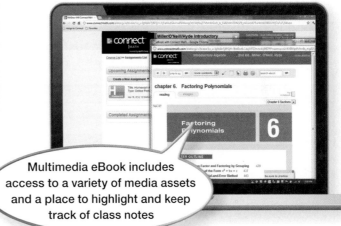

Multimedia eBook includes access to a variety of media assets and a place to highlight and keep track of class notes

ALEKS Corporation's experience with algorithm development ensures a commitment to accuracy and a meaningful experience for students to demonstrate their understanding with a focus towards online learning.

The ALEKS® Initial Assessment is an artificially intelligent (AI), diagnostic assessment that identifies precisely what a student knows. Instructors can then use this information to make more informed decisions on what topics to cover in more detail with the class.

ALEKS is a registered trademark of ALEKS Corporation.

www.successinmath.com

Hosted by **ALEKS Corp.**

ALEKS®

ALEKS is a unique, online program that significantly raises student proficiency and success rates in mathematics, while reducing faculty workload and office-hour lines. ALEKS uses artificial intelligence and adaptive questioning to assess precisely a student's knowledge, and deliver individualized learning tailored to the student's needs. With a comprehensive library of math courses, ALEKS delivers an unparalleled adaptive learning system that has helped millions of students achieve math success.

ALEKS Delivers a Unique Math Experience:

- **Research-Based, Artificial Intelligence** precisely measures each student's knowledge
- **Individualized Learning** presents the exact topics each student is most **ready to learn**
- **Adaptive, Open-Response Environment** includes comprehensive tutorials and resources
- **Detailed, Automated Reports** track student and class progress toward course mastery
- **Course Management Tools** include textbook integration, custom features, and more

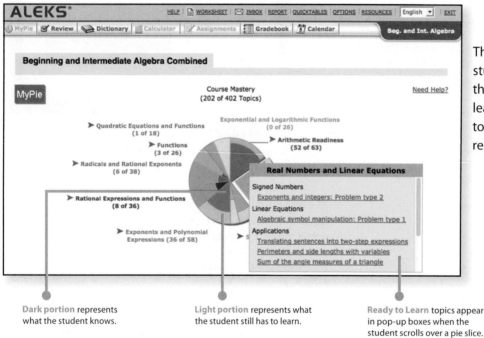

The ALEKS Pie summarizes a student's current knowledge, then delivers an individualized learning path with the exact topics the student is most ready to learn.

Dark portion represents what the student knows.

Light portion represents what the student still has to learn.

Ready to Learn topics appear in pop-up boxes when the student scrolls over a pie slice.

"My experience with ALEKS has been effective, efficient, and eloquent. **Our students' pass rates improved from 49 percent to 82 percent with ALEKS.** We also saw student retention rates increase by 12% in the next course. Students feel empowered as they guide their own learning through ALEKS."

—Professor Eden Donahou, *Seminole State College of Florida*

To learn more about ALEKS, please visit: **www.aleks.com/highered/math**

ALEKS is a registered trademark of ALEKS Corporation.

ALEKS® Prep Products

ALEKS Prep products focus on prerequisite and introductory material, and can be used during the first six weeks of the term to ensure student success in math courses ranging from Beginning Algebra through Calculus. ALEKS Prep quickly fills gaps in prerequisite knowledge by assessing precisely each student's preparedness and delivering individualized instruction on the exact topics students are most ready to learn. As a result, instructors can focus on core course concepts and see improved student performance with fewer drops.

> **"**ALEKS is wonderful. It is a professional product that takes very little time as an instructor to administer. Many of our students have taken Calculus in high school, but they have forgotten important algebra skills. ALEKS gives our students an opportunity to review these important skills.**"**
>
> —**Professor Edward E. Allen**, *Wake Forest University*

 **A Total Course Solution**

With *eBook* Integration

A cost-effective total course solution: fully integrated, interactive eBook combined with the power of ALEKS adaptive learning and assessment.

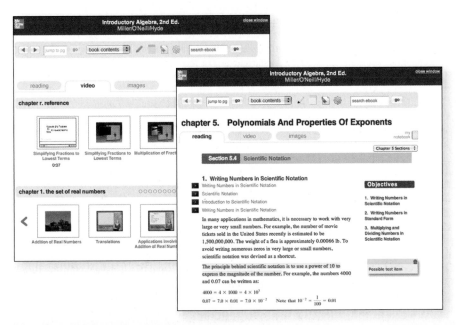

Students can easily access the full eBook content, multimedia resources, and their notes from within their ALEKS Student Accounts.

To learn more about ALEKS, please visit: **www.aleks.com/highered/math**

Acknowledgments

Manuscript Reviewers and Focus Group Participants

Thank you to all of the dedicated instructors who reviewed manuscript, participated in focus groups, and provided thoughtful feedback throughout the development of the *P.O.W.E.R.* series.

Darla Aguilar, *Pima Community College;* Scott Albert, *College of DuPage;* Bhagirathi Anand, *Long Beach City College;* Raul Arana, *Lee College;* Jan Archibald, *Ventura College;* Morgan Arnold, *Central Georgia Technical College;* Christy Babu, *Laredo Community College;* Michele Bach, *Kansas City Kansas Community College;* Kelly Bails, *Parkland College;* Vince Bander, *Pierce College, Pullallup;* Kim Banks, *Florence Darlington Technical College;* Michael Bartlett, *University of Wisconsin—Marinette;* Sarah Baxter, *Gloucester County College;* Michelle Beard, *Ventura College;* Annette Benbow, *Tarrant County College, Northwest;* Abraham Biggs, *Broward College;* Leslie Bolinger Horton, *Quinsigamond Community College;* Jessica Bosworth, *Nassau Community College;* Joseph Brenkert, *Front Range Community College;* Michelle Briles, *Gloucester County College;* Kelly Brooks, *Daytona State College (and Pierce);* Connie Buller, *Metropolitan Community College;* Rebecca Burkala, *Rose State College;* Gail Burkett, *Palm Beach State College;* Gale Burtch, *Ivy Tech Community College;* Jennifer Caldwell, *Mesa Community College;* Edie Carter, *Amarillo College;* Allison Cath, *Ivy Tech Community College of Indiana, Indianapolis;* Dawn Chapman, *Columbus Tech College;* Christopher Chappa, *Tyler Junior College;* Chris Chappa, *Tyler Junior College;* Charles Choo, *University of Pittsburgh at Titusville;* Patricia Clark, *Sinclair Community College;* Judy Kim Clark, *Wayne Community College;* Karen Cliffe, *Southwestern College;* Sherry Clune, *Front Range Community College;* Ela Coronado, *Front Range Community College;* Heather Cotharp, *West Kentucky Community & Tech College;* Danny Cowan, *Tarrant County College, Northwest;* Susanna Crawford, *Solano College;* George Daugavietis, *Solano Community College;* Joseph De Guzman, *Norco College;* Michaelle Downey, *Ivy Tech Community College;* Dale Duke, *Oklahoma City Community College;* Rhonda Duncan, *Midlands Technical College;* Marcial Echenique, *Broward College;* Sarah Ellis, *Dona Ana Community College;* Onunwor Enyinda, *Stark State College;* Chana Epstein, *Sullivan County Community College;* Karen Ernst, *Hawkeye Community College;* Stephen Ester, *St. Petersburg College;* Rosemary Farrar, *Southern West Virginia Community & Technical College;* John Fay, *Chaffey College;* Stephanie Fernandes, *Lewis and Clark Community College;* James Fiebiger, *Front Range Community College;* Angela Fipps, *Durham Technical Community College;* Jennifer Fisher, *Caldwell Community College & Technical Institute;* Elaine Fitt, *Bucks County Community College;* Carol Fletcher, *Hinds Community College;* Claude Fortune, *Atlantic Cape Community College;* Marilyn Frydrych, *Pikes Peak Community College;* Robert Fusco, *Broward College;* Jared Ganson, *Nassau Community College;* Kristine Glasener, *Cuyahoga Community College;* Ernest Gobert, *Oklahoma City Community College;* Linda Golovin, *Caldwell College;* Suzette Goss, *Lone Star College Kingwood;* Sharon Graber, *Lee College;* Susan Grody, *Broward College;* Leonard Groeneveld, *Springfield Tech Community College;* Joseph Guiciardi, *Community College of Allegheny County;* Susanna Gunther, *Solano College;* Lucy Gurrola, *Dona Ana Community College;* Frederick Hageman, *Delaware Technical & Community College;* Tamela Hanebrink, *Southeast Missouri State University;* Deborah Hanus, *Brookhaven College;* John Hargraves, *St. John's River State College;* Michael Helinger, *Clinton Community College;* Mary Hill, *College of DuPage;* Jody Hinson, *Cape Fear Community College;* Kayana Hoagland, *South Puget Sound Community College;* Tracey Hollister, *Casper College;* Wendy Houston, *Everett Community College;* Mary Howard, *Thomas Nelson Community College;* Lisa Hugdahl, *Milwaukee Area Tech College—Milwaukee;* Larry Huntzinger, *Western Oklahoma State College;* Manoj Illickal, *Nassau Community College;* Sharon Jackson, *Brookhaven College;* Lisa Jackson, *Black River Technical College;* Christina Jacobs, *Washington State University;* Gretta Johnson, *Amarillo College;* Lisa Juliano, *El Paso Community College, Northwest Campus;* Elias M. Jureidini, *Lamar State College/Orange;* Ismail Karahouni, *Lamar University;* Cliffe Karen, *Southwestern College;* David Kater, *San Diego City College;* Joe Kemble, *Lamar University;* Esmarie Kennedy, *San Antonio College;* Ahmed Khago, *Lamar University;* Michael Kirby, *Tidewater Community College VA Beach Campus;* Corrine Kirkbride, *Solano Community College;* Mary Ann Klicka, *Bucks County Community College;* Alex Kolesnik, *Ventura College;* Tatyana Kravchuk, *Northern Virginia Community College;* Randa Kress, *Idaho State University;* Julianne Labbiento, *Lehigh Carbon Community College;* Robert Leifson, *Pierce College;* Greg Liano, *Brookdale Community College;* Charyl Link, *Kansas City Kansas Community College;* Wanda Long, *Saint Charles County Community College;* Lorraine Lopez, *San Antonio College;* Luke Mannion, *St. John's University;* Shakir Manshad, *New Mexico State University;* Robert Marinelli, *Durham Technical Community College;* Lydia Matthews-Morales, *Ventura College;* Melvin Mays, *Metropolitan Community College (Omaha NE);* Carrie McCammon, *Ivy Tech Community College;* Milisa Mcilwain, *Meridian Community College;* Valerie Melvin, *Cape Fear Community College;* Christopher Merlo, *Nassau Community College;* Leslie Meyer, *Ivy Tech Community College/Central Indiana;* Beverly Meyers, *Jefferson College;* Laura Middaugh, *McHenry County College;* Karen Mifflin, *Palomar College;* Kris Mudunuri, *Long Beach City College;* Donald Munsey, *Louisiana Delta Community College;* Randall Nichols, *Delta College;* Joshua Niemczyk, *Saint Charles County Community College;* Katherine Ocker Stone, *Tusculum College;* Karen Orr, *Roane State;* Staci Osborn, *Cuyahoga Community College;* Steven Ottmann, *Southeast Community College, Lincoln Nebraska;* William Parker, *Greenville Technical College;* Joanne Peeples, *El Paso Community College;* Paul Peery, *Lee College;* Betty Peterson, *Mercer County Community College;* Carol Ann Poore, *Hinds Community College;* Hadley Pridgen, *Gulf Coast State College;* William Radulovich, *Florida State College @ Jacksonville;* Lakshminarayan Rajaram, *St. Petersburg College;* Kumars Ranjbaran, *Mountain View College;* Darian Ransom, *Southeastern Community College;* Nimisha Raval, *Central Georgia Technical College;* Amy Riipinen, *Hibbing Community College;* Janet Roads, *Moberly Area Community College;* Marianne Roarty, *Metropolitan Community College;* Jennifer Robb, *Scott Community College;* Marie Robison, *McHenry County College;* Daphne Anne Rossiter, *Mesa Community College;* Anna Roth, *Gloucester County College;* Daria Santerre, *Norwalk Community College;* Kala Sathappan, *College of Southern Nevada;* Patricia Schubert, *Saddleback College;* William H. Shaw,

Coppin State University; Azzam Shihabi, Long Beach City College; Jed Soifer, Atlantic Cape Community College; Lee Ann Spahr, Durham Technical Community College; Marie St. James, Saint Clair County Community College; Mike Stack, College of DuPage; Ann Starkey, Stark State College of Technology; Thomas Steinmann, Lewis and Clark Community College; Claudia Stewart, Casper College; Kim Taylor, Florence Darlington Technical College; Laura Taylor, Cape Fear Community College; Janet Teeguarden, Ivy Tech Community College; Janine Termine, Bucks County Community College; Yan Tian, Palomar College; Lisa Tolliver, Brown Mackie South Bend; David Usinski, Erie Community College; Hien Van Eaton, Liberty University; Theresa Vecchiarelli, Nassau Community College; Val Villegas, Southwestern College; David Walker, Hinds Community College; Ursula Walsh, Minneapolis Community & Tech College; Dottie Walton, Cuyahoga Community College; LuAnn Walton, San Juan College; Thomas Wells, Delta College; Kathryn Wetzel, Amarillo College; Marjorie Whitmore, North West Arkansas Community College; Ross Wiliams, Stark State College of Technology; Gerald Williams, San Juan College; Michelle Wolcott, Pierce College, Puyallup; Mary Young, Brookdale Community College; Loris Zucca, Lone Star College, Kingwood; Michael Zwilling, University of Mount Union

Student Focus Group Participants

Thanks to the students who reviewed elements of P.O.W.E.R. and talked candidly with the editorial team about their experiences in math courses.

Eire Aatnite, Roosevelt University; Megan Bekker, Northeastern Illinois University; Hiran Crespo, Northeastern Illinois University; John J. Frederick, Jr., Harold Washington College; Omar Gonzalez, Wright College; Yamizaret Guzman, Western Illinois University; Ashley Grayson, Northeastern Illinois University; Nathan Hurde, University of Illinois at Chicago; Zainab Khomusi, University of Illinois at Chicago; Amanda Koger, Roosevelt University; Diana Kotchounian, Roosevelt University; Adrana Martinez, DePaul University; Laurien Mosley, Western Illinois University; Jeffrey Moy, University of Illinois at Chicago; Jaimie O'Leary, Northeastern Illinois University; Trupti Patel, University of Illinois at Chicago; Pete Rodriguez, Truman College; Kyaw Sint Lay Wu, University of Illinois at Chicago; Shona L. Thomas, Northeastern Illinois University; Nina Turnage, Roosevelt University; Brittany K. Vernon, Roosevelt University; Kyaw Sint Lay Wu, University of Illinois at Chicago

Digital Contributors

Special thanks go to the faculty members who contributed their time and expertise to the digital offerings with P.O.W.E.R.

Jennifer Caldwell, Mesa Community College
Chris Chappa, Tyler Junior College
Kim Cozean, Saddleback College
Cindy Cummins, Ozarks Technical Community College
Rob Fusco, Bergen Community College
Sharon Jackson, Brookhaven College

Corrine Kirkbride, Solano Community College
Brianna Kurtz, Daytona State College
Christy Peterson, College of DuPage
Janine Termine, Bucks County Community College
Linda Schott, Ozarks Technical Community College

From the Authors

The authors would like to thank many people at McGraw-Hill. First, our editorial team: Elizabeth O'Brien, Liz Recker, and most of all, Dawn "Dawesome" Bercier, who believed in, championed, and put never-ending energy into our project from the beginning. To Ryan Blankenship, Marty Lange, Kurt Strand, and Brian Kibby: thank you for your continued support and vision that allows us to help students far beyond our own classrooms. Also, Kim Leistner, Nicole Lloyd, Peggy Selle, Peter Vanaria and Stewart Mattson have been instrumental in what they do to help bring our books and digital products to completion.

We offer sincere thanks to Vicki Garringer, Jennifer Caldwell and Sharon Bailey for their contributions to the series.

From Larry Perez: Thank you to my wife, Georgette, for your patience, support, and understanding throughout this endeavor. Thank you to Patrick Quigley and Candice Harrington for your friendship and support. Also, I must thank Dr. Harriet Edwards and Dr. Raghu Mathur for modeling inspirational and innovative pedagogy, examples which I still strive to emulate.

From Bob Feldman: I am grateful to my children, Jonathan, Joshua, and Sarah; my daughters-in-law Leigh and Julie; my smart, handsome, and talented grandsons Alex and Miles, and most of all to my wife, Katherine (who no longer can claim to be the sole mathematician in our family). I thank them all, with great love.

From Sherri Messersmith: Thank you to my daughters, Alex and Cailen, for being the smart, strong, supportive young women that you are; and to my husband, Phil, for understanding the crazy schedule I must keep that often does not complement your own. To Sue, Mary, Sheila, and Jill: everyone should have girlfriends like you. Thank you to the baristas at my hometown Starbucks for your always-smiling faces at 6 am and for letting me occupy the same seat for hours on end. Larry and Bob, thank you for agreeing to become my coauthors and for bringing your expertise to these books. Bill Mulford, we are immensely grateful for your hard work and creativity and for introducing Bob, Larry, and me in the first place. Working with our team of four has been a joy. And, finally, thank you Bill, for your friendship, your patience, and for working with me since the very beginning more than 8 years ago, without question the best student I've ever had.

Sherri Messersmith
Larry Perez
Bob Feldman

Application Index

height of building, 414, 425, 691
height of flagpole, 415, 691
height of ladder, 683
height of rocket, 709
height of statue, 691
height of telephone pole, 688
insect spray amount, 187
land for lots, 187
length of board remaining, 470
length of fence, 200, 661
length of flag pole shadow, 415
length of garden, 627
length of metal piping, 489
length of wire attached to pole, 680
lumber for houses, 185
minutes spent babysitting, 443
oil for lawn mower, 416
oil for two-stroke engine, 416
paint to cover wall space, 414
paper perimeter and area, 626
perimeter of garden, 659
plaster of Paris mixture, 475
ratio of bookshelf dimensions, 390
ratio of oil painting dimensions, 390
ratio of stained glass window dimensions, 390
rooms in a hotel, 93
rubber tubing for water feature, 202
sale price on table saw, 558
strips from sheet metal, 194
surface area of reflecting pool, 202
time for daily chores, 194
time spent on activities, 23
trim for window, 23
volume of cannonball, 674
volume of corn silo, 674, 675
volume of Great Pyramid of Giza, 674
weather stripping for door, 287
wheel barrel capacity, 201
wood for picture frame, 24
wood for project, 215
yellow tape for construction site, 24, 41

cost of gym membership, 80
cost of light fixtures, 124
cost of postage stamps, 53
cost of road trip, 491
cost with sales tax, 374
cost of tickets and fees, 118
cost of tiki torches, 330
cost of t-shirts, 79
cost of youth retreat, 118
cost per lip gloss application, 471
cost per square foot, 397
coupon book usage, 539
diapers received by hospital, 105
discount on price of batteries, 290
discount on price of boots, 286
discount on price of pencil, 290
discount on price of shoes, 390
discount on wedding reception, 557
estimated cost of winter clothes, 374
expenses for new car, 62
fee for economy lot parking, 105
flood insurance subscribers, 427
flowers sold for Mother's Day, 270
graduation party attendees, 114
hair salon total and tip, 521
hotel rooms for smokers *vs.* nonsmokers, 177
manicure and pedicure total and tip, 521
median cost of facial, 362
median cost of manicure, 362
median hotel price, 363
mileages for used cars, 375
monthly coffee shop spending, 330
monthly payment for gardener, 522
monthly payment for pool service, 522
monthly spending categories, 177
newspaper delivery cost, 414
paper napkin unit price, 424
percent decrease in car value, 558
percent decrease in heating bill, 591
percent increase in gas price, 558
percent increase in postage stamp price, 558
perfume applications, 489
price of discounted shirt, 386–387
price of gold nugget, 479
rent per roommate, 115
rent per year, 80
restaurant bill total and tip, 518–519, 521, 545, 546
sale price and tax on bedroom set, 557
sale price and tax on jeans, 557
sale price and tax on raincoat, 557
sale price on boots, 522
sale price on coat, 552
sale price on diapers, 545
sale price on dress, 522, 557, 590
sale price on gas grill, 553
sale price on gloves, 557
sale price on handbag, 557
sale price on jeans, 522
sale price on pet grooming, 557
sale price on refrigerator, 522
sale price on shirt, 427
sale price on washer and dryer, 559, 589
sales tax amount, 289–290, 314
sales tax on engagement ring, 549
sales tax on jeans, 548
sales tax on microwave, 556
sales tax on tableware, 556
sales tax on tennis shoes, 556

sales tax rate, 590
sales tax rate on coffeemaker, 556
sales tax rate on dress, 556
sales tax rate on picture frame, 556
sales tax rate on sweater, 556
savings on purse sale, 519
shampoo per bottle, 468–469
shoe shine total and tip, 521
shoppers making impulse purchases, 173–174
spending at home improvement store, 314
spending at toy store, 314
sticker price on car, 37
time spent waiting in line, 41
toothpaste per tube, 470
tree service total and tip, 522
volume of dime, 674
wait for sofa delivery, 80
water heater capacity, 489
water used by dishwasher, 199, 479
water used by washing machines, 479
weight of cat litter, 479
weight of dog food, 479
weight of lipstick application, 470

Addition and Subtraction of Whole Numbers

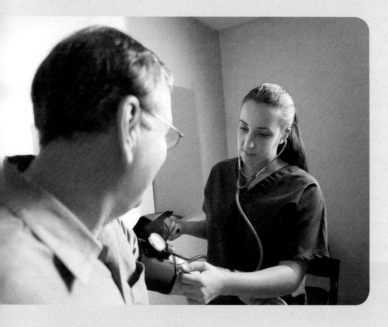

Math at Work:

Physician's Assistant

Delia Cruz has always had an instinct to help people. Growing up, she was a volunteer tutor to younger students in her school, and she spent her summers interning at a local health clinic. So when it came time to choose a profession, Delia knew she wanted to enter a field that would allow her to make a positive impact on people's lives.

"Medicine was a perfect fit for me," Delia explains. "As a physician's assistant, I have the opportunity to be there for people when it matters the most."

Delia realized quickly that a key to such efforts was one she might not have expected: math. Her use of math on the job ranges from simple arithmetic to track changes in weight or blood pressure to more sophisticated calculations involving prescription dosage and the analysis of lab results.

"Math is part of everything I do to treat my patients," Delia says.

While helping others came naturally to Delia, math did not. But she understood that it was an essential component to the career—and the life—she wanted to build for herself. So she worked hard at it and used smart study skills. Eventually, Delia was able to turn math from a relative weakness into an area of strength—one that benefits her and the patients she treats every day.

In this chapter, we look at some basic concepts in math: addition and subtraction of whole numbers along with place value. Later we introduce the P.O.W.E.R. system, which will help you master the skills of math, or of any subject in the classroom and on the job.

The **P.O.W.E.R.** framework is based on an acronym—a word formed from the first letters of a series of steps—that will help you study, learn, and ultimately make use of new information. P.O.W.E.R. stands for **P**repare, **O**rganize, **W**ork, **E**valuate, and **R**ethink. That's it. It's a simple framework but an effective one. Using the systematic framework that P.O.W.E.R. provides will allow you to master everything from mathematical concepts to filling out a purchase order on the job.

Let's take a closer look at each of the steps.

- Identify your goals, both short-term and long-term.
- **Long-term goals** are aims relating to major accomplishments that take some time to achieve. **Short-term goals** are relatively limited steps you would take on the road to accomplishing your long-term goals.

- Organize the tools you need to accomplish your goals.
- Effective organization involves both gathering the *physical* tools you will need to complete your task and doing the *mental* work to ensure you are ready to succeed.
- In learning math, organize by reminding yourself of the major concepts you will need to apply.

- Using the previous steps as your foundation, do the work to carry out your task.
- Stay motivated, think positively, and focus on controlling the elements of your task that are under your control.

- Consider how well the work you have done matches your goals for it.
- Based on your evaluation, revise your work if you believe it can be improved.

- Think critically about the work you have done.
- Reconsider not only the outcome of your efforts but also your goals and the ideas that shaped them.

Chapter 1 **POWER** Plan

P Prepare

What are your goals for Chapter 1?

1   Be prepared before and during class.

2   Understand the homework to the point where you could do it without needing any help or hints.

3   Use the P.O.W.E.R. framework to help you organize your study: *Who's in Charge?*

4   Write your own goal.

O Organize

How can you accomplish each goal?

- Don't stay out late the night before and be sure to set your alarm clock!
- Bring a pencil, notebook paper, and textbook to class.
- Avoid distractions by turning off your cell phone during class.
- Pay attention, take good notes, and ask questions.
- Complete your homework on time and ask questions on problems you do not understand.

- Read the directions and show all of your steps.
- Go to the professor's office for help.
- Rework homework and quiz problems, and find similar problems for practice.

- Read the Study Strategy that explains how to use P.O.W.E.R.
- What does P.O.W.E.R. stand for?
- Complete the emPOWERme that appears before the Chapter Summary.

- _____

What are your objectives for Chapter 1?

1   Learn the terminology involved with whole numbers and place value.

2   Learn the process of addition and subtraction.

3   Understand how to regroup when adding or subtracting numbers.

4   Solve applied problems using addition or subtraction.

5   Know how to round numbers in order to estimate a sum or difference.

6   Learn how to read different types of graphs and perform operations on the data.

7   Write your own goal.

How can you accomplish each objective?

- Take notes and learn the definitions and procedures in Section 1.1.
- Take good notes in class.

- Master each objective of Sections 1.2–1.5 in order because they build upon each other.
- Understand how to use a number line to perform operations and find missing numbers.
- Know the definition of the *commutative properties* and *associative properties of addition.*

- Know how to carry when adding and how to borrow when subtracting.
- Read the book or reread your notes before doing the homework.
- Watch the exercise videos for extra help if you get stuck on a certain problem.

- Read the problem twice to be sure that you fully understand it.
- Use what you learned about adding and subtracting to solve applied problems.

- Take notes and write the procedure in your own words.
- Complete all of the exercises and ask for help when you need it.

- Know how to recognize and use three different graphs: the pictograph, bar graph, and line graph.
- Use the procedures learned earlier in the chapter to perform operations on the graph(s).

- _____

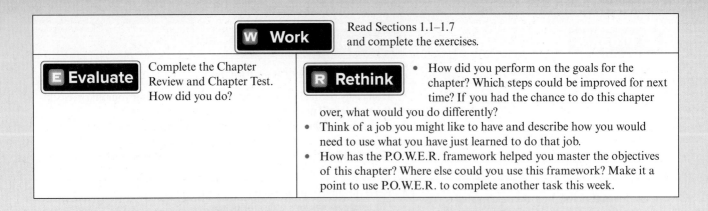

| | Read Sections 1.1–1.7 and complete the exercises. |

W Work

E Evaluate Complete the Chapter Review and Chapter Test. How did you do?

R Rethink
- How did you perform on the goals for the chapter? Which steps could be improved for next time? If you had the chance to do this chapter over, what would you do differently?
- Think of a job you might like to have and describe how you would need to use what you have just learned to do that job.
- How has the P.O.W.E.R. framework helped you master the objectives of this chapter? Where else could you use this framework? Make it a point to use P.O.W.E.R. to complete another task this week.

1.1 Whole Numbers and Place Value

P Prepare   **O Organize**

What are your objectives for Section 1.1?	How can you accomplish each objective?
1 Identify Digits and Place Value	• Understand the definitions of a *digit* and *whole numbers*. • Draw the charts that help identify *place value* and *periods* in your notes. • Complete the given examples on your own. • Complete You Trys 1 and 2.
2 Write a Number in Words or Digits	• Write the procedure for **Writing a Number in Words** in your own words. • Complete the given examples on your own. • Complete You Trys 3–5.
3 Read a Table	• Write the definition of a *table* in your own words. • Complete the given example on your own. • Complete You Try 6.

 **W Work**   **Read the explanations, follow the examples, take notes, and complete the You Trys.**

It is important to understand the language used in mathematics. So, let's start with some definitions.

1 Identify Digits and Place Value

A **digit** is a single character in a numbering system. We use the digits 0, 1, 2, 3, 4, 5, 6, 7, 8, and 9 to write numbers in the **decimal system.** If we put two or more digits together in a certain order, like 58, we get a number. (Single digits, like 5, are both digits and numbers.)

The first group of numbers we will study is the *whole numbers*. The **whole numbers** are

0, 1, 2, 3, 4, 5, 6, 7, 8, 9, 10, 11, 12, 13, 14, 15, …

where the three dots mean that the list continues forever.

Each digit in a whole number represents a **place value** that is determined by where it appears in the whole number. Here is a place-value chart that shows the place value of each digit in the number 5,712,374.

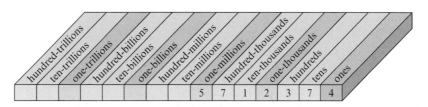

In the *number* 5,712,374, the *digit* 7 appears twice. On the left, the place value of the 7 is 7 hundred-thousands (or 700,000), but the place value of the 7 on the right is 7 tens (or 70).

| **EXAMPLE 1** | Identify the place value of the digit 6 in each whole number. |

In-Class Example 1

Identify the place value of the digit 7 in each whole number.
a) 79   b) 735   c) 247

Answer: a) 7 tens
b) 7 hundreds   c) 7 ones

a) 806   b) 61   c) 659

6 ones   6 tens   6 hundreds

[YOU TRY 1] Identify the place value of the digit 2 in each whole number.

a) 528   b) 293   c) 42

We use commas to separate each group of three digits in a number starting from the right. These groups of numbers are called **periods.**

Periods (or Groups)

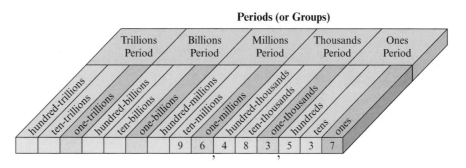

SECTION 1.1   **Whole Numbers and Place Value**

Note

Often, the comma is not written in four-digit numbers. For example, the number 2,758 can also be written as 2758.

EXAMPLE 2

In-Class Example 2

Using the number 81,952,563,
a) identify the place value of each digit in the number.
b) identify the digits in each period of the number.

Answer:

a)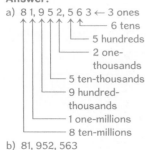

8 1, 9 5 2, 5 6 3 ← 3 ones
⎣— 6 tens
⎣— 5 hundreds
⎣— 2 one-thousands
⎣— 5 ten-thousands
⎣— 9 hundred-thousands
⎣— 1 one-millions
⎣— 8 ten-millions

b)

81, 952, 563
⎣— 563 ones
⎣— 952 thousands
⎣— 81 millions

Using the number 96,483,537 given in the table,

a) identify the place value of each digit in the number.

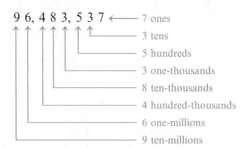

9 6, 4 8 3, 5 3 7 ← 7 ones
3 tens
5 hundreds
3 one-thousands
8 ten-thousands
4 hundred-thousands
6 one-millions
9 ten-millions

Note

Often, the *one* is left off of the place value. For example, 3 one-thousands can be written as 3 thousands, 6 one-millions can be written as 6 millions, etc.

b) identify the digits in each period of the number.

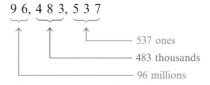

9 6, 4 8 3, 5 3 7
537 ones
483 thousands
96 millions

[YOU TRY 2]

Using the number 815,742,459,

a) identify the place value of each digit in the number.

b) identify the digits in each period of the number.

---

2 Write a Number in Words or Digits

To read a number containing more than three digits, we use the following procedure.

Procedure Writing a Number in Words

Start at the left. Write or say the number in each period (group) followed by the name of the period (group) *except* for "ones." Leave off the plural "s" when reading the period. For example, 123,000 is "123 thousand," not "123 thousands." We do not use the word "ones" when writing or reading a number.

EXAMPLE 3

In-Class Example 3

Write each number in words.
a) 64   b) 937   c) 201

Answer: a) sixty-four
b) nine hundred thirty-seven
c) two hundred one

Write each number in words.

a) 82   b) 317   c) 405

<table>
<tr><td>

W Hint

Look back at the charts in Objective 1 for help if needed.

</td><td>

Solution

a) Write 82 as eighty-two.

b) Write 317 as three hundred seventeen.

c) Write 405 as four hundred five.

</td></tr>
</table>

 BE CAREFUL We do **not** use the word *and* when writing or reading whole numbers. The number 405, for example, is **not** read as *four hundred and five*.

[YOU TRY 3] Write each number in words.

a) 37   b) 629   c) 803

EXAMPLE 4

Write each number in words.

a) 64,189   b) 570,343,016

c) 12,000,080,000   d) 3560

In-Class Example 4

Write each number in words.
a) 58,217
b) 408,955,014
c) 61,000,020,000
d) 7690

Answer:
a) fifty-eight thousand, two hundred seventeen
b) four hundred eight million, nine hundred fifty-five thousand, fourteen
c) sixty-one billion, twenty thousand
d) seven thousand, six hundred ninety

Solution

a) 64,189

sixty-four thousand, one hundred eighty-nine

number in   name of   number in the period
the period   period   (Do not write "ones.")

b) 570,343,016

five hundred seventy million, three hundred forty-three thousand, sixteen

number in the   name of   number in the   name of   number
period   period   period   period   in the
                                                        period

c) 12,000,080,000

twelve billion, eighty thousand

number   name   number   name of
in the   of   in the   period
period   period period

d) Remember that a four-digit number can be written with or without a comma. You should get used to seeing it both ways. Let's insert the comma to help us see the periods more clearly: 3,560.

three thousand, five hundred sixty

number   name of   number in
in the   period   the period
period

[YOU TRY 4] Write each number in words.

a) 172,314   b) 38,206,975   c) 561,000,004,000   d) 7409

Next, let's take a number that is written in words and write it using digits.

EXAMPLE 5

In-Class Example 5

Write each number using digits.
a) two thousand, five hundred forty-three
b) seven hundred eighty-one thousand, ninety-two
c) twenty-seven billion, four hundred forty-one million, three hundred ten

Answer: a) 2,543
b) 781,092
c) 27,441,000,310

EXAMPLE 5

Write each number using digits.

a) five thousand, two hundred ninety-eight

$$5,298 \quad \text{or} \quad 5298 \text{ with no comma}$$

b) seven hundred twenty-six thousand, fifty-three

726,053

↑——There are no hundreds, so use a zero.

c) eighteen billion, three hundred seventy-one million, four hundred twenty

18,371,000,420

↑——There are no thousands, so use zeros.

[YOU TRY 5]   Write each number using digits.

a) eleven thousand, nine hundred seventy-four

b) twenty-one million, five hundred thirty-three thousand, eight

c) one billion, eight hundred fourteen thousand, six hundred twelve

---

3 Read a Table

Next, let's practice reading a table. A table is a way to organize information so that it is easy to understand.

EXAMPLE 6

In-Class Example 6

Use Example 6.

EXAMPLE 6

Use the table to answer the questions. Write the number in digits and in words.

Average Annual Income of Males 25–34 Years Old by Educational Attainment

Year	2005	2006	2007
High School Diploma	$33,866	$37,181	$35,995
Associate's Degree	$42,666	$42,357	$45,691
Bachelor's Degree or Higher	$61,027	$67,195	$66,731

(www.census.gov)

a) What was the average annual income for a male with a high school diploma in 2006?

b) What was the average annual income for a male with a bachelor's degree or higher in 2007?

Solution

a) Find "High School Diploma" in the leftmost column. Move to the right until you get to the column labeled 2006 and stop. The number is $37,181. In words, this is *thirty-seven thousand, one hundred eighty-one dollars.*

b) Find "Bachelor's Degree or Higher" in the leftmost column. Move to the right until you get to the column labeled 2007 and stop. The number is $66,731. In words, this is *sixty-six thousand, seven hundred thirty-one dollars.*

E Evaluate **1.1** Exercises

Do the exercises, and check your work.

*Additional answers can be found in the Answers to Exercises appendix.

Objective 1: Identify Digits and Place Value

1) What is the difference between a digit and a number? A digit is a single character in a numbering system, but a number is what you get when you write digits together in a certain order.

2) Write down two different digits. Then, form a two-digit number with those two digits. Answers may vary.

Identify the place value of the digit 5 in each whole number.

3) 7,591 5 hundreds

4) 257,031 5 ten-thousands

5) 654,988,176 5 ten-millions

6) 5,228,964 5 one-millions

Identify the place value of the digit 2 in each whole number.

7) 452,908 2 one-thousands

8) 8,217,754 2 hundred-thousands

9) 327,055,149,619 2 ten-billions

10) 19,025,411,607 2 ten-millions

Identify the digit with the given place value in each whole number.

11) 83,962,519

a) ten-millions 8

b) one-millions 3

c) ten-thousands 6

d) hundreds 5

12) 94,257,108,637

a) one-billions 4

b) ten-millions 5

c) hundred-thousands 1

d) ones 7

13) 320,963

a) one-thousands 0

b) ones 3

c) hundred-thousands 3

14) 423,574

a) ten-thousands 2

b) hundreds 5

c) tens 7

15) 965,352,654

a) hundred-millions 9

b) ten-thousands 5

c) hundreds 6

16) 807,004,219,505

a) hundred-billions 8

b) ten-millions 0

c) one-thousands 9

Identify the digits in each period of the number.

17) 72,544 72 thousands, 544 ones

18) 956,128 956 thousands, 128 ones

19) 803,001,216 803 millions, 1 thousands, 216 ones

20) 49,223,007,950 49 billions, 223 millions, 7 thousands, 950 ones

21) 52,774,800 52 millions, 774 thousands, 800 ones

22) 6,002,791 6 millions, 2 thousands, 791 ones

23) 735,000,068,004 735 billions, 68 thousands, 4 ones

24) 108,054,000,062 108 billions, 54 millions, 62 ones

Objective 2: Write a Number in Words or Digits

Write each number in words.

25) 601 six hundred one

26) 84,915 eighty-four thousand, nine hundred fifteen

27) 5,000,449 five million, four hundred forty-nine

28) 30,008,723,010 thirty billion, eight million, seven hundred twenty-three thousand, ten

29) 32,043 thirty-two thousand, forty-three

30) 1,201,402 one million, two hundred one thousand, four hundred two

31) 450,629,875 four hundred fifty million, six hundred twenty-nine thousand, eight hundred seventy-five

32) 810,000,060 eight hundred ten million, sixty

Write each number using digits.

33) seven thousand, two hundred eighty-three 7,283

34) two hundred eleven thousand, three hundred ninety-five 211,395

35) forty-eight million, nine hundred two thousand, twenty 48,902,020

36) sixteen billion, five hundred fifty-eight million, four 16,558,000,004

37) one hundred thousand, two hundred twelve 100,212

38) seventeen thousand, three hundred twenty-eight 17,328

39) sixty-four million, nineteen thousand, five 64,019,005

40) eleven billion, two million, four 11,002,000,004

Rewrite each number in the problem using digits.

41) People spend over seven hundred billion minutes on Facebook every month. (www.facebook.com) 700,000,000,000

42) McDonald's serves over forty-seven million customers per day around the world. (www.mcdonalds.ca) 47,000,000

43) During the 2009–2010 season, the Chicago Blackhawks' home attendance was eight hundred fifty-four thousand, two hundred sixty-seven.
(espn.go.com) 854,267

44) The distance from Earth to the sun is approximately ninety-three million, five hundred eighteen miles. 93,000,518

45) The population of California was approximately thirty-six million, nine hundred sixty-one thousand, six hundred sixty-four in 2009. (quickfacts.census.gov) 36,961,664

46) The total area of Alaska is six hundred sixty-four thousand, nine hundred eighty-eight square miles. 664,988

Objective 3: Read a Table

Use the table to answer the questions in Exercises 47–50.

Number of Cosmetic Surgery Procedures Performed in the United States

Year	2006	2007	2008
Lipoplasty (Liposuction)	403,700	456,800	341,100
Rhinoplasty (Nose Reshaping)	141,900	151,800	152,400
Blepharoplasty (Eyelid Surgery)	210,000	240,800	195,100

(www.census.gov)

47) How many blepharoplasty procedures were done in 2007? Write the answer in digits and in words.
240,800; two hundred forty thousand, eight hundred

48) How many lipoplasty procedures were done in 2006? Write the answer in digits and in words.
403,700; four hundred three thousand, seven hundred

49) Which procedure was performed 341,100 times in 2008? lipoplasty

50) Which procedure was performed a greater number of times in 2008 than in 2007? rhinoplasty

R Rethink

R1) Which objective do you still need help mastering?

R2) Where have you encountered a table in the last two weeks and how did you use it?

R3) Create a table that contains your Math, Science, and English scores for the last four terms.

1.2 Introduction to Addition

What are your objectives for Section 1.2?	**How can you accomplish each objective?**
1 Add Numbers Using a Number Line	• Write the definition of a *number line* in your own words. • Complete the given examples on your own. • Complete You Try 1.
2 Use the Commutative Property	• Write the **commutative property of addition** in your own words. • Complete the given examples on your own. • Complete You Trys 2 and 3.
3 Use the Associative Property	• Write the **associative property of addition** in your own words. • Add the numbers inside *parentheses* first. • Complete the given examples on your own. • Complete You Trys 4–8.
4 Find a Missing Addend	• Use the number line from Objective 1 to count the unit gap. • Complete the given examples on your own. • Complete You Trys 9 and 10.

W Work

Read the explanations, follow the examples, take notes, and complete the You Trys.

We can strengthen our addition, subtraction, multiplication, and division skills if we begin with the basics and understand how these operations are related. To do this, we will use a number line.

1 Add Numbers Using a Number Line

Definition

A **number line** is a line used to represent numbers, in order, on evenly spaced, marked points on the line.

Here is a number line marked with the numbers 0 through 10:

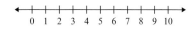

Note

1) It is important that the spacing between the tick marks be the same.

2) As you move from left to right on the number line, the numbers get larger.

We can represent a number on the number line with a dot. For example, the number 4 can be placed on the number line like this:

We can use a number line to add numbers.

EXAMPLE 1

Use a number line to add 2 + 5.

In-Class Example 1

Use a number line to add 3 + 4.

Answer: 7

Solution

Start at 0 and move 2 spaces to the right to reach 2. To add 5, move 5 more spaces to the right. We finish at 7.

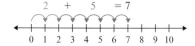

$$2 + 5 = 7$$

W Hint

Does this feel like you are counting?

[YOU TRY 1]

Use a number line to add 7 + 3.

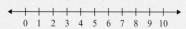

In an addition problem, the numbers being added together are called the **addends,** and the answer is called the **sum.** In Example 1, the addends are 2 and 5. The sum is 7.

2 Use the Commutative Property

If we change the order in which we add numbers, does it change the sum?

EXAMPLE 2

Use a number line to add 5 + 2.

In-Class Example 2

Use a number line to add 4 + 3.

Answer: 7

Solution

Start at 0 and move 5 spaces to the right to reach 5. To add 2, move 2 more spaces to the right. We finish at 7.

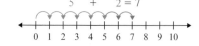

$$5 + 2 = 7$$

Notice that this is the same result we obtained in Example 1 when we found that 2 + 5 = 7.

[YOU TRY 2]

Use a number line to add 3 + 7.

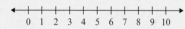

We can add numbers in any order and the result, or sum, will be the same. The *commutative property of addition* tells us this is true.

Property The Commutative Property of Addition

The **commutative property of addition** says that changing the order in which we add numbers does not change the sum.

Note

It may be helpful to remember the commutative property this way: To *commute* to work means that each day we travel from home to our place of business and then back home again. Therefore, commuting refers to changing location. When we *commute* numbers, we are changing the locations of those numbers.

EXAMPLE 3

In-Class Example 3

Add 7 + 2, then rewrite the addition problem using the commutative property.

Answer: 9; 2 + 7 = 9

Add 8 + 1, then rewrite the addition problem using the commutative property.

Solution

8 + 1 = 9. Using the commutative property, we get 1 + 8 = 9.

[YOU TRY 3] Add 4 + 7, then rewrite the addition problem using the commutative property.

3 Use the Associative Property

Let's add three numbers on a number line. Then we will learn another property of addition.

EXAMPLE 4

In-Class Example 4

Use a number line to add 3 + 1 + 9.

Answer: 13

Use a number line to add 3 + 6 + 4.

Solution

We will extend the number line to 15.

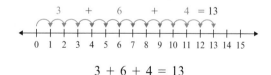

$$3 + 6 + 4 = 13$$

[YOU TRY 4] Use a number line to add 5 + 2 + 8.

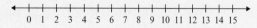

We can also use *parentheses* to add numbers. **Parentheses** are grouping symbols that tell us the order in which we should perform arithmetic operations. Usually, we do the operations in parentheses before other operations in a problem.

EXAMPLE 5

In-Class Example 5

Use a number line to add
(3 + 1) + 9.

Answer: 13

W Hint

Notice that the same numbers are being added in Examples 4, 5, and 6.

Use a number line to add $(3 + 6) + 4$.

Solution

Let's add the numbers in parentheses first; then we will add on the number line.

$(3 + 6) + 4 =$
$\quad 9 \quad + 4 =$
$\quad\quad 13$

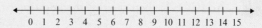

$(3 + 6) + 4 = 13$

[YOU TRY 5] Use a number line to add $(5 + 2) + 8$.

When we add several numbers, can we change the placement of the parentheses without changing the sum?

EXAMPLE 6

In-Class Example 6

Use a number line to add
3 + (1 + 9).

Answer: 13

Use a number line to add $3 + (6 + 4)$.

Solution

Add the numbers in parentheses first.

$3 + (6 + 4) =$
$3 + \quad 10 \quad =$
$\quad\quad 13$

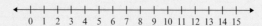

$3 + (6 + 4) = 13$

This is the same as the result in Example 5 when the parentheses were in a different place: $(3 + 6) + 4 = 13$.

[YOU TRY 6] Use a number line to add $5 + (2 + 8)$.

Examples 5 and 6 show that $(3 + 6) + 4 = 3 + (6 + 4) = 13$. Changing the position of the parentheses in an addition problem does *not* change the sum. This is an example of the *associative property of addition*.

Property The Associative Property of Addition

The **associative property of addition** says that we can change the position of grouping symbols when adding numbers and the sum remains the same.

EXAMPLE 7

Add 9 + (3 + 8), then rewrite the addition problem using the associative property.

In-Class Example 7

Add 8 + (3 + 6), then rewrite the addition problem using the associative property.

Answer: 17;
(8 + 3) + 6 = 11 + 6 = 17

Solution

Original Sum	Using the Associative Property
9 + (3 + 8) =	(9 + 3) + 8 =
9 + 11 = 20	12 + 8 = 20

Notice that we changed the position of the parentheses. We did not change the position of the numbers.

[YOU TRY 7] Add (5 + 2) + 8, then rewrite the addition problem using the associative property.

Sometimes, using the commutative and associative properties together makes it easier to find the sum of numbers.

EXAMPLE 8

Add 4 + 7 + 6 + 3.

Solution

The commutative property says that we can add numbers in any order and the sum does not change. Let's rearrange the numbers.

$$4 + 7 + 6 + 3 = 4 + 6 + 7 + 3 \quad \text{Commutative property}$$

W Hint

If possible, rearrange the numbers so that groups add up to 10.

The associative property says that we can *group* the addends in any way.

$$= (4 + 6) + (7 + 3)$$
$$= 10 + 10 = 20$$

[YOU TRY 8] Add 9 + 2 + 7 + 8.

4 Find a Missing Addend

EXAMPLE 9

Fill in the blank: 6 + _____ = 10.

Solution

We can use a number line.

W Hint

Use the number line to count the number of units between the addends given and the sum.

6 + _____ = 10

0 1 2 3 4 5 6 7 8 9 10

How many units must we move to get from 6 to 10? 4
    Therefore, 6 + 4 = 10.

[YOU TRY 9] Fill in the blank: 2 + _____ = 9.

Find the missing length labeled with ?.

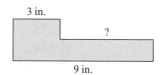

3 in.

?

9 in.

Solution

Notice that the side of length 3 in. *plus* the side of length ? equals the side of length 9 in.

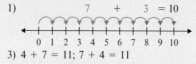

3 in.   ?

9 in.

We can write 3 + _____ = 9. The missing number is 6. Therefore, the length of the missing side is 6 in.

[YOU TRY 10]   Find the missing length labeled with ?.

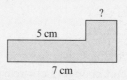

?

5 cm

7 cm

ANSWERS TO [YOU TRY] EXERCISES

1)   7   +   3   = 10

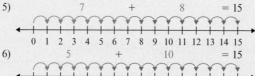

0 1 2 3 4 5 6 7 8 9 10

2)   3   +   7   = 10

0 1 2 3 4 5 6 7 8 9 10

3) 4 + 7 = 11; 7 + 4 = 11

4)   5   +   2   +   8   = 15

0 1 2 3 4 5 6 7 8 9 10 11 12 13 14 15

5)   7   +   8   = 15

0 1 2 3 4 5 6 7 8 9 10 11 12 13 14 15

6)   5   +   10   = 15

0 1 2 3 4 5 6 7 8 9 10 11 12 13 14 15

7) (5 + 2) + 8 = 7 + 8 = 15; Using the associative property: 5 + (2 + 8) = 5 + 10 = 15

8) 26   9) 7   10) 2 cm

E Evaluate **1.2** Exercises   Do the exercises, and check your work.

*Additional answers can be found in the Answers to Exercises appendix.

Objective 1: Add Numbers Using a Number Line

Identify the addends and sum in each addition problem.

Use a number line to add the numbers.

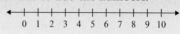

0 1 2 3 4 5 6 7 8 9 10

1) 8 + 7 = 15   addends: 8, 7; sum: 15

2) 1 + 9 = 10   addends: 1, 9; sum: 10

3) 5 + 4

4) 4 + 5

5) 6 + 4

6) 7 + 1

 7) 2 + 3 + 4

8) 5 + 2 + 1

Objective 2: Use the Commutative Property

9) In your own words, explain the commutative property of addition.   Answers may vary.

10) When you are adding numbers, will the order in which you add them affect the answer? Explain.
No. The commutative property says that numbers can be added in any order and the sum will be the same.

Add, then rewrite the problem using the commutative property.

11) 8 + 7   15; 7 + 8   12) 2 + 11   13; 11 + 2

13) 1 + 16   17; 16 + 1   14) 7 + 0   7; 0 + 7

15) 2 + 4 + 8   14; Answers may vary.   16) 9 + 7 + 1   17; Answers may vary.

17) 7 + 6 + 3   16; Answers may vary.   18) 5 + 0 + 8   13; Answers may vary.

Objective 3: Use the Associative Property

19) In your own words, explain the associative property of addition.   Answers may vary.

20) Answer true or false. 7 + (2 + 3) = (7 + 2) + 3
Which property helped you get the answer?
True. The associative property of addition says that we can change the position of parentheses and the sum remains the same.

Add, then rewrite the problem using the associative property.

21) 3 + (7 + 5) 15; (3 + 7) + 5   22) (6 + 3) + 2 11; 6 + (3 + 2)

23) 4 + (7 + 3) 14; (4 + 7) + 3   24) 2 + (4 + 6) 12; (2 + 4) + 6

25) (3 + 5) + 5 13; 3 + (5 + 5)   26) (6 + 2) + 8 16; 6 + (2 + 8)

Objective 4: Find a Missing Addend
Fill in the blank.

27) 2 + _____ = 7   5   28) 5 + _____ = 8   3

29) 4 + _____ = 13   9   30) 8 + _____ = 14   6

31) _____ + 7 = 17   10   32) _____ + 3 = 11   8

33) 3 + 4 + _____ = 12   5   34) 5 + _____ + 2 = 11   4

Answer each question.

35) What number do you add to 3 to get 10?   7

36) What number do you add to 2 to get 8?   6

37) What number do you add to 3 + 1 to get 7?   3

38) What number do you add to 2 + 4 to get 11?   5

Find the missing length labeled with ?.

39)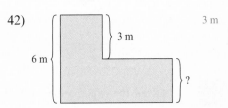

40)

41)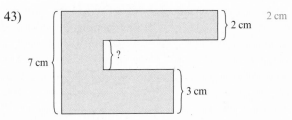

42)

43)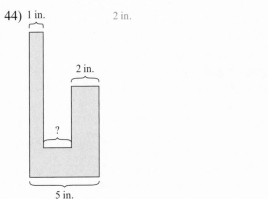

44)

R Rethink

R1) How have you done on the exercises? Were you able to do parts of an exercise or the full exercise in your head?

R2) Which objectives for the section did you master?

R3) How often do you encounter situations where you need to find the missing piece?

1.3 Adding Whole Numbers

P Prepare

O Organize

What are your objectives for Section 1.3?	How can you accomplish each objective?
1 Add Numbers with No Regrouping (Carrying)	• Write the procedure for **Adding Numbers with More Than One Digit** in your own words. • In this objective, the sum of the digits in each column is a single-digit number. • Complete the given examples on your own. • Complete You Trys 1 and 2.
2 Add Numbers with Regrouping (Carrying)	• In this objective, the sum of the digits in each column could be a multidigit number. • Complete the given examples on your own. • Complete You Trys 3 and 4.
3 Solve Applied Problems Using Addition	• Read the applied problem twice and be sure to understand what is being asked. • Write the definition of *perimeter* in your notes. • Complete the given examples on your own. • Complete You Trys 5 and 6.

W Work   **Read the explanations, follow the examples, take notes, and complete the You Trys.**

In this section, we will learn more techniques for adding numbers.

1 Add Numbers with No Regrouping (Carrying)

In Section 1.2, we added more than two numbers using the associative and commutative properties. In this first example, we will add several numbers by aligning them vertically.

EXAMPLE 1

In-Class Example 1

Add $4 + 1 + 8 + 6$.

Answer: 19

Add $5 + 3 + 7 + 2$.

Solution

Line up the numbers vertically, one under the other.

Add the first two numbers, then add that sum to the third number.

We continue until we have added all the numbers.

$$
\begin{array}{r}
5 \\
3 \\
7 \\
+\,2 \\
\hline
17
\end{array}
\begin{array}{l}
5 + 3 = 8 \\
8 + 7 = 15 \\
15 + 2 = 17
\end{array}
$$

← Write the final sum under the horizontal line.

The sum of the numbers is 17.

[YOU TRY 1]   Add $8 + 2 + 6 + 3$.

Next, we will add numbers containing more than one digit.

Procedure Adding Numbers with More Than One Digit

1) Line up the numbers vertically so that the ones digits are in the same column, the tens digits are in the same column, the hundreds digits are in the same column, and so on.

2) Begin the addition process in the column farthest to the right, and then move to the left, adding numbers column by column. That is, add the numbers in the ones place, then add the numbers in the tens place, then add the numbers in the hundreds place, and so on.

Note

Using graph paper to perform operations with numbers can help us line up the numbers in their proper places.

EXAMPLE 2

In-Class Example 2

Add 615 + 20 + 31 + 213.

Answer: 879

ⓦ Hint

Notice that the sum of each column is a single-digit number.

Add 702 + 41 + 33 + 120.

Solution

Line up the numbers in columns starting with the ones at the right.

Begin adding in the ones column, the column farthest to the right.

Next, add the numbers in the tens column.

Then, add the numbers in the hundreds column.

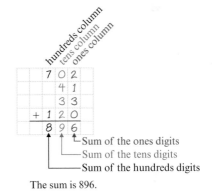

The sum is 896.

[YOU TRY 2]

Add 221 + 12 + 453 + 101.

2 Add Numbers with Regrouping (Carrying)

Let's extend what we have learned about digits and place value.

For example, we can think of the number 18 in different ways:

1) 18 = 18 ones   or   2) 18 = 1 ten + 8 ones

We can think of the number 250 like this:

1) 250 = 250 ones   or   2) 250 = 2 hundreds + 5 tens + 0 ones

or   3) 250 = 25 tens

These other ways of describing numbers are what we use when we add numbers that require **regrouping** or **carrying.**

EXAMPLE 3

Add 38 + 27.

Solution

Line up the numbers in their correct columns.

Add the 8 and 7 in the ones column: $8 + 7 = 15$.

Write the 5 in the ones column and "carry the one" to the tens column. We can do this because we are regrouping 15 as $15 = 1$ ten + 5 ones.

Add all the digits in the tens column, including the 1.

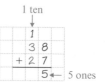

The sum is 65.

[YOU TRY 3] Add 56 + 18.

EXAMPLE 4

Add 256 + 14 + 5,418 + 5 + 743.

Solution

Line up the numbers in their correct columns, and add the digits in the ones column.

> **W Hint**
> As you are reading the example, write it out on your paper too!

```
        2
      2 5 6
        1 4
    5, 4 1 8
          5
  +   7 4 3
          6
```

The sum of the digits in the ones column is 26. Regroup this as 2 tens + 6 ones. Carry the 2 to the tens column.

Add the digits in the hundreds column, including the carried 1.

```
      1 2
      2 5 6
    1   1 4
    5, 4 1 8
          5
  +   7 4 3
      4 3 6
```

The sum of the digits in the hundreds column is 14 hundreds. Regroup this as 1 one-thousand and 4 hundreds. Carry the 1 to the thousands column.

Add the digits in the tens column, including the carried 2.

```
      1 2
      2 5 6
        1 4
    5, 4 1 8
          5
  +   7 4 3
        3 6
```

The sum of the digits in the tens column is 13 tens. Regroup this as 1 hundred and 3 tens. Carry the 1 to the hundreds column.

Add the digits in the thousands column, including the carried 1.

```
      1 2
      2 5 6
    1   1 4
    5, 4 1 8
          5
  +   7 4 3
    6, 4 3 6
```
The final sum is 6,436.

The sum in the thousands column is 6.

The answer is 6,436.

YOU TRY 4 | Add 46 + 7,518 + 947 + 1,136.

3 Solve Applied Problems Using Addition

We use addition in many ways to solve applied problems.

EXAMPLE 5

In-Class Example 5

Use Example 5.

Phil lives in Los Angeles and picked up friends to go to Las Vegas. First, he drove to Bakersfield to pick up Stu, then they drove to Barstow to get Doug and Alan, and then they went on to Las Vegas. Find the total number of miles Phil drove to get to Las Vegas.

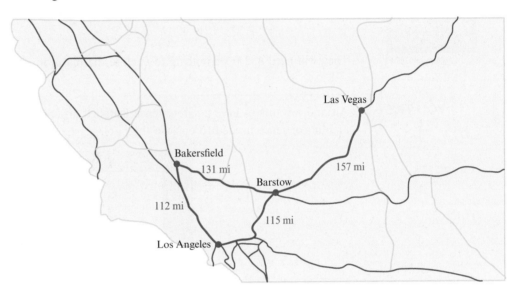

Solution

 Hint

Read the problem carefully, maybe more than once.

 Hint

Do we need the 115-mile distance from LA to Barstow?

The distance from Los Angeles to Bakersfield is 112 mi, the distance from Bakersfield to Barstow is 131 mi, and the distance from Barstow to Las Vegas is 157 mi. Add these numbers to find the total distance that Phil drove.

```
    1 1
    1 1 2 ← Distance from Los Angeles to Bakersfield
    1 3 1 ← Distance from Bakersfield to Barstow
  + 1 5 7 ← Distance from Barstow to Las Vegas
    4 0 0 ← Total number of miles Phil drove
```

Phil drove a total of 400 mi.

YOU TRY 5

Use the map in Example 5. When their vacation was over, Phil, Stu, Doug, and Alan took the shortest route from Las Vegas to Phil's house in Los Angeles. Find the total number of miles they drove back from Las Vegas.

The **perimeter** of a figure is the distance around a figure. We use perimeter to solve many everyday problems.

EXAMPLE 6

A city parks department wants to put a fence around a rectangular playground. How many feet of fencing will they need?

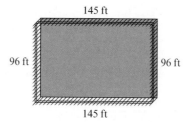

In-Class Example 6

Jocelyn is making a fabric bulletin board for her daughter and wants to put ribbon around the edge. How much ribbon will she need?

Answer: 84 in.

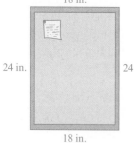

Solution

We must find the *perimeter* of the playground, the total distance around the playground. Add the lengths of all of the sides.

They will need 482 ft of fencing to enclose the playground.

$$
\begin{array}{r}
2\,2 \\
1\,4\,5 \\
9\,6 \\
1\,4\,5 \\
+\ \ 9\,6 \\
\hline
4\,8\,2
\end{array}
$$

[YOU TRY 6]

Alejandra wants to have a safety fence installed around her backyard pool. Find the amount of fence needed to enclose the pool.

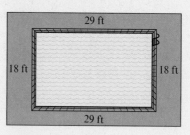

ANSWERS TO [YOU TRY] EXERCISES

1) 19   2) 787   3) 74   4) 9,647   5) 272 mi   6) 94 ft

E Evaluate **1.3** Exercises

Do the exercises, and check your work.

*Additional answers can be found in the Answers to Exercises appendix.

Objective 1: Add Numbers with No Regrouping (Carrying)

Add.

1) 4 + 1 + 7 + 6   18

2) 8 + 5 + 6 + 3   22

3) 56
+ 23   79

4) 67
+ 31   98

5) 432
+ 125   557

6) 608
+ 231   839

7) 4,205
+ 3,581   7,786

8) 1,613
+ 4,152   5,765

9) 2,014
33
+ 921   2,968

10) 16
542
+ 8,431   8,989

11) 375 + 14   389

12) 162 + 23   185

13) 452 + 5,103 + 34   5,589

14) 61 + 8,200 + 137   8,398

22   CHAPTER 1   Addition and Subtraction of Whole Numbers   www.mhhe.com/messersmith

15) 24 + 601 + 3 + 171   16) 410 + 5 + 32 + 251   698
799
17) 60,142 + 11 + 5,200 + 516   65,869

18) 2,431 + 210 + 71,002 + 45   73,688

Objective 2: Add Numbers with Regrouping (Carrying)
Add.

19) 47 + 39   86   20) 75 + 18   93

21) 84 + 36   120   22) 93 + 57   150

23) 375 + 486   861   24) 594 + 187   781

25)   6,594   26)   2,917
     + 1,822   8,416   + 1,846   4,763

27)   5,475   28)   7,692
     + 4,925   10,400   + 2,318   10,010

29)   89   30)   79
       26   132   18   129
     + 17   + 32

31)   8,199   32)   256
         39   8,890   7,654   7,936
     + 652   + 26

33)   571   34)   37,092
     19,680   863
        85   29,808   4,216   50,713
      2,712   28
        803   511
     + 5,957   + 8,003

35) 268 + 564 + 17   849

36) 365 + 52 + 456   873

37) 569 + 956 + 145   1,670

38) 489 + 198 + 363   1,050

39) 8,256 + 936 + 36,589   45,781

40) 1,001 + 89,201 + 199   90,401

41) 12 + 36,987 + 185 + 4 + 2,066   39,254

42) 85,645 + 8 + 3,214 + 198 + 70,301   159,366

43) 23,584 + 1,965 + 354 + 42,000 + 26 + 3,750
71,679
44) 189 + 45,256 + 3,658 + 7,000 + 87 + 810   57,000

45) 9,400 + 78,228 + 55 + 546 + 41,617 + 154   130,000

46) 300 + 20 + 68,000 + 9,500 + 4 + 25,000   102,824

Objective 3: Solve Applied Problems Using Addition
Solve each problem.

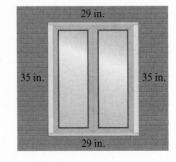

47) A builder installs the window pictured here but still needs to install the trim that goes around it. How many inches of trim will he need?   128 in.

48) Farzan wants to put a fence around his garden to keep out the rabbits. How many feet of fencing will he need?   42 ft

49) Sheng-Li paid $1,199 for a new television and $449 for a home theater system. How much did he pay for these electronics? $1,648

50) For the fall semester, Latrice paid $1,624 for tuition and $582 for books. How much did she pay for tuition and books? $2,206

51) Pauly, Ronnie, and Vinny spend 75 min at the gym, then they go to the tanning salon for 25 min, and finally they spend 110 min doing laundry. How long did they spend on these activities?   210 min

52) Mike did 120 crunches on Monday, 150 crunches on Wednesday, 120 crunches on Friday, and 100 crunches on Sunday. How many crunches did he do all together?   490 crunches

53) A community college has 2,687 students taking math courses on campus, 1,385 at an off-campus facility, and 887 students in online sections. How many total students are enrolled in math courses?
4,959 students
54) An appliance manufacturer has 1,235 employees at its plant in Ohio, 672 employees at its Michigan plant, and 834 people working at its factory in Pennsylvania. Find the total number of employees at these three plants.   2,741 employees

Use the map for Exercises 55–60.

Flying Distances Between Cities

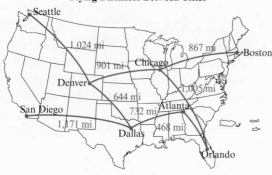

55) Lara is meeting her friends in Colorado to go skiing over Christmas break. She will fly from San Diego to Dallas and then on to Denver. How many miles will she fly to get to Denver?   1,815 mi

56) The Anderson family is flying from Boston to go to Disney World, and they have to change planes in Chicago. Find the total miles they will fly to get from Boston to Orlando.   1,872 mi

57) The cheapest flight that Emilio could find from Seattle to Boston makes stops in Denver and Chicago. How many miles will he travel if he purchases this itinerary?   2,792 mi

58) Corinne gets a cheap flight from her home in Chicago to San Diego if she makes stops in Denver and Dallas. Find the total distance she will travel from Chicago to San Diego.   2,716 mi

59) Find the total, round-trip distance Veronica travels from Dallas to Orlando if she has to change planes in Atlanta.   2,400 mi

60) Using the cities given on the map, find the shortest flying distance from Denver to Orlando.   1,844 mi

Find the perimeter of each figure in Exercises 61 and 62.

61)
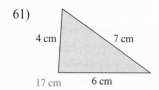
4 cm   7 cm
17 cm   6 cm

62)
4 cm
7 cm
3 cm
20 cm   6 cm

Solve each problem involving perimeter.

24
63) How many inches of wood does James need to make a frame for this picture?   64 in.

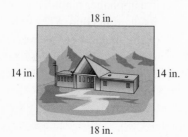
18 in.
14 in.   14 in.
18 in.

64) Mr. Rizzo wants to put a chain-link fence around his property. How many feet of fencing will he need?   376 ft

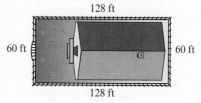
128 ft
60 ft   60 ft
128 ft

65) A community garden is on a corner lot and has the dimensions shown here. If the director wants to put a fence around it, how many feet will she need?   120 ft

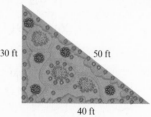
30 ft   50 ft
40 ft

66) Find the length of the border around the backyard ice skating rink.   50 yd

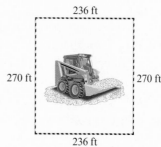
16 yd
9 yd   9 yd
16 yd

67) A construction site is enclosed by yellow tape to keep people out. How many feet of tape were used?   1,012 ft

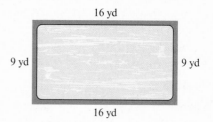
236 ft
270 ft   270 ft
236 ft

68) Haruko is sewing a border around a scarf for her daughter. How many centimeters of the border will she need?   135 cm

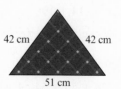
42 cm   42 cm
51 cm

Find the length of each missing side, then find the perimeter of the figure.

69) 2 ft; 3 ft; 28 ft

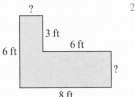

70) 3 in.; 6 in.; 56 in.

R1) Did you use graph paper to help line up the numbers correctly?

R2) Could you explain how to regroup (or carry) to a friend?

R3) Would you be able to complete similar exercises without needing any help?

R4) Think of a situation where you needed to find the sum of two or more "large" numbers. How did you find the sum? How would you find the sum now?

1.4 Introduction to Subtraction

P Prepare

O Organize

What are your objectives for Section 1.4?	How can you accomplish each objective?
1 Subtract Numbers Using a Number Line	• Use the number line to subtract numbers by counting. • Write your own definition of the different parts of a subtraction problem: *minuend, subtrahend,* and *difference.* • Complete the given example on your own. • Complete You Try 1.
2 Relate Subtraction and Addition	• Check a subtraction problem by using addition. • Check an addition problem by using subtraction. • Complete the given examples on your own. • Complete You Trys 2 and 3.
3 Subtract Without Regrouping (Borrowing)	• Write the procedure for **Subtracting Numbers with More Than One Digit** in your own words. • Complete the given examples on your own. • Complete You Trys 4 and 5.
4 Find the Missing Number	• Use the number to line to count the unit gap between the minuend and the difference. • Know that unit gap can be determined by using subtraction. • Complete the given examples on your own. • Complete You Trys 6–8.

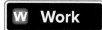
Read the explanations, follow the examples, take notes, and complete the You Trys.

What does $8 - 3$ mean? Let's look at a number line to answer this question.

1 Subtract Numbers Using a Number Line

EXAMPLE 1

In-Class Example 1

Use a number line to subtract $10 - 2$.

Answer: 8

Use a number line to subtract $8 - 3$.

Solution

Start at 0 and move 8 units to the right to reach 8.
To subtract 3, move 3 units to the left. We finish at 5.

$$8 - 3 = 5$$

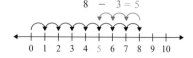

[YOU TRY 1] Use a number line to subtract $9 - 5$.

Note

Notice, also, that if $8 - 3 = 5$, then $8 - 5 = 3$.

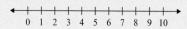

W Hint

Why do you think each number has a different name?

In Example 1, $8 - 3 = 5$, the number 8 is called the **minuend,** the number 3 is called the **subtrahend,** and the number 5 is called the **difference.** You should know the names for the different parts of a subtraction problem.

2 Relate Subtraction and Addition

How is the subtraction problem $8 - 3 = 5$ related to the addition problem $5 + 3 = 8$? Let's look at these problems when they are written vertically.

$$
\begin{array}{c}
8 \\
-\,3 \\
\hline
5
\end{array}
\quad \uparrow 5 + 3 = 8 \quad
\begin{array}{c}
5 \\
+\,3 \\
\hline
8
\end{array}
$$

This means that we can check the answer to a subtraction problem with an addition problem, and we can check the answer to an addition problem with a subtraction problem.

EXAMPLE 2

In-Class Example 2

Subtract $8 - 7$, then check using addition.

Answer: 1; $1 + 7 = 8$

Find $9 - 8$, then check the answer using addition.

Solution

$$
\begin{array}{c}
9 \\
-\,8 \\
\hline
1
\end{array}
\quad \uparrow
\begin{array}{l}
\text{Check:} \\
1 + 8 = 9
\end{array}
\quad \text{Check: }
\begin{array}{c}
1 \\
+\,8 \\
\hline
9
\end{array}
$$

[YOU TRY 2] Find 7 − 2, then check the answer using addition.

EXAMPLE 3

In-Class Example 3

Add 3 + 6, then check using subtraction.

Answer: 9; 9 − 6 = 3

Find 2 + 4, then check the answer using subtraction.

Solution

$$
\begin{array}{r}
2 \\
+\ 4 \\
\hline
6
\end{array}
\quad
\begin{array}{l}
\text{Check:} \\
6 - 4 = 2
\end{array}
\qquad
\text{Check:}
\begin{array}{r}
6 \\
-\ 4 \\
\hline
2
\end{array}
$$

[YOU TRY 3] Find 6 + 1, then check the answer using subtraction.

---

3 Subtract Without Regrouping (Borrowing)

Next, we will subtract numbers containing more than one digit.

> **Procedure** Subtracting Numbers with More Than One Digit
>
> 1) Line up the numbers vertically so that the ones digits are in the same column, the tens digits are in the same column, the hundreds are in the same column, and so on.
> 2) Begin the subtraction process in the column farthest to the right, and then move to the left, subtracting numbers column by column. That is, subtract the numbers in the ones place, then subtract the numbers in the tens place, then subtract the numbers in the hundreds place, and so on.

Once again, we will use graph paper to help us line up our numbers correctly.

EXAMPLE 4

In-Class Example 4

Subtract 65 − 24, then check using addition.

Answer: 41; 41 + 24 = 65

W Hint

Have you tried using graph paper to help you add and subtract?

Subtract 38 − 13, then check the answer using addition.

Solution

Line up the numbers in columns starting with the ones at the right so that the ones are in the same column and the tens are in the same column.

Begin subtracting in the ones column, the column farthest to the right.

Next, subtract the numbers in the tens column.

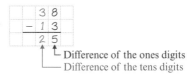

Difference of the ones digits
Difference of the tens digits

The difference is 25. Let's check the answer:

Check:
$$
\begin{array}{r}
2\ 5 \\
+\ 1\ 3 \\
\hline
3\ 8
\end{array}
$$

[YOU TRY 4] Find 75 − 42, then check the answer using addition.

EXAMPLE 5

In-Class Example 5

Subtract 978 − 230, then check using addition.

Answer:
748; 748 + 230 = 978

W Hint

What are the similarities between this procedure and the addition procedure?

Subtract 964 − 250, then check the answer using addition.

Solution

Line up the numbers in columns starting with the ones at the right so that the ones are in the same column, the tens are in the same column, and the hundreds are in the same column.

Begin subtracting in the ones column, the column farthest to the right.

Next, subtract the numbers in the tens column.

Finally, subtract the numbers in the hundreds column.

The difference is 714.

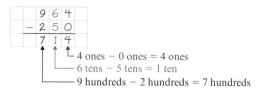

4 ones − 0 ones = 4 ones
6 tens − 5 tens = 1 ten
9 hundreds − 2 hundreds = 7 hundreds

Check:
```
  7 1 4
+ 2 5 0
  9 6 4
```

[YOU TRY 5] Find 498 − 192, then check the answer using addition.

---

4 Find the Missing Number

Let's combine what we know about addition and subtraction to fill in a missing number.

EXAMPLE 6

In-Class Example 6

Fill in the blank:
7 − _____ = 1.

Answer: 6

Fill in the blank: 8 − _____ = 2.

Solution

We can use a number line.

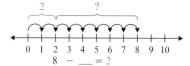

8 − __ = 2

How many units must we move to get from 8 to 2? 6

Therefore, 8 − 6 = 2. We could have also used the related subtraction problem to get the answer. We could have done 8 − 2 = 6 to get that 6 is the missing number.

[YOU TRY 6] Fill in the blank: 10 − _____ = 7.

EXAMPLE 7

In-Class Example 7

Fill in the blank:
354 − _____ = 121.

Answer: 233

W Hint
Which method of finding the missing number is faster? Could it be used to find the missing number in an addition problem?

Fill in the blank: 149 − _____ = 25.

Solution

Use the related subtraction problem, 149 − 25, to get the missing number.

The missing number is 124.

$$
\begin{array}{r}
1\ 4\ 9 \\
-\quad 2\ 5 \\
\hline
1\ 2\ 4
\end{array}
$$

[YOU TRY 7] Fill in the blank: 683 − _____ = 231.

We can find the length of a missing side of a figure using subtraction.

EXAMPLE 8

In-Class Example 8

Use Example 8.

Find the missing length labeled with ?.

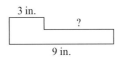

Solution

In Section 1.2, we solved this problem using addition. We can also use subtraction to find the length of the missing side. Notice that the side of length 9 in. *minus* the side of length 3 in. equals the length of the missing side.

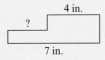

We can write 9 − 3 = _____. The missing number is 6. Therefore, the length of the missing side is 6 in.

[YOU TRY 8] Find the missing length labeled with ?.

4 in.
?
7 in.

ANSWERS TO [YOU TRY] EXERCISES

1)

9 − 5 = 4

0 1 2 3 4 5 6 7 8 9 10

2) 7 − 2 = 5; 5 + 2 = 7

3) 6 + 1 = 7; 7 − 1 = 6
4) 75 − 42 = 33; 33 + 42 = 75
5) 498 − 192 = 306; 306 + 192 = 498
6) 3
7) 452
8) 3 in.

*Additional answers can be found in the Answers to Exercises appendix.

Objective 1: Subtract Numbers Using a Number Line

Identify the minuend, subtrahend, and difference in each subtraction problem.

1) $5 - 4 = 1$
minuend: 5; subtrahend: 4;
difference: 1

2) $6 - 2 = 4$
minuend: 6; subtrahend: 2;
difference: 4

Use a number line to subtract the numbers.

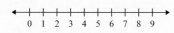

0 1 2 3 4 5 6 7 8 9

3) $9 - 4$

4) $10 - 6$

5) $8 - 5$

6) $9 - 6$

Objective 2: Relate Subtraction and Addition

Subtract. Then, check the answer using addition.

7) $9 - 7$ $2; 2 + 7 = 9$

8) $7 - 3$ $4; 4 + 3 = 7$

9) $5 - 1$ $4; 4 + 1 = 5$

10) $9 - 6$ $3; 3 + 6 = 9$

Add. Then, check the answer using subtraction.

11) $1 + 5$ $6; 6 - 5 = 1$

12) $4 + 3$ $7; 7 - 3 = 4$

13) $7 + 2$ $9; 9 - 2 = 7$

14) $2 + 6$ $8; 8 - 6 = 2$

Objective 3: Subtract Without Regrouping (Borrowing)

Subtract. Then, check the answer using addition.

15) $94 - 52$
$42; 42 + 52 = 94$

16) $69 - 13$ $56; 56 + 13 = 69$

17) $528 - 301$
$227; 227 + 301 = 528$

18) $495 - 260$
$235; 235 + 260 = 495$

19) $156 - 55$
$101; 101 + 55 = 156$

20) $674 - 251$
$423; 423 + 251 = 674$

21) $530 - 410$
$120; 120 + 410 = 530$

22) $398 - 71$
$327; 327 + 71 = 398$

23) $4,859 - 614$
$4,245; 4,245 + 614 = 4,859$

24) $9,227 - 3,024$
$6,203; 6,203 + 3,024 = 9,227$

Objective 4: Find the Missing Number

Fill in the blank.

25) $6 - \underline{\quad} = 2$ 4

26) $8 - \underline{\quad} = 3$ 5

27) $35 - \underline{\quad} = 23$ 12

28) $48 - \underline{\quad} = 23$ 25

29) $439 - \underline{\quad} = 125$
314

30) $172 - \underline{\quad} = 62$ 110

31) $6,570 - \underline{\quad} = 6,030$
540

32) $2,759 - \underline{\quad} = 1,307$
1,452

Answer each question.

33) What number results when you subtract 2 from 9?
7

34) What number results when you subtract 1 from 6?
5

35) What number results when you subtract 32 from 79?
47

36) What number results when you subtract 65 from 88?
23

37) What number results when you subtract 518 from 948?   430

38) What number results when you subtract 122 from 726?   604

39) What number results when you subtract the sum of 3 and 2 from 7?   2

40) What number results when you subtract the sum of 1 and 4 from 9?   4

Find the missing length labeled with ?.

41)

? | 9 in. | 2 in.
11 in.

42)
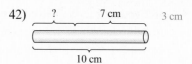
? | 7 cm | 3 cm
10 cm

43)
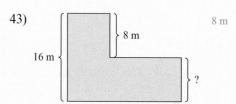
16 m | 8 m | 8 m | ?

44)
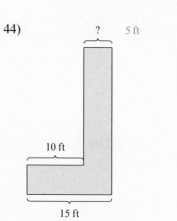
? | 5 ft
10 ft
15 ft

45)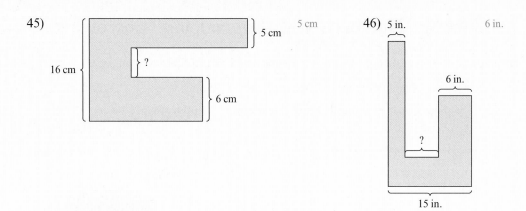

46)

R Rethink

R1) Do you have a firm grasp on subtraction?

R2) Were you able to check all of your answers?

R3) What would happen if you changed the order of a subtraction problem? Give an example of what that would look like. Do you get the same answer?

1.5 Subtracting Whole Numbers

P Prepare

O Organize

What are your objectives for Section 1.5?	How can you accomplish each objective?
1 Subtract Numbers with Regrouping (Borrowing)	• Follow the examples and add any additional steps needed to your procedure you wrote for **Subtracting Numbers with More Than One Digit.** • Complete the given examples on your own. • Complete You Trys 1 and 2.
2 Subtract Numbers Involving Zeros	• Follow the examples and write your own procedure for regrouping numbers that contain zeros. • Complete the given examples on your own. • Complete You Trys 3 and 4.
3 Solve Applied Problems Using Subtraction	• Read the applied problem twice and be sure to understand what is being asked. • Complete the given example on your own. • Complete You Try 5.

W Work

Read the explanations, follow the examples, take notes, and complete the You Trys.

In Section 1.4, we were introduced to subtraction. Now let's look at some subtraction problems where we must regroup or *borrow*.

1 Subtract Numbers with Regrouping (Borrowing)

Sometimes, we have to regroup when we subtract. For example, we can write

8 tens = 7 tens + 1 ten = 7 tens + 10 ones

5 hundreds = 4 hundreds + 1 hundred = 4 hundreds + 10 tens

EXAMPLE 1

Subtract
$$\begin{array}{r} 83 \\ -\ 16 \end{array}$$

In-Class Example 1

Subtract
$$\begin{array}{r} 62 \\ -\ 37 \end{array}$$

Answer: 25

Solution

Normally, we would begin by subtracting $3 - 6$ in the ones column, but because 6 is greater than 3 we must regroup the 8 tens in 83.

Look at the number 83. We will "borrow" one ten from the tens column and add it to the ones column as 10 ones.

Borrow 1 ten from the 8 tens: →
$$\begin{array}{r} {}^{7}\ {}^{13} \\ \cancel{8}\ \cancel{3} \\ -\ 1\ 6 \end{array}$$
← Add the 1 ten to the 3 ones:

8 tens − 1 ten = 7 tens   1 ten + 3 ones = 10 ones + 3 ones
= 13 ones

Next, subtract the numbers in the ones column. Then, subtract the numbers in the tens column.

$$\begin{array}{r} {}^{7}\ {}^{13} \\ \cancel{8}\ \cancel{3} \\ -\ 1\ 6 \\ \hline 6\ 7 \end{array}$$

7 tens − 1 ten = 6 tens   13 ones − 6 ones = 7 ones

The difference is 67.

Check using addition:

$$\begin{array}{r} 1\ \\ 6\ 7 \\ +\ 1\ 6 \\ \hline 8\ 3 \end{array}$$

[YOU TRY 1]

Subtract
$$\begin{array}{r} 72 \\ -\ 38 \end{array}$$

EXAMPLE 2

Subtract.

a) $$\begin{array}{r} 572 \\ -\ 249 \end{array}$$

b) $$\begin{array}{r} 341 \\ -\ 263 \end{array}$$

c) $$\begin{array}{r} 1,254 \\ -\ 178 \end{array}$$

In-Class Example 2

Subtract.

a) $\begin{array}{r} 853 \\ -\ 318 \end{array}$ b) $\begin{array}{r} 721 \\ -\ 566 \end{array}$

c) $\begin{array}{r} 1{,}831 \\ -\ 754 \end{array}$

Answer:

a) 535   b) 155   c) 1,077

Hint

Notice how each part of this example is different from the others.

Solution

a) We cannot just subtract the numbers in the ones column because the 9 is bigger than the 2. So, we have to borrow a ten from the tens column:

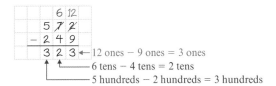

$7 \text{ tens} - 1 \text{ ten} = 6 \text{ tens}$ $\begin{array}{r} 6\ \ 12 \\ 5\ \cancel{7}\ \cancel{2} \\ -\ 2\ 4\ 9 \end{array}$ $1 \text{ ten} + 2 \text{ ones} =$
$10 \text{ ones} + 2 \text{ ones} = 12 \text{ ones}$

Subtract the numbers in the ones column, then the numbers in the tens column, then the numbers in the hundreds column.

$\begin{array}{r} 6\ \ 12 \\ 5\ \cancel{7}\ \cancel{2} \\ -\ 2\ 4\ 9 \\ \hline 3\ 2\ 3 \end{array}$ ← 12 ones − 9 ones = 3 ones
6 tens − 4 tens = 2 tens
5 hundreds − 2 hundreds = 3 hundreds

The difference is 323.

b) First, regroup in the tens column.

$4 \text{ tens} - 1 \text{ ten} = 3 \text{ tens}$ $\begin{array}{r} 3\ \ 11 \\ 3\ \cancel{4}\ \cancel{1} \\ -\ 2\ 6\ 3 \end{array}$ $1 \text{ ten} + 1 \text{ one} =$
$10 \text{ ones} + 1 \text{ one} = 11 \text{ ones}$

The 6 in the tens column is bigger than the 3 in the tens column. So, we have to regroup again. Then, subtract.

$3 \text{ hundreds} - 1 \text{ hundred} = 2 \text{ hundreds}$ $\begin{array}{r} 13 \\ 2\ \cancel{3}\ 11 \\ \cancel{3}\ \cancel{4}\ \cancel{1} \\ -\ 2\ 6\ 3 \\ \hline 7\ 8 \end{array}$ $1 \text{ hundred} + 3 \text{ tens} =$
$10 \text{ tens} + 3 \text{ tens} = 13 \text{ tens}$
Subtract.

The difference is 78.

c) How do we start? Regroup in the tens column because the 8 in the ones column is larger than the 4.

$5 \text{ tens} - 1 \text{ ten} = 4 \text{ tens}$ $\begin{array}{r} 4\ \ 14 \\ 1{,}2\ \cancel{5}\ \cancel{4} \\ -\ \ \ 1\ 7\ 8 \end{array}$ $1 \text{ ten} + 4 \text{ ones} =$
$10 \text{ ones} + 4 \text{ ones} = 14 \text{ ones}$

The 7 in the tens column is bigger than the 4 above it. Regroup again, then subtract.

$2 \text{ hundreds} - 1 \text{ hundred} = 1 \text{ hundred}$ $\begin{array}{r} 14 \\ 1\ \cancel{4}\ 14 \\ 1{,}\cancel{2}\ \cancel{5}\ \cancel{4} \\ -\ \ \ 1\ 7\ 8 \\ \hline 1{,}0\ 7\ 6 \end{array}$ $1 \text{ hundred} + 4 \text{ tens} =$
$10 \text{ tens} + 4 \text{ tens} = 14 \text{ tens}$
Subtract.

The difference is 1,076.

[YOU TRY 2] Subtract.　a) $\begin{array}{r} 985 \\ -\ 317 \end{array}$　b) $\begin{array}{r} 634 \\ -\ 159 \end{array}$　c) $\begin{array}{r} 1{,}623 \\ -\ \ \ 596 \end{array}$

2 Subtract Numbers Involving Zeros

EXAMPLE 3

In-Class Example 3

Subtract $\begin{array}{r} 6{,}702 \\ -\ 2{,}368 \end{array}$

Answer: 4,334

Subtract $\begin{array}{r} 9{,}502 \\ -\ 4{,}356 \end{array}$

Solution

In the ones column, the 6 is greater than the 2 so we must regroup and borrow from the tens column. However, there are no tens in the tens column. Therefore, we must regroup 1 hundred as 10 tens.

W Hint

If you have to regroup during subtraction, you will need to regroup when checking your answer.

5 hundreds − 1 hundred = 4 hundreds

$$\begin{array}{r} {\scriptstyle 4\ \ 10} \\ 9{,}\cancel{5}\cancel{0}\ 2 \\ -\ 4{,}3\ 5\ 6 \end{array}$$

1 hundred + 0 tens = 10 tens + 0 tens = 10 tens

Now we can borrow from the tens column.

10 tens − 1 ten = 9 tens

$$\begin{array}{r} {\scriptstyle 9} \\ {\scriptstyle 4\ \ 10\ \ 12} \\ 9{,}\cancel{5}\cancel{0}\cancel{2} \\ -\ 4{,}3\ 5\ 6 \\ \hline 5{,}1\ 4\ 6 \end{array}$$

1 ten + 2 ones = 10 ones + 2 ones = 12 ones
Subtract.

The difference is 5,146. Verify that 5,146 + 4,356 = 9,502.

[YOU TRY 3] Subtract $\begin{array}{r} 5{,}804 \\ -\ 1{,}287 \end{array}$

EXAMPLE 4

In-Class Example 4

Subtract.

a) $\begin{array}{r} 380 \\ -\ 142 \end{array}$　b) $\begin{array}{r} 906 \\ -\ 388 \end{array}$

c) $\begin{array}{r} 3{,}000 \\ -\ 1{,}299 \end{array}$

Answer: a) 238
b) 518　c) 1,701

Subtract.

a) $\begin{array}{r} 890 \\ -\ 514 \end{array}$　b) $\begin{array}{r} 601 \\ -\ 273 \end{array}$　c) $\begin{array}{r} 4{,}000 \\ -\ 1{,}699 \end{array}$

Solution

a)　Regroup 1 ten as 10 ones. Then, subtract.

9 tens − 1 ten = 8 tens

$$\begin{array}{r} {\scriptstyle 8\ \ 10} \\ 8\ \cancel{9}\ \cancel{0} \\ -\ 5\ 1\ 4 \\ \hline 3\ 7\ 6 \end{array}$$

1 ten + 0 ones = 10 ones + 0 ones = 10 ones
Subtract.

The difference is 376.

34　CHAPTER 1　**Addition and Subtraction of Whole Numbers**　www.mhhe.com/messersmith

b) To subtract in the ones column, we have to "borrow" a ten from the tens column. But, as the problem is written now, there are zero tens. Therefore, regroup 1 hundred as 10 tens. Then, borrow.

Regroup 1 hundred as 10 tens.

$$\begin{array}{r} 5\ \ 10\ \ \ \\ \cancel{6}\ \ \cancel{0}\ \ 1 \\ -\ 2\ \ 7\ \ 3 \end{array}$$

Regroup 1 ten as 10 ones.

$$\begin{array}{r} 9\ \ \ \\ 5\ \ \cancel{10}\ \ 11 \\ \cancel{6}\ \ \cancel{0}\ \ \cancel{1} \\ -\ 2\ \ 7\ \ 3 \\ \hline 3\ \ 2\ \ 8 \end{array}\ \ \text{Subtract.}$$

The difference is 328.

c) We have to regroup 1 thousand, 1 hundred, *and* 1 ten in order to subtract.

$$\begin{array}{r} 9\ \ 9\ \ \ \ \\ 3\ \ \cancel{10}\ \ \cancel{10}\ \ 10 \\ \cancel{4},\ \cancel{0}\ \ \cancel{0}\ \ \cancel{0} \\ -\ 1,\ 6\ \ 9\ \ 9 \\ \hline 2,\ 3\ \ 0\ \ 1 \end{array}$$

The difference is 2,301.

[**YOU TRY 4**]

Subtract.   a) $\begin{array}{r}470\\-238\end{array}$ b) $\begin{array}{r}705\\-389\end{array}$ c) $\begin{array}{r}8,000\\-4,899\end{array}$

3 Solve Applied Problems Using Subtraction

We use subtraction in many ways to solve applied problems.

EXAMPLE 5

In-Class Example 5

Use the table in Example 5. How much more did Cristie Kerr win than Paula Creamer?

Answer: $639,772

The table shows the amount of money won by certain golfers on the LPGA tour in 2010 through October 17, 2010. Who won more money, Michelle Wie or Morgan Pressel? How much more money did she win?

Golfer	Tournament Winnings
Paula Creamer	$740,721
Cristie Kerr	$1,380,493
Morgan Pressel	$699,313
Jiyai Shin	$1,463,833
Michelle Wie	$848,485

(www.lpga.com)

Solution

Michelle Wie won more money because $848,485 is more than the $699,313 won by Morgan Pressel. To determine how much *more* money Michelle won, we subtract the smaller number from the larger one.

$$\begin{array}{r} 13\ \ \ \ \ \ \ \ \ \\ 7\ \ \cancel{14}\ \ 18\ \ \ \ \ \\ \cancel{8}\ \ \cancel{4}\ \ \cancel{8},\ 4\ \ 8\ \ 5 \\ -\ 6\ \ 9\ \ 9,\ 3\ \ 1\ \ 3 \\ \hline 1\ \ 4\ \ 9,\ 1\ \ 7\ \ 2 \end{array}\ \ \text{Subtract.}$$

Michelle Wie won $149,172 more than Morgan Pressel.

YOU TRY 5 Use the table in Example 5. Who won more money, Cristie Kerr or Jiyai Shin? How much more did she win?

ANSWERS TO [YOU TRY] EXERCISES

1) 34   2) a) 668   b) 475   c) 1,027   3) 4,517   4) a) 232   b) 316   c) 3,101
5) Jiyai Shin won $83,340 more than Cristie Kerr.

E Evaluate **1.5** Exercises   Do the exercises, and check your work.

*Additional answers can be found in the Answers to Exercises appendix.

Objective 1: Subtract Numbers with Regrouping (Borrowing)
Subtract.

1) 21
    − 7   14

2) 72
    − 9   63

3) 62
    − 48   14

4) 54
    − 26   28

5) 95
    − 37   58

6) 71
    − 52   19

7) 43
    − 19   24

8) 81
    − 35   46

9) 678
    − 159   519

10) 491
    − 183   308

11) 425
    − 189   236

12) 944
    − 396   548

13) 833
    − 747   86

14) 672
    − 593   79

15) 2,513
    − 364   2,149

16) 4,922
    − 755   4,167

17) 7,436
    − 4,058   3,378

18) 9,227
    − 5,139   4,088

19) 2,549
    − 1,985   564

20) 5,794
    − 4,979   815

Objective 2: Subtract Numbers Involving Zeros
Subtract.

21) 70
    − 7   63

22) 60
    − 8   52

23) 920
    − 207   713

24) 580
    − 151   429

25) 702
    − 325   377

26) 406
    − 218   188

27) 6,074
    − 2,519   3,555

28) 9,063
    − 7,825   1,238

29) 3,008
    − 1,478   1,530

30) 5,003
    − 2,611   2,392

31) 19,021
    − 16,998   2,023

32) 75,106
    − 56,197   18,909

33) 800
    − 164   636

34) 600
    − 358   242

35) 7,000
    − 2,564   4,436

36) 2,000
    − 1,316   684

37) 9,000
    − 3,907   5,093

38) 4,000
    − 2,668   1,332

39) 66,005
    − 37,894   28,111

40) 81,009
    − 22,654   58,355

Mixed Exercises: Objectives 1 and 2
Subtract.

41) 947 − 215   732

42) 4,693 − 1,277   3,416

43) 8,416 − 2,719   5,697

44) 806 − 432   374

45) 5,000
    − 1,799   3,201

46) 7,000
    − 2,999   4,001

47) 8,945
    − 1,898   7,047

48) 87,020
    − 26,415   60,605

49) Subtract 9,614 from 32,884.   23,270

50) Subtract 62,078 from 283,120.   221,042

51) Subtract 15,907 from 85,428.   69,521

52) Subtract 34,040 from 70,026.   35,986

Objective 3: Solve Applied Problems Using Subtraction

Solve each problem.

53) Aris needs to complete 42 semester units to meet his general education requirement to earn his degree. If he has already completed 24 units in this area, how many more units does he need to complete his general education requirement?   18

54) Sumaya received $2,378 in financial aid last year. This year she received $2,501. How much more money did she receive this year? $123

55) A Burger King Double Whopper with cheese has 990 calories, while the BK Big Fish Sandwich has 640 calories. How many fewer calories does the fish sandwich have? (www.bk.com)   350

56) The Applegate subdivision contains 365 homes while the Tallgrass subdivision contains 473 homes. How many more homes are in the Tallgrass subdivision?
108

57) The average annual salary of a registered nurse in Montana in 2009 was $56,380. In Texas, the average annual salary was $64,670. How much more was the average annual salary in Texas? (www.bls.gov) $8,290

58) The sticker price on a car was $24,145, but Jignesh paid $21,300. How much money did he save off the sticker price? $2,845

59) In 2012, a university had 5,366 students. This is 371 more than in 2010. How many students attended in 2010?   4,995

60) At Seneca High School, 694 students are taking Spanish. This is 257 more than the number of students studying French. How many are taking French?   437

61) In 2006, approximately 6,071,000 people participated in a book club at least once. The estimate for 2008 was 6,720,000. In which year did more people participate in a book club? How many more? (www.census.gov)   2008; 649,000

62) In 2008, the population of Vermont was approximately 621,000, and the population of Delaware was about 873,000. Which state had the larger population? By how much? (www.census.gov)
Delaware; 252,000

63) The driving distance from Washington, D.C., to Des Moines, IA, is about 1,060 mi. The distance from Washington, D.C., to Oklahoma City, OK, is about 1,330 mi. How much farther is it from Washington D.C. to Oklahoma City?   270 mi

64) In 2008, 43,257 people attended the championship game of the NCAA Final Four tournament. In 2009, that number was 72,922. How many fewer people attended the championship game in 2008? (web1.ncaa.org)   29,665

65) If the perimeter of the figure is 21 in., find the missing side length.   7 in.

66) If the perimeter of the figure is 40 cm, find the missing side length.   8 cm

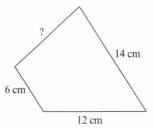

R Rethink

R1) Do you understand how to subtract when you have to borrow?

R2) Did you check all of your answers?

R3) Did you get help on any problems you could not do or that you got wrong?

Putting It All Together

P Prepare | **O Organize**

What are your objectives?	How can you accomplish each objective?
1 Review the Concepts of Sections 1.1–1.5	• Be sure that you can apply the objectives you have learned in the previous sections. • If you are not confident on a certain example, go back to the section that gives more explanation. • Complete the given examples on your own. • Complete You Try 1.

W Work

Read the explanations, follow the examples, take notes, and complete the You Try.

1 Review the Concepts of Sections 1.1–1.5

In Section 1.1, we learned about whole numbers and place value, and we learned how to write numbers in words.

EXAMPLE 1

In-Class Example 1

Write the number 5,238,014 in words, then identify the place value of the digits 2 and 0.

Answer:
five million, two hundred thirty-eight thousand, fourteen; 2 hundred-thousands; 0 hundreds

Write the number 653,072 in words, then identify the place value of the digits 5 and 0.

Solution

In words, we write 653,072 as *six hundred fifty-three thousand, seventy-two.*

Identifying the place values, we get

$$6\ 5\ 3,\ 0\ 7\ 2$$

5 ten-thousands   0 hundreds

Next, let's look at addition and subtraction problems together.

EXAMPLE 2

In-Class Example 2

Perform the indicated operation.
a) 8,946 + 31 + 578
b)   95,171
  − 2,864

Answer:
a) 9,555   b) 92,307

 Hint

Be sure to notice whether the problem is addition or subtraction!

Perform the indicated operation.

a)   2,472 + 85 + 621   b)   38,152
      − 5,347

Solution

a) Line up the numbers in their correct columns. Begin adding in the ones column, the column farthest to the right. Then, add the numbers in the tens column, the hundreds column, and the thousands column. Regroup (carry) where it is necessary.

The sum is 3,178.

$$\begin{array}{r} 1\ 1\ \\ 2,4\ 7\ 2 \\ 8\ 5 \\ +\ \ 6\ 2\ 1 \\ \hline 3,1\ 7\ 8 \end{array}$$

b) Line up the numbers in the correct columns, and begin subtracting in the ones column. Because the 7 is larger than the 2, we have to regroup and "borrow" from the tens column. We must regroup in other columns, too.

The difference is 32,805.

$$\begin{array}{r} 7\ 11\ 4\ 12 \\ 3\ 8,1\ 5\ 2 \\ -\ \ 5,3\ 4\ 7 \\ \hline 3\ 2,8\ 0\ 5 \end{array}$$

The commutative and associative properties of addition can make it easier for us to add numbers.

EXAMPLE 3

In-Class Example 3

Add 8 + 6, then rewrite the addition problem using the commutative property.

Answer: 14; 6 + 8

Add 5 + 7, then rewrite the addition problem using the commutative property.

Solution

5 + 7 = 12. The commutative property says that changing the order in which we add numbers does not change the sum. Therefore, 5 + 7 = 7 + 5.

EXAMPLE 4

In-Class Example 4

Add 1 + (9 + 8), then rewrite the addition problem using the associative property.

Answer: 18; (1 + 9) + 8

Add 6 + (4 + 9), then rewrite the addition problem using the associative property.

Solution

The associative property says that we can change the position of the grouping symbols and the sum remains the same.

Original Sum	Using the Associative Property
6 + (4 + 9) =	(6 + 4) + 9 =
6 + 13 = 19	10 + 9 = 19

We can use addition and subtraction to solve applied problems. One application is finding the *perimeter* of a figure. Remember that the **perimeter** is the distance around a figure.

EXAMPLE 5

In-Class Example 5

Use Example 5.

Byron wants to enclose his garden with a fence to keep out the rabbits. The garden has the dimensions shown here. How many feet of fencing will he need?

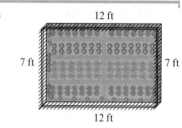

Solution

Because the fence will go *around* the garden, the number of feet of fencing Byron needs is the same as the *perimeter* of the garden. To find the perimeter, add the lengths of all of the sides:

$$12 \text{ ft} + 7 \text{ ft} + 12 \text{ ft} + 7 \text{ ft} = 38 \text{ ft}$$

The perimeter of the garden is 38 ft, so Byron will need 38 ft of fencing.

[YOU TRY 1]

a) Write the number 85,061,973 in words, then identify the place value of the digits 8 and 0.

b) Subtract 52,736 − 18,192.

c) Add 354 + 67,909 + 81 + 5,547.

d) Subtract 4,288 − 935.

e) Add 7 + (3 + 14), then rewrite the addition problem using the associative property.

f) Add 9 + 2, then rewrite the addition problem using the commutative property.

g) Find the perimeter of the figure:

7 cm

11 cm   11 cm

13 cm

Putting It All Together Exercises

 **Evaluate**   Do the exercises, and check your work.

Additional answers can be found in the Answers to Exercises appendix.

Objective 1: Review the Concepts of Sections 1.1–1.5

Identify the digit with the given place value in each whole number.

1) 72,963

   a) ones   b) hundreds   c) one-thousands
      3   9   2

2) 207,498,365

   a) ten-thousands   b) hundred-millions
      9   2

   c) one-millions   7

3) Write the number 720,653,008 in words, then identify the place value of the digits 2 and 5.

4) Write the number 5,000,744,216 in words, then identify the place value of the digits 5 and 1.   five billion, seven hundred forty-four thousand, two hundred sixteen; 5 one-billions; 1 tens

5) Write *thirty-two billion, seventy million, nine hundred eighty-eight thousand, eleven* using digits.
   32,070,988,011

6) Write *two hundred million, four hundred fifty-three thousand, eight hundred one* using digits.
   200,453,801

Perform the indicated operation.

7)   123
      256
   + 368
   —————
      747

8)   52
   − 29
   ———
     23

9)   13,589
   − 10,895
   ————
     2,694

10) 711 + 7,668 + 59 + 34,026   42,464

11) 8,023 − 926   7,097

12) 4,000 − 2,718   1,282

13) 273,551 + 387 + 9,066 + 32,174   315,178

14)   62,900,588
        83,044
    7,892,521   71,094,060
          977
   + 216,930

15) Subtract 34,617 from 80,000.   45,383

16) Find the sum of 9,004 and 2,798.   11,802

17) Subtract 293 from the sum of 756 and 1,366.   1,829

18) Subtract 41 from the sum of 128 and 72.   159

19) Add (12 + 7) + 6, then rewrite the addition problem using the associative property.   25; 12 + (7 + 6)

20) Add 32 + 67, then rewrite the addition problem using the commutative property.   99; 67 + 32

21) Add 271 + 588, then rewrite the addition problem using the commutative property.   859; 588 + 271

22) Add 153 + (47 + 89), then rewrite the addition problem using the associative property.
   289; (153 + 47) + 89

Find the missing number.

23) 7 + _____ = 12   5   24) 19 − _____ = 11   8

25) 64 + _____ = 98   34   26) 4 + _____ = 10   6

27) 47 − _____ = 28   19   28) 83 − _____ = 25   58

Find the missing length.

29)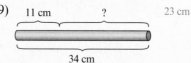

30)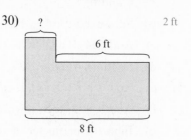

Find the perimeter of the figures in Exercises 31 and 32.

31)

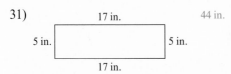

44 in.

32)

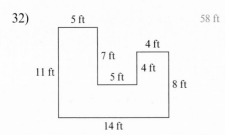

58 ft

Solve each problem.

33) A public works department is repairing some water pipes and must enclose the area with tape to keep people out. How much tape will they need?   120 ft

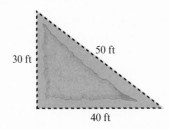

34) Guillermo is building a rectangular dog run with the dimensions shown here. How much fencing will he need?   124 ft

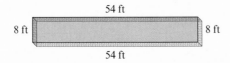

35) One week, Kristen skated for 45 min on Monday and Wednesday, 30 min on Tuesday, 60 min on Thursday, 40 min on Friday, and 75 min on Saturday and Sunday. How many minutes did she skate that week?   370 min

36) Last year, Kayla paid a total of $367 for her textbooks. This year she paid $403. How much more did she pay this year for her books? $36

37) Tache needs to complete 126 semester units to earn his Bachelor of Science degree. If he has already completed 97 semester units, how many more units does he need to graduate?   29 semester units

38) When Dontrell went to Cedar Point, he waited in line 25 min for the maXair ride, 80 min for Top Thrill Dragster, 65 min for Raptor, and 75 min for Thunder Canyon. How long did he spend waiting in line for these rides?   245 min

The table shows the number of games played by selected Major League Baseball players from 2007 to 2009. Use the information to solve the problems in Exercises 39–42. (mlb.mlb.com)

Player	2007	2008	2009
Ryan Howard	144	162	160
Derek Jeter	156	150	153
Paul Konerko	151	122	152
Alex Rodriguez	158	138	124

39) Find the total number of games played by the four players in 2007.   609

40) In 2009, Ryan Howard played in how many more games than Alex Rodriguez?   36

41) In 2008, Paul Konerko played in how many fewer games than Derek Jeter?   28

42) Find the total number of games played by Alex Rodriguez during these three years.   420

R Rethink

R1) Discuss how you use both subtraction and addition outside of the math classroom.

R2) Where could you go if you needed help on some of the problems?

1.6 Rounding and Estimation

What are your objectives for Section 1.6?	How can you accomplish each objective?
1 Round Numbers	• Write the procedure for **Rounding Numbers** in your own words. • Complete the given examples on your own. • Complete You Trys 1–3.
2 Round Numbers to Estimate a Sum or Difference	• Round to the indicated place by using the procedure for rounding numbers, and add or subtract. • Complete the given examples on your own. • Complete You Trys 4 and 5.

W Work   Read the explanations, follow the examples, take notes, and complete the You Trys.

To **round** a number means to find another number close to the original number. Think about a number line. If we had to round the number 43 to the nearest ten, we could think about a number line on which each tick mark represents 10 units.

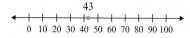

43

0 10 20 30 40 50 60 70 80 90 100

Is 43 closer to 40 or 50 on the number line? It is closer to 40. Therefore, we can say that 43 rounded to the nearest ten is 40.

Usually, we round numbers to make them easier to work with. Let's list the steps for rounding numbers.

1 Round Numbers

We can use these steps to round numbers:

> **Procedure** Rounding Numbers
>
> **Step 1:** Find the place to which we are asked to round. Underline the digit in that place.
>
> **Step 2:** Look at the digit to the right of the underlined digit.
> a) If the digit to the right is **less than 5,** leave the underlined digit as it is.
> b) If the digit to the right is **5 or more,** increase the underlined digit by 1.
>
> **Step 3:** Change all the digits to the right of the underlined digit to zeros.

> **Note**
>
> Remember that the one-thousands place can also be called the *thousands* place, the one-millions place can also be called the *millions* place, and so on. From this section onward, we will use *thousands* place, *millions* place, etc.

EXAMPLE 1

Round each number to the indicated place.

a) 62 to the nearest ten   b) 273 to the nearest hundred

c) 8,529 to the nearest thousand

Solution

a) *Step 1:* Because we are asked to round 62 to the tens place, underline the number in that place: 6̲2

Step 2: Look at the digit to the right of the underlined digit. That digit is 2. Since 2 is less than 5, we will leave the underlined digit as it is, 6.

Digit to right is less than 5.

6 2̲

Keep this a 6.

Step 3: Change the digit to the right of the 6 to a zero: 60

62 rounded to the nearest ten is 60. Therefore, 62 is closer to 60 than to 70.

Hint

Why is it important to underline the digit to which you are rounding?

b) *Step 1:* Because we are asked to round 273 to the hundreds place, underline the number in that place: 2̲73

Step 2: Look at the digit to the right of the underlined digit. That digit is 7. Since 7 is greater than 5, we will increase the underlined digit by 1 to make it 3.

Digit to right is 5 or more.

2 7̲ 3

Increase from 2 to 3.

Step 3: Change the digits to the right of the 3 to zeros: 300

273 rounded to the nearest hundred is 300. Therefore, 273 is closer to 300 than to 200.

c) *Step 1:* To round 8,529 to the nearest thousands place, underline the number in that place: 8̲,529

Step 2: Look at the digit to the right of the underlined digit. That digit is 5. Since 5 is 5 or more, we will increase the underlined digit by 1 to make it 9.

Digit to right is 5 or more.

8̲,529

Increase from 8 to 9.

Step 3: Change the digits to the right of the 9 to zeros: 9,000

8,529 rounded to the nearest thousand is 9,000.

[YOU TRY 1] Round each number to the indicated place.

a) 78 to the nearest ten

b) 2,544 to the nearest thousand

c) 526 to the nearest hundred

Next, we will round larger numbers.

EXAMPLE 2

Round each number to the indicated place.
a) 30,691 to the nearest hundred
b) 274,198 to the nearest thousand
c) 80,514,997 to the nearest million

Answer:
a) 30,700   b) 274,000
c) 81,000,000

Round each number to the indicated place.

a) 24,185 to the nearest hundred

b) 421,306 to the nearest thousand

c) 70,522,917 to the nearest million

Solution

a) *Step 1:* Underline the number in the hundreds place: 24,185

  Step 2: Look at the digit to the right of the underlined digit. Since 8 is greater than 5, we will increase the underlined digit by 1 to make it 2.

  ──Digit to right is 5 or more.

  2 4, 1 8 5

  Increase from 1 to 2.──

  Step 3: Change the digits to the right of the underlined digit to zeros: 24,200

  24,185 rounded to the nearest hundred is 24,200. Therefore, 24,185 is closer to 24,200 than to 24,100.

b) *Step 1:* Underline the number in the thousands place: 421,306

  Step 2: Look at the digit to the right of the underlined digit. Since 3 is less than 5, we will keep the underlined digit a 1.

  ──Digit to right is less than 5.

  421, 306

  Keep this a 1.──

  Step 3: Change the digits to the right of the 1 to zeros: 421,000

  421,306 rounded to the nearest thousand is 421,000.

c) *Step 1:* Underline the number in the millions place: 70,522,917

  Step 2: Look at the digit to the right of the underlined digit. Since 5 is 5 or more, we will increase the underlined digit by 1 to make it 1.

  ──Digit to right is 5 or more.

  70, 522,917

  Increase from 0 to 1.──

  Step 3: Change the digits to the right of the 1 to zeros: 71,000,000

  70,522,917 rounded to the nearest million is 71,000,000.

[YOU TRY 2] Round each number to the indicated place.

a) 94,270 to the nearest hundred

b) 578,413 to the nearest thousand

c) 63,503,881 to the nearest million

Sometimes, we have to use regrouping to round numbers.

EXAMPLE 3

In-Class Example 3

Round each number to the indicated place.
a) 6,974 to the nearest hundred
b) 295,318,260 to the nearest ten million

Answer:
a) 7,000   b) 300,000,000

Ⓦ Hint

This example involves rounding and regrouping or carrying!

Round each number to the indicated place.

a) 4,982 to the nearest hundred

b) 596,204,950 to the nearest ten-million

Solution

a) **Step 1:** Underline the digit in the hundreds place: 4,9̲82

Step 2: Look at the digit to the right of the 9. Since 8 is greater than 5, we must increase the underlined digit by 1.

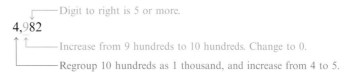

But 9 hundreds + 1 hundred = 10 hundreds, so we have to regroup the 10 hundreds as 1 thousand and add that to the 4 in the thousands place.

Step 3: Change the digits to the right of the underlined digit to zeros: 5,000

4,982 rounded to the nearest hundred is 5,000.

b) **Step 1:** Underline the digit in the ten-millions place: 59̲6,204,950

Step 2: Look at the digit to the right of the underlined digit. Since 6 is greater than 5, we will increase the underlined digit by 1.

```
                  ┌─── Digit to right is 5 or more.
            ↓
59 6,204,950
   ↑ ↑
   │ └────── Increase from 9 ten-millions to 10 ten-millions. Change to 0.
   └─────────── Regroup 10 ten-millions as 1 hundred-million, and increase from 5 to 6.
```

But 9 ten-millions + 1 ten-million = 10 ten-millions, so we have to regroup the 10 ten-millions as 1 hundred-million and add that to the 5 in the hundred-millions place.

Step 3: Change the digits to the right of the underlined digit to zeros: 600,000,000

596,204,950 rounded to the nearest ten million is 600,000,000.

[YOU TRY 3]

Round each number to the indicated place.

a) 275,958 to the nearest hundred

b) 39,801,042 to the nearest million

2 Round Numbers to Estimate a Sum or Difference

Sometimes, we want to find an approximation or *estimation* of the sum or difference of numbers. We can estimate an answer to an addition or subtraction problem by first rounding the numbers in the problem and then performing the operation on those numbers. In this way, we *estimate* the sum or the difference. It is not the exact answer, but it is close to the actual answer. (The estimated answer can be used as a check for the exact answer.) Instead of using an = symbol, we can use the symbol ≈, which means "approximately equal to."

EXAMPLE 4

In-Class Example 4

Estimate the answer of the sum 429 + 645 + 281 by first rounding each number to the nearest
a) ten
b) hundred

Answer: a) 1,360   b) 1,300

Estimate the answer of the sum 217 + 556 + 134 by first rounding each number to the nearest

a)   ten   b)   hundred

Solution

a)   Round each number to the nearest ten, then find the sum.

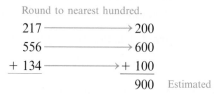

Round to nearest ten.

$$
\begin{aligned}
217 &\longrightarrow 220 \\
556 &\longrightarrow 560 \\
+\,134 &\longrightarrow +\,130 \\
&\ 910 \quad \text{Estimated}
\end{aligned}
$$

Rounded to the nearest ten, 217 + 556 + 134 ≈ 910.

b)   Round each number to the nearest hundred, then find the sum.

Round to nearest hundred.

$$
\begin{aligned}
217 &\longrightarrow 200 \\
556 &\longrightarrow 600 \\
+\,134 &\longrightarrow +\,100 \\
&\ 900 \quad \text{Estimated}
\end{aligned}
$$

Rounded to the nearest hundred, 217 + 556 + 134 ≈ 900.

Note

The exact sum of the numbers is 217 + 556 + 134 = 907. Our estimations in parts a) and b) are very close.

[YOU TRY 4]

Estimate the answer of the sum 385 + 182 + 633 by first rounding each number to the nearest

a)   ten   b)   hundred

EXAMPLE 5

In-Class Example 5

Estimate the answer of the difference 8,623 − 5,296 by first rounding each number to the nearest
a) thousand
b) hundred

Answer: a) 4,000   b) 3,300

Estimate the answer of the difference 5,893 − 2,152 by first rounding each number to the nearest

a)   thousand   b)   hundred

Solution

a)   Round each number to the nearest thousand, then subtract.

Round to nearest thousand.

$$
\begin{aligned}
5,893 &\longrightarrow 6,000 \\
-\,2,152 &\longrightarrow -\,2,000 \\
&\ 4,000 \quad \text{Estimated difference}
\end{aligned}
$$

b)   Round each number to the nearest hundred, then subtract.

Round to nearest hundred.

$$
\begin{aligned}
5,893 &\longrightarrow 5,900 \\
-\,2,152 &\longrightarrow -\,2,200 \\
&\ 3,700 \quad \text{Estimated difference}
\end{aligned}
$$

The exact difference of the two numbers, 5,893 − 2,152, is 3,741.

E Evaluate **1.6** Exercises   Do the exercises, and check your work.

*Additional answers can be found in the Answers to Exercises appendix.

Objective 1: Round Numbers

Use the number line to round each number to the nearest ten.

```
←—+—+—+—+—+—+—+—+—+—+—+—→
  0 10 20 30 40 50 60 70 80 90 100
```

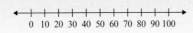 1) 23 20   2) 52 50   3) 39 40

4) 17 20   5) 87 90   6) 76 80

7) 2 0   8) 6 10

Use the number line to round each number to the nearest hundred.

```
←—+—+—+—+—+—+—+—+—→
  0  100 200 300 400 500 600 700 800
```

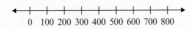 9) 362 400   10) 204 200   11) 123 100

12) 683 700   13) 549 500   14) 451 500

15) 64 100   16) 32 0

17) Explain, in your own words, how to round a number to the nearest hundred. Answers may vary.

18) Explain, in your own words, how to round a number to the nearest thousand. Answers may vary.

Round each number to the indicated place.

19) 38 to the nearest ten 40

20) 12 to the nearest ten 10

21) 157 to the nearest hundred 200

22) 253 to the nearest hundred 300

23) 8,498 to the nearest thousand 8,000

24) 5,703 to the nearest thousand 6,000

25) 76,501 to the nearest thousand 77,000

26) 16,409 to the nearest thousand 16,000

27) 145,528 to the nearest thousand 146,000

28) 235,001 to the nearest thousand 235,000

29) 47 to the nearest hundred 0

30) 85 to the nearest hundred 100

31) 39,762 to the nearest thousand 40,000

32) 709,574 to the nearest thousand 710,000

33) 549,321 to the nearest hundred-thousand 500,000

34) 751,423 to the nearest hundred-thousand 800,000

35) 219,502 to the nearest ten-thousand 220,000

36) 61,775 to the nearest ten-thousand 61,000

37) 3,541,672 to the nearest hundred-thousand 3,500,000

38) 2,499,381 to the nearest hundred-thousand 2,500,000

39) 399,129,721 to the nearest ten-million 400,000,000

40) 199,752,000 to the nearest ten-million 200,000,000

41) 299,318 to the nearest ten-thousand 300,000

42) 699,422 to the nearest ten-thousand 700,000

43) 999 to the nearest thousand 1,000

44) 35,999 to the nearest hundred-thousand 0

Round each number to the nearest ten, nearest hundred, and nearest thousand.

		Ten	Hundred	Thousand
45)	84	80	100	0
46)	45	50	0	0
47)	781	780	800	1,000
48)	523	520	500	1,000
49)	1,397	1,400	1,400	1,000
50)	2,495	2,500	2,500	2,000
(24) 51)	619,755	619,760	619,800	620,000
52)	734,974	734,970	735,000	735,000

Objective 2: Round Numbers to Estimate a Sum or Difference

Estimate the answer to each problem by first rounding each number to the nearest ten. Then, find the exact answer.

(24) 53)
$$\begin{array}{r} 56 \\ + 23 \\ \hline 79 \end{array}\quad \begin{array}{r} 60 \\ + 20 \\ \hline 80 \end{array}$$

54)
$$\begin{array}{r} 72 \\ + 14 \\ \hline 86 \end{array}\quad \begin{array}{r} 70 \\ + 10 \\ \hline 80 \end{array}$$

55)
$$\begin{array}{r} 56 \\ 64 \\ + 23 \\ \hline 143 \end{array}\quad \begin{array}{r} 60 \\ 60 \\ + 20 \\ \hline 140 \end{array}$$

56)
$$\begin{array}{r} 72 \\ 26 \\ + 55 \\ \hline 153 \end{array}\quad \begin{array}{r} 70 \\ 30 \\ + 60 \\ \hline 160 \end{array}$$

57)
$$\begin{array}{r} 65 \\ - 42 \\ \hline 23 \end{array}\quad \begin{array}{r} 70 \\ - 40 \\ \hline 30 \end{array}$$

58)
$$\begin{array}{r} 98 \\ - 52 \\ \hline 46 \end{array}\quad \begin{array}{r} 100 \\ - 50 \\ \hline 50 \end{array}$$

59)
$$\begin{array}{r} 83 \\ - 22 \\ \hline 61 \end{array}\quad \begin{array}{r} 80 \\ - 20 \\ \hline 60 \end{array}$$

60)
$$\begin{array}{r} 44 \\ - 18 \\ \hline 26 \end{array}\quad \begin{array}{r} 40 \\ - 20 \\ \hline 20 \end{array}$$

Estimate the answer to each problem by first rounding each number to the nearest hundred. Then, find the exact answer.

61)
$$\begin{array}{r} 672 \\ + 231 \\ \hline 903 \end{array}\quad \begin{array}{r} 700 \\ + 200 \\ \hline 900 \end{array}$$

62)
$$\begin{array}{r} 318 \\ + 754 \\ \hline 1,072 \end{array}\quad \begin{array}{r} 300 \\ + 800 \\ \hline 1,100 \end{array}$$

63)
$$\begin{array}{r} 183 \\ 579 \\ + 617 \\ \hline 1,379 \end{array}\quad \begin{array}{r} 200 \\ 600 \\ + 600 \\ \hline 1,400 \end{array}$$

64)
$$\begin{array}{r} 850 \\ 238 \\ + 519 \\ \hline 1,607 \end{array}\quad \begin{array}{r} 900 \\ 200 \\ + 500 \\ \hline 1,600 \end{array}$$

65)
$$\begin{array}{r} 726 \\ - 388 \\ \hline 338 \end{array}\quad \begin{array}{r} 700 \\ - 400 \\ \hline 300 \end{array}$$

66)
$$\begin{array}{r} 316 \\ - 172 \\ \hline 144 \end{array}\quad \begin{array}{r} 300 \\ - 200 \\ \hline 100 \end{array}$$

67)
$$\begin{array}{r} 4,063 \\ - 2,419 \\ \hline 1,644 \end{array}\quad \begin{array}{r} 4,100 \\ - 2,400 \\ \hline 1,700 \end{array}$$

68)
$$\begin{array}{r} 9,251 \\ - 8,216 \\ \hline 1,035 \end{array}\quad \begin{array}{r} 9,300 \\ - 8,200 \\ \hline 1,100 \end{array}$$

69) The flying distance from Lisbon, Portugal to Sydney, Australia is 11,302 mi. Round this number to the nearest thousand.   11,000 mi

70) In 2008, 3,912,000 people flew between Los Angeles and New York City. Round this number to the nearest million. (www.census.gov)   4,000,000

(24) 71) The population of the state of California is 36,961,664. Estimate the population to the nearest hundred-thousand and nearest million. (www.census.gov)   37,000,000; 37,000,000

72) In 2007, there were 98,916 public elementary and secondary schools in the United States. Round this number to the nearest thousand. (National Center for Education Statistics)   99,000

73) One day, 654,931,407 shares of stock of a major company were traded. Round that number to the nearest ten-million.   650,000,000

74) In 2008, the United States imported 3,571,000,000 barrels of crude oil from OPEC nations. Round that number to the nearest billion. (www.census.gov)   4,000,000,000

R Rethink

R1) How have you used estimation or rounding in the last week?

R2) Redo a few problems from Exercises 61 to 68, but round to the nearest ten first. Discuss the accuracy of this estimation compared to rounding to the nearest hundred. What can you say about your comparison?

1.7 Reading Pictographs, Bar Graphs, and Line Graphs

P Prepare

O Organize

What are your objectives for Section 1.7?	How can you accomplish each objective?
1 Read a Pictograph	• Write the definition of a *pictograph* in your own words. • Complete the given example on your own. • Complete You Try 1.
2 Read a Bar Graph	• Write the definition of a *bar graph* in your own words. • Complete the given example on your own. • Complete You Try 2.
3 Read a Line Graph	• Write the definition of a *line graph* in your own words. • Complete the given example on your own. • Complete You Try 3.

 **Work**   **Read the explanations, follow the examples, take notes, and complete the You Trys.**

Graphs are visual ways to represent information. We will study three types of graphs in this section: pictographs, bar graphs, and line graphs.

1 Read a Pictograph

A **pictograph** is a graph that uses pictures or symbols to represent information. While this type of graph is visually appealing, it may be difficult to read fractional parts of a whole.

EXAMPLE 1

Use the given pictograph to answer the following questions.

In-Class Example 1

Use Example 1.

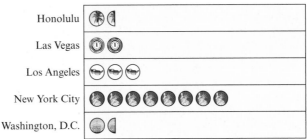

Approximate Number of Foreign Visitors to Selected United States Cities in 2008

Each symbol represents 1 million visitors.
(www.census.gov)

a) Which city had the most foreign visitors, and approximately how many visitors did it have?

b) Which two cities had the same number of visitors?

c) How many fewer people visited Las Vegas than Los Angeles?

Solution

a) New York City had the most foreign visitors because it has the greatest number of symbols. Since there are 8 pictures of the Statue of Liberty and each of them represents 1 million people, there were 8 million foreign visitors to New York City.

b) Because Honolulu and Washington, D.C., have the same number of pictures, they had the same number of visitors.

c) Los Angeles had 3 million visitors and Las Vegas had 2 million visitors, so to determine how many fewer people visited Las Vegas, we subtract:
3 million − 2 million = 1 million fewer visitors to Las Vegas.

[**YOU TRY 1**] Use the pictograph in Example 1 to answer the following questions.

a) How many people visited Honolulu?

b) How many more people visited New York City than Las Vegas?

Note

We can also use multiplication to interpret information in graphs. We will look at this in Chapter 2.

2 Read a Bar Graph

A **bar graph** is another way to display and read information. In Example 2, the graph displays the number of farms in certain states in 2008.

EXAMPLE 2   Use the given bar graph to answer the following questions.

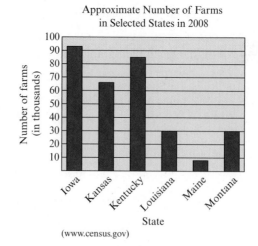

Approximate Number of Farms in Selected States in 2008

(www.census.gov)

a) How many farms did Louisiana have in 2008?

b) Which state had the fewest farms, and approximately how many did it have?

c) Which state had approximately 66,000 farms?

Solution

a) Go to the top of the bar for Louisiana. It touches the line that is a guide for reading the graph. On the left, that line is labeled 30. Notice that the number of farms is in thousands, so the "30" represents 30,000. Therefore, Louisiana had 30,000 farms.

b) The state with the lowest bar had the fewest farms. That state is Maine. To determine how many farms were in Maine, go to the top of the bar for Maine and move in a straight line to the left where you see the scale for the numbers. The top of the bar is a little lower than 10, let's say at 8, so we will estimate it as 8,000 farms.

c) The number 66,000 is a little more than halfway between 60,000 and 70,000. Since the units on the left are in thousands, go to the left of the graph and locate the region between 60 and 70. Move to the right to see that the bar that reaches a little above halfway between 60 and 70 is for Kansas. Therefore, Kansas had approximately 66,000 farms.

[**YOU TRY 2**] Use the bar graph in Example 2 to answer the following questions.

a) Which state had approximately 85,000 farms?

b) How many fewer farms were in Montana than in Kentucky?

3 Read a Line Graph

A **line graph** is another type of graph that is often used to represent information. A line graph is a good way to show trends in information over time. The graph in Example 3 shows the number of hours spent playing video games per person per year for various years.

EXAMPLE 3 Use the given line graph to answer the following questions.

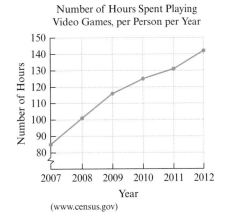

Number of Hours Spent Playing Video Games, per Person per Year

(www.census.gov)

a) How many hours per person per year were spent playing video games in 2007?

b) In what year did the number of hours equal 125?

c) What is the general trend in the number of hours spent playing video games over the time period shown?

Solution

a) Locate the year 2007 at the bottom of the graph. Go up to the graph and move straight to the left. The dot on the line graph is halfway between the 80 and 90, so we will estimate the number at 85. In 2007, the amount of time spent playing video games was about 85 hr per person per year.

b) On the left side of the graph, 125 is halfway between 120 and 130. Locate that place on the left, then move straight over to the right until you reach the line graph. Then, read down; the year is 2010.

c) As we move along the graph from 2007 to 2012, the numbers increase. Therefore, the number of hours people spend playing video games is increasing each year.

[YOU TRY 3] Use the line graph in Example 3 to answer the following questions.

a) In what year did a person spend about 101 hr per year playing video games?

b) How many more hours did a person spend playing video games in 2012 than in 2007?

ANSWERS TO [YOU TRY] EXERCISES

1) a) 1,500,000 b) 6,000,000   2) a) Kentucky b) 55,000
3) a) 2008 b) approximately 57 more hours (Answers may vary.)

E Evaluate **1.7** Exercises   Do the exercises, and check your work.

*Additional answers can be found in the Answers to Exercises appendix.

Objective 1: Read a Pictograph

The pictograph shows the amounts of food items sold at a community fair. Use the pictograph to answer the questions in Exercises 1–6.

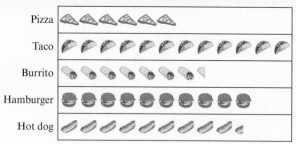

Amount of Food Sold at a Fair

Each symbol = 100 units

1) How many hamburgers were sold at this event? 1,000

2) Approximately how many hot dogs were sold? 950

3) Which food item was the most popular at the fair? How many of these food items were sold? tacos; 1,200

4) Which food item had the least sales? pizza

5) Approximately how many more hamburgers than burritos were sold? 250

6) Approximately how many hot dogs and hamburgers were sold at this event? 1,950

Objective 2: Read a Bar Graph

The bar graph shows the number of miles of interstate highways for six selected states. Use the graph to answer the questions in Exercises 7–14.

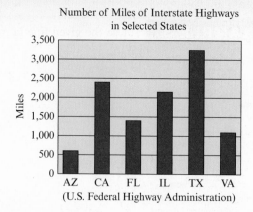

Number of Miles of Interstate Highways in Selected States

(U.S. Federal Highway Administration)

7) Which state has the greatest number of miles of interstate highways? Texas

8) Which state has the least interstate mileage? Arizona

9) Which state has approximately 2,400 mi of interstate highways? California

10) Which states have less than 1,500 mi of interstate highways? Arizona, Florida, Virginia

11) How many more miles of interstate highway does Texas have than Illinois? Approximate your answer. 1,100 mi

12) How many more miles of interstate highway does California have than Arizona? Approximate your answer. 1,800 mi

13) How many miles of interstate highway do Florida and Virginia have combined? Approximate your answer. 2,500 mi

14) How many miles of interstate highway do California and Texas have combined? Approximate your answer. 5,650 mi

Objective 3: Read a Line Graph

The line graph shows the cost of a U.S. first-class postage stamp for various years. Use the graph to answer the questions in Exercises 15–22.

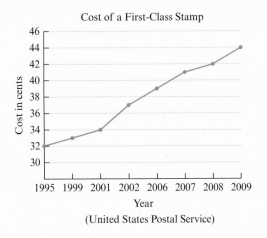

Cost of a First-Class Stamp

(United States Postal Service)

15) What was the cost of a stamp in 1995? 32 cents

16) What was the cost of a stamp in 2007? 41 cents

17) In what year was the cost of a stamp 37 cents? 2002

18) In what year was the cost of a stamp 42 cents? 2008

19) By how much did the price of a stamp increase between 1995 and 2001? 2 cents

20) By how much did the price of a stamp increase between 2001 and 2007? 7 cents

21) How much less did a first-class stamp cost in 1995 than in 2009? 12 cents less

22) What is the general trend in the cost of a first-class stamp? The cost is increasing.

R Rethink

R1) What did you find most interesting about these types of problems?

R2) Which of the three graphs did you find easiest to work with, and why?

Group Activity – Rounding and Estimation

- Students should work in teams of two.
- After reading the problems, each team will decide on a proper estimate for the answer to the problem. It is up to the team members to decide the most appropriate place value for rounding and estimating. Teams should record their estimates, and the chosen place value, on a sheet of paper.

- After each team has determined all the estimates, two teams will get together and share their estimates. Then, the two teams will work together to find the exact answer to each of the problems and compare the exact answers to the estimates.
- The members of the team whose estimate was the closest to the exact answer should share their strategy for finding the estimate with the other team.

1) The distance between Dallas, Texas and Scottsdale, Arizona is 873 mi, and the distance between Dallas, Texas and Cleveland, Ohio is 1,027 mi. How much farther is Dallas from Cleveland than it is from Scottsdale?

2) A home improvement store advertises a washing machine on sale for $899 and a dryer on sale for $599. What is the cost for both appliances?

3) The Lincoln family took a cross-country trip this summer. The daily distances traveled during the first week of the trip are shown below.

Day 1	677 mi
Day 2	589 mi
Day 3	327 mi
Day 4	141 mi
Day 5	216 mi
Day 6	442 mi
Day 7	57 mi

What is the total distance traveled by the Lincoln family during the first week of the trip?

4) A certain sport utility vehicle (SUV) at one car dealership has a sticker price of $24,585. The same SUV has a sticker price of $26,899 at a different dealership. What is the difference in price between the two dealerships?

5) According to the 2010 United States Census, the population of Indiana is 6,483,802 and the population of Illinois is 12,830,632. How much larger is the population of Illinois than Indiana?

Challenge Exercise

Answer the next question with your team members.

- Sometimes your estimate is higher than the exact answer and sometimes it is lower. Why is this so?

Group Activity Answers

1) Estimates will vary. Possible estimate: 160 mi. Exact: 154 mi
2) Estimates will vary. Possible estimate: $1,500. Exact: $1,498.
3) Estimates will vary. Possible estimate: 2,460 mi. Exact: 2,449 mi
4) Estimates will vary. Possible estimate: $2,300. Exact: $2,314.
5) Estimates will vary. Possible estimate: 6,500,000 people. Exact: 6,346,830 people.

Student responses to the last question will vary. An appropriate response will refer to the place value that is chosen and the operation used in the problem (addition or subtraction).

 em**POWER**me Who's in Charge?

One essential component to success—in the classroom and beyond—is taking responsibility for your results. Yes, there will always be things that happen that are beyond your control. But if you blame the alarm that didn't go off or the mosquito that wouldn't stop buzzing during the test for your poor results on a math test, you will never improve. You have the power, and the responsibility, to achieve your goals.

To get a sense of your ideas of why things happen to you, circle the statement from each of the pairs below that best describes your views.

1. A. In the long run, people get the respect they deserve in this world.
   B. Unfortunately, an individual's value often goes unrecognized no matter how hard he or she tries.

2. A. The idea that teachers are unfair to students is nonsense.
   B. Most students don't realize the extent to which their exam results are influenced by random events.

3. A. I have found that much of what happens will happen no matter what I do.
   B. Trusting fate has never turned out as well for me as making a decision to take a definite course of action.

4. A. For a well-prepared student, there is rarely, if ever, such a thing as an unfair exam.
   B. Many times, exam questions are unrelated to coursework, and studying is often useless.

5. A. Becoming a success is a matter of hard work; luck has little or nothing to do with it.
   B. Getting a good job depends mainly on being in the right place at the right time.

6. A. It is not always wise to plan too far ahead because you can never predict what's going to happen to you.
   B. When I make plans, I am almost certain that I can make them work.

7. A. In my case, getting what I want has little or nothing to do with luck.
   B. I often feel like I might as well decide what to do by flipping a coin.

8. A. In general, I feel that I have little influence over the things that happen to me.
   B. It is impossible for me to believe that chance or luck plays an important role in my life.

9. A. What happens to me is my own doing.
   B. Sometimes I feel that I don't have enough control over the direction my life is taking.

10. A. Sometimes I can't understand how teachers arrive at the grades they give.
    B. There is a direct connection between how hard a person studies and the grades he or she gets.

Scoring: Give yourself one point for each of the following answers and then add up your score:

1. A 2. A 3. B 4. A 5. A 6. B 7. A 8. B 9. A 10. B

Your total score can range from 0 to 10. The higher your score, the more you believe that you have a strong influence over what happens to you and that you are in control of your life and your own behavior. The lower your score, the more you believe that your life is outside of your control and what happens to you is caused by luck or fate.

If you score below 5 on this questionnaire, consider how rethinking your views of the causes of what happens to you might lead to greater success.

―――――

Adapted from "Do you control what happens to you?" in Nathenson, M. (1985). *The Book of Tests.* New York: Penguin.

Chapter 1: Summary

Definition/Procedure	Example

1.1 Whole Numbers and Place Value

A **digit** is a single character in a numbering system. **(p. 5)**

The **decimal system** consists of the digits 0, 1, 2, 3, 4, 5, 6, 7, 8, and 9. **(p. 5)**

The **whole numbers** are 0, 1, 2, 3, 4, 5, 6, 7, 8, 9, 10, 11, 12, ... **(p. 5)**

Each digit in a whole number represents a **place value** that is determined by where it appears in the number. **(p. 5)**

Write the number 78,250,361 in words and identify the place value of the digits 7 and 0.

In words, the number is *seventy-eight million, two hundred fifty thousand, three hundred sixty-one.*

The place value of 7 is 7 ten-millions, and the place value of the 0 is 0 thousands or 0 one-thousands.

1.2 Introduction to Addition

We can use a **number line** to add numbers. **(p. 11)**

The numbers being added together are called the **addends,** and the answer is called the **sum. (p. 12)**

Use a number line to add 3 + 2.

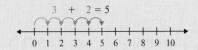

3 + 2 = 5. The addends are 3 and 2. The sum is 5.

The **commutative property of addition** says that changing the order in which we add numbers does not change the sum. **(p. 12)**

The commutative property tells us that 9 + 4 = 4 + 9.

The **associative property of addition** says that we can change the position of grouping symbols when adding numbers and the sum remains the same. **(p. 13)**

The associative property tells us that (7 + 6) + 2 = 7 + (6 + 2).

1.3 Adding Whole Numbers

Adding Numbers with More Than One Digit

1) Line up the numbers vertically so that the ones digits are in the same column, the tens digits are in the same column, the hundreds digits are in the same column, and so on.

2) Begin the addition process in the column farthest to the right, and then move to the left, adding numbers column by column. **(p. 19)**

Add 403 + 52 + 8,124.

$$\begin{array}{r} 4\,0\,3 \\ 5\,2 \\ +\,8,1\,2\,4 \\ \hline 8,5\,7\,9 \end{array}$$

The sum is 8,579.

Sometimes, adding numbers requires **regrouping** or **carrying. (p. 19)**

Add 6,472 + 2,063.

We have to regroup, or carry, when adding these numbers.

$$\begin{array}{r} 1 \\ 6,4\,7\,2 \\ +\,2,0\,6\,3 \\ \hline 8,5\,3\,5 \end{array}$$

The sum of the digits in the tens column is 13 tens. Regroup this as 1 hundred and 3 tens. Carry the 1 to the hundreds column.

The sum is 8,535.

Definition/Procedure	Example
The **perimeter** of a figure is the distance around the figure. To find the perimeter, find the sum of the lengths of the sides around the figure. **(p. 21)**	Find the perimeter of this rectangle. 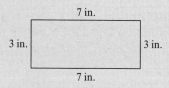 7 in. + 3 in. + 7 in. + 3 in. = 20 in. The perimeter is 20 in.

1.4 Introduction to Subtraction

We can use a number line to subtract numbers. **(p. 26)** The answer to a subtraction problem is called the **difference.** We can check the answer to a subtraction problem by adding, and we can check our answer to an addition problem by subtracting. **(p. 26)**	Use a number line to subtract 7 − 4. 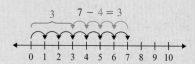 7 − 4 = 3. The **minuend** is 7, and the **subtrahend** is 4. The **difference** is 3. We can check our answer using addition: 3 + 4 = 7.
Subtracting Numbers with More Than One Digit 1) Line up the numbers vertically so that the ones digits are in the same column, the tens digits are in the same column, the hundreds are in the same column, and so on. 2) Begin the subtraction process in the column farthest to the right, and then move to the left, subtracting numbers column by column. That is, subtract the numbers in the ones place, then subtract the numbers in the tens place, then subtract the numbers in the hundreds place, and so on. **(p. 27)**	Subtract 685 − 271. $$\begin{array}{r} 6\ 8\ 5 \\ -\ 2\ 7\ 1 \\ \hline 4\ 1\ 4 \end{array}$$ The difference is 414.

1.5 Subtracting Whole Numbers

Sometimes, we have to **regroup** or **borrow** when we subtract numbers. **(p. 32)**	Subtract $\begin{array}{r} 5,736 \\ -\ 2,254 \end{array}$ 7 hundreds − 1 hundred = 6 hundreds $\begin{array}{r} 6\ 13 \\ 5,\cancel{7}\ \cancel{3}\ 6 \\ -\ 2,2\ 5\ 4 \\ \hline 3,4\ 8\ 2 \end{array}$ 1 hundred + 3 tens = 10 tens + 3 tens = 13 tens The difference is 3,482. Check by adding: 3,482 + 2,254 = 5,736.

Definition/Procedure	Example

1.6 Rounding and Estimation

Rounding Numbers

To **round** a number means to find another number close to the original number. We can use these steps to round numbers.

Step 1: Find the place to which we are asked to round. Underline the digit in that place.

Step 2: Look at the digit to the right of the underlined digit.

    a) If the digit to the right is **less than 5,** leave the underlined digit as it is.

    b) If the digit to the right is **5 or more,** increase the underlined digit by 1.

Step 3: Change all the digits to the right of the underlined digit to zeros. **(p. 43)**

Round 2,378,541 to the nearest

a) million   b) thousand

        — Digit to right is less than 5.

a) 2,378,541

Since the digit to the right of the 2 is less than 5, keep the underlined digit 2. Make all digits to the right of the underlined digit zeros.

Rounding to the nearest million, we get 2,000,000.

        — Digit to right is 5 or more.

b) 2,378,541

Since the digit to the right of the 2 is 5 or more, increase the 8 by 1 to make it 9. Make all digits to the right of the underlined digit zeros.

Rounding to the nearest thousand, we get 2,379,000.

We can **estimate** the sum or difference of numbers by first rounding the numbers in the problem.

The symbol ≈ means "approximately equal to." **(p. 46)**

Estimate the answer of the sum $687 + 326$ by first rounding each number to the nearest hundred. Then, find the exact sum.

Round to nearest hundred.

$$687 \longrightarrow 700$$
$$+\ 326 \longrightarrow +\ 300$$
$$1,000 \quad \text{Estimated sum}$$

The exact sum is 1,013.

1.7 Reading Pictographs, Bar Graphs, and Line Graphs

Graphs are visual ways to represent information. In this section, we learned how to read and interpret **pictographs, bar graphs,** and **line graphs. (p. 50)**

Use the given bar graph to answer the following questions.

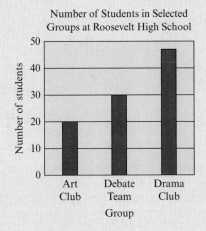

Number of Students in Selected Groups at Roosevelt High School

a) Which group is the largest, and approximately how many students are in it? The Drama Club is the largest with about 47 students.

b) How many more people are on the Debate Team than in the Art Club? The Debate Team has 10 more members since $30 - 20 = 10$.

Chapter 1: Review Exercises

*Additional answers can be found in the Answers to Exercises appendix.

(1.1) Identify the place value of the digit 7 in each whole number.

1) 7,015,388,602
   7 one-billions

2) 972,429
   7 ten-thousands

Identify the digits in each period.

3) 138,952,600
   138 millions, 952 thousands, 600 ones

4) 56,033,421,007
   56 billions, 33 millions, 421 thousands, 7 ones

Write each number in words.

5) 490,617,005,915

6) 98,468,040

(1.2) Use a number line to add the numbers.

0 1 2 3 4 5 6 7 8 9 10

7) 6 + 3

8) 4 + 3 + 1

9) In your own words, explain the commutative property of addition.

10) In your own words, explain the associative property of addition.

Add, then rewrite the problem using the commutative property.

11) 3 + 8   11; 8 + 3

12) 8 + 7   15; 7 + 8

13) 6 + 3 + 4   13; Answers may vary.

14) 4 + 1 + 6   11; Answers may vary.

Add, then rewrite the problem using the associative property.

15) 1 + (9 + 5)   15; (1 + 9) + 5

16) (2 + 5) + 6   13; 2 + (5 + 6)

Fill in the blank.

17) 7 + _____ = 10   3

18) 2 + _____ = 8   6

Find the length of the missing side.

19)
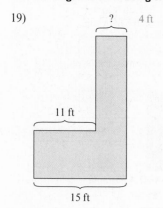
? 4 ft
11 ft
15 ft

20) What number do you add to 2 to get 9?   7

(1.3) Add.

21)   43
    + 52   95

22)   381
    + 405   786

23) 74 + 112 + 3   189

24) 5,223 + 31 + 402 + 3   5,659

25)   2,752
    + 5,439   8,191

26)   78,504
    + 21,658   100,162

27)   6,576
       4,258   14,198
    + 3,364

28)   499
       384   1,082
    + 199

29) 6,317 + 290,405 + 52,033 + 245   349,000

30) 422 + 54,778 + 67 + 8,495 + 706   64,468

Find the perimeter of each figure.

31)
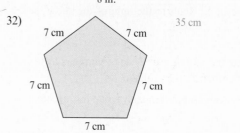
8 in.   24 in.
4 in.   4 in.
8 in.

32)
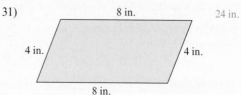
7 cm   35 cm
7 cm
7 cm   7 cm
7 cm

Solve each problem.

33) Javier has 543 Facebook friends, and Ivette has 329. How many Facebook friends do they have all together?   872

34) The first week of April, Marta paid $280 for her son's child care, the second week she paid $220, the third week she paid $240, and the fourth week she paid $260. How much did Marta pay for child care in April? $1,000

35) A landscaper has to put edging around a flower bed. How much will he need?   38 ft

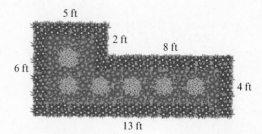
5 ft
2 ft   8 ft
6 ft
4 ft
13 ft

36) A community college is remodeling its football field and needs to put a fence around it. How many feet of fencing are needed?   1,410 ft

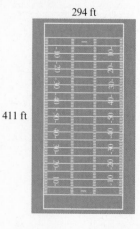
294 ft
411 ft

(1.4) Use a number line to subtract the numbers.

```
0  1  2  3  4  5  6  7  8  9  10
```

37) $10 - 4$ 38) $8 - 3$

Subtract. Check your answer using addition.

39) $7 - 4$ 3; 3 + 4 = 7   40) $8 - 6$ 2; 2 + 6 = 8

41) $38 - 17$ 42) $682 - 150$
     21; 21 + 17 = 38   532; 532 + 150 = 682

43)   19,605   44)   89,377
    $-\ 3,203$ $-\ 54,164$
16,402; 16,402 + 3,203 = 19,605   35,213; 35,213 + 54,164 = 89,377

Add. Check your answer using subtraction.

45) $24 + 61$ 46) $536 + 201$
    85; 85 − 61 = 24   737; 737 − 201 = 536

47)   622,130   48)   32,401
   $+\ 270,025$ $+\ 16,594$
892,155; 892,155 − 270,025 = 622,130   48,995; 48,995 − 16,594 = 32,401

Fill in the blank.

49) $97 - \underline{\quad} = 26$ 71   50) $458 - \underline{\quad} = 136$ 322

51) What number results when you subtract 5 from 9?   4

52) What number results when you subtract 42 from 78?   36

53) What number results when you subtract 3,614 from 8,915?
    5,301

54) Find the missing length.   23 in.

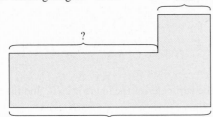

31 in.

(1.5) Subtract.

55)   83   56)   60
   $-\ 27$ 56 $-\ 36$ 24

57)   523   58)   945
  $-\ 328$ 195 $-\ 656$ 289

59) $6,177 - 789$ 5,388   60) $9,452 - 1,468$ 7,984

61)   7,831   62) $81,913 - 72,856$ 9,057
  $-\ 2,994$ 4,837

63) $9,438 - 2,919$ 6,519   64)   78,101
                        $-\ 55,099$ 23,002

65)   3,101   66)   7,000
  $-\ 2,979$ 122 $-\ 1,999$ 5,001

Solve each problem.

67) In one month, Serena sent
3,208 texts while Blair sent
4,107. How many fewer texts
did Serena send?   899

68) In 2012, the Richards family paid $6,014 in real estate taxes. Their bill in 2011 was $5,823. By how much did their tax bill increase? $191

69) In July 2010, the population of India was 1,156,897,766. The population of China was 1,338,612,968. How many more people were there in China? (www.cia.gov)   181,715,202

70) In October 2004, there were 16,557,273 registered voters in California. In October 2008, that number had risen to 17,304,091. How many more people were registered to vote in 2008? (www.sos.ca.gov)   746,818

(1.6) Round each number as indicated.

71) 6,239 to the nearest hundred   6,200

72) 8,731 to the nearest thousand   9,000

73) 31,508 to the nearest thousand   32,000

74) 423,892 to the nearest hundred-thousand   400,000

75) 9,622,563 to the nearest million   10,000,000

76) 82,495,907 to the nearest ten-thousand   82,500,000

Estimate the answer to each problem by rounding each number to the nearest ten. Then, find the exact answer.

77)   79   80   78)   943   940
  $+\ 64$ $+\ 60$ $-\ 427$ $-\ 430$
   143   140   516   510

Estimate the answer to each problem by rounding each number to the nearest hundred. Then, find the exact answer.

79)   5,358   5,400   80)   871   900
  $-\ 1,149$ $-\ 1,100$ $-\ 254$ $-\ 300$
   4,209   4,300   617   600

81) In 2009, the population of Georgia was 9,829,211. Round this number to the nearest hundred-thousand. (quickfacts.census.gov)   9,800,000

82) In 2008, men's clothing sales in the United States totaled $8,630,000,000. Round this number to the nearest billion. (www.census.gov) $9,000,000,000

(1.7) The following line graph shows the number of ticket sales in thousands over a seven-month period. Use the graph to answer the questions in Exercises 83–88.

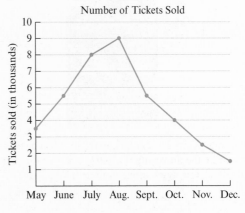

Number of Tickets Sold

83) What month had the greatest number of ticket sales and how many tickets were sold?   August; 9,000

84) What month had the lowest number of ticket sales and how many tickets were sold?   December; 1,500

85) Between what two consecutive months did the greatest decrease in ticket sales occur?   August and September

86) Between what two consecutive months did the greatest increase in ticket sales occur?   June and July

87) Approximately how much did the ticket sales increase between May and August?   5,500

88) Approximately how much did the ticket sales decrease between August and September?   3,500

Mixed Exercises

Perform the indicated operation.

89) $\begin{array}{r} 758 \\ -\ 379 \end{array}$ 379

90) $\begin{array}{r} 598 \\ 198 \\ +\ 399 \end{array}$ 1,195

91) $\begin{array}{r} 4,315 \\ +\ 5,641 \end{array}$ 9,956

92) $\begin{array}{r} 74,329 \\ -\ 17,897 \end{array}$ 56,432

93) 37,092 + 688 + 198,634 + 52 + 7,059   243,525

94) 72 + 83,755 + 4 + 893 + 570,632   655,356

95) $\begin{array}{r} 85,005 \\ -\ 26,374 \end{array}$ 58,631

96) $\begin{array}{r} 8,000 \\ -\ 3,999 \end{array}$ 4,001

97) Find the sum of 7,984 and 1,013   8,997

98) Subtract 438 from 985.   547

Fill in the blank.

99) 856 − _____ = 374   482

100) 162 + _____ = 458   296

Solve each problem.

101) Adriana decides to purchase a new car for $15,580. The state sales tax for the purchase is $1,168 while the license and registration fees are $345. How much must Adriana pay? $17,093

102) Antonio received a scholarship of $9,500. The cost of attending the university is $16,021 per year for tuition and fees. How much money will he have to pay? $6,521

103) In 2004, the average 8–18-yr-old spent 381 min per day using media. In 2009, that number jumped to 458 min per day. How much more time did they spend using media in 2009? (www.businessweek.com)   77 min per day

104) Janice decided to record her caloric intake on a random day. Her breakfast was 210 calories, her lunch was 420 calories, and her dinner was 825 calories. What was her total caloric intake for this day?   1,455 calories

Find the perimeter of each figure.

105)   48 cm

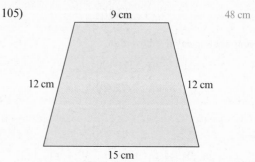

106)   70 in.

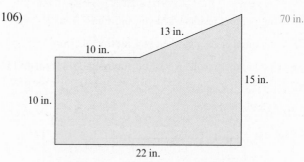

107) If the perimeter of the figure is 26 ft, find the missing side length.   4 ft

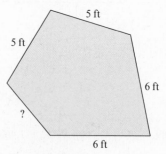

108) If the perimeter of the figure is 39 cm, find the missing side length.   11 cm

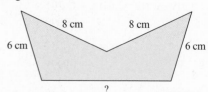

Chapter 1:   Test

*Additional answers can be found in the Answers to Exercises appendix.

Identify the place value of the digit 8 in each whole number.

1) 286,275   8 ten-thousands   2) 8,902,544   8 millions
or 8 one-millions

3) Write the number 17,008,632 in words.
seventeen million, eight thousand, six hundred thirty-two

4) Use the commutative property to rewrite the addition problem 45 + 71.   71 + 45

5) Use the associative property to rewrite the addition problem (8 + 14) + 7.   8 + (14 + 7)

Fill in the blank.

6) 54 − _____ = 37   17   7) 871 + _____ = 1,209   338

8) Subtract. Check your answer using addition. 695 − 231.
464; 464 + 231 = 695

Perform the indicated operation.

9) 5 + 4 + 3   12

10)   71
       − 19   52

11)   8,749
      − 2,760   5,989

12)   349,652
      + 530,381   880,033

13) 7,558 + 14 + 200,789 + 64,853   273,214

14)   97,000
      − 39,641   57,359

15) Subtract 7,038 from 12,519.   5,481

16) Find the sum of 2,613,884 and 35,060,912.   37,674,796

17) Round 635,027 to the nearest

   a) hundred-thousand   600,000

   b) ten-thousand   640,000

Estimate the answer to this problem by first rounding each number to the nearest hundred. Then, find the exact answer.

18)   7,413   7,400
      − 2,993   − 3,000
       4,420   4,400

19) Find the perimeter of this figure.   50 cm

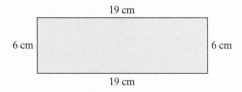
19 cm
6 cm   6 cm
19 cm

20) Find the length of the missing side.   9 in.

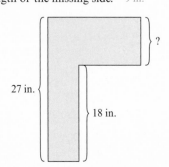
27 in.
18 in.
?

21) If the perimeter of the figure is 22 inches, find the missing side length.   6 in.

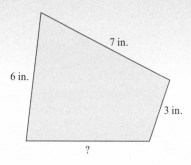
7 in.
6 in.
3 in.
?

Solve each problem.

22) For her new apartment, Houng purchased a new refrigerator for $872, a new sofa for $458, and a new bedroom set for $1,350. How much did she spend on all these items? $2,680

23) The television show *E.R.* filmed 331 episodes. This is 61 more episodes than were filmed for *Cheers*. How many episodes of *Cheers* were there? (www.imdb.com)
270 episodes

24) In his chemistry lab class, Bryce must make an acid solution by mixing 25 mL of hydrochloric acid with 165 mL of pure water. How many milliliters is the total solution?   190 mL

The bar graph shows the number of ships operated by the North America Cruise Industry in the United States. Use the graph to answer the following exercises.

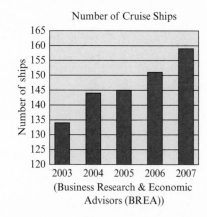
Number of Cruise Ships
Number of ships
165 160 155 150 145 140 135 130 125 120
2003 2004 2005 2006 2007
(Business Research & Economic Advisors (BREA))

25) How many ships were being operated in 2004?   144 ships

26) Between what two consecutive years did the number of ships increase the most and by how many?
2003 and 2004; 10 ships

27) Between what two consecutive years did the number of ships increase the least and by how many?
2004 and 2005; 1 ship

28) How many more ships were being operated in 2007 than in 2003?   25 ships

Multiplication and Division of Whole Numbers

Math at Work:

Regional Sales Manager

Twenty-five copy machines were sold to a customer for $2,000 each, and 52 copy machines were sold to a larger customer for $1,800 dollars each. Two salespeople in a region generate $23,000 in sales per month, while one salesperson in a neighboring region generates $13,500 per month.

Andre Mathers went into sales because he was good with people and enjoyed the rush of closing a deal. But he found that the higher he rose in the office equipment supply company where he started as a salesperson, the more math came in handy.

"I always used math on the job," Andre says. "For example, customers would ask me how much it would cost for a certain number of units, and I had to be able to quickly do the multiplication in my head. Now, as a sales manager for an entire region, math is an even bigger part of my job." Whether Andre is dividing a sales bonus across his staff or determining the cost of giving a discounted price to a customer for 12 months, math in general—and multiplication and division in particular—is essential to his success.

"Sales is all about trust," Andre notes. "Your customers need to be able to trust you'll deliver what you tell them, and just as importantly, they need to know that any figures you give them are accurate."

In this chapter, we'll cover multiplying and dividing, and we'll introduce some strategies to help you read textbooks and master the skills you'll need to succeed in math class and on the job.

Math textbooks can be intimidating. They are often long, and they contain equations and formulas that may look complicated. Here are some strategies for reading and studying math texts (this one included!) that can help you perform better:

- Study the frontmatter of the book, such as the preface and the introduction. Here, the author will help you understand the goals and strategies behind the book.
- Look over any advance organizers—outlines, overviews, section objectives, or other clues to the meaning and organization of new material—before you start reading.

- Gather the tools you'll need, including a pen or pencil, highlighters, a copy of the assignment (so you'll be sure to read the right material), a pad of paper, index cards, or a computer for taking notes.
- Be sure to give yourself enough time to complete the reading.

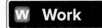

- Write while you read. Jot notes to yourself, place check marks on the page, draw arrows, and make diagrams.
- Highlight and underline selectively, marking only key material.
- Complete all the exercises. More than anything else, they will help you master the material!
- Pay particular attention to formulas. Look at them, think about them, annotate them, and make them concrete by substituting actual numbers for abstract letters.

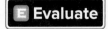

- Identify main ideas and concepts, and think about their relevance to you personally.
- Pretend that you are explaining the material (talking—out loud!—about the material) to a fellow classmate who didn't read the assignment.

- Look over the assignment again, along with any notes you've taken. If you do this within 24 hours of first reading the assignment, it can save you hours of work later.

Chapter 2 **POWER** Plan

P Prepare	**O** Organize
What are your goals for Chapter 2?	**How can you accomplish each goal?**
1 Be prepared before and during class.	• Don't stay out late the night before and be sure to set your alarm clock! • Bring a pencil, notebook paper, and textbook to class. • Avoid distractions by turning off your cell phone during class. • Pay attention, take good notes, and ask questions. • Complete your homework on time and ask questions on problems you do not understand.
2 Understand the homework to the point where you could do it without needing any help or hints.	• Read the directions and show all of your steps. • Go to the professor's office for help. • Rework homework and quiz problems and find similar problems for practice.
3 Use the P.O.W.E.R. framework to learn how to read a textbook: *Discover your reading attention span.*	• Read the Study Strategy that explains how to read a math textbook. • Be sure to personalize the strategy and notice where you might be able to improve. • Complete the emPOWERme that appears before the Chapter Summary.
4 Write your own goal. _____ _____	• _____ _____
What are your objectives for Chapter 2?	**How can you accomplish each objective?**
1 Learn how to multiply various types of numbers.	• Understand how to use a number line to multiply and find a missing factor. • Learn and apply the commutative property and associative property of multiplication. • Learn procedures for multiplying numbers.
2 Learn how to divide various types of numbers.	• Know the different parts of a division problem and that division is the opposite of multiplying. • Learn and apply the divisibility rules. • Be able to perform short and long division, and check your answer. • Learn the procedure for dividing numbers.
3 Use exponents, square roots, and the order of operations.	• Learn and apply the common powers of whole numbers. • Understand how to find a square root. • Use **P**lease **E**xcuse **M**y **D**ear **A**unt **S**ally to help you remember the order of operations.
4 Solve applied problems using multiplication or division.	• Learn the key words to look for when solving a problem. • Learn the five steps for solving any applied problem.
5 Write your own goal. _____ _____	• _____ _____

 **Work**	Read Sections 2.1–2.7 and complete the exercises.

Evaluate Complete the Chapter Review and Chapter Test. How did you do?	**Rethink** • How did you perform on the goals for the chapter? Which steps could be improved for next time? If you had the chance to do this chapter over, what would you do differently? • Think of a job you might like to have and describe how you would need to use what you have just learned to effectively do that job. • How has the reading strategy helped you master the objectives of this chapter? Where else could you use this strategy? • What were you able to learn about yourself by completing the emPOWERme at the end of the chapter?

2.1 Introduction to Multiplication

Prepare · **Organize**

What are your objectives for Section 2.1?	How can you accomplish each objective?
1 Understand the Meaning of Multiplication	• Write the definition of *multiplication* in your own words. • Understand the terms *multiplicand, multiplier, factor,* and *product.* • Memorize the multiplication facts from 1 through 12 by reviewing the table provided. • Complete the given examples on your own. • Complete You Trys 1 and 2.
2 Use the Commutative Property of Multiplication	• Learn the commutative property of multiplication. • Complete the given example on your own. • Complete You Try 3.
3 Find a Missing Factor	• Use a number line to find a missing factor. • Complete the given example on your own. • Complete You Try 4.

W Work Read the explanations, follow the examples, take notes, and complete the You Trys.

1 Understand the Meaning of Multiplication

What is multiplication? **Multiplication** is a shorthand way to represent repeated addition of the same number.

Let's add $3 + 3 + 3 + 3$ on a number line then see how we can write it as a multiplication problem.

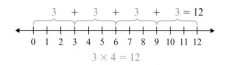

$$3 \times 4 = 12$$

We found that $3 + 3 + 3 + 3 = 12$. Since we are adding the 3 *four times,* we can say that 3 *times* 4 *equals* 12, which can be written as $3 \times 4 = 12$. The 3 is called the **multiplicand,** and 4 is called the **multiplier.** The numbers being multiplied together are also called **factors,** so 3 and 4 are factors of 12. The answer to a multiplication problem is called the **product.** So, 12 is the product of 3 and 4.

We can also write the multiplication problem vertically:

$$\begin{array}{r} 3 \leftarrow \\ \times\ 4 \leftarrow \\ \hline 1\ 2 \leftarrow \end{array}$$
$\leftarrow$ Multiplicand
$\leftarrow$ Multiplier
$\leftarrow$ Product
3 and 4 are *factors.*

EXAMPLE 1

In-Class Example 1

Use Example 1.

Use a number line to add $2 + 2 + 2$. Then,

a) write the addition problem as a multiplication problem.

b) identify the multiplicand and the multiplier.

c) identify the factors and the product.

Solution

We can add $2 + 2 + 2$ on the number line like this:

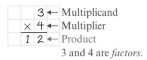

W Hint

Pay attention to the relationship between addition and multiplication.

a) Since we are adding 2 *three times,* we can write $2 + 2 + 2 = 6$ as the multiplication problem $2 \times 3 = 6$.

b) The multiplicand is 2, and the multiplier is 3.

c) The factors are 2 and 3. The product is 6.

[YOU TRY 1]

Use a number line to add $5 + 5$. Then,

a) write the addition problem as a multiplication problem.

b) identify the multiplicand and the multiplier.

c) identify the factors and the product.

Multiplication can be written in several different ways. For example, other ways to write $2 \times 3 = 6$ are

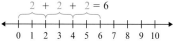

No operation symbol means multiplication.

$$\begin{array}{r} 2 \\ \times\ 3 \\ \hline 6 \end{array} \quad \text{or} \quad 2 \cdot 3 = 6 \quad \text{or} \quad 2(3) = 6 \quad \text{or} \quad (2)(3) = 6$$

Multiplication dot

So multiplication may also be represented by a multiplication dot or with no symbol at all before or between parentheses.

EXAMPLE 2

Find each product.

a) 4 · 5   b) 9(3)   c) (0)(8)

Solution

a) Here, the multiplication dot is used.   4 · 5 = 20

b) In this problem, there is no operation symbol between the 9 and the parenthesis right next to it. So the operation is multiplication.   9(3) = 27

c) There is no operation symbol between the parentheses, so the operation is multiplication. (0)(8) = 0   (Zero times any number equals zero.)

[YOU TRY 2]   Find each product.

a) 3 · 7   b) 5(0)   c) (9)(6)

If you do not remember the multiplication facts from 1 through 12, you can review them using this table.

Multiplication Table

×	1	2	3	4	5	6	7	8	9	10	11	12
1	1	2	3	4	5	6	7	8	9	10	11	12
2	2	4	6	8	10	12	14	16	18	20	22	24
3	3	6	9	12	15	18	21	24	27	30	33	36
4	4	8	12	16	20	24	28	32	36	40	44	48
5	5	10	15	20	25	30	35	40	45	50	55	60
6	6	12	18	24	30	36	42	48	54	60	66	72
7	7	14	21	28	35	42	49	56	63	70	77	84
8	8	16	24	32	40	48	56	64	72	80	88	96
9	9	18	27	36	45	54	63	72	81	90	99	108
10	10	20	30	40	50	60	70	80	90	100	110	120
11	11	22	33	44	55	66	77	88	99	110	121	132
12	12	24	36	48	60	72	84	96	108	120	132	144

W Hint

Make yourself some flash cards to review the multiplication facts.

2 Use the Commutative Property of Multiplication

Earlier, we learned that addition is commutative. Is multiplication commutative? In Example 1, we found that 2 × 3 = 6. Does 3 × 2 = 6? Yes, 2 × 3 = 6 and 3 × 2 = 6. This is just one example that shows that multiplication is commutative.

Property The Commutative Property of Multiplication

The **commutative property of multiplication** says that changing the order in which we multiply numbers does not change the product. For example,

$$2 \times 3 = 6 \text{ and } 3 \times 2 = 6$$

EXAMPLE 3

Multiply 8 · 9, then rewrite the problem using the commutative property of multiplication.

In-Class Example 3

Multiply 5 · 3, then rewrite the problem using the commutative property of multiplication.

Answer: 5 · 3 = 15; 3 · 5 = 15

Solution

8 · 9 = 72. Using the commutative property of multiplication, we get 9 · 8 = 72.

[**YOU TRY 3**]

Multiply 7 × 6, then rewrite the problem using the commutative property of multiplication.

W Hint

This procedure is similar to what you did for finding a missing addend.

3 Find a Missing Factor

Sometimes, it is useful to find a missing factor.

EXAMPLE 4

Fill in the missing factor: 2 · _____ = 10.

In-Class Example 4

Fill in the missing factor:
7 · ___ = 14.

Answer: 2

Solution

Ask yourself, "Two times what number equals 10?" That number is 5.
Therefore, 2 · 5 = 10.

[**YOU TRY 4**]

Fill in the missing factor: 3 × ___ = 18.

As you become more comfortable with the multiplication facts, filling in the missing factor will become easier.

ANSWERS TO [YOU TRY] **EXERCISES**

1)
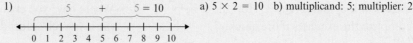
5 + 5 = 10

a) 5 × 2 = 10   b) multiplicand: 5; multiplier: 2

c) factors: 5 and 2; product: 10   2) a) 21   b) 0   c) 54   3) 7 × 6 = 42; 6 × 7 = 42   4) 6

E Evaluate **2.1** Exercises   Do the exercises, and check your work.

*Additional answers can be found in the Answers to Exercises appendix.

Objective 1: Understand the Meaning of Multiplication

Use a number line to add the following numbers. Then,

a) write the addition problem as a multiplication problem.

b) identify the multiplicand and the multiplier.

c) identify the factors and the product.

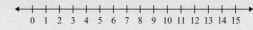

1) 4 + 4 + 4   2) 5 + 5 + 5

3) 3 + 3 + 3 + 3 + 3   4) 2 + 2 + 2 + 2

Find each product.

5) a) 9×3 27

   b) $4(7)$ 28

   c) $5 \cdot 11$ 55

6) a) 6×5 30

   b) $12(3)$ 36

   c) $7 \cdot 9$ 63

7) a) $(10)(6)$ 60

   b) 2×9 18

   c) $12 \cdot 4$ 48

8) a) $4 \cdot 3$ 12

   b) $(5)(9)$ 45

   c) 7×8 56

9) a) 6×6 36

   b) $1 \cdot 7$ 7

   c) $\begin{array}{r} 12 \\ \times\ 8 \\ \hline 96 \end{array}$

10) a) 4×0 0

    b) $(9)(9)$ 81

    c) $\begin{array}{r} 6 \\ \times\ 7 \\ \hline 42 \end{array}$

Objective 2: Use the Commutative Property of Multiplication

11) Explain, in your own words, the commutative property of multiplication. Answers may vary.

12) Rewrite $8(3)$ in three other ways.
Answers may vary.

Find each product, then rewrite the problem using the commutative property.

13) 3×5 15; $5 \times 3 = 15$ 14) 10×7 70; $7 \times 10 = 70$

15) $12 \cdot 9$ 108; $9 \cdot 12 = 108$ 16) $9 \cdot 6$ 54; $6 \cdot 9 = 54$

17) $8(4)$ 32; $4(8) = 32$ 18) $3(11)$ 33; $11(3) = 33$

19) $0 \cdot 2$ 0; $2 \cdot 0 = 0$ 20) $7 \cdot 0$ 0; $0 \cdot 7 = 0$

21) 10×1 10; $1 \times 10 = 10$ 22) $1 \cdot 5$ 5; $5 \cdot 1 = 5$

Objective 3: Find a Missing Factor

Fill in the missing factor.

23) $4 \cdot \underline{\hspace{1em}} = 24$ 6

24) $9 \cdot \underline{\hspace{1em}} = 45$ 5

25) $12 \times \underline{\hspace{1em}} = 60$ 5

26) $6 \times \underline{\hspace{1em}} = 66$ 11

27) $\underline{\hspace{1em}} \cdot 7 = 49$ 7

28) $\underline{\hspace{1em}} \cdot 8 = 96$ 12

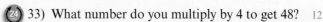

29) $9 \times \underline{\hspace{1em}} = 27$ 3

30) $11 \times \underline{\hspace{1em}} = 99$ 9

31) $\underline{\hspace{1em}} \times 2 = 0$ 0

32) $\underline{\hspace{1em}} \times 1 = 8$ 8

Answer the following questions.

33) What number do you multiply by 4 to get 48? 12

34) What number do you multiply by 9 to get 36? 4

35) 7 times what number equals 56? 8

36) 6 times what number equals 54? 9

R Rethink

R1) Do you know the "times table"? How did it help you complete the exercises more quickly?

R2) Where have you encountered multiplication in the last week? How did you handle it?

2.2 Finding the Product with Whole Numbers

P Prepare

O Organize

What are your objectives for Section 2.2?	How can you accomplish each objective?
1 Use the Associative Property of Multiplication	• Learn the associative property of multiplication. • Complete the given example on your own. • Complete You Try 1.
2 Multiply a Number by a One-Digit Number	• Follow the examples, and write a procedure for multiplying a number by a one-digit number. • Complete the given examples on your own. • Complete You Trys 2 and 3.
3 Multiply a Number by a Number with More Than One Digit	• Be sure to follow each example carefully, as each one will point out different scenarios you might encounter while multiplying. • Follow the examples, and write a procedure for multiplying a number by a number with more than one digit. • Complete the given examples on your own. • Complete You Trys 4 and 5.
4 Multiply a Number by a Number Ending in Zero	• Write the procedure for **Multiplying a Number by 10, 100, 1000, 10,000, etc.** in your own words. • Complete the given example on your own. • Complete You Try 6.
5 Solve Applied Problems Using Multiplication	• Be sure to carefully read the application problem and understand what you are being asked to find. • Complete the given example on your own. • Complete You Try 7.

 **W Work**   Read the explanations, follow the examples, take notes, and complete the You Trys.

1 Use the Associative Property of Multiplication

In Section 1.2, we learned that addition is associative. The associative property also applies to multiplication.

> **Property** The Associative Property of Multiplication
>
> The **associative property of multiplication** says that we can group factors in any order and the product will remain the same.

EXAMPLE 1

Multiply 2 × 4 × 3.

Solution

When we are multiplying more than two numbers, we can group them any way we like. Let's do this two ways.

1) 2 × 4 × 3 = (2 × 4) × 3   Use the associative property of multiplication to group the factors.
              =   8   × 3   Perform the operation inside the parentheses first.
              = 24   Multiply.

Or,

2) 2 × 4 × 3 = 2 × (4 × 3)   Use the associative property of multiplication to group the factors.
              = 2 ×   12   Perform the operation inside the parentheses first.
              = 24   Multiply.

No matter which way we group the factors, the product is the same.

[**YOU TRY 1**]   Multiply 7 × 1 × 6.

So far, the multiplication problems we have seen all use the basic multiplication facts from 1 through 12. Next we will learn how to multiply larger numbers by one-digit numbers.

2   Multiply a Number by a One-Digit Number

EXAMPLE 2

Multiply.

a)   21
    × 3

b)   102
    × 4

Solution

a) Begin with the multiplier, 3. We will multiply each place in the number 21 by 3, starting with the ones column of 21. So, first multiply 3 × 1 one = 3 ones. Then, multiply 3 × 2 tens = 6 tens.

		2	1
	×		3
			3

3 × 1 one = 3 ones

		2	1
	×		3
		6	3

3 × 2 tens = 6 tens

The product is 63.

b) Begin with the multiplier, 4. Multiply each place in the number 102 by 4, starting with the ones column of 102. So, first multiply 4 × 2 ones = 8 ones, then multiply 4 × 0 tens = 0 tens, and finally multiply 4 × 1 hundred = 4 hundreds.

	1	0	2
×			4
4	0	8	

← 4 × 2 ones = 8 ones
← 4 × 0 tens = 0 tens
← 4 × 1 hundred = 4 hundreds

The product is 408.

<table>
<tr><td>**[YOU TRY 2]**</td><td>Multiply.</td></tr>
</table>

a)
$$\begin{array}{r} 14 \\ \times\ 2 \\ \hline \end{array}$$

b)
$$\begin{array}{r} 204 \\ \times\ 2 \\ \hline \end{array}$$

Sometimes we need to use regrouping to multiply numbers.

EXAMPLE 3

Multiply.

a)
$$\begin{array}{r} 473 \\ \times\ 2 \\ \hline \end{array}$$

b)
$$\begin{array}{r} 738 \\ \times\ 5 \\ \hline \end{array}$$

In-Class Example 3

Multiply.

a)
$$\begin{array}{r} 361 \\ \times\ 3 \\ \hline \end{array}$$

b)
$$\begin{array}{r} 796 \\ \times\ 5 \\ \hline \end{array}$$

Answer: a) 1,083 b) 3,980

Solution

a) Begin with the multiplier, 2. Multiply 2 × 3 ones = 6 ones.

W Hint

Can you write a procedure to generalize this objective?

Now, multiply 2 × 7 tens = 14 tens. Regroup this as 1 hundred + 4 tens. Write the 4 in the tens column of the product and write the 1 above the 4 in the hundreds column.

Multiply 2 × 4 hundreds = 8 hundreds and add the 1 hundred above the 4 to get 9 hundreds in the product.

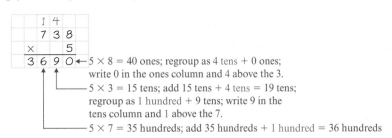

The product is 946.

b) Multiply each digit in 738 by 5 as shown here.

The product is 3,690.

<table>
<tr><td>**[YOU TRY 3]**</td><td>Multiply.</td></tr>
</table>

a)
$$\begin{array}{r} 291 \\ \times\ 3 \\ \hline \end{array}$$

b)
$$\begin{array}{r} 845 \\ \times\ 6 \\ \hline \end{array}$$

3 Multiply a Number by a Number with More Than One Digit

How do we multiply 34×16?
Since $16 = 1$ ten $+ 6$ ones, one way to find 34×16 is like this:

$$
\begin{array}{r}
{\scriptstyle 2} \\
3\,4 \\
\times\quad 6 \\
\hline
2\,0\,4
\end{array}
\qquad
\begin{array}{r}
3\,4 \\
\times 1\,0 \\
\hline
3\,4\,0
\end{array}
$$

Add the results to get

$$
\begin{array}{r}
3\,4 \\
\times\,1\,6 \\
\hline
2\,0\,4 \\
+\,3\,4\,0 \\
\hline
5\,4\,4
\end{array}
$$

$\leftarrow 34 \times 6$
$\leftarrow 34 \times 10$
Add to get the product.

204 and 340 are called **partial products.** We can also find 34×16 by multiplying in a single step using partial products. Usually, we do not write the 0 in 340.

$$
\begin{array}{r}
3\,4 \\
\times\,1\,6 \\
\hline
2\,0\,4 \\
3\,4 \\
\hline
5\,4\,4
\end{array}
$$

Leave off the 0. Line up the 4 in the tens column.

The product is 544.

Let's look at another example.

EXAMPLE 4

In-Class Example 4

Multiply.

a) $\begin{array}{r} 131 \\ \times\,123 \end{array}$ b) $\begin{array}{r} 548 \\ \times\,67 \end{array}$

Answer: a) 16,113 b) 36,716

Multiply.

a) $\begin{array}{r} 322 \\ \times\,213 \end{array}$ b) $\begin{array}{r} 268 \\ \times\,49 \end{array}$

Solution

a) We will use partial products to write all multiplication steps in a single problem.

$$
\begin{array}{r}
3\,2\,2 \\
\times\,2\,1\,3 \\
\hline
9\,6\,6 \\
3\,2\,2 \\
6\,4\,4 \\
\hline
6\,8,5\,8\,6
\end{array}
$$

Multiply 3 ones $\times$ 322. Line up the rightmost digit in the ones column.
Multiply 1 ten $\times$ 322. Line up on the right in the tens column.
Multiply 2 hundreds $\times$ 322. Line up on the right in the hundreds place.
Add to get the product.

The product is 68,586.

b) Begin by multiplying by 9. Notice that we must regroup.

$$
\begin{array}{r}
{\scriptstyle 6\,7} \\
2\,6\,8 \\
\times\quad 4\,9 \\
\hline
2,4\,1\,2
\end{array}
$$

Multiply 268 by 9.

Now, multiply by 4. Again, we must regroup.

$$
\begin{array}{r}
{\scriptstyle 2\,3} \\
{\scriptstyle 6\,7} \\
2\,6\,8 \\
\times\quad 4\,9 \\
\hline
2\,4\,1\,2 \\
1\,0\,7\,2 \\
\hline
1\,3,1\,3\,2
\end{array}
$$

$\leftarrow$ This is the regrouping from multiplying by 4.
$\leftarrow$ This is the regrouping from multiplying by 9.

Multiply 268 by 9; line up in the ones column.
Multiply 268 by 4; line up in the tens column.
Add to get the product.

The product is 13,132.

W Hint

Remember, work out the example on your paper as you are reading it!

[**YOU TRY 4**] Multiply.

a) $\begin{array}{r} 413 \\ \times\, 122 \\ \hline \end{array}$ b) $\begin{array}{r} 276 \\ \times\, 83 \\ \hline \end{array}$

Be careful when the multiplier contains zeros. We still have to account for their positions in the multiplication problem.

EXAMPLE 5

In-Class Example 5

Multiply.
a) $\begin{array}{r} 483 \\ \times\, 206 \\ \hline \end{array}$ b) $\begin{array}{r} 8,217 \\ \times\, 2,006 \\ \hline \end{array}$

Answer:
a) 99,498 b) 16,483,302

Multiply.

a) $\begin{array}{r} 254 \\ \times\, 301 \\ \hline \end{array}$ b) $\begin{array}{r} 6,132 \\ \times\, 4,003 \\ \hline \end{array}$

Solution

a)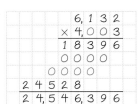

		2	5	4	
	×	3	0	1	
		2	5	4	Multiply 254 by 1. Line up in the ones column.
	0	0	0		Multiply 254 by 0. Line up in the tens column.
7	6	2			Multiply 254 by 3. Line up in the hundreds column.
7	6,	4	5	4	Add to get the product.

The product is 76,454.

b) Let's look at two methods for working with zeros.

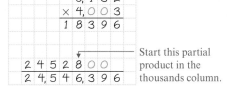

The product is 24,546,396. The method on the right is a shorthand way to account for the two zeros in the multiplier.

[**YOU TRY 5**] Multiply.

a) $\begin{array}{r} 186 \\ \times\, 204 \\ \hline \end{array}$ b) $\begin{array}{r} 5,283 \\ \times\, 3,007 \\ \hline \end{array}$

Multiplying a whole number by 10 or 100 or 1,000 can be simple if we notice a pattern.

4 Multiply a Number by a Number Ending in Zero

Let's multiply 25 by 10, 100, 1,000, and 10,000 and see what happens:

$$25 \times 10 = 250$$
$$25 \times 100 = 2,500$$
$$25 \times 1,000 = 25,000$$
$$25 \times 10,000 = 250,000$$

Do you notice the pattern?

Procedure Multiplying a Whole Number by 10, 100, 1,000, 10,000, etc.

When you multiply a whole number by 10, 100, 1,000, 10,000, and so on, the result is the number followed by the number of zeros in the multiplier. For example, $382 \times 100 = 38,200$.

We can use this property to multiply a whole number by other *multiples* of 10 as well. For example, 20 is a multiple of 10 since $2 \cdot 10 = 20$. (A product is a **multiple** of each of its factors.) So if we use what we know about multiplying a whole number by 10 or 100 or 1,000, we can also use a shortcut to multiply by other multiples of 10.

EXAMPLE 6

In-Class Example 6

Multiply.
a) $6,918 \times 1,000$
b) $56 \cdot 80$
c) 420×300

Answer:
a) 6,918,000 b) 4,480
c) 126,000

W Hint

What does "adding zero(s)" really mean?

Multiply.

a) $9,722 \times 1,000$ b) $83 \cdot 20$ c) 240×300

Solution

a) $9,722 \times 1,000 = 9,722,000$ Add three zeros to the end of 9,722.

b) 20 is a multiple of 10. So, to find $83 \cdot 20$ we can multiply 83 by 2, then add one zero to the end of that result.

$$83 \cdot 2 = 166, \text{ then add one zero to } 166: 1,660$$
$$83 \cdot 20 = 1,660$$

c) In 240×300, 240 is a multiple of 10 and 300 is a multiple of 100. To find 240×300, we can multiply 24 by 3 then add three zeros to the end of that result since there are a total of three zeros in the multiples of 10 and 100.

$$24 \times 3 = 72, \text{ then add three zeros to } 72: 72,000$$
$$240 \times 300 = 72,000$$

[YOU TRY 6]

Multiply.

a) $68 \cdot 100$ b) 32×40 c) $530 \cdot 600$

---

5 Solve Applied Problems Using Multiplication

Multiplication is often used to solve real-world problems.

EXAMPLE 7

In-Class Example 7

Leslie bought 14 bags of dry dog food for her kennel. Each bag cost $18. How much did she spend?

Answer: $252

Adelita bought 17 gift cards worth $25 each for her employees. How much did she spend?

Solution

To determine the total amount of money Adelita spent, we multiply the value of each gift card, $25, by the number she bought, 17.

Adelita spent $425 on the gift cards.

$$
\begin{array}{r}
2\ 5 \leftarrow \text{Value of each gift card} \\
\times\ 1\ 7 \leftarrow \text{Number of cards} \\
\hline
1\ 7\ 5 \\
2\ 5\ \\
\hline
4\ 2\ 5
\end{array}
$$

ANSWERS TO [YOU TRY] EXERCISES

1) 42   2) a) 28   b) 408   3) a) 873   b) 5,070   4) a) 50,386   b) 22,908
5) a) 37,944   b) 15,885,981   6) a) 6,800   b) 1,280   c) 318,000   7) $1,044

E Evaluate **2.2** Exercises   Do the exercises, and check your work.

*Additional answers can be found in the Answers to Exercises appendix.

Objective 1: Use the Associative Property of Multiplication

1) In your own words, explain the associative property of multiplication.   Answers may vary.

2) How can using the associative property of multiplication make multiplying three numbers easier? Give an example.   Answers may vary.

Multiply in two different ways using the associative property of multiplication.

3) $3 \times 2 \times 4$

4) $6 \times 1 \times 9$

5) $9 \cdot 0 \cdot 7$

6) $2 \cdot 4 \cdot 0$

Objective 2: Multiply a Number by a One-Digit Number

Multiply.

7) 31
   $\times\ 2$ 62

8) 22
   $\times\ 3$ 66

9) 413
   $\times\ 3$ 1,239

10) 701
   $\times\ 4$ 2,804

11) 804
   $\times\ 2$ 1,608

12) 633
   $\times\ 2$ 1,266

13) 94
   $\times\ 7$ 658

14) 56
   $\times\ 8$ 448

15) 461
   $\times\ 6$ 2,766

16) 794
   $\times\ 2$ 1,588

17) 635
   $\times\ 9$ 5,715

18) 423
   $\times\ 6$ 2,538

19) $185 \cdot 8$ 1,480

20) $872 \cdot 5$ 4,360

21) 525(4)   2,100

22) 825(4)   3,300

23) (6)(4,809)   28,854

24) (7)(6,044)   42,308

Objective 3: Multiply a Number by a Number with More Than One Digit

25) 14
   $\times 12$ 168

26) 32
   $\times 21$ 672

27) 312
   $\times 23$ 7,176

28) 879
   $\times 11$ 9,669

29) 83
   $\times 65$ 5,395

30) 42
   $\times 36$ 1,512

31) 38
   $\times 25$ 950

32) 55
   $\times 34$ 1,870

33) 613
   $\times 64$ 39,232

34) 228
   $\times 93$ 21,204

35) 1,773
   $\times\ \ 48$ 85,104

36) 9,161
   $\times\ \ 29$ 265,669

37) 599
   $\times 781$ 467,819

38) 806
   $\times 322$ 259,532

39) 8,104
   $\times\ 216$ 1,750,464

40) 4,043
   $\times\ 597$ 2,413,671

41) 2,295
   $\times 4,831$ 11,087,145

42) 6,337
   $\times 9,214$ 58,389,118

43) $403 \cdot 517$ 208,351

44) $602 \cdot 773$ 465,346

45) (2,533)(5,004)   12,675,132

46) (1,882)(7,006)   13,185,292

47) 5,630(1,077)   6,063,510

48) 3,200(8,001)   25,603,200

Objective 4: Multiply a Number by a Number Ending in Zero

49) In your own words, explain how to multiply a number by 100. Then, give an example.

The product is the number followed by two zeros. Examples may vary.

50) Fill in the blank: $38 \times \underline{\hspace{1cm}} = 38,000$.   1,000

Multiply.

51) a) 94×10 940
    b) 55×100 5,500
    c) $67 \times 1,000$ 67,000

52) a) 58×10 580
    b) 86×100 8,600
    c) $23 \times 1,000$ 23,000

53) a) $817 \cdot 10,000$ 8,170,000
    b) $261 \cdot 100$ 26,100
    c) $150 \cdot 100$ 15,000

54) a) $995 \cdot 10,000$ 9,950,000
    b) $384 \cdot 100$ 38,400
    c) $670 \cdot 100$ 67,000

55) a) $41 \cdot 20$ 820
    b) $9 \cdot 50$ 450
    c) $256 \cdot 30$ 7,680

56) a) $32 \cdot 20$ 640
    b) $8 \cdot 40$ 320
    c) $198 \cdot 50$ 9,900

57) a) 150×300 45,000
    b) $70 \times 8,000$ 560,000
    c) $490 \times 6,000$ 2,940,000

58) a) 120×700 84,000
    b) $40 \times 3,000$ 120,000
    c) $580 \times 5,000$ 2,900,000

59) Find the product of 900 and 300.   270,000

60) Find the product of 60 and 8,000.   480,000

61) What is the product when you multiply 420 and 650?   273,000

62) What is the product when you multiply 700 and 340?   238,000

Objective 5: Solve Applied Problems Using Multiplication

63) A classroom contains 5 rows of desks. If each row contains 9 desks, how many desks are in the classroom?   45

64) Kim stores her collection of horror movies on shelves. If she has 5 shelves of movies and there are 10 movies on each shelf, how many horror movies does Kim have?   50

65) A box contains 24 packages of paper cups, and each package holds 30 cups. Find the total number of cups in the box.   720

66) If Pete did 80 push-ups every day for 30 days in a row, find the total number of push-ups he did.   2,400

67) Cora bought 7 packages of coffee costing $6 each. How much did she spend? $42

68) Johnny sold 54 bales of hay for $23 each. How much money did he get for the hay? $1,242

69) Haishin pays $129 per month for his gym membership. How much does he pay in a year? $1,548

70) Lily's rent is $635 per month. How much rent does she pay in a year? $7,620

71) Valeria has to wait 8 weeks for her new sofa to be delivered. How many days does she have to wait?   56

72) Rajnish's birthday is 6 weeks away. How many days is it until his birthday?   42

R Rethink

R1) Were you able to complete these exercises without looking back at the times table?

R2) Check some of your answers for Exercises 25 to 36 by rounding the numbers before multiplying. Was this an effective way to spot-check your answers?

R3) Write an application problem similar to those you just solved.

2.3 Introduction to Division

What are your objectives for Section 2.3?	How can you accomplish each objective?
1 Understand the Meaning of Division	• Understand how to divide by using a number line. • Know the terms *dividend, divisor,* and *quotient.* • Recognize that division is the opposite of multiplication. • Complete the given example on your own. • Complete You Try 1.
2 Perform Division Involving Zero	• Learn the properties for **Dividing a Number by Zero** and **Dividing Zero by a Nonzero Number.** • Complete the given examples on your own. • Complete You Trys 2 and 3.

 **Read the explanations, follow the examples, take notes, and complete the You Trys.**

1 Understand the Meaning of Division

What does $12 \div 3$ mean? The expression $12 \div 3$ is read as "12 divided by 3," and it means that we have to figure out how many threes it takes to make 12. Let's look at this on a number line.

How many threes does it take to make 12? 4

It takes 4 threes to make 12, so $12 \div 3 = 4$. In a division problem, the number being divided is called the **dividend,** the number you are dividing by is the **divisor,** and the result is the **quotient.**

$$\text{Dividend} \rightarrow 12 \div 3 = 4 \leftarrow \text{Quotient}$$

with Divisor labeled above the 3.

There are several different ways to write a division problem. $12 \div 3 = 4$ can also be written as

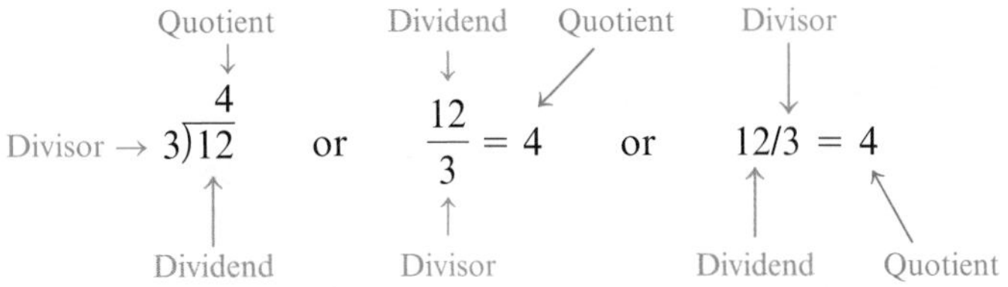

$$\text{Divisor} \rightarrow 3\overline{)12} \quad \text{or} \quad \frac{12}{3} = 4 \quad \text{or} \quad 12/3 = 4$$

with Quotient above the 4, Dividend below; Dividend above 12, Quotient above 4, Divisor below 3; Divisor above, Dividend and Quotient below.

Division and multiplication are opposite operations. Let's see how the division problem $12 \div 3 = 4$ is related to the multiplication problem $3 \times 4 = 12$.

(Remember that in the multiplication problem $3 \times 4 = 12$, the multiplier is 4.) We can represent $3 \times 4 = 12$ on a number line as

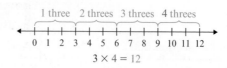

$$3 \times 4 = 12$$

Notice that the number line for $12 \div 3 = 4$ and the number line for $3 \times 4 = 12$ look the same. We can use this relationship to help us perform division by thinking of it in terms of multiplication.

EXAMPLE 1

 Hint

Think in terms of multiplying or finding the missing factor to help you divide.

Divide. Then identify the dividend, the divisor, and the quotient.

a) $10 \div 2$ b) $\dfrac{32}{8}$ c) $1\overline{)3}$ d) $\dfrac{4}{4}$

Solution

a) To find $10 \div 2$, ask yourself, "*How many twos does it take to make* 10?" or "*Two times what number equals* 10?" That number is 5; $2 \times 5 = 10$. We can verify this on the number line.

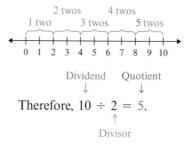

Therefore, $10 \div 2 = 5$.

b) To find $\dfrac{32}{8}$, ask yourself, "*Eight times what number equals* 32?" That number is 4.

$$\text{Dividend} \to \dfrac{32}{8} \overset{\text{Quotient}}{=} 4 \text{ since } 8 \cdot 4 = 32$$
$$\text{Divisor} \to $$

c) To find $1\overline{)3}$, ask yourself, "*One times what number equals* 3?" That number is 3 since $1 \cdot 3 = 3$.

$$\text{Divisor} \to \overset{3 \leftarrow \text{Quotient}}{1\overline{)3}}$$
$$\underset{\text{Dividend}}{\uparrow}$$

 Note

Any number divided by 1 equals itself.

d) To find $\dfrac{4}{4}$, ask yourself, "*Four times what number equals* 4?" That number is 1.

$$\text{Dividend} \to \dfrac{4}{4} \overset{\text{Quotient}}{=} 1 \text{ since } 4 \cdot 1 = 4$$
$$\text{Divisor} \to $$

Note

Any nonzero number divided by itself equals 1.

Because of this relationship between division and multiplication, we can use multiplication to check a division problem. We will do this in the next section.

[**YOU TRY 1**] Divide. Then identify the dividend, the divisor, and the quotient.

a) $\dfrac{35}{7}$ b) $3\overline{)24}$ c) $10 \div 10$ d) $\dfrac{7}{1}$

---

2 Perform Division Involving Zero

Next we will look at division problems involving zero.

EXAMPLE 2

In-Class Example 2

Divide $\dfrac{9}{0}$.

Answer: undefined

Divide $\dfrac{8}{0}$.

Solution

Ask yourself, "*Zero times what number equals* 8?" **There is no such number!** We say that $\dfrac{8}{0}$ is *undefined*. This means there is no answer to $\dfrac{8}{0}$.

W Hint

Visualize these properties by drawing a number line to represent Examples 2 and 3.

Property Dividing a Number by Zero

Any number divided by zero is **undefined.** That is, there is no answer to a number divided by zero. For example, $\dfrac{8}{0}$ is undefined.

[**YOU TRY 2**] Divide $6 \div 0$.

EXAMPLE 3

In-Class Example 3

Divide $0 \div 8$.

Answer: 0

Divide $0 \div 5$.

Solution

Ask yourself, "*Five times what number equals* 0?" That number is 0. Therefore,

$$0 \div 5 = 0 \quad \text{since} \quad 5 \cdot 0 = 0$$

Because any number multiplied by 0 equals 0, we have the following property.

Property Dividing Zero by a Nonzero Number

Zero divided by any nonzero number equals zero. Example: $0 \div 5 = 0$.

[YOU TRY 3]   Divide $\dfrac{0}{2}$.

Note

$0 \div 0$ is undefined.

ANSWERS TO [YOU TRY] EXERCISES

1) a) 5; dividend: 35; divisor: 7; quotient: 5   b) 8; dividend: 24; divisor: 3; quotient: 8
   c) 1; dividend: 10; divisor: 10; quotient: 1   d) 7; dividend: 7; divisor: 1; quotient: 7
2) undefined   3) 0

E Evaluate **2.3** Exercises   Do the exercises, and check your work.

*Additional answers can be found in the Answers to Exercises appendix.

Objective 1: Understand the Meaning of Division

Use a number line to divide the numbers. Then,
  a) identify the dividend, divisor, and quotient.
  b) rewrite the problem using two other notations.

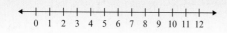

0 1 2 3 4 5 6 7 8 9 10 11 12

 1) $6 \div 2$ 2) $10 \div 5$

3) $6\overline{)12}$ 4) $4\overline{)12}$

5) $\dfrac{7}{1}$ 6) $\dfrac{5}{5}$

Find the quotient, and write a related multiplication problem.

7) $\dfrac{36}{9}$ 4; $9 \cdot 4 = 36$ 8) $\dfrac{42}{6}$ 7; $6 \cdot 7 = 42$

9) $7\overline{)84}$ 12; $7 \cdot 12 = 84$ 10) $5\overline{)40}$ 8; $5 \cdot 8 = 40$

11) $3 \div 1$ 3; $1 \cdot 3 = 3$ 12) $8 \div 8$ 1; $8 \cdot 1 = 8$

Objective 2: Perform Division Involving Zero

13) Is it possible to divide 0 by a nonzero number? Explain your answer.
    Yes. 0 divided by a nonzero number equals 0.

14) Is it possible to divide a number by 0? Explain your answer.   No. A number divided by 0 is undefined.

Divide, if possible.

15) $6 \div 0$ undefined   16) $11 \div 0$ undefined

17) $\dfrac{0}{7}$ 0   18) $\dfrac{0}{6}$ 0

19) $0\overline{)8}$ undefined   20) $0\overline{)5}$ undefined

21) $0 \div 10$ 0   22) $0 \div 9$ 0

Mixed Exercises: Objectives 1 and 2

Fill in the missing number.

23) $20 \div$ _____ $= 4$ 5   24) $21 \div$ _____ $= 3$ 7

25) _____ $\div 5 = 6$ 30   26) _____ $\div 6 = 10$ 60

27) _____ $\div 9 = 7$ 63   28) _____ $\div 7 = 8$ 56

29) $18 \div$ _____ $= 9$ 2   30) $121 \div$ _____ $= 11$ 11

31) $5 \div$ _____ $= 1$ 5   32) $4 \div$ _____ $= 4$ 1

Answer the following questions.

33) What is the quotient when you divide 60 by 5?   12

34) What is the quotient when you divide 36 by 12?   3

35) What number do you divide by 6 to get 9?   54

36) What number do you divide by 4 to get 7?   28

37) By what number do you divide 24 to get 8?   3

38) By what number do you divide 72 to get 6?   12

39) By what number do you divide 10 to get 10?   1

40) By what number do you divide 9 to get 1?   9

Divide, if possible.

41) $\dfrac{35}{7}$ 5

42) $144 \div 12$ 12

43) $0\overline{)3}$ undefined

44) $6\overline{)42}$ 7

45) $64 \div 8$ 8

46) $\dfrac{0}{4}$ 0

47) $9\overline{)54}$ 6

48) $\dfrac{72}{8}$ 9

49) $0 \div 5$ 0

50) $21 \div 0$ undefined

Find the quotient, and write a related multiplication problem.

51) $4\overline{)28}$ $7; 4 \cdot 7 = 28$

52) $9 \div 1$ $9; 1 \cdot 9 = 9$

R Rethink

R1) Look back at Chapter 1 to see how the relationships between addition and subtraction are similar to the relationships between multiplication and division. Use that information to make a statement about the associative and commutative properties.

R2) As you moved through the exercise set, which techniques or processes helped you move more quickly?

2.4 Divisibility Rules and Short Division

P Prepare

O Organize

What are your objectives for Section 2.4?	How can you accomplish each objective?
1 Understand Remainders and Check a Division Problem Using Multiplication	• Write a statement that summarizes two different results when dividing numbers and include the word *remainder*. • Write the procedure for **Checking a Division Problem Using Multiplication** in your own words. • Complete the given examples on your own. • Complete You Trys 1 and 2.
2 Use the Divisibility Rules	• Write the definition of *divisible* in your own words. • Spend some time to understand and then learn the divisibility rules. • Complete the given examples on your own. • Complete You Trys 3–7.
3 Use Short Division	• Understand that *short division* involves division by a one-digit number. • Write a procedure that outlines how to perform short division. • Complete the given examples on your own. • Complete You Trys 8–10.
4 Solve Applied Problems Using Division	• Carefully read the application problem and understand what you are being asked to find. • Complete the given example on your own. • Complete You Try 11.

Read the explanations, follow the examples, take notes, and complete the You Trys.

1 Understand Remainders and Check a Division Problem Using Multiplication

All of the division problems we have seen so far divide exactly. For example, $12 \div 3 = 4$. But what happens if the division does *not* work out to be exact? Then, we get a *remainder*.

Let's look at $9 \div 2$. On a number line we can think of this as, "*How many twos does it take to make 9?*"

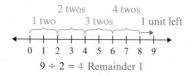

$9 \div 2 = 4$ Remainder 1

$9 \div 2$ does *not* divide exactly. After reaching 8 on the number line, there is no more room for another 2. It takes 4 twos to get to 8, then it takes 1 more unit to get to 9. We say that

$$9 \div 2 = 4 \quad \text{Remainder 1} \quad \text{or} \quad 9 \div 2 = 4 \, \text{R1}$$

The quotient is 4 and the *remainder* is 1. The **remainder** is how many units are left when you divide the dividend by the divisor. The remainder is always less than the divisor. If the remainder equals 0, we say that the dividend **divides evenly** by the divisor. One such example is $12 \div 3 = 4$. We say that 12 divides evenly by 3. If the remainder is not equal to 0, we say that the dividend **does not divide evenly** by the divisor, as in $9 \div 2 = 4$ R1. In this case, 9 does *not* divide evenly by 2.

EXAMPLE 1	Find

In-Class Example 1

Find
a) $45 \div 9$ b) $13 \div 5$

Answer: a) 5 b) 2 R3

a) $42 \div 7$ b) $11 \div 4$

Solution

a) $42 \div 7 = 6$ Since there is no remainder, 42 divides evenly by 7. To check our answer, we can write the related multiplication problem $7 \times 6 = 42$. This is how we can check to be sure that our quotient is correct.

b) The number line shows that there are 2 fours in 11 and then there are 3 units left over. So, $11 \div 4 = 2$ R3.

W Hint

After seeing this number line (for part b), do you think you could solve a similar problem without a number line?

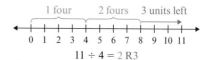

$11 \div 4 = 2$ R3

The number line also shows how we can check our result to this division problem with multiplication and division:

$$\underset{\text{Quotient}}{\underset{\uparrow}{(4 \times \overset{\text{Divisor}}{\overset{\downarrow}{2})} + \overset{\text{Remainder}}{\overset{\downarrow}{3}}} = 11} \leftarrow \text{Dividend}$$

Find

a) $32 \div 8$ b) $37 \div 5$

Let's generalize this procedure for checking a division problem with multiplication.

Procedure Checking a Division Problem Using Multiplication

To check a division problem using multiplication, multiply the divisor by the quotient, then add the remainder. The result should be the dividend.

$$(\text{Divisor} \times \text{Quotient}) + \text{Remainder} = \text{Dividend}$$

Perform the multiplication in parentheses first, then add the remainder.

EXAMPLE 2

Check each division problem to determine whether the statement is true or false.

a) $78 \div 6 = 13$ b) $\dfrac{52}{9} = 5\,R7$ c) $7\overline{)47}^{6\,R3}$

Solution

a)   The statement $78 \div 6 = 13$ is true since $6 \times 13 = 78$.

b)   To determine whether $\dfrac{52}{9} = 5\,R7$ is true, multiply the divisor by the quotient, then add the remainder. The result should be the dividend.

$$(9 \times 5) + 7 = 45 + 7 = 52 \checkmark$$

The statement $\dfrac{52}{9} = 5\,R7$ is true.

c)   To determine whether $7\overline{)47}^{6\,R3}$ is true, multiply the divisor by the quotient, then add the remainder. The result should be the dividend.

$$(7 \times 6) + 3 = 42 + 3 = 45$$

Since $45 \neq 47$, the statement $7\overline{)47}^{6\,R3}$ is false.

Check each division problem to determine whether the statement is true or false.

a) $98 \div 7 = 14$ b) $\dfrac{67}{4} = 16\,R2$ c) $6\overline{)53}^{8\,R5}$

This characteristic of one number dividing evenly by another number leads us to the important topic of divisibility and the divisibility rules.

2 Use the Divisibility Rules

Definition

A whole number is **divisible** by another whole number if the remainder equals 0.

In Example 2a), we can say that 78 *is divisible by* 6 since $78 \div 6 = 13$. But in Example 2b), 52 is not divisible by 9 since there is a remainder when dividing 52 by 9.

EXAMPLE 3

a) Is 66 divisible by 11? Yes, because $66 \div 11 = 6$.

b) Is 37 divisible by 9? No, because $37 \div 9 = 4\,R1$.

In-Class Example 3

a) Is 16 divisible by 8?
b) Is 38 divisible by 5?

Answer: a) yes b) no

[YOU TRY 3]

a) Is 25 divisible by 3?   b) Is 54 divisible by 6?

When we are working with larger numbers, it is helpful to have rules to determine whether one number is divisible by another number. These are called the **divisibility rules.** We have not included a divisibility rule for 7 because it is difficult to use.

Divisibility Rules

A number is divisible by	Example
…2 if it ends in 0, 2, 4, 6, or 8. If a number is divisible by 2, it is an **even number.**	7,394 is divisible by 2 because it ends in 4. It is an even number.
…3 if the sum of its digits is divisible by 3.	837—Add its digits: $8 + 3 + 7 = 18$. Since 18 is divisible by 3, the number 837 is divisible by 3.
…4 if its last two digits form a number that is divisible by 4.	5,932—The last two digits form the number 32. Since 32 is divisible by 4, the number 5,932 is divisible by 4.
…5 if the number ends in 0 or 5.	645 is divisible by 5 since it ends in 5.
…6 if it is divisible by 2 and by 3.	1,248—The number is divisible by 2 since it is an even number. The number is divisible by 3 since the sum of its digits is divisible by 3: $1 + 2 + 4 + 8 = 15$. Therefore, the number 1,248 is divisible by 6.
…8 if its last three digits form a number that is divisible by 8.	5,800—The last three digits form the number 800. Since 800 is divisible by 8, the number 5,800 is divisible by 8.
…9 if the sum of its digits is divisible by 9.	79,542—Add its digits: $7 + 9 + 5 + 4 + 2 = 27$. Since 27 is divisible by 9, the number 79,542 is divisible by 9.
…10 if it ends in a zero.	490 is divisible by 10 because it ends in 0.

W Hint

The fastest way to memorize this table is to practice!

The tests we use most often are those for 2, 3, 5, and 10. We will use these rules when we learn how to write fractions in lowest terms in Chapter 3, so it is very important to learn them!

EXAMPLE 4

Determine whether each number is divisible by 2.

a) 823   b) 7,456

In-Class Example 4

Determine whether each
number is divisible by 2.
a) 751   b) 3,238

Answer: a) no   b) yes

Solution

a) A number is divisible by 2 if it is an even number—that is, if it is a number that ends in 0, 2, 4, 6, or 8. 823 is *not* divisible by 2 since the number ends in 3.

b) 7,456 *is* divisible by 2 because it ends in 6; 7,456 is an even number.

[YOU TRY 4] Determine whether each number is divisible by 2.

a) 9,752   b) 175

EXAMPLE 5

Determine whether each number is divisible by 3.

a) 4,128   b) 983

In-Class Example 5

Determine whether each
number is divisible by 3.
a) 8,637   b) 283

Answer: a) yes   b) no

Solution

a) First, add the digits in 4,128: $4 + 1 + 2 + 8 = 15$
Because 15 is divisible by 3, the number 4,128 *is* divisible by 3.

b) Add the digits in 983: $9 + 8 + 3 = 20$
Because 20 is not divisible by 3, the number 983 is *not* divisible by 3.

[YOU TRY 5] Determine whether each number is divisible by 3.

a) 714   b) 12,253

EXAMPLE 6

Determine whether each number is divisible by 5.

a) 26,915   b) 3,640   c) 5,014

In-Class Example 6

Determine whether each
number is divisible by 5.
a) 19,645   b) 6,790
c) 5,206

Answer: a) yes   b) yes
c) no

Solution

a) A number is divisible by 5 if it ends in 0 or 5. The number 26,915 ends in 5, so it *is* divisible by 5.

b) 3,640 ends in 0, so it *is* divisible by 5.

c) 5,014 does not end in a 0 or 5. Therefore, it is *not* divisible by 5.

[YOU TRY 6] Determine whether each number is divisible by 5.

a) 8,800   b) 451   c) 92,195

EXAMPLE 7

In-Class Example 7

Determine whether each
number is divisible by 10.
a) 4,300 b) 702

Answer: a) yes b) no

Determine whether each number is divisible by 10.

a) 1,700   b) 409

Solution

a) A number is divisible by 10 if it ends in 0. So 1,700 *is* divisible by 10.

b) 409 does not end in 0, so it is *not* divisible by 10.

[**YOU TRY 7**] Determine whether each number is divisible by 10.

a) 6,402   b) 54,090

Next, we will learn how to divide larger numbers by one-digit numbers using a method called *short division*.

3 Use Short Division

Short division is a method for dividing a number by a one-digit divisor.

EXAMPLE 8

In-Class Example 8

Use short division to
find $2\overline{)84}$.

Answer: 42

Use short division to find $2\overline{)68}$.

Solution

First, divide 6 by 2: $\quad 2\overline{)68}^{\;3}\quad$ $\qquad 6 \div 2 = 3$

Next, divide 8 by 2: $\quad 2\overline{)68}^{\;34}\quad$ $\qquad 8 \div 2 = 4$

Therefore, $2\overline{)68}^{\;34}$. Notice that there is no remainder. We can check the answer using multiplication: $2 \times 34 = 68$. ✓

[**YOU TRY 8**] Use short division to find $3\overline{)93}$.

EXAMPLE 9

In-Class Example 9

Use short division to
find $\dfrac{692}{2}$.

Answer: 346

Use short division to find $\dfrac{958}{3}$.

Solution

Rewrite the problem as $3\overline{)958}$.

Divide 9 by 3: $\qquad 3\overline{)958}^{\;3}\qquad$ $9 \div 3 = 3$

Next, divide 5 by 3:

$$3\overline{)95^{2}8}^{\;31}\qquad 5 \div 3 = 1\,\text{R}2$$

Write the remainder of **2** in front of the 8. The remainder together with the 8 forms the number 28.

Now, divide 28 by 3:

$$3\overline{)95^28}\;\;\;\overset{31\,9\quad R1}{}\qquad\qquad 28 \div 3 = 9\,R1$$

Since we have reached the end of the number 958, we have finished the division process. Therefore, $\dfrac{958}{3} = 319\,R1$.

Check: $(3 \times 319) + 1 = 957 + 1 = 958.$ ✓

[YOU TRY 9] Use short division to find $\dfrac{475}{4}$.

EXAMPLE 10

In-Class Example 10

Use short division to divide 3,489 by 8.

Answer: 436 R1

W Hint

Can you make a general statement that outlines how to perform short division?

Use short division to divide 1,967 by 6.

Solution

Rewrite the problem as $6\overline{)1,967}$. Since 1 does not divide by 6, look at the first two digits of 1,967 together. Divide 19 by 6: $6\overline{)1,9^{1}67}\;\;\overset{3}{}$ $19 \div 6 = 3\,R1$

Next, divide 16 by 6: $6\overline{)1,9^{1}6^{4}7}\;\;\overset{3\;2}{}$ $16 \div 6 = 2\,R4$

Finally, divide 47 by 6:

$$6\overline{)1,9^{1}6^{4}7}\;\;\overset{3\;2\;7\;R5}{}\qquad 47 \div 6 = 7\;\;R5$$

So 1,967 divided by 6 is 327 R5.

Check: $(6 \times 327) + 5 = 1,962 + 5 = 1,967.$ ✓

[YOU TRY 10] Use short division to divide 2,053 by 7.

---

4 Solve Applied Problems Using Division

EXAMPLE 11

In-Class Example 11

Vernon buys a box of 25 packages of gum and will distribute the packages evenly among his friends. If there are 7 people including himself, how many packages will each person receive? How many packages are left over?

Answer: 3; 4 left over

Jessica buys a package of 48 cookies for her daughter's playgroup of 9 children. If she gives the same number of cookies to each child, how many cookies can each child have? Will there be any left over?

Solution

We need to determine how many times 9 divides into 48.

$$48 \div 9 = 5\,R3$$

Each child can have 5 cookies, and there will be 3 left over.

SECTION 2.4   **Divisibility Rules and Short Division**

E Evaluate **2.4** Exercises   Do the exercises, and check your work.

*Additional answers can be found in the Answers to Exercises appendix.

Objective 1: Understand Remainders and Check a Division Problem Using Multiplication

1) What does it mean to say that a dividend divides evenly by a divisor?   The remainder equals 0.

2) What does it mean to say that a dividend does not divide evenly by a divisor?   The remainder does not equal 0.

3) Find
   a) $18 \div 6$ 3
   b) $20 \div 6$ 3 R2

4) Find
   a) $30 \div 5$ 6
   b) $34 \div 5$ 6 R4

5) Find
   a) $9\overline{)45}$ 5
   b) $9\overline{)51}$ 5 R6

6) Find
   a) $8\overline{)56}$ 7
   b) $8\overline{)57}$ 7 R1

7) Find
   a) $\dfrac{36}{4}$ 9
   b) $\dfrac{39}{4}$ 9 R3

8) Find
   a) $\dfrac{21}{7}$ 3
   b) $\dfrac{26}{7}$ 3 R5

9) How do you check the result of a division problem?

10) Nivaj checks the division problem $43 \div 4 = 10$ R3 like this: $(10 \times 3) + 4 = 34$. Is the division result wrong, or did he make a mistake when checking the answer? Explain.   His check is wrong. The correct way to check the answer is $(10 \times 4) + 3 = 43$.

Check each division problem to determine whether the statement is true or false.

11) $\dfrac{32}{4} = 8$ $4 \times 8 = 32$; true   12) $\dfrac{21}{3} = 7$ $3 \times 7 = 21$; true

13) $95 \div 9 = 10$ R5
    $(9 \times 10) + 5 = 95$; true

14) $46 \div 8 = 5$ R6
    $(8 \times 5) + 6 = 46$; true

15) $\dfrac{58}{6} = 9$ R2
    $(6 \times 9) + 2 = 56$; false

16) $\dfrac{16}{7} = 2$ R3
    $(7 \times 2) + 3 = 17$; false

17) $4\overline{)85}$ R1
    $(4 \times 21) + 1 = 85$; true

18) $7\overline{)61}$ R5
    $(7 \times 8) + 5 = 61$; true

19) True or False: $31 \div 6 = 4$ R7. Explain your answer.
    False. The remainder is larger than the divisor.

20) True or False: $18 \div 0 = 0$. Explain your answer.
    False. A number divided by 0 is undefined.

21) Does 14 divide evenly by 2? Explain your answer.
    Yes. When you divide 14 by 2, there is no remainder.

22) Does 23 divide evenly by 3? Explain your answer.
    No. When you divide 23 by 3, the remainder is not zero.

Divide. Then, check your answer.

23) $4\overline{)29}$
    7 R1; $(4 \times 7) + 1 = 29$

24) $9\overline{)53}$
    5 R8; $(9 \times 5) + 8 = 53$

25) $\dfrac{62}{7}$
    8 R6; $(7 \times 8) + 6 = 62$

26) $\dfrac{23}{8}$
    2 R7; $(8 \times 2) + 7 = 23$

27) $3\overline{)15}$ 5; $3 \times 5 = 15$

28) $6\overline{)24}$ 4; $6 \times 4 = 24$

29) $48 \div 5$
    9 R3; $(5 \times 9) + 3 = 48$

30) $37 \div 7$
    5 R2; $(7 \times 5) + 2 = 37$

31) $\dfrac{77}{12}$
    6 R5; $(12 \times 6) + 5 = 77$

32) $\dfrac{51}{11}$ 4 R7; $(11 \times 4) + 7 = 51$

Objective 2: Use the Divisibility Rules

33) What is an even number?
    a number that is divisible by 0, 2, 4, 6, or 8

34) Every even number is divisible by what number?
    2

35) How do you know whether a number is divisible by 2?
    The number ends in 0, 2, 4, 6, or 8.

36) How do you know whether a number is divisible by 10?
    The number ends in 0.

37) How do you know whether a number is divisible by 3?

38) Make up an example of a three-digit number that is divisible by 3.   Answers may vary.

Determine whether each number is divisible by 2, 3, 5, and/or 10, or none of these.

39) 52   2

40) 75   3, 5

41) 810   2, 3, 5, 10

42) 708   2, 3

43) 659   none of these

44) 319   none of these

45) 4,863   3

46) 1,740   2, 3, 5, 10

47) 92,725   5

48) 73,660   2, 5, 10

49) 100,176   2, 3

50) 872,619   3

51) 54,623   none of these

52) 6,089   none of these

If a number is divisible by both 2 *and* 3, then the number is also divisible by 6. Determine whether each of the following numbers is divisible by 6.

53) 84   yes

54) 78   yes

55) 172   no

56) 166   no

57) 429   no

58) 513   no

59) 2,520   yes

60) 4,110   yes

Objective 3: Use Short Division

61) Can short division be used to divide 748 by 12? Explain your answer.
No, we cannot use short division because the divisor has two digits.

62) Can short division be used to divide 953 by 7? Explain your answer.
Yes, we can use short division because the divisor has one digit.

Use short division to divide.

63) $2\overline{)46}$ 23

64) $3\overline{)39}$ 13

65) $\dfrac{492}{4}$ 123

66) $\dfrac{684}{6}$ 114

67) $959 \div 3$ 319 R2

68) $871 \div 2$ 435 R1

69) $6\overline{)7,526}$ 1,254 R2

70) $3\overline{)5,350}$ 1,783 R1

71) Divide 2,496 by 8.   312

72) Divide 3,598 by 7.   514

73) Divide 6,711 by 9.   745 R6

74) Divide 5,903 by 6.   983 R5

75) $\dfrac{3,380}{6}$ 563 R2

76) $\dfrac{7,954}{8}$ 994 R2

77) $4\overline{)81,920}$ 20,480

78) $5\overline{)53,450}$ 10,690

Objective 4: Solve Applied Problems Using Division

79) At the end of business Thursday, a tip jar contains $54. The six people who worked that day will split the tips evenly. How much tip money will each employee receive? $9

80) A banquet room can hold a total of 216 people. If each table seats eight people, how many tables are in the room?   27

81) A high school French class is studying in Paris for the summer. Each student checked two pieces of luggage, and a total of 78 bags were checked. How many students went to Paris?   39

82) Tyra runs a modeling agency, and each day, Monday through Friday, she interviews the same number of potential models. If she interviews 30 people per week, how many does she see each day?   6

83) A lecture hall holds 204 people. If six people can sit at each table, how many tables are in the lecture hall?   34

84) Manoli is cleaning out his office and is stacking his books in piles of eight. If he has a total of 112 books, how many stacks are there?   14

85) Tickets to a college play cost $9 each. If the ticket revenue was $2,016, how many people attended the play?   224

86) Tickets to a college rugby game cost $7 each. If the ticket revenue was $441, how many people watched the game?   63

87) Min did the same number of sit-ups every day for a week. If she did a total of 420 sit-ups, how many did she do each day?   60

88) A hotel is being remodeled, and every room will have three lamps. The supplier delivers 138 lamps. How many rooms are in the hotel?   46

R1) Explain the procedure used to check an answer that contains a remainder. Why must you always multiply inside the parentheses first?

R2) After completing the exercises, which divisibility rules do you still need to review?

R3) Where have you encountered a division problem in the last week?

2.5 Long Division

P **Prepare**   **O** **Organize**

What are your objectives for Section 2.5?	How can you accomplish each objective?
1 Use Long Division	• Understand the difference between *long division* and *short division*. • Complete the given examples on your own. • Complete You Trys 1–3.
2 Divide Numbers Ending in Zeros	• Write the procedure for **Dividing Whole Numbers Ending in Zeros by 10, 100, 1,000, etc.** in your own words. • Complete the given examples on your own. • Complete You Trys 4 and 5.
3 Solve Applied Problems Using Long Division	• Read the applied problem twice and be sure to understand what is being asked. • Complete the given example on your own. • Complete You Try 6.

W **Work**   **Read the explanations, follow the examples, take notes, and complete the You Trys.**

If the total cost for 23 art history students to visit a museum is $322, what is the cost per student? We will answer this question using *long division* in Example 6. **Long division** is a method for dividing a number by a divisor with any number of digits. (Recall from the previous section that short division can be used to divide a number by a *one-digit* divisor.)

1 Use Long Division

EXAMPLE 1

Use long division to find $8\overline{)2{,}520}$.

In-Class Example 1

Use long division to find $6\overline{)4{,}428}$.

Answer: 738

Solution

We begin as we do with short division. Since 8 does not divide into the first 2 in the dividend, ask yourself, "*How many times does* 25 *divide evenly by* 8?"   3; Write 3 above the 5, then perform the following steps.

Multiply 3×8 to get 24. Write the 24 under the 25 and subtract.

Bring down the 2.

```
         3
   8)2,5 2 0
    - 2 4  ←————— 3 × 8 = 24
        1  ←————— 25 − 24 = 1
```

```
         3
   8)2,5 2 0
    - 2 4 ↓
        1 2
```

Ask yourself, "*How many times does* 12 *divide evenly by* 8?" 1; Write 1 above the second 2 in the dividend, then

Multiply 1×8 to get 8. Write 8 under the 2 in 12, and subtract.

Bring down the 0.

```
        3 1
   8)2,5 2 0
    - 2 4
        1 2
    -     8  ←————— 1 × 8 = 8
          4  ←————— 12 − 8 = 4
```

```
        3 1
   8)2,5 2 0
    - 2 4      ↓
        1 2    ↓
    -     8    ↓
          4 0
```

Ask yourself, "*How many times does* 40 *divide evenly by* 8?" 5;

Multiply 5×8 to get 40. Write this 40 under the 40, and subtract. The remainder is 0.

```
        3 1 5
   8)2,5 2 0
    - 2 4
        1 2
    -     8
          4 0
    -     4 0  ←——— 5 × 8 = 40
            0  ←——— 40 − 40 = 0
```

Therefore, $8\overline{)2{,}520}$ with quotient $\overset{315}{}$.

Check using multiplication: $8 \times 315 = 2{,}520$. ✓

[YOU TRY 1] Use long division to find $7\overline{)4{,}151}$.

If the divisor has more than one digit, we cannot use short division. We will use long division.

EXAMPLE 2

Use long division to find $19\overline{)6{,}217}$.

Solution

Ask yourself, "*How many times does* 62 *divide evenly by* 19?" We can estimate this by rounding 19 to 20: $\dfrac{62}{20} = 3$ R2. So, we will try 3 as the first digit in the quotient. Write 3 above the 2, then

Multiply 3×19 to get 57. Write the 57 under the 62 and subtract.

Bring down the 1.

```
          3
   1 9)6,2 1 7
      - 5 7  ←——— 3 × 19 = 57
          5  ←——— 62 − 57 = 5
```

```
          3
   1 9)6,2 1 7
      - 5 7 ↓
          5 1
```

Ask yourself, "*How many times does* 51 *divide evenly by* 19?" Again, round 19 to 20 and divide to estimate: $\frac{51}{20} = 2\,\text{R}11$. So, we will try 2 as the second digit in the quotient. Write 2 above the 1 in the dividend, then

Multiply 2 × 19 to get 38. Write 38 under the 51, and subtract.

```
          3 2
  1 9)6,2 1 7
    - 5 7
      5 1
    - 3 8 ←— 2 × 19 = 38
      1 3 ←— 51 − 38 = 13
```

Bring down the 7.

```
          3 2
  1 9)6,2 1 7
    - 5 7
      5 1
    - 3 8 ↓
      1 3 7
```

Ask yourself, "*How many times does* 137 *divide evenly by* 19?" Round 19 to 20 and divide: $\frac{137}{20} = 6\,\text{R}17$. Write 6 above the 7, then

Multiply 6 × 19 to get 114. Write the 114 under the 137, and subtract. We get 23. Since the remainder is greater than the divisor, increase the 6 in the quotient to 7.

Hint

Notice that, like in this example, you will not always guess the correct number in the quotient the first time around!

```
              3 2 6 ←— Change the 6 to 7.
      → 1 9)6,2 1 7
        - 5 7
          5 1
        - 3 8
          1 3 7
        - 1 1 4 ←— 6 × 19 = 114
        → 2 3 ←— 137 − 114 = 23
```
The remainder, 23, is greater than the divisor, 19.

The remainder cannot be greater than the divisor.

Change the 6 in the quotient to 7. Multiply 7 × 19 to get 133. Write the 133 under the 137, and subtract. The remainder is 4.

```
              3 2 7
      1 9)6,2 1 7
        - 5 7
          5 1
        - 3 8
          1 3 7
        - 1 3 3 ←— 7 × 19 = 133
        → 4 ←— 137 − 133 = 4
```
The remainder is less than the divisor.

Therefore, $19)\overline{6{,}217}$ gives $327\,\text{R}4$.

Check: $(19 × 327) + 4 = 6{,}213 + 4 = 6{,}217.$ ✓

[YOU TRY 2]   Use long division to find $17)\overline{8{,}372}$.

In Example 3, we will see that, sometimes, we must write a 0 in the quotient.

EXAMPLE 3   Find 12,782 ÷ 42.

Solution

Begin by setting up the problem as $42)\overline{12{,}782}$.

```
            3
  4 2)1 2,7 8 2
    - 1 2 6 ↓
        1 8
```

1) How many times does 127 divide evenly by 42?   3

2) Multiply 3 × 42 = 126.

3) Subtract 127 − 126 = 1.

4) Bring down the 8.

Start the process again. Ask yourself, "*How many times does* 18 *divide evenly by* 42?"   0

$$
\begin{array}{r}
3\,0 \leftarrow \\
42\overline{)12{,}782} \\
-\,1\,2\,6 \\
\hline
1\,8
\end{array}
$$
Write 0 in the quotient as a placeholder.

Bring down the 2, and do the division process again.

$$
\begin{array}{r}
3\,0\,4 \\
42\overline{)12{,}782} \\
-\,1\,2\,6\;\downarrow \\
\hline
1\,8\,2 \\
-\,1\,6\,8 \\
\hline
1\,4 \leftarrow
\end{array}
$$
Remainder

1) How many times does 182 divide evenly by 42?   4

2) Multiply $4 \times 42 = 168$.

3) Subtract $182 - 168 = 14$.

4) The remainder is 14.

Therefore, $12{,}782 \div 42 = 304\ \text{R}14$.

Check: $(42 \times 304) + 14 = 12{,}768 + 14 = 12{,}782.$ ✓

Hint

Get in the habit of asking yourself the questions that are asked in the solutions of the examples!

[YOU TRY 3]   Find $21{,}557 \div 53$.

2 Divide Numbers Ending in Zeros

In Section 2.2, we saw a pattern for multiplying a number by a number ending in 0. For example, $36 \times 1{,}000 = 36{,}000$. That is, to multiply a number by 1,000, we add three zeros to the end of the number.

Similarly, there is a pattern for dividing a number ending in zeros by another number ending in zeros. Do you see the pattern below?

$$15{,}000 \div 1 = 15{,}000$$
$$15{,}000 \div 10 = 1{,}500$$
$$15{,}000 \div 100 = 150$$
$$15{,}000 \div 1{,}000 = 15$$

Procedure Dividing Whole Numbers Ending in Zeros by 10, 100, 1,000, etc.

When you divide a whole number ending in zeros by

1) 10, you get the quotient by dropping one zero from the whole number.

Example: $2{,}700 \div 10 = 270$

2) 100, you get the quotient by dropping two zeros from the whole number.

Example: $630{,}000 \div 100 = 6{,}300$

3) 1,000, you get the quotient by dropping three zeros from the whole number.

Example: $78{,}000 \div 1{,}000 = 78$

This pattern continues for divisors 10,000, 100,000, and so on.

EXAMPLE 4

In-Class Example 4

Divide.
a) 850 ÷ 10
b) 670,000 ÷ 1,000
c) 14,000 ÷ 7,000

Answer:
a) 85 b) 670 c) 2

Divide.

a) 940 ÷ 10   b) 810,000 ÷ 1,000   c) 8,000 ÷ 200

Solution

a) Since we are dividing by 10, we get the quotient by dropping one zero from 940.
940 ÷ 10 = 94

b) Dividing by 1,000 means that we get the quotient by dropping three zeros from
810,000.   810,000 ÷ 1,000 = 810

c) Here we are dividing 8,000 by a *multiple* of 100. To find 8,000 ÷ 200, first drop
two zeros from each number to get 80 ÷ 2. (This is the same as dividing each
number by 100.) Now, finish the division: 80 ÷ 2 = 4. So, 8,000 ÷ 200 = 4 since
80 ÷ 2 = 4.

[**YOU TRY 4**]   Divide.

a) 420 ÷ 10   b) 39,000 ÷ 1,000   c) 6,000 ÷ 300

Example 4c) shows that we can use this pattern of dropping zeros to divide by
multiples of 10.

EXAMPLE 5

Find 1,200$)\overline{18,000}$.

Solution

Because the divisor, 1,200, is a multiple of 100, we can drop two zeros from each number.

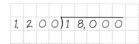   Drop two zeros to get

Divide.

$$\begin{array}{r} 1\ 5 \\ 1\ 2\overline{)1\ 8\ 0} \\ -\ 1\ 2 \\ \hline 6\ 0 \\ -\ 6\ 0 \\ \hline 0 \end{array}$$

Since 180 ÷ 12 = 15, it follows that 18,000 ÷ 1,200 = 15.

Check using multiplication: 1,200 × 15 = 18,000. ✓

[**YOU TRY 5**]   Find 1,500$)\overline{45,000}$.

3 Solve Applied Problems Using Long Division

In the next example, we will answer the question that was asked at the beginning of
this section.

EXAMPLE 6

In-Class Example 6

Leroy pays $288 for the 16 children at his daughter's birthday party. What is the cost per child?

Answer: $18 per child

If the total cost for 23 art history students to visit a museum is $322, what is the cost per student?

Solution

We will use long division to find the answer.

```
        1 4
   2 3)3 2 2
     - 2 3
         9 2
       - 9 2
           0
```

The cost is $14 per student.

[**YOU TRY 6**] Clarissa pays a caterer $2,698 to feed her 142 guests. What is the cost per person?

ANSWERS TO [YOU TRY] **EXERCISES**

1) 593   2) 492 R8   3) 406 R39   4) a) 42   b) 39   c) 20   5) 30   6) $19 per person

---

E Evaluate **2.5** Exercises   Do the exercises, and check your work.

*Additional answers can be found in the Answers to Exercises appendix.

Objective 1: Use Long Division

Use long division to find each quotient. Check your answer.

1) 3)192   64

2) 4)312   78

3) 6)3,486   581

4) 7)3,031   433

5) 4)1,071   267 R3

6) 9)6,478   719 R7

7) 4,272 ÷ 13   328 R8

8) 8,849 ÷ 18   491 R11

9) 4,758 ÷ 61   78

10) 5,394 ÷ 93   58

11) 52)4,940   95

12) 75)1,650   22

13) $\frac{2,834}{39}$ 72 R26

14) $\frac{1,139}{42}$ 27 R5

15) 47)65,153   1,386 R11

16) 86)97,822   1,137 R40

17) 7,923 ÷ 4   1,980 R3

18) 16,204 ÷ 5   3,240 R4

19) 71)61,118   860 R58

20) 63)29,639   470 R29

21) 4,015 ÷ 5   803

22) 2,472 ÷ 8   309

23) $\frac{15,042}{25}$ 601 R17

24) $\frac{12,692}{31}$ 409 R13

25) 68)170,279   2,504 R7

26) 49)279,696   5,708 R4

27) a) Find 5,396 ÷ 8 using short division.   674 R4

   b) Find 5,396 ÷ 8 using long division.   674 R4

   c) Which method do you prefer? Why?   Answers may vary.

28) Can we use short division to find 32,714 ÷ 27? Explain your answer.   No. The divisor has two digits.

Objective 2: Divide Numbers Ending in Zeros

29) If you divide a whole number ending in 0 by 10, how do you get the quotient?
   Drop one zero from the whole number.

30) If you divide a whole number ending in zeros by 100, how do you get the quotient?
   Drop two zeros from the whole number.

31) Divide.

   a) 30 ÷ 10   3

   b) 4,800 ÷ 100   48

   c) 312,000 ÷ 1,000   312

32) Divide.

   a) 70 ÷ 10   7

   b) 6,100 ÷ 100   61

   c) 177,000 ÷ 1,000   177

33) Divide.

   a) 9,260,000 ÷ 10   926,000

   b) 21,100,000 ÷ 1,000   21,100

   c) 78,000 ÷ 10   7,800

34) Divide.

　　a) 835,000 ÷ 10　83,500

　　b) 670,000 ÷ 100　6,700

　　c) 554,000,000 ÷ 1,000　554,000

Find each quotient.

35) 50)‾850　17　　　　36) 30)‾390　13

37) 237,900 ÷ 3,900　61　38) 275,600 ÷ 5,300　52

39) 4,600)‾3,358,000　730　40) 2,100)‾1,764,000　840

41) $\dfrac{7,000,000}{28,000}$　250　　42) $\dfrac{11,160,000}{36,000}$　310

Objective 3: Solve Applied Problems Using Long Division

Solve each problem.

43) Landon is the captain of his intramural soccer team and orders uniforms for each of the 18 players. If the total cost of the uniforms is $756, how much does each player owe?　$42

44) A company spends $6,600 to send 24 employees to a conference. What is the cost per employee?　$275

45) Each of the 230 guests at a fundraising dinner paid the same amount to attend. If $34,500 was raised, what was the cost per person?　$150

46) On opening day, the revenue for single-day adult lift tickets at a ski resort was $34,776. If each of these lift tickets cost $92, how many were sold?　378

47) In 2009, the average American spent approximately 1,095 hours watching television. How many hours per day does the average American watch television? (Hint: 1 year = 365 days) (www.bls.gov)　3 hr

48) In 2008, approximately 66,650,000 bushels of corn were harvested from 430,000 acres. How many bushels were harvested per acre? (www.census.gov)　155

R Rethink

49) In 2009, approximately 46,000,000 turkeys weighing a total of 736,000,000 lb were eaten on Thanksgiving day. Find the average weight of a turkey cooked on Thanksgiving day. (National Turkey Federation)　16 lb

50) Five hundred full-grown turkeys have about 1,750,000 feathers. How many feathers does one turkey have?　3,500

51) A whale migrated 3,000 miles in about 60 days. Find the average number of miles the whale traveled each day.　50 mi

52) A company will give each of its 132 employees the same end-of-the-year bonus. How much will each person receive if the total set aside for the bonuses is $330,000?　$2,500

Mixed Exercises: Objectives 1–3

Divide.

53) 40,693 ÷ 67　607 R24　54) 413,000 ÷ 1,000　413

55) $\dfrac{1,280}{40}$　32　　　　56) 9)‾2,214　246

57) 8,600 ÷ 10　860　　58) $\dfrac{9,180}{16}$　573 R12

Solve each problem.

59) A group of 16 friends went out to dinner and split the bill evenly. With tax and tip, the total bill was $336. How much did each person owe?　$21

60) According to the U.S. Census Bureau, Americans ate citrus fruits at a rate of 18 lb per year in 2007. Find the population of a town if it was expected that the people in that town ate 41,400 lb of citrus fruits in 2007. (www.census.gov)　2,300

R1) Are you using graph paper to help you line up numbers correctly?

R2) Where do you need more help in this section?

R3) Did the Mixed Exercises trip you up at all?

Putting It All Together

P Prepare

O Organize

What are your objectives?	How can you accomplish each objective?
1 Review the Concepts of Sections 2.1–2.5	• Be sure that you can apply the objectives you have learned in the previous sections. • If you are not confident on a certain example, go back to the section that gives more explanation. • Complete the given examples on your own. • Complete You Try 1.

W Work

Read the explanations, follow the examples, take notes, and complete the You Try.

1 Review the Concepts of Sections 2.1–2.5

In Sections 2.1–2.5, we learned how to multiply and divide whole numbers. Let's look at multiplication and division problems together.

EXAMPLE 1

Perform the indicated operation.

a) $\begin{array}{r} 4{,}293 \\ \times\ 605 \end{array}$ b) $4\overline{)2{,}516}$ c) $16{,}259 \div 23$

In-Class Example 1

Perform the indicated operation.

a) $\begin{array}{r} 3{,}192 \\ \times\ 508 \end{array}$

b) $6\overline{)3{,}162}$

c) $12{,}694 \div 31$

Answer:
a) 1,621,536   b) 527
c) 409 R15

Solution

a) Line up the digits in the correct columns and multiply. Since the multiplier, 605, contains a zero, we must remember to account for its position in the multiplication process.

$\begin{array}{r} 4{,}2\ 9\ 3 \\ \times\ \ 6\ 0\ 5 \\ \hline 2\ 1\ 4\ 6\ 5 \\ 0\ 0\ 0\ 0 \\ 2\ 5\ 7\ 5\ 8 \\ \hline 2{,}5\ 9\ 7{,}2\ 6\ 5 \end{array}$

Multiply 4,293 by 5; line up in the ones column on right.
Multiply 4,293 by 0; line up in the tens column on right.
Multiply 4,293 by 6; line up in the hundreds column on right.
Add to get the product.

The product is 2,597,265.

b) The dividend is 2,516 and the divisor is 4. Since the divisor is only one digit, we can use either short or long division. Let's use short division.

Divide 25 by 4: $4\overline{)2{,}5^{1}16}$ $\overset{6}{}$ $25 \div 4 = 6$ R1

Next, divide 11 by 4: $4\overline{)2{,}5^{1}1^{3}6}$ $\overset{6\ 2}{}$ $11 \div 4 = 2$ R3

Finally, divide 36 by 4:

$\overset{6\ 2\ 9}{4\overline{)2{,}5^{1}1^{3}6}}$ $36 \div 4 = 9$

So, 2,516 divided by 4 is 629.   Check: $4 \times 629 = 2{,}516.$ ✔

c) The divisor, 23, has two digits so we cannot use short division. We will use long division.

Begin by setting up the problem as $23\overline{)16{,}259}$.

$$
\begin{array}{r}
7 \\
23\overline{)16{,}259} \\
-161\downarrow \\
\hline
15
\end{array}
$$

1) How many times does 162 divide evenly by 23?   7

2) Multiply $7 \times 23 = 161$.

3) Subtract $162 - 161 = 1$.

4) Bring down the 5.

Start the process again. Ask yourself, "*How many times does* 15 *divide evenly by* 23?"   0

$$
\begin{array}{r}
7\ 0 \\
23\overline{)16{,}259} \\
-161 \\
\hline
15
\end{array}
$$
— Write 0 in the quotient as a placeholder.

Bring down the 9, and do the division process again.

$$
\begin{array}{r}
7\ 0\ 6 \\
23\overline{)16{,}259} \\
-161\downarrow \\
\hline
159 \\
-138 \\
\hline
21
\end{array}
$$
← Remainder

1) How many times does 159 divide evenly by 23?   6

2) Multiply $6 \times 23 = 138$.

3) Subtract $159 - 138 = 21$.

4) The remainder is 21.

Therefore, $16{,}259 \div 23 = 706 \text{ R}21$.
Check: $(23 \times 706) + 21 = 16{,}238 + 21 = 16{,}259$.   ✓

We can use the commutative and associative properties to multiply numbers.

EXAMPLE 2

Multiply $7 \cdot 3$, then rewrite the problem using the commutative property.

Solution

$7 \cdot 3 = 21$. The commutative property says that changing the order in which we multiply numbers does not change the product. Therefore, $3 \cdot 7 = 21$.

EXAMPLE 3

Multiply $(4 \times 2) \times 10$, then rewrite the problem using the associative property.

Solution

The associative property says that we can group factors in any order and the product will remain the same.

Original Product	Using the Associative Property
$(4 \times 2) \times 10 =$	$4 \times (2 \times 10) =$
$8 \times 10 = 80$	$4 \times 20 = 80$

In Section 2.2, we learned that when we multiply a whole number by 10, 100, 1,000, etc., the result is the number followed by the number of zeros in the multiplier. We can use this to multiply a whole number by other multiples of 10 as well.

EXAMPLE 4

Multiply.

a) $881 \times 10,000$ b) $12 \cdot 400$

Solution

a) $881 \times 10,000 = 8,810,000$ Add four zeros to the end of 881.

b) 400 is a multiple of 100. So, to find $12 \cdot 400$, we can multiply 12 by 4 then add two zeros to the end of that result.

$$12 \cdot 4 = 48, \text{ then add two zeros to } 48: 4,800$$
$$12 \cdot 400 = 4,800$$

In a similar way, when we divide a whole number ending in zeros by 10, 100, 1,000, etc., we drop the appropriate number of zeros from the end of the whole number.

EXAMPLE 5

Divide $\dfrac{2,600,000}{1,000}$.

Solution

Since we are dividing 2,600,000 by 1,000, get the quotient by dropping three zeros from 2,600,000. $\dfrac{2,600,000}{1,000} = 2,600$

We learned in Section 2.4 that a whole number is **divisible** by another whole number if the remainder is 0. The divisibility rules help us determine whether one number is divisible by another number.

EXAMPLE 6

Determine whether each number is divisible by 2, 3, 5, and/or 10.

a) 765   b) 9,380

Solution

a) The number 765 is not divisible by 2 since it is not an even number, and it is not divisible by 10 because it does not end in 0.

To determine whether 765 is divisible by 3, add the digits: $7 + 6 + 5 = 18$. Because 18 is divisible by 3, the number 765 is divisible by 3.

A number is divisible by 5 if it ends in 0 or 5. Therefore, 765 is divisible by 5.

Therefore, 765 is divisible by 3 and 5.

b) The number 9,380 is divisible by 2 because it is an even number, and it is divisible by 5 and 10 because it ends in 0. Is it divisible by 3? Add the digits:

$9 + 3 + 8 + 0 = 20$. Because 20 is not divisible by 3, the number 9,380 is not divisible by 3.

YOU TRY 1

a) Perform the indicated operation.

i) $92,341 \div 7$ ii) $\begin{array}{r} 870 \\ \times\ 96 \end{array}$ iii) $(64)(1,000)$

iv) $\dfrac{78,000,000}{100}$ v) $3,566 \times 2,004$ vi) $46\overline{)5,087}$ vii) $25 \cdot 300$

b) Multiply $5 \cdot (4 \cdot 8)$, then rewrite the problem using the associative property.

c) Multiply 6×11, then rewrite the problem using the commutative property.

d) Determine whether 6,285 is divisible by 2, 3, 5, and/or 10.

ANSWERS TO YOU TRY **EXERCISES**

1) a) i) 13,191 R4   ii) 83,520   iii) 64,000   iv) 780,000   v) 7,146,264   vi) 110 R27   vii) 7,500
  b) $5 \cdot (4 \cdot 8) = 160$; $(5 \cdot 4) \cdot 8 = 160$ c) $6 \times 11 = 66$; $11 \times 6 = 66$
  d) 6,285 is divisible by 3 and 5.

Putting It All Together Exercises

E Evaluate   Do the exercises, and check your work.

Additional answers can be found in the Answers to Exercises appendix.

Objective 1: Review the Concepts of Sections 2.1–2.5

1) In the multiplication problem $7 \cdot 3 = 21$,

 a) identify the factors.   3, 7

 b) identify the product.   21

2) In the division problem $32 \div 8 = 4$,

 a) identify the divisor.   8

 b) identify the dividend.   32

 c) identify the quotient.   4

Fill in the blank.

3) Any number divided by 0 is ____undefined____.

4) Zero divided by any nonzero number is ____0____.

Perform the indicated operation.

5) 9×8 72

6) 12×7 84

7) $42 \div 6$ 7

8) $20 \div 4$ 5

9) $12\overline{)144}$ 12

10) $8\overline{)64}$ 8

11) $5 \cdot 7$ 35

12) $6 \cdot 9$ 54

13) $8(0)$ 0

14) $1(4)$ 4

15) $\dfrac{11}{0}$ undefined

16) $\dfrac{0}{5}$ 0

Fill in the blank.

17) $56 \div \underline{} = 7$ 8

18) $28 \div \underline{} = 4$ 7

19) $\underline{} \cdot 12 = 60$ 5

20) $\underline{} \cdot 6 = 18$ 3

21) $8 \times \underline{} = 96$ 12

22) $5 \times \underline{} = 55$ 11

23) $\underline{} \div 4 = 0$ 0

24) $\underline{} \div 7 = 1$ 7

25) $9 \cdot \underline{} = 9$ 1

26) $12 \cdot \underline{} = 0$ 0

Use short division to find the quotient.

27) $7\overline{)4,158}$ 594

28) $4\overline{)2,932}$ 733

29) $8,221 \div 6$ 1,370 R 1

30) $7,447 \div 8$ 930 R7

Perform the indicated operation.

31) $\begin{array}{r} 3,174 \\ \times\ 523 \end{array}$ 1,660,002

32) $\dfrac{620,000}{100}$ 6,200

33) $\dfrac{10,488}{38}$ 276

34) $4 \cdot 5 \cdot 6 \cdot 3$ 360

35) $832(207)$ 172,224

36) $14\overline{)9,880}$ 705 R10

37) $95 \cdot 100,000$ 9,500,000

38) $\begin{array}{r} 2,553 \\ \times\ 1,006 \end{array}$ 2,568,318

39) $17\overline{)68,039}$ 4,002 R5

40) $40\overline{)2,800}$ 70

41) $15,270,000 \div 100$ 152,700

42) 739×52 38,428

43) $\dfrac{8,032}{9}$ 892 R4

44) $905 \cdot 68$ 61,540

45) $800\overline{)24,000}$ 30

46) $904 \div 7$ 129 R 1

Find each product, then rewrite the problem using the commutative property.

47) $8 \cdot 7$ 56; $7 \cdot 8 = 56$

48) $(2)(9)$ 18; $(9)(2) = 18$

Find each product, then rewrite the problem using the associative property.

49) $(3 \times 7) \times 2$ 42; $3 \times (7 \times 2) = 42$

50) $5 \cdot (3 \cdot 4)$ 60; $(5 \cdot 3) \cdot 4 = 60$

51) How do you know whether a number is divisible by 3? Add the digits in the number. If that sum is divisible by 3, then the number is divisible by 3.

52) How do you know whether a number is divisible by 2? The number ends in 0, 2, 4, 6, or 8.

Determine whether each number is divisible by 2, 3, 5, and/or 10, or none of these.

53) 858 2 and 3

54) 470 2, 5, and 10

55) 5,220 2, 3, 5, and 10

56) 7,257 3

Answer the following questions.

57) What is the product of 8 and 72? 576

58) What is the remainder when 94 is divided by 6? 4

59) What number do you divide by 9 to get 12? 108

60) What number do you multiply by 7 to get 56? 8

Solve each problem.

61) One week, Trequanda babysat for 32 hours and earned $352. How much did she earn per hour? $11

62) A factory ships its paper to office supply stores. Each box contains 24 reams of paper. How many boxes are needed to hold 16,800 reams of paper? 700 boxes

63) A college offers 59 sections of its Introduction to Psychology course in the spring semester. If each section can have 35 students, how many students can register for this psychology course in the spring? 2,065 students

64) A hospital orders 120 packages of diapers, and each package contains 48 diapers. Find the total number of diapers the hospital will receive. 5,760 diapers

65) Henry is a marketing manager and earns $1,250 per week. How much does he earn each year? $65,000

66) A college computer lab has a total of 180 computers in 12 rows. If each row contains the same number of computers, how many are in each row? 15 computers

67) Each shelf in a display case in a store can hold 18 coffee cups. How many shelves are needed to hold 216 cups? 12 shelves

68) The economy lot at O'Hare airport in Chicago costs $17 per day. How much will Eileen pay to park her car for a week? (www.flychicago.com) $119

R Rethink

R1) Discuss how you used multiplication and division in every problem if you checked your answer.

R2) You have learned many different properties, procedures, and techniques in the last five sections. What has been the most effective way to learn the material?

2.6 Exponents, Roots, and Order of Operations

P Prepare

O Organize

What are your objectives for Section 2.6?	How can you accomplish each objective?
1 Use Exponents	• Understand why exponents are used and write a sentence describing exponential expressions using the words *base* and *power*. • Learn the common powers of whole numbers listed on page 107. • Complete the given example on your own. • Complete You Try 1.
2 Find Square Roots	• Understand how to find a *square root* and note what makes a *perfect square*. • Complete the given example on your own. • Complete You Try 2.
3 Use the Order of Operations	• Write the procedure for **The Order of Operations** in your own words using **P**lease **E**xcuse **M**y **D**ear **A**unt **S**ally. • Complete the given examples on your own. • Complete You Trys 3 and 4.

W Work   Read the explanations, follow the examples, take notes, and complete the You Trys.

1 Use Exponents

Exponents are used to represent repeated multiplication. For example,

$$3 \cdot 3 = 3^2 \leftarrow \text{Exponent or Power}$$
$$\uparrow$$
$$\text{Base}$$

The **base** is 3, and the **exponent,** or **power,** is 2. The exponent tells us how many times to use the base as a factor in the multiplication problem. We read the exponential expression 3^2 as "3 squared" or "3 to the second power." When we find that $3^2 = 9$, we are *evaluating* 3^2.

EXAMPLE 1

Identify the base and the exponent, then evaluate each expression.

a) 8^2 b) 5^3 c) 2^5

In-Class Example 1

Identify the base and the exponent, then evaluate each expression.
a) 4^2 b) 5^3 c) 2^5

Answer:
a) base: 4; exponent: 2; 16
b) base: 5; exponent: 3; 125
c) base: 2; exponent: 5; 32

Solution

a) $8^2 \leftarrow \text{Exponent}$ The exponent 2 tells us to use 8 as a factor 2 times.
$\uparrow$
Base

$$8^2 = 8 \cdot 8 = 64$$

---

b) 5^3 ← Exponent   The exponent 3 tells us to use 5 as a factor 3 times.
   ↑
  Base

$$5^3 = 5 \cdot 5 \cdot 5 = 125$$

We read 5^3 as "5 to the third power" or "5 cubed."

c) 2^5 ← Exponent   The exponent 5 tells us to use 2 as a factor 5 times.
   ↑
  Base

$$2^5 = 2 \cdot 2 \cdot 2 \cdot 2 \cdot 2 = 32$$

We read 2^5 as "2 to the fifth power."

[YOU TRY 1]   Identify the base and the exponent, then evaluate each expression.

a) 7^2 b) 4^3 c) 2^6

Certain powers of whole numbers are used often in mathematics. We list them here for you to memorize.

 Hint

Quiz yourself by making flash cards!

Powers to Memorize						
$2^1 = 2$	$3^1 = 3$	$4^1 = 4$	$5^1 = 5$	$6^1 = 6$	$8^1 = 8$	$10^1 = 10$
$2^2 = 4$	$3^2 = 9$	$4^2 = 16$	$5^2 = 25$	$6^2 = 36$	$8^2 = 64$	$10^2 = 100$
$2^3 = 8$	$3^3 = 27$	$4^3 = 64$	$5^3 = 125$			$10^3 = 1,000$
$2^4 = 16$	$3^4 = 81$					
$2^5 = 32$				$7^1 = 7$	$9^1 = 9$	$11^1 = 11$
$2^6 = 64$				$7^2 = 49$	$9^2 = 81$	$11^2 = 121$
						$12^1 = 12$
						$12^2 = 144$
						$13^1 = 13$
						$13^2 = 169$
						$14^1 = 14$
						$14^2 = 196$
						$15^1 = 15$
						$15^2 = 225$

2 Find Square Roots

Hint

This is the opposite of squaring a whole number!

At the beginning of this section, we found that $3^2 = 9$. We say that 3 is the *square root* of 9. The **square root** of a number is a number that, when squared, results in the given number. We use the symbol $\sqrt{}$ to represent a square root. Therefore, we can write $\sqrt{9} = 3$ because $3^2 = 9$. We say that 9 is a **perfect square** because it is the square of a whole number.

EXAMPLE 2

Evaluate.

a) $\sqrt{49}$ b) $\sqrt{144}$ c) $\sqrt{1}$ d) $\sqrt{0}$

In-Class Example 2

Evaluate.
a) $\sqrt{36}$ b) $\sqrt{81}$
c) $\sqrt{1}$ d) $\sqrt{0}$

Answer: a) 6 b) 9
c) 1 d) 0

Solution

a) $\sqrt{49} = 7$ since $7^2 = 49$.   b) $\sqrt{144} = 12$ since $12^2 = 144$.

c) $\sqrt{1} = 1$ since $1^2 = 1$.   d) $\sqrt{0} = 0$ since $0^2 = 0$.

[**YOU TRY 2**]   Evaluate.

a) $\sqrt{4}$ b) $\sqrt{25}$ c) $\sqrt{121}$ d) $\sqrt{100}$

3 Use the Order of Operations

If we are asked to evaluate an expression that contains different operation symbols, like $6 \times 7 - 5^2 + 12$, we need rules to tell us the order in which to perform the operations. We call these rules the **order of operations.**

Procedure The Order of Operations

Simplify expressions in the following order:

1) If **parentheses** or **other grouping symbols** appear in an expression, simplify what is inside these grouping symbols first.

2) Simplify expressions with **exponents** and **square roots.**

3) **Multiply** or **divide** moving from left to right.

4) **Add** or **subtract** moving from left to right.

Note

It may be helpful to remember the order of operations by remembering this sentence: **P**lease **E**xcuse **M**y **D**ear **A**unt **S**ally. The first letter of each word tells us the order in which we perform operations: **P**arentheses, **E**xponents, **M**ultiplication and **D**ivision (from left to right), and **A**ddition and **S**ubtraction (from left to right).

EXAMPLE 3

Simplify each expression using the order of operations.

a) $19 - 10 + 3$ b) $30 \div 3 \cdot 2$

c) $32 + 48 \div 8$ d) $6 \times 7 - 5^2 + 12$

In-Class Example 3

Simplify each expression
using the order of operations.
a) $28 - 11 + 4$
b) $40 \div 2 \cdot 4$
c) $14 + 21 \div 7$
d) $9 \times 5 - 6^2 + 25$

Answer:
a) 21 b) 80 c) 17 d) 34

Solution

a) When an expression contains only addition and subtraction, perform the operations from left to right.

$$19 - 10 + 3 =$$

$$9 \quad + 3 = 12$$

b) When an expression contains only multiplication and division, perform the operations from left to right.

$$30 \div 3 \cdot 2 =$$
$$10 \quad \cdot 2 = 20$$

c) Perform division before addition.

$$32 + 48 \div 8 =$$
$$32 + \quad 6 \quad = 38$$

d)
$$6 \times 7 - 5^2 + 12 =$$
$$6 \times 7 - 25 + 12 = \qquad \text{Evaluate exponents before multiplication, addition, and subtraction.}$$
$$42 - 25 \ + 12 = \qquad \text{Multiply before adding or subtracting.}$$
$$17 \qquad + \ 12 = \qquad \text{Perform operations from left to right.}$$
$$29 \qquad\qquad\qquad \text{Add.}$$

[YOU TRY 3] Simplify each expression using the order of operations.

a) $23 - 8 + 7$ b) $84 \div 4 \times 3$

c) $10 + 35 \div 5$ d) $3 \cdot 12 - 4^2 + 9$

When an expression contains parentheses or other grouping symbols, simplify what is inside these first.

EXAMPLE 4 Simplify each expression using the order of operations.

a) $\sqrt{100} \div (11 - 6)$

b) $6^2 - 12 \div 4 + (6 - 1)^2$

c) $4 \cdot \sqrt{49} - \dfrac{24}{8} \cdot (5 + 1)$

d) $8(10) - 2^3 \cdot 3^2 + 5(3 + 4)$

e) $52 + 3[100 \div (7 - 2)^2]$

Solution

a)
$$\sqrt{100} \div (11 - 6) =$$
$$\sqrt{100} \div \quad 5 \quad = \qquad \text{First, perform the operation in parentheses.}$$
$$10 \div \quad 5 \quad = \qquad \text{Evaluate the square root.}$$
$$2 \qquad\qquad \text{Divide.}$$

b)
$$6^2 - 12 \div 4 + (6 - 1)^2 =$$
$$6^2 - 12 \div 4 + \quad 5^2 \quad = \qquad \text{Perform the operation in parentheses first.}$$
$$36 - 12 \div 4 + \quad 25 \quad = \qquad \text{Evaluate exponents.}$$
$$36 - \quad 3 \ + \ 25 \quad = \qquad \text{Perform division before adding or subtracting.}$$
$$33 \qquad + \ 25 \quad = \qquad \text{Subtract.}$$
$$58 \qquad\qquad\qquad \text{Add.}$$

c) $4 \cdot \sqrt{49} - \dfrac{24}{8} \cdot (5 + 1) =$

$\quad 4 \cdot \sqrt{49} - \dfrac{24}{8} \cdot \quad 6 \quad =$ Perform the operation in parentheses first.

$\quad 4 \cdot \quad 7 \quad - \dfrac{24}{8} \cdot \quad 6 \quad =$ Evaluate the square root.

$\quad\quad 28 \quad - \dfrac{24}{8} \cdot \quad 6 \quad =$ Multiply $4 \cdot 7$.

$\quad\quad 28 \quad - \quad 3 \cdot \quad 6 \quad =$ Divide.

$\quad\quad 28 \quad - \quad\quad 18 \quad =$ Multiply before subtracting.

$\quad\quad\quad\quad\quad 10$ Subtract.

d) $8(10) - 2^3 \cdot 3^2 + 5(3 + 4) =$

$\quad 8(10) - 2^3 \cdot 3^2 + \quad 5(7) \quad =$ Perform the operation in parentheses first.

$\quad 8(10) - 8 \cdot 9 \; + \quad 5(7) \quad =$ Evaluate exponents.

$\quad\; 80 \quad - \; 72 \; + \quad 35 \quad =$ Multiply.

$\quad\quad\quad 8 \quad\quad + \quad 35 \quad =$ Subtract.

$\quad\quad\quad\quad\quad 43$ Add.

e) This expression contains two sets of grouping symbols: parentheses and brackets. When one set of grouping symbols is inside another, simplify what is in the innermost grouping symbols first.

$52 + 3[100 \div (7 - 2)^2] =$

$52 + 3[100 \div (5)^2] \quad =$ Perform the operation in the innermost grouping symbols first.

$52 + 3[100 \div 25] \quad\;\; =$ Evaluate exponent.

$52 \; + \; 3[4] \quad\quad\quad =$ Perform the operation in the brackets.

$52 \; + \; 12 \quad\quad\quad\quad =$ Multiply.

$\quad 64$ Add.

[YOU TRY 4]

Simplify each expression using the order of operations.

a) $(58 + 19) \div \sqrt{121}$ b) $8^2 - 20 \div (9 - 7)^2$

c) $\dfrac{72}{9}(17 - 11) + 2\sqrt{25}$ d) $3^4 \cdot 2^2 - 12(1 + 5) - 2(12)$

e) $\sqrt{169} \cdot \sqrt{49} - 3[(4 + 1)^3 \div 5] - 2^4$

ANSWERS TO [YOU TRY] EXERCISES

1) a) base: 7; exponent: 2; 49   b) base: 4; exponent: 3; 64   c) base: 2; exponent: 6; 64
2) a) 2   b) 5   c) 11   d) 10   3) a) 22   b) 63   c) 17   d) 29
4) a) 7   b) 59   c) 58   d) 228   e) 0

[E] Evaluate   **2.6** Exercises   Do the exercises, and check your work.

*Additional answers can be found in the Answers to Exercises appendix.

Objective 1: Use Exponents

Identify the base and the exponent, then evaluate each expression.

1) 8^2 base: 8; exponent: 2; 64   2) 10^2 base: 10; exponent: 2; 100

3) 13^2 base: 13; exponent: 2; 169

4) 12^2 base: 12; exponent: 2; 144

5) 0^2 base: 0; exponent: 2; 0   6) 1^2 base: 1; exponent: 2; 1

7) 2^3 base: 2; exponent: 3; 8   8) 3^3 base: 3; exponent: 3; 27

9) 3^4 base: 3; exponent: 4; 81   10) 2^6 base: 2; exponent: 6; 64

11) 20^2 base: 20; exponent: 2; 400   12) 30^2 base: 30; exponent: 2; 900

13) 10^5 base: 10; exponent: 5; 100,000   14) 11^4 base: 11; exponent: 4; 14,641

Rewrite each product as an exponential expression. Do *not* evaluate.

15) $9 \cdot 9 \cdot 9 \cdot 9$ 9^4

16) $5 \cdot 5 \cdot 5 \cdot 5 \cdot 5 \cdot 5 \cdot 5$ 5^7

17) $4 \cdot 4 \cdot 4 \cdot 4 \cdot 4 \cdot 4$ 4^6

18) $7 \cdot 7 \cdot 7$ 7^3

Objective 2: Find Square Roots

19) Explain how to find the square root of a whole number.   Answers may vary.

20) How do we know that $\sqrt{25} = 5$?
$\sqrt{25} = 5$ because $5^2 = 25$.

Evaluate.

21) $\sqrt{16}$ 4

22) $\sqrt{36}$ 6

23) $\sqrt{81}$ 9

24) $\sqrt{100}$ 10

25) $\sqrt{1}$ 1

26) $\sqrt{0}$ 0

27) $\sqrt{49}$ 7

28) $\sqrt{4}$ 2

29) $\sqrt{196}$ 14

30) $\sqrt{225}$ 15

31) $\sqrt{400}$ 20

32) $\sqrt{900}$ 30

Objective 3: Use the Order of Operations

33) Explain, in your own words, the order of operations.   Answers may vary.

34) Prof. Spahr asks her students to simplify this expression: $21 + 15 \div 3$. Laurel's answer is 12. Is this the correct answer? Why or why not?

Simplify each expression using the order of operations.

35) $8 - 2 + 3$ 9

36) $9 - 5 + 2$ 6

37) $48 \div 12 \times 2$ 8

38) $90 \div 2 \times 3$ 135

39) $2 \cdot 3 + 4$ 10

40) $5 \cdot 4 + 1$ 21

41) $4 \cdot 2^3 + \dfrac{6}{3}$ 34

42) $6 \cdot 3^2 + \dfrac{0}{5}$ 54

43) $15 - 9 \div 3 + 6$ 18

44) $20 - 12 \div 4 + 2$ 19

45) $10^2 - 40 \div 5 + 3(8)$ 116

46) $9^2 + 12(2) - 42 \div 7$ 99

47) $5 \cdot \sqrt{9} - 3(2)$ 9

48) $4 \cdot \sqrt{25} - 5(3)$ 5

49) $3 + 4(3 + 2)$ 23

50) $5 + 3(1 + 4)$ 20

51) $6 \cdot 5 - (3 + 4) \cdot 2$ 16

52) $8 \cdot 4 - (5 + 2) \cdot 3$ 11

53) $8\sqrt{16} - 6\sqrt{9}$ 14

54) $6\sqrt{49} - 5\sqrt{36}$ 12

55) $3^2 \cdot 2^3 - (10 - 2) \div 4$ 70

56) $4^2 \cdot 2^2 - (14 - 6) \div 2$ 60

57) $2(\sqrt{25})^2 - 3^3$ 23

58) $5(\sqrt{9})^2 - 2^3$ 37

59) $\sqrt{16} \div \sqrt{4} \cdot 6 - 3 + 9$ 18

60) $\sqrt{100} \div \sqrt{25} \cdot 6 - 8 + 4$ 8

61) $15 - (6 + 2) + 5\sqrt{81} \div \sqrt{9} \cdot 3 - 5$ 47

62) $21 - (4 + 5) + 8\sqrt{49} \div \sqrt{16} \cdot 4 - 7$ 61

63) $\dfrac{32}{4} + 2[7^2 - (4 - 1)^3]$ 52

64) $\dfrac{50}{25} + 3[8^2 - (7 - 3)^3]$ 2

65) $[5 + (8 - 1)^2] \div (3 \cdot 2)$ 9

66) $[20 + (10 - 4)^2] \div (2 \cdot 4)$ 7

67) $9 \cdot 8 + 3[(7 + 9) \div 2]$ 96

68) $6 \cdot 10 + 4[(12 + 16) \div 7]$ 76

69) $4\sqrt{100} + [12^2 \div (11 - 2)] \cdot \dfrac{40}{8}$ 120

70) $3\sqrt{64} + [10^2 \div (17 - 12)] \cdot \dfrac{33}{11}$ 84

R Rethink

R1) Do you have a firm grasp on exponents, square roots, and using the order of operations?

R2) Did you use flash cards to help memorize the commonly used powers? Could flash cards help you with other topics?

2.7 Solving Applied Problems

What are your objectives for Section 2.7?	How can you accomplish each objective?
1 Recognize Key Words	• Understand what the *key words* mean in an application problem and spend some time memorizing them. • Complete the given examples on your own. • Complete You Trys 1 and 2.
2 Solve Applied Problems	• Write the **Steps for Solving Applied Problems** in your own words. • Complete the given examples on your own. • Complete You Trys 3–6.

Organize

W Work   **Read the explanations, follow the examples, take notes, and complete the You Trys.**

Mathematics is used to solve all kinds of everyday problems. In this section, we will learn some strategies to help us solve applications.

1 Recognize Key Words

Identifying *key words* in a problem is one strategy that can help us solve applications. Here are some key words to look for that will help us determine whether we add, subtract, multiply, or divide to solve a problem.

Add	Subtract	Multiply	Divide	Equals
plus	minus	product	quotient	equals
sum	subtracted from	times	divided by	is
more than	difference	double	divided into	are
increased by	less than	twice	divided equally	is the same as
total	decreased by	triple	per	
added to	fewer	of		

EXAMPLE 1

Find the number that is 74 more than 159.

In-Class Example 1

Find the number that is 83 more than 134.

Answer: 217

W Hint

Solving these short problems will help you solve longer word problems later on.

Solution

The words *more than* indicate that we should add.

```
  1 1
  1 5 9
+   7 4
  2 3 3
```

233 is 74 more than 159.

[YOU TRY 1]   What number do you get when 142 is increased by 107?

EXAMPLE 2

In-Class Example 2

What number is twice 78?

Answer: 156

What number is twice 93?

Solution

The key word *twice* means *two times*. To find the number that is twice 93, we multiply 93 by 2.

$$\begin{array}{r} 9\;3 \\ \times\quad 2 \\ \hline 1\;8\;6 \end{array}$$

186 is twice 93.

[YOU TRY 2] What number do you get when you triple 57?

---

2 Solve Applied Problems

Recognizing key words is just one part of solving applied problems. It is helpful to have a general strategy for solving applications. We will use these steps.

> **Procedure** Steps for Solving Applied Problems
>
> *Step 1:* **Read** the problem carefully, more than once if necessary, until you understand it. Restate the problem in your own words. Draw a picture, if applicable. Identify what you are being asked to find.
>
> *Step 2:* **Make a plan** for solving the problem. Underline important words that might help you solve the problem.
>
> *Step 3:* **Solve** the problem using your plan and the information given. Look at the important words you have underlined.
>
> *Step 4:* **State the answer** in a complete sentence.
>
> *Step 5:* **Check** the answer.

EXAMPLE 3

In-Class Example 3

During the 2008–2009 season, the Chicago Blackhawks' home attendance was 912,155. The next season, 57,888 fewer people were in attendance at home games. Find the home attendance at Blackhawks' games during the 2009–2010 season. (espn.go.com)

Answer: 854,267

Kahlima flies often for her job and collects frequent-flyer miles. In 2010, she flew 51,278 miles. In 2011, she flew 3,115 fewer miles than in 2010. How many miles did Kahlima fly in 2011?

Solution

Step 1: **Read** the problem carefully, and restate it in your own words.

In 2010, Kahlima flew <u>51,278 miles,</u> and in 2011 she flew <u>3,115 miles less than that number.</u> We must <u>find the number of miles she flew in 2011.</u>

Step 2: **Make a plan.** Let's underline important words in our restatement of the problem in Step 1. What do the key words *less than* indicate? Subtraction.

Plan: Subtract 3,115 from 51,278 to determine the number of miles Kahlima flew in 2011.

Step 3: **Solve** the problem.

```
    4  11
    5  1  2  7  8
 −     3, 1  1  5
    4  8, 1  6  3
```

Step 4: **State the answer** in a complete sentence.

Kahlima flew 48,163 miles in 2011.

Step 5: **Check** the answer. We can use addition to check our subtraction.

The answer is correct.

```
       1
    4  8, 1  6  3
 +     3, 1  1  5
    5  1, 2  7  8
```

[**YOU TRY 3**] In the fall semester, Keith had 157 students. In the spring semester, he had 38 fewer students. How many students did he teach in the spring?

EXAMPLE 4

In-Class Example 4

On Wednesday, Leticia received $68 in tips, on Friday she received $115, on Saturday she received $134, and on Sunday her tips totaled $93. Find the total amount of tips Leticia earned.

Answer: $410

Jorge's math class meets three days each week. On Monday, his professor assigned 34 homework problems, on Wednesday she assigned 29, and on Friday he had 45 problems for homework. Find the total number of problems Jorge had to do this week.

Solution

Step 1: **Read** the problem carefully, and restate it in your own words.

Jorge was assigned <u>34</u> problems on Monday, <u>29</u> on Wednesday, and <u>45</u> on Friday. We must find the <u>total number of homework problems</u> Jorge had this week.

Step 2: **Make a plan.** Underline important words in our restatement of the problem in Step 1. What does the key word *total* tell us to do? Add.

Plan: Add 34, 29, and 45 to find the total number of homework problems.

Step 3: **Solve** the problem.

```
      1
      3 4    Number of problems on Monday
      2 9    Number of problems on Wednesday
   +  4 5    Number of problems on Friday
   1  0 8    Total number of homework problems
```

Step 4: **State the answer** in a complete sentence.

Jorge had 108 problems for homework this week.

Step 5: **Check** the answer. Add the numbers again to verify that 108 is the correct sum.

[**YOU TRY 4**] At Kaitlyn's graduation party, there were 47 family members, 23 college friends, and 11 friends from high school. Find the total number of people at Kaitlyn's party.

EXAMPLE 5

Vince, Eric, Johnny, and Turtle are roommates and split the rent equally among themselves. If their rent is $1,300 per month, how much does each of them pay monthly?

Solution

Step 1: **Read** the problem carefully, and restate it in your own words.

Four friends divide the $1,300 rent equally among themselves. We must determine how much each person pays.

Step 2: **Make a plan.** Let's underline important words in our restatement of the problem in Step 1.

Plan: Dividing $1,300 equally among four people means we must divide 1,300 by 4 to determine how much each person pays for rent.

Step 3: **Solve** the problem.

$$
\begin{array}{r}
3\ 2\ 5 \quad \leftarrow \text{Amount each person pays}\\
4\overline{)1,3\ 0\ 0} \quad \leftarrow \text{Amount of rent}\\
-1\ 2\\
\hline
1\ 0\\
-\ \ 8\\
\hline
2\ 0\\
-2\ 0\\
\hline
0
\end{array}
$$

Divide equally among 4 people.

Step 4: **State the answer** in a complete sentence.

Each person pays $325 each month for rent.

Step 5: **Check** the answer. We can use multiplication to check the division.

$$
\begin{array}{r}
1\ 2\\
3\ 2\ 5\\
\times \quad\ \ 4\\
\hline
1,3\ 0\ 0
\end{array}
$$

Amount of rent each person pays
Number of people
Total rent

The answer is correct.

[YOU TRY 5]

Vanessa buys 192 cans of soda divided equally in 8 packages. How many cans are in each package?

Sometimes, we must use more than one type of arithmetic operation to solve a problem.

EXAMPLE 6

A community college charges $98 per credit hour plus fees. If Phuong registers for 16 hours and has to pay $103 in fees, find the amount she must pay to register for classes.

Solution

Step 1: **Read** the problem carefully, and restate it in your own words.

Phuong registers for 16 credit hours and pays $98 for each credit hour. She also pays $103 in fees. We must find the total amount she owes the college.

Step 2: **Make a plan.** Let's underline important words in our restatement of the problem in Step 1.

Plan: Multiply $98 × 16 to determine the amount she owes for taking 16 credit hours. Then, add $103 for the fees to get the total amount Phuong owes.

Step 3: **Solve** the problem.

Cost of taking 16 credit hours   Add the fees.

			9	8	Cost per credit hour
		×	1	6	Number of credit hours
		5	8	8	
		9	8		
1,	5	6	8		Cost of 16 credit hours

	1,	5	6	8	Cost of 16 credit hours
+		1	0	3	Fees
	1,	6	7	1	Total cost to register for classes

Step 4: **State the answer** in a complete sentence.

Phuong must pay $1,671 to register for classes.

Step 5: **Check** the answer. Reverse what we did in Step 4.

Subtract the fees from the total.   Divide $1,568 by 16.

		6	11	
1,	6	7̶	1̶	
−		1	0	3
	1,	5	6	8

				9	8
1 6)1,	5	6	8		
− 1	4	4			
	1	2	8		
−	1	2	8		
			O		

The answer is correct.

[YOU TRY 6] Mr. Kirilenko bought five tickets for his family to see *The Nutcracker*. If he paid $67 for each ticket and $20 for parking, find the total amount he paid.

ANSWERS TO [**YOU TRY**] **EXERCISES**

1) 249   2) 171   3) 119   4) 81   5) 24   6) $355

E Evaluate **2.7** Exercises   Do the exercises, and check your work.

*Additional answers can be found in the Answers to Exercises appendix.

Objective 1: Recognize Key Words

1) List four key words that indicate subtraction.
   Answers may vary.

2) List four key words that indicate division.
   Answers may vary.

3) List four key words that indicate multiplication.
   Answers may vary.

4) List four key words that indicate addition.
   Answers may vary.

5) What number is 52 increased by 39?   91

6) What number is 68 increased by 19?   87

7) Find the product of 22 and 16.   352

8) Find the product of 74 and 41.   3,034

9) What number is 193 less than 460?   267

10) What number is 217 less than 855?   638

11) What number results when you divide 204 into 6 equal parts?   34

12) What number results when you divide 196 into 7 equal parts?   28

13) What number results when you double 53?   106

14) What number results when you double 31?   62

15) What number results when you triple 8?   24

16) What number results when you triple 19?   57

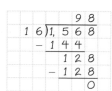17) What number results when 231 is decreased by 108?   123

18) What number results when 314 is decreased by 159?   155

19) What number is twice 175? 350

20) What number is twice 146? 292

21) What number is 23 more than 461? 484

22) What number is 54 more than 298? 352

Objective 2: Solve Applied Problems
Solve each application.

23) In one week, a family-
owned pizza parlor
sold 78 cheese pizzas,
189 pepperoni pizzas,
210 sausage pizzas, and
410 various multi-
topping pizzas. Find
the total number of
pizzas sold that week.
They sold 887 pizzas.

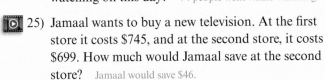

24) A whale-watching tour
company ran four boats
one day during the win-
ter months. One boat
had 15 passengers, another carried 18 tourists, the
third boat had 22 passengers, and the fourth boat
carried 19 people. How many people went whale-
watching on this day? 74 people went whale-watching.

25) Jamaal wants to buy a new television. At the first
store it costs $745, and at the second store, it costs
$699. How much would Jamaal save at the second
store? Jamaal would save $46.

26) Camille spent $568 on textbooks last semester and
$493 this semester. How much less did she spend on
books this semester? Camille spent $75 less this semester.

The graph shows the number of births in the United
States for selected states during 2006. Use the graph for
Exercises 27–32.

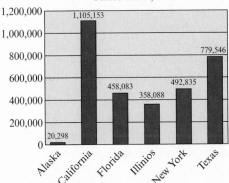

Number of Births by Place of Birth:
United States, 2006.

(National Vital Statistics Reports, Vol. 58, No. 11,
March 3, 2010)

27) What was the total number of births in all six
selected states? 3,214,003

28) How many more births occurred in California when
compared with Texas? 325,607

29) How many fewer births occurred in Alaska when
compared with Illinois? 337,790

30) What was the total number of births in Florida,
Illinois, and New York? 1,309,006

31) What was the total number of births in California
and Texas? 1,884,699

32) How many fewer births occurred in Florida, Illinois,
and New York when compared with California and
Texas? 575,693

33) Sierra is a makeup artist and has 23 pairs of fake
eyelashes in her makeup kit. How much did she pay
for the eyelashes if each pair cost $6? $138

34) Miriam found the *Call of Duty: Black Ops* video
game online for $56. She bought five of them for her
son and nephews for Christmas. How much did she
spend? $280

35) A parking structure is to be built in New York City.
The cost per space is $20,326. How much will the
parking structure cost if the structure needs to house
1,500 vehicles? (www.vtpi.org/tca/tca0504.pdf) $30,489,000

36) The average ticket price at University of Phoenix
Stadium in 2008 was $45. The stadium can seat
63,400 fans. If a game was sold out, how much
money did the stadium take in from ticket sales?
(football.ballparks.com) $2,853,000

37) A group of 12 lottery
players share a winning
ticket that is worth
$7,039,680 after taxes.
If the money is divided
up evenly, how much
will each person
receive? $586,640

38) A small business with 18 employees rents a new
office building that has 1,152 sq ft of workspace.
If the workspace is divided evenly among the
employees, how many square feet of workspace
does each employee receive? 64 sq ft

39) The average cost to build a 4,000 sq ft fast-food
restaurant in San Francisco is about $952,000.
Find the average cost per square foot to build a
fast-food restaurant. (evstudio.com) $238 per sq ft

40) In 2009, the population of Tokyo was approximately 12,996,000, and the size of Tokyo is about 855 sq mi. Find the population density of Tokyo in people per square mile. (www.metro.tokyo.jp)
15,200 people per square mile

41) Marco buys four tickets to Blue Man Group for $72 each. There is an additional processing fee of $32. Find the total cost of the tickets. (www.blueman.com)
$320

42) A group of students in a dorm order 18 sandwiches that cost $6 each and then pay a delivery fee of $8. Find the total cost of the order. $116

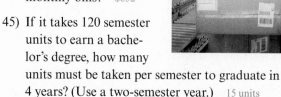

43) Carrie uses her student loan of $3,500 to buy some new furniture for her apartment. She pays $215 for a love seat, $245 for a new bed, $189 for a mattress set, $265 for a dresser, and $389 for a small dining table. How much money does Carrie have left? $2,197

44) Jason has a part-time job that pays him $1,350 a month. His rent is $425, his car payment is $250, and his share of the utilities is $43. How much money does Jason have left after paying these monthly bills? $632

45) If it takes 120 semester units to earn a bachelor's degree, how many units must be taken per semester to graduate in 4 years? (Use a two-semester year.)   15 units

46) Charlie works 20 hours per week and is taking 15 units of classes at a community college, for which he will spend 15 hours a week in class. His advisor tells him he must set aside 3 hours of study time per week for each unit of class. How many total hours per week must Charlie dedicate to school and his part-time job?   80 hr per wk

47) A group of 12 teenagers wishes to attend a retreat that costs $350 per person. The group organizes a fundraising event and raises $5,775. The expenses to run the event cost the group $1,875. How much profit did the group earn? If the profit is divided up evenly among the teenagers, how much must each person pay to attend the youth retreat? $3,900; $25

48) A 16-member glee club held an event in the school auditorium and sold 187 $8 tickets. The refreshment and souvenir stand sold 96 $1 cups of fruit punch and 42 t-shirts for $20 per shirt. How much money did the glee club earn? If this amount were divided up evenly among the 16 members, how much would each member receive? $2,432; $152

49) Ruby earns $16 an hour for the first 8 hours of work per day and earns $24 per hour after that. On holidays, she is paid double-time, which is $32 per hour. Her hours for a holiday workweek are recorded in the table.

Monday	Tuesday	Wednesday	Thursday	Friday
8 hr	12 hr	8 hr	10 hr	6 hr

How much did she earn this week if Thursday was a national holiday? $896

50) Sandra earns $12 per hour for the first 8 hours of work per day and earns $18 per hour after that. On holidays, she is paid double-time, which is $24 per hour. Her hours for a holiday workweek are recorded in the table.

Monday	Tuesday	Wednesday	Thursday	Friday
8 hr	6 hr	6 hr	12 hr	8 hr

How much did she earn this week if Friday was a national holiday? $600

The accompanying graph shows the lift ticket prices at Deer Valley Ski Resort in Utah. Use the graph for Exercises 51–56.

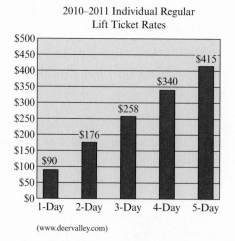

2010–2011 Individual Regular Lift Ticket Rates

(www.deervalley.com)

51) How much money does a skier save if he purchases a 5-day lift ticket instead of five 1-day lift tickets? What is the cost per day? $35; $83

52) How much money does a skier save if she purchases a 3-day lift ticket instead of three 1-day lift tickets? What is the cost per day? $12; $86

53) If Lisa, Jody, Sharron, and Tasha each purchase a 5-day lift ticket, what is their total cost? $1,660

54) If Giuseppe, Francisco, Dante, Victor, and Alexander each purchase a 4-day lift ticket, what is their total cost? $1,700

55) If Jerome and Michael each buy a 2-day lift ticket, Lamar buys a 3-day lift ticket, and Steven and Terrell each purchase a 4-day lift ticket, what is their total cost? $1,290

56) If Houng and Lan each buy a 3-day lift ticket while Vivian and Tian each buy a 4-day lift ticket, what is their total cost? $1,196

R Rethink

R1) How often do you encounter money problems that involve more than one operation?

R2) How did recognizing basic key words and sentences in Exercises 5–22 help you prepare for more complex applied problems?

Group Activity – Order of Operations

Activity #1: "Make the Number"

- Students should work in pairs.
- Using the numbers 3, 5, 6, and 11, create an expression that will equal 24. You may use any operations, and you may use the numbers as many times as you want. You may use all of the numbers or just some of the numbers.
- Students should create their own expressions, then switch papers with their partners to verify that each expression simplifies to 24.
- To really challenge yourself, try to create an expression that includes a fraction bar!

    Example: $(6 - 3)^3 - [11 - (5 + 3)]$

Activity #2: "Around the World"

- Work in groups of three students (students should work on the same piece of paper).
- One student performs the first step in simplifying one of the expressions below. That student then passes the paper to the next student, who performs the second step. Continue this pattern until the expression is simplified.
- Change the order of students for each new expression.

1) $\dfrac{4 + [20^2 - (3 + 8)]}{10 - 7}$

2) $7 + (8 - 5)^3 \div 9$

3) $12^2 \div 6(4 - 1) + (6 - 2)^3$

4) $6 \cdot [11 - (2^2 + 1)] \div 4$

Group Activity Answers

Activity 1: Answers will vary. Possible answers are $6(5) - 6$; $\dfrac{11(6) - 5(3) - 3}{5 - 3}$

Activity 2: 1) 131   2) 10   3) 136   4) 9

You should know your reading attention span, the length of time you usually are able to sustain attention to a task, as you prepare for reading assignments. To get an idea of the length of your current attention span for reading, perform this exercise over the next few days.

1. Choose one of the textbooks that you've been assigned to read this semester.

2. Start reading a chapter, without any preparation, noting in the chart below the time that you start reading.

3. As soon as your mind begins to wander and think about other subjects, stop reading and note the time on the chart below.

4. Using the same textbook, repeat this process four more times over the course of a few days, entering the data on the chart below.

5. To find your reading attention span, calculate the average number of minutes across the five trials.

    Trial #1: Starting time: _____ Ending time: _____
    Number of minutes between start and end times: _____

    Trial #2: Starting time: _____ Ending time: _____
    Number of minutes between start and end times: _____

    Trial #3: Starting time: _____ Ending time: _____
    Number of minutes between start and end times: _____

    Trial #4: Starting time: _____ Ending time: _____
    Number of minutes between start and end times: _____

    Trial #5: Starting time: _____ Ending time: _____
    Number of minutes between start and end times: _____

Reading attention span (the average of the number of minutes in the last column, found by adding up the five numbers and dividing by 5) = _____ minutes

Ask yourself these questions about your reading attention span:

1. Are you surprised by the length of your reading attention span? In what way?

2. Does any number in the set of trials stand out from the other numbers? For instance, is any number much higher or lower than the average? If so, can you account for this? For example, what time of day was it?

3. Do the numbers in your trials show any trend? For instance, did your attention span tend to increase slightly over the course of the trials, did it decrease, or did it stay about the same? Can you explain any trend you may have noted?

4. Do you think your attention span times would be very different if you had chosen a different textbook? Why or why not?

Chapter 2:   Summary

Definition/Procedure	Example

2.1 Introduction to Multiplication

Multiplication is a shorthand way to represent repeated addition of the same number.

We can rewrite $3 + 3 = 6$ as $3 \times 2 = 6$.

The 3 is called the **multiplicand,** the 2 is called the **multiplier,** and the 6 is called the **product.** The numbers being multiplied together, the 3 and 2, are called **factors. (p. 68)**

Use a number line to find 3×2.

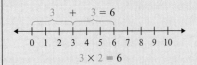

$$3 \times 2 = 6$$

The multiplier, 2, tells us that 3 is being added 2 times.

Multiplication can be written several different ways. **(p. 69)**

3×2 can also be written as $3 \cdot 2$, $3(2)$, $(3)(2)$, and $\begin{array}{r} 3 \\ \times\, 2 \\ \hline \end{array}$

The **commutative property of multiplication** says that changing the order in which we multiply numbers does not change the product. **(p. 70)**

The commutative property tells us that $5 \cdot 8 = 8 \cdot 5$.

2.2 Finding the Product with Whole Numbers

The **associative property of multiplication** says that we can group factors in any order and the product remains the same. **(p. 73)**

$(4 \cdot 5) \cdot 2 = 4 \cdot (5 \cdot 2) = 40$

To multiply numbers containing more than one digit, we line them up vertically. We may need to use **regrouping.** Be sure to line up the numbers in the correct columns. **(p. 74)**

Multiply 347×56.

		2	3	←	This is the regrouping from multiplying by 5.
		2	4	←	This is the regrouping from multiplying by 6.
		3	4	7	
	×		5	6	
	2	0	8	2	Multiply 347 by 6.
1	7	3	5		Multiply 347 by 5.
1	9,	4	3	2	Add to get the product.

$347 \times 56 = 19{,}432$

When you multiply a whole number by 10, 100, 1,000, 10,000, and so on, the result is the number followed by the number of zeros in the multiplier. **(p. 77)**

$78 \cdot 1{,}000 = 78{,}000$

2.3 Introduction to Division

A division problem like $8 \div 2$ means that we have to figure out how many twos it takes to make 8. It takes 4 twos to make 8, so $8 \div 2 = 4$.

Use a number line to find $8 \div 2$.

How many twos does it take to make 8?   4

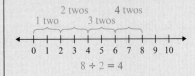

$$8 \div 2 = 4$$

In a division problem, the number being divided is called the **dividend,** the number you are dividing by is called the **divisor,** and the result is called the **quotient.** In the problem $8 \div 2 = 4$, the dividend is 8, the divisor is 2, and the quotient is 4. **(p. 81)**

Division Involving Zero

Any number divided by zero is undefined.

Zero divided by any nonzero number equals 0. **(p. 83)**

$\dfrac{4}{0}$ is undefined.

$\dfrac{0}{6} = 0$

Definition/Procedure	Example

2.4 Divisibility Rules and Short Division

The **remainder** in a division problem is the number left over when you divide the dividend by the divisor. If the remainder equals 0, we say that the dividend **divides evenly** by the divisor. If the remainder does not equal 0, then the dividend **does not divide evenly** by the divisor. **(p. 86)**

$15 \div 5 = 3$ Since there is no remainder when 15 is divided by 5, we say that 15 divides evenly by 5.

$15 \div 2 = 7 \, R1$ There are 7 twos in 15, and then there is 1 unit left over. Since there is a remainder when 15 is divided by 2, we say that 15 does *not* divide evenly by 2.

Checking a Division Problem Using Multiplication
To check the answer to a division problem, do the following:

(Divisor × Quotient) + Remainder = Dividend   **(p. 86)**

Check $48 \div 5 = 9 \, R3$.

$(5 \times 9) + 3 = 45 + 3 = 48$ ✓

Divisibility Rules
The divisibility rules we use most often are for 2, 3, 5, and 10.

A number is divisible by . . .

2 if it ends in 0, 2, 4, 6, or 8. If a number is divisible by 2, it is an **even number.**

3 if the sum of its digits is divisible by 3.

5 if the number ends in 0 or 5.

10 if it ends in a 0.

Other divisibility rules are listed on p. 88.

Determine whether each number is divisible by 2, 3, 5, or 10.

a) 740

Since 740 ends in 0, it is divisible by 2, 5, and 10. It is not divisible by 3 because when we add the digits, $7 + 4 + 0 = 11$, the sum 11 is not divisible by 3.

b) 5,838

Since the number ends in 8, 5,838 is divisible by 2. It is not divisible by 5 or 10. The number is divisible by 3 because when we add the digits, $5 + 8 + 3 + 8 = 24$, the sum 24 is divisible by 3.

Short Division
Short division is a method for dividing a number by a one-digit divisor. **(p. 90)**

Find $4\overline{)74}$.

$\frac{1}{4\overline{)7^34}}$ $7 \div 4 = 1 \, R3$

$\frac{1 \ 8}{4\overline{)7^34}} \, R2$ $34 \div 4 = 8 \, R2$

$74 \div 4 = 18 \, R2$ Check: $(4 \times 18) + 2 = 72 + 2 = 74$ ✓

2.5 Long Division

Long division is a method for dividing a whole number by a divisor with any number of digits **(p. 94).**

Find $238 \div 14$.

$$\begin{array}{r} 1 \\ 14\overline{)238} \\ -14 \quad \leftarrow 1 \times 14 = 14 \\ \overline{9} \quad \leftarrow 23 - 14 = 9 \end{array}$$

$$\begin{array}{r} 17 \\ 14\overline{)238} \\ -14 \downarrow \text{ Bring down the 8.} \\ \overline{98} \\ -98 \leftarrow 7 \times 14 = 98 \\ \overline{0} \leftarrow 98 - 98 = 0 \end{array}$$

$238 \div 14 = 17$

Dividing Whole Numbers Ending in Zeros by 10, 100, 1,000, etc.
To divide a whole number ending in zeros by 10, 100, 1,000, etc., drop the appropriate number of zeros from the end of the whole number. **(p. 97)**

Divide.

a) $578,000 \div 100 = 5,780$

b) $\dfrac{93,400,000}{1,000} = 93,400$

2.6 Exponents, Roots, and Order of Operations

An **exponent** represents repeated multiplication of the same number.

The **base** is the number that is being repeatedly multiplied. The **exponent,** or **power,** tells us the number of times to use the base as a factor in the multiplication problem. **(p. 106)**

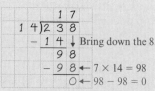

$5^3 = 5 \cdot 5 \cdot 5 = 125$

Definition/Procedure	Example
The **square root** of a number is the number that, when squared, equals the original number. **(p. 107)**	$\sqrt{49} = 7$ because $7^2 = 49$ We read $\sqrt{49}$ as "the square root of 49."

Order of Operations

Simplify expressions in the following order:

1) If **parentheses** or **other grouping symbols** appear in an expression, simplify what is in these grouping symbols first.

2) Simplify expressions with **exponents** and **square roots.**

3) **Multiply** or **divide** moving from left to right.

4) **Add** or **subtract** moving from left to right. **(p. 108)**

Remember "**P**lease **E**xcuse **M**y **D**ear **A**unt **S**ally" to help you remember the order of operations.

Simplify $40 + 10^2 \div (23 - 3)$.

$$40 + 10^2 \div (23 - 3) =$$

$40 + 10^2 \div$	20	= First, perform the operation in parentheses.
$40 + 100 \div$	20	= Simplify the expression with the exponent.
$40 +$	5	= Do division before addition.
45		Add.

2.7 Solving Applied Problems

Identifying key words and using the following steps can help us solve applied problems.

Solve the problem.

The average ticket price at Qualcomm Stadium in 2008 was $81. The stadium can seat 71,294 fans. If the game was sold out, how much money did the stadium take in from ticket sales? (football.ballparks.com)

Steps for Solving Applied Problems

Step 1: **Read** the problem carefully, more than once if necessary, until you understand it. Restate the problem in your own words. Draw a picture, if applicable. Identify what you are being asked to find.

Step 1: **Read** the problem carefully, and restate it in your own words.

The cost of each ticket was $81, and 71,294 tickets were sold. We must determine the total amount of money made from ticket sales.

Step 2: **Make a plan** for solving the problem. Underline important words that might help you solve the problem.

Step 2: **Make a plan.** Let's underline important words in our restatement of the problem in Step 1.

Plan: Multiply the number of tickets sold by the cost of each ticket to determine the total amount of money made from ticket sales.

Step 3: **Solve** the problem using your plan and the information given. Look at the important words you have underlined.

Step 3: **Solve** the problem.

$$\begin{array}{r} \overset{1\ 2\ 7\ 3}{71{,}294} \\ \times\ \ \ \ \ \ 81 \\ \hline 71294 \\ 570352\ \ \\ \hline 5{,}774{,}814 \end{array}$$

Step 4: **State the answer** in a complete sentence.

Step 4: **State the answer** in a complete sentence.

The total amount in ticket sales was $5,774,814.

Step 5: **Check** the answer. **(p. 113)**

Step 5: **Check** the answer. We can use division to check a multiplication problem.

$$81\overline{)5{,}774{,}814} \quad \checkmark$$
$$71{,}294$$

The answer is correct.

Chapter 2: Review Exercises

*Additional answers can be found in the Answers to Exercises appendix.

(2.1)

1) Use a number line to add 2 + 2 + 2 + 2 + 2. Then,

   a) write the addition problem as a multiplication problem.

   b) identify the multiplicand and the multiplier.
     multiplicand: 2; multiplier: 5
   c) identify the factors and the product.
     factors: 2 and 5; product: 10

Find each product.

2) 9(7)　63

3) 5 × 12　60

4) 3 · 0　0

Find each product, then rewrite the expression using the commutative property.

5) 12 × 6　72; 6 × 12 = 72

6) 2 · 7　14; 7 · 2 = 14

Fill in the missing factor.

7) 5 · _____ = 45　9

8) _____ × 8 = 56　7

9) What number do you multiply by 2 to get 24?　12

10) 6 times what number equals 30?　5

(2.2)

11) In your own words, explain the associative property of multiplication.　Answers may vary.

12) Multiply 5 × 4 × 8 in two different ways using the associative property.
(5 × 4) × 8 = 20 × 8 = 160 and 5 × (4 × 8) = 5 × 32 = 160

Multiply.

13) 64
× 7　448

14) 907
× 8　7,256

15) 252
× 43　10,836

16) 5,774
× 79　456,146

17) (3,061)(285)　872,385

18) (8,912)(736)　6,559,232

19) 9,208 · 4,003　36,859,624

20) 5,400 · 3,009　16,248,600

Multiply.

21) 291 × 1,000　291,000

22) 88 × 10,000　880,000

23) 34 · 200　6,800

24) 12 · 3,000　36,000

25) Find the product of 54 and 9.　486

26) What is the product when you multiply 800 and 300?　240,000

27) Eva bought four outdoor light fixtures that cost $39 each. How much did she spend?　$156

28) Pilar's son wants to take his friends bowling for his birthday party. It will cost $18 per child. Find the cost of the party if there will be a total of 14 children.　$252

(2.3) Divide. Then identify the dividend, the divisor, and the quotient.

29) 27 ÷ 9　3; dividend: 27; divisor: 9; quotient: 3

30) $\frac{24}{4}$　6; dividend: 24; divisor: 4; quotient: 6

Find the quotient, and write a related multiplication problem.

31) 12)84　7; 12 · 7 = 84

32) 0 ÷ 5　0; 5 · 0 = 0

33) Is it possible to divide a number by 0? Explain.
No. A number divided by 0 is undefined.

34) Is it possible to divide 0 by a nonzero number? Explain.
Yes. 0 divided by a nonzero number equals 0.

Fill in the missing number.

35) 12 ÷ _____ = 3　4

36) _____ ÷ 11 = 8　88

37) What number do you divide by 5 to get 12?　60

38) What is the quotient when you divide 28 by 4?　7

(2.4)

39) How do you check the result of a division problem?

Check each division problem to determine whether the answer is true or false.

40) 4)59 → 14 R3　true

41) $\frac{97}{6}$ = 16 R1　true

42) 77 ÷ 5 = 15 R3　false

43) How do you know whether a number is divisible by 10?
The number ends in 0.

44) How do you know whether a number is divisible by 3?

Determine whether each number is divisible by 2, 3, 5, and/or 10, or none of these.

45) 365　5

46) 6,492　2 and 3

47) 7,800　2, 3, 5, and 10

48) 49,060　2, 5, and 10

Use short division to divide. Check your answer.

49) 847 ÷ 6　141 R1

50) 3)957　319

51) $\frac{7,480}{8}$　935

52) $\frac{45,880}{9}$　5,097 R7

53) A kindergarten class has six tables for 24 students. How many students sit at each table if the students are divided equally among the tables?　4 students per table

54) Professor Mulford is moving out of his office and has to pack his books. He has 136 books and will put eight books in each box. How many boxes will he need?   17 boxes

(2.5) Divide using long division.

55) $735 \div 5$ 147

56) $984 \div 6$ 164

57) $28\overline{)1,764}$ 63

58) $36\overline{)2,628}$ 73

59) $\dfrac{4,647}{54}$ 86 R3

60) $\dfrac{2,441}{64}$ 38 R9

61) $42,854 \div 14$ 3,061

62) $71,451 \div 17$ 4,203

63) $\dfrac{73,893}{211}$ 350 R43

64) $\dfrac{30,813}{219}$ 140 R153

Divide.

65) $251,000 \div 100$ 2,510

66) $\dfrac{6,080,000}{100}$ 60,800

Find each quotient.

67) $20\overline{)1,080}$ 54

68) $\dfrac{3,116,000}{4,100}$ 760

69) Owen organized a bachelor party for his best friend and invited 15 people. Each person, including Owen but not the groom, contributed the same amount for the party, and Owen collected a total of $2,240. How much did each person pay? $140

70) A high-speed copier can copy and staple a seven-page math exam in 16 seconds. How many exams can the copier produce in 12 minutes (720 seconds)?   45 exams

(2.6) Identify the base and the exponent, then evaluate each expression.

71) 7^2 base: 7; exponent: 2; 49

72) 12^2 base: 12; exponent: 2; 144

73) 2^6 base: 2; exponent: 6; 64

74) 3^3 base: 3; exponent: 3; 27

Evaluate.

75) $\sqrt{25}$ 5

76) $\sqrt{9}$ 3

77) $\sqrt{144}$ 12

78) $\sqrt{1}$ 1

Simplify each expression using the order of operations.

79) $8 + 6 \div 2 + 3 \cdot 5$ 26

80) $16 + 12 \div 4 + 3 \cdot 5$ 34

81) $6^2 \div 9 - \dfrac{18}{6}$ 1

82) $4^3 \div 8 - \dfrac{12}{3}$ 4

83) $6\sqrt{49} - 2(9 - 5)$ 34

84) $3\sqrt{100} - 4(12 - 7)$ 10

85) $30 \div 3\sqrt{25} \div 5 \cdot 4 - 2^4$ 24

86) $48 \div 4\sqrt{36} \div 3 \cdot 4 - 7^2$ 47

87) $10 + 2[60 - (5 - 2)^3] - 55 \div 11$ 71

88) $72 - 48 \div 4[84 - (1 + 8)^2]$ 36

89) $45 - [(84 - 20) \div 2^4] + 5(9 + 1)$ 91

90) $5 + 3[54 \div (7 - 4)^3 - 2] - 5$ 0

(2.7) Solve each problem.
The graph shows the lift ticket prices at Mammoth Mountain Ski Resort in California. Use the graph for Exercises 91–94.

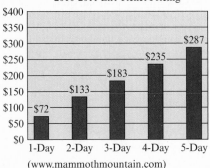

2010-2011 Lift Ticket Pricing

(www.mammothmountain.com)

91) How much money does a skier save if she purchases a 5-day lift ticket instead of five 1-day lift tickets? $73

92) If Angel, David, Joe, and Victor each purchase a 4-day lift ticket, what is their total cost? $940

93) If a skier purchases a 3-day lift ticket, what is her cost per day? $61

94) If Cantu buys a 2-day lift ticket while Duyen and Thu each buy a 3-day lift ticket, what is their total cost? $499

95) Cheryl has two roommates, and the three women split their apartment costs equally. In March, their cable bill was $68, their utility bills totaled $241, and their rent was $1,200. How much does each woman owe for the expenses in March? $503

96) In 2007, Atlanta Hartsfield Airport was the nation's busiest, serving about 42,704,000 people. This is 10,011,000 more than the number of people it served in 1997. How many people went through this airport in 1997? (www.census.gov)   32,693,000 people

Mixed Exercises

Perform the indicated operations.

97) $18\overline{)45,059}$ 2,503 R5

98) $859 + 25,007 + 6,438 + 94$ 32,398

99) $\begin{array}{r} 5,682 \\ -1,915 \end{array}$ 3,767

100) $421 \cdot 10,000$ 4,210,000

101) $\begin{array}{r} 694 \\ \times 362 \end{array}$ 251,228

102) $\dfrac{4,896}{32}$ 153

103) $72 + 38,556 + 9,032$ 47,660

104) $\begin{array}{r} 900 \\ -647 \end{array}$ 253

105) $\dfrac{2,670}{7}$ 381 R3

106) $1,950 \times 844$ 1,645,800

Chapter 2:   Test

1) Fill in the missing number.

   a) $8 \cdot$ _____ $= 24$ 3   b) _____ $\div 6 = 9$ 54

   c) $132 \div$ _____ $= 11$ 12   d) _____ $\times 4 = 0$ 0

2) Given the division problem $703 \div 12$,

   a) perform the division.   58 R7

   b) check your answer. $(12 \times 58) + 7 = 703$

   c) identify the divisor, dividend, quotient, and remainder if there is one.
     divisor: 12; dividend: 703; quotient: 58; remainder: 7

3) Determine whether each number is divisible by 2, 3, 5, and/or 10.

   a) 588   2 and 3   b) 74,115   3 and 5

Perform the indicated operation.

4) $\begin{array}{r} 873 \\ \times\ 24 \end{array}$ 20,952

5) $\dfrac{3,655}{54}$ 67 R37

6) $15 \div 0$ undefined

7) $8\overline{)2,856}$ 357

8) $32(10,000)$ 320,000

9) $6,410,000 \div 1,000$ 6,410

10) $1,500\overline{)870,000}$ 580

11) $\dfrac{0}{9}$ 0

12) $2,596 \cdot 405$ 1,051,380

13) $24,942 \div 23$ 1,084 R10

14) a) Evaluate $(7 \cdot 2) \cdot 5$.   70

   b) Rewrite the multiplication problem using the associative property and evaluate. $7 \cdot (2 \cdot 5) = 70$

15) Identify the base and the exponent, and evaluate each expression.

   a) 9^2 base: 9; exponent: 2; 81

   b) 2^5 base: 2; exponent: 5; 32

   c) 5^3 base: 5; exponent: 3; 125

16) Evaluate.

   a) $\sqrt{16}$ 4   b) $\sqrt{121}$ 11

   c) $\sqrt{0}$ 0

Simplify each expression using the order of operations.

17) $18 + 24 \div 6$ 22   18) $7\sqrt{64} - 5^2 + 2 \cdot 9$ 49

19) $3^4 - 5(1 + 3)^2 - \dfrac{8}{8}$ 0

20) $\sqrt{100} \div \sqrt{4} \cdot 3[5 + (1 + 1)^3]$ 195

Solve each problem.

21) What is the product of 36 and 4?   144

22) If a part-time student takes eight units of classes every semester and a bachelor's degree requires 120 units, how many semesters will it take to earn the bachelor's degree?   15 semesters

23) The table shows the different flavors of frozen yogurt sold at a shop and the number of ounces sold in a day.

Vanilla	Chocolate	Strawberry	Mango	Peanut Butter
995 oz	789 oz	825 oz	479 oz	638 oz

   a) Find the total amount of yogurt sold.   3,726 oz

   b) How much less mango yogurt was sold compared with the amount of strawberry yogurt sold?   346 oz

24) The Photron FASTCAM BC2 high-definition video camera is capable of capturing high-speed images at 2,000 frames per second. How many frames are recorded in 1 min? (1 min = 60 sec) (www.photron.com)   120,000 frames

25) Dale just bought several parts to restore his 1968 Mustang Convertible. He bought one standard grill for $138, two racing mirrors for $117 each, four wire-spoke hub caps for $79 each, and a convertible top for $375. How much did he spend on all of these parts? $1,063

*Additional answers can be found in the Answers to Exercises appendix.

1) Write the number 67,004,031 in words.
   sixty-seven million, four thousand, thirty-one

2) In your own words, explain the commutative property of addition.   Numbers can be added in any order and the sum will remain the same.

3) Round 87,513 to the nearest thousand.   88,000

4) If the perimeter of the figure shown here is 22 centimeters, find the missing side length.   8 cm

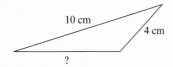

Perform the indicated operation.

5) $32,106 - 4,749$ 27,357

6) $\dfrac{9,700,000}{10,000}$ 970

7) $\begin{array}{r} 8,375 \\ \times\ \ \ 81 \end{array}$ 678,375

8) $563 + 21,994 + 18 + 5 + 6,722$ 29,302

9) $9)\overline{3,847}$ 427 R4

10) $\dfrac{7}{0}$ undefined

11) Simplify $\sqrt{144} + 2^3 \cdot 3^2 - (27 - 3) \div (2 + 6)$ 81

Fill in the blank.

12) $47 +$ _____ $= 195$ 148

13) $7 \cdot$ _____ $= 84$ 12

14) _____ $\div 16 = 54$ 864

15) $859 -$ _____ $= 137$ 722

16) Check the division problem $353 \div 12 = 29$ R5 to determine whether the answer is correct.
    $(12 \times 29) + 5 = 348 + 5 = 353$; The answer is correct.

17) What number results when 685 is subtracted from 1,339?   654

18) Find the product of 120 and 6.   720

19) What number do you get when you find the sum of 716 and 584 and then divide by 4?   325

20) A parking structure is to be built at a community college located in Seattle, Washington, at a cost of $12,118,500. If the structure will hold 750 vehicles, what is the cost per parking space? (www.vtpi.org) $16,158 per space

21) The Bell 427 Legacy Series helicopter has a maximum cruising speed of approximately 158 miles per hour. Find the number of miles traveled in 4 hours at maximum cruising speed. (www.bellhelicopter.textron.com)   632 mi

22) Jake submitted his expenses for a business trip. His airfare was $328, he spent three nights in a hotel that cost $189 per night, he took a shuttle to and from the airport for $13 per trip, and his meals cost a total of $157. If he received $500 in advance, how much more money does his company owe him for the trip? $578

The graph shows the number of animals treated at the Village Veterinary Practice each day during a certain week. Use the graph for Exercises 23–25.

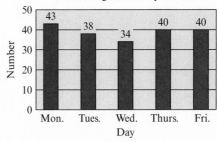

Number of Animals Treated at the Village Veterinary Practice

23) Find the total number of animals treated this week.   195

24) On which days were the same number of animals treated?   Thursday and Friday

25) On which day was the office the busiest? On which day did the least number of animals visit the vet? How many more animals were treated on the busiest day compared with the slowest day?   Monday; Wednesday; 9

Multiplying, Dividing, and Simplifying Fractions

Math at Work:

Chef

For chef Jim Dion, the dream of opening his own restaurant has finally come true. Although Chez Dion Restaurant is a small place, with seating for just under 40 customers, he is thrilled.

Jim credits much of his success as a chef to the training he received in culinary arts school and to his creativity in combining unexpected flavors. However, he also credits his skill in math, which he uses on a daily basis. Cooking requires the regular use of fractions, as recipe ingredients are multiplied and divided according to the number of people being served. Jim routinely cuts ingredients into halves or quarters, or multiplies amounts in order to adjust the size of a recipe. In addition, he uses math to determine the amount of supplies that he needs to order depending on seasonal changes in the number of customers and to figure out whether or not he is making a profit.

Math is also key to another skill Jim applies on a daily basis: time management. "As the chef and owner of a restaurant, there are always a thousand things I need to do," Jim says. "So, I am very careful and organized about dividing the time I have during the day among all the tasks I need to accomplish."

In this chapter, we'll learn about multiplying, dividing, and reducing fractions, and we'll also explore some strategies you can use to help improve your own time management when it comes to studying for a test.

It seems that some people are forever rushing from one task to the next, while others appear to have all the time they need. The difference? Time management. The strategies described below will help you balance all demands on your time more effectively—so you can be one of those people who seems to have more than 24 hours in a day!

- Learn where your time is going by creating a **time log:** a record of how you actually spend your time, including interruptions, noting blocks of time in increments as short as 15 minutes.
- List and rank your priorities, so that you can structure your time around what is most important to you.

- Create a **master calendar** that includes every week of the term on a single page. Write in every major class assignment you have, as well as significant upcoming events in your personal life.
- Create a **weekly timetable,** a master grid with the days of the week across the top and the hours of the day along the side. Use this to record all your regularly scheduled activities, as well as one-time appointments when they arise.
- Finally, create an easily portable **daily to-do list** to record what you want to accomplish on a daily basis.

- Use the priorities you've identified and the schedules you've made to manage how you spend your time.
- Avoid procrastination! (The emPOWERme exercise on page 205 can help.)

- Look at your daily to-do list to determine whether you are accomplishing your short-term tasks.
- Use your weekly timetable and master calendar to see whether you are on target to meet the obligations you have down the road.

- Reassess your priorities. Are you making time for what really matters to you?

Chapter 3 **POWER** Plan

P Prepare

What are your goals for Chapter 3?	

O Organize

How can you accomplish each goal?	

1 Be prepared before and during class.

- Don't stay out late the night before and be sure to set your alarm clock!
- Bring a pencil, notebook paper, and textbook to class.
- Avoid distractions by turning off your cell phone during class.
- Pay attention, take good notes, and ask questions.
- Complete your homework on time and ask questions on problems you do not understand.

2 Understand the homework to the point where you could do it without needing any help or hints.

- Read the directions and show all of your steps.
- Go to the professor's office for help.
- Rework homework and quiz problems and find similar problems for practice.

3 Use the P.O.W.E.R. framework to learn how to manage your time: *Find Your Procrastination Quotient.*

- Read the Study Strategy that explains how to manage your time.
- Be sure to personalize the strategy and notice where you might be able to improve.
- Complete the emPOWERme that appears before the Chapter Summary.

4 Write your own goal.

_____

_____

- _____

  _____

What are your objectives for Chapter 3?	How can you accomplish each objective?

1 Learn how to identify different types of fractions, including mixed numbers, and change from one form to another.

- Take notes and learn the definitions and procedures in Sections 3.1 and 3.2.
- Take good notes in class.

2 Use the definitions of prime and composite numbers to find the prime factorization of a number and apply it to writing fractions in lowest terms.

- Master each objective in the sections, in order, because they build upon each other.
- Understand the two different methods to write fractions in lowest terms.
- Watch the exercise videos for extra help if you get stuck on a certain problem.

3 Learn how to multiply and divide fractions and mixed numbers.

- Take good notes on the different procedures you will need to use.
- Read the book or reread your notes before doing the homework.

4 Learn how to solve applications containing multiplication and division of fractions.

- Believe that you *can* do word problems.
- Slow down when reading the word problem. Read it at least twice.
- Underline key words in the problem.

5 Write your own goal.

_____

_____

- _____

  _____

W Work	Read Sections 3.1–3.8 and complete the exercises.

E Evaluate Complete the Chapter Review and Chapter Test. How did you do?	**R Rethink**
	• How did you perform on the goals for the chapter? Which steps could be improved for next time? If you had the chance to do this chapter over, what would you do differently?
	• Think of a job you might like to have and describe how you would need to use what you have just learned to effectively do that job.
	• How has the time management strategy helped you master the objectives of this chapter? Where else could you use this strategy?
	• What were you able to learn about yourself by completing the emPOWERme at the end of the chapter?

3.1 Introduction to Fractions

P Prepare

O Organize

What are your objectives for Section 3.1?	How can you accomplish each objective?
1 Understand What Fractions Represent	• Write your own definition of a *fraction* and include the words *numerator* and *denominator*. • Complete the given examples on your own. • Complete You Trys 1 and 2.
2 Identify Proper and Improper Fractions	• Write the definition of a **proper fraction** and **improper fraction** in your own words and be sure to include the words *numerator* and *denominator*. • Compare the relationship between the numerator and the denominator in the definitions. • Complete the given examples on your own. • Complete You Trys 3–5.

Read the explanations, follow the examples, take notes, and complete the You Trys.

1 Understand What Fractions Represent

What is a *fraction*? A **fraction** is a part of a whole. We will look at some figures and number lines to understand fractions. Let's begin with a circle divided into three equal parts.

Each of these parts is *one-third*, or $\frac{1}{3}$, of the circle.

The number $\frac{1}{3}$ is an example of a fraction.

Let's identify the parts of a fraction using the number $\frac{1}{3}$.

$$\text{Fraction bar} \rightarrow \frac{1}{3} \begin{array}{l} \leftarrow \text{Numerator} \\ \leftarrow \text{Denominator} \end{array}$$

The **denominator** is the number *below* the fraction bar. It represents the total number of equally-sized parts of a whole. The **numerator** is the number *above* the fraction bar. It represents the number of parts being considered.

 Note

Remember from Chapter 2 that the fraction bar represents division.

Example: $\frac{1}{3} = 1 \div 3$

BE CAREFUL Because division by 0 is undefined, a fraction with a denominator of 0 is undefined.

Example: $8 \div 0$ is undefined, so $\frac{8}{0}$ is undefined.

Let's write fractions for shaded parts of the circle divided into thirds and also represent these numbers on a number line.

Each circle is divided into 3 equal parts, so *the denominator of each fraction is 3.*

Number of → $\frac{1}{3}$ of the circle is shaded. $\frac{2}{3}$ of the circle is shaded. $\frac{3}{3}$ of the circle is shaded.
shaded parts.

Where is each fraction on the number line? A fraction is a part of *one whole,* so let's look at the number line from 0 to 1 and divide it into 3 equal parts.

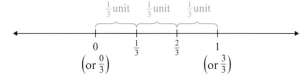

Just as each piece of the circle is $\frac{1}{3}$ of the circle, the space between each tick mark is $\frac{1}{3}$ of the distance from 0 to 1.

So, 0 can also be labeled as $\frac{0}{3}$, the next tick mark is $\frac{1}{3}$, the next is $\frac{2}{3}$, and 1 is equivalent to $\frac{3}{3}$.

EXAMPLE 1

In-Class Example 1

Use Example 1.

Use a fraction to represent the shaded part of the rectangle, and represent the fraction on a number line.

Solution

The rectangle is divided into 4 equal parts: The denominator is 4.

Three parts are shaded: The numerator is 3.

Then, $\frac{3}{4}$, read as "three-fourths", of the rectangle is shaded. $\Big($Notice that $\frac{1}{4}$, read as "one-fourth", of the rectangle is *not* shaded and that the shaded portion *plus* the unshaded portion is 1 whole.$\Big)$

To represent $\frac{3}{4}$ on the number line, first divide the number line from 0 to 1 into 4 equal parts. The space between consecutive tick marks is $\frac{1}{4}$ of a unit. Label the number line beginning at 0 with $\frac{0}{4}$.

Place the dot on $\frac{3}{4}$.

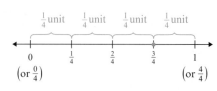

[YOU TRY 1] Use a fraction to represent the shaded part of the rectangle, and represent the fraction on a number line.

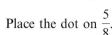

EXAMPLE 2

In-Class Example 2

Use a fraction to represent the *unshaded* part of the circle, and represent the fraction on a number line.

Answer: $\frac{2}{3}$;

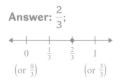

Use a fraction to represent the *unshaded* part of the circle, and represent the fraction on a number line.

Solution

The circle is divided into 8 equal parts: The denominator is 8.

Five parts are not shaded: The numerator is 5.

Therefore, $\frac{5}{8}$ (five-eighths) of the circle is *not* shaded. $\Big($Notice that $\frac{3}{8}$ of the circle *is* shaded and that the shaded portion *plus* the unshaded portion is 1 whole.$\Big)$

Divide the region on the number line from 0 to 1 into 8 equal parts. The space between consecutive tick marks is $\frac{1}{8}$ (one-eighth) of a unit. Label the number line beginning at 0 with $\frac{0}{8}$.

Place the dot on $\frac{5}{8}$.

Use a fraction to represent the *unshaded* part of the circle, and represent the fraction on a number line.

Note

$$\frac{0}{\text{Number}} = 0, \text{ as long as the denominator does not equal zero.}$$

$$\frac{\text{A number}}{\text{Itself}} = 1, \text{ as long as the denominator does not equal zero.}$$

2 Identify Proper and Improper Fractions

Let's learn more vocabulary associated with fractions.

Definition

If the numerator of a fraction is less than the denominator, then the fraction is a **proper fraction.** A proper fraction represents less than 1 whole.

Example: $\frac{5}{8}$ is a proper fraction.

W Hint

Compare the relationship between the numerator and the denominator in the definitions.

Most of the fractions we've seen so far have been proper fractions. However, on p. 133 we saw the following circle:

We said that $\frac{3}{3}$ of the circle is shaded, and that equals 1 whole circle. $\frac{3}{3}$ is an example of an *improper fraction.*

Definition

If the numerator of a fraction is greater than or equal to the denominator, then the fraction is an **improper fraction.** An improper fraction represents a quantity greater than or equal to 1 whole.

Examples

$\frac{3}{3}$ is an improper fraction.
Numerator equals denominator.

$\frac{9}{2}$ is an improper fraction.
Numerator is greater than denominator.

EXAMPLE 3

In-Class Example 3

Identify each fraction as proper or improper.

a) $\dfrac{7}{4}$ b) $\dfrac{3}{10}$ c) $\dfrac{8}{8}$

Answer:
a) improper fraction
b) proper fraction
c) improper fraction

EXAMPLE 3   Identify each fraction as proper or improper.

a) $\dfrac{9}{8}$ b) $\dfrac{6}{11}$ c) $\dfrac{5}{5}$

Solution

a) $\dfrac{9}{8}$ is an *improper fraction* because the numerator is greater than the denominator.

b) $\dfrac{6}{11}$ is a *proper fraction* because the numerator is less than the denominator.

c) $\dfrac{5}{5}$ is an *improper fraction* because the numerator equals the denominator.

[**YOU TRY 3**]   Identify each fraction as proper or improper.

a) $\dfrac{10}{10}$ b) $\dfrac{13}{4}$ c) $\dfrac{1}{2}$

EXAMPLE 4

In-Class Example 4

Use a fraction to represent the shaded part of the figure. Then, represent the fraction on a number line.

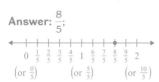

Answer: $\dfrac{8}{5}$;

$0 \; \frac{1}{5} \; \frac{2}{5} \; \frac{3}{5} \; \frac{4}{5} \; 1 \; \frac{6}{5} \; \frac{7}{5} \; \frac{8}{5} \; \frac{9}{5} \; 2$
(or $\frac{0}{5}$)   (or $\frac{5}{5}$)   (or $\frac{10}{5}$)

EXAMPLE 4   Use a fraction to represent the shaded part of the figure. Then, represent the fraction on a number line.

Solution

Notice that *more than 1 whole rectangle is shaded*. Therefore, the fraction will be improper.

Each rectangle is divided into 5 equal parts: The denominator is 5.

Seven parts are shaded: The numerator is 7.

$\dfrac{7}{5}$ of the figure is shaded.

Let's put $\dfrac{7}{5}$ on a number line. Notice that the number of *whole rectangles* shaded is greater than 1 and less than 2. Draw the number line from 0 to 2. Divide the region from 0 to 1 into 5 equal parts, and divide the region from 1 to 2 into 5 equal parts.

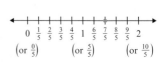

$0 \; \frac{1}{5} \; \frac{2}{5} \; \frac{3}{5} \; \frac{4}{5} \; 1 \; \frac{6}{5} \; \frac{7}{5} \; \frac{8}{5} \; \frac{9}{5} \; 2$
(or $\frac{0}{5}$)   (or $\frac{5}{5}$)   (or $\frac{10}{5}$)

The space between consecutive tick marks is $\dfrac{1}{5}$ of a unit. Label each tick mark. Put a dot on $\dfrac{7}{5}$.

[**YOU TRY 4**]   Use a fraction to represent the shaded part of the figure, and represent the fraction on a number line.

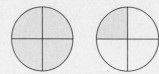

Note

You may also notice in Example 4 that 1 *whole rectangle* and then $\frac{2}{5}$ of the second rectangle are shaded. We can also represent the figure in Example 4 with the *mixed number* $1\frac{2}{5}$. We will learn about mixed numbers in the next section.

EXAMPLE 5

In-Class Example 5

Use a fraction to represent the shaded part of the figure. Then, represent the fraction on a number line.

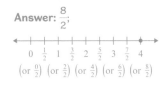

Answer: $\frac{8}{2}$;

$0 \quad \frac{1}{2} \quad 1 \quad \frac{3}{2} \quad 2 \quad \frac{5}{2} \quad 3 \quad \frac{7}{2} \quad 4$
(or $\frac{0}{2}$) (or $\frac{2}{2}$) (or $\frac{4}{2}$) (or $\frac{6}{2}$) (or $\frac{8}{2}$)

Use a fraction to represent the shaded part of the figure. Then, represent the fraction on a number line.

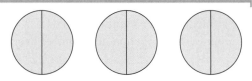

Solution

More than 1 *whole circle is shaded,* so the fraction will be improper.

Each circle is divided into 2 equal parts: The denominator is 2.

Six parts are shaded: The numerator is 6.

$\frac{6}{2}$ of the figure is shaded.

Because 3 whole circles are shaded, draw the number line from 0 to 3. Each circle is divided into 2 equal parts, so divide the region from 0 to 1 into 2 equal parts, divide the region from 1 to 2 into 2 equal parts, and divide 2 to 3 into 2 equal parts.

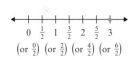

$0 \quad \frac{1}{2} \quad 1 \quad \frac{3}{2} \quad 2 \quad \frac{5}{2} \quad 3$
(or $\frac{0}{2}$) (or $\frac{2}{2}$) (or $\frac{4}{2}$) (or $\frac{6}{2}$)

The space between consecutive tick marks is $\frac{1}{2}$ of a unit. Label each tick mark.

Place a dot on $\frac{6}{2}$ or 3. It makes sense that $\frac{6}{2} = 3$ because the fraction bar represents division: $\frac{6}{2} = 6 \div 2 = 3$.

[YOU TRY 5]

Use a fraction to represent the shaded part of the figure, and represent the fraction on a number line.

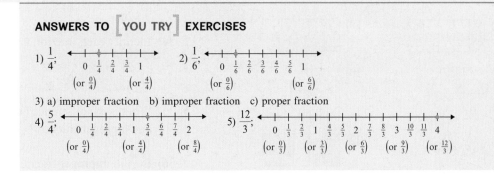

ANSWERS TO [YOU TRY] EXERCISES

1) $\frac{1}{4}$;

$0 \quad \frac{1}{4} \quad \frac{2}{4} \quad \frac{3}{4} \quad 1$
(or $\frac{0}{4}$) (or $\frac{4}{4}$)

2) $\frac{1}{6}$;

$0 \quad \frac{1}{6} \quad \frac{2}{6} \quad \frac{3}{6} \quad \frac{4}{6} \quad \frac{5}{6} \quad 1$
(or $\frac{0}{6}$) (or $\frac{6}{6}$)

3) a) improper fraction   b) improper fraction   c) proper fraction

4) $\frac{5}{4}$;

$0 \quad \frac{1}{4} \quad \frac{2}{4} \quad \frac{3}{4} \quad 1 \quad \frac{5}{4} \quad \frac{6}{4} \quad \frac{7}{4} \quad 2$
(or $\frac{0}{4}$) (or $\frac{4}{4}$) (or $\frac{8}{4}$)

5) $\frac{12}{3}$;

$0 \quad \frac{1}{3} \quad \frac{2}{3} \quad 1 \quad \frac{4}{3} \quad \frac{5}{3} \quad 2 \quad \frac{7}{3} \quad \frac{8}{3} \quad 3 \quad \frac{10}{3} \quad \frac{11}{3} \quad 4$
(or $\frac{0}{3}$) (or $\frac{3}{3}$) (or $\frac{6}{3}$) (or $\frac{9}{3}$) (or $\frac{12}{3}$)

Additional answers can be found in the Answers to Exercises appendix.

Objective 1: Understand What Fractions Represent

1) Identify the numerator and denominator of $\frac{4}{7}$.
   The numerator is 4, and the denominator is 7.

 2) Does $\frac{0}{6} = \frac{6}{0}$? Explain your answer.
   No. $\frac{0}{6} = 0$ but $\frac{6}{0}$ is undefined.

Use a fraction to represent the shaded part of the figure, and represent the fraction on a number line.

 3)   4)   5)

 6)   7)   8)

 9)   10)   11)

 12)   13)   14)

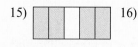 15)   16)

Use a fraction to represent the *unshaded* part of the figure, and represent the fraction on a number line.

17)    18)

19)   20)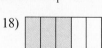

 21) 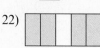   22)

23) 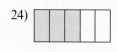   24)

Exercises 25–30 show two circles with equally shaded areas. Each shaded area can be represented by a fraction, and the two fractions are equal. Write the two fractions that are equal to each other.

24 25) 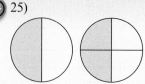   26)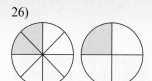

27) 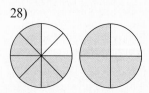   28)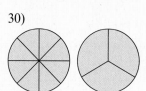

29) 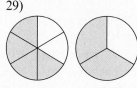   30)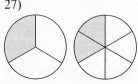

Objective 2: Identify Proper and Improper Fractions

31) Identify each fraction as proper or improper.

   a) $\frac{13}{7}$ b) $\frac{5}{9}$ c) $\frac{12}{13}$
   improper fraction   proper fraction   proper fraction

32) Identify each fraction as proper or improper.

   a) $\frac{7}{17}$ b) $\frac{13}{3}$ c) $\frac{9}{11}$
   proper fraction   improper fraction   proper fraction

24 33) Identify each fraction as proper or improper.

   a) $\frac{21}{20}$ b) $\frac{14}{15}$ c) $\frac{23}{23}$
   improper fraction   proper fraction   improper fraction

34) Identify each fraction as proper or improper.

   a) $\frac{21}{32}$ b) $\frac{52}{25}$ c) $\frac{11}{11}$
   proper fraction   improper fraction   improper fraction

35) What is the difference between an improper fraction and a proper fraction?

36) Is $\frac{2}{0}$ an improper fraction or a proper fraction?
   Neither. It is undefined.

Use a fraction to represent the shaded part of the figure, and represent the fraction on a number line.

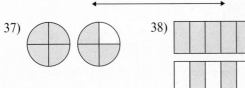

37) 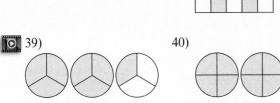 38)

39) 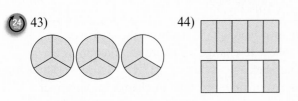 40)

41) 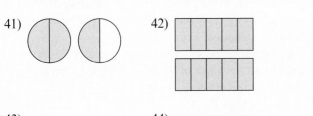 42)

43) 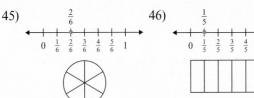 44)

Shade an appropriate amount of area on the figure according to the fraction represented on the number line.

45) $\frac{2}{6}$

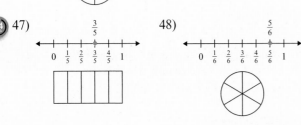

46) $\frac{1}{5}$

47) $\frac{3}{5}$

48) $\frac{5}{6}$

49) $\frac{3}{4}$ 50) $\frac{4}{5}$

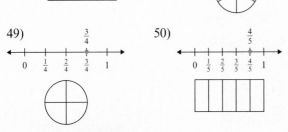

R Rethink

51) $\frac{2}{5}$ 52) $\frac{1}{4}$

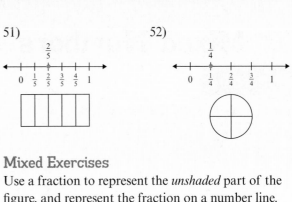

Mixed Exercises
Use a fraction to represent the *unshaded* part of the figure, and represent the fraction on a number line.

53) 54)

55) 56)

Use a fraction to represent the shaded part of the figure, and represent the fraction on a number line.

57) 58)

59) 60)

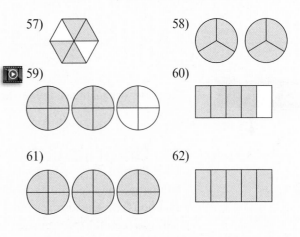

61) 62)

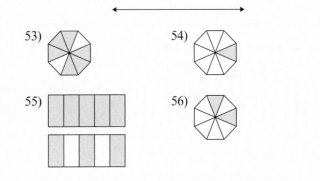

Identify each fraction as proper or improper.

63) $\frac{1}{3}$ proper fraction   64) $\frac{5}{5}$ improper fraction

65) $\frac{11}{10}$ improper fraction   66) $\frac{9}{16}$ proper fraction

67) $\frac{2}{2}$ improper fraction   68) $\frac{7}{6}$ improper fraction

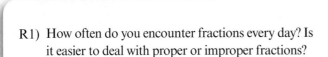

R1) How often do you encounter fractions every day? Is it easier to deal with proper or improper fractions?

R2) Which concepts do you need to spend more time practicing?

3.2 Mixed Numbers

P Prepare

O Organize

What are your objectives for Section 3.2?	How can you accomplish each objective?
1 Understand Mixed Numbers	• Write the definition of a *mixed number* in your own words. • Notice the relationship between improper fractions and mixed numbers. • Complete the given examples on your own. • Complete You Trys 1 and 2
2 Change a Mixed Number to an Improper Fraction	• In your own words, take notes on the steps you would follow to change a mixed number to an improper fraction. • Compare your notes on how to change a mixed number to an improper fraction to the example. • Complete the given example on your own. • Complete You Try 3.
3 Change an Improper Fraction to a Mixed Number	• In your own words, take notes on the steps you would follow to change an improper fraction to a mixed number. • Compare your notes on how to change an improper fraction to a mixed number to the example. • Complete the given example on your own. • Complete You Try 4.

W Work

Read the explanations, follow the examples, take notes, and complete the You Trys.

1 Understand Mixed Numbers

In this section, we will learn about *mixed numbers*. What *is* a mixed number? Let's say that you have friends over for a barbeque, and you have drunk two pitchers of iced tea plus another half of a pitcher of iced tea. All together, you have had

$2 + \dfrac{1}{2} = 2\dfrac{1}{2}$ pitchers of iced tea

The number $2\dfrac{1}{2}$ is called a *mixed number*.

Definition

A **mixed number** consists of a whole number and a fraction.

Example: $2\frac{1}{2}$ is a mixed number.

A mixed number represents more than 1 whole.

Let's see how mixed numbers and improper fractions are related. In Example 4 of Section 3.1, we were given this figure:

W Hint

Note the relationship between improper fractions and mixed numbers.

$\frac{7}{5}$ of the figure is shaded, and $\frac{7}{5}$ is an improper fraction because it represents a quantity greater than 1. Any fraction that is greater than 1 can be written as a mixed number. How can we write $\frac{7}{5}$ as a mixed number? Let's look at an example.

EXAMPLE 1

In-Class Example 1

Use Example 1.

Use a mixed number to describe what portion of the figure is shaded, and represent the mixed number on a number line.

Solution

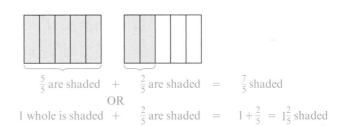

$\frac{5}{5}$ are shaded $+$ $\frac{2}{5}$ are shaded $=$ $\frac{7}{5}$ shaded

OR

1 whole is shaded $+$ $\frac{2}{5}$ are shaded $=$ $1+\frac{2}{5} = 1\frac{2}{5}$ shaded

To represent $1\frac{2}{5}$ on a number line, first notice that this number is greater than 1 and less than 2. Draw the number line from 0 to 2. Because $1\frac{2}{5}$ means $1 + \frac{2}{5}$, start at 1 and then divide the region between 1 and 2 into 5 equal parts. Label the tick marks.

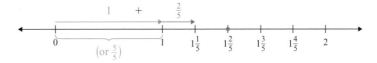

Perform addition on the number line as we did in Chapter 1. Start at 0 and move 1 space to the right to reach 1. Then, move $\frac{2}{5}$ of a unit to the right to reach $1\frac{2}{5}$. $\left(\text{This is the same as } \frac{7}{5}.\right)$

[YOU TRY 1] Use a mixed number to describe what portion of the figure is shaded, and represent the mixed number on a number line.

EXAMPLE 2   Use a mixed number to describe what portion of the figure is shaded, and represent the mixed number on a number line.

In-Class Example 2

Use a mixed number to represent what portion of the figure is shaded, and represent the mixed number on a number line.

Answer: $3\frac{1}{4}$;

Solution

How much is shaded? $4 \text{ whole} + \frac{2}{3} \text{ whole} = 4 + \frac{2}{3} = 4\frac{2}{3}$

$4\frac{2}{3}$ circles are shaded. Because $4\frac{2}{3}$ is between 4 and 5, draw a number line from 0 to 5. To place $4\frac{2}{3}$ on the number line, think of $4\frac{2}{3}$ as $4 + \frac{2}{3}$. Start at 0 and move to 4. Then divide the space between 4 and 5 into 3 equal parts. Move another $\frac{2}{3}$ of a unit.

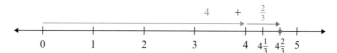

Place the dot on $4\frac{2}{3}$.

[YOU TRY 2] Use a mixed number to describe what portion of the figure is shaded, and represent the mixed number on a number line.

---

2 Change a Mixed Number to an Improper Fraction

How can we change a mixed number to an improper fraction?

Let's look at Example 2 again. We can count the shaded regions to determine that $\frac{14}{3}$ are shaded, or we can think of it like this:

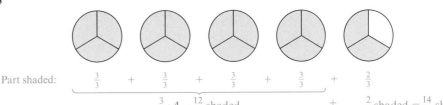

Part shaded:
$$\underbrace{\frac{3}{3} + \frac{3}{3} + \frac{3}{3} + \frac{3}{3}}_{\frac{3}{3} \cdot 4 = \frac{12}{3} \text{ shaded}} + \frac{2}{3}$$
$$+ \quad \frac{2}{3} \text{ shaded} = \frac{14}{3} \text{ shaded}$$

So, $4\frac{2}{3} = \frac{14}{3}$.

Here is another way to change a mixed number to an improper fraction.

 Hint

In your own words, explain the steps you would take to change a mixed number to an improper fraction.

Procedure Change a Mixed Number to an Improper Fraction

Step 1: Multiply the denominator and the whole number.

Step 2: Add the numerator to the result in Step 1.

Step 3: Write the improper fraction. The numerator is the result in Step 2, and the denominator is the original denominator.

EXAMPLE 3

In-Class Example 3

Write each mixed number as an improper fraction.

a) $2\frac{3}{4}$ b) $5\frac{6}{7}$

Answer: a) $\frac{11}{4}$ b) $\frac{41}{7}$

Write each mixed number as an improper fraction.

a) $4\frac{2}{3}$ b) $7\frac{3}{5}$

Solution

a) $4\frac{2}{3}$	b) $7\frac{3}{5}$
Step 1: Multiply the denominator and whole number: $3 \cdot 4 = 12$	**Step 1:** Multiply the denominator and whole number: $5 \cdot 7 = 35$
Step 2: Add the numerator to the result in Step 1: $12 + 2 = 14$	**Step 2:** Add the numerator to the result in Step 1: $35 + 3 = 38$
Step 3: Write the improper fraction: $4\frac{2}{3} = \frac{14}{3}$ ← Numerator found in Step 2 ← Original denominator	**Step 3:** Write the improper fraction: $7\frac{3}{5} = \frac{38}{5}$ ← Numerator found in Step 2 ← Original denominator

---

[YOU TRY 3]   Write each mixed number as an improper fraction.

a) $6\frac{1}{2}$ b) $2\frac{5}{8}$

3 Change an Improper Fraction to a Mixed Number

To change an improper fraction to a mixed number, follow these steps.

> ## Procedure Change an Improper Fraction to a Mixed Number
>
> **Step 1:** Divide the numerator by the denominator.
>
> **Step 2:** Write the mixed number. The *quotient* is the whole-number part. The *remainder* is the numerator of the fractional part, and the denominator is the same as the denominator of the improper fraction.

EXAMPLE 4

In-Class Example 4

Write each improper fraction as a mixed number.

a) $\dfrac{13}{5}$ b) $\dfrac{49}{6}$ c) $\dfrac{27}{3}$

Answer:

a) $2\dfrac{3}{5}$ b) $8\dfrac{1}{6}$ c) 9

Write each improper fraction as a mixed number.

a) $\dfrac{9}{4}$ b) $\dfrac{52}{9}$ c) $\dfrac{48}{6}$

Solution

a) **Step 1:** Divide the numerator by the denominator.

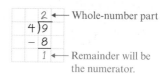

Step 2: Write the mixed number. $\dfrac{9}{4} = 2\dfrac{1}{4}$

The denominator stays the same.

Let's look at a figure to see that these are the same.

1 whole	+	1 whole	+	$\frac{1}{4}$ whole	= $2\frac{1}{4}$ shaded

$\frac{4}{4}$ shaded + $\frac{4}{4}$ shaded + $\frac{1}{4}$ shaded = $\frac{9}{4}$ shaded

b) **Step 1:** Divide the numerator by the denominator.

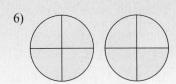

$$\frac{52}{9} = 5\frac{7}{9}$$

Step 2: Write the mixed number.

The denominator stays the same.

c) **Step 1:** Divide the numerator by the denominator.

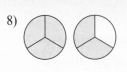

Since $\frac{48}{6} = 8$ (with *no* remainder), the improper fraction $\frac{48}{6}$ can be written as the whole number 8.

[**YOU TRY 4**] Write each improper fraction as a mixed number.

a) $\frac{10}{7}$ b) $\frac{75}{8}$ c) $\frac{30}{5}$

ANSWERS TO [**YOU TRY**] **EXERCISES**

1) $1\frac{3}{4}$;  2) $3\frac{1}{2}$;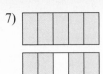

3) a) $\frac{13}{2}$ b) $\frac{21}{8}$ 4) a) $1\frac{3}{7}$ b) $9\frac{3}{8}$ c) 6

 E Evaluate **3.2** Exercises   Do the exercises, and check your work.

*Additional answers can be found in the Answers to Exercises appendix.

Objective 1: Understand Mixed Numbers

Use a mixed number to describe which portion of the figure is shaded, and represent the mixed number on a number line.

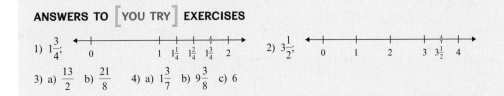

1)

2)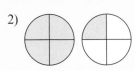

3)

4)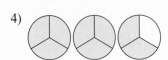

5)

6)

7)

8)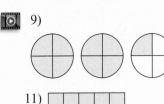

9)

10)

11)

12)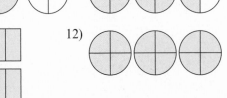

Objective 2: Change a Mixed Number to an Improper Fraction

13) Explain, in your own words, how to change a mixed number to an improper fraction.   Answers may vary.

14) Explain, in your own words, how to change an improper fraction to a mixed number.
Answers may vary.

Write each mixed number as an improper fraction.

15) $1\frac{1}{3}$ $\frac{4}{3}$

16) $3\frac{1}{2}$ $\frac{7}{2}$

17) $2\frac{3}{5}$ $\frac{13}{5}$

18) $1\frac{1}{5}$ $\frac{6}{5}$

19) $6\frac{1}{4}$ $\frac{25}{4}$

20) $5\frac{3}{7}$ $\frac{38}{7}$

21) $6\frac{4}{9}$ $\frac{58}{9}$

22) $3\frac{7}{8}$ $\frac{31}{8}$

23) $10\frac{5}{6}$ $\frac{65}{6}$

24) $11\frac{5}{9}$ $\frac{104}{9}$

25) $9\frac{5}{8}$ $\frac{77}{8}$

26) $10\frac{7}{11}$ $\frac{117}{11}$

27) $12\frac{2}{3}$ $\frac{38}{3}$

28) $13\frac{4}{5}$ $\frac{69}{5}$

29) Write down your own rule for changing a mixed number to an improper fraction.   Answers may vary.

30) How are mixed numbers and improper fractions related?   Answers may vary.

Fill in the blank with *proper* or *improper*.

31) A mixed number is the sum of a whole number and a(n) _____ fraction.   proper

32) A _____ fraction is a fraction that is less than one.
proper

33) A(n) _____ fraction cannot be written as a mixed number.   proper

34) A mixed number can always be represented by a(n) _____ fraction.   improper

Objective 3: Change an Improper Fraction to a Mixed Number

Write each improper fraction as a mixed number or whole number.

35) $\frac{5}{3}$ $1\frac{2}{3}$

36) $\frac{11}{8}$ $1\frac{3}{8}$

37) $\frac{9}{4}$ $2\frac{1}{4}$

38) $\frac{24}{7}$ $3\frac{3}{7}$

39) $\frac{11}{2}$ $5\frac{1}{2}$

40) $\frac{37}{5}$ $7\frac{2}{5}$

41) $\frac{42}{7}$ 6

42) $\frac{15}{3}$ 5

43) $\frac{28}{3}$ $9\frac{1}{3}$

44) $\frac{21}{2}$ $10\frac{1}{2}$

45) $\frac{105}{5}$ 21

46) $\frac{121}{11}$ 11

47) $\frac{55}{9}$ $6\frac{1}{9}$

48) $\frac{14}{13}$ $1\frac{1}{13}$

49) $\frac{64}{5}$ $12\frac{4}{5}$

50) $\frac{31}{3}$ $10\frac{1}{3}$

51) $\frac{289}{3}$ $96\frac{1}{3}$

52) $\frac{567}{11}$ $51\frac{6}{11}$

53) $\frac{1328}{23}$ $57\frac{17}{23}$

54) $\frac{1225}{12}$ $102\frac{1}{12}$

R Rethink

R1) Is it easier to explain the value of a mixed number or an improper fraction?

R2) Which objectives do you need to spend more time on to master?

3.3 Factors

P Prepare	**O Organize**
What are your objectives for Section 3.3?	**How can you accomplish each objective?**
1 Find the Factors of a Number	• Review what you learned about factors in Section 2.1. • Complete the given example on your own. • Complete You Try 1.
2 Identify Composite and Prime Numbers	• Learn and compare the definitions of a *composite number* and a *prime number*. • Review the divisibility rules from Section 2.4 to help you check whether a number is prime. • Complete the given example on your own. • Complete You Try 2.
3 Find the Prime Factorization of a Number	• How will the information you learned in Objectives 1 and 2 help you in Objective 3? • Write the definition of *prime factorization* in your own words. • Note the different procedures you can use to find the prime factorization of a number. • Complete the given examples on your own. • Complete You Trys 3–6.

W Work   **Read the explanations, follow the examples, take notes, and complete the You Trys.**

Before we continue our study of fractions, let's review what we have learned about *factors* in Section 2.1 and add some new information.

1 Find the Factors of a Number

Factors are numbers that are multiplied together to get a product. (We consider only natural numbers as factors.) For example, 2 and 9 are factors of 18 because $2 \cdot 9 = 18$. Does 18 have any other factors?

EXAMPLE 1

Find all factors of 18.

In-Class Example 1

Find all factors of 20.

Answer: 1, 2, 4, 5, 10, and 20

Solution

List the different pairs of numbers whose product is 18.

$$1 \cdot 18 = 18 \qquad 2 \cdot 9 = 18 \qquad 3 \cdot 6 = 18$$

All of these are ways to write 18 as the product of two numbers.
The factors of 18 are 1, 2, 3, 6, 9, and 18.

$\big[$ **YOU TRY 1** $\big]$ Find all factors of 30.

---

2 Identify Composite and Prime Numbers

The number 18 is an example of a *composite number*.

Definition

A **composite number** is a number with factors other than 1 and itself.

The number 18 is composite because it has factors other than 1 and 18. Its other factors are 2, 3, 6, and 9.

Note

Another way to think of the factors of 18 is that 18 *divides evenly* by 1, 2, 3, 6, 9, and 18:

$18 \div 1 = 18$ $18 \div 2 = 9$ $18 \div 3 = 6$ $18 \div 6 = 3$ $18 \div 9 = 2$ $18 \div 18 = 1$

Because 18 *divides evenly* by 1, 2, 3, 6, 9, and 18, they are factors of 18.

What if the only factors of a number are 1 and itself? Then it is a *prime number*.

Definition

A **prime number** is a number whose only two different factors are 1 and itself.

For example, 5 is *prime* because $1 \cdot 5$ is the only way to write 5 as the product of two different numbers. So, the only factors of 5 are 1 and 5.

We can think of this in terms of division as well. Since 5 divides evenly *only* by 1 and 5, 5 is a prime number. ($5 \div 1 = 5$ and $5 \div 5 = 1$)

Note

1) Since the only factor of 1 is 1, $1 \cdot 1 = 1$, it is not a prime number.

2) The numbers 0 and 1 are neither prime nor composite.

It is helpful to remember the divisibility rules from Section 2.4 when trying to determine whether a number is composite or prime.

EXAMPLE 2

Identify each number as composite or prime.

a) 35   b) 19   c) 87   d) 2

In-Class Example 2

Identify each number as composite or prime.
a) 45 b) 17 c) 51 d) 2

Answer:
a) composite   b) prime
c) composite   d) prime

Solution

a) Because 35 is divisible by 5, it is *not* prime: $35 \div 5 = 7$, which means that $5 \cdot 7 = 35$. So 35 has factors other than 1 and 35. Therefore, **35 is composite.**

b) Does 19 divide evenly by any numbers other than 1 and 19? *No.* **19 is prime.**

c) Think about 87 and the divisibility rules. Is it divisible by 2, 3, 5, or 10? Yes, it is divisible by 3. (87 is divisible by 3 since 8 + 7 = 15 and 15 is divisible by 3.) Since 87 has factors other than 1 and itself, **87 is composite.**

d) The only way to write 2 as a product of two different numbers is 1 · 2. Therefore, **2 is a prime number.**

[YOU TRY 2] Identify each number as composite or prime.

a) 13   b) 4000   c) 171   d) 83

 The only even number that is prime is 2. All of the other prime numbers are odd. But, not all odd numbers are prime! For example, 9 and 15 are odd but not prime.

Here is a list of the prime numbers from 1 to 100.

2	3	5	7	11	13	17	19	23
29	31	37	41	43	47	53	59	61
	67	71	73	79	83	89	97	

W Hint

Write the definition of prime factorization in your own words.

3 Find the Prime Factorization of a Number

To write fractions in lowest terms and to add and subtract fractions, it can be helpful to write a number as a product of its prime factors.

Definition

Finding the **prime factorization** of a number means writing the number as a *product* of prime factors.

We can find the prime factorization of a number using a *factor tree*.

EXAMPLE 3   Find the prime factorization of 18.

In-Class Example 3

Find the prime factorization of 20.

Answer:
$20 = 2 \cdot 2 \cdot 5$ or $20 = 2^2 \cdot 5$

Solution

To make a factor tree, write 18 at the top. Then, think of *any* two numbers (except 1 and 18) that multiply to 18. When a factor is prime, circle it, and that part of the factor tree is complete.

$$18$$
2 is prime, so → ②· 9   Think of *any* two numbers
circle it.   that multiply to 18.

Can 9 be written as the product of two numbers other than 1 and 9? *Yes.* $3 \cdot 3 = 9$. Continue with the tree.

18
②· 9
③·③ ← Circle the threes because they are prime.

$$18 = 2 \cdot 3 \cdot 3 \quad \text{or} \quad 2 \cdot 3^2$$

When all of the factors at the end of the tree are primes, you have finished the tree. **The prime factorization is the product of all the circled primes.**

The prime factorization of 18 is $2 \cdot 3 \cdot 3$ or $2 \cdot 3^2$.

[**YOU TRY 3**]   Find the prime factorization of 28.

Note

1) The factors in the prime factorization are written from smallest to largest.

2) The prime factorization may be written with or without exponents.

BE CAREFUL   In Example 1, we found that the *factors of 18* are 1, 2, 3, 6, 9, and 18. In Example 3, we found that the *prime factorization of 18* is $2 \cdot 3 \cdot 3$ or $2 \cdot 3^2$. Finding all the factors of a number and finding the prime factorization of a number are two different things.

EXAMPLE 4

In-Class Example 4

Find the prime factorization of each number.
a) 50   b) 414

Answer:
a) $50 = 2 \cdot 5 \cdot 5$ or $50 = 2 \cdot 5^2$
b) $414 = 2 \cdot 3 \cdot 3 \cdot 23$ or $414 = 2 \cdot 3^2 \cdot 23$

Find the prime factorization of each number.

a) 60   b) 462

Solution

a) Write 60 at the top, then think of *any* two numbers that multiply to 60. Let's use 10 and 6. We do *not* circle them because they are not prime.

60
10 · 6 ← Do *not* circle these numbers because they are not prime.

Now, think of two numbers that multiply to 10 and two numbers that multiply to 6: $10 = 2 \cdot 5$ and $6 = 2 \cdot 3$.

60
10 · 6
②·⑤·②·③ ← Circle these numbers because they are prime.

The tree is finished because all of the numbers at the end are prime. Here is the prime factorization of 60:

$$60 = 2 \cdot 2 \cdot 3 \cdot 5 \quad \text{or} \quad 60 = 2^2 \cdot 3 \cdot 5$$

Remember, write the factors from smallest to largest.

b) Can you think of two numbers that multiply to 462? Use the divisibility rules.

Is 462 divisible by 2? *Yes!* It is an even number.

Since 2 is a factor of 462, we can find another factor using long division.

$$\begin{array}{r} 2\ 3\ 1 \\ 2\overline{)4\ 6\ 2} \end{array}$$

Since $462 \div 2 = 231$, it follows that $231 \cdot 2 = 462$. Put these on the factor tree.

$$462$$
2 is prime, → ② · 231
so circle it.

Is 231 prime or composite? Let's use the divisibility rules again. 231 is not divisible by 2, 5, or 10. Is 231 divisible by 3? *Yes!* (Add the digits: $2 + 3 + 1 = 6$. Because 6 is divisible by 3, 231 is divisible by 3.)

Using long division, we get $231 \div 3 = 77$. It follows that $77 \cdot 3 = 231$. Put these on the factor tree.

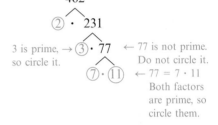

462
② · 231
3 is prime, → ③ · 77   ← 77 is not prime.
so circle it.   Do not circle it.
⑦ · ⑪   ← $77 = 7 \cdot 11$
Both factors are prime, so circle them.

Write the prime factorization of 462: $462 = 2 \cdot 3 \cdot 7 \cdot 11$.

[YOU TRY 4]

Find the prime factorization of each number.

a) 90   b) 396

We can also find the prime factorization of a number by modifying the long division procedure. When we use this method, *all* divisors must be prime.

EXAMPLE 5

In-Class Example 5

Use Example 5.

Find the prime factorization of 12.

Solution

First ask yourself, *"What prime number divides evenly into 12?"* We could use either 2 or 3. Let's use 2.

$$\begin{array}{r} 6 \\ 2\overline{)12} \end{array}$$ Divide 12 by 2.

Now ask yourself, *"What prime number divides evenly into 6?"* We could use 2 or 3. We will use 2.

$$\begin{array}{r} 3 \\ 2\overline{)6} \end{array}$$ Divide 6 by 2.

Ask yourself, *"What prime number divides evenly into 3?"* That number is 3.

$$\begin{array}{r} 1 \\ 3\overline{)3} \end{array}$$ Divide 3 by 3.

When the quotient is 1, the division is finished. The prime factorization consists of the prime factors, in blue.

Write the prime factorization: $12 = 2 \cdot 2 \cdot 3$ or $12 = 2^2 \cdot 3$.

[YOU TRY 5]

Find the prime factorization of 63.

We can write the steps used in Example 5 as a continuous string of division problems.

EXAMPLE 6

Find the prime factorization of 180.

Solution

Remember, *all* divisors must be prime numbers. So, ask yourself, *"What prime number divides evenly into 180?"* Since 180 ends in 0, it is divisible by 2.

$$2\overline{)180} \quad \overset{90}{} \quad \text{Divide 180 by 2.}$$

$$2\overline{)90} \quad \overset{45}{} \quad \text{Divide 90 by 2.}$$

$$5\overline{)45} \quad \overset{9}{} \quad \text{Divide 45 by 5.}$$

$$3\overline{)9} \quad \overset{3}{} \quad \text{Divide 9 by 3.}$$

$$3\overline{)3} \quad \overset{1}{} \quad \text{Divide 3 by 3.}$$

When the quotient is 1, the division is finished. The prime factorization consists of the prime factors, in blue.

Write the prime factorization: $180 = 2 \cdot 2 \cdot 3 \cdot 3 \cdot 5$ or $180 = 2^2 \cdot 3^2 \cdot 5$.

> **[YOU TRY 6]** Find the prime factorization of 364.

ANSWERS TO [YOU TRY] EXERCISES

1) 1, 2, 3, 5, 6, 10, 15, and 30   2) a) prime   b) composite   c) composite   d) prime
3) $28 = 2 \cdot 2 \cdot 7$ or $28 = 2^2 \cdot 7$
4) a) $90 = 2 \cdot 3 \cdot 3 \cdot 5$ or $90 = 2 \cdot 3^2 \cdot 5$ b) $396 = 2 \cdot 2 \cdot 3 \cdot 3 \cdot 11$ or $396 = 2^2 \cdot 3^2 \cdot 11$
5) $63 = 3 \cdot 3 \cdot 7$ or $63 = 3^2 \cdot 7$ 6) $364 = 2 \cdot 2 \cdot 7 \cdot 13$ or $364 = 2^2 \cdot 7 \cdot 13$

W Hint
Write out the example as you are reading it!

E Evaluate **3.3** Exercises   Do the exercises, and check your work.

*Additional answers can be found in the Answers to Exercises appendix.

Objective 1: Find the Factors of a Number

Find all factors of each number.

1) 8   1, 2, 4, and 8   2) 6   1, 2, 3, and 6

3) 9   1, 3, and 9   4) 15   1, 3, 5, and 15

5) 35   1, 5, 7, and 35   6) 26   1, 2, 13, and 26

7) 17   1 and 17   8) 11   1 and 11

9) 63   1, 3, 7, 9, 21, and 63   10) 45   1, 3, 5, 9, 15, and 45

11) 40   1, 2, 4, 5, 8, 10, 20, and 40   12) 50   1, 2, 5, 10, 25, and 50

13) 24   1, 2, 3, 4, 6, 8, 12, and 24   14) 42   1, 2, 3, 6, 7, 14, 21, and 42

15) 25   1, 5, and 25   16) 49   1, 7, and 49

17) 59   1 and 59   18) 37   1 and 37

Objective 2: Identify Composite and Prime Numbers

19) In your own words, explain the difference between a prime number and a composite number.
Answers may vary.

20) Is 1 a prime number? Why or why not?
The number 1 is not prime because it does not have two different factors.

21) What is the smallest prime number?   2

22) Are there any prime numbers that are even? If so, give an example.   Yes. The number 2 is prime.

Identify each number as composite or prime.

23) 5 prime

24) 9 composite

25) 21 composite

26) 17 prime

27) 31 prime

28) 75 composite

29) 43 prime

30) 80 composite

31) 41 prime

32) 59 prime

33) 56 composite

34) 63 composite

35) 101 prime

36) 105 composite

37) 183 composite

38) 67 prime

39) 540 composite

40) 895 composite

41) 7227 composite

42) 1401 composite

43) Is the product of two prime numbers *never, sometimes,* or *always* a prime number? never

44) Is the sum of two prime numbers *never, sometimes,* or *always* a prime number? sometimes

Objective 3: Find the Prime Factorization of a Number

45) What does it mean to write the prime factorization of a number? Writing the prime factorization of a number means writing the number as a product of its prime factors.

46) Is $4 \cdot 5$ the prime factorization of 20? Explain your answer. It is not the prime factorization of 20 because 4 is not a prime number. The prime factorization of 20 is $2 \cdot 2 \cdot 5$ or $2^2 \cdot 5$.

Find the prime factorization of each number.

47) 15 $15 = 3 \cdot 5$

48) 35 $35 = 5 \cdot 7$

49) 8 $8 = 2 \cdot 2 \cdot 2$ or 2^3

50) 27 $27 = 3 \cdot 3 \cdot 3$ or 3^3

51) 24 $24 = 2 \cdot 2 \cdot 2 \cdot 3$ or $2^3 \cdot 3$

52) 50 $50 = 2 \cdot 5 \cdot 5$ or $2 \cdot 5^2$

53) 81 $81 = 3 \cdot 3 \cdot 3 \cdot 3$ or 3^4

54) 64 $64 = 2 \cdot 2 \cdot 2 \cdot 2 \cdot 2 \cdot 2$ or 2^6

55) 99 $99 = 3 \cdot 3 \cdot 11$ or $3^2 \cdot 11$

56) 75 $75 = 3 \cdot 5 \cdot 5$ or $3 \cdot 5^2$

57) 62 $62 = 2 \cdot 31$

58) 82 $82 = 2 \cdot 41$

59) 78 $78 = 2 \cdot 3 \cdot 13$

60) 98 $98 = 2 \cdot 7 \cdot 7$ or $2 \cdot 7^2$

61) 270 $270 = 2 \cdot 3 \cdot 3 \cdot 3 \cdot 5$ or $2 \cdot 3^3 \cdot 5$

62) 210 $210 = 2 \cdot 3 \cdot 5 \cdot 7$

63) 330 $330 = 2 \cdot 3 \cdot 5 \cdot 11$

64) 324 $324 = 2 \cdot 2 \cdot 3 \cdot 3 \cdot 3 \cdot 3$ or $2^2 \cdot 3^4$

65) 495 $495 = 3 \cdot 3 \cdot 5 \cdot 11$ or $3^2 \cdot 5 \cdot 11$

66) 525 $525 = 3 \cdot 5 \cdot 5 \cdot 7$ or $3 \cdot 5^2 \cdot 7$

67) 1300 $1300 = 2 \cdot 2 \cdot 5 \cdot 5 \cdot 13$ or $2^2 \cdot 5^2 \cdot 13$

68) 3600 $3600 = 2 \cdot 2 \cdot 2 \cdot 2 \cdot 3 \cdot 3 \cdot 5 \cdot 5$ or $2^4 \cdot 3^2 \cdot 5^2$

69) a) List all the factors of 24.
    1, 2, 3, 4, 6, 8, 12, and 24
    b) Find the prime factorization of 24.
    $24 = 2 \cdot 2 \cdot 2 \cdot 3$ or $2^3 \cdot 3$

70) a) List all the factors of 45.
    1, 3, 5, 9, 15, and 45
    b) Find the prime factorization of 45.
    $45 = 3 \cdot 3 \cdot 5$ or $3^2 \cdot 5$

71) a) List all the factors of 70.
    1, 2, 5, 7, 10, 14, 35, and 70
    b) Find the prime factorization of 70.
    $70 = 2 \cdot 5 \cdot 7$

72) a) List all the factors of 42.
    1, 2, 3, 6, 7, 14, 21, and 42
    b) Find the prime factorization of 42.
    $42 = 2 \cdot 3 \cdot 7$

R Rethink

R1) Which skills that you have learned so far in this class have helped you complete the exercises more quickly?

R2) Which method do you prefer for finding the prime factorization of a number? Why?

3.4 Writing Fractions in Lowest Terms

P Prepare

O Organize

What are your objectives for Section 3.4?	How can you accomplish each objective?
1 Understand Equivalent Fractions	• Write the definition of *equivalent fractions* in your own words. • Write the definition of *lowest terms* in your own words. • Complete the given example on your own. • Complete You Try 1.
2 Write Fractions in Lowest Terms Using Common Factors	• In your own words, take notes on the steps you would take to write a fraction in lowest terms using common factors. • Write the definition of a *greatest common factor* in your own words. • Complete the given examples on your own. • Complete You Trys 2 and 3.
3 Write Fractions in Lowest Terms Using Prime Factorization	• In your own words, take notes on the steps you would use to write a fraction in lowest terms using prime factorization. • Complete the given examples on your own. • Complete You Trys 4 and 5.
4 Determine Whether Two Fractions Are Equivalent	• Write down the steps you would use to determine whether two fractions are equivalent. • Complete the given example on your own. • Complete You Try 6.

W Work

Read the explanations, follow the examples, take notes, and complete the You Trys.

1 Understand Equivalent Fractions

Different fractions can describe the same quantity. For example, compare these two pizzas of the same size.

$\frac{1}{2}$ of the pizza is left. 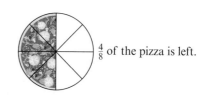 $\frac{4}{8}$ of the pizza is left.

Both of the fractions represent the same amount of pizza, so $\frac{1}{2} = \frac{4}{8}$. We say that $\frac{1}{2}$ and $\frac{4}{8}$ are *equivalent fractions*.

Definition

Equivalent fractions are different fractions that represent the same part of the whole.

Example: $\frac{1}{2}$ and $\frac{4}{8}$ are equivalent fractions.

Although $\frac{1}{2}$ and $\frac{4}{8}$ represent the same amount of pizza, $\frac{1}{2}$ is in *lowest terms* and $\frac{4}{8}$ is not. $\frac{4}{8}$ is *not* in lowest terms because 4 and 8 share at least one *common factor:*

1, 2, and 4 are **common factors** of 4 and 8 because 1, 2, and 4 are factors of 4 and factors of 8. The number 4 is the **greatest common factor** of 4 and 8 because 4 is the largest of their common factors.

Definition

The **greatest common factor, or GCF,** of a group of numbers is the *largest* number that is a factor of each number in the group.

Example: The greatest common factor of 10 and 15 is 5 because 5 is the largest number that is a factor of 10 and of 15.

The fraction $\frac{1}{2}$ *is* in lowest terms because the numerator and denominator do not have any common factor other than 1.

 Hint
Did you write these definitions in your own words?

Definition

A fraction is in **lowest terms** if the numerator and denominator have no common factors other than 1.

Example: $\frac{1}{2}$ is in lowest terms.

Note
Writing a fraction in lowest terms is also called **simplifying** a fraction.

EXAMPLE 1

Determine whether each fraction is in lowest terms.

a) $\frac{5}{9}$ b) $\frac{14}{21}$

In-Class Example 1

Determine whether each fraction is in lowest terms.

a) $\frac{3}{8}$ b) $\frac{10}{35}$

Answer: a) yes b) no

Solution

a) List the factors of 5 and 9.

Factors of 5: 1 and 5   Factors of 9: 1, 3, and 9

$\frac{5}{9}$ *is* in lowest terms because 5 and 9 have no common factor other than 1.

b) Look at the fraction $\frac{14}{21}$. ← 14 is divisible by 7.
    ← 21 is divisible by 7.

14 and 21 have a common factor of 7. Therefore, $\frac{14}{21}$ is *not* in lowest terms.

[YOU TRY 1] Determine whether each fraction is in lowest terms.

a) $\frac{16}{40}$ b) $\frac{11}{18}$

---

2 Write Fractions in Lowest Terms Using Common Factors

Knowing how to write a fraction in lowest terms is a skill that we need in *many* areas of mathematics as well as in other subject areas like nursing, science, culinary arts, and more. There are two common methods for writing a fraction in lowest terms. The first method we will learn involves dividing the numerator and denominator by a common factor.

EXAMPLE 2

In-Class Example 2

Write $\frac{21}{28}$ in lowest terms.

Answer: $\frac{3}{4}$

Write $\frac{15}{20}$ in lowest terms.

Solution

Ask yourself, *"What number divides evenly into both 15 and 20?"* That number is 5. (We do not use 1. It will not help us simplify the fraction.)

Divide the numerator and denominator by 5: $\frac{15}{20} = \frac{15 \div 5}{20 \div 5} = \frac{3}{4}$

Always look at the result and ask yourself, *"Is the fraction in lowest terms?"* Yes; the numbers 3 and 4 have no common factor other than 1.

Therefore, $\frac{15}{20} = \frac{3}{4}$, and $\frac{3}{4}$ is in lowest terms.

[YOU TRY 2] Write $\frac{18}{33}$ in lowest terms.

Dividing the numerator and denominator by the same number will give us an equivalent fraction. Follow these steps for writing a fraction in lowest terms.

Procedure Writing a Fraction in Lowest Terms Using Common Factors

To write a fraction in lowest terms:

1) Ask yourself, *"What number divides evenly into both the numerator and denominator?"* (Use any number except 1.) Divide the numerator and denominator by that number.

2) Look at the result and ask yourself, *"Is the fraction in lowest terms?"* If the numerator and denominator still contain a common factor, repeat Steps 1 and 2.

Note

It is **very** important that you always look at the result and ask yourself, *"Is the fraction in lowest terms?"* If you divided by the greatest common factor, then it will be in lowest terms. But if you have *not* divided by the greatest common factor, the fraction will *not* be in lowest terms, and you will have to simplify it more.

EXAMPLE 3

Write each fraction in lowest terms.

a) $\dfrac{50}{80}$ b) $\dfrac{198}{294}$

Solution

a) Ask yourself, *"What number divides evenly into both 50 and 80?"* Let's use 10. (We could have used 2 or 5, but 10 is the **greatest common factor** of 50 and 80.) We will use the greatest common factor, 10, because that will simplify the fraction most quickly.

$$\frac{50}{80} = \frac{50 \div 10}{80 \div 10} = \frac{5}{8}$$

Ask yourself, *"Is $\dfrac{5}{8}$ in lowest terms?"* Yes it is, because 5 and 8 have no common factor other than 1.

Therefore, $\dfrac{50}{80} = \dfrac{5}{8}$, and $\dfrac{5}{8}$ is in lowest terms.

b) The numerator and denominator of $\dfrac{198}{294}$ are large numbers, so we probably will not divide by the *greatest* common factor the first time. But that is fine; we can divide by *any* common factor. Ask yourself, *"What number divides evenly into both 198 and 294?"* Both numbers divide by 2.

$$\frac{198}{294} = \frac{198 \div 2}{294 \div 2} = \frac{99}{147}$$

Ask yourself, *"Is $\frac{99}{147}$ in lowest terms?"* No! Think about the divisibility rules. Each number is divisible by 3.

$$\frac{99}{147} = \frac{99 \div 3}{147 \div 3} = \frac{33}{49}$$

"Is $\frac{33}{49}$ in lowest terms?" Yes. Therefore, in lowest terms, $\frac{198}{294} = \frac{33}{49}$.

[YOU TRY 3] Write each fraction in lowest terms.

a) $\frac{35}{60}$ b) $\frac{1620}{2340}$

BE CAREFUL   Example 3b shows why it is so important to look at the result to determine whether it can be simplified more. If you did not divide by the greatest common factor the first time, you will still be able to divide out a common factor.

3 Write Fractions in Lowest Terms Using Prime Factorization

We can also use the prime factorizations of the numerator and denominator to write a fraction in lowest terms.

EXAMPLE 4

In-Class Example 4

Write $\frac{18}{30}$ in lowest terms.

Answer: $\frac{3}{5}$

Write $\frac{12}{42}$ in lowest terms.

Solution

Use one of the methods of Section 3.3 to write the prime factorizations of 12 and 42: $\frac{12}{42} = \frac{2 \cdot 2 \cdot 3}{2 \cdot 3 \cdot 7}$ Write the prime factorizations of 12 and 42.

Divide the numerator and denominator by the common factors. Write a 1 by each factor to indicate that you have performed that division.

$$\frac{12}{42} = \frac{\overset{1}{2} \cdot 2 \cdot \overset{1}{3}}{\underset{1}{2} \cdot \underset{1}{3} \cdot 7}$$

Multiply the factors that are left: $\frac{12}{42} = \frac{1 \cdot 2 \cdot 1}{1 \cdot 1 \cdot 7} = \frac{2}{7}$

Is $\frac{2}{7}$ in lowest terms? Yes. Therefore, $\frac{12}{42} = \frac{2}{7}$.

[**YOU TRY 4**] Write $\dfrac{28}{98}$ in lowest terms.

W Hint

In your own words, take notes on the steps you would take to write a fraction in lowest terms using prime factorization.

Procedure Writing a Fraction in Lowest Terms Using Prime Factorization

To write a fraction in lowest terms:

1) Write the prime factorization of the numerator and denominator.

2) Divide out common factors. Write a 1 by each factor to indicate that you have performed the division.

3) Multiply the factors that are left in the numerator and in the denominator.

Note

Always look at the result and ask yourself, *"Is the fraction in lowest terms?"* in case you have not divided out all common factors. Divide out remaining common factors, if necessary.

EXAMPLE 5

In-Class Example 5

Write each fraction in lowest terms.

a) $\dfrac{15}{105}$ b) $\dfrac{756}{42}$

Answer:

a) $\dfrac{1}{7}$ b) 18

Write each fraction in lowest terms.

a) $\dfrac{21}{126}$ b) $\dfrac{540}{45}$

Solution

a) Use one of the methods of Section 3.3 to write the prime factorizations of 21 and 126.

$$\frac{21}{126} = \frac{3 \cdot 7}{2 \cdot 3 \cdot 3 \cdot 7} \qquad \text{Write the prime factorizations of 21 and 126.}$$

Divide out the common factors and write a 1 by each of these factors that have been divided.

$$\frac{21}{126} = \frac{\overset{1}{3} \cdot \overset{1}{7}}{2 \cdot \underset{1}{3} \cdot 3 \cdot \underset{1}{7}}$$

Multiply the factors that are left: $\dfrac{21}{126} = \dfrac{1 \cdot 1}{2 \cdot 1 \cdot 3 \cdot 1} = \dfrac{1}{6}$

Is $\dfrac{1}{6}$ in lowest terms? Yes. So, $\dfrac{21}{126} = \dfrac{1}{6}$, and $\dfrac{1}{6}$ is in lowest terms.

 BE CAREFUL

When all of the factors of the numerator were divided out, we were left with 1 so that the answer is $\dfrac{1}{6}$, *not* 6.

---

b) Write the prime factorization, and divide out the common factors.

$$\frac{540}{45} = \frac{2 \cdot 2 \cdot \overset{1}{\cancel{3}} \cdot \overset{1}{\cancel{3}} \cdot 3 \cdot \overset{1}{\cancel{5}}}{\underset{1}{\cancel{3}} \cdot \underset{1}{\cancel{3}} \cdot \underset{1}{\cancel{5}}} = \frac{2 \cdot 2 \cdot 1 \cdot 1 \cdot 3 \cdot 1}{1 \cdot 1 \cdot 1} = \frac{12}{1}$$

Ask yourself, *"Is $\frac{12}{1}$ in lowest terms?"* No! We can write $\frac{12}{1}$ as 12. In lowest terms, $\frac{540}{45} = 12$.

[YOU TRY 5] Write each fraction in lowest terms.

a) $\dfrac{18}{72}$ b) $\dfrac{378}{63}$

---

4   Determine Whether Two Fractions Are Equivalent

At the beginning of this section, a picture of two pizzas showed that $\dfrac{1}{2} = \dfrac{4}{8}$. That is, $\dfrac{1}{2}$ and $\dfrac{4}{8}$ are equivalent fractions. To determine whether two fractions are equivalent, write each of them in lowest terms.

EXAMPLE 6

In-Class Example 6

Determine whether each pair of fractions is equivalent.

a) $\dfrac{16}{36}$ and $\dfrac{28}{63}$

b) $\dfrac{34}{51}$ and $\dfrac{102}{162}$

Answer: a) yes   b) no

W Hint

Write down the steps you would use to determine whether two fractions are equivalent.

Determine whether each pair of fractions is equivalent.

a) $\dfrac{6}{27}$ and $\dfrac{16}{72}$ b) $\dfrac{22}{176}$ and $\dfrac{28}{154}$

Solution

a) Write each fraction in lowest terms and see whether we get the same result. Let's simplify these fractions by dividing out the greatest common factor.

$$\frac{6}{27} = \frac{6 \div 3}{27 \div 3} = \frac{2}{9} \qquad\qquad \frac{16}{72} = \frac{16 \div 8}{72 \div 8} = \frac{2}{9}$$

Since $\dfrac{6}{27} = \dfrac{2}{9}$ and $\dfrac{16}{72} = \dfrac{2}{9}$, the fractions *are* equivalent.

b) Let's use prime factorization to write each fraction in lowest terms.

$$\frac{22}{176} = \frac{2 \cdot \overset{1}{\cancel{11}}}{2 \cdot 2 \cdot 2 \cdot 2 \cdot \underset{1}{\cancel{11}}} = \frac{1 \cdot 1}{1 \cdot 2 \cdot 2 \cdot 2 \cdot 1} = \frac{1}{8}$$

$$\frac{28}{154} = \frac{2 \cdot 2 \cdot \overset{1}{\cancel{7}}}{2 \cdot \underset{1}{\cancel{7}} \cdot 11} = \frac{1 \cdot 2 \cdot 1}{1 \cdot 1 \cdot 11} = \frac{2}{11}$$

$\dfrac{22}{176}$ and $\dfrac{28}{154}$ are *not* equivalent.

[YOU TRY 6] Determine whether each pair of fractions is equivalent.

a) $\frac{7}{42}$ and $\frac{12}{84}$ b) $\frac{540}{1980}$ and $\frac{45}{165}$

ANSWERS TO [YOU TRY] EXERCISES

1) a) no b) yes   2) $\frac{6}{11}$ 3) a) $\frac{7}{12}$ b) $\frac{9}{13}$ 4) $\frac{2}{7}$ 5) a) $\frac{1}{4}$ b) 6   6) a) no b) yes

---

E Evaluate **3.4** Exercises   Do the exercises, and check your work.

*Additional answers can be found in the Answers to Exercises appendix.

Objective 1: Understand Equivalent Fractions

1) How do you know whether a fraction is in lowest terms?   A fraction is in lowest terms if the numerator and denominator have no common factors other than 1.

2) What is the greatest common factor of two numbers?   The greatest common factor of two numbers is the largest factor that the numbers have in common.

Determine whether each fraction is in lowest terms.

3) $\frac{2}{3}$ yes

4) $\frac{2}{5}$ yes

5) $\frac{8}{10}$ no

6) $\frac{4}{9}$ yes

7) $\frac{3}{32}$ yes

8) $\frac{7}{28}$ no

9) $\frac{7}{24}$ yes

10) $\frac{17}{30}$ yes

11) $\frac{11}{22}$ no

12) $\frac{4}{28}$ no

13) $\frac{23}{69}$ no

14) $\frac{17}{34}$ no

15) $\frac{7}{31}$ yes

16) $\frac{12}{23}$ yes

17) $\frac{63}{207}$ no

18) $\frac{36}{324}$ no

Objective 2: Write Fractions in Lowest Terms Using Common Factors

19) In your own words, explain how to write a fraction in lowest terms using common factors.
Answers may vary.

20) If you have divided the numerator and denominator by a common factor, will the result always be a fraction in lowest terms? Explain your answer.
No, it will not always be in lowest terms. Sometimes, you can divide out another common factor.

Write each fraction in lowest terms by dividing out common factors.

21) $\frac{10}{16}$ $\frac{5}{8}$

22) $\frac{14}{21}$ $\frac{2}{3}$

23) $\frac{33}{77}$ $\frac{3}{7}$

24) $\frac{27}{36}$ $\frac{3}{4}$

25) $\frac{4}{8}$ $\frac{1}{2}$

26) $\frac{7}{42}$ $\frac{1}{6}$

27) $\frac{44}{28}$ $\frac{11}{7}$ or $1\frac{4}{7}$

28) $\frac{84}{30}$ $\frac{14}{5}$ or $2\frac{4}{5}$

29) $\frac{60}{12}$ 5

30) $\frac{49}{7}$ 7

31) $\frac{48}{36}$ $\frac{4}{3}$ or $1\frac{1}{3}$

32) $\frac{88}{55}$ $\frac{8}{5}$ or $1\frac{3}{5}$

33) $\frac{30}{90}$ $\frac{1}{3}$

34) $\frac{20}{80}$ $\frac{1}{4}$

35) $\frac{20}{35}$ $\frac{4}{7}$

36) $\frac{50}{65}$ $\frac{10}{13}$

37) $\frac{108}{9}$ 12

38) $\frac{132}{12}$ 11

39) $\frac{480}{680}$ $\frac{12}{17}$

40) $\frac{630}{900}$ $\frac{7}{10}$

41) $\frac{153}{171}$ $\frac{17}{19}$

42) $\frac{117}{261}$ $\frac{13}{29}$

43) $\frac{225}{525}$ $\frac{3}{7}$

44) $\frac{205}{615}$ $\frac{1}{3}$

45) $\frac{800}{1400}$ $\frac{4}{7}$

46) $\frac{1190}{1700}$ $\frac{7}{10}$

Objective 3: Write Fractions in Lowest Terms Using Prime Factorization

Write each fraction in lowest terms using prime factorization.

47) $\dfrac{6}{15}$ $\dfrac{2}{5}$

48) $\dfrac{15}{35}$ $\dfrac{3}{7}$

49) $\dfrac{36}{81}$ $\dfrac{4}{9}$

50) $\dfrac{72}{84}$ $\dfrac{6}{7}$

51) $\dfrac{70}{154}$ $\dfrac{5}{11}$

52) $\dfrac{72}{192}$ $\dfrac{3}{8}$

53) $\dfrac{24}{288}$ $\dfrac{1}{12}$

54) $\dfrac{15}{135}$ $\dfrac{1}{9}$

55) $\dfrac{168}{6}$ 28

56) $\dfrac{272}{8}$ 34

57) $\dfrac{51}{39}$ $\dfrac{17}{13}$ or $1\dfrac{4}{13}$

58) $\dfrac{92}{76}$ $\dfrac{23}{19}$ or $1\dfrac{4}{19}$

59) $\dfrac{350}{70}$ 5

60) $\dfrac{325}{25}$ 13

61) $\dfrac{868}{1488}$ $\dfrac{7}{12}$

62) $\dfrac{1312}{2460}$ $\dfrac{8}{15}$

Objective 4: Determine Whether Two Fractions Are Equivalent

Determine whether each pair of fractions is equivalent.

63) $\dfrac{12}{18}$ and $\dfrac{16}{24}$ yes

64) $\dfrac{28}{35}$ and $\dfrac{16}{20}$ yes

65) $\dfrac{72}{40}$ and $\dfrac{42}{18}$ no

66) $\dfrac{24}{16}$ and $\dfrac{36}{21}$ no

67) $\dfrac{45}{25}$ and $\dfrac{54}{30}$ yes

68) $\dfrac{14}{12}$ and $\dfrac{63}{54}$ yes

69) $\dfrac{63}{168}$ and $\dfrac{51}{136}$ yes

70) $\dfrac{112}{512}$ and $\dfrac{49}{224}$ yes

71) $\dfrac{63}{144}$ and $\dfrac{84}{182}$ no

72) $\dfrac{126}{288}$ and $\dfrac{168}{384}$ yes

73) $\dfrac{224}{512}$ and $\dfrac{175}{400}$ yes

74) $\dfrac{104}{120}$ and $\dfrac{960}{1200}$ no

75) $\dfrac{147}{462}$ and $\dfrac{1260}{3960}$ yes

76) $\dfrac{162}{468}$ and $\dfrac{1980}{5720}$ yes

Determine whether each statement is true or false.

77) Two equivalent fractions have the same location on a number line. true

78) On the number line, $\dfrac{1}{10}$ is to the left of $\dfrac{1}{2}$. true

79) All fractions are less than 1. false

80) $\dfrac{10}{10,000} = \dfrac{1}{1000}$ true

81) $\dfrac{1}{1000}$ is greater than $\dfrac{1}{100}$. false

82) $\dfrac{1}{3}$ is less than $\dfrac{1}{4}$. false

R Rethink

R1) What is the first thing you think when you see a fraction?

R2) What is the difference between prime factorization and the GCF?

R3) Is it easier for you to compare two improper fractions or two mixed numbers? Why?

3.5 Multiplying Fractions

What are your objectives for Section 3.5?	How can you accomplish each objective?
1 Multiply Fractions	• Write the procedure for **Multiplying Fractions** in your own words. • Complete the given example on your own. • Complete You Try 1.
2 Divide Out Common Factors Before Multiplying	• Add the step of dividing out a common factor before multiplying to the procedure you wrote for multiplying fractions. • Complete the given examples on your own. • Complete You Trys 2–4.
3 Multiply a Fraction and a Whole Number	• Write the procedure for **Multiplying a Fraction and a Whole Number** in your own words. • Complete the given example on your own. • Complete You Try 5.

W Work   **Read the explanations, follow the examples, take notes, and complete the You Trys.**

1   Multiply Fractions

When we use the word *of* with fractions, it usually means multiplication. Why is that true? Let's consider this situation.

    Rich is having a party and orders a party-size sub sandwich. He cuts the sandwich in half.

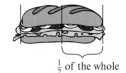

$\frac{1}{2}$ of the whole

He cuts each piece in half again and eats one piece. Rich eats $\frac{1}{2}$ *of* $\frac{1}{2}$ of the sandwich. What fraction of the whole sandwich did Rich eat?

    We can see from the figure that he ate $\frac{1}{4}$ of the whole sandwich. If we do not have a picture to look at, how can we find $\frac{1}{2}$ *of* $\frac{1}{2}$? We multiply.

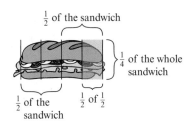

$\frac{1}{2}$ of the sandwich

$\frac{1}{4}$ of the whole sandwich

$\frac{1}{2}$ of the sandwich $\frac{1}{2}$ of $\frac{1}{2}$

W Hint

Write the procedure for multiplying fractions in your own words.

Procedure Multiplying Fractions

To multiply fractions, multiply the numerators and multiply the denominators. Write the result in lowest terms.

    Example: $\frac{1}{2}$ *of* $\frac{1}{2}$ means $\frac{1}{2} \cdot \frac{1}{2} = \frac{1 \cdot 1}{2 \cdot 2} = \frac{1}{4}$

EXAMPLE 1

Multiply. Write all answers in lowest terms.

a) $\dfrac{2}{5} \cdot \dfrac{4}{9}$ b) $\dfrac{7}{9} \cdot \dfrac{1}{4} \cdot \dfrac{5}{2}$ c) $\dfrac{3}{8} \cdot \dfrac{5}{6}$

In-Class Example 1

Multiply. Write all answers in lowest terms.

a) $\dfrac{7}{10} \cdot \dfrac{3}{5}$ b) $\dfrac{1}{2} \cdot \dfrac{3}{7} \cdot \dfrac{5}{4}$

c) $\dfrac{4}{9} \cdot \dfrac{5}{8}$

Answer:

a) $\dfrac{21}{50}$ b) $\dfrac{15}{56}$ c) $\dfrac{5}{18}$

Solution

a) Multiply the numerators, and multiply the denominators.

$$\frac{2}{5} \cdot \frac{4}{9} = \frac{2 \cdot 4}{5 \cdot 9} = \frac{8}{45}$$ Multiply numerators, and multiply denominators.

Is $\dfrac{8}{45}$ in lowest terms?   Yes. So, the product is $\dfrac{8}{45}$.

b) $\dfrac{7}{9} \cdot \dfrac{1}{4} \cdot \dfrac{5}{2} = \dfrac{7 \cdot 1 \cdot 5}{9 \cdot 4 \cdot 2} = \dfrac{35}{72}$

Is $\dfrac{35}{72}$ in lowest terms?   Yes. The answer is $\dfrac{35}{72}$.

c) $\dfrac{3}{8} \cdot \dfrac{5}{6} = \dfrac{3 \cdot 5}{8 \cdot 6} = \dfrac{15}{48}$

Is $\dfrac{15}{48}$ in lowest terms? No! We must write it in lowest terms.

$$\frac{15}{48} = \frac{15 \div 3}{48 \div 3} = \frac{5}{16}$$

Is $\dfrac{5}{16}$ in lowest terms?   Yes. The answer is $\dfrac{5}{16}$.

[YOU TRY 1] Multiply. Write all answers in lowest terms.

a) $\dfrac{8}{11} \cdot \dfrac{2}{3}$ b) $\dfrac{2}{9} \cdot \dfrac{7}{3} \cdot \dfrac{1}{5}$ c) $\dfrac{5}{21} \cdot \dfrac{7}{2}$

 BE CAREFUL   Whenever you get a result that is a fraction, ask yourself, *"Is it in lowest terms?"* If it is not, write it in lowest terms.

2 Divide Out Common Factors Before Multiplying

In Example 1c, the product was *not* in lowest terms: $\dfrac{3}{8} \cdot \dfrac{5}{6} = \dfrac{15}{48}$. We had to perform

one more step to write the result in lowest terms: $\dfrac{15}{48} = \dfrac{15 \div 3}{48 \div 3} = \dfrac{5}{16}$.

Another way to multiply fractions is to divide out common factors *before* finding the final product. We can write the prime factorization of 8 and 6 and divide out common factors.

$$\frac{3}{8} \cdot \frac{5}{6} = \frac{3 \cdot 5}{2 \cdot 2 \cdot 2 \cdot \overset{1}{\cancel{3}}} = \frac{1 \cdot 5}{2 \cdot 2 \cdot 2 \cdot 1} = \frac{5}{16}$$

Because we have divided out all prime factors, the product, $\frac{5}{16}$, is in lowest terms.

EXAMPLE 2

Multiply $\frac{4}{9} \cdot \frac{3}{10}$ by writing the prime factorization of each number and dividing out the common factors. Be sure the answer is in lowest terms.

Solution

$$\frac{4}{9} \cdot \frac{3}{10} = \frac{4 \cdot 3}{9 \cdot 10} = \frac{\overset{1}{\cancel{2}} \cdot 2 \cdot \overset{1}{\cancel{3}}}{\underset{1}{\cancel{3}} \cdot 3 \cdot \underset{1}{\cancel{2}} \cdot 5} = \frac{1 \cdot 2 \cdot 1}{1 \cdot 3 \cdot 1 \cdot 5} = \frac{2}{15}$$

The product is $\frac{2}{15}$, and it is in lowest terms.

[YOU TRY 2]

Multiply $\frac{15}{28} \cdot \frac{14}{25}$ by writing the prime factorization of each number and dividing out the common factors. Be sure the answer is in lowest terms.

Note

From this point onward, all fractional answers should be written in lowest terms unless stated otherwise.

There is another way to divide out common factors. We can divide them out *before* we multiply. Let's find the product in Example 2 another way.

EXAMPLE 3

Multiply $\frac{4}{9} \cdot \frac{3}{10}$ by dividing out common factors before multiplying.

Solution

First look at the 4 and 10 in $\frac{4}{9} \cdot \frac{3}{10}$. What is the greatest common factor of 4 and 10? It is 2. Divide 4 and 10 by 2.

$$4 \div 2 = 2 \rightarrow 2$$
$$\frac{\overset{}{4}}{9} \cdot \frac{3}{\underset{5}{\cancel{10}}}$$
$$5 \leftarrow 10 \div 2 = 5$$

Now, look at the 3 and 9. What is the greatest common factor of 3 and 9? It is 3.

$$\frac{\overset{2}{4}}{\underset{3}{9}} \cdot \frac{\overset{1 \leftarrow\, 3 \div 3 = 1}{3}}{\underset{5}{10}}$$

$$9 \div 3 = 3 \rightarrow 3$$

Multiply the numerators, and multiply the denominators: $\frac{2 \cdot 1}{3 \cdot 5} = \frac{2}{15}$.

This is the same as the result in Example 2.

[YOU TRY 3] Multiply $\frac{15}{28} \cdot \frac{14}{25}$ by dividing out common factors before multiplying.

BE CAREFUL Be sure you divide the numerator and the denominator by the *same number*. If you divide out all common factors, the answer will be in lowest terms. *Always* look at the product to be sure it is in lowest terms!

EXAMPLE 4

In-Class Example 4

Multiply by first dividing out common factors.

a) $\frac{3}{8} \cdot \frac{12}{13}$ b) $\frac{5}{28} \cdot \frac{21}{25}$

c) $\frac{10}{7} \cdot \frac{7}{2}$ d) $\frac{4}{11} \cdot \frac{5}{9} \cdot \frac{21}{40}$

e) $\frac{44}{27} \cdot \frac{45}{11}$

Answer: a) $\frac{9}{26}$ b) $\frac{3}{20}$

c) 5 d) $\frac{7}{66}$ e) $\frac{20}{3}$ or $6\frac{2}{3}$

Multiply by first dividing out common factors.

a) $\frac{9}{10} \cdot \frac{15}{16}$ b) $\frac{7}{40} \cdot \frac{16}{21}$ c) $\frac{8}{3} \cdot \frac{3}{2}$

d) $\frac{4}{11} \cdot \frac{2}{15} \cdot \frac{9}{16}$ e) $\frac{36}{25} \cdot \frac{35}{12}$

Solution

a) First, look at 9 and 16 in $\frac{9}{10} \cdot \frac{15}{16}$. What is the greatest common factor of 9 and 16? It is 1. So, we cannot divide out common factors from 9 and 16.

Now, look at 10 and 15. What is the largest number that divides evenly into 10 and 15? It is 5. Divide 10 and 15 by 5.

$$\frac{9}{\underset{2}{10}} \cdot \frac{\overset{3 \leftarrow\, 15 \div 5 = 3}{15}}{16}$$

$$10 \div 5 = 2 \rightarrow 2$$

Multiply: $\frac{9 \cdot 3}{2 \cdot 16} = \frac{27}{32}$. Is $\frac{27}{32}$ in lowest terms? Yes. The product is $\frac{27}{32}$.

b) In $\frac{7}{40} \cdot \frac{16}{21}$, we will divide 7 and 21 by 7, and divide 40 and 16 by 8. Then, multiply.

$$\frac{\overset{1}{7}}{\underset{5}{40}} \cdot \frac{\overset{2}{16}}{\underset{3}{21}} = \frac{1 \cdot 2}{5 \cdot 3} = \frac{2}{15} \qquad \text{The answer is in lowest terms.}$$

c) Before multiplying $\dfrac{8}{3} \cdot \dfrac{3}{2}$, divide the 3's by 3, and divide 8 and 2 by 2.

$$\dfrac{\overset{4}{\cancel{8}}}{\underset{1}{\cancel{3}}} \cdot \dfrac{\overset{1}{\cancel{3}}}{\underset{1}{\cancel{2}}} = \dfrac{4 \cdot 1}{1 \cdot 1} = \dfrac{4}{1} = 4$$

Remember, the fraction $\dfrac{4}{1}$ can be written in lowest terms as 4.

d) When we multiply more than two fractions, we can pair up *any* numerator and denominator to divide out common factors. Let's begin by dividing out 4 from the 4 in the numerator and the 16 in the denominator.

$$\overset{4 \div 4 = 1 \to 1}{\dfrac{4}{11} \cdot \dfrac{2}{15} \cdot \dfrac{9}{\underset{4 \leftarrow 16 \div 4 = 4}{16}}}$$

Next, let's divide out 2 from the 2 in the numerator and the 4 in the denominator.

$$\dfrac{\overset{1}{4}}{11} \cdot \dfrac{\overset{1 \leftarrow 2 \div 2 = 1}{2}}{15} \cdot \dfrac{9}{\underset{2 \leftarrow 4 \div 2 = 2}{\cancel{4}}}$$

Can we divide out any other common factors? Yes! Divide 9 and 15 by 3.

$$\dfrac{\overset{1}{4}}{11} \cdot \dfrac{\overset{1}{2}}{\underset{15 \div 3 = 5 \to 5}{\cancel{15}}} \cdot \dfrac{\overset{3 \leftarrow 9 \div 3 = 3}{9}}{\underset{2}{4}}$$

Can we divide out any other common factors? No. Multiply.

$$\dfrac{\overset{1}{4}}{11} \cdot \dfrac{\overset{1}{2}}{\underset{5}{\cancel{15}}} \cdot \dfrac{\overset{3}{9}}{\underset{2}{\cancel{16}}} = \dfrac{1 \cdot 1 \cdot 3}{11 \cdot 5 \cdot 2} = \dfrac{3}{110} \qquad \dfrac{3}{110} \text{ is in lowest terms.}$$

e) Before multiplying $\dfrac{36}{25} \cdot \dfrac{35}{12}$, divide 36 and 12 by 12, and divide 25 and 35 by 5.

$$\dfrac{\overset{3}{\cancel{36}}}{\underset{5}{\cancel{25}}} \cdot \dfrac{\overset{7}{\cancel{35}}}{\underset{1}{\cancel{12}}} = \dfrac{21}{5} \text{ or } 4\dfrac{1}{5}$$

The answer may be written as an improper fraction or as a mixed number.

[**YOU TRY 4**] Multiply by first dividing out common factors.

a) $\dfrac{1}{16} \cdot \dfrac{12}{13}$

b) $\dfrac{14}{15} \cdot \dfrac{5}{8}$

c) $\dfrac{11}{2} \cdot \dfrac{6}{11}$

d) $\dfrac{5}{18} \cdot \dfrac{21}{40} \cdot \dfrac{8}{35}$

e) $\dfrac{21}{10} \cdot \dfrac{25}{14}$

Note

If a product is an improper fraction, the answer can be written either as an improper fraction or as a mixed number. Just be sure the fraction is in lowest terms.

3 Multiply a Fraction and a Whole Number

In Example 4c, we saw that $\dfrac{4}{1} = 4$. In fact, every whole number can be written with a denominator of 1. For example,

$$\frac{4}{1} = 4 \qquad \frac{9}{1} = 9 \qquad \frac{20}{1} = 20$$

We use this fact to multiply a fraction and a whole number.

W Hint

Write the procedure for multiplying a fraction and a whole number in your own words.

Procedure Multiplying a Fraction and a Whole Number

To multiply a fraction and a whole number, rewrite the whole number as a fraction with a denominator of 1. Then, multiply.

EXAMPLE 5

In-Class Example 5

Multiply.

a) $\dfrac{3}{5} \cdot 10$ b) $18 \cdot \dfrac{7}{12}$

Answer: a) 6   b) $\dfrac{21}{2}$ or $10\dfrac{1}{2}$

Multiply.

a) $\dfrac{2}{3} \cdot 12$ b) $10 \cdot \dfrac{3}{8}$

Solution

a) $\dfrac{2}{3} \cdot 12 = \dfrac{2}{3} \cdot \dfrac{12}{1}$ Write 12 with a denominator of 1.

$= \dfrac{2}{\underset{1}{3}} \cdot \dfrac{\overset{4}{12}}{1}$ Divide 3 and 12 by 3.

$= \dfrac{2 \cdot 4}{1 \cdot 1}$ Multiply numerators, and multiply denominators.

$= \dfrac{8}{1} = 8$ Multiply, and write the answer in lowest terms.

b) $10 \cdot \dfrac{3}{8} = \dfrac{10}{1} \cdot \dfrac{3}{8}$ Write 10 with a denominator of 1.

$= \dfrac{\overset{5}{10}}{1} \cdot \dfrac{3}{\underset{4}{8}}$ Divide 10 and 8 by 2.

$= \dfrac{5 \cdot 3}{1 \cdot 4}$ Multiply numerators, and multiply denominators.

$= \dfrac{15}{4} = 3\dfrac{3}{4}$ Multiply. Write the answer as an improper fraction or mixed number.

[YOU TRY 5]   Multiply.

a) $14 \cdot \dfrac{4}{7}$ b) $32 \cdot \dfrac{9}{20}$

E Evaluate 3.5 Exercises

Do the exercises, and check your work.

*Additional answers can be found in the Answers to Exercises appendix.

Objective 1: Multiply Fractions

Multiply. Write all answers in lowest terms.

1) $\frac{3}{4} \cdot \frac{5}{8}$ $\frac{15}{32}$

2) $\frac{2}{7} \cdot \frac{5}{9}$ $\frac{10}{63}$

3) $\frac{3}{7} \cdot \frac{8}{11}$ $\frac{24}{77}$

4) $\frac{7}{4} \cdot \frac{5}{12}$ $\frac{35}{48}$

5) $\frac{7}{8} \cdot \frac{4}{13}$ $\frac{7}{26}$

6) $\frac{9}{8} \cdot \frac{5}{12}$ $\frac{15}{32}$

7) $\frac{12}{13} \cdot \frac{11}{6}$ $\frac{22}{13}$ or $1\frac{9}{13}$

8) $\frac{7}{5} \cdot \frac{15}{2}$ $\frac{21}{2}$ or $10\frac{1}{2}$

9) $\frac{4}{15} \cdot \frac{3}{2}$ $\frac{2}{5}$

10) $\frac{5}{6} \cdot \frac{9}{10}$ $\frac{3}{4}$

11) $\frac{7}{24} \cdot \frac{16}{9}$ $\frac{14}{27}$

12) $\frac{3}{10} \cdot \frac{15}{7}$ $\frac{9}{14}$

13) $\frac{15}{2} \cdot \frac{3}{11}$ $\frac{45}{22}$ or $2\frac{1}{22}$

14) $\frac{14}{9} \cdot \frac{4}{5}$ $\frac{56}{45}$ or $1\frac{11}{45}$

15) $\frac{1}{5} \cdot \frac{3}{4} \cdot \frac{2}{3}$ $\frac{1}{10}$

16) $\frac{1}{6} \cdot \frac{4}{5} \cdot \frac{3}{4}$ $\frac{1}{10}$

17) $\frac{13}{4} \cdot \frac{1}{9} \cdot \frac{3}{2}$ $\frac{13}{24}$

18) $\frac{1}{8} \cdot \frac{4}{3} \cdot \frac{1}{2}$ $\frac{1}{12}$

Fill in the blank.

19) $\frac{7}{9} \cdot \underline{\hspace{1cm}} = \frac{14}{45}$ $\frac{2}{5}$

20) $\frac{4}{11} \cdot \underline{\hspace{1cm}} = \frac{32}{99}$ $\frac{8}{9}$

21) $\underline{\hspace{1cm}} \cdot \frac{1}{6} = \frac{1}{24}$ $\frac{1}{4}$

22) $\underline{\hspace{1cm}} \cdot \frac{1}{2} = \frac{1}{10}$ $\frac{1}{5}$

Objective 2: Divide Out Common Factors Before Multiplying

Multiply by first dividing out common factors.

23) $\frac{8}{9} \cdot \frac{7}{10}$ $\frac{28}{45}$

24) $\frac{3}{4} \cdot \frac{10}{13}$ $\frac{15}{26}$

25) $\frac{1}{6} \cdot \frac{3}{4}$ $\frac{1}{8}$

26) $\frac{2}{3} \cdot \frac{1}{8}$ $\frac{1}{12}$

27) $\frac{11}{2} \cdot \frac{9}{11}$ $\frac{9}{2}$ or $4\frac{1}{2}$

28) $\frac{4}{5} \cdot \frac{5}{3}$ $\frac{4}{3}$ or $1\frac{1}{3}$

29) $\frac{12}{77} \cdot \frac{55}{144}$ $\frac{5}{84}$

30) $\frac{14}{63} \cdot \frac{27}{7}$ $\frac{6}{7}$

31) $\frac{54}{25} \cdot \frac{50}{9}$ 12

32) $\frac{33}{10} \cdot \frac{90}{11}$ 27

33) $\frac{120}{21} \cdot \frac{49}{12}$ $\frac{70}{3}$ or $23\frac{1}{3}$

34) $\frac{56}{27} \cdot \frac{81}{32}$ $\frac{21}{4}$ or $5\frac{1}{4}$

35) $\frac{36}{7} \cdot \frac{14}{15} \cdot \frac{10}{27}$ $\frac{16}{9}$ or $1\frac{7}{9}$

36) $\frac{27}{14} \cdot \frac{10}{7} \cdot \frac{28}{45}$ $\frac{12}{7}$ or $1\frac{5}{7}$

37) $\frac{45}{14} \cdot \frac{21}{5} \cdot \frac{1}{27}$ $\frac{1}{2}$

38) $\frac{63}{62} \cdot \frac{31}{26} \cdot \frac{13}{36}$ $\frac{7}{16}$

39) $\frac{72}{17} \cdot \frac{1}{6} \cdot \frac{17}{8}$ $\frac{3}{2}$ or $1\frac{1}{2}$

40) $\frac{36}{11} \cdot \frac{1}{2} \cdot \frac{121}{36}$ $\frac{11}{2}$ or $5\frac{1}{2}$

41) $\frac{52}{5} \cdot \frac{15}{6} \cdot \frac{18}{13}$ 36

42) $\frac{102}{9} \cdot \frac{27}{24} \cdot \frac{36}{51}$ 9

43) Explain two different ways to multiply fractions.
Answers may vary.

44) Is the product of fractions always a fraction? no

Objective 3: Multiply a Fraction and a Whole Number

45) Explain how to multiply a fraction and a whole number. Write the whole number with a denominator of 1, then multiply.

46) Is the product of a fraction and a whole number always a whole number? no

Multiply.

47) $20 \cdot \frac{3}{5}$ 12

48) $40 \cdot \frac{7}{8}$ 35

49) $\frac{7}{3} \cdot 21$ 49

50) $\frac{4}{9} \cdot 72$ 32

51) $\frac{5}{14} \cdot 24$ $\frac{60}{7}$ or $8\frac{4}{7}$ 52) $\frac{5}{12} \cdot 40$ $\frac{50}{3}$ or $16\frac{2}{3}$

53) $72 \cdot \frac{1}{16}$ $\frac{9}{2}$ or $4\frac{1}{2}$ 54) $56 \cdot \frac{1}{32}$ $\frac{7}{4}$ or $1\frac{3}{4}$

55) $5 \cdot \frac{2}{15}$ $\frac{2}{3}$ 56) $2 \cdot \frac{3}{8}$ $\frac{3}{4}$

57) $\frac{3}{8} \cdot 4 \cdot \frac{7}{15}$ $\frac{7}{10}$ 58) $\frac{5}{18} \cdot 9 \cdot \frac{3}{10}$ $\frac{3}{4}$

59) $14 \cdot \frac{3}{50} \cdot \frac{25}{21}$ 1 60) $21 \cdot \frac{33}{14} \cdot \frac{4}{9}$ 22

61) $36 \cdot \frac{27}{20} \cdot \frac{7}{9}$ $\frac{189}{5}$ or $37\frac{4}{5}$ 62) $80 \cdot \frac{7}{8} \cdot \frac{5}{4}$ $\frac{175}{2}$ or $87\frac{1}{2}$

Mixed Exercises: Objectives 1–3
Multiply.

63) $\frac{5}{3} \cdot \frac{9}{14} \cdot \frac{7}{2}$ $\frac{15}{4}$ or $3\frac{3}{4}$ 64) $\frac{15}{2} \cdot \frac{1}{18}$ $\frac{5}{12}$

65) $\frac{21}{2} \cdot \frac{1}{14}$ $\frac{3}{4}$ 66) $\frac{108}{39} \cdot \frac{13}{27}$ $\frac{4}{3}$ or $1\frac{1}{3}$

67) $24 \cdot \frac{2}{3}$ 16 68) $\frac{1}{2} \cdot \frac{5}{18} \cdot \frac{3}{2}$ $\frac{5}{24}$

69) $\frac{125}{39} \cdot \frac{13}{50}$ $\frac{5}{6}$ 70) $\frac{25}{12} \cdot \frac{3}{20} \cdot 12$ $\frac{15}{4}$ or $1\frac{1}{4}$

71) $\frac{8}{9} \cdot \frac{1}{11}$ $\frac{8}{99}$ 72) $\frac{5}{3} \cdot 7 \cdot \frac{7}{10}$ $\frac{49}{6}$ or $8\frac{1}{6}$

R Rethink

R1) Did you find yourself automatically deciding to divide out a common factor first when completing the Mixed Exercises? Explain.

R2) Do you think that if you divide out a common factor first, the product you get after multiplying seems to be simplified? Why might that be?

3.6 Applications of Multiplication

P Prepare

O Organize

What are your objectives for Section 3.6?	How can you accomplish each objective?
1 Use a Chart to Solve a Problem	• Remember the procedure for **Multiplying a Fraction and a Whole Number.** • Complete the given example on your own. • Complete You Try 1.
2 Solve Applied Problems Involving Multiplication	• Review the notes you took for Section 2.7 on the **Five Steps for Solving Applied Problems,** and compare them to the examples for this objective. • Complete the given examples on your own. • Complete You Trys 2–4.
3 Find the Area of a Rectangle	• Write the procedure for **Finding the Area of a Rectangle** in your own words. • Complete the given examples on your own, and note the similarities between Examples 5 and 6. • Complete You Trys 5 and 6.

Read the explanations, follow the examples, take notes, and complete all the You Trys.

Many real-world problems use multiplication involving fractions.

1 Use a Chart to Solve a Problem

EXAMPLE 1

In-Class Example 1

Use Example 1.

The large, deep-dish sausage pizza at Mario's Pizzeria is portioned by weight according to the following pie chart. The pizza weighs 5 lb.

a) How many pounds of crust are used to make the pizza?

b) How many pounds of sausage are used to make the pizza?

Five-Pound Pizza Portions

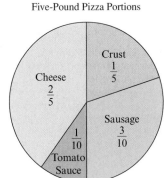

Solution

a) Find the fraction in the *crust* section of the pie chart. The $\frac{1}{5}$ means that $\frac{1}{5}$ *of* the total weight of the pizza is the crust. The *of* indicates multiplication. To determine the number of pounds of crust in the pizza, find $\frac{1}{5}$ of 5 lb or $\frac{1}{5} \cdot 5$.

$$\text{Number of pounds of crust} = \frac{1}{5} \cdot 5 = \frac{1}{5} \cdot \frac{5}{1} = \frac{1}{\cancel{5}} \cdot \frac{\cancel{5}^{1}}{1} = 1$$

One pound of crust is used to make the pizza.

b) Find the fraction in the *sausage* section of the pie chart. The $\frac{3}{10}$ means that $\frac{3}{10}$ *of* the total weight of the pizza is the sausage. The *of* indicates multiplication. The number of pounds of sausage in the pizza is $\frac{3}{10}$ of 5 lb or $\frac{3}{10} \cdot 5$.

$$\text{Number of pounds of sausage} = \frac{3}{10} \cdot 5 = \frac{3}{10} \cdot \frac{5}{1} = \frac{3}{\cancel{10}_{2}} \cdot \frac{\cancel{5}^{1}}{1} = \frac{3}{2} \text{ or } 1\frac{1}{2}$$

$1\frac{1}{2}$ lb of sausage are used to make the pizza.

[YOU TRY 1] Use the pie chart in Example 1 to answer these questions.

a) How many pounds of sauce are used to make the pizza?

b) How many pounds of cheese are used to make the pizza?

2 Solve Applied Problems Involving Multiplication

We learned in Section 2.7 that the following key words indicate multiplication: *product, times, double, twice, triple,* and *of.* Let's look at some problems involving multiplication of fractions.

EXAMPLE 2

In-Class Example 2

In a parking lot, $\frac{7}{9}$ of the 108 cars are American brands. How many American cars are in the parking lot? How many are foreign cars?

Answer:
There are 84 American cars and 24 foreign cars.

Professor Hill teaches at a community college at night, and $\frac{5}{12}$ of her 144 students work full-time. How many students work full-time? How many do not?

Solution

The problem says that: $\frac{5}{12}$ *of* 144 students work full-time. The *of* indicates multiplication.

Plan: Multiply $\frac{5}{12}$ and 144 to find the number of students who work full-time.

Then, subtract that number from the total number of students to find how many do *not* work full-time.

$$\frac{5}{12} \cdot 144 = \frac{5}{12} \cdot \frac{144}{1} = \frac{5}{\overset{1}{12}} \cdot \frac{\overset{12}{144}}{1} = \frac{60}{1} = 60$$

$12 \leftarrow 144 \div 12 = 12$
$12 \div 12 = 1 \rightarrow 1$

60 students work full-time. $144 - 60 = 84$ students do not work full-time.
To check the answer, notice that

Number who work full time	+	Number who do not work full time	=	Total number of students
60	+	84	=	144 students

YOU TRY 2

On a city bus, $\frac{3}{8}$ of the 56 passengers are using an electronic device such as an MP3 player, a cell phone, or an iPad. How many people are using an electronic device? How many are not?

Let's use the five-step process to solve the next problem.

EXAMPLE 3

In-Class Example 3

In 1950, the number of members of the United Nations was $\frac{5}{16}$ of the number in 2011. If there were 192 members in 2011, how many countries were part of the United Nations in 1950? (www.un.org)

Answer:
In 1950, there were 60 members in the United Nations.

The number of female drivers in fatal, alcohol-related crashes in 2008 in Hawaii was $\frac{3}{4}$ of the number involved in fatal crashes in 2007. If 40 women were involved in fatal, alcohol-related crashes in 2007, find the number in 2008. (www.nhtsa.gov)

Solution

Step 1: **Read** the problem carefully, and restate it in your own words.

In 2007, 40 women were involved in fatal, alcohol-related crashes in Hawaii. In 2008, the figure was $\frac{3}{4}$ of that number. Find the number of women involved in fatal, alcohol-related crashes in 2008.

Step 2: **Make a plan.** Let's underline important words in our restatement of the problem in step 1. The *of* means multiplication.

Statement: Number in 2008 is $\frac{3}{4}$ *of* the number in 2007

↓ times

Math: Number in 2008 $= \frac{3}{4} \cdot$ 40

Plan: Multiply $\frac{3}{4}$ and 40.

Step 3: **Solve** the problem.

$$\frac{3}{4} \cdot 40 = \frac{3}{4} \cdot \frac{40}{1} = \frac{3}{4} \cdot \frac{\overset{10 \leftarrow 40 \div 4 = 10}{40}}{1} = \frac{30}{1} = 30$$
$$\underset{4 \div 4 = 1 \to 1}{}$$

Step 4: **State the answer** in a complete sentence.

In 2008, 30 women were involved in fatal, alcohol-related crashes in Hawaii.

Step 5: **Check** the answer. Double-check your work to verify that the answers are correct.

[YOU TRY 3]

In 2002, the number of people working in a service industry was $\frac{7}{9}$ of the number in 2009. If 90,000 people worked in the service industry in 2009, how many were employed in this field in 2002? (www.census.gov)

Some situations involve more than one fractional part.

EXAMPLE 4

A market research company has determined that $\frac{47}{50}$ of shoppers make a list when they go to the grocery store. Of these shoppers, $\frac{1}{4}$ will buy on impulse; that is, they buy things that are not on their lists. If a grocery store had 2400 customers on a Saturday, what fraction of the shoppers are impulse buyers? How many shoppers made an impulse purchase? (www.npd.com)

The eighth-grade class at Washington Middle School has 210 students, and $\frac{4}{5}$ of them have at least one pet. If $\frac{5}{7}$ of these students have dogs, what fraction of the eighth-graders have dogs? How many students have dogs?

Answer:
$\frac{4}{7}$ of the eighth-graders have dogs. 120 students have at least one dog.

Solution

Step 1: **Read** the problem carefully, and restate it in your own words.

Out of the $\frac{47}{50}$ <u>of shoppers</u> who make a grocery list, $\frac{1}{4}$ <u>of them buy on impulse.</u> <u>What fraction of the shoppers are impulse buyers, and how many of the 2400 shoppers made an impulse purchase?</u>

Step 2: **Make a plan.** Let's underline important words in our restatement of the problem in Step 1. We will make a plan to answer each question. So, how can we think of this problem in terms of arithmetic?

What fraction of the shoppers are impulse buyers?

Statement: Fraction who are impulse buyers $= \frac{1}{4}$ *of* fraction who make a list

$\downarrow$ times

Math: Fraction who are impulse buyers $= \frac{1}{4} \cdot \frac{47}{50}$

Plan: Multiply $\frac{1}{4}$ and $\frac{47}{50}$.

How many of the 2400 shoppers made an impulse purchase?

Plan: Multiply the fraction who are impulse buyers by 2400.

Step 3: **Solve** the problem.

Find the *fraction* of shoppers who are impulse buyers:

$$\frac{1}{4} \cdot \frac{47}{50} = \frac{47}{200}$$

Find the *number* of shoppers who made an impulse purchase:

$$\text{Number who made impulse purchase} = \text{Fraction who are impulse buyers} \cdot \text{Number of shoppers}$$

$$= \frac{47}{200} \cdot 2400$$

$$= \frac{47}{200} \cdot \frac{2400}{1}$$

$$= \frac{47}{\underset{200 \div 200 = 1 \,\to\, 1}{200}} \cdot \frac{\overset{12 \leftarrow 2400 \div 200 = 12}{2400}}{1} = \frac{564}{1} = 564$$

Step 4: **State the answer** in a complete sentence.

According to the marketing research company, $\frac{47}{200}$ of shoppers are impulse buyers, and 564 of the 2400 shoppers made an impulse purchase.

Step 5: **Check** the answer. Double-check your work to verify that the answers are correct.

A survey of 600 adults revealed that $\frac{2}{3}$ of them check their email every day. Of those who check email daily, $\frac{9}{10}$ say they get spam every day. What fraction of the adults get spam every day, and how many of the adults surveyed get spam daily?

3 Find the Area of a Rectangle

The **area** of a figure is the size of the region enclosed in the figure. In this section, we will solve problems involving the area of a rectangle. In Chapter 9, we will learn how to find the areas of other figures.

Look at this rectangle:

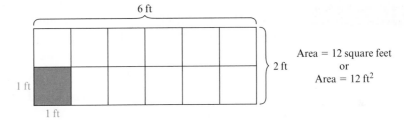

6 ft

1 ft

1 ft

2 ft

Area = 12 square feet
or
Area = 12 ft^2

Each square inside this rectangle has a length and width of 1 foot. The **area** of each *square* is 1 *square* foot. This can be abbreviated as 1 ft^2.

How many squares are inside the rectangle? There are 12 squares. Therefore, the **area of the rectangle** is 12 *square* feet or 12 ft^2.

We can also find the area of a rectangle by multiplying its length and width.

W Hint

Explain in your own words how to find the area of a rectangle.

Procedure Find the Area of a Rectangle

Use this formula to find the area of a rectangle:

$$\text{Area} = \text{Length} \cdot \text{Width}$$

The units for area are *square* units—for example, square inches (in^2), square feet (ft^2), square yards (yd^2), and square miles (mi^2).

For the rectangle pictured above, we can use the formula to find the area of the rectangle:

$$\text{Area} = \text{Length} \cdot \text{Width}$$
$$\text{Area} = \quad 6\,\text{ft} \quad \cdot \quad 2\,\text{ft} \quad = 12\,\text{ft}^2$$

EXAMPLE 5

Find the area of this rectangle.

In-Class Example 5

Find the area of this rectangle.

8 yd

2 yd

Answer: 16 yd^2

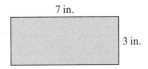

7 in.

3 in.

Solution

$$\text{Area} = \text{Length} \cdot \text{Width} = 7\,\text{in.} \cdot 3\,\text{in.} = 21\,\text{in}^2$$

YOU TRY 5 Find the area of this rectangle.

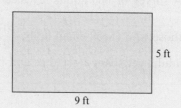

5 ft

9 ft

BE CAREFUL Be sure to include the correct units with your answer!

EXAMPLE 6

A city park is in the shape of a rectangle and has the dimensions shown here. Find the area of the park.

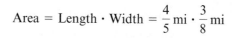

$\frac{4}{5}$ mi

$\frac{3}{8}$ mi

In-Class Example 6

The Rodriguez family's home sits on a rectangular piece of land with the dimensions shown here. Find the area of their property.

$\frac{3}{4}$ mi

$\frac{4}{9}$ mi

Answer:

$\frac{1}{3}$ mi^2

Solution

Use the formula for the area of a rectangle and substitute the values.

$$\text{Area} = \text{Length} \cdot \text{Width} = \frac{4}{5}\text{ mi} \cdot \frac{3}{8}\text{ mi}$$

Multiply the fractions.

$$\overset{1}{\frac{4}{5}} \cdot \frac{3}{\underset{2}{8}} = \frac{3}{10}$$

The area of the park is $\frac{3}{10}$ mi^2.

YOU TRY 6

A rectangular horse stall is $\frac{27}{2}$ ft wide and $\frac{44}{3}$ ft long. What is the area of the stall?

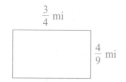
Hint

Did you check your answers by hand before looking here?

ANSWERS TO YOU TRY EXERCISES

1) a) $\frac{1}{2}$ lb   b) 2 lb   2) 21 people are using an electronic device and 35 are not.

3) 70,000 people were employed in the service industry in 2002.

4) a) $\frac{3}{5}$ of adults get spam every day.   b) Of the adults surveyed, 360 get spam every day.

5) 45 ft^2 6) 198 ft^2

Additional answers can be found in the Answers to Exercises appendix.

Objective 1: Use a Chart to Solve a Problem

The pie chart below shows how Kimi spends her monthly earnings of $2360. Use the information for Exercises 1–6.

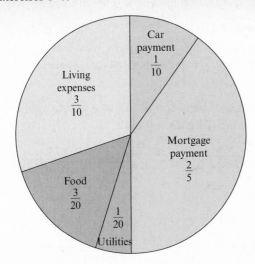

(24) 1) How much does Kimi spend on her food each month? $354

2) What is her monthly mortgage payment? $944

3) What is her car payment? $236

4) What is her combined budget for living expenses and utilities? $826

5) If Kimi decides to place $\frac{1}{3}$ of her living expenses budget into a savings account, how much will she deposit into the account? $236

6) Verify that the sum of the living expenses and car payment equals the mortgage payment. What does this tell you about the sum of $\frac{3}{10}$ and $\frac{1}{10}$? Their sum must equal $\frac{2}{5}$.

A small manufacturing company recently moved into a new facility that has 18,000 square feet of floor space. The pie chart at the top of the next column shows how much floor space will be given to each department. Use this information for Exercises 7–12.

7) How much floor space is given to the break room? 900 ft²

8) How much floor space is given to the tool room? 2700 ft²

9) How much floor space is provided for office space? 3600 ft²

10) What is the combined area for manufacturing and assembly? 9000 ft²

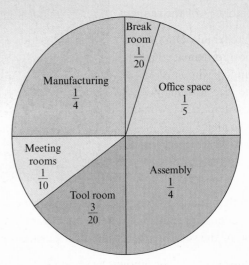

11) Verify that the sum of the floor space for breaks, offices, and assembly equals half of the 18,000 square-foot facility. What does this tell you about the sum of $\frac{1}{20}$, $\frac{1}{5}$, and $\frac{1}{4}$? Their sum must equal $\frac{1}{2}$.

12) Verify that the sum of the floor space for meetings and tools equals the floor space of the assembly area. What does this tell you about the sum of $\frac{1}{10}$ and $\frac{3}{20}$? Their sum must equal $\frac{1}{4}$.

Objective 2: Solve Applied Problems Involving Multiplication

Solve each problem.

13) Professor Velez's music class has 40 students. If $\frac{3}{5}$ of the class is female, how many students are female? How many students are male?
There are 24 female students and 16 male students.

14) Professor Harding's math classroom at a community college has 45 students. If $\frac{2}{3}$ of the students are recent high school graduates, how many students are recent high school grads? How many are not?
There are 30 recent high school graduates and 15 who are not recent high school graduates.

(24) 15) A hotel with 354 rooms allows smoking in $\frac{1}{6}$ of its rooms. How many rooms does the hotel offer to smokers? How many rooms are offered to nonsmokers?
There are 59 rooms for smokers and 295 rooms for nonsmokers.

16) In the 2010 Chicago Marathon, approximately $\frac{9}{20}$ of the runners were female. Out of the approximate 36,000 runners who finished the race, how many were female? How many were male?

(www.chicagomarathon.com)

16,200 were female; 19,800 were male

17) Stephan set up a savings account to pay for college. He deposited $300 every month for 1 year. At the end of the year, Stephan's parents deposited an additional $\frac{2}{3}$ of the amount he saved to the account. How much money did Stephan's parents deposit into the account? What is the total amount in the savings account including the amount his parents deposited? The parents deposited $2400; the total amount is $6000.

18) Lester earns his living selling home furniture in a department store. The salary he receives is $\frac{2}{7}$ the amount of his total sales. If Lester sold $1680 worth of furniture this week, what is his salary for this week? What amount of his sales goes to the department store? His salary is $480; $1200 goes to the department store.

19) A local 24-hour diner offers $\frac{1}{4}$ of its dinner plates as vegetarian meals. Of these vegetarian meals, $\frac{1}{3}$ are vegan. If the diner offers 36 different dinner plates, what fraction of the dinner plates are vegan? How many different vegan plates are there?

20) Concetta donates $\frac{1}{8}$ of her salary to a local women's group. The women's group uses $\frac{3}{4}$ of its collected donations to pay for its community services. If Concetta's salary is $2304, what fractional amount of her salary goes toward paying for community services? What amount is this?

21) A department store decides to have a $\frac{1}{2}$-off sale. Additionally, the first 50 customers get an additional $\frac{3}{5}$ off. If one of the first 50 customers purchases an item with an original sale price of $240, what fraction of the original sale price will she pay, and what is the sale price?

22) In a company that manufactures electrical motors, $\frac{4}{5}$ of its employees joined the electricians' labor union. Of these union members, $\frac{2}{3}$ voted to strike over a proposed reduction in health benefits. If the company has 630 employees, what fraction voted for the strike? How many voted for a strike?

$\frac{8}{15}$ of its employees voted to strike; 336 out of 630 employees voted for a strike.

Objective 3: Find the Area of a Rectangle

Find the area of each rectangle.

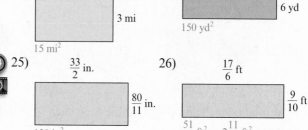

23) 5 mi, 3 mi — 15 mi²

24) 25 yd, 6 yd — 150 yd²

25) $\frac{33}{2}$ in., $\frac{80}{11}$ in. — 120 in²

26) $\frac{17}{6}$ ft, $\frac{9}{10}$ ft — $\frac{51}{20}$ ft² or $2\frac{11}{20}$ ft²

27) Find the area of the shaded region. $\frac{21}{4}$ ft² or $5\frac{1}{4}$ ft²

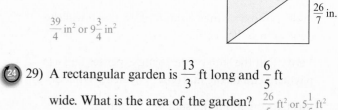

$\frac{35}{6}$ ft, $\frac{9}{5}$ ft

28) Find the area of the shaded region.

$\frac{39}{4}$ in² or $9\frac{3}{4}$ in²

$\frac{21}{4}$ in., $\frac{26}{7}$ in.

29) A rectangular garden is $\frac{13}{3}$ ft long and $\frac{6}{5}$ ft wide. What is the area of the garden? $\frac{26}{5}$ ft² or $5\frac{1}{5}$ ft²

30) A 3 × 3 Rubik's cube has a side length of approximately $\frac{9}{4}$ in. Find the area of one face of the cube. $\frac{81}{16}$ in² or $5\frac{1}{16}$ in²

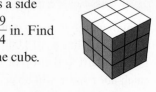

31) A football field, including the end zones, is 120 yd long and $\frac{160}{3}$ yd wide. What is the area of this field? 6400 yd²

32) An acre-size rectangular lot measures $\frac{121}{2}$ yd long and 80 yd wide. How many square yards are in 1 acre? 4840 yd²

3.7 Dividing Fractions

P Prepare	**O Organize**
What are your objectives for Section 3.7?	**How can you accomplish each objective?**
1 Find the Reciprocal of a Number	• Write the definition of a *reciprocal* in your own words. • Complete the given example on your own. • Complete You Try 1.
2 Divide Fractions	• Write the procedure for **Dividing Fractions** in your own words. • Complete the given examples on your own, and notice the slight differences between them. • Complete You Trys 2–4.
3 Solve Applied Problems Involving Division of Fractions	• Review the notes you took for Section 3.6 on the **Five Steps for Solving Applied Problems** and compare them to the examples for this objective. • Complete the given examples on your own, and notice the slight differences between them. • Complete You Trys 5 and 6.

W Work   **Read the explanations, follow the examples, take notes, and complete all the You Trys.**

Let's use a number line to understand how to divide fractions. In Section 2.3, we said that $12 \div 3$ means, *"How many threes does it take to make 12?"*

Likewise, the problem $2 \div \dfrac{1}{3}$ means, *"How many one-thirds does it take to make 2?"*

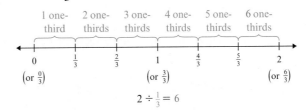

It takes 6 *one-thirds* to make 2, so $2 \div \dfrac{1}{3} = 6$.

It is not a coincidence that $2 \div \frac{1}{3} = 6$ and $2 \cdot 3 = 6$. The numbers $\frac{1}{3}$ and 3 are *reciprocals*. We need to learn more about reciprocals before we learn more about dividing.

1 Find the Reciprocal of a Number

Definition

Two numbers are **reciprocals** if their product is 1. To find the reciprocal of a number, we interchange the numerator and denominator.

Example: The reciprocal of $\frac{2}{5}$ is $\frac{5}{2}$.

Check: $\frac{2}{5}$ and $\frac{5}{2}$ are reciprocals because $\frac{2}{5} \cdot \frac{5}{2} = \frac{10}{10} = 1$.

W Hint
Write the definition of a reciprocal in your own words.

Note
We also say that we *invert* or *flip* a fraction to find its reciprocal.

EXAMPLE 1

Find the reciprocal of each number.

a) $\frac{3}{4}$ b) $\frac{9}{7}$ c) 2   d) $\frac{1}{3}$

Solution

a) The reciprocal of $\frac{3}{4}$ is $\frac{4}{3}$. We *flipped* $\frac{3}{4}$ to find its reciprocal. We can verify that $\frac{3}{4}$ and $\frac{4}{3}$ are reciprocals by multiplying.

$$\frac{3}{4} \cdot \frac{4}{3} = \frac{12}{12} = 1 \qquad \text{The product is 1, so they are reciprocals.}$$

b) The reciprocal of $\frac{9}{7}$ is $\frac{7}{9}$.

Check: $\frac{9}{7} \cdot \frac{7}{9} = \frac{63}{63} = 1$ ✓

c) How do we find the reciprocal of 2? First, write 2 as a fraction with a denominator of 1: $2 = \frac{2}{1}$

Then, flip $\frac{2}{1}$ to get its reciprocal, $\frac{1}{2}$. The reciprocal of 2 is $\frac{1}{2}$.

Check: $2 \cdot \frac{1}{2} = \frac{2}{1} \cdot \frac{1}{2} = \frac{2}{2} = 1$ ✓

d) The reciprocal of $\frac{1}{3}$ is $\frac{3}{1}$ or 3.

Check: $\frac{1}{3} \cdot 3 = \frac{1}{3} \cdot \frac{3}{1} = \frac{3}{3} = 1$ ✓   The product is 1, so they are reciprocals.

[YOU TRY 1]   Find the reciprocal of each number.

a) $\frac{7}{8}$ b) $\frac{10}{3}$ c) $\frac{1}{5}$ d) 6

Note

To find the reciprocal of a natural number, first write it as a fraction with a denominator of 1, then flip it.

Example: To find the reciprocal of 8, first write 8 as $\frac{8}{1}$, then flip it: $\frac{1}{8}$. The reciprocal of 8 is $\frac{1}{8}$.

Does 0 have a reciprocal? *No.* The number 0 does *not* have a reciprocal because there is no number that can be multiplied by 0 to get 1. The product of any number and 0 is 0.

Note

The number 0 does *not* have a reciprocal.

2 Divide Fractions

Now that we understand reciprocals, we can learn how to divide fractions. At the beginning of this section, we found that

$$2 \div \frac{1}{3} = 6 \text{ because it takes 6 one-thirds to make 2.}$$

We also said that it is not a coincidence that $2 \div \frac{1}{3} = 6$ and $2 \cdot 3 = 6$. *To perform division involving fractions, multiply the first number by the reciprocal of the second number.*

W Hint

Write the procedure for dividing fractions in your own words.

Procedure Dividing Fractions

To perform division involving fractions, multiply the first number by the reciprocal of the second number.

Example: $\frac{1}{5} \div \frac{2}{3} = \frac{1}{5} \cdot \frac{3}{2} = \frac{3}{10}$

Change division to multiplication by the reciprocal.

Remember, write all answers in lowest terms.

EXAMPLE 2

In-Class Example 2

Divide.

a) $\dfrac{2}{5} \div \dfrac{3}{4}$ b) $\dfrac{11}{12} \div \dfrac{2}{3}$

Answer: a) $\dfrac{8}{15}$ b) $\dfrac{11}{8}$ or $1\dfrac{3}{8}$

Divide.

a) $\dfrac{5}{8} \div \dfrac{6}{7}$ b) $\dfrac{9}{10} \div \dfrac{2}{5}$

Solution

a) To divide fractions, *multiply by the reciprocal* of the second fraction.

$$\frac{5}{8} \div \frac{6}{7} = \frac{5}{8} \cdot \frac{7}{6} = \frac{35}{48}$$

Change division to multiplication
by the reciprocal.

Is $\dfrac{35}{48}$ in lowest terms? Yes.

b) $\dfrac{9}{10} \div \dfrac{2}{5} = \dfrac{9}{10} \cdot \dfrac{5}{2} = \dfrac{9}{\overset{}{10}} \cdot \dfrac{\overset{1}{5}}{2}$ Divide 5 and 10 by 5.

Change division to
multiplication by
the reciprocal.

$= \dfrac{9 \cdot 1}{2 \cdot 2}$ Multiply.

$= \dfrac{9}{4}$ or $2\dfrac{1}{4}$ Write the answer in lowest terms as an
improper fraction or as a mixed number.

[YOU TRY 2]

Divide.

a) $\dfrac{1}{3} \div \dfrac{7}{8}$ b) $\dfrac{13}{18} \div \dfrac{3}{10}$

Note

Do not divide out common factors until *after* changing the problem to multiplication.

If a division problem contains a fraction and a natural number, the first step is to write the natural number as a fraction with a denominator of 1.

EXAMPLE 3

In-Class Example 3

Divide.

a) $\dfrac{5}{9} \div 10$ b) $8 \div \dfrac{1}{3}$

Answer: a) $\dfrac{1}{18}$ b) 24

Divide.

a) $\dfrac{3}{8} \div 6$ b) $4 \div \dfrac{1}{7}$

---

a) First, write 6 as $\frac{6}{1}$. Then, follow the procedure for dividing fractions.

$$\frac{3}{8} \div 6 = \frac{3}{8} \div \frac{6}{1} \qquad \text{Begin by writing 6 as } \frac{6}{1}.$$

$$= \frac{3}{8} \cdot \frac{1}{6} \qquad \text{Change division to multiplication by the reciprocal.}$$

$$= \frac{\overset{1}{3}}{8} \cdot \frac{1}{\underset{2}{6}} \qquad \text{Divide 3 and 6 by 3.}$$

$$= \frac{1 \cdot 1}{8 \cdot 2} = \frac{1}{16} \qquad \text{Multiply.}$$

b) $4 \div \frac{1}{7} = \frac{4}{1} \div \frac{1}{7} \qquad \text{Begin by writing 4 as } \frac{4}{1}.$

$$= \frac{4}{1} \cdot \frac{7}{1} \qquad \text{Change division to multiplication by the reciprocal.}$$

$$= \frac{28}{1} = 28 \qquad \text{Multiply.}$$

[YOU TRY 3] Divide.

a) $\frac{1}{11} \div 16$ b) $7 \div \frac{1}{5}$

A division problem can also take the form of a *complex fraction*. **A complex fraction** contains a fraction in its numerator, its denominator, or both.

EXAMPLE 4

In-Class Example 4

Divide $\dfrac{\frac{5}{8}}{\frac{9}{14}}$.

Answer: $\frac{35}{36}$

Divide $\dfrac{\frac{2}{9}}{\frac{5}{12}}$.

Solution

The fraction bar represents → division. $\dfrac{\frac{2}{9}}{\frac{5}{12}} = \frac{2}{9} \div \frac{5}{12} = \frac{2}{9} \cdot \frac{12}{5} \qquad \text{Change division to multiplication by the reciprocal.}$

$$= \frac{2}{\underset{3}{9}} \cdot \frac{\overset{4}{12}}{5} \qquad \text{Divide 12 and 9 by 3.}$$

$$= \frac{2 \cdot 4}{3 \cdot 5} = \frac{8}{15} \qquad \text{Multiply.}$$

3 Solve Applied Problems Involving Division of Fractions

Many applied problems are solved using division of fractions. Recall from Section 2.7 that some key words indicating division are *quotient, divided by, divided into, divided equally,* and *per.*

EXAMPLE 5

In-Class Example 5

A carton contains 6 cups of heavy cream, and Jon uses $\dfrac{3}{4}$ of a cup to make whipped cream to frost each of the birthday cakes in his bakery. How many cakes can he frost with the carton?

Answer:
Jon can frost 8 cakes.

A jar contains 4 cups of spaghetti sauce. The label says that a serving size is $\dfrac{2}{3}$ of a cup. How many servings of sauce are in the jar?

Solution

We can think about the problem this way: How many $\dfrac{2}{3}$-cup servings does it take to make 4 cups? *Divide* 4 by $\dfrac{2}{3}$ to find the answer.

$$4 \div \frac{2}{3} = \frac{4}{1} \div \frac{2}{3} \qquad \text{Write 4 as } \frac{4}{1}.$$

$$= \frac{4}{1} \cdot \frac{3}{2} \qquad \text{Change division to multiplication by the reciprocal.}$$

$$= \frac{\overset{2}{4}}{1} \cdot \frac{3}{\underset{1}{2}} \qquad \text{Divide 4 and 2 by 2.}$$

$$= \frac{6}{1} = 6 \qquad \text{Multiply and simplify.}$$

The jar contains six $\dfrac{2}{3}$-cup servings of spaghetti sauce.

To check the answer, multiply the number of servings and the serving size to find the total amount of spaghetti sauce in the jar.

$$\text{Number of servings} \rightarrow 6 \cdot \frac{2}{3} = \frac{6}{1} \cdot \frac{2}{3} = \frac{\overset{2}{6}}{1} \cdot \frac{2}{\underset{1}{3}} = \frac{4}{1} = 4 \leftarrow \begin{array}{l} \text{Total amount of} \\ \text{sauce in the jar.} \end{array}$$

Size of each serving

Write 6 as $\dfrac{6}{1}$.

The answer is correct.

[YOU TRY 5]

A 5-gallon office water cooler dispenses glasses of water in a serving size of $\dfrac{1}{20}$ of a gallon. How many servings of water are in the water cooler?

Let's use the five-step process to solve the next problem.

EXAMPLE 6

In-Class Example 6

A sports drink company gives $\frac{2}{9}$ of its budget to the marketing department. The marketing director then divides the money equally among her 8 regional managers. What fraction of the total budget does each manager receive?

Answer:
Each manager receives $\frac{1}{36}$ of the total budget.

W Hint
Review the notes you took for Section 3.6 on the **Five Steps for Solving Applied Problems,** and compare them to the examples for this objective.

A construction company sets aside $\frac{9}{10}$ of its lumber for single-family homes. If the company plans to divide the lumber equally among 36 houses, what fraction of all of the lumber is used for each house?

Solution

Step 1: **Read** the problem carefully, and restate it in your own words.

A company <u>divides</u> $\frac{9}{10}$ <u>of all its lumber equally among 36 houses.</u>
<u>What fraction of the lumber is used for each house?</u>

Step 2: **Make a plan.** Let's underline important words in our restatement of the problem in Step 1 and think about what is happening in this problem. $\frac{9}{10}$ of the lumber is divided equally into 36 parts. *Divide* $\frac{9}{10}$ by 36 to find the answer.

Plan: Divide $\frac{9}{10}$ by 36 to find the fraction of the total lumber that is used for each house.

Step 3: **Solve** the problem.

$$\frac{9}{10} \div 36 = \frac{9}{10} \div \frac{36}{1} \qquad \text{Write 36 as } \frac{36}{1}.$$

$$= \frac{9}{10} \cdot \frac{1}{36} \qquad \text{Change division to multiplication by the reciprocal.}$$

$$= \frac{\overset{1}{9}}{10} \cdot \frac{1}{\underset{4}{36}} \qquad \text{Divide 9 and 36 by 9.}$$

$$= \frac{1}{40} \qquad \text{Multiply.}$$

Step 4: **State the answer** in a complete sentence.

Each house uses $\frac{1}{40}$ of the company's lumber.

Step 5: **Check** the answer. Multiply the fraction used by each house and the number of houses to find the fraction of the total lumber used for single-family homes.

$$\frac{1}{40} \cdot 36 = \frac{1}{40} \cdot \frac{36}{1} = \frac{1}{\underset{10}{40}} \cdot \frac{\overset{9}{36}}{1} = \frac{9}{10} \; \checkmark$$

$$\underset{\text{Write 36 as } \frac{36}{1}.}{}$$

The answer is correct.

E Evaluate 3.7 Exercises   Do the exercises, and check your work.

*Additional answers can be found in the Answers to Exercises appendix.

Objective 1: Find the Reciprocal of a Number

1) If two numbers are reciprocals, then their product is _____. 1

2) Does every number have a reciprocal? Explain your answer. No. The number 0 does not have a reciprocal because there is no number that, when multiplied by 0, equals 1.

3) In your own words, explain how to find the reciprocal of a fraction. Answers may vary.

4) In your own words, explain how to find the reciprocal of a natural number like 7. Answers may vary.

Find the reciprocal of each number.

5) $\frac{4}{5}$ $\frac{5}{4}$

6) $\frac{6}{13}$ $\frac{13}{6}$

7) $\frac{9}{2}$ $\frac{2}{9}$

8) $\frac{12}{7}$ $\frac{7}{12}$

9) $\frac{1}{7}$ 7

10) $\frac{1}{4}$ 4

11) 2 $\frac{1}{2}$

12) 3 $\frac{1}{3}$

13) $\frac{11}{4}$ $\frac{4}{11}$

14) $\frac{21}{5}$ $\frac{5}{21}$

15) 13 $\frac{1}{13}$

16) 6 $\frac{1}{6}$

17) $\frac{1}{12}$ 12

18) $\frac{1}{15}$ 15

Objective 2: Divide Fractions

19) In your own words, explain how to divide two fractions. Answers may vary.

20) When dividing fractions, when can you divide out common factors? Divide out common factors after changing the problem to multiplication.

Divide.

21) $\frac{3}{10} \div \frac{2}{5}$ $\frac{3}{4}$

22) $\frac{5}{8} \div \frac{7}{4}$ $\frac{5}{14}$

23) $\frac{15}{16} \div \frac{25}{21}$ $\frac{63}{80}$

24) $\frac{7}{8} \div \frac{21}{10}$ $\frac{5}{12}$

25) $\frac{35}{16} \div \frac{5}{12}$ $\frac{21}{4}$ or $5\frac{1}{4}$

26) $\frac{28}{11} \div \frac{32}{33}$ $\frac{21}{8}$ or $2\frac{5}{8}$

27) $\frac{9}{7} \div 3$ $\frac{3}{7}$

28) $\frac{4}{5} \div 2$ $\frac{2}{5}$

29) $\frac{34}{9} \div 10$ $\frac{17}{45}$

30) $\frac{36}{11} \div 8$ $\frac{9}{22}$

31) $\frac{1}{2} \div 6$ $\frac{1}{12}$

32) $\frac{1}{3} \div 15$ $\frac{1}{45}$

33) $5 \div \frac{3}{8}$ $\frac{40}{3}$ or $13\frac{1}{3}$

34) $2 \div \frac{3}{5}$ $\frac{10}{3}$ or $3\frac{1}{3}$

35) $6 \div \frac{1}{3}$ 18

36) $10 \div \frac{1}{5}$ 50

37) What is a complex fraction? It is a fraction that contains a fraction in its numerator, its denominator, or both.

38) Is a complex fraction another way to write a division problem? Explain. Yes. It means that you divide the numerator by the denominator.

Divide.

39) $\dfrac{\frac{2}{7}}{\frac{1}{3}}$ $\frac{6}{7}$

40) $\dfrac{\frac{1}{8}}{\frac{3}{5}}$ $\frac{5}{24}$

41) $\dfrac{\frac{3}{5}}{\frac{6}{7}}$ $\frac{7}{10}$

42) $\dfrac{\frac{7}{24}}{\frac{9}{16}}$ $\frac{14}{27}$

www.mhhe.com/messersmith

43) $\dfrac{\dfrac{4}{3}}{\dfrac{2}{9}}$ 6

44) $\dfrac{\dfrac{40}{21}}{\dfrac{10}{63}}$ 12

45) $\dfrac{\dfrac{121}{15}}{\dfrac{22}{25}}$ $\dfrac{55}{6}$ or $9\dfrac{1}{6}$

46) $\dfrac{\dfrac{88}{13}}{\dfrac{12}{5}}$ $\dfrac{110}{39}$ or $2\dfrac{32}{39}$

47) $\dfrac{\dfrac{1}{5}}{20}$ $\dfrac{1}{100}$

48) $\dfrac{18}{\dfrac{2}{9}}$ 81

Objective 3: Solve Applied Problems Involving Division of Fractions

Solve each problem.

49) Alexa makes 6 cups of vanilla frosting for her cupcakes. If each cupcake requires $\dfrac{1}{8}$ cup of frosting, how many cupcakes can Alexa frost? 48 cupcakes

50) Abhinav owns 12 acres of land and wants to subdivide the land into lots. If each lot is to be $\dfrac{1}{3}$ of an acre, how many lots can Abhinav make?
36 lots

51) A pharmacist needs to divide $\dfrac{3}{4}$ of a quart of saline solution into 6 equal portions. What fraction of the saline solution is used for each portion? $\dfrac{1}{8}$ of a quart

52) A company needs to divide $\dfrac{5}{8}$ of its inventory into 10 equally sized shipments. What fraction of the total inventory is each shipment?
$\dfrac{1}{16}$ of the company's inventory

53) On a map, $\dfrac{3}{8}$ in. represents 1 mile. If two cities are 9 in. apart on the map, how many miles apart are the two cities? 24 mi

54) Brandy needs to measure 2 cups of sugar for a recipe. She has only a $\dfrac{1}{8}$ cup measuring spoon. How many measuring spoons of sugar are required to get 2 cups of sugar? 16 measuring spoons

55) If $\dfrac{5}{6}$ yd of decorative ribbon is required to decorate a single gift, how many gifts can be decorated with 30 yd of decorative ribbon? 36 gifts

56) A pest control worker uses $\dfrac{2}{7}$ of a gallon of insect spray to treat the exterior boundary of a home. How many homes can the worker treat with 10 gal of insect spray? 35 homes

57) If $\dfrac{2}{3}$ of a gallon of cleaning solution needs to be divided into 4 equal portions, how much of a gallon is each portion? $\dfrac{1}{6}$ of a gallon

58) If $\dfrac{7}{8}$ of a liter of cooking oil is divided into 3 equal portions, how much of a liter is each portion?
$\dfrac{7}{24}$ of a liter

59) Tamara donates $\dfrac{1}{5}$ of her summer earnings to a local church group. The church divides its summer donations into 3 equal portions and gives one portion to a local homeless shelter. What portion of Tamara's summer earnings went to the homeless shelter? $\dfrac{1}{15}$

60) A home improvement store moves $\dfrac{2}{3}$ of its outdoor furniture collection outside for display. At closing, only $\dfrac{1}{2}$ of the furniture is brought inside. What portion of the outdoor furniture collection remains outside after closing? $\dfrac{1}{3}$

61) Lorenzo has completed 45 hr of his student teaching assignment. If he has completed $\dfrac{3}{4}$ of his total required hours, how many hours is he required to student teach? 60 hr

62) A jetliner has flown 700 mi, completing $\dfrac{1}{3}$ of its flight. What is the total mileage of the entire flight?
2100 mi

63) A hybrid vehicle has traveled 240 mi, with $\dfrac{1}{3}$ of a tank of gas remaining. How many miles can the hybrid vehicle travel on a full tank of gas? 360 mi

64) After completely charging her laptop's battery, Jenny used her laptop computer for 90 minutes straight. If her laptop now indicates that she has $\frac{3}{4}$ battery life remaining, how long can Jenny's laptop run on a fully charged battery? 360 min

65) The shaded area here represents $\frac{3}{4}$ of a circle. If this shaded area is separated into 6 equal portions, what fractional amount of the entire circle is each portion? Represent one shaded portion on the blank circle.

66) The figure here represents $\frac{1}{2}$ of a circle. If this shaded area is separated into 3 equal portions, what fractional amount of the entire circle is each portion? Represent one shaded portion on the blank circle.

Mixed Exercises
Divide.

67) $\frac{32}{7} \div 8$ $\frac{4}{7}$

68) $\frac{8}{5} \div \frac{6}{7}$ $\frac{28}{15}$ or $1\frac{13}{15}$

69) $\frac{5}{18} \div \frac{11}{4}$ $\frac{10}{99}$

70) $2 \div \frac{2}{5}$ 5

71) $\dfrac{\frac{9}{2}}{\frac{4}{27}}$ $\frac{243}{8}$

72) $\frac{1}{4} \div \frac{2}{3}$ $\frac{3}{8}$

73) $\frac{8}{9} \div \frac{1}{6}$ $\frac{16}{3}$ or $5\frac{1}{3}$

74) $\dfrac{\frac{11}{16}}{\frac{3}{20}}$ $\frac{55}{12}$ or $4\frac{7}{12}$

75) $\dfrac{\frac{15}{3}}{8}$ 40

76) $\frac{3}{20} \div \frac{1}{4}$ $\frac{3}{5}$

Solve each problem.

77) Carlos has 1800 songs on his MP3 player, and he shares $\frac{2}{3}$ of them with his sister Mariana. She divides the songs equally into 8 playlists. How many songs are in each of Mariana's playlists? 150 songs

78) A can contains 3 cups of chili, and each serving is $\frac{3}{4}$ cup. How many servings of chili are in the can? 4 servings

R Rethink

R1) Describe the last time you encountered a situation where you needed to divide by a fraction.

R2) Write an application problem similar to the problems you just solved, and have a friend solve it.

Putting It All Together

P Prepare

O Organize

What are your objectives for Putting It All Together?	How can you accomplish the objective?
1 Review the Concepts of Sections 3.1–3.7	• Review the definitions and procedures that you have learned so far in this chapter. • Complete the given examples on your own and, if you struggled with specific concepts, go back to previous sections for more information on those concepts. • Complete You Trys 1–4.

Read the explanations, follow the examples, take notes, and complete all the You Trys.

1 Review the Concepts of Sections 3.1–3.7

Let's review what we have learned about fractions so far.

A **fraction** is a part of a whole. In a **proper fraction,** like $\frac{2}{5}$, the numerator is less than the denominator. It represents a number less than one whole. In an **improper fraction,** like $\frac{11}{4}$, the numerator is greater than or equal to the denominator, and it represents a quantity greater than or equal to one whole. A **mixed number** such as $2\frac{5}{6}$ consists of a whole number and a fraction. It represents more than one whole.

We can write mixed numbers as improper fractions. For example, to write $2\frac{5}{6}$ as an improper fraction, multiply $6 \cdot 2 = 12$, add that to the numerator, $12 + 5 = 17$, then write the fraction using the original denominator: $\frac{17}{6}$. So, $2\frac{5}{6} = \frac{17}{6}$.

We can write improper fractions as mixed numbers using division. For example, to write $\frac{11}{4}$ as a mixed number, divide 11 by 4.

W Hint

If some of the concepts seem unfamiliar, go back and review the definitions and procedures from earlier sections in this chapter.

The quotient is the whole-number part of the mixed number, and the remainder is the numerator of the fractional part. The denominator is the same as the original denominator.

When we perform operations with fractions, we write the answers in lowest terms. To be sure a fraction is in lowest terms, you should ask yourself two questions: *"What number divides evenly into both the numerator and denominator?"* and, after dividing out the common factors, look at the result and ask, *"Is the fraction in lowest terms?"*

EXAMPLE 1

In-Class Example 1

Determine whether each fraction is in lowest terms. If it is not, write it in lowest terms.

a) $\frac{28}{63}$ b) $\frac{12}{19}$ c) $\frac{360}{400}$

Answer:

a) $\frac{4}{9}$

b) $\frac{12}{19}$ is in lowest terms.

c) $\frac{9}{10}$

Determine whether each fraction is in lowest terms. If it is not, write it in lowest terms.

a) $\frac{12}{42}$ b) $\frac{10}{17}$ c) $\frac{210}{350}$

Solution

a) Look at $\frac{12}{42}$. Ask yourself, *"What number divides evenly into both 12 and 42?"* Let's use 6.

$$\frac{12}{42} = \frac{12 \div 6}{42 \div 6} = \frac{2}{7}$$

Ask yourself, *"Is $\frac{2}{7}$ in lowest terms?"* Yes. Therefore, $\frac{12}{42} = \frac{2}{7}$, and $\frac{2}{7}$ is in lowest terms.

b) Look at $\dfrac{10}{17}$ and ask yourself, *"What number divides evenly into both 10 and 17?"* Their only common factor is 1. Therefore, $\dfrac{10}{17}$ is in lowest terms.

c) Look at $\dfrac{210}{350}$ and ask yourself, *"What number divides evenly into both 210 and 350?"* Because both numbers end in 0, they are divisible by 10.

$$\frac{210}{350} = \frac{210 \div 10}{350 \div 10} = \frac{21}{35}$$

Ask yourself, *"Is $\dfrac{21}{35}$ in lowest terms?"* No! 21 and 35 are divisible by 7.

$$\frac{21}{35} = \frac{21 \div 7}{35 \div 7} = \frac{3}{5}$$

"Is $\dfrac{3}{5}$ in lowest terms?" Yes. Therefore, in lowest terms, $\dfrac{210}{350} = \dfrac{3}{5}$.

[YOU TRY 1] Determine whether each fraction is in lowest terms. If it is not, write it in lowest terms.

a) $\dfrac{35}{48}$ b) $\dfrac{9}{72}$ c) $\dfrac{1620}{5280}$

BE CAREFUL Example 1c shows why it is so important to look at the result to determine whether it can be simplified more. When we divided the numerator and denominator of $\dfrac{210}{350}$ by 10, we obtained the fraction $\dfrac{21}{35}$, which was still not in lowest terms.

We can also use prime factorizations of numbers to write a fraction in lowest terms.

EXAMPLE 2

In-Class Example 2

Write $\dfrac{126}{630}$ in lowest terms using the prime factorizations of the numerator and denominator.

Answer: $\dfrac{1}{5}$

Write $\dfrac{56}{168}$ in lowest terms using the prime factorizations of the numerator and denominator.

Solution

Let's find the prime factorizations of 56 and 168 using factor trees.

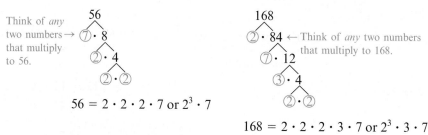

So, $\dfrac{56}{168} = \dfrac{2 \cdot 2 \cdot 2 \cdot 7}{2 \cdot 2 \cdot 2 \cdot 3 \cdot 7} = \dfrac{\overset{1}{2} \cdot \overset{1}{2} \cdot \overset{1}{2} \cdot \overset{1}{7}}{\underset{1}{2} \cdot \underset{1}{2} \cdot \underset{1}{2} \cdot 3 \cdot \underset{1}{7}} = \dfrac{1}{3}$ Is $\dfrac{1}{3}$ in lowest terms? Yes.

Write $\dfrac{102}{156}$ in lowest terms using the prime factorizations of the numerator and denominator.

Let's review how to multiply and divide fractions.

EXAMPLE 3

In-Class Example 3

Multiply or divide. Write the answer in lowest terms.

a) $\dfrac{9}{32} \div \dfrac{21}{40}$ b) $6 \cdot \dfrac{5}{11}$

c) $\dfrac{44}{21} \cdot \dfrac{49}{60} \cdot \dfrac{18}{55}$ d) $\dfrac{2}{9} \div 8$

e) $\dfrac{\frac{3}{10}}{\frac{4}{5}}$

Answer:

a) $\dfrac{15}{28}$ b) $\dfrac{30}{11}$ or $2\dfrac{8}{11}$

c) $\dfrac{14}{25}$ d) $\dfrac{1}{36}$ e) $\dfrac{3}{8}$

W Hint

In your own words, summarize how to multiply and divide fractions.

Multiply or divide. Write the answer in lowest terms.

a) $\dfrac{10}{21} \div \dfrac{45}{56}$ b) $5 \cdot \dfrac{3}{7}$ c) $\dfrac{10}{63} \cdot \dfrac{27}{32} \cdot \dfrac{7}{5}$

d) $\dfrac{2}{9} \div 8$ e) $\dfrac{\frac{3}{10}}{\frac{4}{5}}$

Solution

a) To divide fractions, *multiply by the reciprocal* of the second fraction.

$$\dfrac{10}{21} \div \dfrac{45}{56} = \dfrac{10}{21} \cdot \dfrac{56}{45}$$
Change division to multiplication by the reciprocal.

$$= \dfrac{\overset{2}{\cancel{10}}}{\underset{3}{\cancel{21}}} \cdot \dfrac{\overset{8}{\cancel{56}}}{\underset{9}{\cancel{45}}}$$
Divide 10 and 45 by 5; divide 21 and 56 by 7.

$$= \dfrac{2 \cdot 8}{3 \cdot 9}$$
Multiply.

$$= \dfrac{16}{27}$$
The answer is in lowest terms.

b) What should we do *before* we multiply $5 \cdot \dfrac{3}{7}$? We should write the natural number, 5, as $\dfrac{5}{1}$.

Write 5 as $\dfrac{5}{1}$.

$$5 \cdot \dfrac{3}{7} = \dfrac{5}{1} \cdot \dfrac{3}{7} = \dfrac{5 \cdot 3}{1 \cdot 7} = \dfrac{15}{7} \text{ or } 2\dfrac{1}{7}$$
Write the answer as an improper fraction or mixed number.

c) When we multiply more than two fractions, we can pair up any numerator with any denominator to divide out common factors.

$$\dfrac{\overset{\overset{1}{\cancel{2}}}{\cancel{10}}}{\underset{\underset{1}{\cancel{7}}}{\cancel{63}}} \cdot \dfrac{\overset{3}{\cancel{27}}}{\underset{16}{\cancel{32}}} \cdot \dfrac{\overset{1}{\cancel{7}}}{\underset{1}{\cancel{5}}} = \dfrac{1 \cdot 3 \cdot 1}{1 \cdot 16 \cdot 1} = \dfrac{3}{16}$$

d) Remember, when you are given a division problem involving a natural number and a fraction, always begin by changing the natural number to a fraction. Then, follow the procedure for dividing fractions.

Write 8 as $\frac{8}{1}$.

$$\frac{2}{9} \div 8 = \frac{2}{9} \div \frac{8}{1} = \frac{2}{9} \cdot \frac{1}{8} = \frac{\overset{1}{2}}{9} \cdot \frac{1}{\underset{4}{8}} = \frac{1}{36}$$

Change division to multiplication by the reciprocal.

e) Remember that $\dfrac{\frac{3}{10}}{\frac{4}{5}}$ is called a **complex fraction.** It is another way to represent a division problem.

The fraction bar means division. → $\dfrac{\frac{3}{10}}{\frac{4}{5}} = \frac{3}{10} \div \frac{4}{5} = \frac{3}{10} \cdot \frac{5}{4} = \frac{3}{\underset{2}{10}} \cdot \frac{\overset{1}{5}}{4} = \frac{3}{8}$

Change division to multiplication by the reciprocal.

[**YOU TRY 3**] Multiply or divide. Write the answer in lowest terms.

a) $\dfrac{21}{25} \div \dfrac{7}{15}$ b) $3 \cdot \dfrac{7}{18}$ c) $\dfrac{14}{15} \cdot \dfrac{3}{10} \cdot \dfrac{50}{21}$

d) $\dfrac{4}{7} \div 10$ e) $\dfrac{\frac{3}{2}}{\frac{3}{8}}$

Many applications use multiplication or division of fractions.

EXAMPLE 4

In-Class Example 4

A survey of 2000 recent college graduates revealed that $\dfrac{7}{10}$ of them said they would move back in with their parents until they get a job. How many people said they would move back home? (www.collegegrad.com)

Answer: 1400 recent graduates said they plan to move back home with their parents.

Daria spends $\dfrac{3}{10}$ of her income on rent. Determine how much rent she pays if she earns $2800 per month.

Solution

The amount of her rent is $\dfrac{3}{10}$ *of* $2800. The *of* means multiply.

$$\frac{3}{10} \cdot 2800 = \frac{3}{10} \cdot \frac{2800}{1} = \frac{3}{\underset{1}{10}} \cdot \frac{\overset{280}{2800}}{1} = \frac{840}{1} = 840$$

Write 2800 as $\dfrac{2800}{1}$.

Daria's rent is $840 per month. Double-check your work to verify that the answers are correct.

[YOU TRY 4] Of the approximately 2800 white-collar workers surveyed, $\frac{6}{25}$ of them said they play video games at work. How many play games at work? (www.marketingcharts.com)

ANSWERS TO [YOU TRY] EXERCISES

1) a) $\frac{35}{48}$ is in lowest terms.   b) $\frac{1}{8}$ c) $\frac{27}{88}$

2) $\frac{17}{26}$ 3) a) $\frac{9}{5}$ or $1\frac{4}{5}$ b) $\frac{7}{6}$ or $1\frac{1}{6}$ c) $\frac{2}{3}$ d) $\frac{2}{35}$ e) 4

4) 672 of the white-collar workers surveyed play video games at work.

Putting It All Together Exercises

E Evaluate   Do the exercises, and check your work.

*Additional answers can be found in the Answers to Exercises appendix.

Objective 1: Review the Concepts of Sections 3.1–3.7

Use a proper fraction or mixed number to represent the shaded portion of the figure, and represent the number on a number line.

1)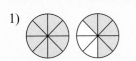

2)

Determine whether each statement is true or false. If it is false, explain why.

3) The denominator of a fraction can be any number.
False. The denominator cannot equal 0.

4) The fraction $\frac{7}{1}$ is in lowest terms.
False. In lowest terms, $\frac{7}{1} = 7$.

5) The number 35 is a prime number.
False. 35 has factors other than 1 and 35. Other factors are 5 and 7.

6) The prime factorization of 36 is $2^2 \cdot 3^2$.   true

Change each number to an improper fraction.

7) $3\frac{1}{8}$ $\frac{25}{8}$

8) $1\frac{7}{10}$ $\frac{17}{10}$

9) $12\frac{6}{11}$ $\frac{138}{11}$

10) $15\frac{4}{9}$ $\frac{139}{9}$

Change each improper fraction to a mixed number.

11) $\frac{10}{7}$ $1\frac{3}{7}$

12) $\frac{37}{8}$ $4\frac{5}{8}$

13) $\frac{179}{12}$ $14\frac{11}{12}$

14) $\frac{218}{13}$ $16\frac{10}{13}$

15) a) Find all factors of 48.   1, 2, 3, 4, 6, 8, 12, 16, 24, and 48

   b) Write the prime factorization of 48.
   $2 \cdot 2 \cdot 2 \cdot 2 \cdot 3$ or $2^4 \cdot 3$

16) a) Find all factors of 60.
   1, 2, 3, 4, 5, 6, 10, 12, 15, 20, 30, and 60

   b) Write the prime factorization of 60.
   $2 \cdot 2 \cdot 3 \cdot 5$ or $2^2 \cdot 3 \cdot 5$

Write each fraction in lowest terms.

17) $\frac{40}{75}$ $\frac{8}{15}$

18) $\frac{24}{96}$ $\frac{1}{4}$

19) $\frac{510}{102}$ 5

20) $\frac{2520}{9900}$ $\frac{14}{55}$

Determine whether each pair of fractions is equivalent.

21) $\frac{28}{63}$ and $\frac{12}{27}$ yes

22) $\frac{24}{40}$ and $\frac{48}{60}$ no

23) Explain how to multiply $7 \cdot \frac{3}{4}$, then find the product.
First write 7 as $\frac{7}{1}$, then multiply. $7 \cdot \frac{3}{4} = \frac{7}{1} \cdot \frac{3}{4} = \frac{21}{4}$ or $5\frac{1}{4}$

24) Explain how to divide two fractions.
Multiply the first number by the reciprocal of the second number.

Multiply or divide.

25) $\frac{5}{18} \cdot \frac{12}{13}$ $\frac{10}{39}$

26) $\frac{8}{9} \cdot 15$ $\frac{40}{3}$ or $13\frac{1}{3}$

27) $10 \div \frac{1}{2}$ 20

28) $\frac{3}{4} \div 6$ $\frac{1}{8}$

29) $\dfrac{\frac{8}{21}}{\frac{16}{7}}$ $\frac{1}{6}$

30) $\frac{1}{6} \cdot \frac{10}{21} \cdot \frac{18}{25}$ $\frac{2}{35}$

31) $\frac{24}{35} \cdot \frac{25}{44} \cdot \frac{7}{60}$ $\frac{1}{22}$ 32) $20 \cdot \frac{9}{16}$ $\frac{45}{4}$ or $11\frac{1}{4}$

 33) $\frac{35}{66} \div \frac{30}{77}$ $\frac{49}{36}$ or $1\frac{13}{36}$ 34) $\dfrac{\frac{1}{4}}{\frac{2}{5}}$ $\frac{5}{8}$

35) What is the formula for the area of a rectangle?
Area = Length · Width

36) If the length and width of a rectangle are measured in inches, what are the units of the area?
square inches or in²

Solve each problem.

 37) Find the area of this note card. $\frac{5}{48}$ ft²

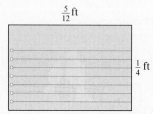
$\frac{5}{12}$ ft

$\frac{1}{4}$ ft

38) Soledad spent $4104 on tuition, books, and other supplies, and $\frac{7}{9}$ of the amount was for tuition. How much did Soledad pay for tuition? $3192

39) A coffeemaker holds 3 gal of coffee. How many travel containers can Arthur fill if each one holds $\frac{3}{4}$ gal?   4 travel containers

40) Amritpal sold 145 boxes of Girl Scout Cookies and $\frac{3}{5}$ of them were Thin Mints. How many boxes of Thin Mints did she sell? How many boxes of the other types of cookies did she sell?
87 boxes of Thin Mints and 58 boxes of the other types of cookies

41) In 2009, a survey revealed that $\frac{1}{5}$ of men spend some time during an average day doing housework. Of these men, $\frac{2}{5}$ did food preparation or cleanup. What fraction of all the men surveyed do food preparation or cleanup on an average day? (www.bls.gov)

$\frac{2}{25}$ of all men

42) When Sean gets home from the grocery store, he opens the 6-lb package of ground beef and stores it in $\frac{2}{3}$-lb packages in the freezer. How many packages can he make?   9 packages

43) A worker has a 10-ft piece of sheet metal that must be cut into strips that are $\frac{5}{8}$ ft long. How many strips can be made?   16 strips

44) An insurance agent handles 240 accounts, and $\frac{3}{4}$ of the accounts are with married people. Of the married couples, $\frac{4}{9}$ have children.

a) What fraction of all the accounts involve married couples with children? $\frac{1}{3}$ of the accounts

b) How many of the accounts involve married couples with children?   80 accounts

R Rethink

R1) What is the purpose of having you complete exercises that contain all the concepts of this chapter in one section?

R2) Did you find any problems that you needed to look up to answer? What do you need to practice more?

3.8 Multiplying and Dividing Mixed Numbers

Organize

What are your objectives for Section 3.8?	How can you accomplish each objective?
1 Multiply Mixed Numbers	• Write the procedure for **Multiplying Mixed Numbers** in your own words. • Complete the given example. • Complete You Try 1.
2 Divide Mixed Numbers	• Write the procedure for **Dividing Mixed Numbers** in your own words. • Complete the given example. • Complete You Try 2.
3 Solve Applied Problems Involving Mixed Numbers	• Review the notes you took for Section 3.7 on the **Five Steps for Solving Applied Problems,** and compare them to the examples for this objective. • Complete the given examples. • Complete You Trys 3–5.

W Work   **Read the explanations, follow the examples, take notes, and complete all the You Trys.**

In this section, we will learn how to multiply and divide mixed numbers.

1 Multiply Mixed Numbers

We use what we learned about changing a mixed number to an improper fraction to multiply mixed numbers.

W Hint
Write the procedure for multiplying mixed numbers in your own words.

Procedure Multiplying Mixed Numbers

To multiply mixed numbers,

1) Change each mixed number to an improper fraction.

2) Multiply the fractions.

3) Write the answer in lowest terms. If it is an improper fraction, change it to a mixed number.

Note

In general, if we perform operations with mixed numbers and the result is an improper fraction, the final answer should be written as a mixed number.

EXAMPLE 1

Multiply.

a) $1\dfrac{5}{6} \cdot 2\dfrac{2}{3}$ b) $5\dfrac{1}{3} \cdot 4\dfrac{1}{2}$ c) $2\dfrac{5}{9} \cdot \dfrac{3}{10}$

In-Class Example 1

Multiply.

a) $3\dfrac{2}{9} \cdot 4\dfrac{1}{2}$ b) $2\dfrac{1}{4} \cdot 6\dfrac{2}{3}$

c) $2\dfrac{1}{10} \cdot \dfrac{2}{11}$

Answer:

a) $14\dfrac{1}{2}$ b) 15 c) $\dfrac{21}{55}$

Solution

a) First, change each mixed number to an improper fraction.

$$1\frac{5}{6} = \frac{11}{6} \qquad\qquad 2\frac{2}{3} = \frac{8}{3}$$

Multiply.

$$1\frac{5}{6} \cdot 2\frac{2}{3} = \frac{11}{6} \cdot \frac{8}{3} = \frac{11}{\cancel{6}_{3}} \cdot \frac{\cancel{8}^{4}}{3} \qquad \text{Divide 6 and 8 by 2.}$$

$$= \frac{11 \cdot 4}{3 \cdot 3} \qquad \text{Multiply.}$$

$$= \frac{44}{9} = 4\frac{8}{9} \qquad \text{Write the final answer as a mixed number.}$$

b) Change each mixed number to an improper fraction.

$$5\frac{1}{3} = \frac{16}{3} \qquad\qquad\qquad\qquad 4\frac{1}{2} = \frac{9}{2}$$

Multiply.

$$5\frac{1}{3} \cdot 4\frac{1}{2} = \frac{16}{3} \cdot \frac{9}{2} = \frac{\cancel{16}^{8}}{\cancel{3}_{1}} \cdot \frac{\cancel{9}^{3}}{\cancel{2}_{1}} = \frac{8 \cdot 3}{1 \cdot 1} = \frac{24}{1} = 24 \qquad \text{Simplify } \frac{24}{1} \text{ to 24.}$$

c) Write $2\dfrac{5}{9}$ as an improper fraction: $2\dfrac{5}{9} = \dfrac{23}{9}$

Multiply: $2\dfrac{5}{9} \cdot \dfrac{3}{10} = \dfrac{23}{9} \cdot \dfrac{3}{10} = \dfrac{23}{\cancel{9}_{3}} \cdot \dfrac{\cancel{3}^{1}}{10} = \dfrac{23}{30}$

As you can see here, sometimes the product is a *proper* fraction.

[YOU TRY 1] Multiply.

a) $5\dfrac{1}{8} \cdot 1\dfrac{3}{7}$ b) $3\dfrac{1}{5} \cdot 2\dfrac{3}{16}$ c) $3\dfrac{1}{18} \cdot \dfrac{4}{11}$

2 Divide Mixed Numbers

To divide mixed numbers, we use the following steps.

Procedure Dividing Mixed Numbers

W Hint

Write the procedure for dividing mixed numbers in your own words.

1) Change each mixed number to an improper fraction.

2) Rewrite the division problem containing mixed numbers as a division problem with fractions.

3) Multiply the first number by the reciprocal of the second number.

4) Write the answer in lowest terms. If it is an improper fraction, change it to a mixed number.

EXAMPLE 2

In-Class Example 2

Divide.

a) $5\frac{1}{2} \div 3\frac{2}{3}$ b) $4\frac{2}{5} \div 8$

c) $18 \div 2\frac{1}{7}$

Answer:

a) $1\frac{1}{2}$ b) $\frac{11}{20}$ c) $8\frac{2}{5}$

Divide.

a) $3\frac{3}{4} \div 2\frac{1}{8}$ b) $6\frac{1}{4} \div 15$ c) $12 \div 4\frac{2}{7}$

Solution

a) First, change each mixed number to an improper fraction.

$$3\frac{3}{4} = \frac{15}{4} \qquad 2\frac{1}{8} = \frac{17}{8}$$

Write the division problem using improper fractions.

$$3\frac{3}{4} \div 2\frac{1}{8} = \frac{15}{4} \div \frac{17}{8} \qquad \text{Change the mixed numbers to improper fractions.}$$

$$= \frac{15}{4} \cdot \frac{8}{17} \qquad \text{Change division to multiplication by the reciprocal.}$$

$$= \frac{15}{\overset{}{\underset{1}{4}}} \cdot \frac{\overset{2}{8}}{17} \qquad \text{Divide 4 and 8 by 4.}$$

$$= \frac{30}{17} = 1\frac{13}{17} \qquad \text{Multiply and write the answer as a mixed number.}$$

Therefore, $3\frac{3}{4} \div 2\frac{1}{8} = 1\frac{13}{17}$.

b) Change $6\frac{1}{4}$ to an improper fraction, and write 15 as $\frac{15}{1}$.

$$6\frac{1}{4} = \frac{25}{4} \qquad\qquad 15 = \frac{15}{1}$$

Rewrite the division problem using the fractions.

$$6\frac{1}{4} \div 15 = \frac{25}{4} \div \frac{15}{1} = \frac{25}{4} \cdot \frac{1}{15} = \frac{\overset{5}{25}}{4} \cdot \frac{1}{\underset{3}{15}} = \frac{5}{12}$$

Change division to multiplication by the reciprocal.

c) Write 12 as $\frac{12}{1}$, and change $4\frac{2}{7}$ to an improper fraction.

$$12 = \frac{12}{1} \qquad\qquad 4\frac{2}{7} = \frac{30}{7}$$

Multiply.

$$12 \div 4\frac{2}{7} = \frac{12}{1} \div \frac{30}{7} = \frac{12}{1} \cdot \frac{7}{30} = \frac{\overset{2}{\cancel{12}}}{1} \cdot \frac{7}{\underset{5}{\cancel{30}}} = \frac{14}{5} = 2\frac{4}{5}$$

Change division to
multiplication by the reciprocal.

[YOU TRY 2] Divide.

a) $7\frac{1}{5} \div 2\frac{7}{10}$　　　b) $11\frac{2}{3} \div 5$　　　c) $4 \div 5\frac{1}{5}$

---

3 Solve Applied Problems Involving Mixed Numbers

Many applications involve multiplying or dividing mixed numbers.

EXAMPLE 3

In-Class Example 3

Martha buys 10 quarts of potting soil to plant some herbs. If each pot uses $1\frac{1}{4}$ quarts of soil, how many pots of herbs can she plant?

Answer:
Martha can plant 8 pots of herbs.

Amber sews dresses for Little Dresses for Africa, an organization that provides dresses for girls. Amber buys 14 yd of fabric, and each dress requires $1\frac{3}{4}$ yd. How many dresses can she make?

Solution

Step 1: **Read** the problem carefully, and restate it in your own words.

Amber buys <u>14 yd of fabric</u> and <u>uses $1\frac{3}{4}$ yd</u> <u>for each dress</u>. <u>How many dresses can she make</u>?

W Hint
Review the notes you took for Section 3.7 on the **Five Steps for Solving Applied Problems,** and compare them to the examples for this objective.

Step 2: **Make a plan.** Let's underline important words in our restatement of the problem in Step 1, and think about the problem this way: How many $1\frac{3}{4}$-yd pieces of fabric are in 14 yd?

Plan: Divide 14 by $1\frac{3}{4}$ to find the number of dresses Amber can make.

Step 3: **Solve** the problem.

$$14 \div 1\frac{3}{4} = \frac{14}{1} \div \frac{7}{4}$$ Write 14 as $\frac{14}{1}$, and write $1\frac{3}{4}$ as an improper fraction.

$$= \frac{14}{1} \cdot \frac{4}{7}$$ Change division to multiplication by the reciprocal.

$$= \frac{\overset{2}{\cancel{14}}}{1} \cdot \frac{4}{\underset{1}{\cancel{7}}}$$ Divide 14 and 7 by 7.

$$= \frac{8}{1} = 8$$ Multiply and simplify.

Step 4: **State the answer** in a complete sentence.

Amber can make 8 dresses.

Step 5: **Check** the answer. Multiply the 8 dresses she can make by the amount of fabric needed for each dress. The answer should be the total amount of fabric she bought.

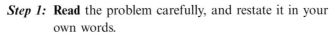

$$8 \cdot 1\frac{3}{4} = \frac{8}{1} \cdot \frac{7}{4} = \frac{\overset{2}{\cancel{8}}}{1} \cdot \frac{7}{\underset{1}{\cancel{4}}} = \frac{14}{1} = 14 \leftarrow \text{Total amount}$$

Number of dresses Amber can make   Amount of fabric for each dress   of fabric

The answer is correct.

[YOU TRY 3]

When the restaurant closes, Vijay must drain 9 gal of oil from the deep fryer and put it into $1\frac{1}{2}$-gal containers. How many containers will he need?

EXAMPLE 4

In-Class Example 4

Every day, Jameer goes on a $12\frac{1}{2}$-mi training ride at 6 A.M. How many miles does he ride each week?

Answer:
Jameer rides $87\frac{1}{2}$ mi per week.

An energy-efficient dishwasher uses $5\frac{1}{3}$ gal of water per load. If the Yamoto family uses their dishwasher 4 times each week, how many gallons of water do they use?

Solution

Step 1: **Read** the problem carefully, and restate it in your own words.

If a dishwasher is run <u>4 times per week</u> and uses $5\frac{1}{3}$ <u>gal of water each time, find the total amount of water used.</u>

Step 2: **Make a plan.** Let's underline important words in our restatement of the problem in Step 1, and think about what is happening in this problem.

Plan: Multiply $5\frac{1}{3}$ by 4 to find the total amount of water the dishwasher uses each week.

Step 3: **Solve** the problem.

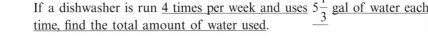

$$5\frac{1}{3} \cdot 4 = \frac{16}{3} \cdot \frac{4}{1} = \frac{64}{3} = 21\frac{1}{3} \leftarrow \text{Total amount of water used each week}$$

Number of gallons per load   Number of loads

Step 4: **State the answer** in a complete sentence.

The dishwasher uses $21\frac{1}{3}$ gal of water each week.

Step 5: **Check** the answer. Verify that $21\frac{1}{3} \div 4 = 5\frac{1}{3}$.

The fence at the back of Liliana's property consists of 10 wooden panels, each of which is $6\frac{1}{2}$ ft long. How long is the fence?

We can use what we learned in Section 3.6 to solve problems involving area.

EXAMPLE 5

In-Class Example 5

Phil's rectangular garden is $20\frac{1}{3}$ ft long and $11\frac{1}{4}$ ft wide. Find the area of the garden.

Answer:
The area of the garden is $228\frac{3}{4}$ ft².

Igal's rectangular garden is $19\frac{1}{2}$ ft long and $10\frac{2}{3}$ ft wide. Find the area of the garden.

Solution

Step 1: **Read** the problem carefully, and restate it in your own words.

We must find the <u>area of a rectangular garden that is $19\frac{1}{2}$ ft long and $10\frac{2}{3}$ ft wide</u>.

Step 2: **Make a plan.** Underline important words in the restatement of the problem in Step 1. Also, let's draw a picture and label it with the length and width.

What is the formula for the area of a rectangle?

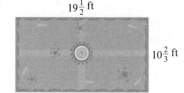

$$\text{Area} = \text{Length} \cdot \text{Width}$$

Identify the numbers given in the problem: length = $19\frac{1}{2}$ ft, width = $10\frac{2}{3}$ ft.

Plan: Use the formula, and substitute the values for the length and width.

Step 3: **Solve** the problem.

$$\text{Area} = \text{Length} \cdot \text{Width}$$

$$\text{Area} = 19\frac{1}{2} \cdot 10\frac{2}{3} \qquad \text{Substitute the values for length and width.}$$

$$= \frac{39}{2} \cdot \frac{32}{3} \qquad \text{Change the mixed numbers to improper fractions.}$$

$$= \frac{\overset{13}{\cancel{39}}}{\underset{1}{\cancel{2}}} \cdot \frac{\overset{16}{\cancel{32}}}{\underset{1}{\cancel{3}}} \qquad \text{Divide 39 and 3 by 3; divide 2 and 32 by 2.}$$

$$= \frac{208}{1} = 208 \qquad \text{Multiply and simplify.}$$

Step 4: **State the answer** in a complete sentence.

The area of the garden is 208 ft².

Step 5: **Check** the answer. Double-check your arithmetic to verify that the answer is correct.

A rectangular painting is $2\frac{5}{6}$ ft long and $1\frac{1}{2}$ ft wide. What is the area of the painting?

ANSWERS TO YOU TRY **EXERCISES**

1) a) $7\frac{9}{28}$ b) 7 c) $1\frac{1}{9}$ 2) a) $2\frac{2}{3}$ b) $2\frac{1}{3}$ c) $\frac{10}{13}$ 3) Vijay will need 6 containers.

4) The fence is 65 ft long.   5) The area of the painting is $4\frac{1}{4}$ ft².

E Evaluate **3.8** Exercises   Do the exercises, and check your work.

*Additional answers can be found in the Answers to Exercises appendix.

Objective 1: Multiply Mixed Numbers

1) In your own words, explain how to multiply mixed numbers.   Answers may vary.

2) When you multiply two mixed numbers, will the answer always be a mixed number?
No. The answer can be a natural number or a proper fraction.

Multiply.

3) $1\frac{2}{3} \cdot 2\frac{1}{7}$ $3\frac{4}{7}$

4) $2\frac{1}{6} \cdot 4\frac{2}{7}$ $9\frac{2}{7}$

5) $2\frac{4}{5} \cdot 3\frac{1}{2}$ $9\frac{4}{5}$

6) $7\frac{1}{3} \cdot 1\frac{1}{6}$ $8\frac{5}{9}$

7) $6\frac{3}{7} \cdot 2\frac{1}{3}$ 15

8) $3\frac{2}{3} \cdot 6\frac{3}{11}$ 23

9) $8 \cdot 2\frac{1}{6}$ $17\frac{1}{3}$

10) $12 \cdot 1\frac{3}{8}$ $16\frac{1}{2}$

11) $1\frac{9}{14} \cdot \frac{7}{8}$ $1\frac{7}{16}$

12) $3\frac{3}{4} \cdot \frac{7}{30}$ $\frac{7}{8}$

13) $8\frac{3}{4} \cdot 3\frac{1}{7}$ $27\frac{1}{2}$

14) $9\frac{1}{3} \cdot 2\frac{3}{7}$ $22\frac{2}{3}$

15) $11\frac{3}{5} \cdot \frac{2}{29}$ $\frac{4}{5}$

16) $7\frac{7}{8} \cdot 4\frac{8}{21}$ $34\frac{1}{2}$

Objective 2: Divide Mixed Numbers

17) In your own words, explain how to divide mixed numbers.   Answers may vary.

18) If you perform division involving one or more mixed numbers and the result is an improper fraction, how should you write the final answer?
Write the answer as a mixed number.

Divide.

19) $7\frac{1}{5} \div 4\frac{1}{2}$ $1\frac{3}{5}$

20) $4\frac{1}{6} \div 1\frac{1}{9}$ $3\frac{3}{4}$

21) $3\frac{3}{4} \div 5\frac{5}{8}$ $\frac{2}{3}$

22) $1\frac{5}{9} \div 1\frac{5}{6}$ $\frac{28}{33}$

23) $6\frac{3}{4} \div 8$ $\frac{27}{32}$

24) $7\frac{2}{3} \div 10$ $\frac{23}{30}$

25) $4\frac{7}{8} \div 3$ $1\frac{5}{8}$

26) $8\frac{2}{5} \div 6$ $1\frac{2}{5}$

27) $15 \div 4\frac{1}{2}$ $3\frac{1}{3}$

28) $6 \div 5\frac{1}{3}$ $1\frac{1}{8}$

29) $8 \div 6\frac{2}{5}$ $1\frac{1}{4}$

30) $10 \div 4\frac{2}{3}$ $2\frac{1}{7}$

31) $12\frac{5}{6} \div 1\frac{5}{9}$ $8\frac{1}{4}$

32) $14\frac{1}{4} \div 1\frac{9}{10}$ $7\frac{1}{2}$

Objective 3: Solve Applied Problems Involving Mixed Numbers

Solve each problem.

33) Sunny is going to crochet small squares for a throw blanket she wants to make. If each square requires $3\frac{3}{4}$ yd of yarn, how many squares can she make using 60 yd of yarn?   16 squares

34) Colin needs to move 69 cubic feet of dirt to a truck using a wheel barrel that can carry $5\frac{3}{4}$ cubic feet of dirt. How many times will Colin have to fill the wheel barrel to move all the dirt?   12 times

35) Spiro's study schedule requires that he spend $2\frac{1}{2}$ hr of study each week for every unit of class he is enrolled in. How many hours will he study per week if he is taking 15 units?
$37\frac{1}{2}$ hr per week

36) Fatima's commute to work is $1\frac{1}{4}$ hr each way every day. How many hours does she spend commuting to work and back each week if she works Monday through Friday only?
$12\frac{1}{2}$ hr each week

37) Clarissa's chocolate chip cookie recipe requires $2\frac{1}{4}$ cups of all-purpose flour to make 5 dozen cookies. How much flour does Mary Jo need to make $2\frac{1}{2}$ dozen cookies? $1\frac{1}{8}$ cups

38) Heinrich's cheesecake recipe requires $1\frac{1}{2}$ cups of white sugar to make one cheesecake. If he needs to make one dozen cheesecakes for a conference event, how many cups of white sugar does he need?
18 cups

39) A homeowner wants to use hardwood flooring in his living room. The living room measures 20 ft long and 12 ft wide. If each individual piece of wood flooring covers $1\frac{1}{3}$ ft², how many individual pieces are required to cover the entire living room floor?
180 individual pieces

40) How many quarter-pound hamburger patties can be made from $8\frac{3}{4}$ lb of ground beef? 35 patties

41) Nora's rectangular home office desk measures $3\frac{1}{2}$ ft long and $2\frac{1}{3}$ ft wide. What is the area of Nora's desk? $8\frac{1}{6}$ ft²

42) A rectangular reflecting pool measures $12\frac{3}{4}$ ft long and $5\frac{1}{3}$ ft wide. Find the area of the surface of the reflecting pool. 68 ft²

43) Romeo's digital camera takes digital pictures that are $2\frac{3}{4}$ megabytes each. How many megabytes are required to store 300 of Romeo's digital pictures?
825 megabytes

44) If an MP3 song is encoded such that its file size is $1\frac{1}{5}$ megabytes per minute, how much memory is required to store an hour's length of music? 72 megabytes

45) What is the area of a standard $8\frac{1}{2}$- by 11-in. sheet of paper? $93\frac{1}{2}$ in²

46) Manny and Becky are planning to build a backyard sundeck measuring $6\frac{1}{3}$ yd by $4\frac{1}{2}$ yd. Find the area of the sundeck. $28\frac{1}{2}$ yd²

47) One gallon of water weighs approximately $8\frac{1}{3}$ lb. What is the approximate weight of a quart of water if a quart is $\frac{1}{4}$ gallon? $2\frac{1}{12}$ lb

48) One gallon of salt water weighs approximately $8\frac{3}{5}$ lb. What is the approximate water weight of a 60-gal saltwater aquarium? 516 lb

49) A 5-in.-radius wheel travels approximately $31\frac{2}{5}$ in. for each complete revolution it makes. Approximately how many inches will the wheel travel if it makes 100 complete revolutions? How many feet is this? 3140 in.; $261\frac{2}{3}$ ft

50) To create a complex water feature, Valarie needs to cut rubber tubing into lengths measuring $4\frac{1}{2}$ in. each. How many $4\frac{1}{2}$-in. pieces can she make with 2 yd of rubber tubing? 16 pieces

In Exercises 51–56, the shaded areas can be represented by a mixed number. First, write down the mixed number that represents the shaded area. Next, try to find half the amount of the shaded area by inspection. Check your result by dividing the mixed number by 2.

Multiply or divide.

51) 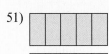 $1\frac{3}{5}; \frac{4}{5}$ 52)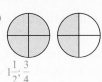

$1\frac{1}{2}; \frac{3}{4}$

53)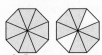

$1\frac{3}{4}; \frac{7}{8}$

54)

$1\frac{2}{3}; \frac{5}{6}$

55)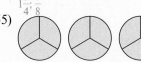

$2\frac{2}{3}; 1\frac{1}{3}$

56)

$2\frac{1}{2}; 1\frac{1}{4}$

57) $8\frac{6}{7} \cdot 2\frac{1}{2}$ $22\frac{1}{7}$

58) $4\frac{8}{9} \div 11$ $\frac{4}{9}$

59) $12 \div 2\frac{1}{4}$ $5\frac{1}{3}$

60) $\frac{10}{27} \cdot 5\frac{2}{5}$ 2

61) $4\frac{7}{8} \div 6\frac{1}{2}$ $\frac{3}{4}$

62) $8 \div 3\frac{1}{2}$ $2\frac{2}{7}$

▶ 63) $9\frac{3}{8} \div 40$ $\frac{15}{64}$

64) $1\frac{4}{7} \cdot 4\frac{2}{3}$ $7\frac{1}{3}$

65) $6\frac{7}{8} \cdot 2\frac{6}{11}$ $17\frac{1}{2}$

66) $9\frac{6}{7} \div 6\frac{3}{4}$ $1\frac{29}{63}$

R Rethink

R1) Discuss a situation that you encountered in the last week or two that required you to multiply or divide two mixed numbers.

R2) Using the situation you just wrote about, write an application similar to the ones you just solved, and have a friend solve it.

R3) How comfortable do you feel working with fractions? Discuss how having a plan or procedure to help start any of these problems has helped you.

Group Activity – Multiplying and Dividing Fractions

The state of Florida produces the most tomatoes in the United States. In fact, Florida produced 1.455 billion pounds of tomatoes in 2007. Work with a partner to answer the questions below. (http://www.growingproduce.com/floridagrower/?storyid=206)

1) The Rodriquez family lives in Florida. The backyard of the Rodriquez house is in the shape of a rectangle and has the dimensions $25\frac{1}{3}$ ft $\times$ $32\frac{5}{8}$ ft. Find the area of the backyard of the Rodriquez home. Express your answer as a mixed number.

2) Mr. and Mrs. Rodriquez want to plant a tomato garden. They have reserved $\frac{1}{5}$ of the area of their backyard for the garden. Find the area of the tomato garden. Express your answer as a mixed number.

3) There are 4 boys in the Rodriquez family. Mr. and Mrs. Rodriquez are going to give each child his own section of the garden to plant tomatoes. Each child shall have an equal area to plant his tomatoes. Find the area of each child's portion of the garden. Express your answer as a mixed number.

4) One student says that to find the answer to Exercise 3, you should divide the area of the garden by 4. Another student says that you should multiply the area of the garden by $\frac{1}{4}$ to find the answer. Which student is correct? Explain.

5) Give a general rule for dividing a fraction by a whole number.

6) In Exercises 1, 2, and 3, the numerators of the improper fractions stayed the same, but the denominators increased. Why is this so?

Challenge Exercise

Find three possible sets of dimensions (length and width) for the tomato garden that will give the area found in Exercise 2. Express your dimensions as whole numbers, mixed numbers, or fractions. Draw a sketch of the garden that will match each set of dimensions.

Group Activity Answers

1) $826\frac{1}{2}$ ft^2 2) $165\frac{3}{10}$ ft^2 3) $41\frac{13}{40}$ ft^2

4) Both students are correct. Explanations may vary.
5) When you divide a fraction by a whole number, you put the whole number over 1 and then multiply the fraction by the reciprocal of the whole number. For example, dividing by 2 is the same as multiplying by $\frac{1}{2}$.
6) The numerators stayed the same because we were dividing by a whole number. The denominators increased because the area was getting smaller after each step. First we took $\frac{1}{5}$ of the entire backyard, and then we took $\frac{1}{4}$ of that area.

Challenge Exercise
Answers may vary. Three possible answers are shown below.

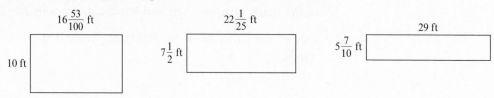

www.mhhe.com/messersmith

Do you procrastinate? To find out, circle the number that best applies for each question using the following scale:

1. I invent reasons and look for excuses for not acting on a problem.
   Strongly agree   4   3   2   1   Strongly disagree

2. It takes pressure to get me to work on difficult assignments.
   Strongly agree   4   3   2   1   Strongly disagree

3. I take half measures that will avoid or delay unpleasant or difficult tasks.
   Strongly agree   4   3   2   1   Strongly disagree

4. I face too many interruptions and crises that interfere with accomplishing my major goals.
   Strongly agree   4   3   2   1   Strongly disagree

5. I sometimes neglect to carry out important tasks.
   Strongly agree   4   3   2   1   Strongly disagree

6. I schedule big assignments too late to get them done as well as I know I could.
   Strongly agree   4   3   2   1   Strongly disagree

7. I'm sometimes too tired to do the work I need to do.
   Strongly agree   4   3   2   1   Strongly disagree

8. I start new tasks before I finish old ones.
   Strongly agree   4   3   2   1   Strongly disagree

9. When I work in groups, I try to get other people to finish what I don't.
   Strongly agree   4   3   2   1   Strongly disagree

10. I put off tasks that I really don't want to do but know that I must do.
    Strongly agree   4   3   2   1   Strongly disagree

Scoring: Total the numbers you have circled. If the score is below 15, you are not a chronic procrastinator and you probably have only an occasional problem. If your score is 16–25, you have a minor problem with procrastination. If your score is above 25, you procrastinate quite often and should work on breaking the habit.

Now, consider the following:

- If you do procrastinate often, why do you think you do it? What are some things you can do to complete tasks in a timely manner?
- Are there particular kinds of tasks that you are more likely to procrastinate on?
- Is there something that you are putting off doing right now? How might you get started on it?

Adapted from Ferner, J. D. (1980). *Successful Time Management*. NY: Wiley. p. 33.

Chapter 3:   Summary

Definition/Procedure	Example

3.1 Introduction to Fractions

A **fraction** is a part of a whole.

The **denominator** is the number *below* the fraction bar. It represents the total number of equally-sized parts of a whole.

The **numerator** is the number *above* the fraction bar. It represents the number of parts being considered. **(p. 132)**

$\frac{2}{3}$ of this circle is shaded.

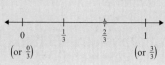

The *numerator* of the fraction is 2, and the *denominator* is 3.

We can put the number $\frac{2}{3}$ on a number line.

1) $\dfrac{0}{\text{Number}} = 0$ if the denominator is not 0.

2) $\dfrac{\text{Number}}{0}$ is undefined. **(p. 133)**

$\frac{0}{9} = 0$

$\frac{4}{0}$ is undefined.

If the numerator of a fraction is less than the denominator, then the fraction is a **proper fraction.** A proper fraction represents less than 1 whole. **(p. 135)**

$\frac{3}{5}$ is a proper fraction.

If the numerator of a fraction is greater than or equal to the denominator, then the fraction is an **improper fraction.** An improper fraction represents a quantity greater than or equal to 1 whole. **(p. 135)**

$\frac{11}{6}$ and $\frac{2}{2}$ are improper fractions.

3.2 Mixed Numbers

A **mixed number** consists of a whole number and a fraction. **(p. 141)**

$1\frac{3}{4}$ is a mixed number.

A mixed number represents more than 1 whole.

Use a mixed number to represent the portion of the figure that is shaded. Then, represent the mixed number on a number line.

Mixed numbers can also be written as improper fractions. **(p. 143)**

$1\frac{3}{4}$ of the figure is shaded. $\Big($ By counting each shaded region, we can also say that $\frac{7}{4}$ of the figure is shaded. $\Big)$

Let's put $1\frac{3}{4}$ on a number line.

Definition/Procedure	Example
Change a Mixed Number to an Improper Fraction ***Step 1:*** Multiply the denominator and the whole number. ***Step 2:*** Add the numerator to the result in Step 1. ***Step 3:*** Write the improper fraction. The numerator is the result in Step 2, and the denominator is the original denominator. **(p. 144)**	Write $1\dfrac{3}{4}$ as an improper fraction. ***Step 1:*** Multiply the denominator and the whole number: $4 \cdot 1 = 4$ ***Step 2:*** Add the numerator to the result in Step 1: $4 + 3 = 7$ ***Step 3:*** Write the improper fraction: $$1\dfrac{3}{4} = \dfrac{7}{4}$$ This is the same as the result we obtained in the previous box when we determined the portion of the figure that was shaded.
Change an Improper Fraction to a Mixed Number ***Step 1:*** Divide the numerator by the denominator. ***Step 2:*** Write the mixed number. The *quotient* is the whole-number part. The *remainder* is the numerator of the fractional part, and the denominator is the same as the denominator of the improper fraction. **(p. 145)**	Write $\dfrac{17}{5}$ as a mixed number. ***Step 1:*** Divide the numerator by the denominator. 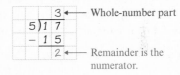 ***Step 2:*** Write the mixed number. $$\dfrac{17}{5} = 3\dfrac{2}{5}$$ Use the same denominator.

3.3 Factors

Factors are numbers that are multiplied together to get a product. (We consider only natural numbers as factors.) **(p. 147)**	The factors of 12 are 1, 2, 3, 4, 6, and 12. Another way to think of the factors of 12 is that 12 *divides evenly* by 1, 2, 3, 4, 6, and 12.
Composite and Prime Numbers A **composite number** is a number with factors other than 1 and itself. A **prime number** is a number whose only two different factors are 1 and itself. The numbers 0 and 1 are neither prime nor composite. **(p. 148)**	Identify each number as composite or prime. a) 11 b) 15 a) 11 is *prime* because its only factors are 1 and 11. b) 15 is *composite* because it has factors other than 1 and 15. For example, because 15 is divisible by 5, 5 is a *factor* of 15: $5 \cdot 3 = 15$.
Prime Factorization Finding the **prime factorization** of a number means writing the number as a product of prime factors. We can find the prime factorization of a number using a factor tree or by modifying the long division procedure. **(p. 149)**	Find the prime factorization of 18 a) using a factor tree. b) using division. $18 = 2 \cdot 3 \cdot 3$ or $2 \cdot 3^2$

Definition/Procedure	Example

3.4 Writing Fractions in Lowest Terms

Equivalent fractions are different fractions that represent the same part of the whole. **(p. 155)**

$\frac{1}{2}$ and $\frac{2}{4}$ are equivalent fractions.

$\frac{1}{2}$ of the figure is shaded. $\frac{2}{4}$ of the figure is shaded.

A fraction is in **lowest terms** if the numerator and denominator have no common factors other than 1. **(p. 155)**

$\frac{1}{2}$ is in lowest terms. $\frac{2}{4}$ is not in lowest terms because 2 and 4 have a common factor of 2.

Write a Fraction in Lowest Terms Using Common Factors

To write a fraction in lowest terms:

1) Ask yourself, *"What number divides evenly into both the numerator and denominator?"* (Use any number except 1.) Divide the numerator and denominator by that number.

2) Look at the result and ask yourself, *"Is the fraction in lowest terms?"* If the numerator and denominator still contain a common factor, repeat Steps 1 and 2.

Writing a fraction in lowest terms is also called **simplifying** a fraction. **(p. 157)**

Write $\frac{36}{60}$ in lowest terms.

Ask yourself, *"What number divides evenly into both* 36 *and* 60*?"* Let's use 12. (We could have chosen other factors, but 12 is the **greatest common factor** of 36 and 60.)

$$\frac{36}{60} = \frac{36 \div 12}{60 \div 12} = \frac{3}{5}$$

Ask yourself, *"Is $\frac{3}{5}$ in lowest terms?"* Yes, it is, because 3 and 5 have no common factor other than 1.

Therefore, $\frac{36}{60} = \frac{3}{5}$, and $\frac{3}{5}$ is in lowest terms.

Write a Fraction in Lowest Terms Using Prime Factorization

To write a fraction in lowest terms:

1) Write the prime factorization of the numerator and denominator.

2) Divide out common factors. Write a 1 by each factor to indicate that you have performed the division.

3) Multiply the factors that are left in the numerator and denominator. **(p. 159)**

Write $\frac{90}{15}$ in lowest terms.

Write the prime factorization, and divide out the common factors.

$$\frac{90}{15} = \frac{2 \cdot \overset{1}{\cancel{3}} \cdot 3 \cdot \overset{1}{\cancel{5}}}{\underset{1}{\cancel{3}} \cdot \underset{1}{\cancel{5}}} = \frac{2 \cdot 1 \cdot 3 \cdot 1}{1 \cdot 1} = \frac{6}{1}$$

Ask yourself, *"Is $\frac{6}{1}$ in lowest terms?"* No! We can write $\frac{6}{1}$ as 6. In lowest terms, $\frac{90}{15} = 6$.

Determine Whether Two Fractions Are Equivalent

To determine whether two fractions are equivalent, write each of them in lowest terms. **(p. 160)**

Determine whether $\frac{8}{14}$ and $\frac{20}{35}$ are equivalent fractions.

Begin by writing each fraction in lowest terms.

$$\frac{8}{14} = \frac{8 \div 2}{14 \div 2} = \frac{4}{7} \qquad \frac{20}{35} = \frac{20 \div 5}{35 \div 5} = \frac{4}{7}$$

Each fraction equals $\frac{4}{7}$ in lowest terms. Therefore,

$\frac{8}{14}$ and $\frac{20}{35}$ are equivalent fractions.

Definition/Procedure	Example

3.5 Multiplying Fractions

Multiply Fractions

To multiply fractions, multiply the numerators and multiply the denominators. *Always write the result in lowest terms.*

We can divide out common factors from numerators and denominators before multiplying. **(p. 163)**

Multiply.

a) $\dfrac{2}{9} \cdot \dfrac{21}{16} = \dfrac{\overset{1}{2}}{\underset{3}{9}} \cdot \dfrac{\overset{7}{21}}{\underset{8}{16}}$ Divide 2 and 16 by 2; divide 9 and 21 by 3.

$= \dfrac{1 \cdot 7}{3 \cdot 8}$ Multiply numerators; multiply denominators.

$= \dfrac{7}{24}$ The answer is in lowest terms.

b) $\dfrac{2}{7} \cdot \dfrac{3}{5}$

We cannot divide out common factors from the numerators and denominators. So, just multiply.

$$\dfrac{2}{7} \cdot \dfrac{3}{5} = \dfrac{2 \cdot 3}{7 \cdot 5} = \dfrac{6}{35}$$

Multiply a Fraction and a Whole Number

To multiply a fraction and a whole number, rewrite the whole number as a fraction with a denominator of 1. Then, multiply. **(p. 168)**

Multiply $\dfrac{5}{8} \cdot 6$.

$\dfrac{5}{8} \cdot 6 = \dfrac{5}{8} \cdot \dfrac{6}{1}$ Write 6 with a denominator of 1.

$= \dfrac{5}{\underset{4}{8}} \cdot \dfrac{\overset{3}{6}}{1}$ Divide 6 and 8 by 2.

$= \dfrac{5 \cdot 3}{4 \cdot 1}$ Multiply numerators; multiply denominators.

$= \dfrac{15}{4}$ or $3\dfrac{3}{4}$ Write the answer as an improper fraction or mixed number in lowest terms.

3.6 Applications of Multiplication

We can use the five-step process to solve applications involving multiplication with fractions. **(p. 173)**

Solve the problem.

In 2011, a survey of about 2400 adults revealed that $\dfrac{4}{25}$ of them have driven a car without auto insurance. How many of the people surveyed have driven without insurance? (www.motorwayamerica.com)

Step 1: **Read** the problem carefully, and restate it in your own words.

$\dfrac{4}{25}$ *of* 2400 people surveyed have <u>driven without auto insurance.</u> We must <u>find the number of people who have driven without insurance.</u>

Step 2: **Make a plan.** Let's underline important words in our restatement of the problem in Step 1.

The *of* in $\dfrac{4}{25}$ *of* 2400 means we should multiply.

Plan: Multiply $\dfrac{4}{25}$ by 2400 to determine the number of people who have driven without insurance.

Definition/Procedure	Example
	Step 3: Solve the problem. $$\frac{4}{25} \cdot 2400 = \frac{4}{25} \cdot \frac{2400}{1} = \frac{4}{\overset{}{25}} \cdot \frac{\overset{96}{2400}}{1} = \frac{4 \cdot 96}{1 \cdot 1} = \frac{384}{1} = 384$$ Write 2400 as $\frac{2400}{1}$. **Step 4: State the answer** in a complete sentence. 384 of the 2400 people surveyed have driven without auto insurance. **Step 5: Check** the answer. Double-check your work to verify that the answer is correct.

3.7 Dividing Fractions

Definition/Procedure	Example
Find the Reciprocal of a Number Two numbers are **reciprocals** if their product is 1. To find the reciprocal of a number, we interchange the numerator and denominator. We also say that we *invert* or *flip* a fraction to find its reciprocal. The number 0 does *not* have a reciprocal. **(p. 180)**	The reciprocal of $\frac{2}{11}$ is $\frac{11}{2}$. We can check by multiplying. $$\frac{2}{11} \cdot \frac{11}{2} = \frac{22}{22} = 1$$
Find the Reciprocal of a Natural Number To find the reciprocal of a natural number, first write it as a fraction with a denominator of 1, then flip it. **(p. 180)**	Find the reciprocal of 3. Write 3 as a fraction with a denominator of 1: $\quad 3 = \frac{3}{1}$ Then, flip $\frac{3}{1}$ to get its reciprocal, $\frac{1}{3}$. The reciprocal of 3 is $\frac{1}{3}$.
Divide Fractions To perform division involving fractions, multiply the first number by the reciprocal of the second number. If a division problem contains a fraction and a natural number, the first step is to write the natural number as a fraction with a denominator of 1. **(p. 181)**	Divide. a) $\frac{7}{10} \div \frac{42}{5}$ $$\frac{7}{10} \div \frac{42}{5} = \frac{7}{10} \cdot \frac{5}{42} = \frac{\overset{1}{7}}{\underset{2}{10}} \cdot \frac{\overset{1}{5}}{\underset{6}{42}} = \frac{1 \cdot 1}{2 \cdot 6} = \frac{1}{12}$$ Change division to multiplication by the reciprocal. Do not divide out common factors until the problem has been changed to multiplication! b) $\frac{9}{10} \div 8$ $\frac{9}{10} \div 8 = \frac{9}{10} \div \frac{8}{1}$ Begin by writing 8 as $\frac{8}{1}$. $\quad = \frac{9}{10} \cdot \frac{1}{8}$ Change division to multiplication by the reciprocal. $\quad = \frac{9}{80}$ Multiply.

Definition/Procedure	Example
Solving Applications We can use the five-step process to solve applications involving division with fractions. **(p. 185)**	Solve the problem. A 6-ft-long piece of lumber must be cut into pieces that are $\frac{3}{4}$ ft long. How many pieces can be cut? ***Step 1:*** **Read** the problem carefully, and restate it in your own words. We must determine <u>how many $\frac{3}{4}$-ft-long boards can be cut from a 6-ft piece of lumber.</u> ***Step 2:*** **Make a plan.** Let's underline important words in our restatement of the problem in Step 1, and think of the problem this way: How many $\frac{3}{4}$-ft-long pieces does it take to make a 6-ft-long board? $\left(\text{Or, } divide \text{ the 6-ft piece of lumber into } \frac{3}{4}\text{-ft pieces.}\right)$ *Plan:* Divide 6 by $\frac{3}{4}$ to find the answer. ***Step 3:*** **Solve** the problem. $$6 \div \frac{3}{4} = \frac{6}{1} \div \frac{3}{4} = \frac{6}{1} \cdot \frac{4}{3} = \frac{\overset{2}{\cancel{6}}}{1} \cdot \frac{4}{\underset{1}{\cancel{3}}} = \frac{8}{1} = 8$$ Change division to multiplication by the reciprocal. ***Step 4:*** **State the answer** in a complete sentence. Eight $\frac{3}{4}$-ft-long pieces can be cut from the 6-ft piece of lumber. ***Step 5:*** **Check** the answer. Since each of 8 pieces is $\frac{3}{4}$-ft long, multiply 8 by $\frac{3}{4}$ to find the total length of the piece of lumber. Length of each piece ↓ Number of pieces → $8 \cdot \frac{3}{4} = \frac{8}{1} \cdot \frac{3}{4} = \frac{\overset{2}{\cancel{8}}}{1} \cdot \frac{3}{\underset{1}{\cancel{4}}} = \frac{6}{1} = 6$ ← Total length

Definition/Procedure	Example

3.8 Multiplying and Dividing Mixed Numbers

Multiply Mixed Numbers

To multiply mixed numbers,

1) Change each mixed number to an improper fraction.

2) Multiply the fractions.

3) Write the answer in lowest terms. If it is an improper fraction, change it to a mixed number. **(p. 195)**

Multiply $2\frac{1}{2} \cdot 1\frac{3}{4}$.

$2\frac{1}{2} \cdot 1\frac{3}{4} = \frac{5}{2} \cdot \frac{7}{4}$ Change each mixed number to an improper fraction.

$= \frac{35}{8}$ Multiply.

$= 4\frac{3}{8}$ Write the answer as a mixed number.

Divide Mixed Numbers

1) Change each mixed number to an improper fraction.

2) Rewrite the division problem containing mixed numbers as a division problem with fractions.

3) Multiply the first number by the reciprocal of the second number.

4) Write the answer in lowest terms. If it is an improper fraction, change it to a mixed number. **(p. 197)**

Divide $3\frac{4}{7} \div 6\frac{1}{4}$.

$3\frac{4}{7} \div 6\frac{1}{4} = \frac{25}{7} \div \frac{25}{4}$ Change each mixed number to an improper fraction.

$= \frac{25}{7} \cdot \frac{4}{25}$ Change division to multiplication by the reciprocal.

$= \frac{\overset{1}{25}}{7} \cdot \frac{4}{\underset{1}{25}}$ Divide by 25.

$= \frac{4}{7}$ Multiply.

Chapter 3:   Review Exercises

*Additional answers can be found in the Answers to Exercises appendix.

(3.1) Use a fraction to represent the shaded part of the figure, and represent the fraction on a number line.

1)

2)

3)   4)

Use a fraction to represent the *unshaded* part of the figure, and represent the fraction on a number line.

5)   6)

7)

8)

9) Does $\frac{0}{4} = \frac{4}{0}$? Explain your answer.
No. $\frac{0}{4} = 0$ but $\frac{4}{0}$ is undefined.

10) In your own words, explain the difference between a proper and an improper fraction.   Answers may vary.

11) Identify each fraction as proper or improper.

a) $\frac{24}{11}$ b) $\frac{7}{23}$ c) $\frac{6}{6}$

improper fraction   proper fraction   improper fraction

12) Identify each fraction as proper or improper.

a) $\frac{11}{11}$ b) $\frac{29}{27}$ c) $\frac{4}{5}$ proper fraction

improper fraction   improper fraction

Shade an appropriate amount of area on the figure according to the represented fraction on the number line.

13)

14)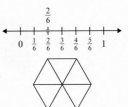

(3.2) Write each improper fraction as a mixed number.

15) $\dfrac{37}{6}$ $6\dfrac{1}{6}$

16) $\dfrac{11}{8}$ $1\dfrac{3}{8}$

17) $\dfrac{41}{9}$ $4\dfrac{5}{9}$

18) $\dfrac{78}{11}$ $7\dfrac{1}{11}$

Write each mixed number as an improper fraction.

19) $7\dfrac{8}{9}$ $\dfrac{71}{9}$

20) $8\dfrac{5}{6}$ $\dfrac{53}{6}$

21) $6\dfrac{10}{11}$ $\dfrac{76}{11}$

22) $9\dfrac{5}{6}$ $\dfrac{59}{6}$

Use a mixed number to describe which portion of the figure is shaded, and represent the mixed number on a number line.

23)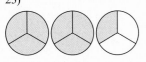

24)

(3.3)

 25) In your own words, explain the difference between a prime number and a composite number.   Answers may vary.

26) What is the smallest prime number?   2

Find all factors of each number.

27) 16   1, 2, 4, 8, and 16

28) 63   1, 3, 7, 9, 21, and 63

29) 19   1 and 19

30) 67   1 and 67

Identify each number as composite or prime.

31) 48   composite

32) 60   composite

33) 17   prime

34) 43   prime

35) 1413   composite

36) 9700   composite

37) a) List all the factors of 36.   1, 2, 3, 4, 6, 9, 12, 18, and 36

   b) Find the prime factorization of 36.
   $36 = 2 \cdot 2 \cdot 3 \cdot 3$ or $2^2 \cdot 3^2$

38) a) List all the factors of 28.   1, 2, 4, 7, 14, and 28

   b) Find the prime factorization of 28.
   $28 = 2 \cdot 2 \cdot 7$ or $2^2 \cdot 7$

39) Find the prime factorization of 252.
   $252 = 2 \cdot 2 \cdot 3 \cdot 3 \cdot 7$ or $2^2 \cdot 3^2 \cdot 7$

40) Find the prime factorization of 360.
   $360 = 2 \cdot 2 \cdot 2 \cdot 3 \cdot 3 \cdot 5$ or $2^3 \cdot 3^2 \cdot 5$

(3.4) Determine whether each fraction is in lowest terms.

41) $\dfrac{3}{18}$ no

42) $\dfrac{3}{17}$ yes

43) $\dfrac{9}{61}$ yes

44) $\dfrac{43}{129}$ no

Write each fraction in lowest terms.

45) $\dfrac{16}{40}$ $\dfrac{2}{5}$

46) $\dfrac{12}{45}$ $\dfrac{4}{15}$

47) $\dfrac{4}{8}$ $\dfrac{1}{2}$

48) $\dfrac{7}{42}$ $\dfrac{1}{6}$

49) $\dfrac{4020}{7140}$ $\dfrac{67}{119}$

50) $\dfrac{434}{31}$ 14

Determine whether each pair of fractions is equivalent.

51) $\dfrac{45}{75}$ and $\dfrac{24}{40}$ yes

52) $\dfrac{24}{36}$ and $\dfrac{8}{12}$ yes

53) $\dfrac{63}{336}$ and $\dfrac{96}{498}$ no

54) $\dfrac{130}{432}$ and $\dfrac{160}{512}$ no

Determine whether each statement is true or false.

55) On the number line, $\dfrac{1}{4}$ is to the right of $\dfrac{1}{5}$.   true

56) On the number line, $\dfrac{1}{8}$ is to the left of $\dfrac{1}{7}$.   true

57) $\dfrac{7}{8}$ is greater than $\dfrac{3}{2}$.   false

58) 1 is less than $\dfrac{7}{6}$.   true

(3.5) Multiply. Write all answers in lowest terms.

59) $\dfrac{5}{24} \cdot \dfrac{8}{10}$ $\dfrac{1}{6}$

60) $\dfrac{9}{15} \cdot \dfrac{25}{6}$ $\dfrac{5}{2}$ or $2\dfrac{1}{2}$

61) $\dfrac{7}{27} \cdot 3$ $\dfrac{7}{9}$

62) $2 \cdot \dfrac{4}{11}$ $\dfrac{8}{11}$

63) $\dfrac{25}{33} \cdot \dfrac{11}{4} \cdot \dfrac{18}{35}$ $\dfrac{15}{14}$ or $1\dfrac{1}{14}$

64) $\dfrac{52}{5} \cdot \dfrac{25}{6} \cdot \dfrac{24}{13}$ 80

65) $\dfrac{5}{3} \cdot 3 \cdot \dfrac{3}{10}$ $\dfrac{3}{2}$ or $1\dfrac{1}{2}$

66) $\dfrac{21}{44} \cdot 22 \cdot \dfrac{33}{14}$ $\dfrac{99}{4}$ or $24\dfrac{3}{4}$

67) Does multiplying a whole number by a proper fraction *always, never,* or *sometimes* result in a number larger than the whole number?   never

68) Is the product of two improper fractions *always, never,* or *sometimes* greater than 1?   sometimes

(3.6) Miss Sorenson teaches a math class that meets 140 min per day, two days per week. The pie chart shows how Miss Sorenson manages her class time. Use this information for Exercises 69–74.

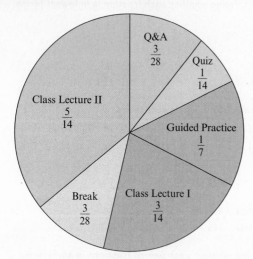

69) How much break time does Miss Sorenson give her students? 15 min

70) How much time is allowed for the Quiz? 10 min

71) What is the combined Lecture time? 80 min

72) What is the combined Q&A and Quiz time? 25 min

73) Verify that the sum of the Quiz and Guided Practice time equals the Class Lecture I time. What does this tell you about the sum of $\frac{1}{14}$ and $\frac{1}{7}$? The sum must equal $\frac{3}{14}$.

74) Based on the pie chart, what is the sum of all six fractions: $\frac{3}{28} + \frac{1}{14} + \frac{1}{7} + \frac{3}{14} + \frac{3}{28} + \frac{5}{14} = ?$ The sum must equal 1.

Solve each problem.

75) Every month for a year, Kasia deposited $250 into a bank account. At the end of the year, her grandparents deposited an additional $\frac{2}{3}$ of the amount she saved into the account. How much money did Kasia's grandparents deposit into the account? What is the total amount in the savings account including the amount her grandparents deposited? Grandparents deposited $2000; total amount is $5000.

76) In a manufacturing plant, $\frac{7}{8}$ of the employees are in the labor union. Of these union members, $\frac{4}{5}$ voted to strike over proposed pay cuts. The plant has 140 employees. Determine the fraction of employees that voted for the strike as well as the number of employees who voted to strike. $\frac{7}{10}$ of the employees voted to strike; 98 out of 140 employees voted yes on the strike.

77) A rectangular-shaped wheat field is $\frac{3}{4}$ mi long and $\frac{3}{8}$ mi wide. What is the area of the field? $\frac{9}{32}$ mi^2

78) Find the area of the shaded region. $\frac{28}{3}$ in^2 or $9\frac{1}{3}$ in^2

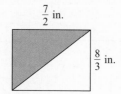

(3.7) Find the reciprocal of each number.

79) $\frac{13}{6}$ $\frac{6}{13}$

80) 8 $\frac{1}{8}$

81) $\frac{1}{7}$ 7

82) $\frac{15}{13}$ $\frac{13}{15}$

Divide. Write all answers in lowest terms.

83) $\frac{3}{8} \div \frac{2}{5}$ $\frac{15}{16}$

84) $\frac{7}{8} \div \frac{7}{4}$ $\frac{1}{2}$

85) $\frac{35}{16} \div \frac{5}{12}$ $\frac{21}{4}$ or $5\frac{1}{4}$

86) $\frac{11}{28} \div \frac{33}{32}$ $\frac{8}{21}$

87) $\frac{\frac{1}{10}}{\frac{3}{8}}$ $\frac{4}{15}$

88) $\frac{\frac{12}{13}}{\frac{4}{9}}$ $\frac{27}{13}$ or $2\frac{1}{13}$

89) $\frac{1}{3} \div 6$ $\frac{1}{18}$

90) $\frac{15}{4} \div 2$ $\frac{15}{8}$ or $1\frac{7}{8}$

91) $5 \div \frac{5}{8}$ 8

92) $4 \div \frac{4}{5}$ 5

93) The shaded area represents $\frac{3}{4}$ of a circle. If this shaded area is separated into 3 equal portions, what fractional amount of the entire circle is each portion? Represent one shaded portion on the blank circle below.

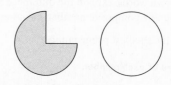

94) The figure represents $\frac{1}{2}$ of a circle. If this shaded area is separated into 4 equal portions, what fractional amount of the entire circle is each portion? Represent one shaded portion on the blank circle.

Solve each problem.

95) If $\frac{2}{3}$ of a gallon of cleaning solution needs to be divided into 8 equal portions, how much of a gallon is each portion? $\frac{1}{12}$ of a gallon

96) If $\frac{3}{4}$ of a liter of olive oil is divided into 6 equal portions, how much of a liter is each portion? $\frac{1}{8}$ of a liter

(3.8) Multiply or divide. Write all answers in lowest terms.

97) $1\frac{5}{6} \cdot 3\frac{3}{10}$ $6\frac{1}{20}$

98) $4\frac{1}{6} \cdot 3\frac{1}{5}$ $13\frac{1}{3}$

99) $4\frac{7}{8} \div 3$ $1\frac{5}{8}$

100) $8\frac{2}{5} \div 6$ $1\frac{2}{5}$

101) $1\frac{3}{7} \div 2$ $\frac{5}{7}$

102) $2\frac{2}{5} \div 2\frac{2}{3}$ $\frac{9}{10}$

103) $3 \cdot 2\frac{1}{6}$ $6\frac{1}{2}$

104) $10 \cdot 1\frac{3}{8}$ $13\frac{3}{4}$

Solve each problem.

105) Toni's recipe for ciabatta bread makes two loaves and uses $2\frac{1}{3}$ cups of bread flour. If she wants to make 8 loaves of bread, how much flour will she need?
$9\frac{1}{3}$ cups

106) For a school project, Cyrus needs to cut a 3-yd length of wood into pieces measuring $2\frac{1}{4}$ in. How many pieces measuring $2\frac{1}{4}$ in. can he make? 48 pieces

Mixed Exercises

107) Write the prime factorization of 96.
$96 = 2 \cdot 2 \cdot 2 \cdot 2 \cdot 2 \cdot 3$ or $2^5 \cdot 3$

108) Write $\frac{315}{600}$ in lowest terms. $\frac{21}{40}$

Multiply or divide. Write all answers in lowest terms.

109) $\frac{9}{4} \cdot \frac{36}{7}$ $\frac{81}{7}$ or $11\frac{4}{7}$

110) $\frac{3}{8} \div 9$ $\frac{1}{24}$

111) $\dfrac{\frac{2}{5}}{\frac{1}{6}}$ $\frac{12}{5}$ or $2\frac{2}{5}$

112) $5\frac{1}{3} \cdot 3\frac{3}{4}$ 20

113) $6\frac{1}{4} \div 12\frac{1}{2}$ $\frac{1}{2}$

114) $\frac{5}{16} \cdot \frac{21}{72} \cdot \frac{54}{35}$ $\frac{9}{64}$

115) $15 \cdot \frac{4}{9}$ $\frac{20}{3}$ or $6\frac{2}{3}$

116) $\frac{10}{33} \div \frac{1}{12}$ $\frac{40}{11}$ or $3\frac{7}{11}$

Solve each problem.

117) Basam's car needs new ball joints, and the repairs will cost $\frac{2}{3}$ of one paycheck. If he makes $900 per week, how much will it cost for Basam to get his car fixed? $600

118) A large tin contains 24 cups of popcorn. How many $1\frac{1}{2}$-cup portions of popcorn can Imelda make using all of the popcorn in the tin? 16 portions

Chapter 3:   Test

*Additional answers can be found in the Answers to Exercises appendix.

Use a fraction to represent the shaded part of each figure, and represent the fraction on a number line.

1)

2)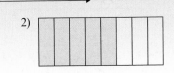

3) What is the difference between a proper fraction and an improper fraction? Give an example of each.

4) Use a mixed number to describe what portion of the figure is shaded, and represent the mixed number on a number line.

5) Write $5\frac{4}{7}$ as an improper fraction. $\frac{39}{7}$

6) Write $\dfrac{89}{3}$ as mixed number. $29\dfrac{2}{3}$

7) Find all factors of 24.   1, 2, 3, 4, 6, 8, 12, and 24

8) Identify each number as prime or composite.

    a) 10   composite   b) 7   prime

    c) 43   prime   d) 87   composite

Find the prime factorization of each number.

9) 24 $2 \cdot 2 \cdot 2 \cdot 3$ or $2^3 \cdot 3$ 10) 140 $2 \cdot 2 \cdot 5 \cdot 7$ or $2^2 \cdot 5 \cdot 7$

11) 585 $3 \cdot 3 \cdot 5 \cdot 13$ or $3^2 \cdot 5 \cdot 13$

Write each fraction in lowest terms.

12) $\dfrac{6}{16}$ $\dfrac{3}{8}$ 13) $\dfrac{18}{72}$ $\dfrac{1}{4}$

14) $\dfrac{420}{1050}$ $\dfrac{2}{5}$

15) Are $\dfrac{9}{12}$ and $\dfrac{24}{32}$ equivalent fractions? Explain your answer.

Perform the indicated operation. Write all answers in lowest terms.

16) $\dfrac{7}{10} \cdot \dfrac{4}{9}$ $\dfrac{14}{45}$ 17) $\dfrac{5}{12} \div \dfrac{25}{28}$ $\dfrac{7}{15}$

18) $3 \cdot \dfrac{4}{7}$ $\dfrac{12}{7}$ or $1\dfrac{5}{7}$ 19) $6\dfrac{2}{3} \cdot 1\dfrac{1}{5}$ 8

20) $\dfrac{8}{11} \div 16$ $\dfrac{1}{22}$ 21) $\dfrac{\dfrac{3}{4}}{\dfrac{3}{10}}$ $\dfrac{5}{2}$ or $2\dfrac{1}{2}$

22) $\dfrac{21}{40} \cdot \dfrac{11}{14} \cdot \dfrac{5}{9}$ $\dfrac{11}{48}$ 23) $22 \div 4\dfrac{5}{7}$ $4\dfrac{2}{3}$

24) $2\dfrac{3}{4} \cdot 9\dfrac{3}{5}$ $26\dfrac{2}{5}$

Solve each problem.

25) The label on a 20-oz bottle of root beer says that it contains $2\dfrac{1}{2}$ servings. How many ounces are in each serving?   8 oz

26) A sewage treatment plant produces $\dfrac{4}{5}$ of a ton of sludge in one day. How much sludge would it produce in $\dfrac{1}{2}$ of a day? $\dfrac{2}{5}$ of a ton

27) A sticky note is $4\dfrac{1}{2}$ in. long and $2\dfrac{3}{4}$ in. wide. What is the area of the sticky note? $12\dfrac{3}{8}$ in^2

28) Sig is a crab fisherman, and his crew hauled up a pot containing 320 opi crabs. Because they cannot keep females or crabs that are too small, the crew had to throw back $\dfrac{3}{8}$ of their catch. How many crabs did they keep?   200

Chapter 3:   Cumulative Review for Chapters 1–3

*Additional answers can be found in the Answers to Exercises appendix.

1) Identify the digit with the given place value in the whole number 867,584.

    a) thousands   7

    b) ones   4

    c) hundred-thousands   8

Find the missing length.

2)   ?   7 in.   3 in.

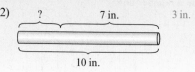

10 in.

3)

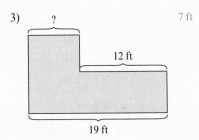

7 ft

12 ft

19 ft

Fill in the blank.

4) $7 + 2 +$ _____ $= 12$ 3

5) $12 -$ _____ $= 5$ 7

Add, subtract, multiply, or divide as indicated.

6) $\begin{array}{r} 342 \\ 158 \\ + 56 \end{array}$ 556

7) $\begin{array}{r} 7226 \\ - 5899 \end{array}$ 1327

8) $\begin{array}{r} 6000 \\ - 2657 \end{array}$ 3343

9) $\begin{array}{r} 517 \\ \times 302 \end{array}$ 156,134

10) $\begin{array}{r} 2678 \\ \times 1356 \end{array}$ 3,631,368

11) $8\overline{)2963}$ 370 R3

12) $12\overline{)3852}$ 321

Round 525 to the nearest ten, nearest hundred, and nearest one-thousand.

	Ten	Hundred	One-thousand
13) 525	520	500	1000

Simplify each expression.

14) $8^2 - 5^2 - 10 - 3$ 26

15) $46 - 4\sqrt{79 - 15} \div 4 \cdot 3 - \sqrt{144}$ 10

16) A group of students on spring break order 8 large pizzas that cost $12 each and then pay a delivery fee of $8. Find the total cost of the order. $104

17) A community college charges $46 per credit hour plus fees. If Kara registers for 12 hours and has to pay $89 in fees, find the amount she must pay to register for classes. $641

Multiply or divide as indicated.

18) $\dfrac{27}{2} \cdot \dfrac{8}{13} \cdot \dfrac{26}{63}$ $\dfrac{24}{7}$ or $3\dfrac{3}{7}$

19) $1\dfrac{3}{5} \cdot 6\dfrac{1}{4}$ 10

20) $\dfrac{9}{11} \div 4$ $\dfrac{9}{44}$

21) $\dfrac{35}{16} \div \dfrac{25}{12}$ $\dfrac{21}{20}$ or $1\dfrac{1}{20}$

22) $\dfrac{3}{28} \cdot 1\dfrac{5}{9}$ $\dfrac{1}{6}$

23) Is the product of two proper fractions *always, never,* or *sometimes* less than 1?   always

24) Colette owns $16\dfrac{1}{4}$ acres of land. If she wants to divide her land into $\dfrac{5}{8}$-acre lots, how many lots can she make?
26 lots

25) Find the area of the shaded region.   7 ft²

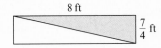

8 ft

$\dfrac{7}{4}$ ft

Adding and Subtracting Fractions

Math at Work:

Civil Drafter

It takes a lot of people to build a highway. One of the most important is Tanya Richards.

As a civil drafter, Tanya is responsible for creating the drawings and plans for the construction of civil projects such as new highways or sewer systems. Her plans have to detail not only the visual aspects of a project, but also the physical features of the land, the types and amounts of materials to be used, and how construction can be completed to meet specifications.

"I think of my job as translating ideas into reality," Tanya says. "My plans are like instructions for completing these massive undertakings."

Not surprisingly, math is a core component of Tanya's work. Every drawing she makes involves hours of measurement and calculation. Skill in using fractions, she says, is particularly important. "I need to be able to make different parts fit together on a single plan," she explains. "So I'm always adding $\frac{2}{5}$ of a mile here to $\frac{1}{3}$ of a mile there, removing half a ton of weight from a support that had been carrying $\frac{7}{8}$ of a ton before."

In this chapter, we continue our work with fractions, exploring how they can be added and subtracted. Later, we'll look at a skill that, like drafting, involves bringing together many different kinds of information into a single, organized document: note-taking.

Taking good notes in class is not easy, especially in math courses, but in-class note-taking is critical to college success. What an instructor says in class usually reflects what he or she thinks are the most important points on a given subject. Here are some proven techniques to help improve the quality of the notes you take:

P Prepare

- Complete any assignments before arriving in class.
- Find a seat that lets you see and hear the instructor clearly.
- Warm up your mind by looking over notes from the previous class or any assigned materials.

O Organize

- Choose the right writing tool. In math classes, this is usually a pencil, as you'll likely be working through problems in class.
- Use a loose-leaf notebook to write your notes in, and plan to take notes on *only one side of the page*.

W Work

- Listen actively. Don't just passively take in the information. Concentrate on the subject at hand, and try to make sense of it. (The emPOWERme exercise on page 279 will help you determine how active your listening is.)
- Don't try to write down everything. Instead, focus on writing down the key ideas.
- Ask questions. Remember, if you are confused about a point, chances are other people in the class are, too.

E Evaluate

- Look over your notes toward the end of class, and if you realize you missed anything, take the opportunity to ask the instructor for further information, either before the class ends or right after.

R Rethink

- As soon as the class is finished, *read over your notes*. This helps transfer the information into long-term memory and will literally save you hours of study time later.

Chapter 4 **POWER** Plan

P Prepare

O Organize

What are your goals for Chapter 4?	How can you accomplish each goal?
1 Be prepared before and during class.	• Don't stay out late the night before, and be sure to set your alarm clock! • Bring a pencil, notebook paper, and textbook to class. • Avoid distractions by turning off your cell phone during class. • Pay attention, take good notes, and ask questions. • Complete your homework on time, and ask questions on problems you do not understand.
2 Understand the homework to the point where you could do it without needing any help or hints.	• Read the directions, and show all of your steps. • Go to the professor's office for help. • Rework homework and quiz problems, and find similar problems for practice.
3 Use the P.O.W.E.R. framework to learn how to effectively take notes in class: *Active Listening*	• Read the Study Strategy as it is outlined in the P.O.W.E.R. framework. • Decide which steps you might need to improve. • Complete the emPOWERme that appears before the Chapter Summary.
4 Write your own goal.	• _____

What are your objectives for Chapter 4?	How can you accomplish each objective?
1 Learn to add and subtract like fractions.	• Understand and visualize the difference between like and unlike fractions. • Recognize the quickest way to add, and subtract like fractions.
2 Master the process of finding least common multiples, and understand how it helps you find a least common denominator.	• Learn the four different ways to find the LCM and which process is most efficient for you. • Practice, and learn the procedure for **Writing a Fraction with a Different Denominator** in your own words. • Apply the process of finding the LCM to finding the LCD.
3 Learn to add and subtract unlike fractions, and solve applied problems.	• Recognize why fractions must be like fractions before adding or subtracting. • Notice that you must master finding the LCD and writing a fraction with a different denominator first! • Use the Five Steps for Solving Applied Problems.
4 Add and subtract mixed numbers.	• Know the procedure for adding and subtracting mixed numbers. • Understand how to regroup a mixed number for subtraction or addition. • Recognize and master a new way to add or subtract using improper fractions.
5 Compare fractions, and use the order of operations.	• Take notes, and write the procedures and definitions in your own words. • Complete all the exercises, and ask for help when you need it.
6 Write your own goal.	• _____

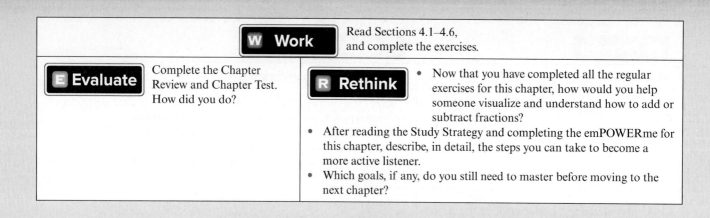

Read Sections 4.1–4.6, and complete the exercises.

W Work — Read Sections 4.1–4.6, and complete the exercises.

E Evaluate — Complete the Chapter Review and Chapter Test. How did you do?

R Rethink
- Now that you have completed all the regular exercises for this chapter, how would you help someone visualize and understand how to add or subtract fractions?
- After reading the Study Strategy and completing the emPOWERme for this chapter, describe, in detail, the steps you can take to become a more active listener.
- Which goals, if any, do you still need to master before moving to the next chapter?

4.1 Adding and Subtracting Like Fractions

P Prepare | **O Organize**

What are your objectives for Section 4.1?	How can you accomplish each objective?
1 Use a Figure and a Number Line to Add Fractions	• Refer to Section 1.2 if you need to brush up on adding using a number line. • Write the definitions of *like fractions* and *unlike fractions* in your notes. • Complete the given example on your own. • Complete You Try 1.
2 Add Like Fractions	• Learn the procedure for **Adding Like Fractions.** • Complete the given example on your own. • Complete You Try 2.
3 Subtract Like Fractions	• Learn the procedure for **Subtracting Like Fractions.** • Complete the given example on your own. • Complete You Try 3.

 **W Work** — Read the explanations, follow the examples, take notes, and complete the You Trys.

In this chapter, we will learn how to add and subtract fractions and mixed numbers. Let's begin by using figures and number lines to help us add fractions.

1 Use a Figure and a Number Line to Add Fractions

In-Class Example 1

Use Example 1.

EXAMPLE 1

Add $\dfrac{3}{5} + \dfrac{1}{5}$:

a) by drawing a figure to represent each fraction.

b) using a number line.

Solution

a) Let's shade $\dfrac{3}{5}$ of a rectangle and $\dfrac{1}{5}$ of a rectangle to find the sum $\dfrac{3}{5} + \dfrac{1}{5}$.

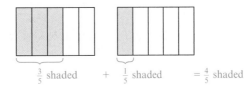

$\dfrac{3}{5}$ shaded $\quad + \quad$ $\dfrac{1}{5}$ shaded $\quad = \dfrac{4}{5}$ shaded

How many total fifths are shaded? *4 fifths.* Therefore, $\dfrac{3}{5} + \dfrac{1}{5} = \dfrac{4}{5}$.

b) Now let's use a number line to add these fractions just like we used a number line to add whole numbers in Section 1.2.

To add $\dfrac{3}{5} + \dfrac{1}{5}$, start at 0 and move $\dfrac{3}{5}$ unit to reach $\dfrac{3}{5}$. To add $\dfrac{1}{5}$ unit, move $\dfrac{1}{5}$ unit more to the right. We finish at $\dfrac{4}{5}$.

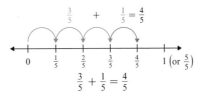

$\dfrac{3}{5} + \dfrac{1}{5} = \dfrac{4}{5}$

YOU TRY 1

Add $\dfrac{2}{7} + \dfrac{3}{7}$:

a) by drawing a figure to represent each fraction.

b) using a number line.

Notice in Example 1 that the denominators of $\dfrac{3}{5}$ and $\dfrac{1}{5}$ are the same. When fractions have the same denominator, we call them *like fractions.*

Definition

Fractions with the same denominator are called **like fractions.** Fractions with different denominators are called **unlike fractions.**

2 Add Like Fractions

To add like fractions, as in Example 1, we use these steps.

Procedure Adding Like Fractions

To add like fractions:

1) Add the numerators.

2) Use the denominator of the like fractions as the denominator of the sum.

3) Write the answer in lowest terms.

W Hint

Write a group of three unlike fractions.

Note

After you have added fractions, always look at the result and ask yourself, *"Is the answer in lowest terms?"* If it is not, write the answer in lowest terms.

EXAMPLE 2

Add.

In-Class Example 2

Add.

a) $\dfrac{2}{7} + \dfrac{3}{7}$ b) $\dfrac{4}{5} + \dfrac{7}{5}$

c) $\dfrac{1}{9} + \dfrac{4}{9} + \dfrac{1}{9}$

Answer:

a) $\dfrac{5}{7}$ b) $\dfrac{11}{5}$ or $2\dfrac{1}{5}$ c) $\dfrac{2}{3}$

a) $\dfrac{4}{9} + \dfrac{1}{9}$ b) $\dfrac{2}{3} + \dfrac{5}{3}$ c) $\dfrac{7}{15} + \dfrac{1}{15} + \dfrac{2}{15}$

Solution

a) Because the denominators are the same, we add the numerators and use the denominator 9.

$$\frac{4}{9} + \frac{1}{9} = \frac{4+1}{9} = \frac{5}{9}$$ Add the numerators, and keep the denominator the same.

Ask yourself, *"Is $\dfrac{5}{9}$ in lowest terms?"*

Yes. Therefore, $\dfrac{4}{9} + \dfrac{1}{9} = \dfrac{5}{9}$. Let's verify this using a number line.

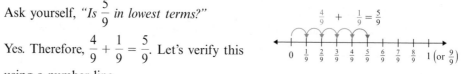

b) $\dfrac{2}{3}$ and $\dfrac{5}{3}$ are like fractions, so add the numerators and use the denominator 3.

$$\frac{2}{3} + \frac{5}{3} = \frac{2+5}{3} = \frac{7}{3} \text{ or } 2\frac{1}{3}$$ Write the answer as an improper fraction or as a mixed number.

Ask yourself, *"Are $\dfrac{7}{3}$ and $2\dfrac{1}{3}$ in lowest terms?"*

Yes. Therefore, $\dfrac{2}{3} + \dfrac{5}{3} = \dfrac{7}{3}$ or $2\dfrac{1}{3}$. Let's look at this on a number line.

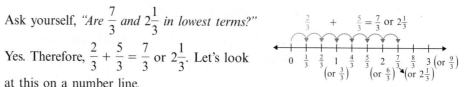

c) $\dfrac{7}{15}$, $\dfrac{1}{15}$, and $\dfrac{2}{15}$ are like fractions, so add the numerators and use the denominator 15.

$$\dfrac{7}{15} + \dfrac{1}{15} + \dfrac{2}{15} = \dfrac{7 + 1 + 2}{15} = \dfrac{10}{15} \qquad \text{Add the numerators, and keep the denominator the same.}$$

Ask yourself, *"Is $\dfrac{10}{15}$ in lowest terms?"* No! We must write it in lowest terms.

$$\dfrac{10}{15} = \dfrac{10 \div 5}{15 \div 5} = \dfrac{2}{3}$$

So, $\dfrac{7}{15} + \dfrac{1}{15} + \dfrac{2}{15} = \dfrac{10}{15} = \dfrac{2}{3}$.

[YOU TRY 2]   Add.

a) $\dfrac{8}{11} + \dfrac{2}{11}$ b) $\dfrac{1}{8} + \dfrac{5}{8}$ c) $\dfrac{5}{12} + \dfrac{7}{12} + \dfrac{11}{12}$

 BE CAREFUL

1) We can add fractions only if they are like fractions.

2) Always look at the sum and ask yourself, *"Is it in lowest terms?"* If it is not, write it in lowest terms.

3 Subtract Like Fractions

Now, we will learn how to subtract fractions. Let's start with rectangles divided into sixths to find the difference $\dfrac{5}{6} - \dfrac{4}{6}$.

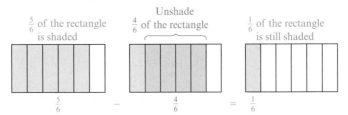

$\dfrac{5}{6}$ of the rectangle is shaded   Unshade $\dfrac{4}{6}$ of the rectangle $\dfrac{1}{6}$ of the rectangle is still shaded

$$\dfrac{5}{6} \quad - \quad \dfrac{4}{6} \quad = \quad \dfrac{1}{6}$$

To use a number line to find $\dfrac{5}{6} - \dfrac{4}{6}$, start at 0 and move $\dfrac{5}{6}$ unit to the right to reach $\dfrac{5}{6}$. To subtract $\dfrac{4}{6}$, move $\dfrac{4}{6}$ unit to the left. We finish at $\dfrac{1}{6}$.

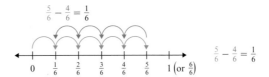

Notice that $\dfrac{5}{6}$ and $\dfrac{4}{6}$ are *like* fractions. They have the same denominator.

Note

We can subtract fractions only if they are like fractions.

The way that we subtract fractions is very similar to the way we add fractions. Recall that the result of a subtraction problem is called the *difference*.

Procedure Subtracting Like Fractions

To subtract like fractions:

1) Subtract the numerators.

2) Use the denominator of the like fractions as the denominator of the difference.

3) Write the answer in lowest terms.

EXAMPLE 3

In-Class Example 3

Subtract.

a) $\dfrac{7}{12} - \dfrac{5}{12}$ b) $\dfrac{19}{3} - \dfrac{7}{3}$

Answer:

a) $\dfrac{1}{6}$ b) 4

W Hint

After you add or subtract fractions, what should you ask yourself before you identify your final answer?

Subtract.

a) $\dfrac{7}{10} - \dfrac{3}{10}$ b) $\dfrac{20}{7} - \dfrac{6}{7}$

Solution

a) $\dfrac{7}{10}$ and $\dfrac{3}{10}$ are like fractions, so we can subtract them.

$$\dfrac{7}{10} - \dfrac{3}{10} = \dfrac{7 - 3}{10} = \dfrac{4}{10}$$ Subtract the numerators, and keep the denominator the same.

Ask yourself, *"Is $\dfrac{4}{10}$ in lowest terms?"* No! Write $\dfrac{4}{10}$ in lowest terms.

$$\dfrac{4}{10} = \dfrac{4 \div 2}{10 \div 2} = \dfrac{2}{5}$$

$$\dfrac{7}{10} - \dfrac{3}{10} = \dfrac{4}{10} = \dfrac{2}{5}$$

b) $\dfrac{20}{7}$ and $\dfrac{6}{7}$ are like fractions, so we can subtract them.

$$\dfrac{20}{7} - \dfrac{6}{7} = \dfrac{20 - 6}{7} = \dfrac{14}{7}$$ Subtract the numerators, and keep the denominator the same.

Ask yourself, *"Is $\dfrac{14}{7}$ in lowest terms?"* No! We will write it in lowest terms.

$$\dfrac{14}{7} = \dfrac{14 \div 7}{7 \div 7} = \dfrac{2}{1} = 2$$

$$\dfrac{20}{7} - \dfrac{6}{7} = \dfrac{14}{7} = 2$$

[YOU TRY 3] Subtract.

a) $\dfrac{17}{18} - \dfrac{5}{18}$ b) $\dfrac{21}{4} - \dfrac{13}{4}$

Note

If a sum or difference is an improper fraction, the answer can be written as either an improper fraction or as a mixed number.

ANSWERS TO [YOU TRY] EXERCISES

1) $\dfrac{5}{7}$; Figures may vary. 2) a) $\dfrac{10}{11}$ b) $\dfrac{3}{4}$ c) $\dfrac{23}{12}$ or $1\dfrac{11}{12}$ 3) a) $\dfrac{2}{3}$ b) 2

E Evaluate **4.1** Exercises Do the exercises, and check your work.

*Additional answers can be found in the Answers to Exercises appendix.

Objective 1: Use a Figure and a Number Line to Add Fractions

Add the like fractions. First, shade the figures appropriately to represent each fraction and the resulting sum. Then, use a number line to demonstrate the operation.

1) $\dfrac{3}{6} + \dfrac{2}{6}$

2) $\dfrac{1}{8} + \dfrac{6}{8}$

3) $\dfrac{1}{5} + \dfrac{2}{5}$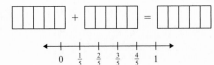

4) $\dfrac{2}{5} + \dfrac{2}{5}$

 5) $\dfrac{4}{8} + \dfrac{4}{8}$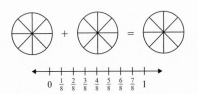

6) $\dfrac{3}{6} + \dfrac{3}{6}$

7) $\dfrac{6}{8} + \dfrac{1}{8}$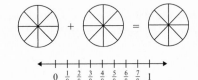

8) $\dfrac{3}{8} + \dfrac{2}{8}$

9) What is the difference between *like* and *unlike* fractions?   *Like* fractions have the same denominator, but *unlike* fractions have different denominators.

10) Look at Exercises 1–8. Explain, in your own words, how to add like fractions.   Answers may vary.

Objective 2: Add Like Fractions

11) After adding fractions, you should look at your answer and ask yourself what question?
Is the answer in lowest terms?

12) When Khinsi adds $\dfrac{1}{10} + \dfrac{3}{10}$, she writes down $\dfrac{4}{10}$ as her final answer. Is this correct? Why or why not?

No, it is not correct. The final answer should be in lowest terms, $\dfrac{2}{5}$.

Add.

13) $\dfrac{3}{11} + \dfrac{5}{11}$ $\dfrac{8}{11}$

14) $\dfrac{3}{7} + \dfrac{1}{7}$ $\dfrac{4}{7}$

15) $\dfrac{2}{7} + \dfrac{4}{7}$ $\dfrac{6}{7}$

16) $\dfrac{5}{9} + \dfrac{2}{9}$ $\dfrac{7}{9}$

17) $\dfrac{1}{4} + \dfrac{1}{4}$ $\dfrac{1}{2}$

18) $\dfrac{1}{10} + \dfrac{1}{10}$ $\dfrac{1}{5}$

19) $\begin{array}{r} \dfrac{5}{4} \\ + \dfrac{2}{4} \\ \hline \end{array}$ $\dfrac{7}{4}$ or $1\dfrac{3}{4}$

20) $\begin{array}{r} \dfrac{7}{5} \\ + \dfrac{4}{5} \\ \hline \end{array}$ $\dfrac{11}{5}$ or $2\dfrac{1}{5}$

21) $\begin{array}{r} \dfrac{13}{6} \\ + \dfrac{7}{6} \\ \hline \end{array}$ $\dfrac{10}{3}$ or $3\dfrac{1}{3}$

22) $\begin{array}{r} \dfrac{13}{8} \\ + \dfrac{7}{8} \\ \hline \end{array}$ $\dfrac{5}{2}$ or $2\dfrac{1}{2}$

23) $\dfrac{12}{5} + \dfrac{3}{5}$ 3

24) $\dfrac{20}{13} + \dfrac{6}{13}$ 2

25) $\dfrac{7}{18} + \dfrac{13}{18} + \dfrac{1}{18}$ $\dfrac{7}{6}$ or $1\dfrac{1}{6}$

26) $\dfrac{8}{15} + \dfrac{2}{15} + \dfrac{11}{15}$ $\dfrac{7}{5}$ or $1\dfrac{2}{5}$

27) $\dfrac{7}{20} + \dfrac{9}{20} + \dfrac{4}{20}$ 1

28) $\dfrac{6}{28} + \dfrac{17}{28} + \dfrac{5}{28}$ 1

29) $\dfrac{93}{40} + \dfrac{81}{40} + \dfrac{77}{40}$ $\dfrac{251}{40}$ or $6\dfrac{11}{40}$

30) $\dfrac{65}{24} + \dfrac{47}{24} + \dfrac{31}{24}$ $\dfrac{143}{24}$ or $5\dfrac{23}{24}$

Objective 3: Subtract Like Fractions

31) Fill in the blank. In order to subtract fractions, they must have the same _____.   denominator

32) What is the last question you should ask yourself after you have subtracted fractions?   Is the answer in lowest terms?

Subtract.

33) $\dfrac{2}{5} - \dfrac{1}{5}$ $\dfrac{1}{5}$

34) $\dfrac{4}{7} - \dfrac{2}{7}$ $\dfrac{2}{7}$

35) $\dfrac{12}{13} - \dfrac{8}{13}$ $\dfrac{4}{13}$

36) $\dfrac{7}{9} - \dfrac{5}{9}$ $\dfrac{2}{9}$

37) $\dfrac{10}{6} - \dfrac{7}{6}$ $\dfrac{1}{2}$

38) $\dfrac{5}{8} - \dfrac{3}{8}$ $\dfrac{1}{4}$

39) $\dfrac{9}{10} - \dfrac{3}{10}$ $\dfrac{3}{5}$

40) $\dfrac{11}{14} - \dfrac{5}{14}$ $\dfrac{3}{7}$

41) $\begin{array}{r} \dfrac{7}{5} \\ - \dfrac{4}{5} \\ \hline \end{array}$ $\dfrac{3}{5}$

42) $\begin{array}{r} \dfrac{11}{9} \\ - \dfrac{7}{9} \\ \hline \end{array}$ $\dfrac{4}{9}$

43) $\begin{array}{r} \dfrac{51}{16} \\ - \dfrac{3}{16} \\ \hline \end{array}$ 3

44) $\begin{array}{r} \dfrac{37}{14} \\ - \dfrac{9}{14} \\ \hline \end{array}$ 2

45) Vikas subtracts $\dfrac{19}{11} - \dfrac{4}{11}$ and gets $\dfrac{15}{11}$ as his final answer. Maura gets $1\dfrac{4}{11}$ as the final answer. Who is right?   Both of them are right. The answer can be written as either an improper fraction or a mixed number.

46) Maeve subtracts $\dfrac{8}{9} - \dfrac{2}{9}$ and gets a final answer of $\dfrac{6}{9}$. Is she right?   No, that is not the final answer because it is not in lowest terms. The final answer is $\dfrac{2}{3}$.

Subtract.

47) $\dfrac{31}{9} - \dfrac{11}{9}$ $\dfrac{20}{9}$ or $2\dfrac{2}{9}$

48) $\dfrac{23}{5} - \dfrac{9}{5}$ $\dfrac{14}{5}$ or $2\dfrac{4}{5}$

49) $\dfrac{13}{24} - \dfrac{5}{24}$ $\dfrac{1}{3}$

50) $\dfrac{19}{30} - \dfrac{3}{30}$ $\dfrac{8}{15}$

51) $\begin{array}{r} \dfrac{21}{10} \\ - \dfrac{9}{10} \\ \hline \end{array}$ $\dfrac{6}{5}$ or $1\dfrac{1}{5}$

52) $\begin{array}{r} \dfrac{23}{8} \\ - \dfrac{5}{8} \\ \hline \end{array}$ $\dfrac{9}{4}$ or $2\dfrac{1}{4}$

53) $\dfrac{89}{15} - \dfrac{28}{15}$ $\dfrac{61}{15}$ or $4\dfrac{1}{15}$

54) $\dfrac{103}{19} - \dfrac{47}{19}$ $\dfrac{56}{19}$ or $2\dfrac{18}{19}$

55) $\dfrac{11}{18} - \dfrac{5}{18} - \dfrac{6}{18}$ 0

56) $\dfrac{17}{12} - \dfrac{9}{12} - \dfrac{8}{12}$ 0

Fill in the blank with a fraction to make both sides of the equation equal.

57) $\dfrac{3}{7} + $ ____ $= \dfrac{5}{7}$ $\dfrac{2}{7}$

58) $\dfrac{4}{9} + $ ____ $= \dfrac{8}{9}$ $\dfrac{4}{9}$

59) $\dfrac{1}{6} + $ ____ $= \dfrac{5}{6}$ $\dfrac{4}{6}$

60) $\dfrac{7}{10} + $ ____ $= \dfrac{9}{10}$ $\dfrac{2}{10}$

61) $\dfrac{1}{2} + $ ____ $= 2$ $\dfrac{3}{2}$

62) $\dfrac{3}{5} + $ ____ $= 1$ $\dfrac{2}{5}$

63) $\dfrac{7}{3} - $ ____ $= \dfrac{1}{3}$ $\dfrac{6}{3}$

64) $\dfrac{7}{4} - $ ____ $= \dfrac{3}{4}$ $\dfrac{4}{4}$

Mixed Exercises: Objectives 2 and 3

Perform the indicated operations.

65) $\dfrac{7}{9} + \dfrac{8}{9} - \dfrac{3}{9}$ $\dfrac{4}{3}$ or $1\dfrac{1}{3}$
66) $\dfrac{4}{5} + \dfrac{13}{5} - \dfrac{1}{5}$ $\dfrac{16}{5}$ or $3\dfrac{1}{5}$

67) $\dfrac{7}{4} - \dfrac{3}{4}$ 1
68) $\dfrac{19}{10} - \dfrac{9}{10}$ 1

69) $\dfrac{19}{16} - \dfrac{7}{16} + \dfrac{2}{16}$ $\dfrac{7}{8}$
70) $\dfrac{17}{20} - \dfrac{12}{20} + \dfrac{3}{20}$ $\dfrac{2}{5}$

71) $\dfrac{2}{11} + \dfrac{5}{11}$ $\dfrac{7}{11}$
72) $\dfrac{4}{17} + \dfrac{8}{17}$ $\dfrac{12}{17}$

73) $\dfrac{27}{12} - \dfrac{17}{12} + \dfrac{22}{12}$ $\dfrac{8}{3}$ or $2\dfrac{2}{3}$
74) $\dfrac{23}{30} - \dfrac{11}{30} + \dfrac{39}{30}$ $\dfrac{17}{10}$ or $1\dfrac{7}{10}$

R Rethink

R1) Write a general statement that will help you add or subtract like fractions.

R2) Write an application problem involving three left-over pizzas, each of which was cut into 10 slices.

R3) Was this a difficult topic to understand? Think about how long it took you to complete the exercises.

4.2 Least Common Multiples

P Prepare

O Organize

What are your objectives for Section 4.2?	How can you accomplish each objective?
1 Find the Least Common Multiple (LCM)	• Describe the process of finding multiples. • Write the definition of the *least common multiple* (*LCM*). • Make a chart that describes the different ways to find the LCM. • Complete the given examples on your own. • Complete You Trys 1–3.
2 Find the LCM Using Prime Factorization	• Write the procedure for **Finding the LCM Using Prime Factorization** in your own words. • Complete the given example on your own by comparing it to the procedure presented. • Complete You Try 4.

W Work

Read the explanations, follow the examples, take notes, and complete the You Trys.

In Section 4.1, we learned that we could add and subtract fractions *only* if they have the same denominator. That is, they must be *like fractions*.

If we are asked to add or subtract *unlike* fractions, such as $\dfrac{2}{5} + \dfrac{1}{3}$ or $\dfrac{8}{9} - \dfrac{5}{6}$, then we must first write the fractions with the same denominator. Before we can do this, we must learn about the *least common multiple,* or *LCM,* of a group of numbers.

1 Find the Least Common Multiple (LCM)

What is a multiple? Let's look at some multiples of 3.

$$1 \cdot 3 = 3 \qquad \text{3 is a multiple of 3.}$$
$$2 \cdot 3 = 6 \qquad \text{6 is a multiple of 3.}$$
$$3 \cdot 3 = 9 \qquad \text{9 is a multiple of 3.}$$
$$4 \cdot 3 = 12 \qquad \text{12 is a multiple of 3.}$$

We find multiples of 3 by multiplying 3 by natural numbers. We can also think of multiples in terms of division. Notice that every multiple of 3 is divisible by 3.

So what is a least common multiple, or LCM?

Definition

The **least common multiple,** or **LCM,** of a group of natural numbers is the smallest natural number divisible by each number in the group.

Example: The LCM of 2 and 3 is 6 because 6 is the smallest number divisible by both 2 and 3.

There are different ways to find the least common multiple of a group of numbers. To use the first method, we begin by listing some multiples of each number. Then, the least common multiple (LCM) is the *smallest* number that appears on each list.

| **EXAMPLE 1** | Find the least common multiple of: |

In-Class Example 1

Find the least common multiple of:
a) 8 and 12.
b) 5, 8, and 20.

Answer:
a) 24 b) 40

a) 4 and 6.   b) 5, 10, and 15.

Solution

a) List some multiples of 4 and 6.

Multiples of 4: 4, 8, 12, 16, 20, 24, ...
Multiples of 6: 6, 12, 18, 24, 30, 36, ...

(The three dots at the end of each list mean that the list continues forever in the same pattern.)

Notice that *two* numbers appear on each list: 12 and 24. So, 12 and 24 are both common multiples of 4 and 6, but **12 is the least common multiple (LCM)** because it is the *smallest* number on each list.

b) List some multiples of 5, 10, and 15.

Multiples of 5: 5, 10, 15, 20, 25, 30, ...
Multiples of 10: 10, 20, 30, 40, 50, 60, ...
Multiples of 15: 15, 30, 45, 60, 75, 90 ...

The LCM of 5, 10, and 15 is 30 because it is the smallest number that appears on each list.

[YOU TRY 1] Find the least common multiple of:

a) 6 and 9.   b) 3, 9, and 12.

Note

The least common multiple of a group of different *prime* numbers is always the product of the primes.

Example: The numbers 5 and 7 are prime. Their LCM is 5 · 7 = 35.

If the numbers are easy to work with, we should be able to find the LCM without making a list or writing anything on paper.

EXAMPLE 2

Find the least common multiple of 4 and 10 by inspection.

Solution

Ask yourself, *"What is the smallest number that is divisible by both 4 and 10?"* That number is 20. Therefore, the LCM of 4 and 10 is 20.

[YOU TRY 2] Find the least common multiple of 4 and 8 by inspection.

We can also find the LCM by first finding multiples of the larger number and then finding the smallest of those that is divisible by the other numbers in the group.

EXAMPLE 3

 Hint

Which process do you find easiest to use?

Find the least common multiple of 12 and 16 by first making a list of multiples of the larger number.

Solution

The larger of the two numbers is 16, so make a list of some multiples of 16.

Multiples of 16: 16, 32, 48, 64, 80, ...

Are any of the numbers on the list divisible by 12? Yes! 48 is divisible by 12.

The LCM of 12 and 16 is 48.

[YOU TRY 3] Find the least common multiple of 15 and 20 by first making a list of multiples of the larger number.

2 Find the LCM Using Prime Factorization

We can also use prime factorization to find the least common multiple of a group of numbers.

Procedure Finding the Least Common Multiple Using Prime Factorization

Step 1: Write the prime factorization of each number.

Step 2: Identify the factors that will be in the least common multiple. The LCM will contain each different factor the *greatest* number of times it appears in any single factorization.

Step 3: The LCM is the *product* of the factors identified in Step 2.

Note

This is a good method to use when we are trying to find the LCM of larger numbers.

EXAMPLE 4

Find the LCM of each group of numbers using prime factorization.

a) 8 and 12   b) 14 and 21   c) 6, 15, and 27

Solution

a)   Begin by writing the prime factorizations of 8 and 12. Use one of the methods from Section 3.3.

$$\text{2 factors of 2}$$

Step 1: $8 = \underbrace{2 \cdot 2 \cdot 2}_{\text{3 factors of 2}}$ and $12 = \overbrace{2 \cdot 2} \cdot \underset{\downarrow}{3}$
$$\text{1 factor of 3}$$

Step 2: The LCM will contain each different factor the *greatest* number of times it appears in any single factorization.

The LCM will contain $\underbrace{2 \cdot 2 \cdot 2}_{\text{Use 3 factors of 2.}}$ and $\underset{\text{Use 1 factor of 3.}}{3}$.

Step 3: The LCM is the *product* of the factors identified in Step 2.

The LCM of 8 and 12 is $2 \cdot 2 \cdot 2 \cdot 3 = 24$.

b)   **Step 1:** Write the prime factorizations of 14 and 21.

$$14 = \underset{\text{1 factor of 2}}{2} \cdot \underset{\text{1 factor of 7}}{7} \quad \text{and} \quad 21 = \underset{\text{1 factor of 3}}{3} \cdot \underset{\text{1 factor of 7}}{7}$$

Step 2: The LCM will contain each different factor the *greatest* number of times it appears in any single factorization.

The LCM will contain 2, 3, and 7.   Use 1 factor of 2, 3, and 7.

Step 3: The LCM is the *product* of the factors identified in Step 2.

The LCM of 14 and 21 is $2 \cdot 3 \cdot 7 = 42$.

c) **Step 1:** Write the prime factorizations of 6, 15, and 27.

$$6 = \underset{\substack{\downarrow \\ \text{1 factor of 2}}}{2} \cdot 3 \qquad 15 = 3 \cdot \underset{\substack{\downarrow \\ \text{1 factor of 5}}}{5} \qquad \text{and} \qquad 27 = \underset{\text{3 factors of 3}}{\underbrace{3 \cdot 3 \cdot 3}}$$

Step 2: The LCM will contain each different factor the *greatest* number of times it appears in any single factorization.

The LCM will contain 2, $\underset{\text{Use 3 factors of 3.}}{\underbrace{3 \cdot 3 \cdot 3}}$, and 5.   Use 1 factor of 2 and 5.

Step 3: The LCM is the *product* of the factors identified in Step 2.

The LCM of 6, 15, and 27 is $2 \cdot 3 \cdot 3 \cdot 3 \cdot 5 = 270$.

$\left[\text{YOU TRY 4}\right]$ Find the LCM of each group of numbers using prime factorization.

a) 18 and 30   b) 15 and 21   c) 18, 54, and 60

Note

It is very important that you understand the different methods for finding the least common multiple. We will use these methods to find least common denominators of fractions with unlike denominators.

ANSWERS TO $\left[\text{YOU TRY}\right]$ **EXERCISES**

1) a) 18 b) 36   2) 8   3) 60   4) a) 90 b) 105 c) 540

E Evaluate **4.2** Exercises   Do the exercises, and check your work.

*Additional answers can be found in the Answers to Exercises appendix.

Objective 1: Find the Least Common Multiple (LCM)

1) In your own words, define the *least common multiple* of a group of numbers.   Answers may vary.

2) Is this statement true or false? Explain your answer.
   The least common multiple of 6 and 12 is 24.
   False. 24 is a multiple of 6 and 12, but the *least common multiple* is 12.

Find the least common multiple of each group of numbers by inspection or by making a list of multiples of both numbers.

 3) 2 and 4   4   4) 3 and 9   9

5) 3 and 12   12   6) 5 and 15   15

7) 4 and 10   20   8) 6 and 8   24

9) 12 and 36 36   10) 10 and 20 20

11) 10, 20, and 40 40   12) 9, 18, and 36 36

13) 2, 5, and 6 30   14) 2, 3, and 8 24

15) 3, 5, and 6 30   16) 4, 5, and 10 20

Find the least common multiple of each group of numbers by first making a list of multiples of the larger number.

17) 3 and 7 21   18) 5 and 9 45

19) 12 and 20 60   20) 10 and 15 30

21) 15 and 25 75   22) 16 and 24 48

23) 3, 5, and 10 30   24) 3, 12, and 18 36

25) 4, 9, and 24 72   26) 6, 15, and 25 150

27) 4, 5, 8, and 10 40   28) 3, 5, 6, and 10 30

29) 6, 8, 9, and 15 360 30) 4, 6, 10, and 36 180

Determine whether each statement is *always, sometimes,* or *never* true.

31) The LCM of two different prime numbers is the product of the two numbers. always

32) The LCM of two different prime numbers is a prime number. never

33) The LCM of two numbers is the product of the two numbers. sometimes

34) The LCM of two even numbers is even. always

35) The LCM of two different odd numbers is odd. always

36) The LCM of an even number and an odd number is odd. never

Objective 2: Find the LCM Using Prime Factorization

Find the LCM of each group of numbers using prime factorization.

37) 7 and 28 28   38) 8 and 56 56

39) 8 and 20 40   40) 9 and 15 45

41) 12 and 54 108   42) 16 and 28 112

43) 50 and 60 300   44) 45 and 54 270

45) 6, 9, and 15 90   46) 6, 16, and 18 144

47) 2, 5, and 11 110   48) 2, 5, and 17 170

49) 8, 24, and 32 96   50) 9, 21, and 30 630

51) 3, 4, 9, and 12 36   52) 2, 3, 6, and 8 24

53) 12, 28, 54, and 126 756   54) 9, 12, 50, and 60 900

R Rethink

R1) Do you know how to use the different methods for finding the least common multiple?

R2) Would you be able to complete exercises similar to those you just finished without any help or notes?

4.3 Finding the Least Common Denominator

P Prepare	**O Organize**

What are your objectives for Section 4.3?	How can you accomplish each objective?
1 Write a Fraction with a Different Denominator	• Understand that this is the opposite process of writing a fraction in lowest terms. • Write the procedure for **Writing a Fraction with a Different Denominator** in your own words. • Complete the given examples on your own. • Complete You Trys 1 and 2.
2 Rewrite Fractions with the Least Common Denominator	• Write the definition of the *least common denominator* (*LCD*) in your own words. • Complete the given examples on your own. • Complete You Trys 3–5.

W Work   **Read the explanations, follow the examples, take notes, and complete the You Trys.**

In Section 3.4, we learned how to write fractions in lowest terms. For example, we can write $\dfrac{18}{27}$ in lowest terms by dividing the numerator and denominator by 9.

$$\frac{18}{27} = \frac{18 \div 9}{27 \div 9} = \frac{2}{3}$$

In order to add and subtract *unlike* fractions, we need to know how to rewrite a fraction as an equivalent fraction with a different denominator. This process is the opposite of writing a fraction in lowest terms.

1   Write a Fraction with a Different Denominator

Let's look at the fractions $\dfrac{1}{2}$ and $\dfrac{3}{6}$ in terms of a figure and on a number line.

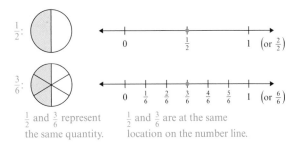

$\dfrac{1}{2}$ and $\dfrac{3}{6}$ represent the same quantity. $\dfrac{1}{2}$ and $\dfrac{3}{6}$ are at the same location on the number line.

The fractions $\dfrac{1}{2}$ and $\dfrac{3}{6}$ are equivalent. We can also show this by writing $\dfrac{3}{6}$ in lowest terms or by beginning with the fraction $\dfrac{1}{2}$ and rewriting it as $\dfrac{3}{6}$ like this:

$$\frac{1}{2} = \frac{1}{2} \cdot \frac{3}{3} = \frac{3}{6}$$

To add and subtract unlike fractions, we must know how to write a given fraction as an equivalent fraction with a different denominator. Let's practice that now.

EXAMPLE 1

In-Class Example 1

Write $\dfrac{2}{5}$ as an equivalent fraction with a denominator of 10.

Answer: $\dfrac{4}{10}$

Write $\dfrac{3}{4}$ as an equivalent fraction with a denominator of 20.

Solution

We must find a fraction that is equivalent to $\dfrac{3}{4}$ so that $\dfrac{3}{4} = \dfrac{?}{20}$.

Ask yourself, *"By what number do I multiply 4 to get 20?"* That number is 5:
$4 \cdot 5 = 20$.

Multiply the numerator *and* denominator of $\dfrac{3}{4}$ by 5: $\dfrac{3}{4} \cdot \dfrac{5}{5} = \dfrac{15}{20}$

$\left(\text{Remember, } \dfrac{5}{5} = 1, \text{ so multiplying } \dfrac{3}{4} \text{ by } \dfrac{5}{5} \text{ does not change the } value \text{ of the fraction;}\right.$
$\left.\text{it gives us an equivalent fraction.}\right)$

[YOU TRY 1]

Rewrite $\dfrac{7}{8}$ as an equivalent fraction with a denominator of 32.

Procedure Writing a Fraction with a Different Denominator

Step 1: Ask yourself, *"By what number do I multiply the original denominator to get the new denominator?"*

Step 2: Multiply the numerator and denominator of the original fraction by that number to get the equivalent fraction.

EXAMPLE 2

In-Class Example 2

Write each fraction with the indicated denominator.

a) $\dfrac{5}{8} = \dfrac{?}{72}$

b) $\dfrac{1}{9} = \dfrac{?}{54}$

Answer:

a) $\dfrac{5}{8} = \dfrac{45}{72}$ b) $\dfrac{1}{9} = \dfrac{6}{54}$

Write each fraction with the indicated denominator.

a) $\dfrac{4}{7} = \dfrac{?}{56}$ b) $\dfrac{1}{12} = \dfrac{?}{72}$

Solution

a) **Step 1:** Ask yourself, *"By what number do I multiply 7 to get 56?"* That number is 8.

Step 2: Multiply the numerator and denominator of $\dfrac{4}{7}$ by 8: $\dfrac{4}{7} \cdot \dfrac{8}{8} = \dfrac{32}{56}$

Therefore, $\dfrac{4}{7} = \dfrac{32}{56}$.

b) **Step 1:** Ask yourself, *"By what number do I multiply 12 to get 72?"* That number is 6.

Step 2: Multiply the numerator and denominator of $\frac{1}{12}$ by 6: $\frac{1}{12} \cdot \frac{6}{6} = \frac{6}{72}$

W Hint

Follow the procedure!

Therefore, $\frac{1}{12} = \frac{6}{72}$.

[YOU TRY 2] Write each fraction with the indicated denominator.

a) $\frac{6}{11} = \frac{?}{77}$ b) $\frac{1}{15} = \frac{?}{45}$

2 Rewrite Fractions with the Least Common Denominator

In the next section, we will learn how to add and subtract fractions with different denominators. First, we must learn how to identify the *least common denominator* of a group of fractions and then write them as equivalent fractions with the least common denominator.

W Hint

How is this different from or similar to finding the LCM?

Definition

The **least common denominator**, or **LCD**, of a group of fractions is the *least common multiple* of the denominators.

Example: The **least common denominator** of $\frac{2}{3}$ and $\frac{1}{6}$ is 6 because 6 is the *least common multiple* of 3 and 6.

EXAMPLE 3

In-Class Example 3

Identify the least common denominator of $\frac{3}{4}$ and $\frac{1}{6}$, then write each fraction as an equivalent fraction with the LCD as its denominator.

Answer:

LCD = 12; $\frac{3}{4} = \frac{9}{12}$, $\frac{1}{6} = \frac{2}{12}$

Identify the least common denominator of $\frac{1}{4}$ and $\frac{5}{6}$, then write each fraction as an equivalent fraction with the LCD as its denominator.

Solution

The least common denominator of $\frac{1}{4}$ and $\frac{5}{6}$ is the least common multiple of 4 and 6. What is the least common multiple of 4 and 6? It is 12. Therefore,

$$LCD = 12$$

Write each fraction with a denominator of 12. We want to find

$$\frac{1}{4} = \frac{?}{12} \qquad \text{and} \qquad \frac{5}{6} = \frac{?}{12}$$

$$\frac{1}{4} \cdot \frac{3}{3} = \frac{3}{12} \qquad\qquad \frac{5}{6} \cdot \frac{2}{2} = \frac{10}{12}$$

W Hint

Always write down the LCD so that you can look at it.

The LCD of $\frac{1}{4}$ and $\frac{5}{6}$ is 12. Then, $\frac{1}{4} = \frac{3}{12}$ and $\frac{5}{6} = \frac{10}{12}$.

Identify the least common denominator of $\frac{4}{5}$ and $\frac{2}{3}$, then write each fraction as an equivalent fraction with the LCD as its denominator.

EXAMPLE 4

In-Class Example 4

For each group of fractions, identify the least common denominator, then write each fraction as an equivalent fraction with the LCD as its denominator.

a) $\frac{9}{10}$ and $\frac{4}{5}$

b) $\frac{11}{24}, \frac{1}{12}$, and $\frac{8}{9}$

Answer:
a) LCD = 10;
$\frac{9}{10}$ already has the LCD,
$\frac{4}{5} = \frac{8}{10}$
b) LCD = 72;
$\frac{11}{24} = \frac{33}{72}, \frac{1}{12} = \frac{6}{72}, \frac{8}{9} = \frac{64}{72}$

For each group of fractions, identify the least common denominator, then write each fraction as an equivalent fraction with the LCD as its denominator.

a) $\frac{7}{9}$ and $\frac{2}{3}$ b) $\frac{9}{20}, \frac{1}{8}$, and $\frac{3}{5}$

Solution

a) The LCD of $\frac{7}{9}$ and $\frac{2}{3}$ is the least common multiple of 9 and 3. The least common multiple of 9 and 3 is 9, so

$$LCD = 9$$

$$\frac{7}{9} = \frac{?}{9} \quad \text{and} \quad \frac{2}{3} = \frac{?}{9}$$

$\frac{7}{9}$ is already written with the LCD. $\frac{2}{3} \cdot \frac{3}{3} = \frac{6}{9}$

The LCD of $\frac{7}{9}$ and $\frac{2}{3}$ is 9, so $\frac{2}{3} = \frac{6}{9}$ and $\frac{7}{9}$ remains the same.

b) Use one of the methods of Section 4.2 to find that the least common multiple of 20, 8, and 5 is 40. Therefore, LCD = 40.

Write each fraction with the LCD.

$$\frac{9}{20} = \frac{?}{40} \qquad \frac{1}{8} = \frac{?}{40} \qquad \frac{3}{5} = \frac{?}{40}$$

$$\frac{9}{20} \cdot \frac{2}{2} = \frac{18}{40} \qquad \frac{1}{8} \cdot \frac{5}{5} = \frac{5}{40} \qquad \frac{3}{5} \cdot \frac{8}{8} = \frac{24}{40}$$

The LCD of $\frac{9}{20}, \frac{1}{8}$, and $\frac{3}{5}$ is 40. Then, $\frac{9}{20} = \frac{18}{40}, \frac{1}{8} = \frac{5}{40}$, and $\frac{3}{5} = \frac{24}{40}$.

$$\left[\text{YOU TRY 4}\right]$$

For each group of fractions, identify the least common denominator, then write each fraction as an equivalent fraction with the LCD as its denominator.

a) $\frac{5}{8}$ and $\frac{9}{16}$ b) $\frac{18}{25}, \frac{7}{10}$, and $\frac{1}{20}$

W Hint

You might need to use the previous methods for finding a LCM to find the LCD.

If the denominators are large, a good way to find their LCD is first to make a list of the multiples of the largest denominator or to use prime factorization.

EXAMPLE 5

In-Class Example 5

Use prime factorization to find the least common denominator of $\frac{5}{36}$ and $\frac{37}{56}$, then write each fraction as an equivalent fraction with the LCD as its denominator.

Answer:
LCD = 504;
$\frac{5}{36} = \frac{70}{504}, \frac{37}{56} = \frac{333}{504}$

Use prime factorization to find the least common denominator of $\frac{25}{36}$ and $\frac{17}{40}$, then write each fraction as an equivalent fraction with the LCD as its denominator.

Solution

The denominators of $\frac{25}{36}$ and $\frac{17}{40}$ are large, so let's use the *prime factorizations* of 36 and 40 to find their least common multiple.

Prime factorizations: $36 = 2 \cdot 2 \cdot 3 \cdot 3$ $40 = 2 \cdot 2 \cdot 2 \cdot 5$

LCM of 36 and 40: $2 \cdot 2 \cdot 2 \cdot 3 \cdot 3 \cdot 5 = 360$

The LCD of $\frac{25}{36}$ and $\frac{17}{40}$ is 360.

Write each fraction with the LCD.

$$\frac{25}{36} = \frac{?}{360} \quad \text{and} \quad \frac{17}{40} = \frac{?}{360}$$

If you do not know, by inspection, what to multiply each fraction by to obtain the fraction with the LCD, go back to each prime factorization. Compare the prime factorizations of the denominators of $\frac{25}{36}$ and $\frac{17}{40}$ to the prime factorization of the LCD of 360 and ask yourself, *"What's missing?"*

Compare

$$36 = 2 \cdot 2 \cdot 3 \cdot 3$$

to

$$360 = 2 \cdot 2 \cdot 2 \cdot 3 \cdot 3 \cdot 5$$

These factors are *not* in 36.

What factors are in 360 that are missing from 36?   2 and 5

Because $2 \cdot 5 = 10$, multiply

$$\frac{25}{36} \cdot \frac{10}{10} = \frac{250}{360}$$

to obtain an equivalent fraction with a denominator of 360.

Compare

$$40 = 2 \cdot 2 \cdot 2 \cdot 5$$

to

$$360 = 2 \cdot 2 \cdot 2 \cdot 3 \cdot 3 \cdot 5$$

These factors are *not* in 40.

What factors are in 360 that are missing from 40? *Two* factors of 3

Because $3 \cdot 3 = 9$, multiply

$$\frac{17}{40} \cdot \frac{9}{9} = \frac{153}{360}$$

to obtain an equivalent fraction with a denominator of 360.

The LCD of $\frac{25}{36}$ and $\frac{17}{40}$ is 360, and $\frac{25}{36} = \frac{250}{360}$ and $\frac{17}{40} = \frac{153}{360}$.

[YOU TRY 5]

Use prime factorization to find the least common denominator of $\frac{59}{84}$ and $\frac{41}{126}$, then write each fraction as an equivalent fraction with the LCD as its denominator.

E Evaluate   **4.3** Exercises   Do the exercises, and check your work.

*Additional answers can be found in the Answers to Exercises appendix.

Objective 1: Write a Fraction with a Different Denominator

In Exercises 1–6, a fraction is given. Use the number lines below to identify its equivalent fraction(s).

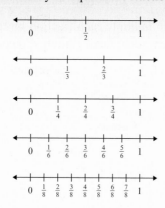

1) $\dfrac{1}{3}$ $\dfrac{2}{6}$

2) $\dfrac{3}{4}$ $\dfrac{6}{8}$

3) $\dfrac{2}{8}$ $\dfrac{1}{4}$

4) $\dfrac{4}{6}$ $\dfrac{2}{3}$

5) $\dfrac{4}{8}$ $\dfrac{3}{6}, \dfrac{2}{4}, \dfrac{1}{2}$

6) $\dfrac{1}{2}$ $\dfrac{2}{4}, \dfrac{3}{6}, \dfrac{4}{8}$

Write each fraction with the indicated denominator.

7) $\dfrac{1}{8} = \dfrac{?}{32}$ $\dfrac{4}{32}$

8) $\dfrac{5}{6} = \dfrac{?}{18}$ $\dfrac{15}{18}$

9) $\dfrac{3}{7} = \dfrac{?}{28}$ $\dfrac{12}{28}$

10) $\dfrac{8}{11} = \dfrac{?}{66}$ $\dfrac{48}{66}$

11) $\dfrac{7}{9} = \dfrac{?}{27}$ $\dfrac{21}{27}$

12) $\dfrac{7}{8} = \dfrac{?}{48}$ $\dfrac{42}{48}$

13) $\dfrac{2}{3} = \dfrac{?}{36}$ $\dfrac{24}{36}$

14) $\dfrac{1}{12} = \dfrac{?}{60}$ $\dfrac{5}{60}$

15) $\dfrac{9}{10} = \dfrac{?}{70}$ $\dfrac{63}{70}$

16) $\dfrac{10}{13} = \dfrac{?}{26}$ $\dfrac{20}{26}$

17) $\dfrac{11}{15} = \dfrac{?}{45}$ $\dfrac{33}{45}$

18) $\dfrac{5}{12} = \dfrac{?}{84}$ $\dfrac{35}{84}$

19) $\dfrac{15}{16} = \dfrac{?}{96}$ $\dfrac{90}{96}$

20) $\dfrac{13}{14} = \dfrac{?}{168}$ $\dfrac{156}{168}$

Objective 2: Rewrite Fractions with the Least Common Denominator

21) What is the least common denominator of a group of fractions?
It is the least common multiple of the denominators.

22) Dana says that the least common denominator of $\dfrac{5}{8}$ and $\dfrac{1}{6}$ is 48, but Inez says that it is 24. Who is right? Inez is right. Although 48 is a common denominator, 24 is the *least* common denominator.

Identify the least common denominator of the two given fractions. Then, write each as an equivalent fraction with the LCD as its denominator.

23) $\dfrac{4}{7}$ and $\dfrac{3}{14}$

24) $\dfrac{3}{4}$ and $\dfrac{11}{12}$

25) $\dfrac{4}{5}$ and $\dfrac{2}{15}$

26) $\dfrac{3}{7}$ and $\dfrac{2}{21}$

27) $\dfrac{3}{8}$ and $\dfrac{5}{12}$

28) $\dfrac{5}{6}$ and $\dfrac{3}{10}$

29) $\dfrac{7}{8}$ and $\dfrac{5}{6}$

30) $\dfrac{4}{9}$ and $\dfrac{3}{4}$

31) $\dfrac{31}{54}$ and $\dfrac{2}{9}$

32) $\dfrac{13}{48}$ and $\dfrac{5}{12}$

33) $\dfrac{7}{12}$ and $\dfrac{3}{20}$

34) $\dfrac{3}{10}$ and $\dfrac{4}{15}$

35) $\dfrac{15}{38}$ and $\dfrac{4}{19}$

36) $\dfrac{21}{22}$ and $\dfrac{9}{11}$

37) $\frac{7}{12}$ and $\frac{8}{9}$ **38)** $\frac{9}{10}$ and $\frac{1}{8}$

39) $\frac{11}{6}$ and $\frac{5}{7}$ **40)** $\frac{10}{7}$ and $\frac{4}{9}$

41) In your own words, explain how to write two fractions as equivalent fractions with the least common denominator.   Answers may vary.

42) Professor Bradley asks his students to write $\frac{1}{4}$ and $\frac{11}{12}$ as equivalent fractions with the least common denominator. Sameer gets $\frac{1}{4} = \frac{6}{24}$ and $\frac{11}{12} = \frac{22}{24}$. Tosh gets $\frac{1}{4} = \frac{3}{12}$ and leaves $\frac{11}{12}$ as it is. Who has used the *least* common denominator?

Identify the least common denominator of the three given fractions. Then, write each as an equivalent fraction with the LCD as its denominator.

43) $\frac{1}{4}, \frac{3}{8},$ and $\frac{1}{16}$ **44)** $\frac{3}{4}, \frac{11}{16},$ and $\frac{1}{32}$

45) $\frac{5}{14}, \frac{1}{2},$ and $\frac{9}{28}$ **46)** $\frac{5}{8}, \frac{1}{6},$ and $\frac{13}{24}$

47) $\frac{5}{12}, \frac{5}{6},$ and $\frac{4}{9}$ **48)** $\frac{1}{20}, \frac{4}{5},$ and $\frac{3}{8}$

49) $\frac{7}{10}, \frac{3}{4},$ and $\frac{1}{5}$ **50)** $\frac{5}{8}, \frac{8}{9},$ and $\frac{1}{6}$

51) $\frac{4}{5}, \frac{1}{6},$ and $\frac{2}{15}$ **52)** $\frac{1}{2}, \frac{2}{3},$ and $\frac{3}{10}$

53) $\frac{2}{9}, \frac{7}{12},$ and $\frac{9}{8}$ **54)** $\frac{5}{12}, \frac{8}{21},$ and $\frac{11}{7}$

Use prime factorization to find the least common denominator of the two fractions. Then, write each fraction as an equivalent fraction with the LCD as its denominator.

55) $\frac{5}{18}$ and $\frac{7}{30}$ **56)** $\frac{3}{16}$ and $\frac{9}{40}$

57) $\frac{5}{32}$ and $\frac{11}{48}$ **58)** $\frac{9}{12}$ and $\frac{7}{28}$

59) $\frac{5}{14}$ and $\frac{3}{26}$ **60)** $\frac{15}{16}$ and $\frac{3}{28}$

61) $\frac{5}{18}$ and $\frac{3}{32}$ **62)** $\frac{13}{28}$ and $\frac{7}{36}$

63) $\frac{13}{78}$ and $\frac{31}{104}$ **64)** $\frac{23}{57}$ and $\frac{45}{76}$

R Rethink

R1) If your friend did not know how to find the least common denominator for a group of fractions, would you be able to explain it to her? How would you explain it?

R2) Which operations would you be able to perform on the fractions in Exercises 55 to 64?

4.4 Adding and Subtracting Unlike Fractions

What are your objectives for Section 4.4?	How can you accomplish each objective?
1 Add Unlike Fractions	• Write the procedure for **Adding or Subtracting Unlike Fractions** in your own words, and add steps from previous sections as needed. • Be sure that the answer is in lowest terms! • Complete the given examples on your own. • Complete You Trys 1–3.
2 Subtract Unlike Fractions	• Use the same procedure you outlined for Objective 1. • Complete the given examples on your own. • Complete You Trys 4 and 5.
3 Add and Subtract Fractions with Large Denominators	• Use prime factorization to find the LCD if needed. • Complete the given example on your own. • Complete You Try 6.
4 Add and Subtract Natural Numbers and Fractions	• Follow Example 7, and outline a procedure for this objective. • Complete the given example on your own. • Complete You Try 7.
5 Solve Applied Problems Involving Adding and Subtracting Fractions	• Use the **Five Steps for Solving Applied Problems** that you previously learned. • Complete the given examples on your own. • Complete You Trys 8 and 9.

W Work   Read the explanations, follow the examples, take notes, and complete the You Trys.

1 Add Unlike Fractions

In this section, we will learn how to add and subtract unlike fractions. Let's think about the addition problem $\frac{1}{2} + \frac{1}{4}$.

As the fractions are written now, we cannot add them because their denominators are different. How *can* we add them? Let's look at some figures as well as some number lines.

We can represent $\frac{1}{2} + \frac{1}{4}$ like this:

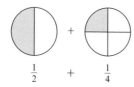

$$\frac{1}{2} \quad + \quad \frac{1}{4}$$

We cannot add halves and fourths because they are not equally-sized pieces of the circles.

If we split the first circle in half again, it will be divided into four equal parts just like the second circle. Now, $\frac{2}{4}$ of the first circle is shaded, and we can add $\frac{2}{4} + \frac{1}{4}$ because fourths are equally-sized pieces of the circle.

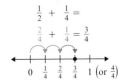

$$\frac{2}{4} \quad + \quad \frac{1}{4} \quad = \quad \frac{3}{4}$$

$\frac{2}{4}$ is equivalent to $\frac{1}{2}$.

Therefore, $\frac{1}{2} + \frac{1}{4} = \frac{2}{4} + \frac{1}{4} = \frac{3}{4}$.

Let's see how we can add $\frac{1}{2} + \frac{1}{4}$ using number lines.

In order to add $\frac{1}{2} + \frac{1}{4}$ using a number line, the denominators must be the same. Do you see on the number lines that $\frac{1}{2} = \frac{2}{4}$?

To add $\frac{1}{2} + \frac{1}{4}$ on a number line, write $\frac{1}{2}$ as $\frac{2}{4}$. Then, use the number line where the space between each tick mark is $\frac{1}{4}$ unit to add the fractions.

$$\frac{1}{2} + \frac{1}{4} =$$
$$\frac{2}{4} + \frac{1}{4} = \frac{3}{4}$$

In order to add $\frac{1}{2} + \frac{1}{4}$ (or any fractions), they must be *like* fractions. In other words, the fractions **must** have a common denominator. The same is true for subtraction.

Note

In order to add or subtract fractions, they **must** have a common denominator.

Procedure Adding or Subtracting Unlike Fractions

Step 1: Determine the least common denominator (LCD), and write it on your paper.

Step 2: Rewrite each fraction with the LCD.

Step 3: Add or subtract.

Step 4: Write the answer in lowest terms.

Note

After finding the sum or difference, look at the result and ask yourself, *"Is the answer in lowest terms?"* If not, write it in lowest terms.

EXAMPLE 1

Add $\dfrac{2}{3} + \dfrac{1}{6}$.

Solution

Step 1: Write down the LCD of $\dfrac{2}{3}$ and $\dfrac{1}{6}$.   LCD = 6

Step 2: Rewrite each fraction with the LCD.

$$\dfrac{2}{3} \cdot \dfrac{2}{2} = \dfrac{4}{6} \qquad \dfrac{1}{6} \text{ already has a denominator of 6.}$$

Step 3: Add.

$$\dfrac{2}{3} + \dfrac{1}{6} = \dfrac{4}{6} + \dfrac{1}{6} = \dfrac{4+1}{6} = \dfrac{5}{6}$$

These fractions are equivalent.

> **W Hint**
> Don't just think about the LCD "in your head." Write it on your paper so you can *look* at it!

Step 4: Ask yourself, *"Is $\dfrac{5}{6}$ in lowest terms?"* Yes. So, $\dfrac{5}{6}$ is the final answer.

[YOU TRY 1]   Add $\dfrac{1}{2} + \dfrac{1}{12}$.

EXAMPLE 2

In-Class Example 2

Add.

a) $\dfrac{1}{6} + \dfrac{6}{8}$ b) $\dfrac{3}{5} + \dfrac{4}{7}$

c) $\dfrac{5}{12} + \dfrac{2}{9} + \dfrac{1}{4}$

Answer:

a) $\dfrac{11}{12}$ b) $\dfrac{41}{35}$ or $1\dfrac{6}{35}$ c) $\dfrac{8}{9}$

Add.

a) $\dfrac{5}{12} + \dfrac{2}{8}$ b) $\dfrac{6}{7} + \dfrac{2}{9}$ c) $\dfrac{2}{15} + \dfrac{1}{6} + \dfrac{3}{10}$

Solution

a) **Step 1:** Write down the LCD of $\dfrac{5}{12}$ and $\dfrac{2}{8}$.   LCD = 24

Step 2: Rewrite each fraction with the LCD.

$$\dfrac{5}{12} \cdot \dfrac{2}{2} = \dfrac{10}{24} \qquad\qquad \dfrac{2}{8} \cdot \dfrac{3}{3} = \dfrac{6}{24}$$

Step 3: Add.

Equivalent fractions

$$\dfrac{5}{12} + \dfrac{2}{8} = \dfrac{10}{24} + \dfrac{6}{24} = \dfrac{10+6}{24} = \dfrac{16}{24}$$

Equivalent fractions

Step 4: Ask yourself, *"Is $\dfrac{16}{24}$ in lowest terms?"* No! Write it in lowest terms.

$$\dfrac{16}{24} = \dfrac{16 \div 8}{24 \div 8} = \dfrac{2}{3}$$

The final answer is $\dfrac{2}{3}$.

b) **Step 1:** Write down the LCD of $\frac{6}{7}$ and $\frac{2}{9}$.   LCD = 63

Step 2: Rewrite each fraction with the LCD.

$$\frac{6}{7} \cdot \frac{9}{9} = \frac{54}{63} \qquad \frac{2}{9} \cdot \frac{7}{7} = \frac{14}{63}$$

Step 3: Add.

Equivalent fractions

$$\frac{6}{7} + \frac{2}{9} = \frac{54}{63} + \frac{14}{63} = \frac{54 + 14}{63} = \frac{68}{63} \text{ or } 1\frac{5}{63}$$

Equivalent fractions

Step 4: Ask yourself, *"Are $\frac{68}{63}$ and $1\frac{5}{63}$ in lowest terms?"* Yes. The final answer is $\frac{68}{63}$ or $1\frac{5}{63}$.

Remember, the final answer may be written as an improper fraction or as a mixed number.

c) **Step 1:** Write down the LCD of $\frac{2}{15}, \frac{1}{6},$ and $\frac{3}{10}.$ LCD = 30

Step 2: Rewrite each fraction with the LCD.

$$\frac{2}{15} \cdot \frac{2}{2} = \frac{4}{30} \qquad \frac{1}{6} \cdot \frac{5}{5} = \frac{5}{30} \qquad \frac{3}{10} \cdot \frac{3}{3} = \frac{9}{30}$$

Step 3: Add.

Equivalent fractions

$$\frac{2}{15} + \frac{1}{6} + \frac{3}{10} = \frac{4}{30} + \frac{5}{30} + \frac{9}{30} = \frac{4 + 5 + 9}{30} = \frac{18}{30}$$

Equivalent fractions   Equivalent fractions

Step 4: Ask yourself, *"Is $\frac{18}{30}$ in lowest terms?"* No! Write it in lowest terms.

$$\frac{18}{30} = \frac{18 \div 6}{30 \div 6} = \frac{3}{5}$$

The final answer is $\frac{3}{5}$.

[YOU TRY 2] Add.

a) $\frac{4}{9} + \frac{2}{6}$ b) $\frac{5}{9} + \frac{5}{8}$ c) $\frac{1}{10} + \frac{7}{15} + \frac{1}{4}$

We can also add fractions vertically.

EXAMPLE 3

In-Class Example 3

Add the fractions vertically.
a) $\frac{2}{9} + \frac{3}{5}$ b) $\frac{11}{12} + \frac{13}{30}$

Answer:
a) $\frac{37}{45}$ b) $\frac{27}{20}$ or $1\frac{7}{20}$

Add the fractions vertically.

a) $\frac{3}{8} + \frac{2}{7}$ b) $\frac{8}{15} + \frac{11}{20}$

Solution

a) Identify the LCD of $\frac{3}{8}$ and $\frac{2}{7}$.

$$LCD = 56$$

Write as equivalent fractions.
↓

$$\frac{3}{8} = \frac{3}{8} \cdot \frac{7}{7} = \frac{21}{56}$$
$$+\frac{2}{7} = \frac{2}{7} \cdot \frac{8}{8} = +\frac{16}{56}$$
$$\frac{37}{56}$$

Ask yourself, *"Is $\frac{37}{56}$ in lowest terms?"*

Yes. The final answer is $\frac{37}{56}$.

b) Identify the LCD of $\frac{8}{15}$ and $\frac{11}{20}$.

$$LCD = 60$$

Write as equivalent fractions.
↓

$$\frac{8}{15} = \frac{8}{15} \cdot \frac{4}{4} = \frac{32}{60}$$
$$+\frac{11}{20} = \frac{11}{20} \cdot \frac{3}{3} = +\frac{33}{60}$$
$$\frac{65}{60}$$

Ask yourself, *"Is $\frac{65}{60}$ in lowest terms?"*

No! Write it in lowest terms.

$$\frac{65}{60} = \frac{65 \div 5}{60 \div 5} = \frac{13}{12} \text{ or } 1\frac{1}{12}$$

Hint

Does adding fractions vertically appear to be more seamless?

[YOU TRY 3]

Add the fractions vertically.

a) $\frac{3}{8} + \frac{6}{11}$ b) $\frac{4}{15} + \frac{9}{10}$

2 Subtract Unlike Fractions

We must write fractions with their least common denominator before subtracting them.

EXAMPLE 4

In-Class Example 4

Subtract.
a) $\frac{5}{6} - \frac{1}{3}$ b) $\frac{7}{8} - \frac{4}{9}$

Answer: a) $\frac{1}{2}$ b) $\frac{31}{72}$

Subtract.

a) $\frac{9}{10} - \frac{2}{5}$ b) $\frac{7}{9} - \frac{5}{12}$

Solution

a) *Step 1:* Write down the LCD of $\frac{9}{10}$ and $\frac{2}{5}$.   LCD = 10

Step 2: Rewrite each fraction with the LCD.

$\frac{9}{10}$ already has the LCD. $\frac{2}{5} \cdot \frac{2}{2} = \frac{4}{10}$

Step 3: Subtract.

$$\frac{9}{10} - \frac{2}{5} = \frac{9}{10} - \frac{4}{10} = \frac{9-4}{10} = \frac{5}{10}$$

These fractions are equivalent.

Step 4: Ask yourself, *"Is* $\frac{5}{10}$ *in lowest terms?"* No! Write it in lowest terms.

$$\frac{5}{10} = \frac{5 \div 5}{10 \div 5} = \frac{1}{2}$$

The final answer is $\frac{1}{2}$.

b) **Step 1:** Write down the LCD of $\frac{7}{9}$ and $\frac{5}{12}$.   LCD = 36

Step 2: Rewrite each fraction with the LCD.

$$\frac{7}{9} \cdot \frac{4}{4} = \frac{28}{36} \qquad \frac{5}{12} \cdot \frac{3}{3} = \frac{15}{36}$$

Step 3: Subtract.

Equivalent fractions

$$\frac{7}{9} - \frac{5}{12} = \frac{28}{36} - \frac{15}{36} = \frac{28-15}{36} = \frac{13}{36}$$

Equivalent fractions

Step 4: Ask yourself, *"Is* $\frac{13}{36}$ *in lowest terms?"* Yes.

[YOU TRY 4]   Subtract.

a) $\frac{11}{12} - \frac{3}{4}$ b) $\frac{5}{6} - \frac{2}{7}$

We can subtract fractions vertically.

EXAMPLE 5

Subtract $\frac{8}{11} - \frac{3}{7}$ vertically.

Solution

Identify the LCD of $\frac{8}{11}$ and $\frac{3}{7}$.   LCD = 77

Write as equivalent fractions.

$$\frac{8}{11} = \frac{8}{11} \cdot \frac{7}{7} = \frac{56}{77}$$
$$-\frac{3}{7} = \frac{3}{7} \cdot \frac{11}{11} = -\frac{33}{77}$$
$$\frac{23}{77}$$

Ask yourself, *"Is* $\frac{23}{77}$ *in lowest terms?"* Yes. The final answer is $\frac{23}{77}$.

[YOU TRY 5] Subtract $\dfrac{10}{11} - \dfrac{7}{12}$ vertically.

3 Add and Subtract Fractions with Large Denominators

If we are asked to add or subtract fractions with large denominators, remember that we can find the least common denominator using prime factorization.

EXAMPLE 6

In-Class Example 6

Add $\dfrac{4}{15} + \dfrac{5}{24}$. Find the LCD using prime factorization.

Answer: $\dfrac{19}{40}$

Add $\dfrac{19}{60} + \dfrac{22}{45}$. Find the LCD using prime factorization.

Solution

Step 1: Find the LCD of $\dfrac{19}{60}$ and $\dfrac{22}{45}$ by first finding the prime factorizations of 60 and 45.

$$60 = 2 \cdot 2 \cdot 3 \cdot 5 \qquad 45 = 3 \cdot 3 \cdot 5$$

The LCD is $2 \cdot 2 \cdot 3 \cdot 3 \cdot 5 = 180$.

Step 2: Rewrite each fraction with the LCD.

$$\dfrac{19}{60} \cdot \dfrac{3}{3} = \dfrac{57}{180} \qquad \dfrac{22}{45} \cdot \dfrac{4}{4} = \dfrac{88}{180}$$

Step 3: Add.

Equivalent fractions

$$\dfrac{19}{60} + \dfrac{22}{45} = \dfrac{57}{180} + \dfrac{88}{180} = \dfrac{57 + 88}{180} = \dfrac{145}{180}$$

Equivalent fractions

Step 4: Ask yourself, *"Is $\dfrac{145}{180}$ in lowest terms?"* No! Write it in lowest terms.

$$\dfrac{145}{180} = \dfrac{145 \div 5}{180 \div 5} = \dfrac{29}{36}$$

The final answer is $\dfrac{29}{36}$.

[YOU TRY 6] Add $\dfrac{5}{18} + \dfrac{3}{28}$. Find the LCD using prime factorization.

Note

When the denominators are large, making a list of multiples of the larger number is also a good way to find the LCD.

4 Add and Subtract Natural Numbers and Fractions

Sometimes, we must add or subtract a group of numbers that includes fractions as well as natural numbers. When we first studied mixed numbers, we learned that $1\frac{3}{4}$ means $1 + \frac{3}{4}$. So, the sum $1 + \frac{3}{4}$ equals the mixed number $1\frac{3}{4}$. (We will learn how to add and subtract mixed numbers in Section 4.5.)

In some situations, however, it is important to understand how to find a sum, like $2 + \frac{3}{8}$, or a difference, like $1 - \frac{2}{5}$, by writing the natural number as a fraction first.

EXAMPLE 7

Hint

Write a procedure in your own words for this objective.

Add or subtract by first changing the natural number to an improper fraction.

a) $2 + \frac{3}{8}$ b) $1 - \frac{2}{5}$

Solution

a) Write 2 as an improper fraction with a denominator of 1: $2 = \frac{2}{1}$

We can write the sum as $2 + \frac{3}{8} = \underbrace{\frac{2}{1}}_{\text{Write 2 as a fraction with a denominator of 1.}} + \frac{3}{8}$.

Now, follow the steps for adding unlike fractions to add $\frac{2}{1} + \frac{3}{8}$.

Step 1: Write down the LCD of $\frac{2}{1}$ and $\frac{3}{8}$.   LCD = 8

Step 2: Rewrite each fraction with the LCD.

$$\frac{2}{1} \cdot \frac{8}{8} = \frac{16}{8} \qquad \frac{3}{8} \text{ is already written with the LCD.}$$

Step 3: Add.

$$2 + \frac{3}{8} = \frac{2}{1} + \frac{3}{8} = \frac{16}{8} + \frac{3}{8} = \frac{19}{8}$$

(Equivalent fractions; Write 2 as $\frac{2}{1}$.)

Step 4: Ask yourself, *"Is $\frac{19}{8}$ in lowest terms?"* Yes. The final answer is $\frac{19}{8}$ or $2\frac{3}{8}$.

b) Write 1 as an improper fraction with a denominator of 1: $1 = \frac{1}{1}$

We can write the difference as $1 - \frac{2}{5} = \frac{1}{1} - \frac{2}{5}$.

Now, follow the steps for subtracting unlike fractions to find $\frac{1}{1} - \frac{2}{5}$.

Step 1: Write down the LCD of $\dfrac{1}{1}$ and $\dfrac{2}{5}$. LCD = 5

Step 2: Rewrite each fraction with the LCD.

$$\dfrac{1}{1}\cdot\dfrac{5}{5}=\dfrac{5}{5}\qquad \dfrac{2}{5}\ \text{is already written with the LCD.}$$

Step 3: Subtract.

Equivalent fractions

$$1-\dfrac{2}{5}=\dfrac{1}{1}-\dfrac{2}{5}=\dfrac{5}{5}-\dfrac{2}{5}=\dfrac{3}{5}$$

Write 1 with a
denominator of 1.

Step 4: Ask yourself, *"Is $\dfrac{3}{5}$ in lowest terms?"* Yes.

[YOU TRY 7] Add or subtract by first changing the natural number to an improper fraction.

a) $4+\dfrac{2}{3}$ b) $1-\dfrac{5}{8}$

Note

In algebra, it is very important to understand how to add and subtract in this way.

Many applications involve adding and subtracting fractions.

5 Solve Applied Problems Involving Adding and Subtracting Fractions

EXAMPLE 8

Mariah has a piece of craft wire that is $\dfrac{7}{8}$ ft long. She cuts off a piece that is $\dfrac{2}{3}$ ft long to make an ornament. How much wire remains?

Solution

Step 1: **Read** the problem carefully, and restate it in your own words.

A piece of <u>wire is $\dfrac{7}{8}$ ft long</u>, and a piece that is $\dfrac{2}{3}$ <u>ft long is cut off</u>. <u>Determine the amount</u> of wire <u>that remains</u>.

Step 2: **Make a plan.** Let's underline important words in our restatement of the problem in Step 1. Then, draw a picture to show what is happening in the problem.

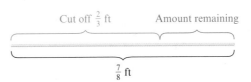

Cut off $\frac{2}{3}$ ft   Amount remaining

$\frac{7}{8}$ ft

Plan: Subtract $\frac{2}{3}$ from $\frac{7}{8}$.

Step 3: **Solve** the problem.

$$\frac{7}{8} - \frac{2}{3} = \frac{21}{24} - \frac{16}{24} \qquad \text{Rewrite each fraction with the LCD.}$$

$$= \frac{5}{24} \qquad \text{Subtract.}$$

Step 4: **State the answer** in a complete sentence.

The amount of wire remaining is $\frac{5}{24}$ ft.

Step 5: **Check** the answer.

$$\begin{array}{ccc} \text{Amount of wire} & + & \text{Amount of wire} & = & \text{Total length} \\ \text{cut off} & & \text{remaining} & & \text{of wire} \end{array}$$

$$\frac{2}{3} \quad + \quad \frac{5}{24} \quad = \quad \frac{16}{24} + \frac{5}{24} = \frac{21}{24} = \frac{7}{8}$$

The total length of the wire is $\frac{7}{8}$ ft. The answer is correct.

[YOU TRY 8]

A carpenter has a piece of window trim that is $\frac{11}{12}$ yd long. He cuts off a piece that is $\frac{3}{4}$ yd long. How much window trim remains?

We can read information from a chart to solve problems.

EXAMPLE 9

W Hint
Recognize that all the pieces add up to 1 in this type of chart.

At an urban elementary school, many students come from homes where English is not the primary language. The pie chart shows the fractions of the 576 students who speak a given language at home.

a) What is the fraction of students who speak English or Chinese at home?

b) How many students speak English or Chinese at home?

c) For what fraction of the students is English *not* the primary language at home?

d) How many students speak a language other than English at home?

Language Spoken at Home as a Fraction of the Student Body

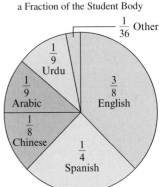

In-Class Example 9

Use the pie chart in Example 9 to answer the following questions.
a) What is the fraction of students who speak Arabic or Spanish at home?
b) How many students speak Arabic or Spanish at home?
c) Use Example 9c.
d) Use Example 9d.

Answer:

a) $\dfrac{13}{36}$ of the students speak Arabic or Spanish at home.

b) 208 students speak Arabic or Spanish at home.

c) See Example 9c.
d) See Example 9d.

Solution

a) Find the English and Chinese sections in the pie chart. The $\dfrac{3}{8}$ in the English section means that $\dfrac{3}{8}$ of the students speak English at home. The $\dfrac{1}{8}$ in the Chinese section means that $\dfrac{1}{8}$ of the students speak Chinese at home. *Add the fractions* to determine the fraction of students who speak English or Chinese at home.

$$
\begin{array}{ccc}
\text{Fraction who} & + & \text{Fraction who} & = & \text{Fraction who speak} \\
\text{speak English} & & \text{speak Chinese} & & \text{English or Chinese} \\
\dfrac{3}{8} & + & \dfrac{1}{8} & = & \dfrac{4}{8}
\end{array}
$$

Write $\dfrac{4}{8}$ in lowest terms: $\dfrac{4}{8} = \dfrac{4 \div 4}{8 \div 4} = \dfrac{1}{2}$

$\dfrac{1}{2}$ of the students speak English or Chinese at home.

b) In part a), we determined that $\dfrac{1}{2}$ *of* the total number of students speak English or Chinese at home. The *of* indicates multiplication. To determine the *number* of students who speak English or Chinese at home, find $\dfrac{1}{2}$ *of* 576 students or $\dfrac{1}{2} \cdot 576$.

$$
\dfrac{1}{2} \cdot 576 = \dfrac{1}{2} \cdot \dfrac{576}{1} = \dfrac{1}{2} \cdot \dfrac{\overset{288}{\cancel{576}}}{\underset{1}{1}} = \dfrac{288}{1} = 288
$$

Write 576 with a denominator of 1.

288 students speak English or Chinese at home.

c) We can determine the fraction of students for whom English is *not* the primary language at home in two ways:

Method 1: Add up all the pieces of the pie *except* for the English piece.

$$
\dfrac{1}{4} + \dfrac{1}{8} + \dfrac{1}{9} + \dfrac{1}{9} + \dfrac{1}{36} = \dfrac{18}{72} + \dfrac{9}{72} + \dfrac{8}{72} + \dfrac{8}{72} + \dfrac{2}{72} = \dfrac{45}{72} = \dfrac{5}{8}
$$

$\dfrac{5}{8}$ of the students do not speak English as the primary language at home.

Method 2: All the fractions in the pie add up to 1 because it is 1 *whole* pie. If we take 1 whole pie and remove the "English slice," we will be left with the fraction of students who do *not* speak English as the primary language at home.

$$
\begin{array}{ccc}
1 \text{ whole pie} & - & \text{Fraction who speak} & = & \text{Fraction who do } not \text{ speak} \\
& & \text{English at home} & & \text{English at home} \\
1 & - & \dfrac{3}{8} & = & \dfrac{8}{8} - \dfrac{3}{8} \qquad \text{Write 1 as } \dfrac{8}{8}. \\
& & & = & \dfrac{5}{8} \qquad\qquad \text{Subtract.}
\end{array}
$$

$\dfrac{5}{8}$ of the students do not speak English as the primary language at home.

While either method gives us the same result, the second method is shorter.

d) In part c), we determined that $\frac{5}{8}$ of the total number of students do not speak English as the primary language at home. The *of* indicates multiplication. To determine the *number* of students who speak a language other than English at home, find $\frac{5}{8}$ of 576 students or $\frac{5}{8} \cdot 576$.

$$\frac{5}{8} \cdot 576 = \frac{5}{8} \cdot \frac{576}{1} = \frac{5}{8} \cdot \frac{\overset{72}{\cancel{576}}}{\underset{1}{1}} = \frac{360}{1} = 360$$

Write 576 with a denominator of 1.

360 of the 576 students speak a language other than English at home.

[YOU TRY 9]

Use the pie chart in Example 9 to answer these questions.

a) What is the fraction of students who speak English, Urdu, or "other" language at home?

b) How many students speak English, Urdu, or "other" language at home?

c) For what fraction of the students is Spanish *not* the primary language spoken at home?

d) How many students speak a language other than Spanish at home?

ANSWERS TO [YOU TRY] EXERCISES

1) $\frac{7}{12}$ 2) a) $\frac{7}{9}$ b) $\frac{85}{72}$ or $1\frac{13}{72}$ c) $\frac{49}{60}$ 3 a) $\frac{81}{88}$ b) $\frac{7}{6}$ or $1\frac{1}{6}$ 4 a) $\frac{1}{6}$ b) $\frac{23}{42}$ 5) $\frac{43}{132}$

6) $\frac{97}{252}$ 7 a) $\frac{14}{3}$ or $4\frac{2}{3}$ b) $\frac{3}{8}$ 8) The amount of window trim remaining is $\frac{1}{6}$ yd.

9) a) $\frac{37}{72}$ of the students speak English, Urdu, or "other" language at home.

b) 296 students speak English, Urdu, or "other" language at home.

c) Spanish is not the primary language spoken at home for $\frac{3}{4}$ of the students.

d) 432 students speak a language other than Spanish at home.

E Evaluate 4.4 Exercises   Do the exercises, and check your work.

*Additional answers can be found in the Answers to Exercises appendix.

Objective 1: Add Unlike Fractions

For Exercises 1–8, use the number lines below to identify the least common denominator, and add the fractions on the appropriate number line.

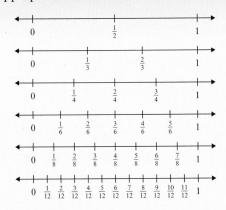

1) $\frac{1}{2}$ and $\frac{1}{3}$ LCD = 6; $\frac{5}{6}$ 2) $\frac{1}{3}$ and $\frac{1}{4}$ LCD = 12; $\frac{7}{12}$

3) $\frac{1}{2}$ and $\frac{1}{6}$ LCD = 6; $\frac{2}{3}$ 4) $\frac{1}{4} + \frac{1}{8}$ LCD = 8; $\frac{3}{8}$

5) $\frac{5}{12}$ and $\frac{1}{4}$ LCD = 12; $\frac{2}{3}$ 6) $\frac{3}{4}$ and $\frac{1}{12}$ LCD = 12; $\frac{5}{6}$

7) $\frac{1}{4} + \frac{1}{6} + \frac{1}{12}$ LCD = 12; $\frac{1}{2}$ 8) $\frac{1}{2} + \frac{1}{3} + \frac{1}{12}$ LCD = 12; $\frac{11}{12}$

9) Diane adds these fractions this way: $\frac{1}{5} + \frac{3}{4} = \frac{4}{9}$. What did she do wrong? What is the right way to add these fractions?

10) Is this statement true or false? *The least common denominator of* $\frac{5}{6}$ *and* $\frac{7}{10}$ *is* 60.   False. The LCD is 30.

11) In your own words, explain how to add unlike fractions.   Answers may vary.

12) If the sum of two fractions is $\frac{13}{5}$, can it also be written as $2\frac{3}{5}$?   Yes. The answer can be written as an improper fraction or as a mixed number.

Add.

13) $\frac{1}{3} + \frac{5}{12}$ $\frac{3}{4}$

14) $\frac{1}{6} + \frac{7}{18}$ $\frac{5}{9}$

15) $\frac{1}{2} + \frac{2}{3}$ $\frac{7}{6}$ or $1\frac{1}{6}$

16) $\frac{2}{3} + \frac{2}{5}$ $\frac{16}{15}$ or $1\frac{1}{15}$

17) $\frac{4}{9} + \frac{15}{27}$ 1

18) $\frac{3}{8} + \frac{35}{56}$ 1

19) $\frac{3}{8} + \frac{5}{12}$ $\frac{19}{24}$

20) $\frac{2}{9} + \frac{1}{6}$ $\frac{7}{18}$

21) $\frac{5}{6} + \frac{9}{20}$ $\frac{77}{60}$ or $1\frac{17}{60}$

22) $\frac{9}{10} + \frac{11}{15}$ $\frac{49}{30}$ or $1\frac{19}{30}$

23) $\frac{7}{12} + \frac{3}{7}$ $\frac{85}{84}$ or $1\frac{1}{84}$

24) $\frac{7}{8} + \frac{2}{9}$ $\frac{79}{72}$ or $1\frac{7}{72}$

25) $\frac{1}{2} + \frac{1}{4} + \frac{1}{8}$ $\frac{7}{8}$

26) $\frac{1}{3} + \frac{1}{6} + \frac{1}{9}$ $\frac{11}{18}$

27) $\frac{3}{10} + \frac{3}{20} + \frac{5}{8}$ $\frac{43}{40}$ or $1\frac{3}{40}$

28) $\frac{5}{6} + \frac{7}{8} + \frac{5}{12}$ $\frac{17}{8}$ or $2\frac{1}{8}$

29) $\frac{1}{4} + \frac{11}{12} + \frac{5}{6}$ 2

30) $\frac{9}{10} + \frac{1}{4} + \frac{17}{20}$ 2

31) $\frac{7}{16} + \frac{11}{24} + \frac{2}{3}$ $\frac{25}{16}$ or $1\frac{9}{16}$

32) $\frac{7}{24} + \frac{5}{9} + \frac{11}{18}$ $\frac{35}{24}$ or $1\frac{11}{24}$

Add the fractions vertically.

33) $\frac{5}{6} + \frac{3}{4}$ $\frac{19}{12}$ or $1\frac{7}{12}$

34) $\frac{3}{8} + \frac{2}{3}$ $\frac{25}{24}$ or $1\frac{1}{24}$

35) $\frac{7}{10} + \frac{1}{6}$ $\frac{13}{15}$

36) $\frac{5}{6} + \frac{1}{10}$ $\frac{14}{15}$

37) $\frac{5}{8} + \frac{3}{14}$ $\frac{47}{56}$

38) $\frac{3}{28} + \frac{1}{12}$ $\frac{4}{21}$

Objective 2: Subtract Unlike Fractions
Subtract.

39) $\frac{6}{7} - \frac{13}{21}$ $\frac{5}{21}$

40) $\frac{3}{4} - \frac{3}{8}$ $\frac{3}{8}$

41) $\frac{5}{8} - \frac{7}{24}$ $\frac{1}{3}$

42) $\frac{4}{5} - \frac{3}{10}$ $\frac{1}{2}$

43) $\frac{8}{9} - \frac{2}{5}$ $\frac{22}{45}$

44) $\frac{10}{11} - \frac{1}{4}$ $\frac{29}{44}$

45) $\frac{6}{8} - \frac{3}{4}$ 0

46) $\frac{9}{15} - \frac{3}{5}$ 0

47) $\frac{11}{15} - \frac{3}{10}$ $\frac{13}{30}$

48) $\frac{7}{8} - \frac{5}{12}$ $\frac{11}{24}$

Subtract the fractions vertically.

49) $\frac{11}{12} - \frac{2}{9}$ $\frac{25}{36}$

50) $\frac{13}{15} - \frac{3}{4}$ $\frac{7}{60}$

51) $\frac{5}{12} - \frac{3}{11}$ $\frac{19}{132}$

52) $\frac{7}{12} - \frac{3}{7}$ $\frac{13}{84}$

53) $\frac{9}{10} - \frac{1}{6}$ $\frac{11}{15}$

54) $\frac{9}{16} - \frac{1}{6}$ $\frac{19}{48}$

55) Do you prefer to add and subtract fractions horizontally or vertically? Why?   Answers may vary.

56) True or false: $\frac{7}{10} - \frac{7}{8} = \frac{0}{2} = 0$ false

Objective 3: Add and Subtract Fractions with Large Denominators

57) When is prime factorization a good method for finding a least common denominator?
when the denominators are large

58) In addition to prime factorization, what is another good method for finding the LCD of fractions with large denominators?
Make a list of multiples of the largest denominator.

Add or subtract as indicated. Find the LCD using prime factorization.

59) $\frac{14}{45} + \frac{17}{30}$ $\frac{79}{90}$

60) $\frac{7}{20} + \frac{12}{35}$ $\frac{97}{140}$

61) $\frac{23}{42} + \frac{13}{24}$ $\frac{61}{56}$ or $1\frac{5}{56}$

62) $\frac{31}{36} + \frac{19}{42}$ $\frac{331}{252}$ or $1\frac{79}{252}$

63) $\frac{11}{24} - \frac{9}{28}$ $\frac{23}{168}$

64) $\frac{31}{36} - \frac{3}{16}$ $\frac{97}{144}$

65) $\frac{47}{56} + \frac{29}{32}$ $\frac{391}{224}$ or $1\frac{167}{224}$

66) $\frac{11}{18} + \frac{17}{26}$ $\frac{148}{117}$ or $1\frac{31}{117}$

67) $\frac{32}{35} - \frac{8}{15} - \frac{8}{21}$ 0

68) $\frac{19}{24} - \frac{3}{56} - \frac{31}{42}$ 0

Objective 4: Add and Subtract Natural Numbers and Fractions

Add or subtract by first changing the natural number to an improper fraction.

69) $5 + \dfrac{1}{4}$ $\frac{21}{4}$ or $5\frac{1}{4}$

70) $3 + \dfrac{1}{8}$ $\frac{25}{8}$ or $3\frac{1}{8}$

 71) $4 + \dfrac{3}{7}$ $\frac{31}{7}$ or $4\frac{3}{7}$

72) $2 + \dfrac{5}{6}$ $\frac{17}{6}$ or $2\frac{5}{6}$

73) $3 - \dfrac{2}{9}$ $\frac{25}{9}$ or $2\frac{7}{9}$

74) $2 - \dfrac{3}{4}$ $\frac{5}{4}$ or $1\frac{1}{4}$

Objective 5: Solve Applied Problems Involving Adding and Subtracting Fractions

Solve the application problem.

75) An electrician has a wire that is $\dfrac{5}{6}$ yd long. He cuts off a piece that is $\dfrac{4}{9}$ yd long. How much wire is left? $\frac{7}{18}$ yd

76) A plumber has a piece of copper pipe that is $\dfrac{3}{4}$ ft long. She cuts off a piece that is $\dfrac{3}{8}$ ft long. How much of the pipe remains? $\frac{3}{8}$ ft

77) A surgeon had a 1-ft-long piece of surgical thread for closing an incision. She used $\dfrac{7}{12}$ ft during the surgery. How much of the thread was not used? $\frac{5}{12}$ ft

78) A computer technician had a 1-in.-long piece of wire, and he used $\dfrac{5}{16}$ in. while making repairs. How much of the wire was not used? $\frac{11}{16}$ in.

79) Rowena opens a lemonade stand. She wishes to line the perimeter of her table with decorative lemon-colored cloth. If the table is $\dfrac{4}{5}$ yd long and $\dfrac{3}{4}$ yd wide, what amount of cloth will she need to line the perimeter of the table?

80) At a science fair, Valerie hopes to impress the judges by lining the perimeter of her two poster boards with a string of blinking lights. If each poster board is $\dfrac{7}{9}$ yd long and $\dfrac{11}{18}$ yd wide, what length of blinking lights is needed to line the perimeter of both poster boards? Valerie needs $5\frac{5}{9}$ yd of blinking lights.

81) A recipe for rum sugar cookies requires $\dfrac{1}{8}$ teaspoon of ground nutmeg, $\dfrac{1}{2}$ teaspoon of almond extract, and 1 teaspoon of rum-flavored extract. What is the total amount of nutmeg, almond extract, and rum-flavored extract required for this recipe?

82) A lifeguard qualification event requires that prospective lifeguards be able to complete an open water swim of $\dfrac{1}{5}$ mi and a $\dfrac{1}{2}$-mi run on the sand within 25 min. What is the total distance traveled by the lifeguard applicants?

83) A performer wears a $\dfrac{2}{3}$-carat diamond earring, a $\dfrac{7}{8}$-carat diamond ring, and a pendant with three $\dfrac{3}{4}$-carat diamonds surrounding a $\dfrac{7}{8}$-carat diamond. What is the total carat weight of the diamonds? The total weight of the diamonds is $4\frac{2}{3}$ carats.

84) Kelsie wears a diamond ring that has a $\dfrac{1}{2}$-carat solitaire diamond with two $\dfrac{1}{8}$-carat diamonds mounted on each side. What is the total carat weight of the ring? Kelsie's ring has a total carat weight of $\frac{3}{4}$ carat.

85) If a student spends $\dfrac{1}{3}$ of her scholarship check on tuition, $\dfrac{1}{4}$ on books, and $\dfrac{1}{8}$ on school supplies, what fraction of her scholarship check remains? The remaining fractional amount of the scholarship is $\frac{7}{24}$.

86) On Sunday just before finals week, Jason spends $\dfrac{1}{8}$ of his day on Facebook, $\dfrac{1}{6}$ watching TV, and $\dfrac{1}{4}$ playing video games. If Jason slept $\dfrac{1}{3}$ of the day (8 hours), what fraction of his day is left for studying? Jason has $\frac{1}{8}$ of a day to study for his final exams.

87) Fiona drives an electric-powered car. When she sets off for work, the battery has $\frac{5}{6}$ of its capacity remaining before it begins using its gas generator. When she arrives at work, $\frac{3}{10}$ of the battery's electric capacity remains. What fraction of the battery's electric capacity was used on Fiona's drive to work? *Fiona's car used $\frac{8}{15}$ of its battery's electric capacity on her way to work.*

88) At the beginning of Lionel's school day, his laptop computer indicated that his battery was charged to $\frac{7}{8}$ capacity. At the end of the day, the battery was charged to $\frac{1}{3}$ capacity. What fraction of the laptop's battery capacity was used during the day? *The laptop used $\frac{13}{24}$ of its battery capacity that day.*

A group of 620 college-bound seniors at Chavez High School was asked to indicate which of the five areas shown they might like to study. The pie chart shows the fraction of the 620 seniors that chose a specific area of study. Use this information for Exercises 89–96.

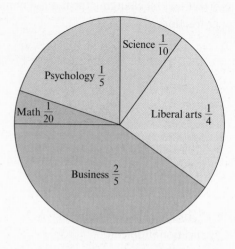

89) What fraction of seniors chose math or science as an area of study? *$\frac{3}{20}$ of the seniors chose math or science as an area of study.*

90) What fraction of seniors chose psychology or liberal arts as an area of study? *$\frac{9}{20}$ of the seniors chose psychology or liberal arts as an area of study.*

91) How many seniors chose math or science as an area of study? *93 seniors chose math or science as an area of study.*

92) How many seniors chose psychology or liberal arts as an area of study? *279 seniors chose psychology or liberal arts as an area of study.*

93) What fraction of seniors did not choose business as an area of study? *$\frac{3}{5}$ of the seniors did not choose business as an area of study.*

94) How many seniors did not choose business as an area of study? *372 seniors did not choose business as an area of study.*

95) Which two areas of study together equal the choice of exactly one-half the senior class? *Exactly one-half the senior class chose business or science as their area of study.*

96) Verify that the five fractional parts have a sum of 1. *Answers may vary.*

R Rethink

R1) Were there any problems you could not do? If so, circle them or write them on your paper, and ask someone for help.

R2) Create a word problem similar to those in Objective 5 from an experience you have had in the past month; then, solve it.

4.5 Adding and Subtracting Mixed Numbers

P Prepare

O Organize

What are your objectives for Section 4.5?	How can you accomplish each objective?
1 Add and Subtract Mixed Numbers in Mixed-Number Form	• Write the procedures for **Adding** and **Subtracting Mixed Numbers** as one procedure. • Complete the given example on your own. • Complete You Try 1.
2 Add Mixed Numbers with Regrouping	• Write your own explanation of how to add mixed numbers when the answer needs regrouping. • Complete the given examples on your own. • Complete You Trys 2 and 3.
3 Subtract Mixed Numbers with Regrouping	• Write your own explanation of how to subtract mixed numbers when regrouping is needed. • Complete the given examples on your own. • Complete You Trys 4–6.
4 Add and Subtract Mixed Numbers Using Improper Fractions	• Write the procedure for **Adding and Subtracting Mixed Numbers Using Improper Fractions** in your own words. • Complete the given example on your own. • Complete You Try 7.

W Work Read the explanations, follow the examples, take notes, and complete the You Trys.

1 Add and Subtract Mixed Numbers in Mixed-Number Form

How do we add mixed numbers? Let's think about how we can add $1\frac{1}{2} + 1\frac{1}{4}$.

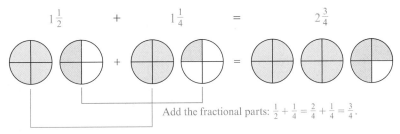

$$1\frac{1}{2} \qquad + \qquad 1\frac{1}{4} \qquad = \qquad 2\frac{3}{4}$$

Add the fractional parts: $\frac{1}{2} + \frac{1}{4} = \frac{2}{4} + \frac{1}{4} = \frac{3}{4}$.

Add the whole-number parts: $1 + 1 = 2$.

$$1\frac{1}{2} + 1\frac{1}{4} = 1\frac{2}{4} + 1\frac{1}{4} = 2\frac{3}{4}$$

Procedure Adding Mixed Numbers

To add mixed numbers, add the whole-number parts and add the fractional parts. Write the answer in lowest terms.

We subtract mixed numbers in a similar way.

Procedure Subtracting Mixed Numbers

To subtract mixed numbers, subtract the whole-number parts and subtract the fractional parts. Write the answer in lowest terms.

EXAMPLE 1

Add or subtract.

a) $2\frac{1}{5} + 7\frac{3}{10}$ b) $9\frac{3}{4} - 5\frac{1}{6}$

Solution

a) Because we will add the whole-number parts and add the fractional parts, begin by writing $\frac{1}{5}$ and $\frac{3}{10}$ as equivalent fractions with their least common denominator.

$$\text{The LCD of } \frac{1}{5} \text{ and } \frac{3}{10} \text{ is } 10.$$

$$\frac{1}{5} \cdot \frac{2}{2} = \frac{2}{10} \qquad \frac{3}{10} \text{ already has the LCD.}$$

$$2\frac{1}{5} + 7\frac{3}{10} = 2\frac{2}{10} + 7\frac{3}{10} \qquad \text{Write the fractions with the LCD.}$$

$$= 9\frac{5}{10} \qquad \text{Add whole-number parts, and add fractions.}$$

$$= 9\frac{1}{2} \qquad \text{Write } \frac{5}{10} \text{ in lowest terms.}$$

b) Begin by writing $\frac{3}{4}$ and $\frac{1}{6}$ as equivalent fractions with their LCD.

$$\text{The LCD of } \frac{3}{4} \text{ and } \frac{1}{6} \text{ is } 12.$$

$$\frac{3}{4} \cdot \frac{3}{3} = \frac{9}{12} \qquad \frac{1}{6} \cdot \frac{2}{2} = \frac{2}{12}$$

$$9\frac{3}{4} - 5\frac{1}{6} = 9\frac{9}{12} - 5\frac{2}{12} \qquad \text{Write the fractions with the LCD.}$$

$$= 4\frac{7}{12} \qquad \text{Subtract whole-number parts, and subtract fractions.}$$

Is $4\frac{7}{12}$ in lowest terms? Yes.

[YOU TRY 1] Add or subtract.

a) $6\frac{3}{7} + 7\frac{2}{5}$ b) $8\frac{5}{6} - 3\frac{11}{15}$

---

2 Add Mixed Numbers with Regrouping

Sometimes, adding mixed numbers involves *regrouping*. Let's learn what regrouping is.

EXAMPLE 2

In-Class Example 2

Explain why $4\dfrac{5}{3}$ is not in simplest form. Then, write it in simplest form.

Answer:
$4\dfrac{5}{3}$ is not in simplest form because the fractional part is an improper fraction.
$4\dfrac{5}{3} = 5\dfrac{2}{3}$

Explain why $5\dfrac{7}{4}$ is not in simplest form. Then, write it in simplest form.

Solution

A mixed number is not in simplest form if its fractional part is an improper fraction.

$5\dfrac{7}{4}$ is not in simplest form because $\dfrac{7}{4}$ is an improper fraction.

To simplify $5\dfrac{7}{4}$, write $\dfrac{7}{4}$ as a mixed number to *regroup* the fractional part with the whole-number part.

$$5\dfrac{7}{4} = 5 + \dfrac{7}{4} \qquad \text{Meaning of a mixed number}$$

$$= 5 + 1\dfrac{3}{4} \qquad \text{Change } \tfrac{7}{4} \text{ to a mixed number to regroup the whole-number part.}$$

$$= 6\dfrac{3}{4} \qquad \text{Add.}$$

Written in simplest form, $5\dfrac{7}{4} = 6\dfrac{3}{4}$. The fractional part is a *proper* fraction, and it is in lowest terms.

W Hint

Write a procedure for regrouping mixed numbers in this way.

[**YOU TRY 2**] Explain why $6\dfrac{8}{5}$ is not in simplest form. Then, write it in simplest form.

Now, let's add two mixed numbers using regrouping.

EXAMPLE 3

In-Class Example 3

Add $4\dfrac{3}{8} + 3\dfrac{5}{6}$.

Answer: $8\dfrac{5}{24}$

Add $3\dfrac{7}{9} + 1\dfrac{1}{2}$.

Solution

Write $\dfrac{7}{9}$ and $\dfrac{1}{2}$ as equivalent fractions with the least common denominator.

The LCD of $\dfrac{7}{9}$ and $\dfrac{1}{2}$ is 18.

$$\dfrac{7}{9} \cdot \dfrac{2}{2} = \dfrac{14}{18} \qquad \qquad \dfrac{1}{2} \cdot \dfrac{9}{9} = \dfrac{9}{18}$$

$$3\dfrac{7}{9} + 1\dfrac{1}{2} = 3\dfrac{14}{18} + 1\dfrac{9}{18} \qquad \text{Write the fractions with the LCD.}$$

$$= 4\dfrac{23}{18} \qquad \text{Add.}$$

Is $4\frac{23}{18}$ in simplest form? No! $\frac{23}{18}$ is an improper fraction. Simplify $4\frac{23}{18}$ by regrouping.

$$4\frac{23}{18} = 4 + \frac{23}{18} = 4 + 1\frac{5}{18} = 5\frac{5}{18}$$

Change to a mixed number.

[YOU TRY 3] Add $5\frac{3}{4} + 9\frac{5}{7}$

Note

When adding mixed numbers, always look at the result and ask yourself, *"Is it in simplest form?"* If it is not, write it in simplest form. As always, the result must also be in lowest terms.

3 Subtract Mixed Numbers with Regrouping

Now let's learn about the type of regrouping, or *borrowing,* we need to use to subtract some mixed numbers.

EXAMPLE 4

In-Class Example 4

Rewrite $3\frac{4}{7}$ as a mixed number with an improper fractional part.

Answer: $2\frac{11}{7}$

Hint

Write a procedure for regrouping mixed numbers in this way.

Rewrite $7\frac{2}{3}$ as a mixed number with an improper fractional part.

Solution

To rewrite the fractional part as an improper fraction, we will regroup, or borrow, 1 from the whole-number part and add it to the fractional part.

Rewrite 7 as 6 + 1.

$$7\frac{2}{3} = 7 + \frac{2}{3} = \overbrace{6 + 1} + \frac{2}{3} = 6 + \frac{3}{3} + \frac{2}{3} = 6\frac{5}{3}$$

Get a common denominator for 1 and $\frac{2}{3}$.

Therefore, $7\frac{2}{3} = 6\frac{5}{3}$.

[YOU TRY 4] Rewrite $5\frac{1}{6}$ as a mixed number with an improper fractional part.

EXAMPLE 5

Subtract $11\frac{2}{5} - 4\frac{3}{4}$.

In-Class Example 5

Subtract $10\frac{2}{7} - 5\frac{3}{4}$.

Answer: $4\frac{15}{28}$

Solution

To find the difference $11\frac{2}{5} - 4\frac{3}{4}$, we must first write the fractional parts with a common denominator.

The LCD of $\frac{2}{5}$ and $\frac{3}{4}$ is 20.

$$\frac{2}{5} \cdot \frac{4}{4} = \frac{8}{20} \qquad \frac{3}{4} \cdot \frac{5}{5} = \frac{15}{20}$$

$$11\frac{2}{5} - 4\frac{3}{4} = 11\frac{8}{20} - 4\frac{15}{20} \qquad \text{Write the fractions with the LCD.}$$

Can we perform the subtraction as it is written here? No! The second fraction is larger than the first.

Regroup (borrow) 1 from the whole-number part of the first mixed number.

Write 11 as $10 + 1$.

$$11\frac{8}{20} = 11 + \frac{8}{20} = 10 + 1 + \frac{8}{20} = 10 + \frac{20}{20} + \frac{8}{20} = 10\frac{28}{20}$$

Get a common denominator for 1 and $\frac{8}{20}$.

Now we can subtract.

$$11\frac{2}{5} - 4\frac{3}{4} = 11\frac{8}{20} - 4\frac{15}{20} \qquad \text{Write the fractions with the LCD.}$$

$$= 10\frac{28}{20} - 4\frac{15}{20} \qquad \text{Rewrite } 11\frac{8}{20} \text{ as } 10\frac{28}{20}.$$

$$= 6\frac{13}{20} \qquad \text{Subtract.}$$

[YOU TRY 5]

Subtract $12\frac{1}{5} - 11\frac{2}{3}$.

SECTION 4.5   **Adding and Subtracting Mixed Numbers**

To find a difference like $8 - 5\frac{2}{3}$, we will regroup, or borrow, 1 from the whole number 8, and write 1 as $\frac{3}{3}$ so that we can represent 8 as a mixed number with an improper fractional part.

Subtract $8 - 5\frac{2}{3}$.

Solution

Because 8 has no fractional part, we must rewrite it so that it does. The fractional part of $5\frac{2}{3}$ has a denominator of 3, so regroup 8 so that its fractional part has a denominator of 3.

Write 1 as $\frac{3}{3}$ so that it has the same denominator as $\frac{2}{3}$.

$$8 = 7 + 1 = 7 + \frac{3}{3} = 7\frac{3}{3}$$

Replace the 8 in $8 - 5\frac{2}{3}$ with $7\frac{3}{3}$.

$$8 - 5\frac{2}{3} = 7\frac{3}{3} - 5\frac{2}{3} = 2\frac{1}{3}$$

[YOU TRY 6]

Subtract $9 - 5\frac{6}{11}$.

4 Add and Subtract Mixed Numbers Using Improper Fractions

Another way to add and subtract mixed numbers is to change them to improper fractions first. If you take an algebra class in the future, you will need to know this method.

> **Procedure** Adding and Subtracting Mixed Numbers Using Improper Fractions
>
> 1) Change each mixed number to an improper fraction.
> 2) Add or subtract the fractions.
> 3) Write the answer in lowest terms. If it is an improper fraction, change it to a mixed number.

EXAMPLE 7

Add or subtract by changing the mixed numbers to improper fractions.

a) $1\dfrac{5}{6} + 4\dfrac{2}{3}$ b) $3\dfrac{1}{4} - 2\dfrac{6}{7}$

Solution

a) $1\dfrac{5}{6} + 4\dfrac{2}{3} = \dfrac{11}{6} + \dfrac{14}{3}$ Write the mixed numbers as improper fractions.

$\qquad = \dfrac{11}{6} + \dfrac{28}{6}$ Multiply $\dfrac{14}{3}$ by $\dfrac{2}{2}$ to get a common denominator.

$\qquad = \dfrac{39}{6}$ Add.

$\qquad = \dfrac{13}{2}$ Divide numerator and denominator by 3 to write in lowest terms.

$\qquad = 6\dfrac{1}{2}$ Write the result as a mixed number.

b) $3\dfrac{1}{4} - 2\dfrac{6}{7} = \dfrac{13}{4} - \dfrac{20}{7}$ Write the mixed numbers as improper fractions.

$\qquad = \dfrac{91}{28} - \dfrac{80}{28}$ Write each fraction with the LCD of 28.

$\qquad = \dfrac{11}{28}$ Subtract.

YOU TRY 7

Add or subtract by changing the mixed numbers to improper fractions.

a) $3\dfrac{2}{9} + 4\dfrac{1}{6}$ b) $7\dfrac{1}{2} - 2\dfrac{3}{5}$

Note

If we use this method for adding and subtracting mixed numbers, we do not have to use regrouping.

ANSWERS TO **YOU TRY** **EXERCISES**

1) a) $13\dfrac{29}{35}$ b) $5\dfrac{1}{10}$ 2) $7\dfrac{3}{5}$ 3) $15\dfrac{13}{28}$ 4) $4\dfrac{7}{6}$ 5) $\dfrac{8}{15}$ 6) $3\dfrac{5}{11}$ 7) a) $7\dfrac{7}{18}$ b) $4\dfrac{9}{10}$

Additional answers can be found in the Answers to Exercises appendix.

Objective 1: Add and Subtract Mixed Numbers in Mixed-Number Form

1) In your own words, explain how to add and how to subtract mixed numbers.

2) Is $4\frac{10}{18}$ in lowest terms? Why or why not?

Add or subtract, as indicated.

3) $1\frac{5}{14} + 3\frac{1}{7}$ $4\frac{1}{2}$ 4) $4\frac{7}{16} + 2\frac{1}{8}$ $6\frac{9}{16}$

5) $5\frac{1}{3} + 6\frac{5}{12}$ $11\frac{3}{4}$ 6) $8\frac{1}{2} + 7\frac{3}{10}$ $15\frac{4}{5}$

7) $9\frac{5}{6} - 7\frac{1}{18}$ $2\frac{7}{9}$ 8) $12\frac{5}{9} - 3\frac{2}{27}$ $9\frac{13}{27}$

9) $14\frac{6}{7} - 9\frac{5}{21}$ $5\frac{13}{21}$ 10) $17\frac{4}{5} - 11\frac{3}{10}$ $6\frac{1}{2}$

11) $5\frac{5}{12} + 4\frac{1}{8}$ $9\frac{13}{24}$ 12) $1\frac{1}{9} + 6\frac{3}{4}$ $7\frac{31}{36}$

13) $23\frac{7}{8} - 19\frac{5}{9}$ $4\frac{23}{72}$ 14) $14\frac{10}{11} - 8\frac{1}{12}$ $6\frac{109}{132}$

Objective 2: Add Mixed Numbers with Regrouping

15) Is $4\frac{8}{7}$ in simplest form? Why or why not?
No. It is not in simplest form because the fractional part is an improper fraction.

16) Is $6\frac{4}{9}$ in simplest form? Why or why not?
Yes. It is in simplest form because the fractional part is a proper fraction in lowest terms.

Write each mixed number in simplest form.

17) $3\frac{7}{5}$ $4\frac{2}{5}$ 18) $1\frac{11}{8}$ $2\frac{3}{8}$

19) $2\frac{8}{7}$ $3\frac{1}{7}$ 20) $7\frac{19}{10}$ $8\frac{9}{10}$

21) $5\frac{23}{14}$ $6\frac{9}{14}$ 22) $9\frac{21}{16}$ $10\frac{5}{16}$

Add.

23) $4\frac{5}{6} + 2\frac{1}{2}$ $7\frac{1}{3}$ 24) $6\frac{2}{3} + 3\frac{7}{9}$ $10\frac{4}{9}$

25) $5\frac{11}{24} + 7\frac{7}{8}$ $13\frac{1}{3}$ 26) $3\frac{9}{20} + 8\frac{4}{5}$ $12\frac{1}{4}$

27) $2\frac{2}{3} + 2\frac{4}{5}$ $5\frac{7}{15}$ 28) $3\frac{1}{4} + 3\frac{5}{6}$ $7\frac{1}{12}$

29) $11\frac{3}{8} + 16\frac{7}{10}$ $28\frac{3}{40}$ 30) $12\frac{4}{9} + 31\frac{11}{12}$ $44\frac{13}{36}$

31) $19\frac{11}{12} + 8\frac{3}{10}$ $28\frac{13}{60}$ 32) $15\frac{6}{7} + 9\frac{5}{6}$ $25\frac{29}{42}$

Objective 3: Subtract Mixed Numbers with Regrouping

Regroup 1 from the whole-number part to rewrite the mixed number with an improper fractional part.

33) $8\frac{1}{2}$ $7\frac{3}{2}$ 34) $2\frac{1}{3}$ $1\frac{4}{3}$

35) $4\frac{3}{5}$ $3\frac{8}{5}$ 36) $3\frac{2}{9}$ $2\frac{11}{9}$

37) $9\frac{13}{16}$ $8\frac{29}{16}$ 38) $6\frac{17}{21}$ $5\frac{38}{21}$

For Exercises 39 and 40, use the problem $5\frac{2}{7} - 2\frac{4}{7}$.

39) Can we subtract these mixed numbers as they appear now? Why or why not?   No. The fractional part of the second mixed number is larger than the fractional part of the first mixed number.

40) Rewrite $5\frac{2}{7}$ with an improper fractional part, then subtract $5\frac{2}{7} - 2\frac{4}{7}$. $5\frac{2}{7} - 2\frac{4}{7} = 4\frac{9}{7} - 2\frac{4}{7} = 2\frac{5}{7}$

Subtract.

41) $9\frac{3}{8} - 5\frac{7}{8}$ $3\frac{1}{2}$ 42) $8\frac{1}{10} - 1\frac{9}{10}$ $6\frac{1}{5}$

43) $5\frac{5}{27} - 3\frac{5}{9}$ $1\frac{17}{27}$ 44) $11\frac{13}{36} - 7\frac{7}{12}$ $3\frac{7}{9}$

45) $16\frac{1}{5} - 8\frac{5}{6}$ $7\frac{11}{30}$ 46) $13\frac{3}{4} - 2\frac{4}{5}$ $10\frac{19}{20}$

47) $14\frac{5}{12} - 13\frac{6}{7}$ $\frac{47}{84}$ 48) $17\frac{5}{9} - 16\frac{10}{11}$ $\frac{64}{99}$

49) $11 - 10\frac{2}{5}$ $\frac{3}{5}$ 50) $3 - 2\frac{5}{8}$ $\frac{3}{8}$

51) $6 - 3\frac{3}{7}$ $2\frac{4}{7}$ 52) $7 - 3\frac{9}{10}$ $3\frac{1}{10}$

53) $14 - 8\frac{5}{6}$ $5\frac{1}{6}$ 54) $12 - 5\frac{4}{9}$ $6\frac{5}{9}$

Objective 4: Add and Subtract Mixed Numbers Using Improper Fractions

Add or subtract by changing the mixed numbers to improper fractions.

55) $3\frac{1}{2} + 2\frac{1}{4}$ $5\frac{3}{4}$

56) $5\frac{1}{3} + 2\frac{5}{6}$ $8\frac{1}{6}$

57) $7\frac{11}{12} - 2\frac{5}{6}$ $5\frac{1}{12}$

58) $5\frac{4}{5} - 3\frac{7}{10}$ $2\frac{1}{10}$

59) $2\frac{2}{5} - 1\frac{2}{3}$ $\frac{11}{15}$

60) $3\frac{3}{7} - 2\frac{3}{4}$ $\frac{19}{28}$

61) $2\frac{5}{6} + 1\frac{1}{4}$ $4\frac{1}{12}$

62) $4\frac{3}{5} + 3\frac{1}{2}$ $8\frac{1}{10}$

63) $2\frac{1}{6} - 1\frac{3}{5}$ $\frac{17}{30}$

64) $4\frac{1}{7} - 3\frac{1}{4}$ $\frac{25}{28}$

65) Do you prefer to add and subtract mixed numbers by leaving them as mixed numbers or by changing them to improper fractions? Why?   Answers may vary.

66) If we add and subtract mixed numbers by first changing them to improper fractions, will we have to do any regrouping?   No

For Exercises 67–70, find the missing length.

67)

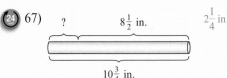

$10\frac{3}{4}$ in. $8\frac{1}{2}$ in.   ? $2\frac{1}{4}$ in.

68)

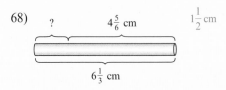

$6\frac{1}{3}$ cm $4\frac{5}{6}$ cm   ? $1\frac{1}{2}$ cm

69)

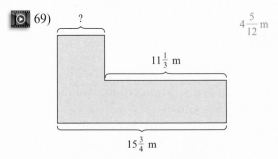

? $4\frac{5}{12}$ m

$11\frac{1}{3}$ m

$15\frac{3}{4}$ m

70)

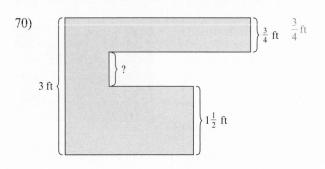

$\frac{3}{4}$ ft $\frac{3}{4}$ ft   3 ft   ? $1\frac{1}{2}$ ft

A healthcare professional monitors the weight of a patient who has been retaining fluids due to an illness. Use the table below for Exercises 71–74.

Day and Time	Weight in Pounds
Day 1, 8:00 A.M.	$141\frac{2}{3}$
Day 2, 9:00 A.M.	$142\frac{1}{2}$
Day 3, 8:00 A.M.	$143\frac{3}{4}$
Day 4, 10:00 A.M.	$144\frac{1}{2}$
Day 5, 8:00 A.M.	$142\frac{3}{4}$
Day 6, 10:00 A.M.	$141\frac{1}{4}$
Day 7, 9:00 A.M.	$139\frac{1}{3}$

71) How much weight did the patient gain from Day 1 to Day 4? $2\frac{5}{6}$ lb

72) How much weight did the patient lose from Day 4 to Day 7? $5\frac{1}{6}$ lb

73) From Day 3 to Day 4, did the patient gain or lose weight and how much?   gain; $\frac{3}{4}$ lb

74) Over the 7-day monitoring period, did the patient gain or lose weight and how much?   lose; $2\frac{1}{3}$ lb

Solve each problem.

75) For breakfast, Julian drank $2\frac{1}{2}$ cups of water, $1\frac{2}{3}$ cups of juice, and $\frac{3}{4}$ cup of milk. How much liquid did Julian consume for breakfast? $4\frac{11}{12}$ cups

76) The Johnsons used $18\frac{2}{3}$  square yards (yd^2) of carpet for their family room, $6\frac{1}{2}$ yd^2 for their hallway, and $12\frac{1}{4}$ yd^2 for their master bedroom. How much carpet did they use for all three areas? $37\frac{5}{12}$ yd^2

77) Ibada has a part-time job and worked $6\frac{1}{2}$ hr on Monday, $3\frac{3}{4}$ hr on Wednesday, and 8 hr on Friday. How many total hours did he work? $18\frac{1}{4}$ hr

78) Araceli's sewing project needs three pieces of fabric with lengths of $\frac{3}{4}$, $2\frac{1}{2}$, and $4\frac{1}{3}$ yd. What is the total amount of fabric she needs? $7\frac{7}{12}$ yd

Mixed Exercises

Perform the indicated operation.

79) $23\frac{1}{8} - 10\frac{5}{24}$ $12\frac{11}{12}$

80) $1\frac{1}{6} + 1\frac{1}{18}$ $2\frac{2}{9}$

81) $5\frac{1}{7} + 4\frac{3}{4}$ $9\frac{25}{28}$

82) $6 - 2\frac{3}{10}$ $3\frac{7}{10}$

83) $4\frac{5}{8} + 7\frac{4}{7}$ $12\frac{11}{56}$

84) $48\frac{11}{16} - 32\frac{1}{4}$ $16\frac{7}{16}$

85) $52\frac{3}{5} - 17\frac{11}{20}$ $35\frac{1}{20}$

86) $15\frac{1}{6} - 8\frac{5}{12}$ $6\frac{3}{4}$

87) $9 - 8\frac{1}{6}$ $\frac{5}{6}$

88) $7 - 6\frac{2}{3}$ $\frac{1}{3}$

89) $2\frac{11}{15} + 7\frac{5}{6} + 4\frac{9}{10}$ $15\frac{7}{15}$

90) $8\frac{4}{5} + 6\frac{7}{10} + 3\frac{7}{8}$ $19\frac{3}{8}$

R Rethink

R1) Explain how regrouping for mixed numbers is similar to regrouping for addition and subtraction of whole numbers. (Hint: Think about place value.)

R2) How do adding and subtracting mixed numbers using improper fractions eliminate the need for regrouping?

Putting It All Together

P Prepare

What are your objectives?

O Organize

How can you accomplish each objective?

What are your objectives?	How can you accomplish each objective?
1 Review Operations with Fractions and Mixed Numbers: Sections 4.1–4.5	• Be sure that you can apply the procedures you have learned in the previous sections. • If you are not confident on a certain example, go back to the section that gives more explanation. • Complete the given examples on your own. • Complete You Try 1.

W Work

Read the explanations, follow the examples, take notes, and complete the You Try.

Hint

In your notes, summarize how to add, subtract, multiply, and divide fractions and mixed numbers.

1 Review Operations with Fractions and Mixed Numbers

Let's put together everything we have learned about adding, subtracting, multiplying, and dividing fractions and mixed numbers.

EXAMPLE 1

Perform the indicated operations.

a) $\dfrac{7}{12} + \dfrac{1}{6} + \dfrac{5}{8}$ b) $1\dfrac{9}{16} \cdot 2\dfrac{2}{15}$ c) $\dfrac{21}{8} \div \dfrac{14}{3}$

d) $8\dfrac{9}{10} - 3\dfrac{4}{5}$ e) $3\dfrac{5}{12} + 9\dfrac{4}{5}$ f) $5 - \dfrac{4}{7}$

In-Class Example 1

Perform the indicated operations.

a) $\dfrac{3}{10} + \dfrac{1}{6} + \dfrac{14}{15}$ b) $3\dfrac{1}{8} \cdot 2\dfrac{4}{5}$

c) $\dfrac{12}{11} \div \dfrac{8}{3}$ d) $10\dfrac{11}{18} - 4\dfrac{5}{9}$

e) $5\dfrac{11}{12} + 4\dfrac{3}{7}$ f) $6 - \dfrac{7}{9}$

Answer:

a) $\dfrac{7}{5}$ or $1\dfrac{2}{5}$ b) $8\dfrac{3}{4}$

c) $\dfrac{9}{22}$ d) $6\dfrac{1}{18}$

e) $10\dfrac{29}{84}$ f) $\dfrac{47}{9}$ or $5\dfrac{2}{9}$

Solution

a) We have to find the sum $\dfrac{7}{12} + \dfrac{1}{6} + \dfrac{5}{8}$. Do we need a common denominator? Yes! Write each fraction with the LCD, then add.

Step 1: Write down the LCD of $\dfrac{7}{12}, \dfrac{1}{6},$ and $\dfrac{5}{8}$.   LCD = 24

Step 2: Rewrite each fraction with the LCD.

$$\frac{7}{12} \cdot \frac{2}{2} = \frac{14}{24} \qquad \frac{1}{6} \cdot \frac{4}{4} = \frac{4}{24} \qquad \frac{5}{8} \cdot \frac{3}{3} = \frac{15}{24}$$

Step 3: Add.

$$\frac{7}{12} + \frac{1}{6} + \frac{5}{8} = \frac{14}{24} + \frac{4}{24} + \frac{15}{24} \qquad \text{Write each fraction with the LCD.}$$

$$= \frac{33}{24} \qquad \text{Add.}$$

Ask yourself, *"Is $\dfrac{33}{24}$ in lowest terms?"* No! Write it in lowest terms.

$$\frac{33}{24} = \frac{33 \div 3}{24 \div 3} = \frac{11}{8} \text{ or } 1\frac{3}{8}$$

Therefore, $\dfrac{7}{12} + \dfrac{1}{6} + \dfrac{5}{8} = \dfrac{11}{8}$ or $1\dfrac{3}{8}$. We can write the answer as an improper fraction or as a mixed number as long as it is in lowest terms.

b) Do we need a common denominator to multiply mixed numbers? No! To multiply $1\dfrac{9}{16} \cdot 2\dfrac{2}{15}$, first change each mixed number to an improper fraction. Then multiply.

$$1\frac{9}{16} \cdot 2\frac{2}{15} = \frac{25}{16} \cdot \frac{32}{15} \qquad \text{Write each mixed number as an improper fraction.}$$

$$= \frac{\overset{5}{\cancel{25}}}{\underset{1}{\cancel{16}}} \cdot \frac{\overset{2}{\cancel{32}}}{\underset{3}{\cancel{15}}} \qquad \text{Divide 25 and 15 by 5; divide 16 and 32 by 16.}$$

$$= \frac{5 \cdot 2}{1 \cdot 3} \qquad \text{Multiply numerators, and multiply denominators.}$$

$$= \frac{10}{3} \text{ or } 3\frac{1}{3}$$

Are $\dfrac{10}{3}$ and $3\dfrac{1}{3}$ in lowest terms? Yes.

c) Do we need a common denominator to find $\dfrac{21}{8} \div \dfrac{14}{3}$? No! *We do not need a common denominator to divide, or multiply, fractions.* To divide fractions, multiply the first fraction by the reciprocal of the second.

$$\dfrac{21}{8} \div \dfrac{14}{3} = \dfrac{21}{8} \cdot \dfrac{3}{14} \qquad \text{Change division to multiplication by the reciprocal.}$$

$$= \dfrac{\overset{3}{\cancel{21}}}{8} \cdot \dfrac{3}{\underset{2}{\cancel{14}}} \qquad \text{Divide 21 and 14 by 7.}$$

$$= \dfrac{3 \cdot 3}{8 \cdot 2} \qquad \text{Multiply.}$$

$$= \dfrac{9}{16}$$

Ask yourself, *"Is $\dfrac{9}{16}$ in lowest terms?"* Yes.

d) What is the first step for finding $8\dfrac{9}{10} - 3\dfrac{4}{5}$? Write $\dfrac{9}{10}$ and $\dfrac{4}{5}$ as equivalent fractions with an LCD.

The LCD of $\dfrac{9}{10}$ and $\dfrac{4}{5}$ is 10.

$\dfrac{9}{10}$ already has the LCD. $\dfrac{4}{5} \cdot \dfrac{2}{2} = \dfrac{8}{10}$

$$8\dfrac{9}{10} - 3\dfrac{4}{5} = 8\dfrac{9}{10} - 3\dfrac{8}{10} \qquad \text{Write the fractions with the LCD.}$$

$$= 5\dfrac{1}{10} \qquad \text{Subtract whole numbers, and subtract fractions.}$$

Is $5\dfrac{1}{10}$ in lowest terms? Yes.

e) How do we find $3\dfrac{5}{12} + 9\dfrac{4}{5}$? Write $\dfrac{5}{12}$ and $\dfrac{4}{5}$ as equivalent fractions with their least common denominator. Then, add the whole-number parts, and add the fractional parts.

$$3\dfrac{5}{12} + 9\dfrac{4}{5} = 3\dfrac{25}{60} + 9\dfrac{48}{60} \qquad \text{Write the fractions with the LCD.}$$

$$= 12\dfrac{73}{60} \qquad \text{Add.}$$

Is $12\dfrac{73}{60}$ in simplest form? No! $\dfrac{73}{60}$ is an improper fraction. Simplify $12\dfrac{73}{60}$ by regrouping.

$$12\dfrac{73}{60} = 12 + \dfrac{73}{60} = 12 + 1\dfrac{13}{60} = 13\dfrac{13}{60}$$

So, $3\dfrac{5}{12} + 9\dfrac{4}{5} = 13\dfrac{13}{60}$. The answer is in lowest terms.

f) To find the difference $5 - \dfrac{4}{7}$, we first need a common denominator. Write 5 as an improper fraction with a denominator of 1: $5 = \dfrac{5}{1}$.

Now, subtract.

Rewrite with a denominator of 7.

$$5 - \frac{4}{7} = \frac{5}{1} - \frac{4}{7} = \frac{35}{7} - \frac{4}{7} = \frac{31}{7} \text{ or } 4\frac{3}{7}$$

Write 5 as a fraction.

BE CAREFUL We need a common denominator *only* when we are adding or subtracting fractions and mixed numbers. When we are multiplying or dividing, a common denominator is *not* needed.

[**YOU TRY 1**] Perform the indicated operations.

a) $\dfrac{4}{15} \div \dfrac{7}{6}$ b) $2\dfrac{1}{8} + 7\dfrac{3}{10}$ c) $9 - 5\dfrac{3}{5}$

d) $\dfrac{1}{24} \cdot \dfrac{18}{25} \cdot \dfrac{10}{63}$ e) $16 \div 3\dfrac{1}{5}$ f) $\dfrac{4}{7} + \dfrac{9}{14} + \dfrac{5}{8}$

ANSWERS TO [YOU TRY] **EXERCISES**

1) a) $\dfrac{8}{35}$ b) $9\dfrac{17}{40}$ c) $3\dfrac{2}{5}$ d) $\dfrac{1}{210}$ e) 5 f) $\dfrac{103}{56}$ or $1\dfrac{47}{56}$

Putting It All Together Exercises

E Evaluate Do the exercises, and check your work.

*Additional answers can be found in the Answers to Exercises appendix.

Objective 1: Review Operations with Fractions and Mixed Numbers

Determine whether each statement is true or false. If it is false, explain why.

 1) To multiply two fractions, we need a common denominator. False. A common denominator is needed only for adding and subtracting fractions.

2) All answers should be written in lowest terms. true

3) Before multiplying or dividing mixed numbers, we must change them to improper fractions. true

4) The mixed number $3\dfrac{11}{6}$ is in simplest form.

5) $\dfrac{1}{2}$ is greater than $\dfrac{3}{2}$.

6) $\dfrac{3}{7}$ is less than 1. true

Perform the indicated operations.

 7) $\dfrac{7}{16} \cdot \dfrac{10}{21}$ $\dfrac{5}{24}$

8) $\dfrac{14}{15} - \dfrac{8}{15}$ $\dfrac{2}{5}$

 9) $3\dfrac{1}{4} + 6\dfrac{2}{7}$ $9\dfrac{15}{28}$

10) $\dfrac{20}{23} \div \dfrac{45}{77}$ $\dfrac{308}{207}$ or $1\dfrac{101}{207}$

11) $\dfrac{11}{18} - \dfrac{1}{6}$ $\dfrac{4}{9}$

12) $7\dfrac{3}{10} + 8\dfrac{4}{15}$ $15\dfrac{17}{30}$

13) $\dfrac{\frac{9}{14}}{\frac{12}{35}}$ $\dfrac{15}{8}$ or $1\dfrac{7}{8}$

14) $5\dfrac{1}{4} \cdot 2\dfrac{3}{14}$ $\dfrac{93}{8}$ or $11\dfrac{5}{8}$

15) $9\dfrac{11}{12} - 8\dfrac{4}{9}$ $1\dfrac{17}{36}$

16) $1\dfrac{17}{20} \div 4\dfrac{4}{9}$ $\dfrac{333}{800}$

17) $4 \cdot 3\dfrac{1}{8}$ $\quad \dfrac{25}{2}$ or $12\dfrac{1}{2}$

18) $\dfrac{7}{8} + \dfrac{5}{9}$ $\quad \dfrac{103}{72}$ or $1\dfrac{31}{72}$

19) $8 \div \dfrac{1}{10}$ $\quad 80$

20) $17 - 16\dfrac{5}{9}$ $\quad \dfrac{4}{9}$

21) $12\dfrac{1}{2} - 5\dfrac{3}{4}$ $\quad 6\dfrac{3}{4}$

22) $\dfrac{35}{54} \cdot \dfrac{8}{21} \cdot \dfrac{45}{32}$ $\quad \dfrac{25}{72}$

23) $3\dfrac{9}{11} \cdot 1\dfrac{5}{7}$ $\quad \dfrac{72}{11}$ or $6\dfrac{6}{11}$

24) $\dfrac{7}{16} + \dfrac{1}{20} + \dfrac{9}{14}$ $\quad \dfrac{633}{560}$ or $1\dfrac{73}{560}$

25) $\dfrac{5}{11} + \dfrac{1}{4}$ $\quad \dfrac{31}{44}$

26) $\dfrac{\dfrac{1}{6}}{\dfrac{4}{4}}$ $\quad \dfrac{1}{24}$

27) $\dfrac{11}{30} + \dfrac{5}{16} + \dfrac{17}{40}$ $\quad \dfrac{53}{48}$ or $1\dfrac{5}{48}$

28) $6\dfrac{5}{7} - 4\dfrac{1}{6}$ $\quad 2\dfrac{23}{42}$

29) $5\dfrac{1}{3} \div 1\dfrac{13}{15}$ $\quad \dfrac{20}{7}$ or $2\dfrac{6}{7}$

30) $3\dfrac{7}{9} + 8\dfrac{3}{5}$ $\quad 12\dfrac{17}{45}$

31) $14 - 5\dfrac{7}{12}$ $\quad 8\dfrac{5}{12}$

32) $\dfrac{5}{36} \cdot \dfrac{12}{13}$ $\quad \dfrac{5}{39}$

33) $\dfrac{15}{28} \cdot \dfrac{16}{33} \cdot \dfrac{21}{40}$ $\quad \dfrac{3}{22}$

34) $11\dfrac{3}{8} - 2\dfrac{9}{16}$ $\quad 8\dfrac{13}{16}$

35) $2\dfrac{4}{5} + 1\dfrac{11}{15}$ $\quad 4\dfrac{8}{15}$

36) $\dfrac{5}{6} + 4\dfrac{7}{10} + \dfrac{8}{15} + 9\dfrac{1}{2}$ $\quad 15\dfrac{17}{30}$

37) $\dfrac{1}{8} + 2\dfrac{5}{6} + \dfrac{1}{2} + 7\dfrac{3}{4}$ $\quad 11\dfrac{5}{24}$

38) $9 \cdot 2\dfrac{2}{3}$ $\quad 24$

Fill in the blank.

39) a) $5 \cdot \underline{\quad} = 40$ $\quad 8$

b) $\dfrac{3}{4} \cdot \underline{\quad} = 18$ $\quad 24$

40) a) $10 + \underline{\quad} = 23$ $\quad 13$

b) $\dfrac{2}{7} + \underline{\quad} = \dfrac{19}{42}$ $\quad \dfrac{1}{6}$

41) a) $\underline{\quad} - 37 = 19$ $\quad 56$

b) $\underline{\quad} - \dfrac{7}{12} = \dfrac{11}{36}$ $\quad \dfrac{8}{9}$

42) a) $\underline{\quad} \div 2 = 6$ $\quad 12$

b) $\underline{\quad} \div \dfrac{4}{9} = \dfrac{3}{10}$ $\quad \dfrac{2}{15}$

Solve each problem.

43) Janae brewed 2 gallons of iced tea. Then, she put $\dfrac{2}{3}$-gallon portions into bottles. How many bottles did she use? $\quad$ 3 bottles

44) A cupcake recipe uses $3\dfrac{1}{2}$ cups of flour and makes 24 cupcakes. If Curtis wants to make 72 cupcakes, how much flour will he need? $\quad 10\dfrac{1}{2}$ cups

45) A builder must enclose a rectangular construction site with a chain-link fence. The width of the site is $60\dfrac{2}{3}$ ft and the length is $115\dfrac{3}{4}$ ft. How much fence will the builder need? $\quad 352\dfrac{5}{6}$ ft

46) On Saturday, Misaki ran $5\dfrac{3}{4}$ mi. On Sunday, she ran $7\dfrac{1}{2}$ mi. How much farther did Misaki run on Sunday than on Saturday? $\quad 1\dfrac{3}{4}$ mi

47) Evan's history class is 50 min long, and he spent $\dfrac{2}{5}$ of the time on Facebook. How much class time did he spend on Facebook during class? $\quad 20$ min

48) During the 2010–2011 NBA regular season, Mike Dunleavy of the Indiana Pacers made $\dfrac{4}{5}$ of his free throws. How many free throws did he make given that he had 125 attempts? (www.nba.com) $\quad$ 100 free throws

49) For Mother's Day, $\dfrac{5}{8}$ of the flowers sold by a florist were roses. What fraction were not roses? $\quad \dfrac{3}{8}$

50) Find the area and perimeter of this rectangle.

$1\dfrac{1}{3}$ yd

$\dfrac{5}{6}$ yd

area $= 1\dfrac{1}{9}$ yd^2; perimeter $= 4\dfrac{1}{3}$ yd

R1) Have you mastered all of the objectives in the chapter so far?

R2) Could you take a quiz or test on these concepts right now?

4.6 Order Relations and Order of Operations

P Prepare **O Organize**

What are your objectives for Section 4.6?	How can you accomplish each objective?
1 Compare Fractions	• Write the definitions of < and >, and write examples in your notes. • Write the procedure for **Comparing Fractions with Unlike Denominators** in your own words. • Complete the given examples on your own. • Complete You Trys 1 and 2.
2 Use Exponents with Fractions	• Remember that exponents indicate repeated multiplication with natural numbers and fractions. • Complete the given example on your own. • Complete You Try 3.
3 Use the Order of Operations with Fractions	• Remember the order of operations and apply it to fractions. • Complete the given example on your own. • Complete You Try 4.

W Work   **Read the explanations, follow the examples, take notes, and complete the You Trys.**

1 Compare Fractions

We have learned about the size of fractions from using figures and number lines. For example, we can see that $\frac{3}{4}$ is greater than $\frac{1}{4}$ by comparing the shaded portions of the figures and by looking at the placement of $\frac{3}{4}$ and $\frac{1}{4}$ on a number line.

We can say that $\frac{3}{4}$ *is greater than* $\frac{1}{4}$ or that $\frac{1}{4}$ *is less than* $\frac{3}{4}$. We can use order relation symbols to represent *is greater than* and *is less than*.

$\frac{3}{4}$ is greater than $\frac{1}{4}$

$\xleftarrow{\quad\;|\;\;|\;\;|\;\;|\;\;\quad}\to$
$\quad 0\;\;\frac{1}{4}\;\;\frac{2}{4}\;\;\frac{3}{4}\;\;1\;(\text{or }\frac{4}{4})$

$\frac{3}{4}$ is to the right of $\frac{1}{4}$.

Definition

The symbol $>$ means *is greater than,* and the symbol $<$ means *is less than.*

Example: $12 > 7$ is read as "12 *is greater than* 7."

$5 < 9$ is read as "5 *is less than* 9."

We can use these symbols to compare $\dfrac{3}{4}$ and $\dfrac{1}{4}$.

$$\frac{3}{4} > \frac{1}{4} \qquad \text{and} \qquad \frac{1}{4} < \frac{3}{4}$$

$\dfrac{3}{4}$ is greater than $\dfrac{1}{4}$. $\qquad$ $\dfrac{1}{4}$ is less than $\dfrac{3}{4}$.

We know that as we move to the right on the number line, the numbers get larger. Therefore, as on the number line above, when two fractions have the same denominator, the fraction with the larger numerator is the larger number.

EXAMPLE 1

Fill in the blank with $>$ or $<$.

a) $\dfrac{4}{7} \underline{\quad} \dfrac{6}{7}$ $\qquad$ b) $\dfrac{11}{8} \underline{\quad} \dfrac{9}{8}$ $\qquad$ c) $\dfrac{2}{3} \underline{\quad} 1$ $\qquad$ d) $3\dfrac{8}{9} \underline{\quad} 3\dfrac{4}{9}$

In-Class Example 1

Fill in the blank with $>$ or $<$.

a) $\dfrac{2}{5} \underline{\quad} \dfrac{4}{5}$

b) $\dfrac{13}{7} \underline{\quad} \dfrac{10}{7}$

c) $\dfrac{3}{4} \underline{\quad} 1$

d) $2\dfrac{5}{6} \underline{\quad} 2\dfrac{1}{6}$

Answer:

a) $<$ $\quad$ b) $>$ $\quad$ c) $<$ $\quad$ d) $>$

Solution

a) To compare these fractions, we can think about a shaded figure or the placement of $\dfrac{4}{7}$ and $\dfrac{6}{7}$ on a number line. Or, notice that the numerator of $\dfrac{4}{7}$ is less than the numerator of $\dfrac{6}{7}$.

$$\frac{4}{7} < \frac{6}{7} \qquad \frac{4}{7} \text{ is less than } \frac{6}{7}.$$

b) $\dfrac{11}{8} > \dfrac{9}{8}$ $\quad$ $\dfrac{11}{8}$ *is greater than* $\dfrac{9}{8}$ because $\dfrac{11}{8}$ is to the right of $\dfrac{9}{8}$ on a number line. Notice that the numerator of $\dfrac{11}{8}$ is greater than the numerator of $\dfrac{9}{8}$.

c) $\dfrac{2}{3} < 1$ $\qquad$ Use $<$ because $\dfrac{2}{3}$ *is less than* 1 whole.

d) $3\dfrac{8}{9} > 3\dfrac{4}{9}$ $\quad$ The whole-number part of each mixed number is the same, so compare the fractional parts. Because $\dfrac{8}{9}$ *is greater than* $\dfrac{4}{9}$, $3\dfrac{8}{9}$ *is greater than* $3\dfrac{4}{9}$.

YOU TRY 1

Fill in the blank with $>$ or $<$.

a) $\dfrac{9}{10} \underline{\quad} \dfrac{3}{10}$ $\qquad$ b) $\dfrac{7}{6} \underline{\quad} \dfrac{19}{6}$ $\qquad$ c) $\dfrac{8}{3} \underline{\quad} 3$ $\qquad$ d) $5\dfrac{2}{11} \underline{\quad} 5\dfrac{6}{11}$

How do we compare fractions with *unlike* denominators? We write them with the least common denominator and compare the numerators.

Procedure Comparing Fractions with Unlike Denominators

1) Rewrite the fractions with the least common denominator.
2) Compare the numerators. The fraction with the greater numerator is the larger fraction.

EXAMPLE 2

Fill in the blank with > or <.

a) $\dfrac{5}{8}$ ___ $\dfrac{9}{16}$ b) $\dfrac{13}{9}$ ___ $\dfrac{7}{4}$

Solution

a) First, write each fraction with the LCD: LCD = 16.

$$\frac{5}{8} \cdot \frac{2}{2} = \frac{10}{16} \qquad \frac{9}{16} \text{ already has the LCD.}$$

Rewrite $\dfrac{5}{8}$ ___ $\dfrac{9}{16}$ as $\dfrac{10}{16}$ ___ $\dfrac{9}{16}$. $\dfrac{5}{8} = \dfrac{10}{16}$

Because the numerator of $\dfrac{10}{16}$ *is greater than* the numerator of $\dfrac{9}{16}$, we write

$$\frac{10}{16} > \frac{9}{16} \qquad \text{or} \qquad \frac{5}{8} > \frac{9}{16}$$

Equivalent fractions

W Hint

You can also draw a picture to visualize each fraction.

b) Write each fraction with a denominator of 36.

$$\frac{13}{9} \cdot \frac{4}{4} = \frac{52}{36} \qquad \frac{7}{4} \cdot \frac{9}{9} = \frac{63}{36}$$

Rewrite $\dfrac{13}{9}$ ___ $\dfrac{7}{4}$ as $\dfrac{52}{36}$ ___ $\dfrac{63}{36}$.

The numerator of $\dfrac{52}{36}$ *is less than* the numerator of $\dfrac{63}{36}$, so

Equivalent

$$\frac{52}{36} < \frac{63}{36} \qquad \text{or} \qquad \frac{13}{9} < \frac{7}{4}$$

Equivalent

[YOU TRY 2]

Fill in the blank with > or <.

a) $\dfrac{5}{12}$ ___ $\dfrac{11}{24}$ b) $\dfrac{9}{5}$ ___ $\dfrac{10}{7}$

---

2 Use Exponents with Fractions

In Chapter 2, we learned that an exponent indicates repeated multiplication. For example,

$$5^2 = 5 \cdot 5 = 25 \quad \text{and} \quad 2^3 = 2 \cdot 2 \cdot 2 = 8$$

We can use exponents with fractions, too.

EXAMPLE 3

Evaluate.

a) $\left(\dfrac{7}{8}\right)^2$ b) $\left(\dfrac{1}{3}\right)^4$

Solution

a) $\left(\dfrac{7}{8}\right)^2 = \dfrac{7}{8} \cdot \dfrac{7}{8} = \dfrac{49}{64}$ The exponent of 2 tells us to use $\dfrac{7}{8}$ as a factor 2 times.

b) $\left(\dfrac{1}{3}\right)^4 = \dfrac{1}{3} \cdot \dfrac{1}{3} \cdot \dfrac{1}{3} \cdot \dfrac{1}{3} = \dfrac{1}{81}$ The exponent of 4 tells us to use $\dfrac{1}{3}$ as a factor 4 times.

[YOU TRY 3]

Evaluate.

a) $\left(\dfrac{2}{5}\right)^3$ b) $\left(\dfrac{1}{12}\right)^2$

---

3 Use the Order of Operations with Fractions

We can use the order of operations to simplify expressions containing fractions. Let's review the order of operations that we first learned in Section 2.6.

Procedure The Order of Operations

Simplify expressions in the following order:

1) If **parentheses** or **other grouping symbols** appear in an expression, simplify what is in these grouping symbols first.
2) Simplify expressions with **exponents** and **square roots.**
3) **Multiply** or **divide,** moving from left to right.
4) **Add** or **subtract,** moving from left to right.

EXAMPLE 4

Simplify each expression using the order of operations.

a) $\dfrac{9}{10} - \dfrac{3}{10} \cdot \dfrac{5}{2}$ b) $\dfrac{7}{20} \div \left(\dfrac{1}{8} + \dfrac{4}{5} \right)$ c) $4 - 3\left(\dfrac{5}{6} \right)^2 + \dfrac{7}{12}$

In-Class Example 4

Simplify each expression using the order of operations.

a) $\dfrac{7}{8} - \dfrac{5}{8} \cdot \dfrac{9}{10}$

b) $\dfrac{4}{15} \div \left(\dfrac{2}{9} + \dfrac{1}{6} \right)$

c) $5 - 4\left(\dfrac{7}{8} \right)^2 + \dfrac{11}{16}$

Answer:

a) $\dfrac{5}{16}$ b) $\dfrac{24}{35}$ c) $\dfrac{21}{8}$ or $2\dfrac{5}{8}$

W Hint

Is this any different from using the order of operations in Section 2.6?

Solution

a) Be careful! Do not subtract first. Remember that we multiply before we subtract.

$$\dfrac{9}{10} - \dfrac{3}{10} \cdot \dfrac{5}{2} = \dfrac{9}{10} - \dfrac{3}{\underset{2}{10}} \cdot \dfrac{\overset{1}{5}}{2} \qquad \text{Divide 10 and 5 by 5.}$$

$$= \dfrac{9}{10} - \dfrac{3}{4} \qquad \text{Multiply.}$$

$$= \dfrac{18}{20} - \dfrac{15}{20} \qquad \text{Write each fraction with the LCD, 20.}$$

$$= \dfrac{3}{20} \qquad \text{Subtract.}$$

b) When an expression contains parentheses or other grouping symbols, simplify what is inside them first.

$$\dfrac{7}{20} \div \left(\dfrac{1}{8} + \dfrac{4}{5} \right) = \dfrac{7}{20} \div \left(\dfrac{5}{40} + \dfrac{32}{40} \right) \qquad \text{Write the fractions in parentheses with the LCD, 40.}$$

$$= \dfrac{7}{20} \div \dfrac{37}{40} \qquad \text{Add the fractions in parentheses.}$$

$$= \dfrac{7}{20} \cdot \dfrac{40}{37} \qquad \text{Change division to multiplication by the reciprocal.}$$

$$= \dfrac{7}{\underset{1}{20}} \cdot \dfrac{\overset{2}{40}}{37} \qquad \text{Divide 20 and 40 by 20.}$$

$$= \dfrac{14}{37} \qquad \text{Multiply.}$$

c) Look at the expression $4 - 3\left(\dfrac{5}{6} \right)^2 + \dfrac{7}{12}$. Notice that there is no operation symbol between the 3 and the expression in parentheses. Remember, this means the operation is multiplication.

What do we do first? Find $\left(\dfrac{5}{6} \right)^2$.

$$4 - 3\left(\dfrac{5}{6} \right)^2 + \dfrac{7}{12} = 4 - 3\left(\dfrac{25}{36} \right) + \dfrac{7}{12} \qquad \text{First, find } \left(\dfrac{5}{6} \right)^2. \text{ Next, multiply.}$$

$$= 4 - \dfrac{\overset{1}{3}}{1} \cdot \dfrac{25}{\underset{12}{36}} + \dfrac{7}{12} \qquad \text{Divide 3 and 36 by 3.}$$

$$= 4 - \dfrac{25}{12} + \dfrac{7}{12} \qquad \text{Multiply.}$$

When an expression contains addition and subtraction, perform the operations from left to right. Therefore, we must first find $4 - \dfrac{25}{12}$. Then, add $\dfrac{7}{12}$.

$$= \dfrac{4}{1} - \dfrac{25}{12} + \dfrac{7}{12} \qquad \text{Write 4 as } \dfrac{4}{1}.$$

$$= \dfrac{48}{12} - \dfrac{25}{12} + \dfrac{7}{12} \qquad \text{Write } \dfrac{4}{1} \text{ and } \dfrac{25}{12} \text{ with the LCD, 12.}$$

$$= \dfrac{23}{12} + \dfrac{7}{12} \qquad \text{Subtract. Perform operations from left to right.}$$

$$= \dfrac{30}{12} \qquad \text{Add.}$$

$$= \dfrac{5}{2} \text{ or } 2\dfrac{1}{2} \qquad \text{Write the answer in lowest terms as an improper fraction or mixed number.}$$

[YOU TRY 4] Simplify each expression using the order of operations.

a) $\dfrac{1}{2} + \dfrac{2}{3} \div 8$ 　　b) $9 - 7\left(\dfrac{3}{2} - \dfrac{5}{7}\right)$ 　　c) $\dfrac{4}{11} + \dfrac{6}{11}\left(\dfrac{1}{3}\right)^2 - \dfrac{14}{33}$

ANSWERS TO [YOU TRY] EXERCISES

1) a) $>$　b) $<$　c) $<$　d) $<$　　2) a) $<$　b) $>$　　3) a) $\dfrac{8}{125}$　b) $\dfrac{1}{144}$　　4) a) $\dfrac{7}{12}$　b) $\dfrac{7}{2}$ or $3\dfrac{1}{2}$　c) 0

E Evaluate **4.6** Exercises　　Do the exercises, and check your work.

*Additional answers can be found in the Answers to Exercises appendix.

Objective 1: Compare Fractions

Fill in the blank with $>$ or $<$.

1) $\dfrac{2}{3}$ _____ $\dfrac{1}{3}$ $>$ 　　2) $\dfrac{1}{8}$ _____ $\dfrac{3}{8}$ $<$

3) $\dfrac{5}{12}$ _____ $\dfrac{7}{12}$ $<$ 　　4) $\dfrac{4}{11}$ _____ $\dfrac{3}{11}$ $>$

5) $\dfrac{12}{5}$ _____ $\dfrac{13}{5}$ $<$ 　　6) $\dfrac{23}{14}$ _____ $\dfrac{19}{14}$ $>$

7) $3\dfrac{5}{7}$ _____ $3\dfrac{4}{7}$ $>$ 　　8) $2\dfrac{8}{9}$ _____ $2\dfrac{7}{9}$ $>$

9) $5\dfrac{1}{6}$ _____ $5\dfrac{5}{6}$ $<$ 　　10) $4\dfrac{5}{8}$ _____ $4\dfrac{3}{8}$ $>$

11) $\dfrac{4}{5}$ _____ 1 $<$ 　　12) 1 _____ $\dfrac{5}{6}$ $>$

13) $\dfrac{63}{6}$ _____ 10 $>$ 　　14) $\dfrac{53}{7}$ _____ 8 $<$

15) Explain, in your own words, how to compare fractions with different denominators. Answers may vary.

16) Is this statement true or false? *As you move to the right on the number line, the numbers get larger.* true

Fill in the blank with $>$ or $<$.

17) $\dfrac{2}{3}$ _____ $\dfrac{5}{6}$ $<$ 　　18) $\dfrac{5}{8}$ _____ $\dfrac{11}{16}$ $<$

19) $\dfrac{5}{6}$ _____ $\dfrac{13}{18}$ $>$ 　　20) $\dfrac{3}{4}$ _____ $\dfrac{19}{24}$ $<$

21) $\dfrac{4}{3}$ _____ $\dfrac{5}{4}$ $>$ 　　22) $\dfrac{11}{7}$ _____ $\dfrac{13}{9}$ $>$

23) $\dfrac{5}{7}$ _____ $\dfrac{5}{6}$ $<$ 　　24) $\dfrac{3}{8}$ _____ $\dfrac{5}{12}$ $<$

25) $\dfrac{1}{2}$ _____ $\dfrac{1}{9}$ $>$ 　　26) $\dfrac{1}{3}$ _____ $\dfrac{1}{8}$ $>$

27) $1\frac{5}{12}$ _____ $1\frac{3}{8}$ >   28) $2\frac{13}{15}$ _____ $2\frac{5}{6}$ >

29) $4\frac{3}{10}$ _____ $4\frac{7}{15}$ <   30) $3\frac{11}{12}$ _____ $3\frac{4}{5}$ >

31) 0 _____ $\frac{1}{12}$ <   32) $\frac{1}{4}$ _____ 0 >

For Exercises 33–38, use the number line to fill in the blank with > or <.

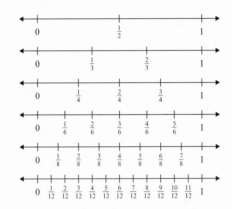

33) $\frac{1}{4}$ _____ $\frac{1}{3}$ <   34) $\frac{1}{6}$ _____ $\frac{1}{4}$ <

35) $\frac{11}{12}$ _____ $\frac{7}{8}$ >   36) $\frac{7}{8}$ _____ $\frac{5}{6}$ >

37) $\frac{5}{6}$ _____ 1 <   38) 1 _____ $\frac{2}{3}$ >

For Exercises 39–46, approximate the location of each fraction or mixed number on the given number line.

39) $\frac{5}{2}$ 40) $\frac{4}{3}$

41) $1\frac{7}{8}$ 42) $3\frac{1}{4}$

43) $\frac{13}{4}$ 44) $\frac{11}{8}$

45) $2\frac{4}{5}$ 46) $1\frac{5}{6}$

Objective 2: Use Exponents with Fractions

Evaluate.

47) $\left(\frac{1}{8}\right)^2$ $\frac{1}{64}$ 48) $\left(\frac{1}{11}\right)^2$ $\frac{1}{121}$

49) $\left(\frac{5}{6}\right)^2$ $\frac{25}{36}$ 50) $\left(\frac{3}{7}\right)^2$ $\frac{9}{49}$

51) $\left(\frac{10}{9}\right)^2$ $\frac{100}{81}$ 52) $\left(\frac{12}{5}\right)^2$ $\frac{144}{25}$

53) $\left(\frac{2}{3}\right)^3$ $\frac{8}{27}$ 54) $\left(\frac{3}{4}\right)^3$ $\frac{27}{64}$

55) $\left(\frac{1}{4}\right)^3$ $\frac{1}{64}$ 56) $\left(\frac{1}{3}\right)^3$ $\frac{1}{27}$

57) $\left(\frac{1}{3}\right)^4$ $\frac{1}{81}$ 58) $\left(\frac{1}{2}\right)^4$ $\frac{1}{16}$

59) $\left(\frac{10}{3}\right)^3$ $\frac{1000}{27}$ 60) $\left(\frac{5}{2}\right)^3$ $\frac{125}{8}$

61) $\left(\frac{2}{3}\right)^4$ $\frac{16}{81}$ 62) $\left(\frac{3}{10}\right)^4$ $\frac{81}{10,000}$

Fill in the blank with > or <.

63) $\left(\frac{1}{3}\right)^2$ _____ $\frac{1}{3}$ <   64) $\left(\frac{1}{4}\right)^2$ _____ $\frac{1}{4}$ <

65) $\frac{2}{9}$ _____ $\left(\frac{2}{9}\right)^2$ >   66) $\frac{3}{10}$ _____ $\left(\frac{3}{10}\right)^2$ >

67) $\left(\frac{3}{2}\right)^2$ _____ $\frac{3}{2}$ >   68) $\left(\frac{4}{3}\right)^2$ _____ $\frac{4}{3}$ >

69) $\frac{5}{4}$ _____ $\left(\frac{5}{4}\right)^2$ <   70) $\frac{7}{6}$ _____ $\left(\frac{7}{6}\right)^2$ <

Objective 3: Use the Order of Operations with Fractions

Simplify each expression using the order of operations.

71) $\left(\frac{5}{3}\right)^2 \cdot \left(\frac{6}{7}\right)^2$ $\frac{100}{49}$ or $2\frac{2}{49}$ 72) $\left(\frac{1}{6}\right)^2 \cdot \left(\frac{3}{10}\right)^2$ $\frac{1}{400}$

73) $\frac{7}{12} - \frac{1}{5} \cdot \frac{1}{12}$ $\frac{17}{30}$ 74) $\frac{13}{6} - \frac{5}{6} \cdot \frac{2}{3}$ $\frac{29}{18}$ or $1\frac{11}{18}$

75) $\frac{40}{9} - \frac{25}{12} \div \frac{3}{5}$ $\frac{35}{36}$ 76) $\frac{7}{9} - \frac{1}{6} \div \frac{3}{8}$ $\frac{1}{3}$

77) $\frac{13}{24} \div \left(\frac{5}{12} + \frac{1}{8}\right)$ 1 78) $\frac{10}{27} \div \left(\frac{1}{6} + \frac{7}{9}\right)$ $\frac{20}{51}$

79) $2 - 4\left(\frac{3}{8}\right)^2 + \frac{9}{16}$ 2 80) $1 - 5\left(\frac{3}{10}\right)^2 + \frac{11}{20}$ $\frac{11}{10}$

81) $10 - 10\left(\frac{4}{5}\right)^2 - \frac{4}{15}$ $\frac{10}{3}$ or $3\frac{1}{3}$ 82) $1 - 3\left(\frac{2}{9}\right)^2 + \frac{5}{9}$ $\frac{38}{27}$ or $1\frac{11}{27}$

83) $\frac{3}{8}\left(\frac{8}{9} - \frac{3}{4}\right)$ $\frac{5}{96}$ 84) $\frac{8}{5}\left(\frac{5}{4} - \frac{7}{6}\right)$ $\frac{2}{15}$

85) $\left(\dfrac{2}{3}\right)^3 - \left(\dfrac{2}{9}\right)^2$ $\dfrac{20}{81}$ 86) $\left(\dfrac{5}{4}\right)^3 - \left(\dfrac{5}{8}\right)^2$ $\dfrac{25}{16}$ or $1\dfrac{9}{16}$ 89) $\left(\dfrac{3}{4}\right)^2 + \left(\dfrac{1}{2}\right)^3 \cdot \left(\dfrac{1}{2} + \dfrac{3}{4}\right)$ $\dfrac{23}{32}$

87) $\dfrac{15}{4} - 5 \div \dfrac{10}{3}$ 88) $\dfrac{18}{5} - 8 \div \dfrac{16}{3}$ $\dfrac{21}{10}$ or $2\dfrac{1}{10}$ 90) $\left(\dfrac{2}{3}\right)^2 \cdot \left(\dfrac{2}{15} + \dfrac{1}{2}\right) \div \dfrac{3}{5}$ $\dfrac{38}{81}$

$\dfrac{9}{4}$ or $2\dfrac{1}{4}$

R Rethink

R1) Why does it make sense to learn how to compare fractions before learning to use exponents and the order of operations?

R2) Based on Exercises 63–66, what happens when you square a proper fraction?

R3) Based on Exercises 67–70, what happens when you square an improper fraction?

Group Activity – Adding and Subtracting Fractions

- Students should work in pairs.
- The object of this activity is to fill in the blank boxes in the 4 × 4 grid below so that the sum of the fractions in each row, column, and the two diagonals is equal to 1.
- There are 10 numbers listed below the grid and there are 10 empty boxes. Use the numbers in the list to fill in the empty boxes. Once you have used a number from the list, you can cross it out. Each number in the list will be used only once.

$\dfrac{31}{60}$	$\dfrac{19}{60}$		$\dfrac{2}{15}$
		$\dfrac{13}{30}$	
$\dfrac{1}{4}$		$\dfrac{17}{60}$	

$\dfrac{1}{30},\quad \dfrac{1}{10},\quad \dfrac{11}{30},\quad \dfrac{7}{30},\quad 0,\quad \dfrac{1}{4},\quad \dfrac{2}{15},\quad \dfrac{1}{3},\quad \dfrac{11}{60},\quad \dfrac{13}{30}$

Group Activity Answers

Row 1: $\dfrac{1}{30}$; Row 2: 0, $\dfrac{2}{15}$, $\dfrac{13}{30}$; Row 3: $\dfrac{7}{30}$, $\dfrac{11}{60}$, $\dfrac{1}{4}$, $\dfrac{1}{3}$; Row 4: $\dfrac{11}{30}$, $\dfrac{1}{10}$

If you want to improve your math skills, just attending class is not enough. You need to do the necessary work outside of class, and when you are in class, you need to listen actively.

To assess whether you are an active listener, consider the following pairs of statements. Place a check next to the statement in each pair that more closely describes your classroom listening style.

☐ 1a. When I'm listening in class, I lean back and get as comfortable as possible.
☐ 1b. When I'm listening in class, I sit upright and even lean forward a little.

☐ 2a. I let the instructor's words wash over me, generally going with the flow of the lecture.
☐ 2b. I try to guess in advance what the instructor is going to say and what direction the lecture is taking.

☐ 3a. I regard each lecture as a separate event, not necessarily related to what the instructor has said before or will say the next time.
☐ 3b. As I listen, I regularly ask myself how this relates to what was said in previous classes.

☐ 4a. When I take notes, I try to reproduce the instructor's words as closely as possible.
☐ 4b. When I take notes, I try to interpret and summarize the ideas behind the instructor's words.

☐ 5a. I don't usually question the importance of what the instructor is saying or why it's the topic of a lecture or discussion.
☐ 5b. I often ask why the content of the lecture is important enough for the instructor to be speaking about it.

☐ 6a. I rarely question the accuracy or logic of a presentation, assuming that the instructor knows the topic better than I do.
☐ 6b. I often ask myself how the instructor knows something and find myself wondering how it could be proved.

☐ 7a. I just about never make eye contact with the instructor.
☐ 7b. I often make eye contact with the instructor.

If you tended to prefer the "a" statements in most pairs, you have a more passive style of listening. If you preferred the "b" statements, you have a more active style of listening. Based on your responses, consider ways that you can become a more active listener.

Chapter 4:   Summary

Definition/Procedure	Example

4.1 Adding and Subtracting Like Fractions

Adding Like Fractions

To add like fractions:

1) Add the numerators.

2) Use the denominator of the like fractions as the denominator of the sum.

3) Write the answer in lowest terms. **(p. 224)**

$$\frac{4}{11} + \frac{3}{11} = \frac{4+3}{11} = \frac{7}{11}$$ The answer is in lowest terms.

Subtracting Like Fractions

To subtract like fractions:

1) Subtract the numerators.

2) Use the denominator of the like fractions as the denominator of the difference.

3) Write the answer in lowest terms. **(p. 226)**

$$\frac{9}{10} - \frac{3}{10} = \frac{9-3}{10} = \frac{6}{10} = \frac{3}{5}$$ Write the answer in lowest terms.

4.2 Least Common Multiples

The **least common multiple,** or **LCM,** of a group of natural numbers is the smallest natural number divisible by each number in the group. **(p. 230)**

The LCM of 4 and 5 is 20 because 20 is the smallest number divisible by both 4 and 5.

Make a List of Multiples to Find the LCM

To find the LCM of a group of numbers, begin by listing some multiples of each number. Then, the least common multiple (LCM) is the *smallest* number that appears on each list. **(p. 230)**

Find the least common multiple of 6 and 8.

List some multiples of 6 and 8.

  Multiples of 6:   6, 12, 18, 24, 30, 36, …
  Multiples of 8:   8, 16, 24, 32, 40, 48, …

The LCM of 6 and 8 is 24.

Find the LCM by Inspection

If the numbers are easy to work with, we should be able to find the LCM without making a list or writing anything on paper. **(p. 231)**

Find the least common multiple of 2 and 10.

Ask yourself, *"What is the smallest number that is divisible by both 2 and 10?"* That number is 10.

The LCM of 2 and 10 is 10.

Make a List of Multiples of the Largest Number to Find the LCM

We can also find the LCM by first finding multiples of the larger number and then finding the smallest of those that is divisible by the other numbers in the group. **(p. 231)**

Find the least common multiple of 5, 6, and 20 by first making a list of multiples of the largest number.

The largest number in the group is 20, so make a list of some multiples of 20.

Multiples of 20:   20, 40, 60, 80, 100, …

Are any of the numbers on the list divisible by 5 and 6? Yes!   60 is divisible by 5 and 6.

The LCM of 5, 6, and 20 is 60.

Definition/Procedure	Example
Find the LCM Using Prime Factorization *Step 1:* Write the prime factorization of each number. *Step 2:* Identify the factors that will be in the least common multiple. The LCM will contain each different factor the *greatest* number of times it appears in any single factorization. *Step 3:* The LCM is the *product* of the factors identified in Step 2. **(p. 232)**	Find the LCM of 9 and 15 using prime factorization. *Step 1:* Write the prime factorization of each number. $$\underbrace{9 = 3 \cdot 3}_{\text{2 factors of 3}} \quad \text{and} \quad \overset{\text{1 factor of 3}}{15 = 3} \cdot \underset{\text{1 factor of 5}}{5}$$ *Step 2:* The LCM will contain each different factor the *greatest* number of times it appears in any single factorization. The LCM will contain $\underbrace{3 \cdot 3}_{\text{2 factors of 3}}$ and 5. *Step 3:* The LCM is the *product* of the factors identified in Step 2. The LCM of 9 and 15 is $3 \cdot 3 \cdot 5 = 45$.

4.3 Finding the Least Common Denominator

Writing a Fraction with a Different Denominator *Step 1:* Ask yourself, *"By what number do I multiply the original denominator to get the new denominator?"* *Step 2:* Multiply the numerator and denominator of the original fraction by that number to get the equivalent fraction. When we multiply the numerator and denominator by the same number, we do *not* change the value of the fraction. We get an equivalent fraction. **(p. 236)**	Write $\dfrac{2}{7}$ as an equivalent fraction with a denominator of 21. *Step 1:* Ask yourself, *"By what number do I multiply 7 to get 21?"* That number is 3. *Step 2:* Multiply the numerator and denominator of $\dfrac{2}{7}$ by 3: $$\frac{2}{7} \cdot \frac{3}{3} = \frac{6}{21}$$ Therefore, $\dfrac{2}{7} = \dfrac{6}{21}$.
Least Common Denominator The **least common denominator,** or **LCD,** of a group of fractions is the least common multiple of the denominators. **(p. 237)**	The least common denominator of $\dfrac{1}{4}$ and $\dfrac{5}{12}$ is 12 because 12 is the least common multiple of 4 and 12.
Writing a Group of Fractions with an LCD To write a group of fractions with their least common denominator, identify the LCM of the denominators, then rewrite each fraction with the LCM as the least common denominator. **(p. 237)**	Write $\dfrac{9}{8}$ and $\dfrac{4}{7}$ as equivalent fractions with the LCD as their denominators. The LCM of 8 and 7 is 56. So, the LCD is 56. Write each fraction with a denominator of 56. We want to find $$\frac{9}{8} = \frac{?}{56} \quad \text{and} \quad \frac{4}{7} = \frac{?}{56}$$ $$\frac{9}{8} \cdot \frac{7}{7} = \frac{63}{56} \qquad \frac{4}{7} \cdot \frac{8}{8} = \frac{32}{56}$$ The LCD of $\dfrac{9}{8}$ and $\dfrac{4}{7}$ is 56, and $\dfrac{9}{8} = \dfrac{63}{56}$ and $\dfrac{4}{7} = \dfrac{32}{56}$.

Definition/Procedure	Example

4.4 Adding and Subtracting Unlike Fractions

In order to add or subtract fractions, they **must** have a common denominator.

Adding or Subtracting Unlike Fractions

Step 1: Determine the least common denominator (LCD), and write it on your paper.

Step 2: Rewrite each fraction with the LCD.

Step 3: Add or subtract.

Step 4: Write the answer in lowest terms. **(p. 242)**

Add $\frac{4}{9} + \frac{5}{6}$.

Step 1: Write down the LCD of $\frac{4}{9}$ and $\frac{5}{6}$. LCD = 18

Step 2: Rewrite each fraction with the LCD.

$$\frac{4}{9} \cdot \frac{2}{2} = \frac{8}{18} \qquad \frac{5}{6} \cdot \frac{3}{3} = \frac{15}{18}$$

Step 3: Add.

Equivalent fractions

$$\frac{4}{9} + \frac{5}{6} = \frac{8}{18} + \frac{15}{18} = \frac{8 + 15}{18} = \frac{23}{18} \text{ or } 1\frac{5}{18}$$

Equivalent fractions

Step 4: Ask yourself, *"Are $\frac{23}{18}$ and $1\frac{5}{18}$ in lowest terms?"*

Yes. We can write the answer as an improper fraction or mixed number.

Add and Subtract Natural Numbers and Fractions

We can add and subtract natural numbers and fractions by changing the natural number to an improper fraction first. (This is a useful method in algebra.) **(p. 249)**

Add or subtract by first changing the natural number to an improper fraction.

a) $3 + \frac{5}{8}$ \qquad b) $1 - \frac{3}{7}$

a) We can say that $3 + \frac{5}{8} = 3\frac{5}{8}$. Or, we can rewrite 3 as a fraction with a denominator of 8.

Rewrite with a denominator of 8.

$$3 + \frac{5}{8} = \frac{3}{1} + \frac{5}{8} = \frac{24}{8} + \frac{5}{8} = \frac{29}{8}$$

Write 3 with a denominator of 1.

b) Write 1 as a fraction with a denominator of 7.

Rewrite with a denominator of 7.

$$1 - \frac{3}{7} = \frac{1}{1} - \frac{3}{7} = \frac{7}{7} - \frac{3}{7} = \frac{4}{7}$$

Write 1 as $\frac{1}{1}$.

Applications of Adding and Subtracting Fractions

Many applications involve adding or subtracting fractions. **(p. 250)**

A rectangular transom window is $\frac{7}{8}$ yd long and $\frac{2}{5}$ yd wide. Find the perimeter of the window.

Step 1: **Read** the problem carefully, and restate it in your own words.

The <u>length</u> of a window <u>is</u> $\frac{7}{8}$ <u>yd</u>, and the <u>width is</u> $\frac{2}{5}$ yd. <u>Find the perimeter</u> of the window.

Definition/Procedure	Example

<table>
<tr><td></td><td>

Step 2: **Make a plan.** Let's underline important words in our restatement of the problem in Step 1, draw a picture, and label the sides.

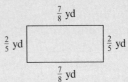

The perimeter of a figure is the distance around the figure.

Plan: Add the lengths of all the sides to find the perimeter.

Step 3: **Solve** the problem.

$$\frac{7}{8} + \frac{7}{8} + \frac{2}{5} + \frac{2}{5} = \frac{14}{8} + \frac{4}{5} \qquad \text{Add the lengths, and add the widths.}$$

$$= \frac{70}{40} + \frac{32}{40} \qquad \text{Rewrite each fraction with the LCD.}$$

$$= \frac{102}{40} \qquad \text{Add.}$$

$$= \frac{51}{20} \qquad \text{Divide the numerator and denominator by 2.}$$

$$= 2\frac{11}{20} \qquad \text{Write the improper fraction as a mixed number.}$$

Step 4: **State the answer** in a complete sentence.

The perimeter of the window is $2\frac{11}{20}$ yd.

Step 5: **Check** the answer. Double-check your work to verify that the answer is correct.

</td></tr>
</table>

4.5 Adding and Subtracting Mixed Numbers

Adding Mixed Numbers To add mixed numbers, add the whole-number parts and add the fractional parts. Write the answer in lowest terms. **(p. 257)** **Subtracting Mixed Numbers** To subtract mixed numbers, subtract the whole-number parts and subtract the fractional parts. Write the answer in lowest terms. **(p. 258)**	Add or subtract. a) $4\frac{1}{12} + 5\frac{4}{9}$ b) $8\frac{1}{2} - 6\frac{3}{8}$ a) First, rewrite each fraction with the LCD, 36. Then, add the whole-number parts and add the fractional parts. $4\frac{1}{12} + 5\frac{4}{9} = 4\frac{3}{36} + 5\frac{16}{36}$ Write each fraction with the LCD. $= 9\frac{19}{36}$ Add the whole numbers, and add the fractions. b) The LCD is 8, so rewrite $\frac{1}{2}$ with a denominator of 8. Then, subtract the whole-number parts and subtract the fractional parts. $8\frac{1}{2} - 6\frac{3}{8} = 8\frac{4}{8} - 6\frac{3}{8}$ Write each fraction with the LCD. $= 2\frac{1}{8}$ Subtract the whole numbers, and subtract the fractions.

Definition/Procedure	Example
Add Mixed Numbers with Regrouping Sometimes, the sum of mixed numbers must be simplified using regrouping. **(p. 259)**	Add $7\frac{3}{4} + 1\frac{2}{3}$. $7\frac{3}{4} + 1\frac{2}{3} = 7\frac{9}{12} + 1\frac{8}{12}$ Write the fractions with the LCD. $= 8\frac{17}{12}$ Add. Is $8\frac{17}{12}$ in simplest form? No! $\frac{17}{12}$ is an improper fraction. Simplify $8\frac{17}{12}$ by regrouping. $8\frac{17}{12} = 8 + \frac{17}{12} = 8 + 1\frac{5}{12} = 9\frac{5}{12}$ Write the improper fraction as a mixed number. The final answer is $9\frac{5}{12}$.
Subtract Mixed Numbers with Regrouping We regroup in a subtraction problem when the fraction in the second mixed number is *larger than* the fraction in the first mixed number. **(p. 260)**	Subtract $6\frac{2}{9} - 3\frac{7}{9}$. The fraction in the second mixed number is larger than the fraction in the first mixed number. Therefore, we must *regroup* or *borrow* 1 from the whole-number part of the *first* mixed number, $6\frac{2}{9}$. Write 6 as 5 + 1. $6\frac{2}{9} = 6 + \frac{2}{9} = 5 + 1 + \frac{2}{9} = 5 + \frac{9}{9} + \frac{2}{9} = 5\frac{11}{9}$ Rewrite 1 as $\frac{9}{9}$. Now, subtract. $6\frac{2}{9} - 3\frac{7}{9} = 5\frac{11}{9} - 3\frac{7}{9} = 2\frac{4}{9}$ These are equivalent.
Add and Subtract Mixed Numbers Using Improper Fractions 1) Change each mixed number to an improper fraction. 2) Add or subtract the fractions. 3) Write the answer in lowest terms. If it is an improper fraction, change it to a mixed number. **(p. 262)**	Add $2\frac{1}{10} + 1\frac{4}{5}$ by changing the mixed numbers to improper fractions. $2\frac{1}{10} + 1\frac{4}{5} = \frac{21}{10} + \frac{9}{5}$ Write the mixed numbers as improper fractions. $= \frac{21}{10} + \frac{18}{10}$ Multiply $\frac{9}{5}$ by $\frac{2}{2}$ to get a common denominator. $= \frac{39}{10}$ Add. $= 3\frac{9}{10}$ Write the result as an improper fraction. Because the numbers in the original problem were mixed numbers, we write the result as a mixed number, if possible.

Definition/Procedure	Example

4.6 Order Relations and Order of Operations

Comparing Numbers with > and <

The symbol > means *is greater than,* and the symbol < means *is less than.*

We can use these symbols to compare the sizes of numbers. **(p. 272)**

9 > 4 is read as "9 *is greater than* 4."

2 < 11 is read as "2 *is less than* 11."

Comparing Fractions

As we move to the right on the number line, the numbers get larger. Therefore, when two fractions have the same denominator, the fraction with the larger numerator is the larger number. **(p. 272)**

Fill in the blank with > or <.

a) $\dfrac{5}{2}$ ——— $\dfrac{3}{2}$ b) $\dfrac{6}{13}$ ——— $\dfrac{10}{13}$

a) $\dfrac{5}{2} > \dfrac{3}{2}$ $\dfrac{5}{2}$ is greater than $\dfrac{3}{2}$.

b) $\dfrac{6}{13} < \dfrac{10}{13}$ $\dfrac{6}{13}$ is less than $\dfrac{10}{13}$.

Comparing Fractions with Unlike Denominators

1) Rewrite the fractions with the least common denominator.

2) Compare the numerators. The fraction with the greater numerator is the larger fraction. **(p. 273)**

Fill in the blank with > or <: $\dfrac{3}{4}$ ——— $\dfrac{5}{7}$

Write each fraction with the LCD, 28.

$$\dfrac{3}{4} \cdot \dfrac{7}{7} = \dfrac{21}{28} \qquad \dfrac{5}{7} \cdot \dfrac{4}{4} = \dfrac{20}{28}$$

Rewrite $\dfrac{3}{4}$ ——— $\dfrac{5}{7}$ as $\dfrac{21}{28}$ ——— $\dfrac{20}{28}$.

The numerator of $\dfrac{21}{28}$ *is greater than* the numerator of $\dfrac{20}{28}$.

Therefore, $\dfrac{21}{28} > \dfrac{20}{28}$ or $\dfrac{3}{4} > \dfrac{5}{7}$.

We can use exponents with fractions. **(p. 274)**

Evaluate $\left(\dfrac{7}{11}\right)^2$.

$$\left(\dfrac{7}{11}\right)^2 = \dfrac{7}{11} \cdot \dfrac{7}{11} = \dfrac{49}{121}$$

The Order of Operations

Simplify expressions in the following order:

1) If **parentheses** or **other grouping symbols** appear in an expression, simplify what is in these grouping symbols first.

2) Simplify expressions with **exponents** and **square roots.**

3) **Multiply** or **divide,** moving from left to right.

4) **Add** or **subtract,** moving from left to right. **(p. 274)**

Simplify $\dfrac{1}{2} + \dfrac{8}{9}\left(\dfrac{3}{4}\right)^3$.

$\dfrac{1}{2} + \dfrac{8}{9}\left(\dfrac{3}{4}\right)^3 = \dfrac{1}{2} + \dfrac{8}{9}\left(\dfrac{27}{64}\right)$ Evaluate the exponent first.

$= \dfrac{1}{2} + \dfrac{\overset{1}{8}}{9} \cdot \dfrac{\overset{3}{27}}{\underset{8}{64}}$ Multiply before adding; divide out common factors.

$= \dfrac{1}{2} + \dfrac{3}{8}$ Multiply.

$= \dfrac{4}{8} + \dfrac{3}{8}$ Get a common denominator.

$= \dfrac{7}{8}$ Add.

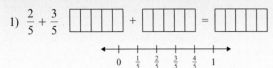

Chapter 4: Review Exercises

*Additional answers can be found in the Answers to Exercises appendix.

(4.1) Add the like fractions. First shade the figures appropriately to represent each fraction and the resulting sum. Then use a number line to demonstrate the operation.

1) $\frac{2}{5} + \frac{3}{5}$ ☐☐☐☐☐ + ☐☐☐☐☐ = ☐☐☐☐☐

2) $\frac{3}{8} + \frac{4}{8}$ ⊗ + ⊗ = ⊗

3) $\frac{1}{6} + \frac{2}{6}$ ⬡ + ⬡ = ⬡

4) $\frac{1}{5} + \frac{2}{5}$ ☐☐☐☐☐ + ☐☐☐☐☐ = ☐☐☐☐☐

Add or subtract.

5) $\frac{4}{13} + \frac{7}{13}$ $\frac{11}{13}$

6) $\frac{1}{9} + \frac{4}{9}$ $\frac{5}{9}$

7) $\frac{7}{15} - \frac{4}{15}$ $\frac{1}{5}$

8) $\frac{17}{18} - \frac{11}{18}$ $\frac{1}{3}$

9) $\frac{13}{30} + \frac{17}{30}$ 1

10) $\frac{27}{28} - \frac{3}{28}$ $\frac{6}{7}$

(4.2) Find the least common multiple of each group of numbers.

11) 3, 6, and 8   24

12) 2, 4, and 7   28

13) 3, 5, and 20   60

14) 3, 12, and 18   36

Find the LCM of each group of numbers using prime factorization.

15) 4, 9, and 12   36

16) 5, 8, and 10   40

17) 15 and 24   120

18) 16 and 28   112

(4.3)

19) *Why* does multiplying $\frac{4}{7}$ by $\frac{5}{5}$ result in a fraction, $\frac{20}{35}$, that is equivalent to $\frac{4}{7}$? $\frac{5}{5} = 1$, so multiplying $\frac{4}{7}$ by 1 does not change the value of the fraction.

20) Explain, in words, how to write $\frac{8}{9}$ as an equivalent fraction with a denominator of 63.   Answers may vary.

21) Write $\frac{3}{8}$ as an equivalent fraction with a denominator of 24. $\frac{9}{24}$

22) Write $\frac{5}{7}$ as an equivalent fraction with a denominator of 84. $\frac{60}{84}$

For each group of fractions, identify the least common denominator. Next, write each fraction as an equivalent fraction with the LCD as its denominator.

23) $\frac{5}{6}$ and $\frac{3}{10}$

24) $\frac{3}{8}$ and $\frac{5}{12}$

25) $\frac{1}{4}, \frac{2}{9},$ and $\frac{7}{6}$

26) $\frac{4}{5}, \frac{7}{8},$ and $\frac{3}{20}$

27) $\frac{5}{24}$ and $\frac{9}{28}$

28) $\frac{13}{28}$ and $\frac{7}{36}$

(4.4)

29) Casimir computes the following sum: $\frac{5}{11} + \frac{4}{9} = \frac{9}{20}$. Is the answer right or wrong? Explain your answer.

30) Explain, in your own words, how to subtract fractions with unlike denominators.   Answers may vary.

Add or subtract, as indicated.

31) $\frac{4}{5} - \frac{3}{10}$ $\frac{1}{2}$

32) $\frac{5}{6} - \frac{1}{3}$ $\frac{1}{2}$

33) $\frac{5}{12} + \frac{4}{7}$ $\frac{83}{84}$

34) $\frac{5}{8} + \frac{1}{9}$ $\frac{53}{72}$

35) $\frac{9}{11} - \frac{3}{8}$ $\frac{39}{88}$

36) $\frac{9}{7} - \frac{7}{8}$ $\frac{23}{56}$

37) $\frac{5}{6} + \frac{1}{8} + \frac{7}{12}$ $\frac{37}{24}$ or $1\frac{13}{24}$

38) $\frac{7}{10} + \frac{7}{20} + \frac{7}{8}$ $\frac{77}{40}$ or $1\frac{37}{40}$

39) $1 - \frac{4}{15}$ $\frac{11}{15}$

40) $2 - \frac{2}{3}$ $\frac{4}{3}$ or $1\frac{1}{3}$

41) $7 + \frac{2}{9}$ $\frac{65}{9}$ or $7\frac{2}{9}$

42) $1 + \frac{3}{4}$ $\frac{7}{4}$ or $1\frac{3}{4}$

Solve each problem.

43) At the beginning of Salomeh's school day, her cell phone battery was charged to $\frac{3}{4}$ capacity. At the end of the day, the battery was charged to $\frac{1}{5}$ capacity. What fraction of the battery capacity was used during the day? $\frac{11}{20}$

44) Crista sees a pair of leather boots on sale for $\frac{1}{4}$ off the regular price. She also has a coupon that gives her an additional discount equal to $\frac{1}{10}$ the regular price. What fraction of the regular price will Crista have to pay for the boots? $\frac{13}{20}$

Students at a community college were surveyed to determine their favorite music genre. The pie chart below shows the fraction of the 540 students who chose a specific genre. Use this information to answer Exercises 45–50.

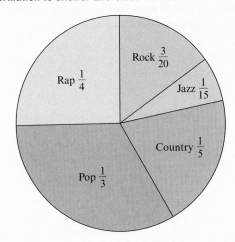

45) What fraction of the students prefer pop or rap music? $\frac{7}{12}$

46) What fraction of the students prefer a genre other than pop or rock? $\frac{31}{60}$

47) How many students prefer rap music? 135 students

48) How many students prefer country or jazz music? 144 students

49) How many students do not prefer pop music?
360 students do not prefer pop music.

50) Verify that the five fractional parts sum to 1.
Answers may vary.

(4.5)

51) Explain two methods for adding mixed numbers.

52) Is $5\frac{10}{7}$ in simplest form? Why or why not?

Add or subtract, as indicated.

53) $3\frac{3}{8} + 8\frac{7}{12}$ $11\frac{23}{24}$

54) $5\frac{1}{4} + 7\frac{5}{9}$ $12\frac{29}{36}$

55) $12\frac{6}{7} - 6\frac{7}{21}$ $6\frac{11}{21}$

56) $15\frac{4}{5} - 7\frac{7}{10}$ $8\frac{1}{10}$

57) $9\frac{4}{5} + 5\frac{9}{20}$ $15\frac{1}{4}$

58) $12\frac{5}{9} + 8\frac{3}{4}$ $21\frac{11}{36}$

59) $23\frac{5}{16} - 17\frac{3}{4}$ $5\frac{9}{16}$

60) $19\frac{3}{5} - 6\frac{22}{35}$ $12\frac{34}{35}$

61) $17\frac{1}{5} - 13\frac{5}{6}$ $3\frac{11}{30}$

62) $11\frac{5}{24} - 6\frac{5}{8}$ $4\frac{7}{12}$

63) $4\frac{5}{8} - 3$ $1\frac{5}{8}$

64) $8\frac{3}{7} - 5$ $3\frac{3}{7}$

65) $8 - 2\frac{7}{10}$ $5\frac{3}{10}$

66) $17 - 9\frac{1}{6}$ $7\frac{5}{6}$

67) $3\frac{13}{15} + 9\frac{5}{6} + 2\frac{9}{10}$ $16\frac{3}{5}$ 68) $10\frac{4}{5} + 7\frac{7}{10} + 3\frac{5}{8}$ $22\frac{1}{8}$

Solve each problem.

69) Herb wants to surround his rectangular rose garden with a small white picket fence. If Herb's garden is $10\frac{1}{2}$ ft long and $6\frac{3}{4}$ ft wide, what length of fence does he need to surround his garden? $34\frac{1}{2}$ ft

70) Deanna wants to apply weather stripping to all four sides of her entry door frame. If the door frame is $6\frac{2}{3}$ ft tall and $2\frac{1}{2}$ ft wide, what length of weather stripping does Deanna need? $18\frac{1}{3}$ ft

71) A police officer needs to mark off a crime scene (in the shape of the figure below) with crime scene tape. What length of tape will she need?

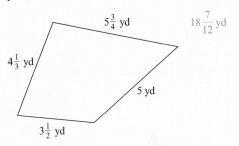

$18\frac{7}{12}$ yd

72) Find the perimeter of the figure below. 21 ft

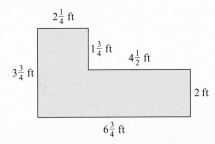

(4.6) For Exercises 73–78, approximate the location of each fraction or mixed number on the given number line.

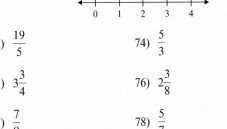

73) $\frac{19}{5}$

74) $\frac{5}{3}$

75) $3\frac{3}{4}$

76) $2\frac{3}{8}$

77) $\frac{7}{9}$

78) $\frac{5}{7}$

Fill in the blank with > or <.

79) $\frac{10}{21}$ ____ $\frac{11}{21}$ $<$

80) $\frac{16}{7}$ ____ $\frac{15}{7}$ $>$

81) $\frac{3}{4}$ ____ $\frac{9}{13}$ $>$

82) $\frac{5}{9}$ ____ $\frac{12}{21}$ $<$

83) If two fractions have the same denominator, the fraction with the smaller numerator is closer to 0 on the number line.　true

84) If two fractions have the same numerator, the fraction with the smaller denominator is closer to 0 on the number line.　false

85) Arrange the fractions in order from smallest to largest.

$$\frac{3}{5}, \frac{7}{8}, \frac{9}{20}, \frac{3}{4}, \frac{7}{10} \quad \frac{9}{20}, \frac{3}{5}, \frac{7}{10}, \frac{3}{4}, \frac{7}{8}$$

86) Arrange the fractions in order from largest to smallest.

$$\frac{7}{5}, \frac{7}{6}, \frac{23}{15}, \frac{3}{2}, \frac{13}{10} \quad \frac{23}{15}, \frac{3}{2}, \frac{7}{5}, \frac{13}{10}, \frac{7}{6}$$

Evaluate.

87) $\left(\frac{11}{12}\right)^2 \quad \frac{121}{144}$

88) $\left(\frac{1}{3}\right)^4 \quad \frac{1}{81}$

Simplify each expression using the order of operations.

89) $\frac{15}{9} - \frac{7}{12} \div \frac{3}{4} \quad \frac{8}{9}$

90) $\left(\frac{3}{4}\right)^3 - \left(\frac{3}{8}\right)^2 \quad \frac{9}{32}$

91) $17 - 8\left(\frac{5}{4}\right)^3 + \frac{1}{8} \quad \frac{3}{2}$ or $1\frac{1}{2}$

92) $\frac{4}{3}\left(\frac{8}{7} - \frac{2}{3}\right) \quad \frac{40}{63}$

93) $\left(\frac{3}{4} + \frac{1}{8}\right)^2 - \left(\frac{1}{8} \div 8\right) \quad \frac{3}{4}$

94) $\frac{1}{10} + \frac{5}{21} \cdot \frac{14}{15} \quad \frac{29}{90}$

Mixed Exercises

The remaining exercises combine adding, subtracting, multiplying, and dividing fractions and mixed numbers.

95) Which operations with fractions require getting a common denominator?　adding and subtracting

96) Explain how to multiply mixed numbers.
First, change them to improper fractions. Then, multiply.

Perform the indicated operations.

97) $\frac{25}{36} \div \frac{20}{63} \quad \frac{35}{16}$ or $2\frac{3}{16}$

98) $1\frac{9}{10} + 6\frac{3}{4} \quad 8\frac{13}{20}$

99) $2\frac{1}{7} \cdot 3\frac{1}{2} \quad 7\frac{1}{2}$

100) $\frac{1}{3}\left(\frac{13}{4} - \frac{5}{2}\right) \quad \frac{1}{4}$

101) $\frac{3}{24} + \frac{5}{8} - \frac{7}{12} \quad \frac{1}{6}$

102) $4\frac{4}{5} \div 6\frac{2}{3} \quad \frac{18}{25}$

103) $7\frac{5}{9} - 2\frac{7}{8} \quad 4\frac{49}{72}$

104) $16 \cdot \frac{11}{40} \quad \frac{22}{5}$ or $4\frac{2}{5}$

105) $\frac{9}{20} \div 12 \quad \frac{3}{80}$

106) $\frac{11}{12} - \frac{3}{4} \quad \frac{1}{6}$

107) $3^2 - \left(\frac{3}{2}\right)^3 \quad \frac{45}{8}$ or $5\frac{5}{8}$

108) $\frac{19}{24} - \frac{3}{56} + \frac{5}{14} \quad \frac{23}{21}$ or $1\frac{2}{21}$

109) $\frac{15}{56} \cdot \frac{42}{55} \cdot \frac{2}{9} \quad \frac{1}{22}$

110) $2 - 9\left(\frac{2}{3}\right)^4 - \frac{2}{9} \quad 0$

Chapter 4:　Test

*Additional answers can be found in the Answers to Exercises appendix.

1) Add $\frac{3}{5} + \frac{1}{5}$:

　a) by drawing a figure to represent each fraction.

　b) using a number line.

Find the least common multiple of each group of numbers.

2) 4 and 6　12

3) 8, 15, and 24　120

4) Write $\frac{1}{2}$ with a denominator of 16.　$\frac{1}{2} = \frac{8}{16}$

5) *Why* does multiplying $\frac{8}{9}$ by $\frac{3}{3}$ result in a fraction, $\frac{24}{27}$, that is equivalent to $\frac{8}{9}$?

6) Identify the least common denominator of $\frac{4}{9}$ and $\frac{1}{6}$, then write each as an equivalent fraction with the LCD as its denominator.

7) Identify the operation(s) that require getting a common denominator to perform the operation between fractions.

　add　　subtract　　multiply　　divide
　add, subtract

8) What is the first step for multiplying or dividing mixed numbers?　Change the mixed numbers to improper fractions.

Perform the indicated operations.

9) $\frac{1}{6} + \frac{4}{9} \quad \frac{11}{18}$

10) $\frac{7}{12} - \frac{1}{4} \quad \frac{1}{3}$

11) $2\frac{4}{9} \div 1\frac{5}{6} \quad 1\frac{1}{3}$

12) $5\frac{2}{7} + 2\frac{3}{8} \quad 7\frac{37}{56}$

13) $\frac{2}{3} + \frac{3}{20} + \frac{1}{4} \quad \frac{16}{15}$ or $1\frac{1}{15}$

14) $1 - \frac{3}{7} \quad \frac{4}{7}$

15) $\frac{5}{8} \cdot \frac{4}{9} \quad \frac{5}{18}$

16) $4\frac{7}{8} + 12\frac{2}{5} \quad 17\frac{11}{40}$

17) $6 - 2\frac{3}{10} \quad 3\frac{7}{10}$

18) $\frac{9}{10} \div 15 \quad \frac{3}{50}$

19) $\frac{19}{24} + \frac{23}{40} \quad \frac{41}{30}$ or $1\frac{11}{30}$

Fill in the blank with > or <.

20) $\frac{5}{11} \underline{\quad} \frac{9}{11} \quad <$

21) $\frac{5}{9} \underline{\quad} \frac{7}{12} \quad <$

22) Evaluate $\left(\frac{2}{5}\right)^3$.　$\frac{8}{125}$

Simplify using the order of operations.

23) $\frac{5}{8} - \frac{1}{12} \div \frac{3}{16}$ $\frac{13}{72}$ 24) $2\frac{1}{4} + 8\left(\frac{1}{2} + \frac{1}{3}\right)$ $\frac{107}{12}$ or $8\frac{11}{12}$

25) $\left(\frac{1}{9}\right)^2 \cdot \left(\frac{3}{2}\right)^4$ $\frac{1}{16}$

Solve the problem.

26) Stephanie is trying to repair a bare spot in her lawn. She buys a rectangular grass seed blanket to lay over the spot. The grass seed blanket is $3\frac{1}{4}$ ft long and $1\frac{1}{2}$ ft wide.

    a) Find the area of the grass seed blanket. $4\frac{7}{8}$ ft^2

    b) Find the perimeter of the grass seed blanket. $9\frac{1}{2}$ ft

Use the pie chart for Exercises 27–30.

Calvin has 2400 songs on his MP3 player. The pie chart shows the fraction of music in each category.

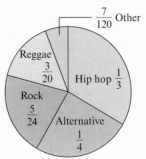

27) What fraction of Calvin's music is hip hop or rock? $\frac{13}{24}$

28) How many reggae songs are on Calvin's MP3 player?   360

29) What fraction of music is *not* classified as alternative? $\frac{3}{4}$

30) How many songs are *not* classified as alternative?   1800

Chapter 4: Cumulative Review for Chapters 1–4

*Additional answers can be found in the Answers to Exercises appendix.

Add, subtract, multiply, or divide as indicated.

1) $\begin{array}{r} 458 \\ 327 \\ + \; 76 \end{array}$ 861

2) $\begin{array}{r} 6435 \\ -4709 \end{array}$ 1726

3) $\begin{array}{r} 628 \\ \times 509 \end{array}$ 319,652

4) $25)\overline{15,042}$ 601 R17

Round each number to the nearest ten, nearest hundred, and nearest thousand.

	Ten	**Hundred**	**Thousand**
5) 675	680	700	1000
6) 58,399	58,400	58,400	58,000

7) A group of 9 lottery players share a winning ticket that is worth $4,007,106 after taxes. If the money is divided up evenly, how much will each person receive? $445,234

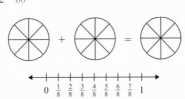

Simplify each expression using the order of operations.

8) $46 - 4\sqrt{79 - 15} \div 4 \cdot 3 - \sqrt{81}$ 13

9) $4^2 \cdot 2^2 - (14 - 6) \div 2$ 60

10) Add the like fractions. First, shade the figures appropriately to represent each fraction and the resulting sum. Then, use a number line to demonstrate the operation. $\frac{1}{8} + \frac{4}{8}$

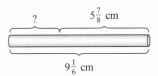

Perform the indicated operations.

11) $\frac{14}{15} \div \frac{8}{25}$ $\frac{35}{12}$ or $2\frac{11}{12}$

12) $\frac{7}{10} - \frac{1}{6}$ $\frac{8}{15}$

13) $5\frac{7}{8} + 6\frac{3}{4}$ $12\frac{5}{8}$

14) $\frac{5}{12} \cdot 18$ $\frac{15}{2}$ or $7\frac{1}{2}$

15) $\frac{20}{27} \cdot \frac{14}{11} \cdot \frac{9}{28}$ $\frac{10}{33}$

For Exercises 16–18, answer true or false.

16) If two fractions have the same numerator, the fraction with the smaller denominator is closer to 0 on the number line.   false

17) $\frac{7}{6} > \frac{9}{8}$ true   18) $\frac{8}{7} < \frac{13}{12}$ false

19) Find the missing length. $3\frac{7}{24}$ cm

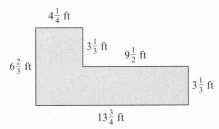

20) Find the perimeter of the figure. $40\frac{5}{6}$ ft

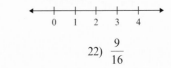

For Exercises 21–22, approximate the location of each fraction or mixed number on the given number line.

21) $2\frac{1}{5}$ 22) $\frac{9}{16}$

Simplify each expression using the order of operations.

23) $\frac{7}{8} - \frac{2}{5} \cdot \frac{3}{8}$ $\frac{29}{40}$ 24) $20 - 20\left(\frac{3}{5}\right)^2 - \frac{2}{5}$ $\frac{62}{5}$ or $12\frac{2}{5}$

25) $\frac{4}{7}\left(\frac{1}{10} + \frac{2}{5}\right)$ $\frac{2}{7}$

Decimals

Math at Work:

Bookkeeper

Uma Patel has always loved math. From elementary school all through college, it was her favorite subject. "It's not that math ever seemed very easy to me," Uma describes. "Like everyone else, I had to work at it. But there's just something about working with numbers that really appeals to me."

It's no surprise, then, that she entered a career as a bookkeeper, managing the financial records for an insurance agency of over 60 people. Her job allows her to apply her math skills on a daily basis: creating profit-and-loss statements, tracking income and expenditures, managing payroll, and so on. "Bookkeeping requires you to use math in a very precise way," Uma says. "A single decimal out of place could potentially cost the company thousands of dollars."

Yet, while Uma was glad to take on the math duties bookkeeping required, one thing she did not expect was how stressful her job became around tax time. "Every spring, there is a huge rush to prepare the documents we need to file our taxes," she says. In order to cope with the pressure and the tight deadlines, Uma calls on strategies she used in a similar context in college: taking math tests. "What worked for me when I was doing math for an exam also works when I'm doing math for my job on April 14th," Uma says.

We'll discuss the use of decimals in this chapter and also introduce some strategies to help you succeed on math tests. As Uma's story suggests, these are skills that will serve you well in any high-intensity situation.

For many students, math tests cause a great deal of anxiety. (To find out whether test anxiety is a problem for you, complete the exercise on pages 365 and 366.) Remember, though: Anyone can do well in math, and anyone can do well on math tests. The strategies below will help you perform your best.

- Practice, practice, practice. Your math skills will benefit from repetition, so do as many practice problems as you can. Use a timer in order to simulate the time period of an actual test.
- Get a good night's sleep before the test.
- Warm up for the test just like athletes do before they play a game. No matter how much you studied the night before, do several "warm-up" problems the same day as the test. This way, you will be in the groove of doing math and won't go into the test cold.

- Bring the right supplies on test day: multiple pens and pencils, plenty of scratch paper, and a watch or other timepiece. If you are allowed to bring a calculator or your textbook, bring those as well.
- Get to the location of the test at least 10 minutes early.

- Answer the easiest questions first. This will build your confidence and allow you more time to work on the harder problems.
- Show your work in a neat and logical way. Your instructor may give you partial credit if you lay out the steps you're going through.
- Throughout the test, manage any anxiety you feel. Take deep breaths, and trust that your preparation has positioned you to succeed.

- Save time at the end of the test to check over your calculations.

- When you receive your grade on the test, rethink the entire test-taking process. Consider what you did that worked and what you could have done better.
- Look over your test and see where you made errors. Ask your instructor for the correct answers, and redo questions you got wrong.

Chapter 5 ⬛POWER⬛ Plan

P Prepare	**O Organize**
What are your goals for Chapter 5?	**How can you accomplish each goal?**
1 Be prepared before and during class.	• Don't stay out late the night before, and be sure to set your alarm clock! • Bring a pencil, notebook paper, and textbook to class. • Avoid distractions by turning off your cell phone during class. • Pay attention, take good notes, and ask questions. • Complete your homework on time, and ask questions on problems you do not understand.
2 Understand the homework to the point where you could do it without needing any help or hints.	• Read the directions, and show all of your steps. • Go to the professor's office for help. • Rework homework and quiz problems, and find similar problems for practice.
3 Use the P.O.W.E.R. framework to learn ways to improve the way you take math tests: *Is Anxiety the Hardest Problem on the Test?*	• Read the Study Strategy as it is outlined in the P.O.W.E.R. framework. • Decide which steps you might need to improve. • Complete the emPOWERme that appears before the Chapter Summary.
4 Write your own goal. _____ _____	• _____ _____
What are your objectives for Chapter 5?	**How can you accomplish each objective?**
1 Learn to read, write, and round decimals.	• Use place value, number lines, and writing a decimal as a fraction or mixed number to help understand what a decimal represents. • The same rounding principles you learned previously still apply to decimals.
2 Learn how to perform basic operations on decimals.	• Write the procedures for adding, subtracting, multiplying, and dividing with decimals in your own words. • Know how to multiply or divide by a power of 10. • Be able to solve applied problems using decimals.
3 Learn to write a fraction as a decimal.	• Understand the two ways to write a fraction as a decimal. One way is to use division, and the other is to write an equivalent fraction with a denominator that is a power of 10. • Know how to compare a decimal and a fraction.
4 Understand how to use measures of central tendency.	• Be able to find a mean, weighted mean, median, and mode. • Know what the different measures represent.
5 Write your own goal. _____ _____	• _____ _____

W Work   Read Sections 5.1–5.7, and complete the exercises.

E Evaluate Complete the Chapter Review and Chapter Test. How did you do?	**R Rethink** <ul><li>Many, if not all, concepts in math build upon each other. How was that true for this chapter?</li><li>Your GPA is important to your academic success. What would your GPA be if it were instead calculated as a median or mode? Would those be good representations of your overall performance? Why or why not?</li><li>What was the most important tip you learned from the Study Strategy or emPOWERme exercise? How can you start applying it now before the next quiz or test?</li></ul>

5.1 Reading and Writing Decimals

P Prepare

O Organize

What are your objectives for Section 5.1?	How can you accomplish each objective?
1 Understand What Decimals Represent	<ul><li>Know the definition of a *decimal* and how it represents a fraction.</li><li>Be able to make the same visual representations of decimals as you did with fractions.</li><li>Complete the given examples on your own.</li><li>Complete You Trys 1 and 2.</li></ul>
2 Use Place Value	<ul><li>Understand the **Place Value Chart** and how it applies to numbers containing decimals.</li><li>Be able to write fractions and mixed numbers as decimals.</li><li>Complete the given examples on your own.</li><li>Complete You Trys 3–5.</li></ul>
3 Read and Write Decimals in Words	<ul><li>Use the procedure for **Reading a Decimal Number**, and write it in your own words.</li><li>Complete the given examples on your own.</li><li>Complete You Trys 6 and 7.</li></ul>
4 Write Decimals as Fractions or Mixed Numbers	<ul><li>Write your own procedure for writing a decimal as a fraction or mixed number.</li><li>Complete the given examples on your own.</li><li>Complete You Trys 8 and 9.</li></ul>

W Work   **Read the explanations, follow the examples, take notes, and complete the You Trys.**

In Chapters 3 and 4, we learned about fractions. We learned how to represent the shaded part of a figure with a fraction, and we learned how to represent the value of a fraction on a number line. Let's do the same with *decimals*.

1 Understand What Decimals Represent

Definition

A **decimal** is a number, containing a *decimal point*, that is another way to represent a fraction with a denominator that is a power of 10.

Example: $0.1 = \dfrac{1}{10}$ Both of these are read as *one tenth*.

↑
Decimal point

Look at the figure.

One tenth of the figure is shaded. We can write this with a fraction or a decimal.

We can say that $\dfrac{1}{10}$ of the figure is shaded, or 0.1 of the figure is shaded.

To represent $\dfrac{1}{10}$ (one tenth) on a number line, divide the number line from 0 to 1 into 10 equal parts so that the space between each tick mark is $\dfrac{1}{10}$ (one tenth) of a unit. Place a dot on $\dfrac{1}{10}$.

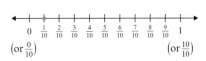

To represent 0.1 (one tenth) on a number line, divide the number line from 0 to 1 into 10 equal parts so that the space between each tick mark is 0.1 (one tenth) of a unit. Label the number line using decimal notation.

Notice from their placement on the number lines that $\dfrac{1}{10}$ and 0.1 represent the same quantity!

Note

Remember, a decimal represents a fraction with a denominator that is a power of 10.

EXAMPLE 1

In-Class Example 1

Use Example 1.

Use a decimal to represent the shaded part of the rectangle, and represent the decimal on a number line.

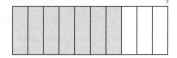

Solution

The rectangle is divided into 10 equal parts. 7 parts are shaded. Therefore,

$$0.7 \text{ (seven tenths) of the rectangle is shaded.}$$

(Notice that, as a fraction, we say $\frac{7}{10}$ is shaded. Both 0.7 and $\frac{7}{10}$ are read as *seven tenths*.) To represent 0.7 on a number line, divide the number line from 0 to 1 into 10 equal parts. The space between each tick mark is 0.1 (one tenth) of a unit. Label the number line using decimal notation.

Place the dot on 0.7.

YOU TRY 1

Use a decimal to represent the shaded part of the rectangle, and represent the decimal on a number line.

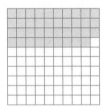

Decimals represent fractions with denominators that are powers of 10. So, let's look at a figure that is divided into 100 equal parts.

Use a decimal to represent the shaded part of the figure.

Solution

The square is divided into 100 equal parts. 43 parts are shaded. As a *fraction*, we say that $\frac{43}{100}$ (forty-three hundredths) is shaded. In *decimal* form, we say that

0.43 (forty-three hundredths) is shaded.

Each small square is $\frac{1}{100}$ (one hundredth) or 0.01 (one hundredth) of the entire figure.

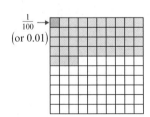

Use a decimal to represent the shaded part of the figure.

2 Use Place Value

Before we discuss decimals based on higher powers of 10, let's learn about place value.

In Chapter 1, we learned about place value of digits in whole numbers. For example, we identified the place value of each digit in a number like 572,364:

The number 572,364 has no fractional parts, so we do not include a decimal point in the number. (If we *did* include a decimal point, it would go at the end of the number: 572,364.) But, what if we have a number like 643,081.29753? What are the place-value names for the digits to the *right* of the decimal point?

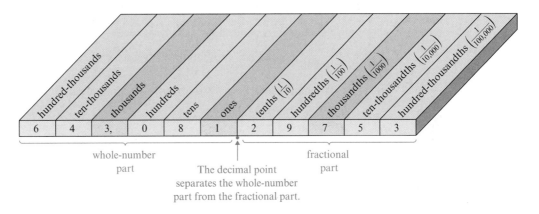

whole-number part

The decimal point separates the whole-number part from the fractional part.

fractional part

Here are some observations about the place-value chart.

Summary The Place-Value Chart

1) The *ones* column is in the middle of the chart.

2) The place values to the *left* of the decimal point (the whole-number part) end in **s.**

3) The place values to the *right* of the decimal point (the fractional part) end in **ths.**

EXAMPLE 3

In-Class Example 3

Write each fraction as a decimal.

a) $\dfrac{3}{100}$ b) $\dfrac{859}{1000}$ c) $\dfrac{273}{10,000}$

Answer: a) 0.03 b) 0.859
c) 0.0273

Write each fraction as a decimal.

a) $\dfrac{9}{100}$ b) $\dfrac{137}{1000}$ c) $\dfrac{421}{10,000}$

Solution

a) Reading the fraction to ourselves will help us determine how to correctly write the decimal.

$$\frac{9}{100} \text{ is read as "nine hundredths."}$$

The 9 must be in the hundredths place when we write $\dfrac{9}{100}$ as a decimal.

hundredths place
$$\text{Therefore, } \frac{9}{100} = 0.09 \qquad \text{Because there are no ones or tenths, we put 0's in those places.}$$
ones   tenths

b) $\dfrac{137}{1000}$ is read as "one hundred thirty-seven thousandths."

The 7 (the number farthest to the right in the numerator) must be written in the thousandths place.

$$\frac{137}{1000} = 0.137$$
thousandths place

c) $\dfrac{421}{10,000}$ is read as "four hundred twenty-one ten-thousandths."

The number farthest to the right in the numerator, 1, must be written in the ten-thousandths place.

ten-thousandths place
$$\frac{421}{10,000} = 0.0421$$
thousandths
hundredths
tenths
ones

[YOU TRY 3]

Write each fraction as a decimal.

a) $\dfrac{7}{100}$ b) $\dfrac{613}{1000}$ c) $\dfrac{909}{10,000}$

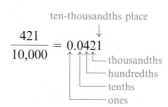

Note

It is not wrong to write $\dfrac{9}{100}$ as .09, leaving off the 0 in the ones place.

Usually, however, if there is no whole-number part, we put a 0 in the ones

place. Therefore, write $\dfrac{9}{100} = 0.09$.

Let's see how we write a decimal when there is a whole-number part.

Write each fraction or mixed number as a decimal.

a) $5\dfrac{3}{10}$ b) $\dfrac{139}{100}$

Solution

a) We read $5\dfrac{3}{10}$ as "five *and* three tenths." The *and* tells us where to put the decimal point, and three *tenths* tells us that 3 goes in the tenths place.

$$5\dfrac{3}{10} = 5.3$$
five and three tenths

Notice that the whole-number part is to the left of the decimal point.

b) There are two methods we can use to write $\dfrac{139}{100}$ as a decimal.

Method 1: $\dfrac{139}{100}$ is read as "one hundred thirty-nine hundredths." The number farthest to the right in the numerator, 9, must be written in the hundredths place.

hundredths place
$$\dfrac{139}{100} = 1.39$$
tenths
ones

Method 2: Write $\dfrac{139}{100}$ as the mixed number $1\dfrac{39}{100}$. Read the mixed number as "one *and* thirty-nine hundredths."

The *and* tells us where to put the decimal point.

$$\dfrac{139}{100} = 1\dfrac{39}{100} = 1.39$$
one and thirty-nine hundredths

[YOU TRY 4]

Write each fraction or mixed number as a decimal.

a) $4\dfrac{87}{100}$ b) $\dfrac{61}{10}$

Note

Because a whole number has no fractional part, it is usually written without a decimal point. We should know, however, that a whole number *can* be written with a decimal point at the end of the number, after the ones place.

$$5 = 5.$$
The decimal point goes at the end of the number.

$$294 = 294.$$
The decimal point goes at the end of the number.

EXAMPLE 5

In-Class Example 5

Identify the place value of each digit.
a) 0.0024 b) 563.08

Answer:
a) 0.—ones
   .0—tenths
   0—hundredths
   2—thousandths
   4—ten-thousandths
b) 5—hundreds
   6—tens
   3—ones
   0—tenths
   8—hundredths

Identify the place value of each digit.

a) 0.0086   b) 372.04

Solution

a)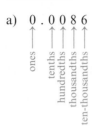

b)   372.04

[YOU TRY 5] Identify the place value of each digit.

a) 0.09058   b) 71.403

3 Read and Write Decimals in Words

We have seen that reading a fraction helps us to write it as a decimal. To read and write a decimal, we must identify the place value of the digit farthest to the right. Let's start with decimals that have no whole-number part.

EXAMPLE 6

In-Class Example 6

Write each decimal in words.
a) 0.4 b) 0.009 c) 0.817
d) 0.0608

Answer:
a) four tenths
b) nine thousandths
c) eight hundred seventeen thousandths
d) six hundred eight ten-thousandths

Write each decimal in words.

a) 0.5   b) 0.008   c) 0.263   d) 0.0701

Solution

a) There is no whole-number part, and the number ends in the *tenths* place. Read the number to the right of the decimal point like you would read the whole number, then follow it with *tenths*.

0.5 is read as "five *tenths*."   Think of 0.5 as $\frac{5}{10}$, read as "five *tenths*."

b) There is no whole-number part, and the number ends in the *thousandths* place. Read the number to the right of the decimal point like you would read the whole number, then follow it with *thousandths*.

0.008 is read as "eight *thousandths*."   Think of 0.008 as $\frac{8}{1000}$, read as "eight *thousandths*."

c) The number ends in the *thousandths* place. Read the number to the right of the decimal point like you would read the whole number, then follow it with *thousandths*.

0.263 is read as "two hundred sixty-three *thousandths*." $0.263 = \frac{263}{1000}$

d) The number ends in the *ten-thousandths* place. Read the number to the right of the decimal point like you would read the whole number, then follow it with *ten-thousandths*.

0.0701 is read as "seven hundred one *ten-thousandths*." $0.0701 = \frac{701}{10,000}$

[YOU TRY 6] Write each decimal in words.

    a) 0.7   b) 0.002   c) 0.926   d) 0.0065

When the decimal contains a whole-number part, read that first. We read the decimal point as "and"; then we read the part to the right of the decimal point.

> ## Procedure Reading a Decimal Number
>
> 1) Read the whole-number part first.
> 2) Read the decimal point as "and."
> 3) Read the fractional part, the digits to the *right* of the decimal point, last.

Note

If the number does not have a whole-number part, we read the part to the right of the decimal point as in Example 6.

EXAMPLE 7

In-Class Example 7

Write each decimal in words.
a) 67.3 b) 802.07 c) 1.495

Answer:
a) sixty seven and three tenths
b) eight hundred two and seven hundredths
c) one and four hundred ninety-five thousandths

Write each decimal in words.

  a) 34.9   b) 207.04   c) 1.625

Solution

a) Read the whole-number part first, read the decimal point as "and," then read the part to the right of the decimal point.

$$34.9$$

thirty-four and nine tenths

Read 34.9 as "thirty-four and nine tenths."

b) Read the whole-number part first, read the decimal point as "and," then read the part to the right of the decimal point.

$$207.04$$

two hundred seven and four hundredths

Read 207.04 as "two hundred seven and four hundredths."

c) Read the whole-number part first, read the decimal point as "and," then read the part to the right of the decimal point.

$$1.625$$

one and six hundred twenty-five thousandths

Read 1.625 as "one and six hundred twenty-five thousandths."

4 Write Decimals as Fractions or Mixed Numbers

Let's learn more about writing decimals as fractions and change decimals to mixed numbers as well.

EXAMPLE 8

In-Class Example 8

Write each decimal as a fraction or mixed number.
a) 0.27 b) 0.0561
c) 4.003

Answer:

a) $\dfrac{27}{100}$ b) $\dfrac{561}{10,000}$

c) $4\dfrac{3}{1000}$

Write each decimal as a fraction or mixed number.

a) 0.93   b) 0.0149   c) 2.007

Solution

a) Read 0.93 as "ninety-three hundredths."

numerator = 93   denominator = 100

$$0.93 = \frac{93}{100}$$

Also notice that in 0.93, the digit farthest to the right is in the *hundredths* place. So, the *denominator* is 100, and the numerator is 93.

$$0.93 = \frac{93}{100}$$

3 is in the *hundredths* place, so the denominator = 100.

b) Read 0.0149 as "one hundred forty-nine ten-thousandths."

numerator = 149   denominator = 10,000

$$0.0149 = \frac{149}{10,000}$$

9 is in the *ten-thousandths* place, so the denominator = 10,000.

Also notice that in 0.0149, the digit farthest to the right, 9, is in the *ten-thousandths* place. So, the *denominator* is 10,000, and the numerator is 149.

c) Because 2.007 has a whole-number part, it will be a mixed number. Read 2.007 as "two and seven *thousandths*."

whole-number   numerator = 7   denominator = 1000
part = 2

$$2.007 = 2\frac{7}{1000}$$

7 is in the *thousandths* place, so the denominator = 1000.

[YOU TRY 8] Write each decimal as a fraction or mixed number.

a) 0.41   b) 0.0903   c) 5.029

In Chapters 3 and 4, we said that all fractional answers must be in lowest terms. The same is true when we change a decimal to a fraction or mixed number.

Note

When we change a decimal to a fraction or mixed number, we *must* write the answer in lowest terms.

EXAMPLE 9

Write each decimal as a fraction or mixed number in lowest terms.

a)   0.6   b)   3.124

Solution

a) $0.6 = \dfrac{6}{10}$

6 is in the *tenths* place, so the denominator = 10.

Ask yourself, "Is $\dfrac{6}{10}$ in lowest terms?" No! Write it in lowest terms.

$$0.6 = \frac{6}{10} = \frac{6 \div 2}{10 \div 2} = \frac{3}{5}$$

b) $3.124 = 3\dfrac{124}{1000}$ Write $\dfrac{124}{1000}$ in lowest terms.

4 is in the *thousandths* place, so the denominator = 1000.

$$3.124 = 3\frac{124}{1000} = 3\frac{124 \div 4}{1000 \div 4} = 3\frac{31}{250}$$

[YOU TRY 9]

Write each decimal as a fraction or mixed number in lowest terms.

a)   0.4   b)   9.528

ANSWERS TO [YOU TRY] EXERCISES

1) 0.3; ◄─┼─┼─┼─┼─┼─┼─┼─┼─┼─┼─►   2) 0.61   3) a) 0.07   b) 0.613   c) 0.0909
          0 0.1 0.2 0.3 0.4 0.5 0.6 0.7 0.8 0.9 1

4) a) 4.87   b) 6.1

5) a) 0.—ones   b) 7—tens
   .0—tenths   1—ones
   9—hundredths   4—tenths
   0—thousandths   0—hundredths
   5—ten-thousandths   3—thousandths
   8—hundred-thousandths

6) a) seven tenths   b) two thousandths   c) nine hundred twenty-six thousandths
   d) sixty-five ten-thousandths   7) a) five hundred twenty-four and six tenths
   b) nine hundred one and six thousandths
   c) two and three thousand eight hundred eight ten-thousandths

8) a) $\dfrac{41}{100}$ b) $\dfrac{903}{10,000}$ c) $5\dfrac{29}{1000}$ 9) a) $\dfrac{2}{5}$ b) $9\dfrac{66}{125}$

---

*Additional answers can be found in the Answers to Exercises appendix.

Objective 1: Understand What Decimals Represent

1) How are decimals and fractions related? Decimals represent fractions with denominators that are powers of 10.

2) Explain how to make a number line, from 0 to 1, that is divided into tenths.   Answers may vary.

Use a fraction with a denominator of 10 to represent the shaded part of the rectangle and represent the fraction as a decimal on a number line.

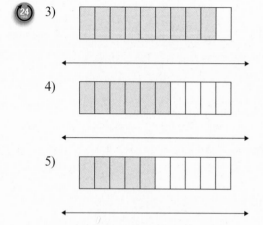

3)

4)

5)

6)

Use a fraction with a denominator of 10 to represent the *unshaded* part of the rectangle, and represent the fraction as a decimal on a number line.

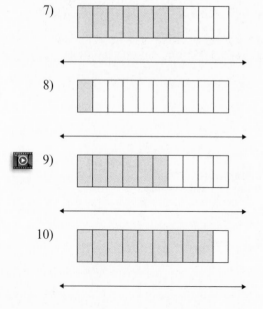

7)

8)

9)

10)

Use a fraction and a decimal to represent the shaded part of the figure. Write the fraction in lowest terms, if possible.

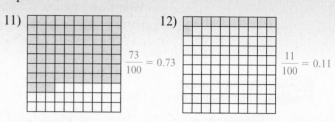

11) $\frac{73}{100} = 0.73$

12) $\frac{11}{100} = 0.11$

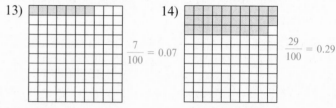

13) $\frac{7}{100} = 0.07$

14) $\frac{29}{100} = 0.29$

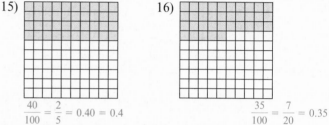

15) $\frac{40}{100} = \frac{2}{5} = 0.40 = 0.4$

16) $\frac{35}{100} = \frac{7}{20} = 0.35$

Approximate the location of the decimal value on the given number line.

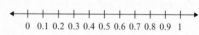

0 0.1 0.2 0.3 0.4 0.5 0.6 0.7 0.8 0.9 1

17) 0.58

18) 0.63

19) 0.06

20) 0.89

Objective 2: Use Place Value

Write each fraction as a decimal.

21) $\frac{3}{100}$ 0.03

22) $\frac{7}{100}$ 0.07

23) $\frac{81}{100}$ 0.81

24) $\frac{29}{100}$ 0.29

25) $\frac{141}{1000}$ 0.141

26) $\frac{719}{1000}$ 0.719

27) $\frac{67}{1000}$ 0.067

28) $\frac{43}{1000}$ 0.043

29) $\frac{893}{10,000}$ 0.0893

30) $\frac{557}{10,000}$ 0.0557

31) $\frac{2051}{10,000}$ 0.2051

32) $\frac{8049}{10,000}$ 0.8049

Write each fraction or mixed number as a decimal.

33) $6\frac{7}{10}$ 6.7

34) $4\frac{1}{10}$ 4.1

35) $7\frac{29}{100}$ 7.29

36) $1\frac{43}{100}$ 1.43

37) $38\frac{1}{1000}$ 38.001

38) $22\frac{7}{1000}$ 22.007

39) $10\frac{533}{1000}$ 10.533

40) $16\frac{829}{1000}$ 16.829

41) $\frac{81}{10}$ 8.1

42) $\frac{57}{10}$ 5.7

43) $\frac{409}{100}$ 4.09

44) $\frac{703}{100}$ 7.03

45) $\frac{1667}{100}$ 16.67

46) $\frac{1841}{100}$ 18.41

47) $\frac{2443}{1000}$ 2.443

48) $\frac{5119}{1000}$ 5.119

Identify the place value of each digit.

49) 0.3572

50) 0.1489

51) 40.16259

52) 90.51437

Objective 3: Read and Write Decimals in Words
Write each decimal in words.

53) 0.4   four tenths

54) 0.8   eight tenths

55) 0.36   thirty-six hundredths

56) 0.52   fifty-two hundredths

57) 0.007   seven thousandths

58) 0.005   five thousandths

59) 0.291   two hundred ninety-one thousandths

60) 0.384   three hundred eighty-four thousandths

61) 0.7415   seven thousand four hundred fifteen ten-thousandths

62) 0.6213   six thousand two hundred thirteen ten-thousandths

63) 57.3   fifty-seven and three tenths

64) 24.1   twenty-four and one tenth

65) 809.56   eight hundred nine and fifty-six hundredths

66) 302.97   three hundred two and ninety-seven hundredths

67) 3.0576   three and five hundred seventy-six ten-thousandths

68) 6.00017   six and seventeen hundred-thousandths

Write each word statement as a decimal.

69) fifteen hundredths   0.15

70) twelve hundredths   0.12

71) ninety-six and seven tenths   96.7

72) forty-nine and three tenths   49.3

73) thirty-two thousandths   0.032

74) sixty-seven thousandths   0.067

75) eight and four ten-thousandths   8.0004

76) one and nine ten-thousandths   1.0009

77) five thousand five and five hundred-thousandths   5005.00005

78) two thousand two and two hundred-thousandths   2002.00002

Objective 4: Write Decimals as Fractions or Mixed Numbers

79) Explain how to write a decimal as a fraction.   Answers may vary.

80) Can a whole number be written with a decimal point? Explain your answer.   Yes. The decimal point goes at the right end of the number.

Write each decimal as a fraction or mixed number in lowest terms.

81) 0.73 $\frac{73}{100}$

82) 0.81 $\frac{81}{100}$

83) 0.0207 $\frac{207}{10,000}$

84) 0.0503 $\frac{503}{10,000}$

85) 4.9 $4\frac{9}{10}$

86) 6.7 $6\frac{7}{10}$

87) 0.6 $\frac{3}{5}$

88) 0.4 $\frac{2}{5}$

89) 0.60 $\frac{3}{5}$

90) 0.40 $\frac{2}{5}$

91) 0.15 $\frac{3}{20}$

92) 0.25 $\frac{1}{4}$

93) 0.68 $\frac{17}{25}$

94) 0.96 $\frac{24}{25}$

95) 5.144 $5\frac{18}{125}$

96) 1.238 $1\frac{119}{500}$

97) 1.00015 $1\frac{3}{20,000}$

98) 2.00035 $2\frac{7}{20,000}$

99) Explain why 0.20 is equivalent to 0.2.   Answers may vary.

100) Explain why 1.3200 is equivalent to 1.32.   Answers may vary.

Mixed Exercises: Objectives 1–4
Write each word statement as a decimal.

101) eight and fourteen ten-thousandths   8.0014

102) three hundred thousand thirty-nine and sixty-two hundredths   300,039.62

Write each decimal in words.

103) 204.8   two hundred four and eight tenths

104) 781.005   seven hundred eighty-one and five thousandths

Use a simplified fraction and a decimal to represent the shaded part of the figure.

105) 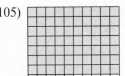 $\frac{3}{4} = 0.75$

Identify the place value of each digit.

106) 574.01368   5—hundreds, 7—tens, 4—ones, 0—tenths, 1—hundredths, 3—thousandths, 6—ten-thousandths, 8—hundred-thousandths

Write each fraction as a decimal.

107) $\dfrac{37}{1000}$ 0.037

108) $\dfrac{189}{10}$ 18.9

Write each decimal as a fraction or mixed number in lowest terms.

109) 2.84 $2\dfrac{21}{25}$

110) 0.0725 $\dfrac{29}{400}$

R1) When do you consistently use decimals? Think about when you buy something!

R2) What did you previously not know about decimals that you learned by completing this section? How will it help you every day?

5.2 Rounding Decimals

P Prepare | **O Organize**

What are your objectives for Section 5.2?	How can you accomplish each objective?
1 Round Decimals	• Write the procedure for **Rounding Decimals** in your own words. • Understand how to regroup with decimals. • Complete the given examples on your own. • Complete You Trys 1–4.
2 Round Money Amounts to the Nearest Cent	• Use the same procedure for rounding decimals for this section. • Complete the given examples on your own. • Complete You Trys 5 and 6.
3 Round Money Amounts to the Nearest Dollar	• Use the same procedure for rounding decimals for this section, and know how to regroup $1 if needed. • Complete the given examples on your own. • Complete You Trys 7 and 8.

W Work **Read the explanations, follow the examples, take notes, and complete the You Trys.**

In Section 1.6, we learned that to *round* a number means to find another number close to the original number. For example, 748 rounded to the nearest ten is 750, and 5391 rounded to the nearest thousand is 5000.

1 Round Decimals

How do we round decimals? Let's use a number line to round 0.67 to the nearest tenth. Put 0.67 on a number line in which each tick mark represents 0.1 unit.

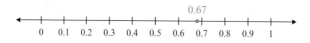

www.mhhe.com/messersmith

Is 0.67 closer to 0.6 or 0.7 on the number line? It is closer to 0.7. Therefore, we can say that 0.67 rounded to the nearest tenth is 0.7.

Rounding decimals is especially useful when working with money. We will see examples using money later in this section.

Here are the rules for rounding decimals.

Procedure Rounding Decimals

Step 1: Find the place to which we are asked to round. Underline the digit in that place, and draw a vertical line after it.

Step 2: Look at the digit to the right of the vertical line.

a) If the digit to the right of the vertical line is **less than 5,** "drop off" the digits to the right of the vertical line and leave the underlined digit as it is.

b) If the digit to the right of the vertical line is **5 or more,** "drop off" the digits to the right of the vertical line and increase the underlined digit by 1.

W Hint

Once again, 5 is the "cutoff" for rounding!

EXAMPLE 1

Round 90.4637 to the nearest hundredth.

In-Class Example 1

Round 50.3821 to the nearest hundredth.

Answer: 50.38

Solution

Step 1: Underline the digit in the hundredths place, and draw a vertical line after it.

$$90.46|37$$

Step 2: Look at the digit to the right of the vertical line. Because 3 is less than 5, we will "drop off" the digits to the right of the vertical line and keep the underlined digit the same.

Keep this digit the same.
3 is less than 5.

$$90.46|37$$

Drop these.

Round to 90.46.

Therefore, 90.4637 rounded to the nearest hundredth is 90.46. We can also say that $90.4637 \approx 90.46$. (Remember, $\approx$ means *is approximately equal to.*)

[YOU TRY 1] Round 19.5439 to the nearest hundredth.

Note

90.4637 rounded to the nearest hundredth is *not* 90.4600. (We do *not* replace the dropped digits with zeros.) **The place to which we are rounding should be the last place in our rounded number.** That is why, rounded to the nearest hundredth, 90.4637 is 90.46.

EXAMPLE 2

Round 7.2814 to the nearest tenth.

Solution

Step 1: Underline the digit in the tenths place and draw a vertical line after it.

$$7.2|814$$

Step 2: Look at the digit to the right of the vertical line. Because 8 is more than 5, "drop off" the digits to the right of the vertical line and increase the underlined digit by 1.

Increase by 1.
8 is more than 5.

$$7.2|814$$

Drop these.

Round to 7.3.

Rounded to the nearest tenth, 7.2814 is 7.3. (Because we are rounding to the *tenths* place, the last digit in the answer will be in the *tenths* place.)

[**YOU TRY 2**] Round 8.1609 to the nearest tenth.

Note

In Example 2, we increased the digit in the *tenths* place by 1. This is the same as adding 1 *tenth* (or 0.1) to the number after dropping off the digits that follow the vertical line.

$$7.2|814 \longrightarrow \begin{array}{r} 7.2 \\ +0.1 \\ \hline 7.3 \end{array}$$ Increase the tenths digit by 1.

Some rounding problems involve regrouping. We can think of regrouping with fractions like this:

$$\frac{9}{10} + \frac{1}{10} = \frac{10}{10}$$ (10 *tenths*) or 1 whole   We can regroup 10 *tenths* as 1 *whole*.

Sometimes, we use a similar approach when rounding decimals.

EXAMPLE 3

Round each number to the indicated place.

a)   12.973 to the nearest tenth

b)   0.8395 to the nearest thousandth

Solution

a) **Step 1:** $12.9|73$ Underline the digit in the tenths place, and draw a vertical line after it.

Step 2: 12.9|73

Increase by 1.
7 is more than 5.

Drop these.

12.9   Increasing the 9 by 1 is the same as adding 1 tenth to 9 tenths.
+ 0.1   9 tenths + 1 tenth = 10 tenths
13.0   Regroup 10 tenths as 1 *whole* (or 1 *one*), and add.

12.973 rounded to the nearest tenth is 13.0.

The correct answer is 13.0 and *not* 13 because we are rounding to the nearest *tenth*. Therefore, we must keep the 0 in the *tenths* place.

W Hint

Be sure you understand why you must keep the zero in the tenths place!

b) **Step 1:** 0.839|5   Underline the digit in the thousandths place, and draw a vertical line after it.

Step 2: 0.839|5

Increase by 1.
5 or more

Drop this digit.

0.839   Increasing the 9 by 1 is the same as adding 1 thousandth to 9 thousandths.
+0.001   9 thousandths + 1 thousandth = 10 thousandths
0.840   Regroup this as 1 hundredth, and add.

0.8395 rounded to the nearest thousandth is 0.840. Remember to keep the 0 at the end because it is in the thousandths place.

[YOU TRY 3]   Round each number to the indicated place.

a)   45.991 to the nearest tenth   b)   0.7295 to the nearest thousandth

---

In some cases, we are asked to round to the *first* decimal place (the *tenths* place), the *second* decimal place (the *hundredths* place), to *three* decimal places (the *thousandths* place), etc. These are different ways to indicate rounding.

EXAMPLE 4

In-Class Example 4

Round 4.23759 to
a) the first decimal place.
b) four decimal places.

Answer: a) 4.2   b) 4.2376

Round 6.71958 to

a)   the first decimal place.   b)   four decimal places.

Solution

a)   Round 6.71958 to the *first* decimal place means to round it to the *tenths* place.

Step 1: 6.7|1958   Underline the digit in the first decimal place (tenths place), and draw a vertical line after it.

Keep this digit the same.
1 is less than 5.

Step 2: 6.7|1958

Drop these digits.

Round to 6.7.

b) Round 6.71958 to *four* decimal places means to round it to the *fourth* place after the decimal point. This is the *ten-thousandths* place.

Step 1: 6.7195|8   Underline the digit in the fourth decimal place, and draw a vertical line after it.

Increase by 1.
8 is more than 5.

Step 2: 6.7195|8

Drop this digit.

Round to 6.7196.

[**YOU TRY 4**] Round 9.04253 to

a) the first decimal place.   b) three decimal places.

---

2 Round Money Amounts to the Nearest Cent

We use decimals every day, especially in terms of money. Let's look at the decimal places in a dollar amount.

$36.28
hundredths place
tenths place

The value of a penny is 1¢ (1 cent). We can also write it in terms of a dollar as $0.01 or 0.01 dollar. $\left(\text{We can also say that it is } \dfrac{1}{100} \text{ dollar.}\right)$ Because it is the smallest denomination of money in the United States, most everyday money amounts are rounded *to the nearest cent*. This is the same as rounding *to the nearest hundredth of a dollar.*

Some *exact* calculations, like computing sales tax or computing the amount of a discount on an item, will actually give a dollar amount with digits to the right of the hundredths place (or number of cents). These are some examples of when money amounts would be rounded to the nearest cent.

EXAMPLE 5

In-Class Example 5

When Rinaldo computes the amount of tax he will owe on the soccer ball he bought, he gets the exact amount of $3.4697. Round this amount to the nearest cent to determine the amount of tax he will actually pay.

Answer: $3.47

When Helena computes the amount of tax she will owe on the makeup she bought, she gets the exact amount of $1.5362. Round this amount to the nearest cent to determine the amount of tax she will actually pay.

Solution

Round $1.5362 *to the nearest cent* means to round it to the *hundredths place.* Underline the 3 in the hundredths place, and round.

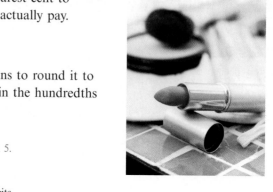

Increase by 1.
6 is more than 5.

$1.53|62

Drop these digits.

Round to $1.54.

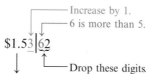

$1.5362 rounded to the nearest cent is $1.54. This answer makes sense because $1.5362 is closer to $1.54 than $1.53.

[YOU TRY 5] Jignesh computes the amount of tax he will owe on the jeans he bought, and that exact amount is $2.7456. Round this to the nearest cent to determine the amount of tax he will actually pay.

EXAMPLE 6

In-Class Example 6

Bridget computed the exact amount of the discount on a birthday card she bought as $0.214. Round this to the nearest cent to determine how much money she will actually save on the card.

Answer: $0.21 or 21¢

Makoto computed the exact amount of the discount on the batteries he bought as $0.783. Round this to the nearest cent to determine how much money he will actually save on the batteries.

Solution

Underline the 8 in the hundredths (or cents) place, and round.

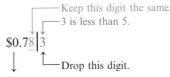

$0.78|3

Round to $0.78.

Makoto will save $0.78. This can also be written as 78¢.

[YOU TRY 6] Oksana computed the exact amount of the discount on a mechanical pencil as $0.352. Round this to the nearest cent to determine how much money she will actually save.

Note

Some stores round all discount amounts *up* to the nearest cent. For example, some stores would round the $0.783 to $0.79 even though the rounding rules tell us to keep the 8 the same.

---

3 Round Money Amounts to the Nearest Dollar

Sometimes we round money amounts to the nearest dollar. We might do this if we want to get an estimate of how much something costs.

Rounding to the nearest *dollar* means rounding to the *ones* place.

EXAMPLE 7

In-Class Example 7

Round $61.24 to the nearest dollar.

Answer: $61

Round $27.39 to the nearest dollar.

Solution

We can solve this problem in two ways.

Method 1: Rounding $27.39 to the nearest dollar means rounding it to the ones place.

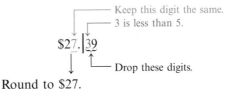

$27.|39

Round to $27.

Write the answer as $27, *not* $27.00. Writing $27.00 would indicate rounding to the nearest cent.

Method 2: $27.39 is between $27 and $28. Ask yourself, "*Is* $27.39 *closer to* $27 *or* $28?" It is closer to $27.

[**YOU TRY 7**] Round $85.42 to the nearest dollar.

 BE CAREFUL When rounding a number like $27.39 to the nearest dollar, the answer is $27 *not* $27.00. The last place in the rounded number should be the ones place.

EXAMPLE 8

In-Class Example 8

Round each number to the nearest dollar.
a) $703.62 b) $0.88
c) $299.78 d) $160.50

Answer:
a) $704 b) $1 c) $300
d) $161

Round each number to the nearest dollar.

a) $406.81   b) $0.59   c) $199.79   d) $320.50

Solution

a) Underline the 6 in $406.81, and round.

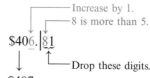

Increase by 1.
8 is more than 5.

$406.|81

Drop these digits.

Round to $407.

Or ask yourself, "*Is* $406.81 *closer to* $406 *or* $407?" It is closer to $407.

b) Underline the 0 in $0.59, and round.

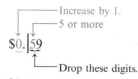

Increase by 1.
5 or more

$0.|59

Drop these digits.

Round to $1.

Or ask yourself, "*Is* $0.59 *closer to* $0 *or* $1?" It is closer to $1.

c) Underline the digit in the *ones* place, and round.

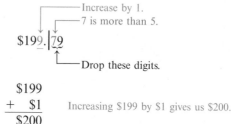

Increase by 1.
7 is more than 5.

$199.|79

Drop these digits.

$199
+ $1   Increasing $199 by $1 gives us $200.
———
$200

$199.79 is closer to $200 than to $199.

---

d) Underline the digit in the ones place, and round.

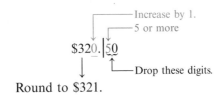

Round to $321.

Although $320.50 is *exactly* halfway between $320 and $321, the rounding rules tell us to round $320.50 to $321.

[**YOU TRY 8**]

Round each number to the nearest dollar.

a) $601.73   b) $0.64   c) $599.89   d) $1270.50

Note

In some areas of science, there are other rules for rounding numbers that are exactly halfway between two numbers. Sometimes, these numbers are not rounded up.

ANSWERS TO [YOU TRY] **EXERCISES**

1) 19.54   2) 8.2   3) a) 46.0   b) 0.730   4) a) 9.0   b) 9.043
5) $2.75   6) $0.35 or 35¢   7) $85   8) a) $602   b) $1   c) $600   d) $1271

E Evaluate **5.2** Exercises   Do the exercises, and check your work.

*Additional answers can be found in the Answers to Exercises appendix.

Objective 1: Round Decimals

Round the given decimal to the nearest tenth. Then represent the rounded decimal on the number line.

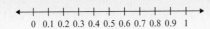

1) 0.39   2) 0.93

3) 0.02   4) 0.97

5) 0.653   6) 0.158

Round each number to the indicated place.

7) 0.683   8) 0.592

   a) tenth 0.7   a) tenth 0.6

   b) hundredth 0.68   b) hundredth 0.59

9) 94.349   10) 34.179

   a) hundredth 94.35   a) tenth 34.2

   b) tens 90   b) ones 34

11) 7620.183849   12) 1195.073264

   a) hundred 7600   a) thousand 1000

   b) ten-thousandth 7620.1838   b) ten-thousandth 1195.0733

13) 0.0982   14) 0.0954

   a) ones 0   a) ones 0

   b) hundredth 0.10   b) hundredth 0.10

15) 5.271   16) 8.629

   a) the first decimal place 5.3   a) the first decimal place 8.6

   b) two decimal places 5.27   b) two decimal places 8.63

17) 43.917995

   a) five decimal
     places   43.91800

   b) four decimal
     places   43.9180

18) 56.618995

   a) three decimal
     places   56.619

   b) five decimal
     places   56.61900

19) Explain, in your own words, how to round a decimal number.   Answers may vary.

20) If you are asked to round 28.4578 to the nearest hundredth, is the answer 28.4600? Explain your answer.   Answers may vary.

For Exercises 21–28, fill in the blank with > or < or =.

21) 0.63 __>__ 0.60

22) 0.40 __<__ 0.43

23) 1.0299 __<__ 1.0300

24) 8.4940 __>__ 8.4900

25) 3.05 __=__ 3.0500

26) 1.0800 __=__ 1.08

27) 0.1 __>__ 0.01

28) 0.0090 __<__ 0.090

Objective 2: Round Money Amounts to the Nearest Cent

Solve each problem.

29) Lyndsey computed the amount of tax she will owe for her new spring outfit as $5.2275. Round to the nearest cent to determine the amount of tax she will actually pay. $5.23

30) When Sheena computes the amount of tax she will owe for her new bedroom set, she gets the exact amount of $85.405. Round to the nearest cent to determine the amount of tax she will actually pay. $85.41

31) When Cameron bought his used car, he computed the amount of tax to be exactly $722.1175. Round to the nearest cent to determine the amount of tax he will actually pay. $722.12

32) Juanita computed the amount of tax she will owe on a purchase of video editing software to be exactly $16.1875. Round to the nearest cent to determine the amount of tax she will actually pay. $16.19

33) Erin purchased a new pair of earrings for $275.50, and she computed the amount of tax she will owe to be exactly $22.72875. How much must Erin pay at the cash register, including the sales tax? $298.23

34) Michael buys a rear spoiler for his sports car. The purchase price is $142.50, and he computes the amount of tax he will owe to be exactly $9.61875. What is the total cost of the rear spoiler, including the sales tax? $152.12

Objective 3: Round Money Amounts to the Nearest Dollar

Round each amount to the nearest dollar.

35) $18.48 $18

36) $11.36 $11

37) $39.05 $39

38) $76.24 $76

39) $42.61 $43

40) $58.73 $59

41) $681.57 $682

42) $912.58 $913

43) $1599.91 $1600

44) $2099.97 $2100

45) $45.50 $46

46) $12.50 $13

47) $0.48 $0

48) $0.76 $1

49) $0.92 $1

50) $0.34 $0

51) Rahim puts the following items into his cart at a home improvement store, and he wants to estimate how much he is spending. Round the price of each item to the nearest dollar, then add the rounded numbers to estimate the total cost of his items. $268

Faucet:	$87.26
Towel bar:	$24.99
Light fixture:	$129.95
Scale:	$19.35
Plunger:	$6.58

52) Sandy puts the following items into her cart at a toy store, and she wants to estimate how much she is spending. Round the price of each item to the nearest dollar, then add the rounded numbers to estimate the total cost of her items. $167

Doll stroller:	$9.49
Doll:	$15.99
Electronic math game:	$27.35
Jump rope:	$4.68
Booster seat:	$109.99

Mixed Exercises: Objectives 1–3
Round each number to the indicated place.

53) 1.85 to the nearest tenth   1.9

54) 46.0944 to the nearest thousandth   46.094

55) 0.00723 to the nearest ten-thousandth   0.0072

56) 925.8996 to the nearest hundredth   925.90

57) 6999.586 to the nearest ones place   7000

58) 74.53 to the nearest tens place   70

Round each amount a) to the nearest cent and b) to the nearest dollar.

59) $375.854   a) $375.85   b) $376

60) $71.9983   a) $72.00   b) $72

61) $0.359   a) $0.36   b) $0

62) $0.573   a) $0.57   b) $1

R Rethink

R1) Since you have learned about rounding in a previous section, explain how it was helpful for understanding how to round decimals.

R2) Where do you encounter scenarios in your life where money is rounded to the nearest dollar?

5.3 Adding and Subtracting Decimals

P Prepare

O Organize

What are your objectives for Section 5.3?	How can you accomplish each objective?
1 Add Decimals	• Write the procedure for **Adding or Subtracting Decimals** in your own words. • Complete the given examples on your own. • Complete You Trys 1 and 2.
2 Subtract Decimals	• Use the same procedure from Objective 1. • Complete the given examples on your own. • Complete You Trys 3–6.
3 Solve an Applied Problem	• Complete the given example on your own. • Complete You Try 7.

W Work

Read the explanations, follow the examples, take notes, and complete the You Trys.

In this section, we will learn how to add and subtract decimals.

1 Add Decimals

To add or subtract *decimal* numbers, we **line up the decimal points**—that is, we line up the numbers in the tenths place, line up the numbers in the hundredths place, and so on. Then, add or subtract.

Procedure Adding or Subtracting Decimals

1) Write the numbers vertically so that the decimal points are lined up.

2) If any numbers are missing digits to the right of the decimal point, insert zeros. Then, add or subtract the same way we add or subtract whole numbers.

3) Place the decimal point in the answer *directly below* the decimal point in the problem.

Note
Using graph paper will help us line up the numbers correctly.

EXAMPLE 1

Add.

a) 9.7 + 2.8   b) 14.223 + 7.501 + 0.884

Solution

a) Write the numbers vertically so that the decimal points are lined up.

Now, add just like we add whole numbers.

Line up the decimal points.

Line up the decimal point in the answer with the decimal points in the problem.

So, 9.7 + 2.8 = 12.5.

b) Write the numbers vertically so that the decimal points are lined up.

Now, add just like we add whole numbers.

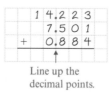

Line up the decimal points.

Line up the decimal point in the answer with the decimal points in the problem.

So, 14.223 + 7.501 + 0.884 = 22.608.

[**YOU TRY 1**] Add.

a) 8.6 + 5.7   b) 27.958 + 9.042 + 0.737

In Example 1a, both numbers had just one decimal place. In Example 1b, all numbers had three decimal places. Sometimes, the numbers in a problem do *not* have the same number of decimal places. When this happens, we insert zeros as placeholders so that they *will* have the same number of decimal places.

EXAMPLE 2

In-Class Example 2

Add.
a) 3.7 + 8.45
b) 12.61 + 6.738 + 9

Answer: a) 12.15 b) 28.348

Add.

a) 6.2 + 5.83   b) 11.36 + 7.295 + 8

Solution

a) Write the numbers vertically so that the decimal points are lined up.

 Hint

As long as you line up the decimal places, you can perform addition.

Line up the decimal points.

5.83 has a digit in the hundredths place, but 6.2 does not. **Insert a 0 in the hundredths place** of 6.2. Then, add.

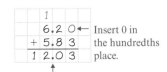

Line up the decimal point in the answer with the decimal points in the problem.

We can insert the 0 in the hundredths place of 6.2 because 6.2 is equivalent to 6.20.

Therefore, 6.2 + 5.83 = 12.03.

b) 11.36 + 7.295 + 8

Write the numbers vertically so that the decimal points are lined up. Remember that 8 can be written as 8.

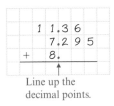

Line up the decimal points.

Insert zeros in the thousandths place of 11.36 and in three places to the right of the decimal point in 8. Then, add.

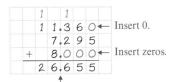

Line up the decimal point in the answer with the decimal points in the problem.

So, the sum is 26.655.

[**YOU TRY 2**] Add.

a) 9.4 + 7.81   b) 25.7 + 7 + 8.643

2 Subtract Decimals

The first step in subtracting decimals is to line up the decimal points. Follow the steps in the Procedure box on page 316.

EXAMPLE 3

Subtract 46.97 − 21.32.

Solution

Write the numbers vertically so that the decimal points are lined up.

Then subtract just like we subtract whole numbers.

Line up the decimal points.

Line up the decimal point in the answer with the decimal points in the problem.

We can check the answer using addition.

$$
\begin{array}{r}
2\,5.6\,5 \\
+\ 2\,1.3\,2 \\
\hline
4\,6.9\,7
\end{array}
$$

If the sum did *not* equal 46.97, then we made a mistake and we need to work the problem again.

[YOU TRY 3] Subtract 85.37 − 55.16.

We regroup with decimal numbers just like we regroup with whole numbers.

EXAMPLE 4

Subtract 48.639 from 129.386.

Solution

Line up the decimal points, then subtract. We will need to regroup (or borrow).

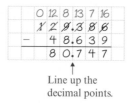

Line up the decimal points.

To check, add 80.747 + 48.639. The sum is 129.386, so the answer is correct.

[YOU TRY 4] Subtract 64.478 from 114.239.

Sometimes, we need to insert zeros as placeholders in subtraction problems.

Find each difference.

a)   29.8 minus 6.174   b)   Subtract 36.2 from 89.06.

Solution

a)   Line up the decimal points.   Insert zeros after the 8 in 29.8. Then, subtract.

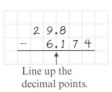

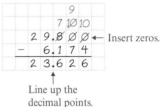

Remember, we can add zeros at the end of 29.8 because 29.8 is equivalent to 29.800.

b)   Line up the decimal points.   Insert 0 after the 2 in 36.2. Then, subtract.

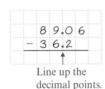

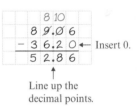

[YOU TRY 5]   Find each difference.

a)   61.7 minus 4.329   b)   Subtract 51.6 from 98.18.

When subtracting decimal numbers and whole numbers, we must remember that a whole number can be written with a decimal point after it. For example, $6 = 6.$.

EXAMPLE 6

Subtract.

a) $863.87 - 45$ b) $12 - 5.386$

Solution

a)   First, we must rewrite 45 with a decimal point: $45 = 45.$.

Line up the decimal points.   Insert zeros after the 5 in 45, then subtract.

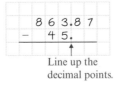

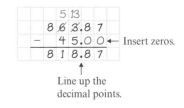

b) First, rewrite 12 with a decimal point: $12 = 12.$.

Line up the decimal points.   Insert zeros and subtract.

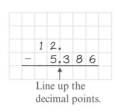

$$\begin{array}{r} 1\,2. \\ -\,5.386 \\ \hline \end{array}$$

Line up the
decimal points.

$$\begin{array}{r} \overset{9}{}\ \overset{9}{} \\ 0\ \ 11\ \ 10\ 10\ 10 \\ \cancel{1}\ 2.\cancel{0}\ \cancel{0}\ \cancel{0} \\ -\quad 5.3\ \ 8\ 6 \\ \hline 6.6\ 1\ 4 \end{array}$$ ← Insert zeros.

Line up the
decimal points.

Remember, we can check the answer with addition.

[YOU TRY 6]   Subtract.

a) $181.55 - 23$ b) $31 - 14.601$

Note

Remember, we can add zeros at the end of decimal numbers to add or subtract because it does not change the *value* of the number.

$$12 = 12.000 \qquad 8.3 = 8.30$$

---

3 Solve an Applied Problem

Decimals are used in many types of real-world problems.

EXAMPLE 7

In-Class Example 7

Mposi's bill at a fast-food restaurant is $7.16. If he pays with a $10 bill, how much change will he receive?

Answer: $2.84

Hint

You can also use the Five Steps for Solving an Applied Problem to solve these problems.

Liam's bill at a fast-food restaurant is $6.83. If he pays with a $10 bill, how much change will he receive?

Solution

To determine the amount of change Liam should get, we subtract 6.83 from 10.

Write 10 with a decimal point: $10.$.
Insert the zeros as placeholders, then subtract.

Liam's change will be $3.17.

We can check by adding: $3.17 + $6.83 = 10.00 ✓

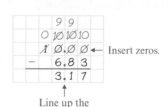

Line up the
decimal points.

[YOU TRY 7]   Tanya's grocery bill is $14.67. If she pays with a $20 bill, how much change will she receive?

Using Technology

When you are adding or subtracting decimal numbers by hand, you must line up the decimal points. A calculator automatically lines up decimal points before making the calculation.

First, calculate 2.1 + 3.0047 by hand. Now enter [2][.][1][+][3][.][0][0][4][7] into the calculator. The display will likely show the correct answer as 5.1047.

Now calculate 5.06 − 4.195 by hand. Now enter [5][.][0][6][−][4][.][1][9][5] into the calculator. The display will likely show the correct answer as 0.865. Did you get both answers correct?

E Evaluate **5.3** Exercises   Do the exercises, and check your work.

*Additional answers can be found in the Answers to Exercises appendix.

Objective 1: Add Decimals

Add.

1) 8.7 + 5.8   14.5

2) 9.3 + 6.8   16.1

3) 0.42 + 0.53   0.95

4) 0.18 + 0.71   0.89

(24) 5) 2.501 + 6.089 + 4.374
    12.964

6) 6.435 + 3.436 + 1.607
   11.478

7) 4.9 + 1.65   6.55

8) 1.3 + 2.88   4.18

9) 3.05 + 5.7   8.75

10) 2.27 + 4.8   7.07

(▶) 11) 17.91 + 2.391 + 1
    21.301

12) 13.2 + 6.482 + 9
    28.682

13) 200.1 + 0.008   200.108

14) 100.05 + 0.009   100.059

(24) 15) 50.009 + 0.003 + 2.3
    52.312

16) 30.005 + 0.0004 + 6.5
    36.5054

17) 8.234 + 419 + 26.076 + 7.39   460.7

18) 14.15 + 6.746 + 582 + 34.904   637.8

19) The sign shows the price of 1 gallon of regular gasoline, in cents, as a mixed number. Represent the mixed number as a sum. Write the exact price of 1 gallon of gas as a dollar amount in decimal form.

$379 + \dfrac{9}{10}$ cents or 379 + 0.9 cents; 3.799 dollars

20) For which gasoline grade is the price displayed incorrectly on the sign? Why is it incorrect?

Regular unleaded; mixed numbers are never written with decimals.

Objective 2: Subtract Decimals

21) Explain, in your own words, how to add and subtract decimals.   Answers may vary.

22) Does 46 = 46.00? Explain your answer.
    Yes. Adding zeros at the end of a decimal number does not change the value of the number.

Subtract.

23) 9.6 − 4.3   5.3

24) 8.7 − 2.5   6.2

25) 36.89 − 12.54   24.35

26) 27.64 − 11.02   16.62

27) 963.381 − 732.482
    230.899

28) 578.036 − 254.139
    323.897

29) 85.14 − 23.8   61.34

30) 64.36 − 18.5   45.86

(▶) 31) 76.5 − 51.34   25.16

32) 59.8 − 12.27   47.53

(24) 33) 120.4 − 38.661
    81.739

34) 140.3 − 75.792
    64.508

Find the difference.

35) 10.003 minus 8.846   1.157

36) 15.006 minus 8.539   6.467

37) Subtract 13.707 from 32.5.   18.793

38) Subtract 9.732 from 11.5.   1.768

39) Subtract 38 from 74.8.   36.8

40) Subtract 59 from 81.6.   22.6

Subtract.

41) 54.47 − 29   25.47   42) 32.25 − 8   24.25

43) 5 − 1.6   3.4   44) 9 − 4.3   4.7

45) 8 − 2.07   5.93   46) 6 − 3.04   2.96

47) 42 − 15.836   26.164   48) 35 − 23.798   11.202

49) 261 − 139.4952   50) 483 − 228.3794   254.6206
121.5048

Objective 3: Solve an Applied Problem

Solve each problem.

51) Namiko buys five pieces of Mochi ice cream for $5.67. If she pays with a $10 bill, how much change will she receive? $4.33

52) Luciano buys four pastries from a bakery for $6.58. If he pays with a $10 bill, how much change will he receive? $3.42

53) DeMarcus buys a small popcorn and a drink at the movie theater for $9.86. If he gives the cashier a $20 bill, how much change will he receive? $10.14

54) Caitlin and her friend each buy a milk tea drink with boba at a local cafe. Their total bill is $7.48. If Caitlin gives the cashier a $20 bill, how much change will she receive? $12.52

55) Ahdoja fills up the gas tank in her hybrid vehicle for $43.67, and she also buys a candy bar and soda for $2.94. If she pays with two $20 bills and a $10 bill, how much change will she receive? $3.39

56) Soren's bill for a taxi ride from the airport to his home is $28.64, and he gives the driver a $4 tip. If he pays the driver with two $20 bills, how much change will he receive? $7.36

57) At a county fair, Kathleen buys three corn dogs and three lemonades for her children. Her total bill is $16.25. If Kathleen gives the cashier a $20 bill, a $1 bill, and a quarter, how much change does she receive? $5.00

58) Ignacio's bill at a sandwich shop is $5.77. He gives the cashier a $10 bill and two pennies. How much change does he receive? $4.25

59) At a farmers' market, Morgan buys some fresh fruit costing $8.51. If Morgan gives the vendor two $5 bills and one penny, how much change does he receive? $1.50

60) Keely's bill at a smoothie café is $6.33. She gives the cashier a $10 bill and eight pennies. How much change does she receive? $3.75

61) Jesse buys the following items and gives the cashier two $20 bills and a $5 bill. If the tax on the items is $2.17, how much change will he receive? $2.62

Sunscreen:	$7.49
Towel:	$10.75
T-shirt:	$9.98
Flip-flops:	$11.99

62) LaVonda buys the following items and gives the cashier a $20 bill and a $10 bill. If the tax on the items is $1.34, how much change will she receive? $0.73

Picture frame:	$6.99
Waste basket:	$8.19
Vase:	$12.75

Mixed Exercises

Perform the indicated operations.

63) 620.7 − 49.58   571.12

64) 9.427 + 138.6 + 58 + 19.09   225.117

65) 185.1 + 0.007   185.107   66) 51 − 0.014   50.986

67) 23.75 − 12   11.75   68) 28.45 − 16.46   11.99

69) 17 + 4.827 + 0.083 + 12.6   34.51

70) 5.978 + 37.201 + 7.846   51.025

71) 46 − 12.597   33.403

72) 762.3 − 255   507.3

73) Find the sum of 19.4 and 6.98.   26.38

74) Subtract 42.6 from 50.37.   7.77

75) Subtract 0.739 from 1.   0.261

76) Find 0.81 minus 0.081.   0.729

Solve each problem.

 77) Before she went away to college, Ileana's grand-mother gave her a $150 gift card. Ileana used the gift card to buy the items listed here. If tax on the items was $7.54, how much money is left on her gift card?
$31.37

Shelves:	$48.99
Shower caddy:	$6.35
Backpack:	$39.98
Desk lamp:	$15.77

78) Takahiro's bills for the month are listed here. If he had $1061.82 in his checking account when he sat down to pay the bills, how much remains after he pays them? $374.68

Rent:	$425
Electricity:	$37.14
Cable:	$41.93
Car payment:	$183.07

R Rethink

R1) Which topics do you still need to master in this section?

R2) Where have you recently encountered the objectives of this section in your life? Write an applied problem similar to the ones you just completed and solve.

5.4 Multiplying Decimals

P Prepare

O Organize

What are your objectives for Section 5.4?	How can you accomplish each objective?
1 Multiply Decimals	• Write the procedure for **Multiplying Decimals** in your own words. • Complete the given examples on your own. • Complete You Trys 1–3.
2 Multiply a Number by a Power of Ten	• Write the procedure for **Multiplying a Number by a Power of 10** in your own words. • Write the procedure for **Multiplying a Number by 0.1, 0.01, 0.001, etc.,** in your own words. • Complete the given examples on your own. • Complete You Trys 4 and 5.
3 Solve Applied Problems	• Complete the given example on your own. • Complete You Try 6.

W Work   Read the explanations, follow the examples, take notes, and complete the You Trys.

1 Multiply Decimals

When we add and subtract decimals, we must line up the decimal points. This is *not* true when we multiply decimals. We can understand why the procedure for multiplying decimals is different if we multiply decimals by changing them to fractions first.

$$0.2 \times 0.37 = \frac{2}{10} \times \frac{37}{100} = \frac{74}{1000} = 0.074$$

1 decimal place + 2 decimal places = 3 decimal places

The number of decimal places in the *product* is the *sum* of the numbers of decimal places in the factors. (Recall that the *factors* are the numbers being multiplied, and the *product* is the answer.)

Procedure Multiplying Decimals

1) **Multiply the numbers (factors) just like you would multiply whole numbers.** (Line up the numbers on the right; the decimal points do *not* have to be lined up.)

2) **Determine the total number of decimal places in the answer (the product).** This will be the *total* number of decimal places in the factors.

3) **Insert the decimal point in the answer.** Start at the right side of the product, and count the *total* number of places you determined in 2). Sometimes, you may need to insert zeros as placeholders on the left side of the answer.

When we *multiply* decimals, we do **not** have to line up the decimal points. When we add or subtract decimals, we **must** line up the decimal points.

EXAMPLE 1

Multiply 15.83 × 4.6.

In-Class Example 1

Multiply 14.75 × 6.3.

Answer: 92.925

Solution

Multiply the numbers just as if they were whole numbers. (Line up the numbers on the right.) Do **not** line up the decimal points.

```
    1 5.8 3
  ×     4.6
    9 4 9 8
  6 3 3 2
  7 2.8 1 8
```

Determine the total number of decimal places in the answer. This will be the total number of decimal places in the factors.

```
    1 5.8 3 →  2 decimal places
  ×     4.6 →  1 decimal place
    9 4 9 8    3 decimal places
  6 3 3 2      in the answer
  7 2.8 1 8
```

Start at the right side of the number and count 3 places to the left. Insert the decimal point.

Therefore, 15.83 × 4.6 = 72.818

[YOU TRY 1] Multiply 51.42 × 7.8.

EXAMPLE 2

In-Class Example 2
Find the product: (26.03)(34).

Answer: 885.02

W Hint
Write out the example on your paper as you are reading it.

Find the product: (34.07)(28).

Solution

Multiply the numbers just as if they were whole numbers. Determine the number of decimal places in the answer, and insert the decimal point.

```
    3 4 . 0 7 →   2 decimal places
  ×       2 8 → + 0 decimal places
    2 7 2 5 6     2 decimal places
  6 8 1 4          in the answer
  9 5 3 . 9 6
```
Start at the right side of the number, and count 2 places to the left.

So, (34.07)(28) = 953.96.

[YOU TRY 2] Find the product: (49.02)(26).

Sometimes, we have to insert zeros on the left side of the product to have the correct number of decimal places in the answer.

EXAMPLE 3

In-Class Example 3
Find each product.
a) 0.027 × 0.08 b) (0.3)^2

Answer:
a) 0.00216 b) 0.09

Find each product.

a) 0.029 × 0.05   b) (0.3)^2

Solution

a) **Multiply the numbers just as if they were whole numbers.** Line up the numbers on the right.

```
    0 . 0 2 9
  ×   0 . 0 5
    1 4 5
```

Determine the total number of decimal places in the answer. This will be the total number of decimal places in the factors.

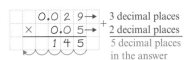

Start at the right side and count 5 places to the left. Insert zeros in the blank spaces.

```
    0 . 0 2 9
  ×   0 . 0 5
  0 0 1 4 5
```
There are 5 places to the right of the decimal point.

Write the final answer with a zero to the left of the decimal point, in the ones place.

$$0.029 \times 0.05 = 0.00145$$

Put a zero in the ones place.

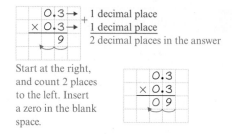

W Hint

Can you think of a faster way to square 0.3?

b) $(0.3)^2$ means 0.3×0.3.

Multiply the numbers just as if they were whole numbers, and determine the number of decimal places in the product.

$$
\begin{array}{r}
0.3 \rightarrow\ 1\ \text{decimal place} \\
\times\ 0.3 \rightarrow\ 1\ \text{decimal place} \\
\hline
9\quad\ 2\ \text{decimal places in the answer}
\end{array}
$$

Start at the right, and count 2 places to the left. Insert a zero in the blank space.

$$
\begin{array}{r}
0.3 \\
\times\ 0.3 \\
\hline
0\ 9
\end{array}
$$

Write the final answer with a zero to the left of the decimal point, in the ones place.

$$(0.3)^2 = 0.09$$

↑

Put a zero in the ones place.

[YOU TRY 3] Find each product.   a) 0.019×0.07 b) $(0.02)^2$

2 Multiply a Number by a Power of Ten

Multiplying a number by a power of 10 can be simple if we notice a pattern. Let's multiply 6.72 by 10, 100, and 1000, and see what happens.

$$
\begin{array}{r}
6.7\ 2 \\
\times\quad 1\ 0 \\
\hline
0\ 0\ 0 \\
6\ 7\ 2\quad \\
\hline
6\ 7.2\ 0
\end{array}
\qquad
\begin{array}{r}
6.7\ 2 \\
\times\ 1\ 0\ 0 \\
\hline
0\ 0\ 0 \\
0\ 0\ 0\quad \\
6\ 7\ 2\quad\quad \\
\hline
6\ 7\ 2.0\ 0
\end{array}
\qquad
\begin{array}{r}
6.7\ 2 \\
\times\ 1\ 0\ 0\ 0 \\
\hline
0\ 0\ 0 \\
0\ 0\ 0\quad \\
0\ 0\ 0\quad\quad \\
6\ 7\ 2\quad\quad\quad \\
\hline
6\ 7\ 2\ 0.0\ 0
\end{array}
$$

$6.72 \times 10 = 67.20$ $6.72 \times 100 = 672.00$ $6.72 \times 1000 = 6720.00$
       or 67.2   or 672   or 6720

Do you notice the pattern?

$6.72 \times 10 = 67.2$ $6.72 \times 100 = 672.$ $6.72 \times 1000 = 6720.$

Multiply by 10, move the decimal point *right* 1 place.

Multiply by 100, move the decimal point *right* 2 places.

Multiply by 1000, move the decimal point *right* 3 places.

The number of zeros in the power of 10 tells us how many places to move the decimal point to obtain the product.

Procedure Multiplying a Number by a Power of 10

To multiply a number by a power of 10,

1) Count the number of zeros in the power of 10.

2) Move the decimal point in the number *to the right* the same number of spaces as the number of zeros in the power of 10.

3) If necessary, add zeros as placeholders on the right.

EXAMPLE 4

Multiply.

a) 0.5941 × 100   b) 23.7 × 10,000   c) 89 × 1000

In-Class Example 4

Multiply.
a) 0.9162 × 100
b) 53.4 × 10,000
c) 78 × 1000

Answer:
a) 91.62   b) 534,000
c) 78,000

Solution

a) 0.5941 × 100 = 59.41

       Move decimal point
    2 zeros 2 places to the right.

b) 23.7 × 10,000 = 23.7000 = 237,000

       Move the decimal point 4 places
    4 zeros to the right and insert zeros.

We write 237,000 instead of 237,000. because we usually do *not* write a decimal point at the end of a number if there are no digits after it.

        3 zeros
        ↓

c) 89 × 1000 = 89. × 1000 = 89.000 = 89,000

   The decimal point comes   Move the decimal point 3 places
   at the end of the number.   to the right and insert zeros.

YOU TRY 4

Multiply.

a) 0.4459 × 1000   b) 608.1 × 100,000   c) 74 × 100

There is a similar procedure for multiplying a number by 0.1, 0.01, 0.001, and so on. Let's multiply 34.9 by 0.1, 0.01, and 0.001 and see whether we notice a pattern.

$$\begin{array}{r} 3\;4.9 \\ \times\quad 0.1 \\ \hline 3.4\;9 \end{array} \qquad \begin{array}{r} 3\;4.9 \\ \times\;0.0\;1 \\ \hline 0.3\;4\;9 \end{array} \qquad \begin{array}{r} 3\;4.9 \\ \times\;0.0\;0\;1 \\ \hline 0.0\;3\;4\;9 \end{array}$$

34.9 × 0.1 = 3.49   34.9 × 0.01 = 0.349   34.9 × 0.001 = 0.0349

1 decimal   Move decimal point   2 decimal   Move decimal point   3 decimal   Move decimal point
place   1 place to the left.   places   2 places to the left.   places   3 places to the left.

W Hint

Compare this with the procedure for multiplying by a power of 10.

Procedure Multiplying a Number by 0.1, 0.01, 0.001, etc.

To multiply a number by:

1) 0.1, move the decimal point in the number 1 place to the left.

2) 0.01, move the decimal point 2 places to the left.

3) 0.001, move the decimal point 3 places to the left.

and so on.

EXAMPLE 5

Multiply.

a) 718.3×0.01 b) 0.299×0.001 c) $650,000 \times 0.0001$

Solution

a) $718.3 \times 0.01 = 7.183$ Move the decimal point 2 places to the left.

2 decimal places

b) $0.299 \times 0.001 = 0.000299$ Move the decimal point 3 places to the left.

3 decimal places

c) $650,000. \times 0.0001 = 65.0000 = 65$ Move the decimal point 4 places to the left.

Insert the decimal point.   4 decimal places

[YOU TRY 5]

Multiply.

a) 1642.5×0.001 b) 0.038×0.01 c) $12,000,000 \times 0.0001$

Note

Notice that when you multiply a number by a power of 10 like 10, 100, 1000, etc., the result is *larger* than the original number.

When you multiply a number by 0.1, 0.01, 0.001, etc., the result is *smaller* than the original number.

This is always true when working with positive numbers.

3 Solve Applied Problems

Let's solve a problem using multiplication of decimals.

EXAMPLE 6

Shu Fang's car payment is $189.65 per month. Determine the total amount she pays in one year.

Solution

Each month, Shu Fang pays $189.65 for her car. *There are* 12 *months in one year,* so multiply $189.65 by 12 to determine the total amount of her car payments in one year.

$$
\begin{array}{r}
1\,8\,9.6\,5 \rightarrow \text{2 decimal places} \\
\times \qquad 1\,2 \rightarrow +\text{0 decimal places} \\
\hline
3\,7\,9\,3\,0 \qquad \text{2 decimal places in} \\
1\,8\,9\,6\,5 \qquad\qquad \text{the answer} \\
\hline
2\,2\,7\,5.8\,0 \qquad\qquad
\end{array}
$$

Shu Fang's total car payment in one year is $2275.80.

We *must* leave the 0 on the end of the number because money amounts are written to the nearest hundredths place, or to the nearest cent.

[YOU TRY 6] Gaurav pays $397.15 per month to repay his student loans. How much does he pay in one year?

ANSWERS TO [YOU TRY] EXERCISES

1) 401.076   2) 1274.52   3) a) 0.00133 b) 0.0004   4) a) 445.9 b) 60,810,000 c) 7400
5) a) 1.6425 b) 0.00038 c) 1200   6) $4765.80

Using Technology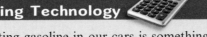

Putting gasoline in our cars is something we often do.

Suppose you pay $379\frac{9}{10}$ cents, or $3.799, for a gallon of gas and the pump indicates you purchased 13.527 gallons of gasoline. To find the amount you should pay in dollars, multiply 3.799 by 13.527. First perform the calculation by hand. Now enter ③ . ⑦ ⑨ ⑨ ⑧ ① ③ . ⑤ ② ⑦ ⑧ into the calculator. The answer is 51.389073. Remember, however, to round the answer to the nearest hundredth since we are working with dollar amounts. The cost of the gas will be $51.39.

E Evaluate   5.4 Exercises   Do the exercises, and check your work.

*Additional answers can be found in the Answers to Exercises appendix.

Objective 1: Multiply Decimals

1) Explain, in your own words, how to multiply decimals.   Answers may vary.

2) Which operations with decimals require that we line up the decimal points?   adding and subtracting

Multiply.

3)   6.3   25.83
    × 4.1

4)   7.5   21.75
    × 2.9

5)   12.7   68.58
    × 5.4

6)   17.4   74.82
    × 4.3

7)   782.29   312.916
    ×   0.4

8)   913.63   730.904
    ×   0.8

9) 27.4(19.35)   530.19

10) 40.8(22.85)   932.28

11) (0.0005)(4018.6)   2.0093

12) (0.0002)(8307.5)   1.6615

13) 31.03(21)   651.63

14) 16.09(14)   225.26

15) 500 × 60.04   30,020

16) 800 × 50.06   40,048

17) 0.024 × 0.03   0.00072

18) 0.032 × 0.06   0.00192

19) (5.004)(32,800)
    164,131.2

20) (7.006)(29,400)
    205,976.4

21) 0.6 × 1005   603

22) 0.2 × 4005   801

23) Given that $\frac{1}{8}$ = 0.125, write a product that is equivalent to the decimal representation of $\frac{5}{8}$. Calculate the decimal representation of $\frac{5}{8}$.   0.125 × 5; 0.625

24) Given that $\frac{1}{16}$ = 0.0625, write a product that is equivalent to the decimal representation of $\frac{9}{16}$. Calculate the decimal representation of $\frac{9}{16}$.
0.0625 × 9; 0.5625

Evaluate each exponential expression.

25) $(0.4)^2$ 0.16

26) $(0.7)^2$ 0.49

27) $(1.2)^2$ 1.44

28) $(1.4)^2$ 1.96

29) $(0.12)^2$ 0.0144

30) $(0.14)^2$ 0.0196

31) $(0.05)^2$ 0.0025
32) $(0.08)^2$ 0.0064
33) $(0.007)^2$ 0.000049
34) $(0.006)^2$ 0.000036

Objective 2: Multiply a Number by a Power of Ten

35) Explain how to multiply a number by 1000.
Move the decimal point in the number 3 places to the right.
36) Explain how to multiply a number by 0.01.
Move the decimal point in the number 2 places to the left.

Find each product.

37) 0.2587×100 25.87
38) 0.7134×100 71.34
39) 3.66×10 36.6
40) 1.09×10 10.9
41) $(0.0000608)(10,000)$ 0.608
42) $(1000)(43.67)$ 43,670
43) $10,000 \times 5.7$ 57,000
44) $10,000 \times 9.6$ 96,000
45) 64×100 6400
46) 73×100 7300

47) $\begin{array}{r} 0.25 \\ \times\ 100 \end{array}$ 25
48) $\begin{array}{r} 0.05 \\ \times\ 100 \end{array}$ 5

Multiply.

49) 38.01×0.1 3.801
50) 70.08×0.1 7.008
51) $(1925.8)(0.01)$ 19.258
52) $0.702(0.01)$ 0.00702
53) 0.001×8.5 0.0085
54) 0.001×2.1 0.0021
55) $0.0001 \times 94,000$ 9.4
56) $0.0001 \times 67,000$ 6.7
57) $0.00001(32,000,000)$ 320
58) $0.00001(56,000,000)$ 560

59) $\begin{array}{r} 3066.47 \\ \times\ 0.001 \end{array}$ 3.06647
60) $\begin{array}{r} 1203.5 \\ \times\ 0.001 \end{array}$ 1.2035

Objective 3: Solve Applied Problems

Solve each problem. For all problems involving money, the final answer should be to the nearest cent.

61) Talog's cable television bill is $54.75 per month. Determine the total amount he pays in one year.
$657.00
62) Molly treats her friends to a late-night snack at a taco stand. If Molly buys 16 tacos costing $1.35 each, what is her total bill? $21.60
63) Kathy is a real estate agent, and she will earn a commission rate of 0.04 for selling a house for $279,000. Find the amount of Kathy's commission. (Multiply the commission rate by the sale price of the house.) $11,160

64) Felipe buys six tiki torches for his backyard. How much did he spend if they cost $11.97 each? $71.82

65) A storage rack holds four canoes and each one weighs 78.6 lb. Find the total weight of the canoes on the rack. 314.4 lb

66) A warehouse worker uses a forklift to stack five boxes on top of each other. If each box is 3.9 ft tall, what is the height of the stack? 19.5 ft

67) Every morning on her way to work, Nicole buys the same drink at her favorite coffee shop. If she spends $3.41 per day, five days each week, how much does she spend in one month? $68.20

68) Jadvyga takes the train to work every day. She buys a monthly pass for $102.25. How much does she spend for her train pass each year? $1227.00

69) Justin downloads 13 songs from iTunes at $1.29 each and six songs at $0.99 each. How much did he spend for his music? $22.71

70) For his son's soccer team, Huang buys 16 bottles of sports drinks at $1.19 each and six boxes of granola bars at $3.49 each. How much did Huang pay for these snacks? $39.98

71) Selena's car gets 27.8 mi per gal. How far can she drive on 10.7 gallons of gas? 297.46 mi

72) Noor drove 3.25 hr at an average speed of 67.8 mi per hr. How far did she go? 220.35 mi

73) Aiko buys 3.5 lb of basmati rice at $1.98 per lb and 2.8 lb of jasmine rice at $2.79 per lb. Find the total cost of the rice. $14.74

74) Bill buys 1.5 lb of a Costa Rican coffee at $6.79 per lb, 3.25 lb of a Kenyan coffee at $9.20 per lb, and 2 lb of Italian espresso beans at $6.29 per lb. How much did Bill pay for the coffee? $52.67

75) Salim is an inspector for his city's building department, and he earns $23.89 per hr. Here is a list of the hours he worked last week:

Monday   7:30 A.M.–3:30 P.M.

Tuesday   8:30 A.M.–4:00 P.M.

Wednesday   9:00 A.M.–5:00 P.M.

Thursday   7:30 A.M.–3:00 P.M.

Friday   7:45 P.M.–3:00 P.M.

a) How many hours did Salim work last week? 38.25 hr

b) Find his gross pay. (Gross pay is the amount earned before deductions.) $913.79

c) Multiply his gross pay by 0.09 to determine the amount of money that will be deducted from his paycheck for taxes. $82.24

d) Find Salim's take-home pay if, in addition to the amount deducted for taxes, $29.36 will be deducted for insurance and $25.68 will be deducted for his retirement plan. (Take-home pay is the gross pay minus the amount of all the deductions.) $776.51

76) Joyce makes three sizes of wreaths that she sells at craft fairs. The small size uses 1.25 ft of wire, the medium size uses 2.50 ft of wire, and the large wreath uses 3.50 ft of wire.

a) If the wire costs $0.64 per ft, how much does it cost to make one of each size wreath?
small: $0.80; medium: $1.60; large: $2.24

b) For the next craft fair, Joyce plans to make 7 small wreaths, 15 medium wreaths, and 8 large wreaths. How much wire will she need? 74.25 ft

c) Find the cost of the wire to make all the wreaths in part b). $47.52

Mixed Exercises: Objectives 1–3

Multiply.

77) 0.076
   × 0.05   0.0038

78) $(2.25)^2$ 5.0625

79) 16,974 × 0.0001 1.6974

80) 100,000(20.06) 2,006,000

81) (3.8)(28.04) 106.552

82) 0.054 × 0.08 0.00432

83) $(1.41)^2$ 1.9881

84) 0.1 × 0.7062 0.07062

85) 1000 × 25.9 25,900

86) 503.06
   ×   25   12,576.5

87) (1.75)(0.001) 0.00175

88) (0.006)(400.8) 2.4048

Solve each problem. The answer should be to the nearest cent.

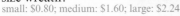

89) Fermin works part-time and earns $9.20 per hr. One week, he worked three days from 4:00 P.M. to 9:30 P.M. How much did Fermin earn? $151.80

90) Laycee purchases 12 yd of cloth costing $5.85 per yd. What is the purchase price for the cloth? $70.20

R Rethink

R1) What is the only extra step in multiplying decimals compared with multiplying whole numbers?

R2) Where do you encounter the multiplication of decimal numbers on a daily basis?

R3) Which objective(s) do you still need help mastering?

5.5 Dividing Decimals and Order of Operations

What are your objectives for Section 5.5?	How can you accomplish each objective?
1 Divide a Decimal by a Whole Number	• Write the procedure for **Dividing a Decimal by a Whole Number** in your own words. • Add details to this procedure as you follow the examples. Include information about *adding extra zeros, nonrepeating decimals,* and *repeating decimals*. • Complete the given examples on your own. • Complete You Trys 1–4.
2 Divide a Number by a Decimal	• Write the procedure for **Dividing a Number by a Decimal** in your own words. • Understand why you are able to move the decimal point in both the dividend and the divisor. • Complete the given examples on your own. • Complete You Trys 5–7.
3 Use the Order of Operations with Decimals	• Use the same rules as before (PEMDAS) for the order of operations, and apply them to decimals. • Complete the given example on your own. • Complete You Try 8.

W Work   **Read the explanations, follow the examples, take notes, and complete the You Trys.**

We first learned how to perform long division with whole numbers in Chapter 2. For example, to find $45 \div 7$, we can divide as follows:

$$
\begin{array}{r}
6 \leftarrow \text{Quotient} \\
\text{Divisor} \rightarrow 7\,\overline{)4\;5} \leftarrow \text{Dividend} \\
-\;4\;2 \\
\hline
3 \leftarrow \text{Remainder}
\end{array}
\qquad 45 \div 7 = 6\,\text{R}3
$$

In this section, we will learn how to divide decimals.

1 Divide a Decimal by a Whole Number

Let's start by learning how to divide a decimal by a whole number. That is, the divisor is a whole number.

> **Procedure** Dividing a Decimal by a Whole Number
>
> 1) Write the problem in long division form.
> 2) Write the decimal point in the quotient directly above the decimal point in the dividend.
> 3) Perform the division as if the numbers were whole numbers.

EXAMPLE 1

Divide.

In-Class Example 1

Divide.
a) $43.74 \div 6$ b) $\dfrac{0.00584}{4}$

Answer:
a) 7.29 b) 0.00146

a) $37.52 \div 4$ b) $\dfrac{0.00945}{7}$

Solution

a) Write the problem in long division form, and write the decimal point in the quotient directly above the decimal point in the dividend.

Perform the division as if the numbers were whole numbers.

Therefore, $37.52 \div 4 = 9.38$.

```
        9.3 8
    4)3 7.5 2
     -3 6
        1 5
       -1 2
          3 2
         -3 2
            0
```

Check by multiplying:

```
      9.3 8
   ×      4
   3 7.5 2  ✓
```

b) Write the problem in long division form, and write the decimal point in the quotient directly above where it appears in the dividend.

Perform the division as if the numbers were whole numbers. Because $0 \div 7 = 0$, we must begin by putting zeros in the quotient.

So, $\dfrac{0.00945}{7} = 0.00135$.

```
      .0 0 1 3 5
   7)0.0 0 9 4 5
       -7
        2 4
       -2 1
          3 5
         -3 5
            0
```

Check by multiplying:

```
   0.0 0 1 3 5
 ×           7
   0.0 0 9 4 5  ✓
```

YOU TRY 1

Divide.

a) $\dfrac{25.41}{3}$ b) $0.00785 \div 5$

In Example 1, both problems had a remainder of zero. Sometimes, however, we reach the end of the dividend, the remainder is *not* zero, and there are no more digits to bring down. If this happens, write extra zeros on the *right* end of the dividend and keep dividing.

EXAMPLE 2

Divide. 8)3.94

Solution

Begin the division process like we did in Example 1.

```
      0. 4 9
  8)3.↓9 4 ←  No more digits
   - 3 2 ↓     to bring down
       7 4
     - 7 2
         2 ←  Remainder ≠ 0
```

We have reached the end of the dividend, the remainder is *not* zero, and there are no more digits to bring down.

Write extra zeros on the *right* end of the dividend and keep on dividing.

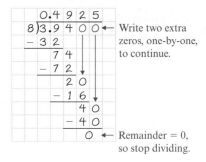

```
      0. 4 9 2 5
  8)3.9 4 0 0 ←  Write two extra
   - 3 2           zeros, one-by-one,
       7 4         to continue.
     - 7 2
         2 0
       - 1 6
           4 0
         - 4 0
             0 ←  Remainder = 0,
                   so stop dividing.
```

The answer is 0.4925.

Check by multiplying: 0.4925 × 8 = 3.94 ✓

Divide. 8)6.26

Note

We can add zeros at the right end of a number containing a decimal point because it does *not* change the value of the number.

Example: 3.94 = 3.9400

Sometimes, the remainder will *never* equal 0. One way to write the answer to such a division problem is to round it.

EXAMPLE 3

In-Class Example 3

Divide 9.3 by 7. Round the answer to the nearest thousandth.

Answer: 1.329

Divide 8.6 by 7. Round the answer to the nearest thousandth.

Solution

Because we will be rounding to the *thousandths* place, we must continue the division until the quotient has a digit in the *ten-thousandths* place, one place to the right of where we must round.

```
                              We have reached the ten-thousandths
      1. 2 2 8 5 ←            place in the quotient.
  7)8.6 0 0 0 ←               Write three zeros, one-by-one,
   - 7                         to continue dividing.
     1 6
   - 1 4 ↓
       2 0
     - 1 4 ↓
         6 0
       - 5 6 ↓
           4 0
         - 3 5
             5 ←  Remainder ≠ 0.
```

This division will never give a remainder of 0. So, our quotient is an approximation.

$$8.6 \div 7 \approx 1.229 \longleftarrow \text{Round the quotient.}$$

Because 1.229 is not the *exact* answer, when we check the answer, it will be different from (but should be very close to) 8.6.

Check: $1.229 \times 7 = 8.603$.   This is very close to 8.6.

[YOU TRY 3]   Divide 8.9 by 7. Round the answer to the nearest thousandth.

Sometimes, a digit (or digits) in a decimal will repeat forever. For example, the fraction $\frac{5}{6}$ is equivalent to the decimal 0.8333..., where the 3 repeats forever. (We will learn how to write fractions as decimals in Section 5.6.) A decimal like 0.8333... is called a *repeating decimal*.

Definition

A **repeating decimal** is a decimal in which a digit or a group of digits repeats forever.

Example: 0.8333...

A repeating decimal can be written in two ways:

1)   Use the three dots at the end of the number.
    0.8333... means the 3 repeats forever.

or   2)   Use a bar above the repeating digit or digits.

    0.8333... can also be written as $0.8\overline{3}$.

    1.4525252... can also be written as $1.4\overline{52}$.

Hint
Add your own details to the procedure for this objective.

Sometimes a quotient will be a repeating decimal.

EXAMPLE 4

Find $7.9 \div 3$. Give the exact answer and an approximation rounded to the nearest thousandth.

In-Class Example 4

Find $8.5 \div 3$. Give the exact answer and an approximation rounded to the nearest thousandth.

Answer:
exact: 2.8333... or $2.8\overline{3}$; approximation: 2.833

Solution

When we divide, notice that we must write extra zeros on the right end of the dividend, 7.9, because the remainder is not 0.

```
      2.6 3 3 3
  3)7.9 0 0 0  ← Write extra zeros.
   - 6
     1 9
   - 1 8↓
       1 0
     -  9↓
         1 0
       -  9↓
           1 0
         -  9
             1  ← Remainder ≠ 0.
```

Also notice that the 3 in the quotient keeps repeating because the remainder of 1 keeps repeating. **This pattern will continue forever, so the remainder will never equal 0.**

We can stop dividing and write the exact answer as

$$7.9 \div 3 = 2.6333\ldots \qquad \text{or} \qquad 7.9 \div 3 = 2.6\overline{3}$$

↑
The dots mean the 3
will repeat forever.

↑
The bar above the 3 means
the 3 will repeat forever.

Rounded to the nearest thousandth, $7.9 \div 3 \approx 2.633$.

Check: $2.633 \times 3 = 7.899$. This is not *exactly* 7.9, but it is very close.

[**YOU TRY 4**] Find $9.1 \div 6$. Give the exact answer and an approximation rounded to the nearest thousandth.

2 Divide a Number by a Decimal

Now we will learn how to divide a number by a decimal. That is, the *divisor* is a decimal.

> **Procedure** Dividing a Number by a Decimal
>
> 1) Move the decimal point to the right end of the divisor. This makes the divisor a whole number. Count the number of decimal places you have moved.
>
> 2) Move the decimal point in the dividend the *same* number of places to the right. (If necessary, write in zeros.)
>
> 3) Write the decimal point in the quotient directly above the decimal point in the dividend. Then, divide.

EXAMPLE 5

Divide. $0.5\overline{)6.85}$

In-Class Example 5

Divide. $0.4\overline{)6.92}$

Answer: 17.3

 Hint

Are you writing out the example as you read it?

Solution

Start with the original problem and *move the decimal point one place to the right in the divisor* to change 0.5 to the whole number 5. Also, *move the decimal point in 6.85 one place to the right*.

Make the
divisor a
whole number.

Divisor → $0.5\overline{)6.85}$ ⟶ $0\,5.\overline{)68.5}$ Move the decimal points one
place to the right.

↑
Dividend

Divide. Rewrite the divisor as just 5.

```
        1 3.7
   5)6 8.5
    - 5
      1 8
    - 1 5
        3 5
      - 3 5
          0
```

Check:
```
      1 3.7
    ×  0.5
      6.8 5 ✓
```

Therefore, when we divide $0.5\overline{)6.85}$, the quotient is 13.7.

[YOU TRY 5]   Divide. $0.8\overline{)9.76}$

Why does this work? Why can we move the decimal points? Let's write $0.5\overline{)6.85}$ as a division problem in fraction form.

$$0.5\overline{)6.85} \quad \text{can be written as} \quad \frac{6.85}{0.5}$$

$$\frac{6.85}{0.5} = \frac{6.85}{0.5} \cdot \frac{10}{10} = \frac{68.5}{5}$$

Multiplying the numerator and denominator of a fraction by the same number gives us an equivalent fraction. Therefore,

$$\frac{6.85}{0.5} = \frac{68.5}{5} \quad \text{and} \quad \frac{68.5}{5} \quad \text{can be written as} \quad 5\overline{)68.5}$$

So, $0.5\overline{)6.85}$ is equivalent to $5\overline{)68.5}$. **Moving the decimal point one place to the right in the divisor and the dividend is the same as multiplying each number by 10.**

EXAMPLE 6

Divide 116.4 by 0.012.

In-Class Example 6

Divide 115.2 by 0.012.

Answer: 9600

Solution

Set up the division problem, then *move the decimal point in the divisor,* 0.012, *three places to the right* so that it is at the end of the number. *Move the decimal point in the dividend three places to the right.* (This is like multiplying both numbers by 1000.) Write in zeros.

$$0.012\overline{)116.4} \quad \longrightarrow \quad 012.\overline{)116400}.$$

Move the decimal points three places to the right. Write the decimal point in the quotient directly above the decimal point in the dividend.

Divide. $12\overline{)116400.}^{9700.}$ Check by multiplying.

[YOU TRY 6]   Divide 124.6 by 0.014.

In the next example, we will divide a whole number by a decimal.

EXAMPLE 7

Divide. Round the answer to the nearest hundredth. $9 \div 2.6$

In-Class Example 7

Divide. Round the answer
to the nearest hundredth.
$6 \div 2.1$

Answer: 2.86

Solution

Set up the division problem. $2.6\overline{)9}$

Because we must move the decimal point *one place to the right,* put a decimal point at the end of the 9.

 Hint

Are you using graph paper to do these division problems?

Move decimal
points one place
$2.6\overline{)9.}$ to the right, $26\overline{)90.}$ Write in one zero and put the
↑   decimal point in the quotient.
Insert the
decimal point.

Divide.

```
            3.4 6 1  ← Because we are rounding to the
  2 6 )9 0.0 0 0        hundredths place, carry out
    - 7 8               the division to the thousandths
      1 2 0             place. Round 3.461 to 3.46.
    - 1 0 4
        1 6 0
      - 1 5 6
            4 0
          - 2 6
            1 4
```

Therefore, $9 \div 2.6 \approx 3.46$.

[YOU TRY 7]   Divide. Round the answer to the nearest hundredth. $5 \div 2.3$

3 Use the Order of Operations with Decimals

We use the order of operations with decimals just like we did with whole numbers and fractions. (See page 108 for the rules.)

EXAMPLE 8

Simplify each expression using the order of operations.

In-Class Example 8

Simplify each expression
using the order of operations.
a) $(0.8)^2 - 3.6 \div 9 + 7.6$
b) $4 + 10(5.2 - 1.93)$

Answer: a) 7.84 b) 36.7

a) $(0.9)^2 - 4.2 \div 7 + 5.3$ b) $2 + 10(8.6 - 1.78)$

Solution

 Hint

Remember "Please Excuse My Dear Aunt Sally."

a) $(0.9)^2 - 4.2 \div 7 + 5.3 = 0.81 - 4.2 \div 7 + 5.3$ Evaluate exponents first.

$= 0.81 - 0.6 + 5.3$ Divide before adding and subtracting.

$= 0.21 + 5.3$ Perform addition and subtraction from left to right.

$= 5.51$ Add.

b) $2 + 10(8.6 - 1.78) = 2 + 10(6.82)$ Perform operations in parentheses first.

$= 2 + 68.2$ Multiply before adding.

$= 70.2$ Add.

YOU TRY 8 Simplify each expression using the order of operations.

    a) $(1.1)^2 + 5.4 \div 6 - 1.29$ b) $9.6 + 100(7 - 4.38)$

ANSWERS TO [YOU TRY] **EXERCISES**

1) a) 8.47   b) 0.00157   2) 0.7825   3) 1.271   4) exact: 1.51666... or $1.51\overline{6}$; approximation: 1.517
5) 12.2   6) 8900   7) 2.17   8) a) 0.82   b) 271.6

Using Technology

Calculators can perform arithmetic operations, but they will give us a wrong answer if we tell the calculator to perform arithmetic operations that do not follow the order of operations.

    First, calculate $4.4 \div 0.2 + 2 \times 0.75$ by hand, using the order of operations. To use a calculator, we must first perform the division operation by entering 4 . 4 ÷ 0 . 2 =. The display will likely show 22. Next, perform the multiplication by entering 2 × 0 . 7 5 = into the calculator. The display will likely show 1.5. Now, find the sum of these two results by entering 2 2 + 1 . 5 = into the calculator. Your final result should be 23.5.

    Note: If your calculator has a parenthesis function, you could use the parenthesis buttons to tell the calculator how to make the calculation. In this case, you would enter (4 . 4 ÷ 0 . 2) + (2 × 0 . 7 5) to get the correct result.

E Evaluate **5.5** Exercises   Do the exercises, and check your work.

*Additional answers can be found in the Answers to Exercises appendix.

Objective 1: Divide a Decimal by a Whole Number

1) Explain, in your own words, how to divide a decimal by a whole number.   *Answers may vary.*

2) What do we do if we reach the end of the dividend and the remainder is not zero?
  Write extra zeros on the right end of the dividend and keep dividing.

Divide.

3) $23.52 \div 8$ 2.94

4) $14.16 \div 6$ 2.36

5) $9\overline{)46.08}$ 5.12

6) $5\overline{)21.85}$ 4.37

7) $\dfrac{0.02112}{4}$ 0.00528

8) $\dfrac{0.01932}{7}$ 0.00276

9) $147.2 \div 16$ 9.2

10) $101.4 \div 13$ 7.8

11) $\dfrac{484.89}{21}$ 23.09

12) $\dfrac{806.52}{26}$ 31.02

13) $6\overline{)2.319}$ 0.3865

14) $8\overline{)4.836}$ 0.6045

15) $\dfrac{12.14}{4}$ 3.035

16) $\dfrac{17.16}{8}$ 2.145

17) $8\overline{)3.46}$ 0.4325

18) $4\overline{)2.07}$ 0.5175

19) Divide 7.5 by 6.   1.25

20) Divide 49.4 by 5.   9.88

Divide. Round the answer to the nearest thousandth.

21) $8.1 \div 7$ 1.157

22) $23.5 \div 9$ 2.611

23) Divide 9.8 by 3.   3.267

24) Divide 12.7 by 6.   2.117

25) $11\overline{)0.144}$ 0.013

26) $16\overline{)0.166}$ 0.010

27) $\dfrac{2472.9}{31}$ 79.771

28) $\dfrac{5358.2}{78}$ 68.695

Divide. Give the exact answer and an approximation rounded to the nearest thousandth.

29) $8.6 \div 6$

30) $7.7 \div 3$

31) $\dfrac{28.34}{3}$

32) $\dfrac{51.28}{9}$

33) $11\overline{)4.7}$

34) $11\overline{)8.1}$

Objective 2: Divide a Number by a Decimal

35) Explain, in your own words, how to divide a number by a decimal. Answers may vary.

36) Is $0.29\overline{)7.283}$ equivalent to $29\overline{)728.3}$? Explain your answer. Yes. Moving the decimal point two places to the right in both the divisor and the dividend is like multiplying both numbers by 100 and does not change the answer.

Divide.

37) $0.4\overline{)4.48}$ 11.2

38) $0.6\overline{)7.62}$ 12.7

39) $0.8\overline{)5.48}$ 6.85

40) $0.4\overline{)1.02}$ 2.55

41) $0.645 \div 0.43$ 1.5

42) $0.756 \div 0.28$ 2.7

43) $\dfrac{0.3552}{9.6}$ 0.037

44) $\dfrac{0.4615}{7.1}$ 0.065

45) Divide 646.8 by 1.32. 490

46) Divide 486.2 by 1.43. 340

47) $2.5\overline{)38}$ 15.2

48) $3.6\overline{)63}$ 17.5

49) Divide 522 by 0.04. 13,050

50) Divide 434 by 0.02. 21,700

Divide. Round the answer to the nearest hundredth.

51) $5.7\overline{)3}$ 0.53

52) $8.3\overline{)4}$ 0.48

53) Divide 150.7 by 4.1. 36.76

54) Divide 287.4 by 3.3. 87.09

55) $\dfrac{0.26}{0.15}$ 1.73

56) $\dfrac{0.94}{0.16}$ 5.88

57) $0.008\overline{)7.309}$ 913.63

58) $0.009\overline{)6.058}$ 673.11

Objective 3: Use the Order of Operations with Decimals

Simplify each expression using the order of operations.

59) $(1.5)^2 - 8.1 \div 9 + 2.7$ 4.05

60) $(1.3)^2 - 6.4 \div 4 + 8.3$ 8.39

61) $5 + 10(2.6 - 1.73)$ 13.7

62) $4 + 10(5.3 - 2.84)$ 28.6

63) $9.7 - 0.8 \times 3.4 \div 2$ 8.34

64) $8.2 - 0.3 \times 1.7 \div 0.6$ 7.35

65) $3 - \dfrac{(2.4)^2}{6}$ 2.04

66) $7 - \dfrac{(2.1)^2}{9}$ 6.51

67) $0.1(1.7 - 0.94) \div 0.002$ 38

68) $0.1(1.5 - 0.86) \div 0.004$ 16

69) $160(0.025) - 2.8 \div 0.7$ 0

70) $200(0.075) - 4.5 \div 0.3$ 0

Solve each problem. For all answers involving money, give the final answer to the nearest cent.

71) Janine buys a package of diapers for $9.99. The package contains 31 diapers. Find the cost of each diaper. $0.32

72) Carlos is a waiter. He worked 7.5 hr and earned $62.25 in tips. How much did he earn per hour? $8.30 per hr

73) During the 2010 regular season of the National Football League, Jamaal Charles of the Kansas City Chiefs ran for 1467 yd in 16 games. Find the average number of yards he ran per game, rounded to the nearest tenth. (This is his total number of yards divided by the number of games.) (www.nfl.com) 91.7 yd per game

74) A baseball player's batting average is the number of hits divided by the number of "at bats." In the Major League Baseball 2010 regular season, Pablo Sandoval of the San Francisco Giants had 151 hits in 563 at bats. What is his batting average rounded to the nearest thousandth? (www.mlb.com) 0.268

75) Razeena spends $55.58 for 14.4 gal of gas. What is the cost per gallon? $3.86 per gal

76) Three boxes of the same size are shipped to a restaurant. The total weight of the boxes is 37.5 lb. How much does each box weigh? 12.5 lb

Mixed Exercises

Divide.

77) $0.0037\overline{)4.81}$ 1300

78) $23.76 \div 6$ 3.96

79) $\dfrac{47.79}{8.1}$ 5.9

80) $0.004\overline{)0.17}$ 42.5

81) $840 \div 4.2$ 200

82) $\dfrac{0.0065}{1.3}$ 0.005

Divide. Give the exact answer and an approximation to the nearest hundredth.

83) $5.23 \div 0.3$
exact: 17.4333... or 17.4̄3;
approximation: 17.43

84) $1.5\overline{)19}$
exact: 12.666... or 12.6̄;
approximation: 12.67

Divide. Round the answer to the nearest thousandth.

85) Divide 8 by 2.1.   3.810

86) $\dfrac{2.5415}{42.5}$ 0.060

Simplify each expression using the order of operations.

87) $59.5 + 2.8 \div 0.7 - 63.5$ 0

88) $16.2(1.5) - (0.09)^2$ 24.2919

Solve each problem. Give the final answer to the nearest cent.

 89) At the end of the year, Trevor receives a bank statement that says he has paid a total of $17,247.36 for his mortgage over the last year. If he pays the same amount each month, what is his monthly mortgage payment? $1437.28

90) Charise fills up her car's gas tank about once each week. Last month, she spent a total of $205.39 on gas. Find the average amount she spent per week. (The average per week is the total amount divided by the number of weeks.) $51.35 per wk

R Rethink

R1) Which procedures from this section would help you divide 1 by 3?

R2) Divide 1 by 3, and round to the nearest thousandth.

R3) Which concepts do you still need help with in this section?

Putting It All Together

P Prepare

O Organize

What are your objectives?	How can you accomplish each objective?
1 Review the Concepts of Sections 5.1–5.5	• Understand what a decimal represents and how to round a decimal. • In your own words, summarize how to perform operations with decimals. • Complete the given examples on your own. • Complete You Trys 1–3.

W Work

Read the explanations, follow the examples, take notes, and complete the You Trys.

1 Review the Concepts of Sections 5.1–5.5

We have learned that a decimal is another way to represent a fraction with a denominator that is a power of 10.

$$0.7 = \frac{7}{10} \qquad 0.61 = \frac{61}{100} \qquad 0.837 = \frac{837}{1000}$$

It is important to understand the place values of the digits in the decimals so that we can understand how to read and write them as well as perform operations with decimals.

EXAMPLE 1

In-Class Example 1

Write 2.084 in words, then write it as a mixed number in lowest terms.

Answer:
two and eighty-four thousandths; $2\dfrac{21}{250}$

Write 3.028 in words, then write it as a mixed number in lowest terms.

Solution

Read 3.028 as "three and twenty-eight thousandths."

thousandths place — whole-number part — numerator = 28 — denominator = 1000

As a mixed number, $3.028 = 3\dfrac{28}{1000}$. Is $\dfrac{28}{1000}$ in lowest terms? No!

$$\frac{28}{1000} = \frac{28 \div 4}{1000 \div 4} = \frac{7}{250}$$

Therefore, $3.028 = 3\dfrac{28}{1000} = 3\dfrac{7}{250}$.

[YOU TRY 1] Write 5.075 in words, then write it as a mixed number in lowest terms.

Note

When we change a decimal to a fraction or a mixed number, we will write the answer in lowest terms.

Often, we round decimals when working with money or when performing operations.

EXAMPLE 2

In-Class Example 2

Round $17.8126 to the nearest cent.

Answer: $17.81

Round $19.6239 to the nearest cent.

Solution

When we are working with a money amount, like $19.6239, we round to the nearest *cent,* which is the nearest *hundredth.*

Step 1: $19.6\underline{2}|39$ Underline the digit in the *cent* place.

Keep this digit the same.
3 is less than 5.

Step 2: $19.6\underline{2}|39$

Drop these digits.

Rounded to the nearest cent, $19.6239 is $19.62. We can also say that $19.6239 \approx $19.62.

[YOU TRY 2] Round $22.9657 to the nearest cent.

Let's review adding, subtracting, multiplying, and dividing decimals.

EXAMPLE 3

In-Class Example 3

Perform the indicated operations. If the remainder will never be 0 in a division problem, give the exact answer and an approximation of the answer rounded to the nearest hundredth.

a) 3.507×8.9
b) $0.256 \div 4$
c) $87.4 - 62.315$
d) $0.18\overline{)5.9}$
e) $(7.2)^2 - 10(19.84 - 15.71)$

Answer: a) 31.2123
b) 0.064 c) 25.085
d) exact: 32.7; approximation: 32.78 e) 10.54

Hint

In your notes, summarize how to add, subtract, multiply, and divide decimals.

Perform the indicated operations. If the remainder will never be 0 in a division problem, give the exact answer and an approximation of the answer rounded to the nearest hundredth.

a) 2.908×7.4
b) $0.147 \div 3$
c) $57.8 - 21.546$
d) $0.18\overline{)4.3}$
e) $(6.7)^2 - 10(14.76 - 11.65)$

Solution

a) When we **multiply** decimals, we do *not* have to line up the decimal points.

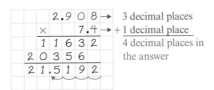

$$\begin{array}{r} 2.908 \rightarrow \\ \times \quad 7.4 \rightarrow \\ \hline 11632 \\ 20356 \\ \hline 21.5192 \end{array}$$

3 decimal places
+1 decimal place
4 decimal places in the answer

b) We are **dividing a decimal by a whole number:** $0.147 \div 3$. Write the decimal point in the quotient directly above the decimal point in the dividend. Then, divide.

$$\begin{array}{r} 0.049 \\ 3\overline{)0.147} \\ -12 \quad\;\; \\ \hline 27 \\ -27 \\ \hline 0 \end{array}$$

So, $0.147 \div 3 = 0.049$.

Check by multiplying.

$$\begin{array}{r} 0.049 \\ \times \quad 3 \\ \hline 0.147 \end{array} \checkmark$$

c) To **subtract decimals,** write the numbers vertically so that the decimal points are lined up.

$$\begin{array}{r} 57.8 \\ -21.546 \\ \hline \end{array} \qquad \begin{array}{r} \overset{9}{}\; \overset{7\;10\;10}{} \\ 57.8\cancel{0}\cancel{0} \\ -21.546 \\ \hline 36.254 \end{array}$$

← Insert two zeros.

The answer is 36.254.

To check, add $36.254 + 21.546$. The sum is 57.800 or 57.8. The answer is correct.

d) In this problem, $0.18\overline{)4.3}$, we are **dividing a number by a decimal.**

Move the decimal points 2 places to the right.

$0.18\overline{)4.3} \xrightarrow{\text{This is the same as multiplying both numbers by 100.}} 018\overline{)430.}$

Write a zero in the dividend, and put the decimal point in the quotient.

Divide.

$$\begin{array}{r} 23.888 \\ 18\overline{)430.000} \\ -36 \\ \hline 70 \\ -54 \\ \hline 160 \\ -144 \\ \hline 160 \\ -144 \\ \hline 160 \\ -144 \\ \hline 16 \end{array}$$

← Write extra zeros to continue dividing.

← Remainder will never equal 0.

The exact answer is $23.\overline{8}$. Rounded to the nearest hundredth, $4.3 \div 0.18 \approx 23.89$.

Check: $23.89 \times 0.18 = 4.3002$. This is not *exactly* 4.3, but it is very close. (When we round a quotient, we will *not* get the exact dividend, but it should be close.)

e) We use the order of operations with decimals in the same way we use them with whole numbers.

$(6.7)^2 - 10(14.76 - 11.65) = 44.89 - 10(14.76 - 11.65)$ Evaluate exponents first.
$= 44.89 - 10(3.11)$ Perform operations in parentheses.
$= 44.89 - 31.1$ Multiply before subtracting.
$= 13.79$ Subtract.

[YOU TRY 3] Perform the indicated operations. If the remainder will never be 0 in a division problem, give the exact answer and an approximation of the answer rounded to the nearest hundredth.

a) $42.1 + 138.976 + 2.05$ b) $100 \times (0.03)^2 + 16 \times 2.7$ c) $6\overline{)0.231}$

d) 91.45×4.1 e) $2.29 \div 0.09$

ANSWERS TO [YOU TRY] EXERCISES

1) a) $\dfrac{91}{100}$ b) $5\dfrac{3}{40}$ 2) a) 4.068   b) $22.97   3) a) 183.126   b) 43.29   c) 0.0385   d) 374.945
e) exact: $25.\overline{4}$; approximation: 25.44

Putting It All Together Exercises

E Evaluate   Do the exercises, and check your work.

*Additional answers can be found in the Answers to Exercises appendix.

Objective 1: Review the Concepts of Sections 5.1–5.5

Write each fraction as a decimal.

1) $\dfrac{79}{10}$ 7.9

2) $\dfrac{23}{1000}$ 0.023

Write each decimal in words; then write it as a fraction or mixed number in lowest terms.

3) 0.31   thirty-one hundredths; $\dfrac{31}{100}$

4) 0.125   one hundred twenty-five thousandths; $\dfrac{1}{8}$

 5) 1.6   one and six tenths; $1\dfrac{3}{5}$

6) Write as a decimal: *two and eight hundredths*.   2.08

Round each number to the indicated place.

7) 831.562 to the nearest tenth   831.6

8) 74.0698 to the nearest thousandth   74.070

9) $33.575 to the nearest dollar $34

10) Explain, in your own words, how to add decimals.

Perform the indicated operations.

11) $527.92 - 82.38$ 445.54   12) $0.001(6.7)$ 0.0067

13) $0.0216 \div 0.8$ 0.027   14) $\dfrac{135.45}{15}$ 9.03

15) $10,000(0.041)$ 4100   16) $7.2 + 4(20.7 - 16.59)$ 23.64

17) 905.47×0.073 66.09931   18) $216.58 + 97 + 36.9$ 350.48

19) $4.216 + 387.5 + 29.96$ 421.676   20) $(1.4)^2$ 1.96

21) $77 - 5.64(3.5)^2$ 7.91   22) $2.5\overline{)160}$ 64

23) $18\overline{)234.918}$ 13.051   24) $53 - 28.09$ 24.91

25) $10 - 10(0.092 + 0.37) + 35 \div 0.7$ 55.38

26) 81.6×7.42 605.472

Divide. Give an exact answer and an approximation to the nearest thousandth.

27) $\dfrac{43}{0.9}$ 28) $7.7 \div 9$
exact: $47.\overline{7}$; approximation: 47.778   exact: $0.8\overline{5}$; approximation: 0.856

29) $0.08 \div 1.1$
exact: 0.072; approximation: 0.073

30) $1.76\overline{)144}$
exact: 81.81;
approximation: 81.818

Divide. Round the answer to the nearest hundredth.

31) $31\overline{)7.2}$ 0.23

32) $\dfrac{6.2}{0.023}$ 269.57

Solve each problem.

33) Nikos buys the following items to make Greek salad. How much did he spend if the tax on his purchase was $2.03?

2 cucumbers at $0.99 each

3 yellow peppers at $2.49 each

2.5 lb of tomatoes at $2.39 per lb

1.6 lb of red onions at $1.25 per lb

1.5 lb of feta cheese at $12.98 per lb
$38.93

34) In February 2009, Facebook had approximately 1.75 million active users. That number rose to 3.5 million in December of the same year. How many more active users were there in December?
(www.facebook.com)
1.75 million

35) General admission tickets for a concert cost $38.50 each. The revenue from these tickets was $10,048.50. How many tickets were sold?   261 tickets

36) Laura earns $13.60 per hour. During a two-week period, she worked 38.5 hours. Determine the amount of her paycheck if $74.92 was deducted for taxes and $56.31 was deducted for health insurance. $392.37

37) Find the missing length.   7.6 in.

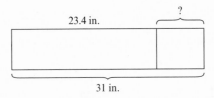

38) Find the perimeter of the triangle.   37.1 in.

R Rethink

R1) When all of the concepts from the first five sections are presented in one exercise set, did you remember how to treat the decimal point?

R2) Where could you spend more time reviewing objectives?

5.6 Writing Fractions as Decimals

What are your objectives for Section 5.6?	How can you accomplish each objective?
1 Write a Fraction as a Decimal Using Division	• Write the procedure for **Writing a Fraction as a Decimal Using Division.** • Complete the given examples on your own. • Complete You Trys 1 and 2.
2 Write a Fraction as a Decimal Using Equivalent Fractions with a Denominator of 10, 100, etc.	• Write your own procedure for **Writing a Fraction as a Decimal Using an Equivalent Fraction with a Denominator of 10, 100, etc.** • Complete the given example on your own. • Complete You Try 3.
3 Compare Fractions and Decimals	• Know the three different ways to compare fractions and decimals: number line, written as fractions, or written as decimals. • Complete the given examples on your own. • Complete You Trys 4 and 5.

W Work   Read the explanations, follow the examples, take notes, and complete the You Trys.

We have learned that a decimal is another way to represent a fraction with a denominator that is a power of 10. For example,

$$\frac{3}{10} = 0.3 \qquad \frac{481}{100} = 4.81 \qquad \frac{257}{1000} = 0.257$$

But how can we write other fractions, like $\frac{5}{8}$, as a decimal?

1   Write a Fraction as a Decimal Using Division

Recall that a fraction is one way to represent division. Therefore, $\frac{5}{8}$ means $5 \div 8$. **To write a fraction in decimal form, divide the numerator by the denominator.**

> **Procedure** Writing a Fraction as a Decimal Using Division
>
> To write a fraction as a decimal, divide the numerator by the denominator.

EXAMPLE 1   Write each fraction or mixed number as a decimal.

In-Class Example 1

Use Example 1.

a) $\frac{5}{8}$ b) $3\frac{4}{5}$

Solution

a) $\frac{5}{8}$ means $5 \div 8$. Divide.

```
    0.6 2 5
8)5.0 0 0 ← Write in zeros.
 -4 8
    2 0
   -1 6
      4 0
     -4 0
        0 ← Remainder = 0.
```

$\frac{5}{8} = 0.625$

b) We can use two different methods to write $3\frac{4}{5}$ as a decimal.

Method 1: Remember, $3\frac{4}{5}$ means $3 + \frac{4}{5}$. Change $\frac{4}{5}$ to a decimal, then add 3.

```
   0.8
5)4.0
 -4 0
    0
```

$\frac{4}{5} = 0.8$, so $3\frac{4}{5} = 3 + \frac{4}{5} = 3 + 0.8 = 3.8$

Method 2: Write $3\frac{4}{5}$ as an improper fraction. Then, divide.

$$3\frac{4}{5} = \frac{19}{5}$$

$\frac{19}{5}$ means $19 \div 5$.

```
    3.8
5)1 9.0
 -1 5
    4 0
   -4 0
      0
```

$3\frac{4}{5} = 3.8$

[YOU TRY 1] Write each fraction or mixed number as a decimal.

a) $\frac{1}{4}$ b) $2\frac{9}{25}$

Sometimes, we will never get a remainder of 0 when we divide.

EXAMPLE 2

In-Class Example 2

Use Example 2.

Write $\frac{2}{3}$ as a decimal. Give the exact answer and an approximation rounded to the nearest thousandth.

Solution

$\frac{2}{3}$ means $2 \div 3$, so divide. In addition to giving the exact answer, we are asked to round the answer to the nearest *thousandth*. Therefore, carry out the division one more place, to the *ten-thousandths* place.

$\dfrac{2}{3}$ means $2 \div 3$.

```
    0.6 6 6 6
3)2.0 0 0 0  ← Write in zeros.
 -1 8
    2 0
   -1 8
      2 0
     -1 8
        2 0
       -1 8
          2  ← The remainder
             will always be 2.
```

The *exact* answer is $\dfrac{2}{3} = 0.\overline{6}$.

The *approximation* to the nearest thousandth is $\dfrac{2}{3} \approx 0.667$.

[YOU TRY 2]

Write $\dfrac{5}{9}$ as a decimal. Give the exact answer and an approximation rounded to the nearest thousandth.

---

2 Write a Fraction as a Decimal Using Equivalent Fractions with a Denominator of 10, 100, etc.

If we can write a fraction as an equivalent fraction with a denominator of 10, 100, 1000, or another power of 10, then we can convert the fraction to a decimal.

EXAMPLE 3

Write each fraction as a decimal.

a) $\dfrac{2}{5}$ b) $\dfrac{18}{25}$

Solution

a) We can write $\dfrac{2}{5}$ with a denominator of 10: $\dfrac{2}{5} \cdot \dfrac{2}{2} = \dfrac{4}{10}$

Write $\dfrac{4}{10}$ as a decimal: 0.4. Therefore, $\dfrac{2}{5} = 0.4$.

b) *Can we write* $\dfrac{18}{25}$ *as a fraction with a denominator of 10 or 100?* Yes, we can write it with a denominator of 100.

$$\frac{18}{25} \cdot \frac{4}{4} = \frac{72}{100}$$

Write $\dfrac{72}{100}$ as a decimal: 0.72. So, $\dfrac{18}{25} = 0.72$.

[**YOU TRY 3**] Write each fraction as a decimal.

          a) $\dfrac{4}{5}$ b) $\dfrac{7}{20}$

Note

Not all fractions can be written as an equivalent fraction with a denominator that is a power of 10.

3   Compare Fractions and Decimals

We used number lines with fractions in Chapters 3 and 4, and we placed decimals on number lines in Sections 5.1 and 5.2. Now, let's compare decimals.

EXAMPLE 4

In-Class Example 4

Use =, >, or < to compare the numbers.
a) 0.7 ___ 0.4
b) 0.5 ___ 0.539

Answer:
a) >   b) <

Use =, >, or < to compare the numbers.

  a)   0.8 _____ 0.2   b)   0.43 _____ 0.461

Solution

a)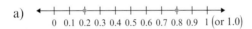

0.8 is to the *right* of 0.2, so 0.8 *is greater than* 0.2:   0.8 > 0.2

b) To compare 0.43 and 0.461, write 0.43 with the same number of decimal places as 0.461 by writing a zero at the end of 0.43.

Compare 0.430 and 0.461.

This is $\dfrac{430}{1000}$.   ⤴   ⤴   This is $\dfrac{461}{1000}$.

$\dfrac{430}{1000}$ *is less than* $\dfrac{461}{1000}$, so 0.43 < 0.461.

[**YOU TRY 4**] Use =, >, or < to compare the numbers.

  a)   0.5 _____ 0.6   b)   0.825 _____ 0.81

To compare fractions and decimals, we can think about where they appear on a number line. Or, we can write both numbers as fractions or both as decimals.

EXAMPLE 5

Use =, >, or < to compare the numbers.

  a) $\dfrac{1}{8}$ _____ 0.6   b)   0.75 _____ $\dfrac{3}{4}$ c)   1.4 _____ $1\dfrac{1}{5}$

Use =, >, or < to compare
the numbers.

a) $\dfrac{1}{3}$ ____ 0.8

b) 0.25 ____ $\dfrac{1}{4}$

c) 1.9 ____ $1\dfrac{4}{5}$

Answer:
a) <   b) =   c) >

Solution

a) Think about where $\dfrac{1}{8}$ and 0.6 appear on a number line.

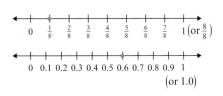

$\dfrac{1}{8}$ is to the *left* of 0.6, so $\dfrac{1}{8} < 0.6$.

b) Let's change 0.75 to a fraction to compare it to $\dfrac{3}{4}$.

$$0.75 = \frac{75}{100} = \frac{75 \div 25}{100 \div 25} = \frac{3}{4}$$

$$0.75 = \frac{3}{4}$$

 Hint

Choose the most efficient
way to compare numbers.

c) Let's change $1\dfrac{1}{5}$ to a decimal to compare it to 1.4.

$1\dfrac{1}{5}$ means $1 + \dfrac{1}{5}$. Change $\dfrac{1}{5}$ to a decimal: $\dfrac{1}{5} \cdot \dfrac{2}{2} = \dfrac{2}{10} = 0.2$

$1\dfrac{1}{5} = 1.2$. Compare 1.4 ____ 1.2.

one and *four* tenths   one and *two* tenths

$1.4 > 1.2$, so $1.4 > 1\dfrac{1}{5}$.

[YOU TRY 5]   Use =, >, or < to compare the numbers.

a) 0.3 ____ $\dfrac{2}{3}$ b) $1\dfrac{9}{20}$ ____ 1.4   c) 0.24 ____ $\dfrac{6}{25}$

Note

In Example 5b, we could have changed $\dfrac{3}{4}$ to the decimal 0.75 to see that $0.75 = \dfrac{3}{4}$.

In Example 5c, we could have changed 1.4 to a mixed number to compare it to $1\dfrac{1}{5}$.

$$1.4 = 1\frac{4}{10} = 1\frac{2}{5} \qquad \text{Divide 4 and 10 by 2.}$$

Then, we can think of 1.4 ____ $1\dfrac{1}{5}$ as $1\dfrac{2}{5}$ ____ $1\dfrac{1}{5}$.

We get $1\dfrac{2}{5} > 1\dfrac{1}{5}$ or $1.4 > 1\dfrac{1}{5}$.

Using Technology

We can use a calculator's division function to change a fraction to a decimal. In many cases, we must represent the displayed answer by indicating that there is a repeating decimal. In some cases, we may be asked to round our answer. For example, convert $\frac{10}{11}$ to a decimal using a calculator by entering [1][0][÷][1][1][=] into the calculator. The display will likely show 0.909090909, indicating that there is a repeating decimal. To represent the displayed repeating decimal, we would write $0.\overline{90}$ for our answer. However, if we are asked to round to the nearest hundredth, we would write 0.91 for the final answer.

E Evaluate **5.6** Exercises   Do the exercises, and check your work.

*Additional answers can be found in the Answers to Exercises appendix.

Objective 1: Write a Fraction as a Decimal Using Division

Use division to write each fraction or mixed number as a decimal.

1) $\frac{1}{2}$ 0.5

2) $\frac{1}{4}$ 0.25

3) $\frac{3}{5}$ 0.6

4) $\frac{4}{5}$ 0.8

5) $\frac{1}{8}$ 0.125

6) $\frac{7}{8}$ 0.875

7) $\frac{7}{16}$ 0.4375

8) $\frac{5}{16}$ 0.3125

9) $2\frac{2}{5}$ 2.4

10) $1\frac{3}{4}$ 1.75

 11) $4\frac{1}{16}$ 4.0625

12) $7\frac{37}{40}$ 7.925

13) When we use a 12-inch ruler to find the length of an object, the measurement often requires that we break up an inch into a fractional amount or a decimal equivalent. To help master this skill, first complete the following tables. Look for a pattern in both columns of the tables. Then using the ruler diagrams to the right, label the tick marks of one diagram with the appropriate fractions in lowest terms, and label the other with their decimal equivalents.

Fraction	Decimal Equivalent	Fraction	Decimal Equivalent
$\frac{1}{16}$	0.0625	$\frac{1}{8}$	0.125
$\frac{2}{16} = \frac{1}{8}$	0.1250	$\frac{2}{8} = \frac{1}{4}$	0.250
$\frac{3}{16}$	0.1875	$\frac{3}{8}$	0.375
$\frac{4}{16} = \frac{2}{8} = \frac{1}{4}$	0.2500	$\frac{4}{8} = \frac{1}{2}$	0.500
$\frac{5}{16}$	0.3125	$\frac{5}{8}$	0.625
$\frac{6}{16} = \frac{3}{8}$	0.3750	$\frac{6}{8} = \frac{3}{4}$	0.750
$\frac{7}{16}$	0.4375	$\frac{7}{8}$	0.875
$\frac{8}{16} = \frac{4}{8} = \frac{1}{2}$	0.5000	$\frac{8}{8} = 1$	1.000
$\frac{9}{16}$	0.5625		
$\frac{10}{16} = \frac{5}{8}$	0.6250		
$\frac{11}{16}$	0.6875		
$\frac{12}{16} = \frac{6}{8} = \frac{3}{4}$	0.7500		
$\frac{13}{16}$	0.8125		
$\frac{14}{16} = \frac{7}{8}$	0.8750		
$\frac{15}{16}$	0.9375		
$\frac{16}{16} = 1$	1.0000		

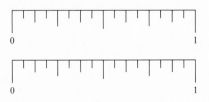

Use the results of Exercise 13 to write the decimal equivalent of the given measurements.

14) $1\frac{1}{4}$ in.   1.25 in.   15) $1\frac{1}{8}$ in.   1.125 in.   16) $4\frac{15}{16}$ in.   4.9375 in.

17) $2\frac{5}{8}$ in.   2.625 in.   18) $5\frac{3}{4}$ in.   5.75 in.

Write each fraction as a decimal. Give the exact answer and the approximation rounded to the nearest thousandth.

19) $\frac{1}{3}$

20) $\frac{1}{9}$

21) $\frac{7}{9}$

22) $\frac{8}{9}$

23) $\frac{5}{6}$

24) $\frac{1}{6}$

25) $\frac{29}{30}$

26) $\frac{1}{11}$

Objective 2: Write a Fraction as a Decimal Using Equivalent Fractions with a Denominator of 10, 100, etc.

27) What are two ways to write the fraction $\frac{17}{20}$ as a decimal?   1) Divide 17 by 20. 2) Write $\frac{17}{20}$ as a fraction with a denominator of 100, then write it as a decimal.

28) Can we change $\frac{8}{13}$ to a decimal by writing it with a denominator that is a power of 10? Explain your answer.   No. It is not possible to multiply 13 by a number so that the result is a power of 10.

Write each fraction or mixed number as a decimal by first getting a denominator of 10, 100, or 1000.

29) $\frac{3}{5}$ 0.6   30) $\frac{1}{5}$ 0.2   31) $\frac{3}{4}$ 0.75

32) $\frac{31}{50}$ 0.62   33) $\frac{16}{25}$ 0.64   34) $\frac{17}{20}$ 0.85

35) $\frac{321}{500}$ 0.642   36) $\frac{189}{200}$ 0.945   37) $\frac{7}{250}$ 0.028

38) $\frac{23}{250}$ 0.092   39) $4\frac{1}{2}$ 4.5   40) $2\frac{3}{4}$ 2.75

41) $1\frac{13}{25}$ 1.52   42) $2\frac{17}{20}$ 2.85

Objective 3: Compare Fractions and Decimals
Use =, >, or < to compare the decimals.

43) 0.4 ____ 0.5   <   44) 0.9 ____ 0.7   >

45) 2.5 ____ 2.4   >   46) 1.3 ____ 1.6   <

47) 0.35 ____ 0.350   =   48) 0.604 ____ 0.6040   =

49) 5.18 ____ 5.09   >   50) 9.42 ____ 9.06   >

51) 0.708 ____ 0.78   <   52) 0.39 ____ 0.309   >

53) 0.0500 ____ 0.05   =   54) 0.07 ____ 0.0700   =

55) 6.002 ____ 6.0015   >   56) 8.004 ____ 8.0042   <

57) 3.35 ____ 3.4   <   58) 1.2 ____ 1.19   >

Use =, >, or < to compare the numbers.

59) $\frac{1}{5}$ ____ 0.8   <   60) 0.6 ____ $\frac{1}{3}$ >

61) 0.8 ____ $\frac{1}{4}$ >   62) $\frac{2}{3}$ ____ 0.1   >

63) $1\frac{7}{20}$ ____ 1.4   <   64) 4.3 ____ $4\frac{6}{25}$ >

65) $\frac{16}{25}$ ____ 0.64   =   66) 0.15 ____ $\frac{3}{20}$ =

67) 2.67 ____ $2\frac{2}{3}$ >   68) 5.17 ____ $5\frac{1}{6}$ >

69) $7\frac{9}{20}$ ____ 7.450   =   70) 2.460 ____ $2\frac{23}{50}$ =

71) 3.004 ____ $3\frac{4}{500}$ <   72) $6\frac{3}{250}$ ____ 6.015   <

73) $4.2\overline{5}$ ____ $4\frac{1}{4}$ >   74) $\frac{1}{5}$ ____ $0.\overline{2}$ <

Arrange each group of numbers in order from smallest to largest.

75) 4.26, $4\frac{3}{10}$, $4\frac{1}{5}$, 4.259   76) $5\frac{1}{2}$, 5.45, $5\frac{7}{10}$, 5.503

77) $2\frac{1}{8}$, 2.75, 2.7, $2\frac{1}{16}$ 78) 3.68, $3\frac{1}{15}$, 3.6, $3\frac{1}{9}$

79) 0.97, $\frac{7}{8}$, $\frac{5}{16}$, 0.3   80) $\frac{3}{8}$, $\frac{15}{16}$, 0.8, 0.38

Mixed Exercises: Objectives 1–3
Write each fraction or mixed number as a decimal. Give the exact answer.

81) $1\frac{4}{5}$ 1.8   82) $\frac{19}{200}$ 0.095

83) $\frac{2}{11}$ $0.\overline{18}$ 84) $\frac{39}{8}$ 4.875

85) $\dfrac{3}{500}$ ___ 0.006

86) $\dfrac{5}{9}$ ___ $0.\overline{5}$

87) $\dfrac{41}{16}$ ___ 2.5625

88) $7\dfrac{3}{25}$ ___ 7.12

Write each fraction as a decimal. Give the exact answer and an approximation rounded to the nearest thousandth.

89) $\dfrac{7}{15}$

exact: $0.4\overline{6}$; approximation: 0.467

90) $\dfrac{3}{11}$

exact: $0.\overline{27}$; approximation: 0.273

Use =, >, or < to compare the numbers.

91) 1.50 _____ $1\dfrac{1}{2}$ =

92) 0.605 _____ 0.61   <

93) $\dfrac{1}{1000}$ _____ 0.0001   >

94) $0.\overline{8}$ _____ $\dfrac{4}{5}$ >

Arrange each group of numbers in order from smallest to largest.

95) $\dfrac{2}{3}$, $\dfrac{59}{100}$, 0.7, 0.6

$\dfrac{59}{100}$, 0.6, $\dfrac{2}{3}$, 0.7

96) $\dfrac{3}{4}$, $\dfrac{11}{16}$, 0.5, $\dfrac{5}{8}$

0.5, $\dfrac{5}{8}$, $\dfrac{11}{16}$, $\dfrac{3}{4}$

R **Rethink**

R1) After completing the exercises, which procedure did you find that you used most often to write a fraction as a decimal? Why?

R2) When would it be easier to understand what a fraction represents if it were written as a decimal?

5.7 Mean, Median, and Mode

P **Prepare**

O **Organize**

What are your objectives for Section 5.7?	How can you accomplish each objective?
1 Find the Mean	• Write the definition of a *mean* (*average*) in your own words. • Complete the given examples on your own. • Complete You Trys 1 and 2.
2 Find the Weighted Mean	• Write your own procedure for **Finding the Weighted Mean.** • Complete the given examples on your own. • Complete You Trys 3 and 4.
3 Find the Median	• Write a definition of *median*. • Write the procedure for **Finding a Median** in your own words. • Complete the given examples on your own. • Complete You Trys 5 and 6.
4 Find the Mode	• Write definitions of *mode* and *bimodal*. • Write the procedure for **Finding a Mode** in your own words. • Complete the given example on your own. • Complete You Try 7.

W **Work**   **Read the explanations, follow the examples, take notes, and complete the You Trys.**

In this section, we will learn about other ways that we use decimals in our everyday lives.

One way to analyze data or a list of numbers is to look for a **measure of central tendency.** This is a number that can be used to represent the entire list of numbers. In this section, we will learn about three measures of central tendency: the mean (or average), the median, and the mode. Let's start with the mean.

1 Find the Mean

What is the *mean,* or *average,* of a list of numbers?

> ### Definition
>
> The **mean (average)** is the sum of all the values in a list of numbers divided by the number of values in the list.
>
> $$\text{Mean} = \frac{\text{Sum of all values}}{\text{Number of values}}$$

EXAMPLE 1

Four friends went bowling. Their scores were 183, 204, 162, and 195. Find the mean, or average, score.

Solution

To find the mean, add the scores and divide by 4, the *number* of scores.

$$\text{Mean} = \frac{183 + 204 + 162 + 195}{4} \qquad \begin{array}{l}\text{Sum of the scores}\\ \text{Number of scores}\end{array}$$

$$= \frac{744}{4} \qquad \text{Add.}$$

$$= 186 \qquad \text{Divide.}$$

The mean, or average, score was 186.

Note

The mean will not necessarily be a value found in the original group of numbers!

[YOU TRY 1]

Tariq's driving times (in minutes) to work Monday through Friday last week were 21, 25, 27, 24, and 23. Find the mean, or average, driving time.

Estrella took six quizzes in her Psychology class this semester. Her scores were 95%, 82%, 88%, 93%, 91%, and 88%. What was her quiz average for the semester?

Solution

To find the average of her quiz scores, add the scores and divide by 6, the *number* of quizzes.

$$\text{Mean} = \frac{95 + 82 + 88 + 93 + 91 + 88}{6} \qquad \text{Sum of the scores} \atop \text{Number of scores}$$

$$= \frac{537}{6} \qquad \text{Add.}$$

$$= 89.5 \qquad \text{Divide.}$$

The average of Estrella's quiz scores was 89.5%.

[YOU TRY 2] Enrique took four exams in his Political Science class this semester. His grades were 82%, 75%, 63%, and 69%. What was his exam average?

2 Find the Weighted Mean

 Hint
How is this different from a "regular" mean?

If some values in a list of numbers appear more than once, then we can compute the *weighted mean* to represent that list of numbers. To find a **weighted mean,** we *weight* each value by multiplying it by the number of times it appears in the list. The number of times an item appears on the list is also called the **frequency.**

EXAMPLE 3

In-Class Example 3

Use Example 3.

The table lists the high temperatures in Dallas during July 2011 and the number of days that each was the high temperature. Find the weighted mean. (www.accuweather.com)

High Temperature, °F	Number of Days
99°	2
100°	2
101°	7
102°	7
103°	4
104°	2
105°	4
106°	3

Solution

The temperature is the value in the list, and the number of days is the number of times the temperature is counted, or the *weight*.

Multiply each temperature by the number of days that it was the high temperature. Then, find the weighted mean by taking the sum of all of these products and dividing by the total number of days. (Notice that this is 31 because July has 31 days.)

High Temperature, °F	Number of Days	Product
99°	2	99 · 2 = **198**
100°	2	100 · 2 = **200**
101°	7	101 · 7 = **707**
102°	7	102 · 7 = **714**
103°	4	103 · 4 = **412**
104°	2	104 · 2 = **208**
105°	4	105 · 4 = **420**
106°	3	106 · 3 = **318**
Totals	**31**	**3177**

$$\text{Weighted mean} = \frac{3177}{31} \qquad \frac{\text{Sum of the products}}{\text{Total number of days}}$$

$$\approx 102.5 \qquad \text{Divide and round to the nearest tenth.}$$

The weighted mean of the high temperatures in July 2011 was approximately 102.5°F.

[YOU TRY 3] The table lists the number of students in each classroom at Prospect School and the number of classrooms containing that number of students. Find the weighted mean number of students per classroom. Round the answer to the nearest tenth.

Number of Students	Number of Classrooms
21	4
22	3
24	5
26	4
27	1

Have you ever wondered how a grade point average (GPA) is calculated? It is usually calculated using a weighted mean.

Let's look at how to find the weighted mean (or GPA) of a student's grades. The grade earned for the course is the value in the list, and the number of credits assigned to the course is the weight.

EXAMPLE 4

In-Class Example 4

Refer to Example 4. Find Bharavi's GPA if she received the following grade report.

Course	Grade	Credits
Chemistry	A	4
Calculus I	B	5
Composition	C	3
Psychology	A	3

Answer: 3.27

Bharavi's grades from last semester are listed in the table. Her school uses a 4-point scale so that an A is 4 points, a B is 3 points, a C is 2 points, a D is 1 point, and an F is 0 points. Find Bharavi's grade point average or GPA.

Course	Grade	Credits
Speech	C	3
Precalculus	A	5
Economics	B	3
Biology	B	4

Solution

The grade earned for the course is the value in the list, and the number of credits assigned to the course is the number of times the grade is counted, or the *weight*.

For each course, multiply the grade, in points, by the number of credits that course is worth. Then, find the weighted mean, or GPA, by taking the sum of all of these numbers and dividing by the total number of credits.

Course	Grade	Grade, in Points	Credits	Points · Credits
Speech	C	2	3	$2 \cdot 3 = 6$
Precalculus	A	4	5	$4 \cdot 5 = 20$
Economics	B	3	3	$3 \cdot 3 = 9$
Biology	B	3	4	$3 \cdot 4 = 12$
Totals			15	47

$$\text{Weighted mean (GPA)} = \frac{47}{15} \quad \frac{\text{Total number of grade points}}{\text{Total number of credits}}$$

$$= 3.1\overline{3} \quad \text{Divide.}$$

Round $3.1\overline{3}$ to the nearest hundredth. Bharavi's GPA was 3.13.

[YOU TRY 4] Determine Wesley's GPA if he received this grade report. Round the answer to the nearest hundredth.

Course	Grade	Credits
French	C	4
Photography	A	3
U.S. History	D	3
Weight Training	B	1
Drawing	A	2

---

3 Find the Median

Another way to represent a list of numbers with a single number is to use the median.

Definition

The **median** of an ordered list of numbers is the middle number.

To find the median of a list of values, follow this three-step process.

Procedure Finding the Median of a List of Values

Step 1: Arrange the values from lowest to highest.

Step 2: Determine whether there is an even or odd number of values in the list.

Step 3: If there is an *odd number* of values, the median is the *middle number*.

If there is an *even number* of values, the median is the *mean (average) of the middle two numbers*.

EXAMPLE 5

In-Class Example 5

Here are the ages of Guillermo's nieces and nephews: 8, 9, 12, 4, 1, 2, 10, 7, 5. Find the median age.

Answer: 7

Here are the ages of Desmond's cousins: 16, 20, 14, 11, 22, 18, 15, 26, 21. Find the median age.

Solution

Follow the three-step process to find the median.

Step 1: Arrange the values from lowest to highest:
11, 14, 15, 16, 18, 20, 21, 22, 26

Step 2: Determine whether there is an even or odd number of values in the list. There are 9 values in the list; therefore, there is an *odd* number of values.

Step 3: Since there is an *odd* number of values, the median is the middle value, 18.

$$11, 14, 15, 16, 18, 20, 21, 22, 26$$

| First four numbers | Middle number | Last four numbers |

The median age of Desmond's cousins is 18.

[YOU TRY 5]

Here are the estimates for installing a new garage door at the O'Reillys' house: $385, $290, $350, $320, $340. Find the median estimate.

EXAMPLE 6

In-Class Example 6

Here are Hiroyuki's phone bills for the previous six months: $93.17, $81.90, $87.65, $92.48, $89.32, $90.43. Find the median phone bill.

Answer: $89.88

Jake finds the following airfares for a round-trip flight from Los Angeles to San Francisco: $155.40, $126.85, $119.38, $131.46, $179.22, $142.03. Find the median airfare.

Solution

Follow the three-step process to find the median.

Step 1: Arrange the values from lowest to highest:

$119.38, $126.85, $131.46, $142.03, $155.40, $179.22

Step 2: Determine whether there is an even or odd number of values in the list. There are 6 values in the list; therefore, there is an *even* number of values.

Step 3: Since there is an *even* number of values, the median is the *mean* of the middle two numbers.

Two middle numbers

$119.38, $126.85, $131.46, $142.03, $155.40, $179.22

| First two numbers | | Last two numbers |

$$\text{Median} = \frac{\$131.46 + \$142.03}{2} = \$136.745$$

Round the answer to the nearest cent, $136.75. The median airfare is $136.75.

[YOU TRY 6] Simone is a real estate agent and is compiling data on home sales. Here are the selling prices of the last 10 homes sold in her town: $265,400, $320,000, $318,500, $299,000, $305,900, $296,800, $332,000, $274,000, $260,000, $340,000. What was the median selling price?

4 Find the Mode

Another measure of central tendency is the *mode*.

Definition

The **mode** is the number that appears most frequently in a list of numbers.

Procedure Finding the Mode of a List of Numbers

Arrange the numbers from lowest to highest, and underline the numbers that are repeated.

1) If one number appears more often than the others, then that number is the **mode.**

2) If there are two numbers that appear most often in a list, then the list has two modes and is said to be **bimodal.** The numbers that appear most often are the modes.

3) The list has **no mode** if no number appears more often than any other number.

EXAMPLE 7

Find the mode for each list of numbers.

a) 40, 90, 70, 20, 50, 20, 60, 10, 80, 50, 30, 20

b) $1.05, $1.19, $1.09, $0.99, $1.19, $1.29, $1.17, $1.09

c) 67, 43, 118, 59, 96, 104, 80

In-Class Example 7

Find the mode for each list of numbers.
a) 58, 31, 47, 58, 65, 47, 20, 61, 84, 43, 47, 39
b) $299, $350, $279, $300, $289, $279, $315, $289
c) 14, 63, 29, 22, 51, 48, 32

Answer:
a) 47
b) The list is bimodal. The modes are $279 and $289.
c) no mode

Solution

a) If the list is long, it is helpful to arrange the numbers from lowest to highest and underline the numbers that are repeated:

10, <u>20</u>, <u>20</u>, <u>20</u>, 30, 40, <u>50</u>, <u>50</u>, 60, 70, 80, 90

The *mode* is 20 because it is the number that appears most often.

b) Write the numbers from smallest to largest, and underline the numbers that are repeated:

$0.99, $1.05, <u>$1.09</u>, <u>$1.09</u>, $1.17, <u>$1.19</u>, <u>$1.19</u>, $1.29

Since $1.09 and $1.19 each appear twice, the list is *bimodal*. The *modes* are $1.09 and $1.19.

c) Writing the numbers in order, we get 43, 59, 67, 80, 96, 104, 118.

No numbers appear more often than any others, so there is *no mode*.

YOU TRY 7 Find the mode for each list of numbers.

a) 25, 15, 40, 75, 35

b) $2.49, $2.79, $2.50, $2.49, $2.59, $2.59, $2.69, $2.59

c) 9.3, 7.8, 10.2, 8.5, 7.8, 8.1, 9.4, 8.1, 8.7

ANSWERS TO YOU TRY **EXERCISES**

1) 24 min 2) 72.25% 3) 23.6 students 4) 2.62 5) $340 6) $302,450

7) a) no mode b) The mode is $2.59. c) The list is bimodal. The modes are 7.8 and 8.1.

Using Technology

We can use a calculator to find the mean (or average) of a list of numbers by first finding the sum of all the values and then dividing by the number of values in the list. For example, find the mean value of 127, 96, 85, and 116. Notice that we have four values in our list. First find the sum of the values by entering $\boxed{1}\boxed{2}\boxed{7}\boxed{+}\boxed{9}\boxed{6}\boxed{+}\boxed{8}\boxed{5}\boxed{+}\boxed{1}\boxed{1}\boxed{6}\boxed{=}$. The display will show 424. Next we divide the sum by 4 by pressing $\boxed{\div}\boxed{4}\boxed{=}$. The display will show 106, which is the mean of our list of numbers.

E Evaluate **5.7** Exercises   Do the exercises, and check your work.

*Additional answers can be found in the Answers to Exercises appendix.

Objective 1: Find the Mean

1) What is another word for the *mean* of a list of numbers?   average

2) Explain, in your own words, how to find the mean of a list of numbers.   Answers may vary.

Solve each problem.

3) The ages of the employees at a bakery are 43, 54, 16, 17, 23, and 21. Find the mean age.   29

4) The numbers of people in Pilates classes are 14, 19, 12, 11, 18, and 16. Find the mean number of people.   15

5) Scott's latest scores on *Halo: Reach* were 11,350, 10,670, 11,020, 12,690, 12,410, 11,880, and 12,160.   11,740

6) Over the past six months, Alma's daughter sent or received the following numbers of text messages each month: 3214, 3107, 3350, 3422, 3069, and 3386. Find the average number of texts per month.   3258 texts

7) In the six games of the 2011 NBA Championship Series against the Miami Heat, Dirk Nowitzki of the Dallas Mavericks scored 27 pts, 24 pts, 34 pts, 21 pts, 29 pts, and 21 pts, respectively. Find the mean number of points he scored per game in this series. (In basketball, this is called the *points-per-game* or *ppg*.) (www.nba.com)   26 ppg

8) See Exercise 7. The numbers of points scored in each championship game by Dwyane Wade of the Miami Heat were 22, 36, 29, 32, 23, and 17. Find the mean number of points he scored per game in this series. (www.nba.com)   26.5 ppg

9) Jagoda looked at several apartments, and these were the rents per month: $525, $480, $600, $570, $542, and $556. Find the average rent. $545.50

10) The last several times Bjorn has filled up his car's gas tank, it cost: $47.20, $48.00, $51.35, $49.70, and $52.80. Find the average cost of filling up the tank. $49.81

11) Opening weekend ticket sales for the *Toy Story* movies were as follows: *Toy Story:* $29.1 million, *Toy Story 2:* $57.4 million, and *Toy Story 3:* $110.3 million. What was the mean revenue from ticket sales? (http://boxofficemojo.com) $65.6 million

12) The *Toy Story* movies were shown in the following numbers of theaters the first weekend of release: *Toy Story:* 2457, *Toy Story 2:* 3236, and *Toy Story 3:* 4028. What was the mean number of theaters? Round to the nearest whole number.
(http://boxofficemojo.com) 3240 theaters

Find the quiz average given the following scores. Round to the nearest tenth of a percent.

13) 79%, 71%, 73%, 64% 71.8%

14) 85%, 92%, 81%, 87% 86.3%

15) Adileh's exam scores are 75%, 61%, and 63%. What is her exam average? Round the answer to the nearest tenth. 66.3%

16) Toby's exam scores are 80%, 84%, and 72%. Round the answer to the nearest tenth. 78.7%

Objective 2: Find the Weighted Mean
Find the weighted mean. Round the answer to the nearest tenth, where necessary.

17) 4.4 people

Family Size	Number of Families
3	2
4	5
5	3
6	2

18) 2.2 houses

Houses Sold per Month	Number of Months
1	3
2	6
3	2
5	1

19) 15.2 cars

Cars Washed per Hour	Frequency
0	2
14	7
15	10
16	12
18	11

20) 6.5 books

Books Read per Year	Frequency
0	8
4	9
6	15
10	10
12	9

21) The table shows the cost of an adult ticket at several movie theaters and the number of theaters charging that price. Find the weighted mean. $9.07

Ticket Price	Number of Theaters
$5.50	2
$7.00	3
$9.00	1
$9.50	5
$10.00	8
$11.00	2

22) The table shows each amount that employees contributed to a going-away gift and the number of employees who contributed that amount. Find the weighted mean. $12.14

Amount	Number of Employees
$5.00	2
$8.00	1
$10.00	9
$12.00	2
$15.00	5
$20.00	3

Find the GPA for each student with the following grade report. Let A = 4 points, B = 3 points, C = 2 points, D = 1 point, and F = 0 points. Round the answer to the nearest hundredth.

23)

Course	Grade	Credits
Study Skills Strategies	B	2
Fundamentals of Writing	C	3
Fundamentals of Reading	A	3
Intro to Child Care	B	3
Aerobic Fitness	A	1

3.08

24)

Course	Grade	Credits
Intermediate Algebra	B	4
English Composition	A	3
Drafting	A	2
Sociology	C	3
Cardio Kickboxing	B	1

3.15

25)

Course	Grade	Credits
World History	C	3
Anatomy and Physiology	F	4
Precalculus	D	5
French	C	4

1.19

26)

Course	Grade	Credits
Automotive Engine Design	C	4
Automotive Electrical Systems	D	4
Technical Math	C	3
Speech	F	3

1.29

27)

Course	Grade	Credits
Art History	B	3
Website Design	A	3
Graphic Design II	B	4
Botany	C	4

2.93

28)

Course	Grade	Credits
Basic Phlebotomy	A	3
Medical Terminology	A	4
Noninvasive EKG	B	2
Speech	B	3

3.58

29)

Course	Grade	Credits
Child Psychology	C	3
Earth Science	C	4
Painting	B	2
English	A	3

2.67

30)

Course	Grade	Credits
Electronics	A	4
Algebra	B	5
Commercial Wiring	B	3
Technical Writing	C	3

3.07

Objective 3: Find the Median

31) What is the difference between the *mean* of a list of numbers and the *median* of the list? To find the *mean*, add all of the numbers in the list and divide by the number of numbers. The *median* is the middle number in the list.

32) Are the mean and the median of a list of numbers *always, sometimes,* or *never* the same value? sometimes

33) If a list has an *odd* number of numbers, how do you find the median? Arrange the numbers from lowest to highest. The number in the middle is the median.

34) If a list has an *even* number of numbers, how do you find the median? Arrange the numbers from lowest to highest. The median is the average of the two numbers in the middle.

Find the median of each list of numbers.

35) The cost of a manicure: $24, $20, $25, $28, $15 $24

36) The cost of a facial: $60, $65, $58, $70, $72 $65

37) The ages of the members of a softball team: 21, 25, 20, 19, 24, 22, 25, 23, 20, 18, 24, 23, 19 22

38) Number of years of experience: 17, 12, 18, 11, 3, 5, 12, 2, 11 11

39) Amount Evelyn spent on coffee each week: $16, $14, $13, $10, $15, $17 $14.50

40) Amount Stanislav spent on textbooks and supplies in previous semesters: $430, $380, $500, $440, $470, $320 $435

41) The attendance at football games: 72,140, 73,632, 75,109, 76,008, 76,150, 75,413, 76,124, 76,235 75,710.5

42) Employees' salaries: $47,540, $49,316, $44,700, $46,215, $45,990, $48,625, $43,180, $48,900 $46,877.50

43) The number of calls made to 911 per hour over a 24-hour period: 1291, 1056, 805, 639, 540, 522, 593, 781, 794, 836, 916, 1062, 1085, 964, 951, 1147, 1002, 1228, 1290, 1053, 997, 1178, 1260, 1359 999.5

44) The number of customers, per hour, at a 24-hour convenience store: 31, 17, 16, 16, 19, 52, 59, 68, 73, 75, 61, 63, 68, 60, 52, 51, 49, 67, 55, 51, 40, 40, 30, 27 51.5

45) The Bertagnoli family's last eight doctor bills: $74.00, $92.00, $120.00, $135.00, $97.00, $103.00, $84.00, $76.00 $94.50

46) Hotel prices for Julia's trip to Florida: $169.00, $129.00, $109.00, $120.00, $139.00, $150.00, $130.00, $158.00 $134.50

Objective 4: Find the Mode

47) What is the *mode* of a list of numbers?
It is the number that appears most frequently in the list.
48) Does every list of numbers have a mode? no

Find the mode of each list of numbers. If the list has no mode or is bimodal, then say so.

49) $5.00, $4.80, $4.90, $5.00, $4.95, $5.00, $5.30, $5.00 $5.00

50) $7.30, $9.10, $8.50, $9.10, $9.20, $8.70, $9.10, $9.10 $9.10

51) 28.3, 28.7, 27.4, 29.0, 27.5, 28.6 no mode

52) 61.8, 60.5, 59.9, 60.2, 61.3, 59.4 no mode

53) 75, 71, 78, 71, 82, 80, 79, 78, 76
The list is bimodal. The modes are 71 and 78.

54) 41, 46, 46, 50, 49, 42, 53, 47, 42
The list is bimodal. The modes are 42 and 46.

55) The heights of the members of a college women's gymnastics team, in inches: 58, 61, 57, 59, 60, 62, 58, 59, 60, 59, 58, 59 59 in.

56) The number of notebooks Levy bought each of the previous seven semesters: 4, 3, 5, 2, 3, 4, 3 3 notebooks

57) Prices for the same laptop at different stores: $409.99, $399.99, $379.99, $389.99, $389.99 $389.99

58) Prices for the same television at different stores: $549.99, $559.99, $539.99, $549.99, $569.99 $549.99

59) The numbers of women job-sharing at several companies: 4, 8, 10, 16, 0, 2, 6 no mode

60) The numbers of cabins at several state parks: 16, 22, 18, 28, 34, 25, 20 no mode

61) The number of patients visiting a free clinic each day over the last week: 102, 114, 96, 114, 120, 102, 85
The list is bimodal. The modes are 102 and 114.

62) The number of students in each section of a PreAlgebra class: 30, 24, 27, 23, 23, 29, 31, 24, 28, 24, 23
The list is bimodal. The modes are 23 and 24.

63) The percent of students at each of twelve schools receiving financial aid: 65%, 80%, 85%, 70%, 80%, 60%, 80%, 85%, 70%, 85%, 65%, 60%
The list is bimodal. The modes are 80% and 85%.

64) The percent of customers who paid their restaurant bill with a credit card over each of the last seven days: 49%, 53%, 61%, 40%, 63%, 79%, 56% no mode

Mixed Exercises: Objectives 1–4

65) The numbers of runs scored by the Detroit Tigers each season from 2000 to 2010 are 823, 724, 575, 591, 827, 723, 822, 887, 821, 743, 751. Find the mean, median, and mode. Round the answer to the nearest tenth, if necessary. (http://detroit.tigers.mlb.com)
mean: 753.4 runs; median: 751 runs; mode: none

66) The numbers of gold medals won by the United States in the Summer Olympics from 1968 in Mexico through 2008 in Beijing are 45, 33, 34, 83, 41, 38, 44, 37, 36, 36. Find the mean, median, and mode. (www.olympic.org)
mean: 42.7 medals; median: 37.5 medals; mode: 36 medals

67) Find the mean, median, and mode of Ms. Darvish's students' test grades: 74%, 85%, 61%, 73%, 92%, 85%, 40%, 78%, 93%, 85%, 73%, 72%, 54%, 66%, 70%, 89%, 81%, 52%, 76%, 65%
mean: 73.2%; median: 73.5%; mode: 85%

68) Find the mean, median, and mode of Mr. Cuesta's students' test grades: 82%, 59%, 73%, 70%, 88%, 65%, 91%, 94%, 67%, 73%, 82%, 39%, 75%, 68%, 80%, 73%, 54%, 82%, 59%   mean: 72.3%; median: 73%; mode: The list is bimodal. The modes are 73% and 82%.

69) The table shows the number of milligrams (mg) of caffeine in a 12-oz serving of each soft drink. Find the average amount of caffeine.

(www.energyfiend.com)   39 mg

Soft Drink	mg of Caffeine
Coca-Cola Classic	35
Pepsi-Cola	38
RC Cola	45
Mountain Dew	54
Barq's Root Beer	23

70) The table shows the percent of the recommended daily calcium in a 1-cup serving of different types of milk. Find the average percent of calcium.   31%

Type of Milk	Percent of Recommended Daily Calcium
Whole Milk (cow)	30
Soy	20
Rice	30
Coconut	45
Almond	30

For Exercises 71 and 72, find the GPA. Let A = 4 points, B = 3 points, C = 2 points, D = 1 point, and F = 0 points. Round the answer to the nearest hundredth.

71)

3.71

Course	Grade	Credits
Architectural Design	B	4
Architectural Drafting	A	2
Calculus I	A	5
Art History	A	3

72)

3.42

Course	Grade	Credits
Technical Writing	B	3
Managerial Accounting	A	4
Computer Accounting	C	2
Finite Math	A	3

R Rethink

R1) You have divided a number by 2 many times now. What statement can you make regarding the quotient?

R2) Where do you often use measures of central tendency? Does one measure of central tendency make sense for certain data sets but not others? Why?

Group Activity – Order of Operations with Decimals

"Around the World"

- Work in groups of three students (students should work on the same piece of paper).
- One student performs the first step in simplifying one of the expressions on p. 365, according to the order of operations. That student then passes the paper to the next student, who performs the second step. Continue this pattern until the expression is simplified.

- Change the order of students for each new expression.
- When appropriate, students should use "mental math" skills (multiplying and dividing by powers of ten, converting common fractions to decimals, etc.).

1) $(6.4 + 3.28) + 10(8.1 - 3.89)$

2) $27 - \dfrac{(9.2)^2}{4}$

3) $(0.5)(3.8 - 2.2) \div 0.0001$

4) $\dfrac{[3.25 + (0.7)^2] \times 100}{0.002 \times 1000}$

5) $(3.5)^2 - 2\dfrac{1}{5} \div 8 + 4\dfrac{3}{4}$

Group Activity Answers

1) 51.78   2) 5.84   3) 8000   4) 187   5) 16.725

emPOWERme Is Anxiety the Hardest Problem on the Test?

Do you feel anxious at the very thought of a math test, or are you cool and calm in the face of this situation? Get a sense of your test-taking style by checking off every statement below that applies to you.

☐ 1. The closer a test date approaches, the more nervous I get.

☐ 2. I am sometimes unable to sleep the night before a test.

☐ 3. I have "frozen up" during a math test, finding myself unable to think or respond.

☐ 4. I can feel my hands shaking as I pick up my pencil to begin the first problem on a test.

☐ 5. The minute I get to a tough question, I forget all the skills I've learned and have no idea how to begin.

☐ 6. I have become physically ill before or during a test.

☐ 7. Nervousness prevents me from studying immediately before a test.

☐ 8. I often dream about an upcoming test.

☐ 9. Even if I successfully answer a number of questions, my anxiety stays with me throughout the test.

☐ 10. I check and recheck the calculations on problems I know how to do, rather than deal with the questions I don't know how to answer.

If you checked off more than four statements, you have experienced fairly serious test anxiety. If you checked off more than six statements, your anxiety is probably interfering with your test performance. In particular, statements 3, 5, 6, and 7 may indicate serious test anxiety.

If, based on your responses to this questionnaire and your previous experience, your level of test anxiety is high, there are several things you can do.

- *Prepare thoroughly.* Good preparation can give you a sense of control and mastery, and it will prevent test anxiety from overwhelming you.
- *Take a realistic view of the test.* Remember that your future success does not hinge on your performance on any single exam. Think of the big picture: Put the task ahead in context, and remind yourself of all the hurdles you've passed so far.
- *Eat right and get enough sleep.* Good mental preparation can't occur without your body being well prepared.
- *Learn relaxation techniques.* You can learn to reduce or even eliminate the jittery physical symptoms of test anxiety by using relaxation techniques. The basic process is straightforward: Breathe evenly, gently inhaling and exhaling. Focus your mind on a pleasant, relaxing scene, or on a restful sound such as that of ocean waves breaking on the beach.
- *Visualize success.* Think of an image of your instructor handing back your test marked with an "A." Positive visualizations that highlight your potential success can help replace images of failure that may fuel test anxiety.

Chapter 5: Summary

Definition/Procedure	Example

5.1 Reading and Writing Decimals

A **decimal** is a number containing a *decimal point* that is another way to represent a fraction with a denominator that is a power of 10. **(p. 295)**

Use a decimal to represent the shaded part of the figure.

The square is divided into 100 equal parts. 27 parts are shaded. As a *fraction,* we say that $\frac{27}{100}$ (twenty-seven hundredths) is shaded. In *decimal* form, we say that 0.27 (twenty-seven hundredths) is shaded.

The Place-Value Chart

1) The *ones* column is in the middle of the chart.

2) The place values to the *left* of the decimal point (the whole number part) end in **s.**

3) The place values to the *right* of the decimal point (the fractional part) end in **ths. (p. 297)**

Identify the place value of each digit of 508.3192.

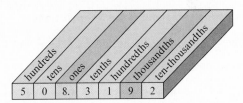

Reading a Decimal Number

1) Read the whole-number part first.

2) Read the decimal point as "*and.*"

3) Read the fractional part, the digits to the *right* of the decimal point, last. **(p. 301)**

Write 43.78 in words.

Read the whole-number part first, read the decimal point as "*and,*" then read the part to the right of the decimal point.

$$43.78$$
$$\uparrow$$
$$\text{and}$$

Read 43.78 as "forty-three and seventy-eight hundredths."

Write Decimals as Fractions or Mixed Numbers

1) If the decimal has a whole number, it will convert to a mixed number. Write the whole number in front of the fraction.

2) The numerator of the fraction will be the digits to the right of the decimal point.

3) The denominator will be the place value of the digit farthest to the right of the decimal point.

4) Write the fraction in lowest terms. **(p. 302)**

Write 5.0789 as a mixed number in lowest terms.

numerator = 789

$$5.0789 = 5\frac{789}{10,000}$$

9 is in the *ten-thousandths* place, so the denominator = 10,000.

Definition/Procedure	Example

5.2 Rounding Decimals

Rounding Decimals

Step 1: Find the place to which we are asked to round. Underline the digit in that place and draw a vertical line after it.

Step 2: Look at the digit to the right of the vertical line.

    a) If the digit to the right of the vertical line is **less than 5,** "drop off" the digits to the right of the vertical line and leave the underlined digit as it is.

    b) If the digit to the right of the vertical line is **5 or more,** "drop off" the digits to the right of the vertical line and increase the underlined digit by 1. **(p. 307)**

Round 45.90825 to the nearest thousandth.

Step 1: Underline the digit in the thousandths place and draw a vertical line after it.

$$45.908|25$$

Step 2: Look at the digit to the right of the vertical line. Because 2 is less than 5, "drop off" the digits to the right of the vertical line and keep the underlined digit as it is.

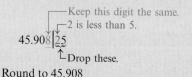

Round to 45.908

Rounded to the nearest thousandth, 45.90825 is 45.908. (Because we are rounding to the *thousandths* place, the last digit in the answer will be in the *thousandths* place.)

Round Money Amounts to the Nearest Cent

The value of a penny is 1¢ (1 cent). We can also write it in terms of a dollar as $0.01 or 0.01 dollar. $\left(\right.$ We can also say that it is $\frac{1}{100}$ dollar. $\left.\right)$ Because it is the smallest denomination of money in the United States, most everyday money amounts are rounded *to the nearest cent.* This is the same as rounding *to the nearest hundredth of a dollar.* **(p. 310)**

Brittany figured out that the exact amount of sales tax for the card she bought for her friend Zoe was $0.2625. Round the sales tax to the nearest cent.

Underline the 6 in the hundredths (or cents) place, and round.

    $0.26|25   Round to $0.26

Brittany will spent $0.26 on sales tax. This can also be written as 26¢.

Round Money Amounts to the Nearest Dollar

Rounding to the nearest *dollar* means rounding to the *ones* place. **(p. 311)**

Round $368.83 to the nearest dollar.

Underline the 8 in the ones place in $368.83 and round.

    $36<u>8</u>. 83   Round to $369

Or ask yourself, "*Is $368.83 closer to $368 or $369?*" It is closer to $369.

Definition/Procedure	Example

5.3 Adding and Subtracting Decimals

Add or Subtract Decimals

1) Write the numbers vertically so that the decimal points are lined up.

2) If any numbers are missing digits to the right of the decimal point, insert zeros. Then, add or subtract the same way we add or subtract whole numbers.

3) Place the decimal point in the answer *directly below* the decimal point in the problem. **(p. 316)**

Add or subtract as indicated.

a) $9.4 + 7.3$ b) $47 - 33.395$

Solution

a) Write the numbers vertically so that the decimal points are lined up. Then, add just like we add whole numbers.

$$\begin{array}{r} 9.4 \\ + 7.3 \\ \hline 1\,6.7 \end{array}$$

↑ Line up the decimal points.

b) First, rewrite 47 with a decimal point: $47 = 47.$ Line up the decimal points. Insert zeros and subtract.

$$\begin{array}{r} 9\ 9 \\ 6\ 10\ 10\ 10 \\ 4\ 7.0\ 0\ 0 \leftarrow \text{Insert 0's.} \\ -\ 3\ 3.3\ 9\ 5 \\ \hline 1\ 3.6\ 0\ 5 \end{array}$$

5.4 Multiplying Decimals

Multiplying Decimals

1) **Multiply the numbers (factors) just like you would multiply whole numbers.** (Line up the numbers on the right; the decimal points do *not* have to be lined up.)

2) **Determine the total number of decimal places in the answer (the product).** This will be the *total* number of decimal places in the factors.

3) **Insert the decimal point in the answer.** Start at the right side of the product and count the *total* number of places you determined in 2). Sometimes, you may need to insert zeros as placeholders on the left side of the answer. **(p. 324)**

Find 65.89×5.4.

Multiply the numbers just like they were whole numbers. Determine the total number of decimal places in the answer. Insert the decimal point in the answer.

$$\begin{array}{r} 6\ 5.8\ 9 \rightarrow \ \text{2 decimal places} \\ \times \quad 5.4 \rightarrow +\ \text{1 decimal place} \\ \hline 2\ 6\ 3\ 5\ 6 \qquad \text{3 decimal places in} \\ 3\ 2\ 9\ 4\ 5 \qquad \text{the answer.} \\ \hline 3\ 5\ 5.8\ 0\ 6 \end{array}$$

$65.89 \times 5.4 = 355.806$

Multiplying a Number by a Power of 10

1) Count the number of zeros in the power of 10.

2) Move the decimal point in the number *to the right* the same number of spaces as the number of zeros in the power of 10.

3) If necessary, add zeros as placeholders on the right. **(p. 326)**

Multiply 34.59×1000.

$$34.59 \times 1\underline{000} = 34.590 = 34{,}590$$

3 decimal places — Move the decimal point 3 places to the right.

Multiplying a Number by 0.1, 0.01, 0.001, etc.

1) 0.1, move the decimal point in the number 1 place to the left;

2) 0.01, move the decimal point 2 places to the left;

3) 0.001, move the decimal point 3 places to the left; and so on. **(p. 327)**

Multiply 27.1×0.01.

Write a 0 in the ones place.
↓

$$27.1 \times 0.01 = .271 = 0.271$$

2 decimal places — Move the decimal point 2 places to the left.

Definition/Procedure	Example

5.5 Dividing Decimals and Order of Operations

Divide a Decimal by a Whole Number

1) Write the problem in long division form.

2) Write the decimal point in the quotient directly above the decimal point in the dividend.

3) Perform the division as if the numbers were whole numbers. **(p. 332)**

Divide $2.748 \div 6$.

Solution

```
      0.4 5 8
  6)2.7 4 8
   -2 4
      3 4
     -3 0
        4 8
       -4 8
          0  ← Remainder = 0
```

Therefore, $2.748 \div 6 = 0.458$.

Divide a Number by a Decimal

1) Move the decimal point to the right end of the divisor. This makes the divisor a whole number. Count the number of decimal places you have moved.

2) Move the decimal point in the dividend the *same* number of places to the right. (If necessary, write in zeros.)

3) Write the decimal point in the quotient directly above the decimal point in the dividend. Then, divide. **(p. 336)**

Divide 61.6 by 0.011.

Move the decimal point 3 places to the right.

$$0.011\overline{)61.6} \longrightarrow 011.\overline{)61600.}$$

Move decimal points 3 places to the right. Write the decimal point in the quotient directly above the decimal point in the dividend.

Divide $11\overline{)61600.}^{\,5600.}$ Check by multiplying.

Use the Order of Operations with Decimals
We use the order of operations with decimals just like we did with whole numbers and fractions. **(p. 338)**

Simplify $8.1 \div 9 - 0.1(1.3)^2$ using the order of operations.

$8.1 \div 9 - 0.1(1.3)^2$

$= 8.1 \div 9 - 0.1(1.69)$ Evaluate exponents first.

$= 0.9 - 0.169$ Divide and multiply before subtracting.

$= 0.731$ Subtract.

5.6 Writing Fractions as Decimals

Write a Fraction as a Decimal Using Division
To write a fraction as a decimal, divide the numerator by the denominator. **(p. 346)**

Write $\dfrac{1}{4}$ as a decimal.

$\dfrac{1}{4}$ means $1 \div 4$. Divide.

```
    0.2 5
  4)1.0 0
   -8
    2 0
   -2 0
      0
```

Therefore, $\dfrac{1}{4} = 0.25$

Definition/Procedure	Example
Write a Fraction as a Decimal Using Equivalent Fractions with a Denominator of 10, 100, etc. If we can write a fraction as an equivalent fraction with a denominator of 10, 100, 1000, or another power of 10, then we can convert it to a decimal. **(p. 348)**	Write $\dfrac{7}{50}$ as a decimal. We can write $\dfrac{7}{50}$ with a denominator of 100. $$\frac{7}{50} \cdot \frac{2}{2} = \frac{14}{100}$$ Write $\dfrac{14}{100}$ as a decimal: 0.14 Therefore, $\dfrac{7}{50} = 0.14$.
To compare two decimals or a fraction and a decimal, we can think about where they appear on a number line. Or, we can write both numbers as fractions or both as decimals. **(p. 349)**	Use $=$, $>$, or $<$ to compare 0.45 _____ $\dfrac{7}{20}$. Let's change 0.45 to a fraction to compare it to $\dfrac{7}{20}$. $$0.45 = \frac{45}{100} = \frac{45 \div 5}{100 \div 5} = \frac{9}{20}$$ Because $0.45 = \dfrac{9}{20}$, compare $\dfrac{9}{20}$ _____ $\dfrac{7}{20}$. $\dfrac{9}{20} > \dfrac{7}{20}$, so $0.45 > \dfrac{7}{20}$.

5.7 Mean, Median, and Mode

Find the Mean The **mean (average)** is the sum of all the values in a list of numbers divided by the number of values in the list. $$\text{Mean} = \frac{\text{Sum of all values}}{\text{Number of values}}$$ The mean will not necessarily be a value found in the list. **(p. 354)**	Find the mean, or average, of 37, 42, 31, and 34. **Solution** To find the mean, add the scores and divide by 4, the *number* of scores. $\text{Mean} = \dfrac{37 + 42 + 31 + 34}{4}$ Sum of the scores / Number of scores $= \dfrac{144}{4}$ Add. $= 36$ Divide. The mean, or average, is 36.

Definition/Procedure	Example

Find the Weighted Mean

If some values in a list of numbers appear more than once, then we can compute the *weighted mean* to represent that list of numbers. To find a **weighted mean,** we *weight* each value by multiplying it by the number of times it appears in the list. **(p. 355)**

Find a Grade Point Average (GPA)

Computing a student's GPA is the same as finding a weighted mean. For each course, multiply the grade, in points, by the number of credits that course is worth. Then, find the weighted mean, or GPA, by taking the sum of all of these numbers and dividing by the total number of credits. **(p. 356)**

Athena's grades from last semester are listed in the table. Her school uses a 4-point scale so that an A is 4 points, a B is 3 points, a C is 2 points, a D is 1 point, and an F is 0 points. Find Athena's grade point average or GPA.

Course	Grade	Credits
Human Services	B	4
Crisis Intervention	A	2
Sociology	C	3
Addictions Counseling	A	4

Solution

Multiply the grade, in points, by the number of credits. Then, add those products and divide by the total number of credits.

Course, Grade, Grade Points	Credits	Points · Credits
Human Services B = 3	4	$3 \cdot 4 = \mathbf{12}$
Crisis Intervention A = 4	2	$4 \cdot 2 = \mathbf{8}$
Sociology C = 2	3	$2 \cdot 3 = \mathbf{6}$
Addictions Counseling, A = 4	4	$4 \cdot 4 = \mathbf{16}$
Totals	13	**42**

$$\text{GPA} = \frac{42}{13} \qquad \frac{\text{Total number of grade points}}{\text{Total number of credits}}$$

$$= 3.23 \qquad \text{Divide. Round to the nearest hundredth.}$$

Athena's GPA was 3.23.

Find the Median

The **median** of an ordered list of numbers is the middle number. To find the median of a list of values, follow this three-step process.

Procedure for Finding the Median of a List of Values

Step 1: Arrange the values from lowest to highest.

Step 2: Determine whether there is an even or odd number of values in the list.

Step 3: If there is an *odd number* of values, the median is the *middle number*. If there is an *even number* of values, the median is the *mean (average) of the middle two numbers*. **(p. 357)**

Find the median of each list of numbers.

a) 19, 25, 27, 20, 26, 18, 23

b) 8.5, 5.4, 6.7, 8.8, 9.2, 7.9

Solution

a) Arrange the numbers from lowest to highest.

$$18, 19, 20, 23, 25, 26, 27$$

Because there is an *odd* number of values in the list (7 values), the median is the *middle number* in the list. The median is 23.

b) Arrange the numbers from lowest to highest.

$$5.4, 6.7, 7.9, 8.5, 8.8, 9.2$$

Because there is an *even* number of values in the list (6 values), the median is the *mean of the middle two numbers* in the list.

$$\text{Median} = \frac{7.9 + 8.5}{2} = 8.2$$

The median is 8.2.

Definition/Procedure	Example
Find the Mode The **mode** is the number that appears most frequently in a list of numbers. **Procedure for Finding the Mode of a List of Numbers** Arrange the numbers from lowest to highest, and underline the numbers that are repeated. 1) If one number appears more often than the others, then that number is the **mode**. 2) If there are two numbers that appear most often in a list, then the list has two modes and is said to be **bimodal.** The numbers that appear most often are the modes. 3) The list has **no mode** if no number appears more often than any other number. **(p. 359)**	Find the mode of each list of numbers. a) 74%, 71%, 76%, 87%, 90%, 71%, 64%, 76%, 71% b) $2.99, $2.69, $2.99, $3.09, $2.89, $3.09, $3.29 c) 51, 58, 49, 56, 50, 62, 68, 54, 57 **Solution** a) It is helpful to arrange the numbers from lowest to highest and underline the numbers that are repeated: 64%, <u>71%</u>, <u>71%</u>, <u>71%</u>, 74%, <u>76%</u>, <u>76%</u>, 87%, 90% The number that appears most often is 71%, so the mode is 71%. b) Arrange the numbers from lowest to highest and underline the numbers that are repeated: $2.69, $2.89, <u>$2.99</u>, <u>$2.99</u>, <u>$3.09</u>, <u>$3.09</u>, $3.29 Both $2.99 and $3.09 appear twice. The list is *bimodal,* and the modes are $2.99 and $3.09. c) Arrange the numbers from lowest to highest. 49, 50, 51, 54, 56, 57, 58, 62, 68 No number appears more often than any other. The list has **no mode.**

Chapter 5:   Review Exercises

*Additional answers can be found in the Answers to Exercises appendix.

(5.1) Use a fraction with a denominator of 10 as well as a decimal to represent the shaded part of the rectangle. Then, represent the fraction as a decimal on a number line.

1)

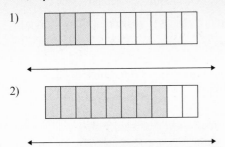

2)

Use a fraction and a decimal to represent the shaded part of the figure. Write the fraction in lowest terms.

3)

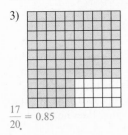

$\frac{17}{20} = 0.85$

4)

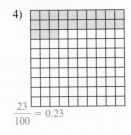

$\frac{23}{100} = 0.23$

Approximate the location of the decimal on the given number line.

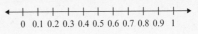

0 0.1 0.2 0.3 0.4 0.5 0.6 0.7 0.8 0.9 1

5) 0.93   6) 0.17

Write each fraction or mixed number as a decimal.

7) $\frac{97}{1000}$ 0.097   8) $4\frac{1}{10}$ 4.1

9) $\frac{3867}{1000}$ 3.867   10) $\frac{1724}{100}$ 17.24

Identify the place value of each digit.

11) 52.406798   12) 3.01584

Write each decimal in words.

13) 0.029   14) 941.0083
     twenty-nine thousandths   nine hundred forty-one and
                                eighty-three ten-thousandths

Write each word statement as a decimal number.

15) Fifty thousand seventy-two and thirty-six hundredths
     50,072.36
16) Four hundred nineteen ten-thousandths   0.0419

Write each decimal as a fraction or mixed number in lowest terms.

17) 0.98 $\dfrac{49}{50}$

18) 0.575 $\dfrac{23}{40}$

19) 1.5 $1\dfrac{1}{2}$

20) 6.0072 $6\dfrac{9}{1250}$

(5.2)

21) Round 39,604.9951 to the indicated place.

    a) thousands   40,000   b) ten-thousands   40,000

    c) tenths   39,605.0   d) hundredths   39,605.00

22) Round 0.0014 to three decimal places.   0.001

Round each money amount to the nearest a) cent and b) dollar.

23) $3.78195
    a) $3.78   b) $4

24) $0.9972
    a) $1.00   b) $1

Solve each problem.

25) Tangaroa bought a surfboard for $549.99, and he computed the amount of sales tax to be exactly $35.74935. How much will Tangaroa pay at the cash register including the sales tax? $585.74

26) Greta takes her son shopping for winter clothes and puts the following items in her shopping cart. Round the price of each item to the nearest dollar, then add the rounded numbers to estimate the total cost of the items. $84

    Coat: $49.99

    Hat: $6.09

    Gloves: $4.85

    Boots: $23.49

(5.3)

27) Explain how to add decimals.

28) What is the first step in performing this subtraction? Do *not* subtract.

$$\begin{array}{r} 19 \\ -\ 2.584 \end{array}$$

Put a decimal point after the 9, and rewrite 19 as 19.000.

Add or subtract as indicated.

29) Find the sum of 4.19 and 3.05.   7.24

30) $\begin{array}{r} 50.042 \\ -\ 39.619 \end{array}$ 10.423

31) 405.293 + 87.55   492.843

32) 53.1 − 43.908   9.192

33) 19 minus 2.584   16.416

34) Subtract 0.0397 from 1.   0.9603

35) Subtract 596.008 from 2104.5.   1508.492

36) 16,001.5 + 42.936 + 579 + 0.02   16,623.456

Solve each problem.

37) Amanda has $817.32 in her checking account. When she uses her debit card, the money comes out of this account. She makes the following purchases with her debit card:

    Boots: $139.87

    Make-Up: $25.09

    Scarf: $32.46

    Jeans: $53.71

    Leather Coat: $206.50

    Purse: $74.83

    a) How much did Amanda spend on this shopping trip? $532.46

    b) How much money is left in her account? $284.86

    c) If Amanda wants to bring her account balance up to $500, how much must she deposit? $215.14

38) At a pet supply store, Anand buys a dog collar and some treats for $16.28. If he gives the cashier a $20 bill and three pennies, how much change will he receive? $3.75

(5.4)

39) Give an example of two decimal numbers that, when multiplied together, will have a product with three decimal places.   Answers may vary.

40) Is it necessary to line up the decimal points when multiplying decimal numbers?   no

Multiply.

41) 43.57(1.08)   47.0556

42) 16 × 62.195   995.12

43) $\begin{array}{r} 0.064 \\ \times\ 0.03 \end{array}$ 0.00192

44) (0.84)(0.009)   0.00756

45) 971.8 × 250   242,950

46) $\begin{array}{r} 31.059 \\ \times\ 2.76 \end{array}$ 85.72284

47) $(1.2)^2$ 1.44

48) $(4.7)^2$ 22.09

49) 100(0.8415)   84.15

50) 3.8 × 1000   3800

51) 200.5 × 0.0001   0.02005

52) (0.00001)(3505)   0.03505

Solve each problem.

53) A rugby field is in the shape of a rectangle and is 157.5 yards long and 76.6 yards wide. What is the area of the field?   12,064.5 sq yd

54) For his daughter's birthday party, Dashiell bought fourteen birthday cupcakes for $2.55 each. Sales tax on this purchase was $2.29. What was the total cost of the cupcakes? If Dashiell pays for the cupcakes by giving the cashier two $20 bills, how much change does he receive? $37.99; $2.01

(5.5) Divide.

55) $45.48 \div 6$ 7.58

56) $\dfrac{15}{0.05}$ 300

57) $1.04\overline{)83.564}$ 80.35

58) $0.03596 \div 6.2$ 0.0058

59) Divide 2146 by 0.029.   74,000

60) $9\overline{)114.687}$ 12.743

Divide. Give the exact answer and an approximation to the nearest thousandth.

61) $\dfrac{59.2}{0.9}$ exact: $65.\overline{7}$;   approximation: 65.778

62) $160.4 \div 6$ exact: $26.7\overline{3}$;   approximation: 26.733

Simplify each expression using the order of operations.

63) $410 - 67.48 \times 3.5 + 7.625$ 181.445

64) $(1.6)^2 + 9.6 \div 0.3$ 34.56

65) $100(51 - 50.328) \div (0.2)^2$ 1680

66) $224.1 - 0.1(72.8 + 95.6)$ 207.26

Solve each problem.

67) Savannah finances $11,654.40 to purchase her new car. Her loan is a 48-month, interest-free loan. If Savannah pays equal amounts per month for 48 months, what is her monthly payment? $242.80

68) The total weight of a shipment of boxes was 317.3 pounds, and each box weighed 16.7 pounds. How many boxes were in the shipment?   19

(5.6) Use division to write each fraction or mixed number as a decimal.

69) $\dfrac{4}{5}$ 0.8

70) $1\dfrac{1}{8}$ 1.125

71) $5\dfrac{1}{16}$ 5.0625

72) $\dfrac{13}{20}$ 0.65

Write each fraction as a decimal. Give the exact answer and an approximation rounded to the nearest hundredth.

73) $\dfrac{2}{11}$ exact: $0.\overline{18}$;   approximation: 0.18

74) $\dfrac{4}{15}$ exact: $0.2\overline{6}$;   approximation: 0.27

Write each fraction as a decimal by first writing the fraction with a denominator of 10, 100, or 1000.

75) $\dfrac{19}{20}$ 0.95

76) $\dfrac{12}{25}$ 0.48

77) $\dfrac{9}{250}$ 0.036

78) $\dfrac{35}{4}$ 8.75

Use =, >, or < to compare the numbers.

79) $6.05 \underline{\hspace{1cm}} 6.049$ >

80) $3\dfrac{4}{500} \underline{\hspace{1cm}} 3.004$ >

81) $\dfrac{2}{3} \underline{\hspace{1cm}} 0.\overline{6}$ =

82) $\dfrac{13}{50} \underline{\hspace{1cm}} 0.27$ <

Arrange each group of numbers in order from smallest to largest.

83) $0.76, \dfrac{1}{2}, 0.7, \dfrac{3}{4}$ $\dfrac{1}{2}, 0.7, \dfrac{3}{4}, 0.76$

84) $0.\overline{8}, 1.01, \dfrac{4}{5}, \dfrac{9}{10}$ $\dfrac{4}{5}, 0.\overline{8}, \dfrac{9}{10}, 1.01$

(5.7)

85) Hillary is looking at four used cars with the following mileages: 51,427, 49,058, 60,229, 55,694. Find the average number of miles on these cars.   54,102 mi

86) A restaurant has seven appetizers on its menu, with the following prices: $6.99, $8.49, $7.89, $7.99, $9.29, $10.99, $8.99. What is the mean price of an appetizer? $8.66

87) Find Paolo's GPA. Let A = 4 points, B = 3 points, C = 2 points, D = 1 point, and F = 0 points. Round the answer to the nearest hundredth.   3.33

Course	Grade	Credits
Constitutional Law	C	3
Criminal Law	A	3
Business Math	A	4
Word Processing	B	2

88) The table shows the number of miles employees drive to work each day and the number of employees who drive that distance. Find the weighted mean rounded to the nearest tenth.   15.6 mi

Distance	Number of Employees
3	1
8	3
15	9
20	6
23	2

89) The numbers of miles Maurice rode his bike each day last week were 18, 17, 25, 20, 28, 25, and 16. Find the median.   20 mi

90) The attendances at a Broadway play for each of its previous ten shows were 1430, 1392, 1571, 1580, 1465, 1609, 1718, 1696, 1381, and 1628. Find the median.   1575.5 people

Find the mode of each list of numbers. If the list is bimodal or has no mode, then say so.

91) 12.5, 9.4, 11.6, 12.1, 11.6, 8.9   11.6

92) 70%, 91%, 64%, 52%, 73%, 85%, 73%, 66%, 52%, 73%   73%

93) 38, 45, 49, 42, 37, 40   no mode

94) $6.29, $6.79, $6.39, $6.99, $6.89, $6.99, $7.19, $6.79   The list is bimodal. The modes are $6.79 and $6.99.

Mixed Exercises: Sections 5.1–5.7

95) Which operations with decimals require lining up the decimals?   adding and subtracting

96) Explain how to multiply a decimal number by 0.01.
Move the decimal point in the number to the left two places.

Perform the indicated operations.

97) 0.098×72.1 7.0658

98) Subtract 14.188 from 23.   8.812

99) $1135.7 + 4.092 + 1135.688 + 730$ 3005.48

100) $2.4\overline{)73.68}$ 30.7

101) $46.5 \times 1.2 - 0.01(87 - 63.94)$ 55.5694

102) $(1.2)^2 - 4.5 \div 15 + 2.8$ 3.94

103) Round $73.8975 to the nearest

   a) dollar $74   b) cent $73.90

104) Identify the place value of each digit of 92.5381.
9—tens, 2—ones, 5—tenths, 3—hundredths,
8—thousandths, 1—ten-thousandths

Write each fraction as a decimal.

105) $\dfrac{11}{8}$ 1.375   106) $\dfrac{39}{10,000}$ 0.0039

Write each decimal as a fraction or mixed number in lowest terms.

107) 7.528 $7\dfrac{66}{125}$ 108) 0.0075 $\dfrac{3}{400}$

Solve each problem.

109) Here is a list of Mr. Carson's students' grades: 62%, 75%, 69%, 81%, 90%, 69%, 72%, 74%, 86%, 72%, 83%, 72%, 51%, 43%, 69%, 79%, 74%, 48%. Find the mean, median, and mode.   mean: 70.5%; median: 72%; mode: The list is bimodal. The modes are 69% and 72%.

110) Find Natasha's GPA. Let A = 4 points, B = 3 points, C = 2 points, D = 1 point, and F = 0 points. Round the answer to the nearest hundredth.   2.36

Course	Grade	Credits
Anatomy and Physiology	D	4
Kinesiology	A	2
Therapeutic Exercise	B	2
Speech	B	3
Psychology	C	3

111) A sandwich shop is open for business from 11:00 A.M. to 9:00 P.M. One day, the tips totaled $61.20. The manager does calculations each day to determine how much each employee earns in tips. Here is the list of employees and the hours they worked:

Vernon   10:00 A.M.–5:30 P.M.

Jane   10:00 A.M.–2:00 P.M.

Aliyah   11:00 A.M.–2:30 P.M.

Domingo   12:00 P.M.–8:00 P.M.

Nayana   3:00 P.M.–10:00 P.M.

Steve   6:00 P.M.–10:00 P.M.

a) Determine the total number of hours worked by all the employees.   34 hours

b) Determine the average amount of tips earned per hour. $1.80 per hour

c) The manager gives each of the employees his or her tips in cash. How much will she give each employee? (Multiply the number of hours worked by each employee by the average amount of tips earned per hour.)

112) If the perimeter of the square is 12.224 in., what is the measure of one side length?   3.056 in.

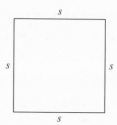

The Daytona 500 is a 500-mile-long NASCAR race held each year at the Daytona International Speedway in Daytona Beach, Florida. Listed here are four winners and their winning times. Use this information for Exercises 113–120. (Note: The average speed will be in miles per hour, mph.) (www.daytonainternationalspeedway.com)

Year	Winner	Time
1961	Marvin Panch	3.34 hours
1981	Richard Petty	2.95 hours
1998	Dale Earnhardt	2.90 hours
2008	Ryan Newman	3.28 hours

113) Who had the fastest time? What was his average speed, rounded to the nearest hundredth?
Dale Earnhardt; 172.41 mph

114) Find Ryan Newman's average speed, rounded to the nearest hundredth.   152.44 mph

115) Who had the slowest time? What was his average speed, rounded to the nearest hundredth?
Marvin Panch; 149.70 mph

116) How much longer did it take Ryan Newman to complete the race than Richard Petty?   0.33 hr

117) How much less time did it take for the fastest driver to complete the course compared to the slowest driver?
It took Dale Earnhardt 0.44 hr less than Marvin Panch.

118) Compare the speeds of Richard Petty and Dale Earnhardt. Who had a faster time and by how much?
Dale Earnhardt's time was faster by 0.05 hr.

119) How many minutes separated the fastest and slowest winning times? (To determine this, multiply the answer in Exercise 117 by 60.)   26.40 min

120) Find the difference, in minutes, between Richard Petty's time and Dale Earnhardt's time. (To do this, multiply the answer in Exercise 118 by 60.)   3.00 min

Chapter 5:   Test

*Additional answers can be found in the Answers to Exercises appendix.

1) Use a decimal to represent the shaded part of the figure, and represent the decimal on a number line.

2) Write each decimal as a fraction or mixed number in lowest terms.

a) 0.73 $\frac{73}{100}$ b) 0.8 $\frac{4}{5}$ c) 2.075 $2\frac{3}{40}$

3) Write each decimal in words.

a) 4.09   b) 0.0614

4) Write as a decimal number: *sixteen and five hundred seventy-three thousandths*   16.573

Round each number to the indicated place.

5) 9.4683 to the nearest hundredth   9.47

6) 310.974 to the nearest tenth   311.0

7) $2375.46 to the nearest dollar $2375

8) $62.1352 to the nearest cent $62.14

9) Explain, in your own words, how to multiply decimals. Do you need to line up the decimal points when you write out the problem?

Perform the indicated operations.

10) 3.86(5.9)   22.774   11) 87 ÷ 0.012   7250

12) 63.14 + 5.9362 + 158.791   227.8672

13) 74.3 − 28.96   45.34   14) $\frac{0.8785}{35}$ 0.0251

15) 3.5(12.7 − 10.1) + (0.9)² − 1.2 × 5   3.91

16) 1000(0.000829)   0.829   17) 273 − 0.406   272.594

18) Find 0.78)‾5.2‾. Give the exact answer and an approximation rounded to the nearest thousandth.
exact: 6.6; approximation: 6.667

19) Write $9\frac{3}{8}$ as a decimal.   9.375

Use =, >, or < to compare the numbers.

20) 0.82 ____ 0.8256   <   21) 0.3 ____ $\frac{1}{10}$ >

22) $2\frac{3}{5}$ ____ 2.6   =   23) $\frac{32}{25}$ ____ 1.44   <

24) Write in order from smallest to largest.

1.207   1.073   0.73   1.25   1.2
0.73, 1.073, 1.2, 1.207, 1.25

Solve each problem.

25) Preet put 12.358 gallons of gas in her car, and the gas cost $3.79 per gallon. How much did she pay for the gas? Round the answer to the nearest cent. $46.84

26) In 2010, the population of Alabama was approximately 4.7 million, and the population of Ohio was approximately 11.5 million. How many more people lived in Ohio? (www.census.gov)   6.8 million

27) Rodrigo had $653.28 in his checking account and deposited his paycheck of $807.14. Then, he paid $66.40 for the electric bill, $120.79 for the cable bill, $195.82 for his credit card, and $19.60 for his water bill. How much money remains in Rodrigo's account? $1057.81

28) A 20-pound bag of dog food costs $18.99. Find the cost per pound to the nearest cent. $0.95

29) A coffee shop is open from 5 A.M. to 7 P.M., and each hour on Thursday it served the following number of customers: 11, 47, 54, 63, 61, 34, 26, 25, 26, 29, 33, 31, 20, 15. Find the mean, median, and mode. Round the answer to the nearest tenth, if necessary.

30) Find Ava's GPA. Let A = 4 points, B = 3 points, C = 2 points, D = 1 point, and F = 0 points. Round the answer to the nearest hundredth.   3.21

Course	Grade	Credits
English Composition	A	4
Advertising	B	3
E-Marketing	A	3
Management	C	4

Chapter 5: Cumulative Review for Chapters 1–5

*Additional answers can be found in the Answers to Exercises appendix.

Perform the indicated operations.

1) $74{,}596 + 103 + 8449 + 62$ 83,210

2) $43{,}000 - 599$ 42,401

3) $\begin{array}{r} 778 \\ \times\ 243 \end{array}$ 189,054

4) $12\overline{)10{,}017}$ 834 R9

5) $\dfrac{8}{15} \div 6$ $\dfrac{4}{45}$

6) $\dfrac{1}{6} + \dfrac{5}{12} + \dfrac{1}{8}$ $\dfrac{17}{24}$

7) If the perimeter of the figure is 60 cm, find the missing side length.   12 cm

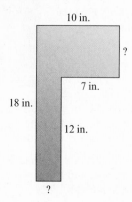

?
21 cm
9 cm
18 cm

8) Find the two missing side lengths, then find the perimeter of the figure.   3 in.; 6 in.; 56 in.

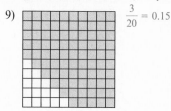

10 in.
?
7 in.
18 in.
12 in.
?

Use a fraction and a decimal to represent the unshaded part of the figure. Reduce the fraction if possible.

9) 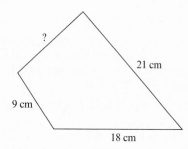 $\dfrac{3}{20} = 0.15$

Approximate the location of the decimal value on the given number line.

10) 0.52
0 0.1 0.2 0.3 0.4 0.5 0.6 0.7 0.8 0.9 1

Identify the place value of each digit.

11) 8416.2573   8—thousands, 4—hundreds, 1—tens, 6—ones, 2—tenths, 5—hundredths, 7—thousandths, 3—ten-thousandths

12) Write *eighty-three and twenty-three ten-thousandths* using numbers.   83.0023

Round each number as indicated.

13) 6,399,699 to the nearest thousand   6,400,000

14) 0.549873 to the nearest ten-thousandth   0.5499

Write each decimal as a fraction or mixed number in lowest terms.

15) 11.8 $11\dfrac{4}{5}$

16) 0.0016 $\dfrac{1}{625}$

Simplify each expression using the order of operations.

17) $9 \cdot \sqrt{16} - 3 + \sqrt{25}$ 38

18) $\left(\dfrac{3}{4}\right)^2 \div \left(\dfrac{3}{2} - \dfrac{5}{4}\right) + \dfrac{3}{8}$ $\dfrac{21}{8}$ or $2\dfrac{5}{8}$

19) $0.96 - 0.001(1002.5 - 132.9)$ 0.0904

20) Find the mode of this list of numbers: 61, 59, 48, 92, 70, 59, 66, 83, 61, 74, 88, 59, 49   59

Solve each problem.

21) Sakura finds a *Hello Kitty* gift set online for $27.30. She buys four of them for her daughter and nieces. How much does she spend? $109.20

22) Alec and his cousin Kullen were playing Nintendo. Kullen's score was 183,204, and Alec's score was 201,037. By how many points did Alec win?   17,833

23) A soup recipe uses $3\dfrac{1}{2}$ cups of milk. If Elijah wants to cut the recipe in half, how much milk should he use? $1\dfrac{3}{4}$ cups

24) Korina and three of her friends purchase a four-pack of 16-GB USB 2.0 flash drives for $50.68. If they are going to split the cost equally among themselves, how much does each person pay? $12.67

25) Opening weekend ticket sales in the United States for the first three *Twilight Saga* movies were $69.6 million, $142.8 million, and $68.5 million. What was the mean revenue from ticket sales? Round the answer to the nearest tenth of a million. (www.imdb.com) $93.6 million

Ratios, Rates, and Proportions

Math at Work:

Physical Therapist

Sam Blekicki's days are filled with broken legs, torn ligaments, and dislocated shoulders. And he wouldn't have it any other way. As a physical therapist, Sam's job is to help people who have suffered such injuries recover their strength and mobility.

"It is very rewarding work," Sam says. "Seeing someone who has been in a wheelchair since a car accident walk across the room... Well, there's just nothing like it."

Even though Sam's work is focused on muscles and joints, he couldn't do his job without math. In order to understand his patients' progress, he determines the proportion of muscle loss and considers the ratio of time spent on therapy to degree of injury. Sometimes he tracks recovery rates so closely that he examines the number of steps per day a patient makes. "In physical therapy, you know that nothing happens overnight," Sam explains. "What you hope for is a rate of slow and steady progress."

The field of physical therapy is changing rapidly. Sam says that if he didn't regularly read medical journals during his off-hours, he wouldn't be able to keep up with the latest advances in treatment. "I always imagined that when I finished school, I'd never have to do homework again," Sam says. "The truth is that if you want to be good at your job, you need to spend time working at it even when you're not in the office."

In this chapter, we explore ratios, rates, and proportions, the same type of math Sam uses to help his patients on the road to recovery. We'll also look at some strategies to help you do your best on your math homework.

If you're like most students, homework is probably not your favorite part of being in college. Yet homework is as important to college success as attending class or studying for exams, particularly in math courses. Below are some strategies that will help you do your math homework as efficiently and effectively as possible.

- Find a place to do your homework that is free of distractions.
- Gather what you need to complete the assignment: a pen, pencils, paper, your textbook, class notes—and, of course, the assignment itself!

- Read over your class notes and the sections in your textbook that relate to the assignment.
- Highlight any essential formulas or definitions that you know you will need to return to as you work.

- While doing your homework, be your own math teacher. Ask yourself why you are taking each step as you solve a problem, and remind yourself of the larger concepts you are using.
- If you can't solve a problem, review the relevant material in your textbook and class notes. If you still can't solve it, complete the rest of the assignment, and plan to get some help from a classmate, math tutor, or your instructor.

- Double-check your answers, and review all your calculations.

- Once an assignment has been returned to you, review it carefully. If it turns out that you didn't understand a major concept, find time to speak to your instructor about it.
- Never throw away your homework! It is an excellent resource for studying for tests.

Chapter 6 POWER Plan

P Prepare

O Organize

What are your goals for Chapter 6?	How can you accomplish each goal?
1 Be prepared before and during class.	• Don't stay out late the night before, and be sure to set your alarm clock! • Bring a pencil, notebook paper, and textbook to class. • Avoid distractions by turning off your cell phone during class. • Pay attention, take good notes, and ask questions. • Complete your homework on time, and ask questions on problems you do not understand.
2 Understand the homework to the point where you could do it without needing any help or hints.	• Read the directions, and show all of your steps. • Go to the professor's office for help. • Rework homework and quiz problems, and find similar problems for practice.
3 Use the P.O.W.E.R. framework to learn a new strategy for doing your math homework: *The Right Approach to Homework.*	• Read the Study Strategy as it is outlined in the P.O.W.E.R. framework. • Think of ways you can apply this strategy beyond your math courses. • Complete the emPOWERme that appears before the Chapter Summary.
4 Write your own goal. _____ _____	• _____ _____

What are your objectives for Chapter 6?	How can you accomplish each objective?
1 Learn how to recognize and write ratios and rates.	• Understand the definitions as well as the similarities and differences between ratios and rates. • Know how to write and simplify ratios and rates. • Be able to use ratios and rates in an applied problem.
2 Determine whether a proportion is true or false.	• Know the definition of a proportion. • Know how to use cross products, and determine whether a proportion is true.
3 Learn to solve a proportion.	• Understand the difference between an expression and an equation. • Know and use the division property of equality, and combine it with using cross products to solve a proportion. • Use the Five Steps for Solving Applied Problems.
4 Write your own goal. _____ _____	• _____ _____

	Read Sections 6.1–6.5, and complete the exercises.
W Work	

E Evaluate	Complete the Chapter Review and Chapter Test. How did you do?	**R** Rethink	• Are you currently taking any courses that don't assign daily homework? What could you do to get consistent practice with the concepts presented in that course?
			• Two important ideas in this chapter were checking your answers and being aware of using units. Were you consistently doing both? Explain how using units in proportions helped you keep problems and applied problems nicely organized.
			• Which goals, if any, do you still need to master before moving to the next chapter?

6.1 Ratios

P Prepare

O Organize

What are your objectives for Section 6.1?	How can you accomplish each objective?
1 Write Basic Ratios	• Write the definition of a *ratio* and your own procedure for **Writing a Ratio as a Fraction.** • Complete the given examples on your own. • Complete You Trys 1 and 2.
2 Write Ratios Comparing Fractions, Mixed Numbers, or Decimals	• Create a list of the different ways to simplify a ratio. • Use the Five Steps for Solving Applied Problems. • Complete the given examples on your own. • Complete You Trys 3 and 4.
3 Write Ratios After Converting Units	• Follow Example 5, and write your own procedure for **Converting Measurements.** • Examine the given relationships between measurements, and memorize them. • Complete the given examples on your own. • Complete You Trys 5–7.

W Work

Read the explanations, follow the examples, take notes, and complete the You Trys.

1 Write Basic Ratios

We hear about *ratios* and use them in many ways in everyday life. But, what is a ratio? A **ratio** is a comparison of two quantities. It can compare numbers or measurements with the same units. (*Rates* compare measurements with different units.) Ratios can be written in several different ways. For example, the ratio of 3 to 4 can be written as

$$3 \text{ to } 4 \qquad \text{or} \qquad \underset{\uparrow}{3} \overset{\downarrow}{:} 4 \qquad \text{or} \qquad \frac{3}{4} \begin{matrix} \leftarrow \text{First number} \\ \leftarrow \text{Second number} \end{matrix}$$

Second number (points to the 4 in 3:4)
First number (points to the 3 in 3:4)

Note

When a ratio is to be written as a fraction, the number that comes first is the numerator and the number that comes second is the denominator.

Let's practice writing ratios.

EXAMPLE 1

Write each ratio as a fraction.

a) $7 to $16   b)   40 min to 15 min   c)   8 ft to 2 ft

Solution

a)   The quantity that comes first is the numerator, and the second quantity is the denominator.

The ratio of $7 to $16 is $\dfrac{\$7}{\$16} \begin{matrix} \leftarrow \text{First number} \\ \leftarrow \text{Second number} \end{matrix}$

$$= \frac{7}{16} \qquad \text{Divide out common units just like common factors.}$$

The ratio of $7 to $16 is $\dfrac{7}{16}$. Notice that we do not write units in a ratio.

b)   Remember, the quantity that comes first is the numerator, and the second quantity is the denominator.

The ratio of 40 min to 15 min is

$$\frac{40 \text{ min}}{15 \text{ min}} = \frac{40}{15} \qquad \text{Divide out common units just like common factors.}$$

$$= \frac{40 \div 5}{15 \div 5} = \frac{8}{3} \qquad \text{Write the ratio in lowest terms.}$$

The ratio of 40 min to 15 min is $\dfrac{8}{3}$. We do *not* write a ratio as a mixed number.

c)   The ratio of 8 ft to 2 ft is

$$\frac{8 \text{ ft}}{2 \text{ ft}} = \frac{8}{2} \qquad \text{Divide out common units just like common factors.}$$

$$= \frac{8 \div 2}{2 \div 2} = \frac{4}{1} \qquad \text{Write the ratio in lowest terms.}$$

The ratio of 8 ft to 2 ft is $\frac{4}{1}$. Notice that even though $\frac{4}{1}$ simplifies to 4, we do *not* write the ratio this way. Because a ratio compares two quantities, we write it as the fraction $\frac{4}{1}$.

Note

Keep in mind the following important facts about ratios.

1) Ratios are not written with units.
2) Ratios are usually written in lowest terms.
3) Ratios are not written as mixed numbers.
4) Ratios are not written as whole numbers.

[YOU TRY 1] Write each ratio as a fraction.

a) $5 to $8   b) 36 ft to 24 ft   c) 9 hr to 3 hr

EXAMPLE 2

In-Class Example 2

The ratio of carbohydrates to protein in a single serving of chicken soup is 14 g to 8 g. Write this ratio as a fraction, and explain what it means.

Answer: $\frac{7}{4}$; for every 7 g of carbohydrates there are 4 g of protein.

The ratio of potassium to sodium in a single serving of oatmeal is 105 mg to 80 mg. Write this ratio as a fraction, and explain what it means.

Solution

The quantity that comes first is the numerator, and the second quantity is the denominator:

$$\frac{\text{Potassium}}{\text{Sodium}} = \frac{105 \ \cancel{\text{mg}}}{80 \ \cancel{\text{mg}}}$$

$$= \frac{105}{80} \qquad \text{Divide out the common units.}$$

$$= \frac{105 \div 5}{80 \div 5} = \frac{21}{16} \qquad \text{Write the ratio in lowest terms.}$$

The ratio of potassium to sodium is $\frac{21}{16}$. This means that for every 21 mg of potassium in the oatmeal, there are 16 mg of sodium. We do *not* write the ratio as a mixed number.

W Hint

Why would it be incorrect to write a ratio as a mixed number?

[YOU TRY 2] The ratio of the number of girls in the choir to the number of boys in the choir is 18 to 10. Write this ratio as a fraction, and explain what it means.

---

2 Write Ratios Comparing Fractions, Mixed Numbers, or Decimals

If a ratio compares fractions, mixed numbers, or decimals, we can rewrite the ratio so that it compares whole numbers.

EXAMPLE 3

Write each ratio so that it compares two whole numbers in lowest terms.

In-Class Example 3

Write each ratio so that it compares two whole numbers in lowest terms.

a) $\dfrac{5}{6}$ to $\dfrac{1}{2}$

b) 4 hr to $4\dfrac{1}{2}$ hr

c) $3.60 to $4.80

Answer:

a) $\dfrac{5}{3}$ b) $\dfrac{8}{9}$ c) $\dfrac{3}{4}$

a) $\dfrac{7}{9}$ to $\dfrac{1}{3}$ b) 2 hr to $2\dfrac{1}{2}$ hr   c) $1.25 to $4.50

Solution

a) Begin by writing the ratio $\dfrac{7}{9}$ to $\dfrac{1}{3}$ as $\dfrac{\frac{7}{9}}{\frac{1}{3}}$. To simplify $\dfrac{\frac{7}{9}}{\frac{1}{3}}$, rewrite it as a division problem.

$$\dfrac{\frac{7}{9}}{\frac{1}{3}} = \dfrac{7}{9} \div \dfrac{1}{3} \qquad \text{Rewrite as a division problem.}$$

$$= \dfrac{7}{9} \cdot \dfrac{3}{1} \qquad \text{Multiply by the reciprocal.}$$

$$= \dfrac{7}{\underset{3}{9}} \cdot \dfrac{\overset{1}{3}}{1} \qquad \text{Divide out common factors.}$$

$$= \dfrac{7}{3} \qquad \text{Multiply.}$$

The ratio of $\dfrac{7}{9}$ to $\dfrac{1}{3}$ is $\dfrac{7}{3}$.

W Hint

You have simplified these types of fractions, or ratios, before!

b) Write the ratio 2 hr to $2\dfrac{1}{2}$ hr as a fraction, and divide out the common units.

$$\dfrac{2 \text{ hr}}{2\frac{1}{2} \text{ hr}} = \dfrac{2}{2\frac{1}{2}}$$

Rewrite $\dfrac{2}{2\frac{1}{2}}$ as a division problem and perform the division.

$$\dfrac{2}{2\frac{1}{2}} = 2 \div 2\dfrac{1}{2} \qquad \text{Rewrite as a division problem.}$$

$$= 2 \div \dfrac{5}{2} \qquad \text{Change the mixed number to an improper fraction.}$$

$$= 2 \cdot \dfrac{2}{5} \qquad \text{Multiply by the reciprocal.}$$

$$= \dfrac{2}{1} \cdot \dfrac{2}{5} = \dfrac{4}{5} \qquad \text{Rewrite 2 as } \dfrac{2}{1}, \text{ and multiply the fractions.}$$

The ratio of 2 hr to $2\dfrac{1}{2}$ hr is $\dfrac{4}{5}$.

c) Begin by writing the ratio of $1.25 to $4.50 as a fraction, and divide out the common units.

$$\dfrac{\$1.25}{\$4.50} = \dfrac{1.25}{4.50}$$

If we multiply the numerator and denominator by 100, we will eliminate the decimal *and* we will not change the value of the fraction.

$$\frac{1.25}{4.50} = \frac{1.25}{4.50} \cdot \frac{100}{100} \qquad \text{Multiply numerator and denominator by 100.}$$

$$= \frac{125}{450} \qquad \text{Multiply to eliminate the decimals.}$$

$$= \frac{125 \div 25}{450 \div 25} = \frac{5}{18} \qquad \text{Write the ratio in lowest terms.}$$

The ratio of \$1.25 to \$4.50 is $\frac{5}{18}$.

[YOU TRY 3] Write each ratio so that it compares two whole numbers in lowest terms.

a) $\frac{9}{10}$ to $\frac{4}{5}$ b) 3 days to $3\frac{1}{2}$ days c) \$2.40 to \$3.20

Let's use the problem-solving steps we first learned in Section 2.7 together with what we have just learned about writing ratios to solve an applied problem.

EXAMPLE 4

In-Class Example 4

The regular price of a necklace was \$20.40, and now it is on sale for \$13.60. Find the ratio of the decrease in the price to the regular price.

Answer: $\frac{1}{3}$

 Hint

You'll see problems similar to these in Chapter 8. How do you normally see discounts represented?

The regular price of a DVD was \$28.00, and now it is on sale for \$22.40. Find the ratio of the decrease in the price to the regular price.

Solution

Step 1: **Read** the problem carefully, and restate it in your own words.

The regular price of a DVD was \$28.00, and the sale price is \$22.40. We must find the ratio of the decrease in the price to the regular price.

Step 2: **Make a plan.** Let's underline important words in our restatement of the problem in Step 1. Is there anything we need to know that we are not given? *Yes, we need to know the decrease in the price.*

Plan: Find the decrease in the price, then write a ratio of the decrease in the price to the regular price. Rewrite the ratio with whole numbers.

Step 3: **Solve** the problem.

Find the decrease in the price of the DVD.

Original price − Sale price = Decrease in price
$28.00 − $22.40 = $5.60

Write the ratio of the decrease in price to the original price.

$$\frac{5.60}{28.00} = \frac{5.60}{28.00} \cdot \frac{10}{10} \qquad \text{Multiplying by } \frac{10}{10} \text{ will eliminate the decimals.}$$

$$= \frac{56}{280} \qquad \text{Multiply.}$$

$$= \frac{56 \div 56}{280 \div 56} = \frac{1}{5} \qquad \text{Write the ratio in lowest terms.}$$

Steps 4 and 5: **State the answer** in a complete sentence.

The ratio of the decrease in price to the regular price is $\frac{1}{5}$. We can double-check our work to be sure our answer is correct.

[YOU TRY 4] The regular price of a shirt was $24.00, and now it is on sale for $16.80. Find the ratio of the decrease in the price to the regular price.

3 Write Ratios After Converting Units

At the beginning of this section, we said that a ratio comparing two measurements must have the same units. If the units are different, we must begin by changing one of the units so that it is the same as the other one.

EXAMPLE 5

In-Class Example 5

Write the ratio of 6 feet to 3 yards.

Answer: $\frac{2}{3}$

Write the ratio of 4 ft to 2 yd.

Solution

Write each quantity with the same units. Let's change yards to feet since a foot is smaller than a yard. (Converting to the smaller unit can help avoid fractions in the conversion.) Since there are 3 ft in 1 yd,

$$2 \text{ yd} = 2 \cdot 3 \text{ ft} = 6 \text{ ft}$$

Then the ratio of 4 ft to 2 yd is

$$\frac{4 \text{ ft}}{2 \text{ yd}} = \frac{4 \text{ ft}}{6 \text{ ft}} = \frac{4 \text{ ft}}{6 \text{ ft}} = \frac{4}{6} = \frac{2}{3}$$

Note

If we had changed feet to yards, the answer would have been the same but the calculations would have been more complicated.

$$4 \text{ ft} = 1\frac{1}{3} \text{ yd}$$

Then the ratio of 4 ft to 2 yd is

$$\frac{4 \text{ ft}}{2 \text{ yd}} = \frac{1\frac{1}{3} \text{ yd}}{2 \text{ yd}} = \frac{1\frac{1}{3} \text{ yd}}{2 \text{ yd}} = 1\frac{1}{3} \div 2 = \frac{4}{3} \cdot \frac{1}{2} = \frac{\overset{2}{4}}{3} \cdot \frac{1}{\underset{1}{2}} = \frac{2}{3}$$

The result is the same, but changing from the larger units to the smaller ones will help avoid these more complicated calculations.

[YOU TRY 5] Write the ratio of 3 ft to 24 in.

EXAMPLE 6

Write the ratio of 8 weeks to 14 days.

Solution

Write each quantity with the same units. Since a day is smaller than a week, we will change weeks to days. There are 7 days in 1 week, so

$$8 \text{ weeks} = 8 \cdot 7 \text{ days} = 56 \text{ days}$$

Then the ratio of 8 weeks to 14 days is

$$\frac{8 \text{ weeks}}{14 \text{ days}} = \frac{56 \text{ days}}{14 \text{ days}} = \frac{56 \text{ days}}{14 \text{ days}} = \frac{4}{1}$$

[YOU TRY 6] Write the ratio of 20 hr to 2 days.

We can use the following list of relationships between measurements to help us write measurements with the same units.

W Hint

Does this chart look familiar? If not, spend some time memorizing these relationships.

Relationships Between Measurements

Length	Time
12 inches = 1 foot	60 seconds = 1 minute
3 feet = 1 yard	60 minutes = 1 hour
5280 feet = 1 mile	24 hours = 1 day
	7 days = 1 week

Volume (Capacity)	Weight
2 cups = 1 pint	16 ounces = 1 pound
2 pints = 1 quart	2000 pounds = 1 ton
4 quarts = 1 gallon	

EXAMPLE 7

The ratio of butternut squash puree to cream in a butternut squash soup recipe is 3 pints to 1 cup. Write the ratio of the puree to the cream.

Solution

Write each quantity with the same units. A cup is smaller than a pint, so let's convert 3 pints to cups.

Then the ratio of 3 pints to 1 cup is

$$\frac{3 \text{ pints}}{1 \text{ cup}} = \frac{6 \text{ cups}}{1 \text{ cup}} = \frac{6 \text{ cups}}{1 \text{ cup}} = \frac{6}{1}$$

The ratio of butternut squash puree to cream is $\dfrac{6}{1}$.

[YOU TRY 7] The ratio of ginger ale to orange juice in a fruit punch recipe is 3 quarts to 4 pints. Write the ratio of the ginger ale to orange juice.

E Evaluate **6.1** Exercises   Do the exercises, and check your work.

*Additional answers can be found in the Answers to Exercises appendix.

Objective 1: Write Basic Ratios

1) What is a ratio?   A ratio is a comparison of two quantities.

2) How are ratios and rates different?
A ratio compares two quantities with the same units, but a rate compares quantities with different units.

Write each ratio as a fraction in lowest terms.

3) 11 min to 16 min $\frac{11}{16}$ 4) 8 oz to 11 oz $\frac{8}{11}$

5) \$13 to \$26 $\frac{1}{2}$ 6) 6¢ to 36¢ $\frac{1}{6}$

7) 75 in. to 50 in. $\frac{3}{2}$ 8) 300 mi to 450 mi $\frac{2}{3}$

9) 72¢ to 18¢ $\frac{4}{1}$ 10) \$80 to \$40 $\frac{2}{1}$

11) At a fast-food restaurant, the ratio of part-time workers to full-time employees is 16 to 6. Write this ratio as a fraction, and explain what it means.
$\frac{8}{3}$; for every 8 part-time employees, there are 3 full-time employees.

12) In a classroom, the ratio of students who play *Words with Friends* on their phones to those who do not is 14 to 10. Write this ratio as a fraction, and explain what it means. $\frac{7}{5}$; for every 7 students who play *Words with Friends,* there are 5 students who do not.

The table shows the number of U.S. music album sales in 2008 sorted by genre. Use this information for Exercises 13–19. Write each ratio as a fraction in lowest terms.

Genre	2008 Sales
Alternative	81 thousand
Classical	13 thousand
Country	48 thousand
Jazz	12 thousand
Latin	25 thousand
Metal	50 thousand
R&B	77 thousand
Rap	33 thousand
Rock	140 thousand
Soundtrack	21 thousand

(Nielsen Soundscan)

13) Find the ratio of metal albums to Latin albums. $\frac{2}{1}$

14) Find the ratio of rock albums to metal albums. $\frac{14}{5}$

15) Find the ratio of rap albums to country albums. $\frac{11}{16}$

16) Find the ratio of R&B albums to soundtrack albums. $\frac{11}{3}$

17) Find the ratio of jazz albums to classical albums. $\frac{12}{13}$

18) Find the ratio of jazz albums to country albums. $\frac{1}{4}$

19) Find the ratio of alternative albums to soundtrack albums. $\frac{27}{7}$

20) Explain how you would use the data above if you owned a music store that sold music CDs.
Answers may vary.

Objective 2: Write Ratios Comparing Fractions, Mixed Numbers, or Decimals

Write each ratio so that it compares two whole numbers in lowest terms.

21) $\frac{8}{9}$ to $\frac{1}{3}$ $\frac{8}{3}$ 22) $\frac{11}{12}$ to $\frac{5}{6}$ $\frac{11}{10}$

23) $\frac{1}{10}$ to $\frac{11}{15}$ $\frac{3}{22}$ 24) $\frac{1}{6}$ to $\frac{3}{4}$ $\frac{2}{9}$

25) 3 to $3\frac{3}{4}$ $\frac{4}{5}$ 26) 2 to $2\frac{1}{2}$ $\frac{4}{5}$

27) 4 min to $6\frac{1}{2}$ min $\frac{8}{13}$ 28) 7 min to $10\frac{1}{2}$ min $\frac{2}{3}$

29) $2\frac{5}{6}$ yd to $1\frac{3}{4}$ yd $\frac{34}{21}$ 30) $3\frac{1}{3}$ hr to $2\frac{3}{4}$ hr $\frac{40}{33}$

31) $4\frac{2}{3}$ mi to $1\frac{1}{6}$ mi $\frac{4}{1}$ 32) $5\frac{1}{2}$ days to $1\frac{5}{6}$ days $\frac{3}{1}$

33) 7.6 to 4.4 $\frac{19}{11}$ 34) 15.6 to 8.8 $\frac{39}{22}$

35) \$4.90 to \$5.60 $\frac{7}{8}$ 36) \$6.00 to \$8.40 $\frac{5}{7}$

37) \$1.05 to \$0.35 $\frac{3}{1}$ 38) \$3.25 to \$0.65 $\frac{5}{1}$

39) 6.4 mi to 9.2 mi $\frac{16}{23}$ 40) 2.7 lb to 14.4 lb $\frac{3}{16}$

Solve each problem.

41) The regular price of a soccer ball was \$42.00, and now it is on sale for \$31.50. Find the ratio of the decrease in the price to the regular price. $\frac{1}{4}$

42) A pair of shoes that normally sells for \$36.00 is marked down to \$24.00. Find the ratio of the decrease in price to the original price. $\frac{1}{3}$

43) In Fall 2011, a community college had an enrollment of 5400. In Fall 2012, that number rose to 5514. Find the ratio of the increase in enrollment to the enrollment in Fall 2011. $\frac{19}{900}$

44) Due to a slowing economy, a company must decrease its normal 40-hr workweek to 32 hr. Find the ratio of the decrease in new hours worked to the normal hourly workweek. $\frac{1}{5}$

45) At birth, a baby weighed 6.8 lb. When she was 4 months old, she weighed 13.2 lb. Find the ratio of the increase in weight to her original weight. $\frac{16}{17}$

46) In 2000, approximately 80.4% of the U.S. population had a high school diploma or higher. In 2009, this percentage rose to 84.6%. Find the ratio of the increase in the percentage to the percentage earning a high school diploma or higher in 2009. (http://factfinder.census.gov) $\frac{7}{141}$

Objective 3: Write Ratios After Converting Units
Write each ratio as a fraction in lowest terms.

47) 14 in. to 2 ft $\frac{7}{12}$ 48) 20 in. to 2 yd $\frac{5}{18}$

49) 8 ft to 4 yd $\frac{2}{3}$ 50) 6 cups to 8 pints $\frac{3}{8}$

51) 12 min to 2 hr $\frac{1}{10}$ 52) 36 min to 4 hr $\frac{3}{20}$

53) 6 qt to 8 gal $\frac{3}{16}$ 54) 8 oz to 8 lb $\frac{1}{16}$

55) 15 weeks to 21 days $\frac{5}{1}$ 56) 9 min to 180 sec $\frac{3}{1}$

57) 14 gal to 8 qt $\frac{7}{1}$ 58) 16 qt to 4 gal $\frac{1}{1}$

Solve each problem.

59) The ratio of the height of a bookshelf to the width of the bookshelf is 6 ft to 32 in. Write the ratio of the height to the width. $\frac{9}{4}$

60) The ratio of the height of a man to the length of his arm is 6 ft to 30 in. Write the ratio of his height to the length of his arm. $\frac{12}{5}$

61) The ratio of heavy cream to whole milk in a vanilla ice cream recipe is 3 cups to 1 pint. Write the ratio of heavy cream to whole milk. $\frac{3}{2}$

62) The ratio of white wine to fish broth in a bouillabaisse recipe is 2 cups to 1.5 pints. Write the ratio of white wine to fish broth. $\frac{2}{3}$

63) The ratio of the width of an oil painting to the length is 10 in. to 1.5 ft. Write the ratio of the width to the length. $\frac{5}{9}$

64) The ratio of the length of a stained glass window to the width is 4 ft to 30 in. Write the ratio of the length to the width. $\frac{8}{5}$

Mixed Exercises: Objectives 1–3
The circle graph shows a family's monthly budget, where the total amount of money shown equals their monthly income. Use the graph for Exercises 65–70. Write each ratio as a fraction in lowest terms.

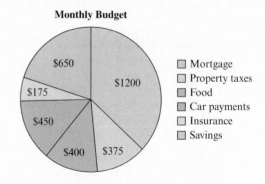

Monthly Budget

$650
$1200
$175
$450
$400 $375

□ Mortgage
□ Property taxes
□ Food
□ Car payments
□ Insurance
□ Savings

65) What is the family's total monthly income? $3250

66) What is the family's combined monthly mortgage, insurance, and property tax payment? $1750

67) Find the ratio of the family's total monthly income to savings. $\frac{5}{1}$

68) Find the ratio of the family's monthly food budget to car payment. $\dfrac{8}{9}$

69) Find the ratio of the family's combined monthly mortgage and property tax payment to insurance payment. $\dfrac{9}{1}$

70) What is the family's yearly savings? $7800

71) Today, a gallon of unleaded gasoline sells for $3.36. Last year, one gallon cost $3.20. Find the ratio of the increase in price to the price last year. $\dfrac{1}{20}$

72) The regular price of a hair dryer is $22.00, and now it is on sale for $16.40. Find the ratio of the decrease in price to the original price. $\dfrac{14}{55}$

Write each ratio as a fraction in lowest terms.

73) 3 gal to 8 qt $\dfrac{3}{2}$ 74) 21 hr to 2 days $\dfrac{7}{16}$

For Exercises 75 and 76, write the ratio of the longest side to the shortest side. Reduce to lowest terms.

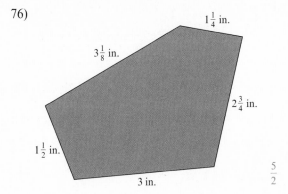

75) $\dfrac{7}{1}$

76) $\dfrac{5}{2}$

6.2 Rates

P Prepare

O Organize

What are your objectives for Section 6.2?	How can you accomplish each objective?
1 Write a Rate as a Fraction	• Write the definition of *rate* in your notes, and be sure to include the units. • Complete the given example on your own. • Complete You Try 1.
2 Find a Unit Rate	• Write the definition of *unit rate*. • Write your own procedure for **Finding a Unit Rate.** • Complete the given example on your own. • Complete You Try 2.
3 Solve Applied Problems Involving Unit Rates	• Complete the given examples on your own. • Complete You Trys 3 and 4.

W Work   **Read the explanations, follow the examples, take notes, and complete the You Trys.**

Rates appear in many different situations. A car's mileage might be 28 miles per gallon. A part-time worker might earn \$9.50/hour. Each of these is an example of a *rate*.

Definition

A **rate** compares quantities with *different* units.

Remember from Section 6.1 that a ratio compares quantities with the *same* units.

1   Write a Rate as a Fraction

Suppose that you drove 170 miles in 4 hours. We can write the *rate* at which you drove as a fraction in lowest terms:

$$\frac{170 \text{ mi}}{4 \text{ hr}} = \frac{170 \text{ mi} \div 2}{4 \text{ hr} \div 2} = \frac{85 \text{ mi}}{2 \text{ hr}}$$

W Hint

Rates are different from ratios!

The rate at which you drove was $\frac{85 \text{ mi}}{2 \text{ hr}}$ or 85 miles in 2 hours. When writing a rate, we *always* include the units.

Note

We can use different words to indicate rate:

in   per   for   from   on

Rates are usually written in lowest terms.

EXAMPLE 1

In-Class Example 1

Write each rate as a fraction in lowest terms.
a) 340 mi on 15 gal of gas
b) 4 lb of apples for \$6
c) \$780 in 3 weeks

Answer:

a) $\frac{68 \text{ mi}}{3 \text{ gal}}$ b) $\frac{2 \text{ lb}}{3 \text{ dollars}}$

c) $\frac{260 \text{ dollars}}{1 \text{ week}}$

Write each rate as a fraction in lowest terms.

a)   600 mi on 21 gal of gas   b)   18 lb of dog food for \$15

c)   \$960 in 4 weeks

Solution

a)   Set this up like we set up ratios. The quantity that comes first goes in the numerator, and the second quantity is the denominator.

$$\frac{600 \text{ mi}}{21 \text{ gal}} = \frac{600 \text{ mi} \div 3}{21 \text{ gal} \div 3} = \frac{200 \text{ mi}}{7 \text{ gal}}$$

b) $\frac{18 \text{ lb}}{15 \text{ dollars}} = \frac{18 \text{ lb} \div 3}{15 \text{ dollars} \div 3} = \frac{6 \text{ lb}}{5 \text{ dollars}}$

c) $\frac{960 \text{ dollars}}{4 \text{ weeks}} = \frac{960 \text{ dollars} \div 4}{4 \text{ weeks} \div 4} = \frac{240 \text{ dollars}}{1 \text{ week}}$

[YOU TRY 1]   Write each rate as a fraction in lowest terms.

a)   450 mi on 20 gal of gas   b)   10 lb of potatoes for 4 dollars

c)   \$1092 in 3 weeks

---

2 Find a Unit Rate

In Example 1c, we wrote "$960 in 4 weeks" in fractional form as $\dfrac{240 \text{ dollars}}{1 \text{ week}}$. Notice that the denominator is 1. This is an example of a *unit rate*.

Definition

A **unit rate** is a rate with a denominator of 1.

The rate $\dfrac{240 \text{ dollars}}{1 \text{ week}}$ can also be written as $240/week or $240 per week. The slash mark, /, means *per*.

EXAMPLE 2

In-Class Example 2

Find each unit rate.
a) 144 mi in 3 hr
b) 259 mi on 14 gal
c) $26.00 for 40 lb of ice melt

Answer:
a) 48 mi/hr or 48 miles per hour
b) 18.5 mi/gal or 18.5 miles per gallon
c) $0.65/lb or $0.65 per pound

Hint

This looks like a procedure to be used for all unit rates!

Find each unit rate.

a) 192 mi in 3 hr

b) 336 mi on 15 gal

c) $13.20 for 20 lb of charcoal

Solution

a) Write the rate as a fraction, then simplify so that the denominator is 1.

$$\frac{192 \text{ mi}}{3 \text{ hr}} = \frac{192 \text{ mi} \div 3}{3 \text{ hr} \div 3} = \frac{64 \text{ mi}}{1 \text{ hr}}$$

The unit rate is 64 mi/hr or 64 miles per hour. This is also called a vehicle's average speed. It can also be written as 64 mph.

b) $\dfrac{336 \text{ mi}}{15 \text{ gal}} = \dfrac{336 \text{ mi} \div 3}{15 \text{ gal} \div 3} = \dfrac{112 \text{ mi}}{5 \text{ gal}}$

Next, divide 112 by 5 to find the unit rate: $5)\overline{112.0}^{\,22.4}$

The unit rate is 22.4 mi/gal or 22.4 miles per gallon. This is also called a vehicle's gas mileage and can be written as 22.4 mpg.

c) Write the rate as $\dfrac{\$13.20}{20 \text{ lb}}$, then divide: $20)\overline{13.20}^{\,0.66}$

The unit rate is $0.66/lb or $0.66 per pound. This is also called unit price. (This is the same as 66¢ per pound.)

[YOU TRY 2] Find each unit rate.

a) 504 mi on 14 gal of gas

b) $198 for 12 hr of work

c) $3.84 for 64 oz of grapefruit juice

3 Solve Applied Problems Involving Unit Rates

We can use unit rates to help us solve many different problems.

EXAMPLE 3

In-Class Example 3

Shannon earned $212.50 for working 17 hr one week. What is her hourly wage? (This is her unit pay.)

Answer: $12.50/hr

> **W Hint**
> It is helpful to know the everyday terminology that is used for unit rates.

Jim earned $253.00 for working 22 hr one week. What is his hourly wage? (This is his unit pay.)

Solution

Jim's hourly wage is the amount of money he earns *per* hour. Set up the rate with his total earnings on the top and hours worked on the bottom.

$$\frac{\$253.00}{22 \text{ hr}} \qquad \text{Divide:} \quad 22)\overline{253.00}^{\,11.50}$$

Jim's hourly wage is $11.50/hr.

[YOU TRY 3] Oksana earned $433.50 for working 34 hr one week. What is her hourly wage?

A unit rate that is used often is the *unit price*. The **unit price** of an item is the cost of the item per unit.

Note

Some examples of unit rates are $0.25 per ounce, $1.98 per pound, $3.00 per gallon, and $49.99 per video game.

We can use the unit price to figure out which item in a store gives us the most value for our money. We call this the **best buy.** The item with the lowest unit price is the best buy.

EXAMPLE 4

In-Class Example 4

A store sells a certain brand of sports drink in three sizes. The 20-oz bottle costs $1.44, the 32-oz bottle costs $1.78, and the price of the 64-oz bottle is $3.69. Which size is the best buy?

Answer:

The 32-oz bottle has the lowest unit price of $0.056/oz, so it is the best buy.

A store sells cornflakes cereal in three different sizes. The sizes and prices are listed here. Which size is the best buy?

Size	Price
12 oz	$3.69
18 oz	$4.89
24 oz	$6.57

Solution

For each box of cereal, we must find the unit price, or how much the cereal costs per ounce. We will find the unit price by dividing.

$$\text{Unit price} = \frac{\text{Price of a box of cereal}}{\text{Number of ounces in the box}} = \text{Cost per ounce}$$

Size	Unit Price
12 oz	$\dfrac{\$3.69}{12\ oz} \approx \$0.308$ per oz
18 oz	$\dfrac{\$4.89}{18\ oz} \approx \$0.272$ per oz
24 oz	$\dfrac{\$6.57}{24\ oz} \approx \$0.274$ per oz

The 18-oz box of cereal has the lowest unit price of $0.272/oz, so it is the best buy.

Note

Round the answers to the thousandths place because, as you can see, if we rounded the unit price of the 18-oz size and the 24-oz size to the nearest hundredth (or nearest cent), they would be the same. Rounding to the thousandths place, however, shows us that the 18-oz size is the best buy.

[YOU TRY 4] A store sells cheddar fish crackers in three sizes. A 7-oz box costs $2.25, a 15-oz box costs $3.96, and the price of a 34-oz box is $8.89. Which size is the best buy, and what is its unit price?

ANSWERS TO [YOU TRY] EXERCISES

1) a) $\dfrac{45\ mi}{2\ gal}$ b) $\dfrac{5\ lb}{2\ dollars}$ c) $\dfrac{364\ dollars}{1\ week}$
2) a) 36 mi/gal b) $16.50/hr c) $0.06/oz   3) $12.75/hr
4) The 34-oz box has the lowest unit price of $0.261/oz, so it is the best buy.

Using Technology

We can use a calculator to find a vehicle's gas mileage in miles per gallon or mpg.

The next time you fill up your tank, record the number of gallons you purchased and the number of miles you have driven since your last fill-up. For example, suppose you drove 284.2 mi using 11.6 gal of gas. We find gas mileage by dividing the number of miles driven by the number of gallons of gas used. To calculate the gas mileage, enter ②⑧④.②÷①①.⑥= into the calculator.

Your display will show 24.5, which means that the car's gas mileage was 24.5 miles per gallon or 24.5 mpg.

E Evaluate 6.2 Exercises   Do the exercises, and check your work.

*Additional answers can be found in the Answers to Exercises appendix.

Objective 1: Write a Rate as a Fraction

1) What is the difference between a rate and a ratio?

2) Is $\dfrac{97\ mi}{2\ hr}$ a rate or a ratio? Explain your answer.

Write each rate as a fraction in lowest terms.

3) 96 ft in 36 sec $\dfrac{8\ ft}{3\ sec}$

4) 150 ft in 20 sec $\dfrac{15\ ft}{2\ sec}$

5) 270 mi on 12 gal $\dfrac{45\ mi}{2\ gal}$

6) 504 mi on 16 gal $\dfrac{63 \text{ mi}}{2 \text{ gal}}$

7) 12 cups for 10 servings $\dfrac{6 \text{ cups}}{5 \text{ servings}}$

8) 10 cups for 6 servings $\dfrac{5 \text{ cups}}{3 \text{ servings}}$

9) 280 mi in 6 hr $\dfrac{140 \text{ mi}}{3 \text{ hr}}$

10) 22 ft in 8 sec $\dfrac{1 \text{ ft}}{4 \text{ sec}}$

11) $12 for 48 daisies $\dfrac{\$1}{4 \text{ daisies}}$

12) $20 for 12 tulips $\dfrac{\$5}{3 \text{ tulips}}$

13) 8 oz of tea for $60 $\dfrac{2 \text{ oz}}{\$15}$

14) 30 boxes of cookies for $110 $\dfrac{3 \text{ boxes}}{\$11}$

15) $597 in 3 weeks $\dfrac{\$199}{1 \text{ wk}}$

16) $2275 in 5 weeks $\dfrac{\$455}{1 \text{ wk}}$

Objective 2: Find a Unit Rate

17) What is a unit rate?   It is a rate with a denominator of 1.

18) Write the rate $\dfrac{\$523}{1 \text{ wk}}$ in two other ways.
$523/wk, $523 per week

Find each unit rate. Round the answer to the nearest tenth where appropriate.

19) 316 mi in 4 hr   79 mi/hr

20) 1143 mi in 3 hr   381 mi/hr

21) 780 mi on 30 gal   26 mpg

22) 425 mi on 25 gal   17 mpg

23) $120 in 3 hr $40/hr

24) $540 in 30 days $18/day

25) $360.75 for 6.5 days $55.50/day

26) $305.25 in 16.5 hr $18.50/hr

27) 421 mi on 18 gal   23.4 mpg

28) 595 mi on 16 gal   37.2 mpg

Find the unit price of each item. Round the answer to the nearest thousandth, if necessary.

29) $5.49 for 4.5 oz of chili powder $1.22/oz

30) $3.15 for 2.5 oz of cinnamon $1.26/oz

31) $3.19 for 15 oz of pasta sauce $0.213/oz

32) $3.39 for 12 oz of molasses $0.283/oz

33) $8.99 for 24 cans of soda $0.375/can

34) $2.59 for 6 individual packs of applesauce $0.432/pack

Objective 3: Solve Applied Problems Involving Unit Rates

Solve each problem. For problems involving money, round to the nearest cent. Otherwise, round to the nearest tenth, where appropriate.

35) Arturo rode 91 mi in 5 hr. What was his average speed?   18.2 mph

36) Monique earns $1424 for a 40-hr workweek. What is her hourly wage? $35.60/hr

37) A minivan can travel 374 mi on 20 gal of gasoline. Find its gas mileage.   18.7 mpg

38) In the 2009–2010 season, Rajon Rondo played 2963 min in 81 games for the Boston Celtics. Find the average number of minutes he played per game.
36.6 min/game

39) The Vespa® GTS 300 scooter can travel approximately 168 mi on its 2.4-gal gas tank. What is the gas mileage for this scooter?
(www.vespausa.com)
70 mpg

40) Marilu drove 234.5 mi on a highway for 3.5 hr. What was her average speed?   67 mph

41) Tuan recorded the number of hours he studied over the past 5 weeks. If he studied a total of 98 hr, what was his rate of study in hours per week? What was his rate of study in hours per day?
19.6 hr/wk; 2.8 hr/day

42) Brandy drove her car 11,830 mi over the past year. What was her driving rate in miles per week? What was her driving rate in miles per day?
227.5 mi/wk; 32.5 mi/day

43) Fumiko has a text messaging plan that allows her 3000 text messages for $9.99/month. For every message above the cap, she is charged $0.18. Last month she sent 3172 text messages. What is her total monthly text message charge? $40.95

44) Jerry has a text messaging plan that allows him 2000 text messages for $7.99/month. For every message above the cap, he is charged $0.15. Last month he sent 2198 text messages. What is his total monthly text message charge? $37.69

45) Alicia buys a two-year health club membership and agrees to pay $1896. What is her monthly payment? $79.00

46) Siyamak buys a used car and agrees to pay $10,800 over four years. What is his monthly payment? $225.00

47) Devin Hester broke the National Football League record for number of touchdowns on kickoffs or punt returns when the Chicago Bears played the Minnesota Vikings on December 20, 2010. In that game, Hester ran back three kickoffs or punts for 146 yd. Find the average number of yards he ran per return. (http://espn.go.com) 48.7 yd/return

48) During his first five seasons in the National Hockey League, Sidney Crosby played a total of 371 games with the Pittsburgh Penguins. Find the average number of games he played per season. (www.nhl.com) 74.2 games/season

49) Tessa's time sheet is shown below. If she was paid $391.50 for working these hours, what is her hourly wage? $13.50/hr

Mon.	Tues.	Wed.	Thurs.	Fri.
6.0 hr	4.5 hr	3.5 hr	8.0 hr	7.0 hr

50) A nursing student sets an intravenous drip rate at 2880 drops per 1 hr. What is the unit drip rate in drops per minute? 48 drops per minute

51) The California high-speed rail authority claims that its proposed high-speed train will travel 600 mi from San Diego to San Francisco in $3\frac{3}{4}$ hr. Find the average speed of the train. (www.cahighspeedrail.ca.gov) 160 mph

52) Corey's morning commute to work is 34.5 mi. In heavy traffic, it took him $1\frac{1}{4}$ hr to get to work. What was his average speed? 27.6 mph

R Rethink

For each item, determine which size is the best buy, and list its unit price.

53) Soy sauce

Size	Price
10 oz	$2.69
24 oz	$4.73
36 oz	$6.39

36 oz; $0.178/oz

54) Cheese

Size	Price
8 oz	$2.99
12 oz	$3.99
16 oz	$6.09

12 oz; $0.333/oz

55) Cups of coffee

Size	Price
12 oz	$1.50
16 oz	$1.95
20 oz	$2.25

20 oz; $0.113/oz

56) Packages of diapers   96 diapers; $0.250/diaper

Number of Diapers in the Package	Price
31	$10.99
96	$23.99
132	$41.99

57) Brand A lightbulbs cost $7.38 for 6 bulbs, and Brand B lightbulbs cost $11.34 for 9 bulbs. Which is the better buy, and what is its unit cost? Brand A; $1.23/lightbulb

58) A 4-pack of AA batteries costs $4.99 while a package of 6 costs $7.39. Which is the better buy, and what is its unit cost? 6-pack; $1.232/battery

The table lists the monthly rental cost for storage units in a city. Use the table for Exercises 59 and 60.

Dimensions in feet	Monthly Cost	Floor Area in square feet	Cost/ft²
15 × 15	$281.25	225	$1.25
10 × 10	$150.00	100	$1.50
8 × 8	$112.00	64	$1.75
8 × 6	$88.80	48	$1.85
5 × 5	$48.75	25	$1.95

59) Find the floor area for each unit and the cost per square foot.

60) How much does it cost to rent the largest storage unit for one year? $3375

R1) How did these exercises compare with those you completed for Section 6.1?

R2) After completing the exercises involving price, have you noticed where you might be able to make better decisions at the store? Explain.

6.3 Proportions

P Prepare

O Organize

What are your objectives for Section 6.3?	How can you accomplish each objective?
1 Write Proportions	• Write the definition of *proportion* in your own words. • Complete the given example on your own. • Complete You Try 1.
2 Determine Whether a Proportion Is True or False	• Know the two different ways to determine whether a proportion is true. • Write the procedure for **Using Cross Products** in your own words. • Complete the given examples on your own. • Complete You Trys 2 and 3.

W Work

Read the explanations, follow the examples, take notes, and complete the You Trys.

1 Write Proportions

A **proportion** is a statement that two ratios or two rates are equal. For example, since $\frac{1}{2}$ and $\frac{3}{6}$ are equivalent fractions, we can write the proportion $\frac{1}{2} = \frac{3}{6}$. This can be read as

$$1 \text{ is to } 2 \quad \overset{=}{\downarrow}{as} \quad 3 \text{ is to } 6.$$
$$\underset{\text{fraction bar}}{\uparrow} \qquad \underset{\text{fraction bar}}{\uparrow}$$

> **Note**
>
> The words *is to* represent the fraction bar, and the word *as* represents =.

Similarly, the proportion $\frac{\$15}{1 \text{ hr}} = \frac{\$30}{2 \text{ hr}}$ says that the two rates are equal. This is true because if the amount of money is multiplied by 2, the hours are also multiplied by 2. We read this proportion as

$$\$15 \text{ is to } 1 \text{ hr} \quad \overset{=}{\downarrow}{as} \quad \$30 \text{ is to } 2 \text{ hr.}$$
$$\underset{\text{fraction bar}}{\uparrow} \qquad \underset{\text{fraction bar}}{\uparrow}$$

EXAMPLE 1

In-Class Example 1

Write each statement as a proportion.
a) 3 in. is to 8 in. as 6 in. is to 16 in.
b) 120 mi is to 2 hr as 360 mi is to 6 hr.

Write each statement as a proportion.

a) 2 in. is to 9 in.   as   14 in. is to 63 in.

b) 100 mi is to 2 hr   as   500 mi is to 10 hr.

Answer: a) $\dfrac{3 \text{ in.}}{8 \text{ in.}} = \dfrac{6 \text{ in.}}{16 \text{ in.}}$

b) $\dfrac{120 \text{ mi}}{2 \text{ hr}} = \dfrac{360 \text{ mi}}{6 \text{ hr}}$

Solution

a) 2 in. is to 9 in. as 14 in. is to 63 in.

$$\text{is to} \rightarrow \dfrac{2 \text{ in.}}{9 \text{ in.}} \underset{\underset{\text{as}}{\uparrow}}{=} \dfrac{14 \text{ in.}}{63 \text{ in.}} \leftarrow \text{is to}$$

b) 100 mi is to 2 hr as 500 mi is to 10 hr

$$\dfrac{100 \text{ mi}}{2 \text{ hr}} = \dfrac{500 \text{ mi}}{10 \text{ hr}}$$

$\left[\text{YOU TRY 1}\right]$ Write each statement as a proportion.

a) 4 in. is to 5 in. as 12 in. is to 15 in.

b) $39 is to 3 hr as $78 is to 6 hr.

---

2 Determine Whether a Proportion Is True or False

One way to determine whether a proportion is true or false is by writing each fraction in lowest terms.

EXAMPLE 2

In-Class Example 2

Determine whether each proportion is true or false by writing each fraction in lowest terms.

a) $\dfrac{8}{11} = \dfrac{27}{66}$ b) $\dfrac{18}{15} = \dfrac{24}{20}$

Answer: a) false b) true

Determine whether each proportion is true or false by writing each fraction in lowest terms.

a) $\dfrac{4}{7} = \dfrac{24}{40}$ b) $\dfrac{10}{6} = \dfrac{15}{9}$

Solution

a) The fraction $\dfrac{4}{7}$ is already in lowest terms. Write $\dfrac{24}{40}$ in lowest terms.

$$\dfrac{24}{40} = \dfrac{24 \div 8}{40 \div 8} = \dfrac{3}{5}$$

Since $\dfrac{4}{7} \neq \dfrac{3}{5}$, the proportion is false.

b) Write each fraction in lowest terms.

$$\dfrac{10}{6} = \dfrac{10 \div 2}{6 \div 2} = \dfrac{5}{3} \qquad \dfrac{15}{9} = \dfrac{15 \div 3}{9 \div 3} = \dfrac{5}{3}$$

Since each fraction simplifies to $\dfrac{5}{3}$, the proportion is true.

$\left[\text{YOU TRY 2}\right]$ Determine whether each proportion is true or false by writing each fraction in lowest terms.

a) $\dfrac{42}{56} = \dfrac{6}{8}$ b) $\dfrac{16}{12} = \dfrac{28}{20}$

Another way to determine whether a proportion is true or false is by finding the *cross products*. The **cross products** are the numbers we get when we *multiply along the diagonals* of the proportion.

For example, the cross products of the proportion $\dfrac{3}{4} = \dfrac{18}{24}$ are

One cross product
$4 \cdot 18 = 72$
$$\dfrac{3}{4} \diagup\!\!\!\!\diagdown \dfrac{18}{24}$$
$3 \cdot 24 = 72$
The other cross product

Procedure Using Cross Products to Determine Whether a Proportion Is True or False

1) If the cross products in a proportion are equal, then the proportion is true.

Example: $\dfrac{3}{4} \diagdown\!\!\!\!\diagup \dfrac{18}{24}$ $\begin{aligned} 4 \cdot 18 &= 72 \\ 3 \cdot 24 &= 72 \end{aligned}$ The cross products are equal. The proportion is true.

2) If the cross products in a proportion are not equal, then the proportion is false.

Example: $\dfrac{8}{12} \diagdown\!\!\!\!\diagup \dfrac{10}{16}$ $\begin{aligned} 12 \cdot 10 &= 120 \\ 8 \cdot 16 &= 128 \end{aligned}$ The cross products are *not* equal. The proportion is false.

Using cross products is especially good when one or both of the fractions contain mixed numbers or decimals.

EXAMPLE 3

In-Class Example 3

Determine whether each proportion is true or false by finding the cross products.

a) $\dfrac{18}{10} = \dfrac{20}{12}$ b) $\dfrac{1\frac{2}{3}}{3\frac{1}{6}} = \dfrac{10}{19}$

Answer: a) false b) true

W Hint

Which procedure do you prefer?

Determine whether each proportion is true or false by finding the cross products.

a) $\dfrac{16}{6} = \dfrac{10}{4}$ b) $\dfrac{2\frac{3}{4}}{4\frac{1}{2}} = \dfrac{11}{18}$

Solution

a) Find the cross products.

$$\dfrac{16}{6} \diagdown\!\!\!\!\diagup \dfrac{10}{4}$$ $\begin{aligned} 6 \cdot 10 &= 60 \\ 16 \cdot 4 &= 64 \end{aligned}$ False. The cross products are *not* equal.

Since the cross products are *not* equal, the proportion is false.

b) Find the cross products.

$$\dfrac{2\frac{3}{4}}{4\frac{1}{2}} \diagdown\!\!\!\!\diagup \dfrac{11}{18}$$

$4\frac{1}{2} \cdot 11 = \dfrac{9}{2} \cdot 11 = \dfrac{9}{2} \cdot \dfrac{11}{1} = \dfrac{99}{2}$

$2\frac{3}{4} \cdot 18 = \dfrac{11}{4} \cdot 18 = \dfrac{11}{\overset{2}{4}} \cdot \dfrac{\overset{9}{18}}{1} = \dfrac{99}{2}$

True. The cross products are equal.

Since the cross products are equal, the proportion is true.

[YOU TRY 3] Determine whether each proportion is true or false by finding the cross products.

a) $\dfrac{45}{18} = \dfrac{20}{8}$

b) $\dfrac{1\frac{4}{7}}{3\frac{2}{3}} = \dfrac{2}{7}$

 BE CAREFUL We use cross products only when we are working with proportions. Cross products are *not* used to multiply, divide, add, or subtract fractions.

ANSWERS TO [YOU TRY] EXERCISES

1) a) $\dfrac{4 \text{ in.}}{5 \text{ in.}} = \dfrac{12 \text{ in.}}{15 \text{ in.}}$ b) $\dfrac{\$39}{3 \text{ hr}} = \dfrac{\$78}{6 \text{ hr}}$ 2) a) true b) false   3) a) true b) false

 Using Technology

A calculator can help us determine whether a proportion is true or false by finding cross products. Suppose we want to know whether the proportion $\dfrac{52}{98} = \dfrac{13}{24.5}$ is true. To find one cross product, we enter ⑤②✕②④．⑤═ into the calculator. The display will show 1274. To calculate the other cross product, we enter ⑨⑧✕①③═ into the calculator. The display will show 1274 again. Since the cross products are equal, the proportion is true.

E Evaluate **6.3** 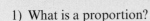 Exercises   Do the exercises, and check your work.

*Additional answers can be found in the Answers to Exercises appendix.

Objective 1: Write Proportions

1) What is a proportion?
   A proportion is a statement that two ratios or two rates are equal.

2) Is the following statement true or false? Because $\dfrac{3}{4}$ and $\dfrac{12}{16}$ are equivalent fractions, we can write the proportion $\dfrac{3}{4} = \dfrac{12}{16}$.   true

Write each statement as a proportion.

 3) 8 is to 11 as 24 is to 33. $\dfrac{8}{11} = \dfrac{24}{33}$

4) 2 is to 7 as 10 is to 35. $\dfrac{2}{7} = \dfrac{10}{35}$

5) 14 is to 8 as 35 is to 20. $\dfrac{14}{8} = \dfrac{35}{20}$

6) 18 is to 12 as 15 is to 10. $\dfrac{18}{12} = \dfrac{15}{10}$

7) \$50 is to \$18 as \$25 is to \$9. $\dfrac{50}{18} = \dfrac{25}{9}$

8) \$84 is to \$28 as \$36 is to \$12. $\dfrac{84}{28} = \dfrac{36}{12}$

9) 2 ft is to 5 ft as 8 ft is to 20 ft. $\dfrac{2}{5} = \dfrac{8}{20}$

10) 3 yd is to 8 yd as 6 yd is to 16 yd. $\dfrac{3}{8} = \dfrac{6}{16}$

11) 480 mi is to 8 hr as 180 mi is to 3 hr. $\dfrac{480 \text{ mi}}{8 \text{ hr}} = \dfrac{180 \text{ mi}}{3 \text{ hr}}$

12) 128 ft is to 8 sec as 48 ft is to 3 sec. $\dfrac{128\ \text{ft}}{8\ \text{sec}} = \dfrac{48\ \text{ft}}{3\ \text{sec}}$

13) 2 in. is to 5 ft as 10 in. is to 25 ft. $\dfrac{2\ \text{in.}}{5\ \text{ft}} = \dfrac{10\ \text{in.}}{25\ \text{ft}}$

14) 3 cm is to 4 m as 12 cm is to 16 m. $\dfrac{3\ \text{cm}}{4\ \text{m}} = \dfrac{12\ \text{cm}}{16\ \text{m}}$

15) $8 is to 12 songs as $16 is to 24 songs. $\dfrac{\$8}{12\ \text{songs}} = \dfrac{\$16}{24\ \text{songs}}$

16) 120 trees is to 1 park as 1320 trees is to 11 parks. $\dfrac{120\ \text{trees}}{1\ \text{park}} = \dfrac{1320\ \text{trees}}{11\ \text{parks}}$

Objective 2: Determine Whether a Proportion Is True or False

17) What are two ways to determine whether a proportion is true or false? 1) Write each fraction in lowest terms. 2) Find the cross products.

18) Explain how to use the cross products to determine whether a proportion is true or false. If the cross products are equal, then the proportion is true. If the cross products are not equal, then the proportion is false.

Determine whether each proportion is true or false by writing each fraction in lowest terms.

19) $\dfrac{9}{27} = \dfrac{1}{3}$ $\dfrac{1}{3} = \dfrac{1}{3}$; true

20) $\dfrac{18}{24} = \dfrac{3}{4}$ $\dfrac{3}{4} = \dfrac{3}{4}$; true

21) $\dfrac{24}{21} = \dfrac{18}{14}$ $\dfrac{8}{7} \neq \dfrac{9}{7}$; false

22) $\dfrac{32}{12} = \dfrac{60}{24}$ $\dfrac{8}{3} \neq \dfrac{5}{2}$; false

23) $\dfrac{150}{225} = \dfrac{20}{36}$ $\dfrac{2}{3} \neq \dfrac{5}{9}$; false

24) $\dfrac{45}{150} = \dfrac{30}{105}$ $\dfrac{3}{10} \neq \dfrac{2}{7}$; false

25) $\dfrac{124}{36} = \dfrac{155}{45}$ $\dfrac{31}{9} = \dfrac{31}{9}$; true

26) $\dfrac{220}{120} = \dfrac{55}{30}$ $\dfrac{11}{6} = \dfrac{11}{6}$; true

27) $\dfrac{18}{4} = \dfrac{63}{14}$ $\dfrac{9}{2} = \dfrac{9}{2}$; true

28) $\dfrac{15}{9} = \dfrac{20}{12}$ $\dfrac{5}{3} = \dfrac{5}{3}$; true

Determine whether each proportion is true or false by finding the cross products.

29) $\dfrac{1}{4} = \dfrac{4}{16}$ 16 = 16; true

30) $\dfrac{7}{21} = \dfrac{1}{3}$ 21 = 21; true

31) $\dfrac{6}{20} = \dfrac{2}{7}$ 42 ≠ 40; false

32) $\dfrac{12}{16} = \dfrac{3}{5}$ 60 ≠ 48; false

33) $\dfrac{19}{5} = \dfrac{76}{20}$ 380 = 380; true

34) $\dfrac{13}{8} = \dfrac{91}{56}$ 728 = 728; true

35) $\dfrac{8}{12} = \dfrac{18}{24}$ 192 ≠ 216; false

36) $\dfrac{4}{30} = \dfrac{6}{50}$ 200 ≠ 180; false

37) $\dfrac{15}{4.3} = \dfrac{17}{6.9}$ 103.5 ≠ 73.1; false

38) $\dfrac{23}{9.8} = \dfrac{18}{5.7}$ 131.1 ≠ 176.4; false

39) $\dfrac{3.2}{12} = \dfrac{1.6}{6}$ 19.2 = 19.2; true

40) $\dfrac{9.8}{21} = \dfrac{1.4}{3}$ 29.4 = 29.4; true

41) $\dfrac{2\frac{5}{6}}{5\frac{3}{8}} = \dfrac{68}{129}$ $\dfrac{731}{2} = \dfrac{731}{2}$; true

42) $\dfrac{1\frac{4}{9}}{3\frac{1}{6}} = \dfrac{26}{57}$ $\dfrac{247}{3} = \dfrac{247}{3}$; true

43) $\dfrac{3\frac{1}{8}}{5} = \dfrac{2}{4\frac{3}{4}}$ $10 \neq 14\frac{27}{32}$; false

44) $\dfrac{4\frac{3}{5}}{9} = \dfrac{3}{6\frac{2}{3}}$ $27 \neq 30\frac{2}{3}$; false

45) $\dfrac{2.5}{6} = \dfrac{5\frac{1}{3}}{12.8}$ 32 = 32; true

46) $\dfrac{2\frac{2}{5}}{1.2} = \dfrac{4\frac{1}{4}}{2.25}$ 5.4 ≠ 5.1; false

47) Do you multiply fractions and determine whether a proportion is true in the same way? Explain.

48) a) Determine whether the proportion $\dfrac{12}{18} = \dfrac{8}{10}$ is true or false. 120 ≠ 144; false

b) Multiply $\dfrac{12}{18} \cdot \dfrac{8}{10}$. $\dfrac{8}{15}$

49) a) Determine whether the proportion $\dfrac{9}{21} = \dfrac{21}{49}$ is true or false. 441 = 441; true

b) Multiply $\dfrac{9}{21} \cdot \dfrac{21}{49}$. $\dfrac{9}{49}$

50) a) Determine whether the proportion $\dfrac{8}{20} = \dfrac{18}{45}$ is true or false. 360 = 360; true

b) Multiply $\dfrac{8}{20} \cdot \dfrac{18}{45}$. $\dfrac{4}{25}$

51) a) Divide $\dfrac{18}{28} \div \dfrac{12}{16}$. $\dfrac{6}{7}$

b) Determine whether the proportion $\dfrac{18}{28} = \dfrac{12}{16}$ is true or false. 336 ≠ 288; false

52) a) Divide $\dfrac{12}{32} \div \dfrac{8}{18}$. $\dfrac{27}{32}$

b) Determine whether the proportion $\dfrac{12}{32} = \dfrac{8}{18}$ is true or false. 256 ≠ 216; false

53) a) Multiply $\dfrac{11}{14} \cdot \dfrac{6}{13}$. $\dfrac{33}{91}$

b) Determine whether the proportion $\dfrac{11}{14} = \dfrac{6}{13}$ is true or false. 84 ≠ 143; false

54) a) Multiply $\dfrac{15}{7} \cdot \dfrac{23}{10}$. $\dfrac{69}{14}$ or $4\frac{13}{14}$

b) Determine whether the proportion $\dfrac{15}{7} = \dfrac{23}{10}$ is true or false. 161 ≠ 150; false

55) Doug got 15 out of 18 problems correct on his quiz and 35 out of 42 problems correct on his exam. He claims that he did equally well on both. Use a proportion and cross products to determine whether Doug's claim is correct.

$\frac{15}{18} = \frac{35}{42}$; 630 = 630; the claim is correct.

56) Janice and Raymond each go to their favorite MP3 download website to get songs. During a holiday sale, Janice downloads 8 songs for $5.20 and Raymond downloads 12 songs for $7.80. Raymond claims that Janice paid more per song than he did. Use a proportion and cross products to determine whether Raymond's claim is correct.

$\frac{8}{5.20} = \frac{12}{7.80}$; 62.4 = 62.4; the claim is incorrect.

R Rethink

R1) How have you done on the exercises?

R2) Where could you go or who could help you with any questions you have?

6.4 Solve Proportions

P Prepare

O Organize

What are your objectives for Section 6.4?	How can you accomplish each objective?
1 Solve an Equation Using the Division Property of Equality	• Know the difference between an *expression* and an *equation*. • Understand the *division property of equality* and write an example. • Complete the given examples on your own, and write a procedure for Example 2. • Complete You Trys 1 and 2.
2 Solve a Proportion	• Review **Using Cross Products** from Section 6.3 if you need to refresh your skills. • Write the procedure for **Solving a Proportion** in your own words. • Complete the given example on your own, and check the answer. • Complete You Try 3.
3 Solve a Proportion Containing Mixed Numbers or Decimals	• Use the same procedure you outlined for Objective 2. • Complete the given examples on your own. • Complete You Try 4.

W Work

Read the explanations, follow the examples, take notes, and complete the You Trys.

Sometimes, a proportion will contain an unknown number and we will have to find the number that makes the proportion true. An example of this is $\frac{2}{5} = \frac{x}{15}$. The process of finding this unknown number is called *solving the proportion*. Before we learn how to solve a proportion, we must learn about expressions and equations.

1 Solve an Equation Using the Division Property of Equality

A **variable** is a symbol, usually a letter, used to represent an unknown number. When we put variables together with operation symbols like $+$, $-$, $\times$, and $\div$, we get an **expression.** For example, the expression $8x$ means $8 \cdot x$. The variable x represents a number. The value of the expression depends on the value of the variable.

EXAMPLE 1

In-Class Example 1

Evaluate $5x$ when
a) $x = 3$.   b) $x = 8$.

Answer: a) 15 b) 40

Evaluate $8x$ when

a) $x = 2$.   b) $x = 9$.

Solution

a) To *evaluate* $8x$ when $x = 2$ means to find the value of the expression $8x$ when $x = 2$. To do this, substitute 2 for x and simplify.

$$\text{Evaluate } 8x \text{ for } x = 2:$$
$$= 8(2) \qquad \text{Substitute 2 for } x.$$
$$= 16 \qquad \text{Multiply.}$$

When $x = 2$, $8x = 16$.

b) Evaluate $8x$ for $x = 9$:

$$= 8(9) \qquad \text{Substitute 9 for } x.$$
$$= 72 \qquad \text{Multiply.}$$

When $x = 9$, $8x = 72$.

[YOU TRY 1] Evaluate $7x$ when

a) $x = 10$.   b) $x = 4$.

When we set two expressions equal to each other, we get an **equation.** Therefore, an equation contains an $=$ sign, and an expression does not.

$$3x \text{ is an expression.} \qquad 3x = 21 \text{ is an equation.}$$

To **solve** an equation means to find the value of the variable that makes the equation true. The number that solves the equation is called the **solution.** For example, the equation $3x = 21$ means $3 \cdot x = 21$. The solution of the equation is $x = 7$ because $3 \cdot 7 = 21$.

We can solve an equation like $3x = 21$ using the *division property of equality.*

Property Division Property of Equality

If both sides of an equation are divided by the same nonzero number, we get an equivalent equation.

Example: $20 = 20$ so $\dfrac{20}{5} = \dfrac{20}{5}$.

Let's practice solving equations using the division property of equality before we solve proportions.

EXAMPLE 2

Solve each equation using the division property of equality.

a) $2x = 10$ b) $27 = 9x$

Solution

a) To solve for x in the equation $2x = 10$, we want to get the x by itself on the left-hand side of the equation. The x is being **multiplied** by 2. To get x by itself, we perform the *opposite* operation. That is, **divide** each side of the equation by 2.

$$2x = 10$$

$$\dfrac{2x}{2} = \dfrac{10}{2} \qquad \text{Divide each side by 2.}$$

$$\dfrac{\overset{1}{\cancel{2}}x}{\underset{1}{\cancel{2}}} = 5 \qquad \text{Divide out the common factor; } 1x \text{ is the same as } x.$$

$$x = 5 \qquad \text{Simplify.}$$

Check: Substitute $x = 5$ into the equation $2x = 10$ to see whether the value makes the equation true.

$$2(5) = 10$$

$$10 = 10 \qquad \text{True}$$

The solution is $x = 5$.

b) To solve for x in the equation $27 = 9x$, we want to get the x by itself on the right-hand side of the equation. The x is being **multiplied** by 9. To get x by itself, we perform the opposite operation. That is, **divide** each side of the equation by 9.

$$27 = 9x$$

$$\dfrac{27}{9} = \dfrac{9x}{9} \qquad \text{Divide each side by 9.}$$

$$3 = \dfrac{\overset{1}{\cancel{9}}x}{\underset{1}{\cancel{9}}} \qquad \text{Divide out the common factor; } 1x \text{ is the same as } x.$$

$$3 = x \qquad \text{Simplify.}$$

Check: Substitute $x = 3$ into the equation $27 = 9x$ to see whether the value makes the equation true.

$$27 = 9(3)$$

$$27 = 27 \qquad \text{True}$$

The solution is $x = 3$.

In-Class Example 2

Solve each equation using the division property of equality.
a) $3x = 12$ b) $48 = 8x$

Answer: a) 4   b) 6

 Hint

Write a procedure in your own words after following this example.

Note

Example 2 shows that whether the variable is on the left-hand side of the equal sign, as in $2x = 10$, or on the right-hand side of the equal sign, as in $27 = 9x$, we divide each side of the equation by the number in front of the variable to solve the equation.

[**YOU TRY 2**] Solve each equation using the division property of equality.

a) $6x = 42$ b) $36 = 4x$

2 Solve a Proportion

Now that we know how to use the division property of equality, we can solve proportions. If a proportion contains one variable and we have to find the number that makes the proportion true, we use cross products and the division property of equality to find that missing value.

> **Procedure** How to Solve a Proportion
>
> **Step 1:** Find the cross products.
>
> **Step 2:** Set the cross products equal to each other, and solve the equation.
>
> **Step 3:** Check the solution by substituting it into the original proportion and finding the cross products.

Let's begin by solving the proportion that appeared at the beginning of the section.

EXAMPLE 3

In-Class Example 3

Solve each proportion.

a) $\dfrac{3}{7} = \dfrac{x}{14}$ b) $\dfrac{x}{15} = \dfrac{8}{6}$

Answer: a) 6 b) 20

W Hint

Write out the example as you are reading it.

Solve each proportion.

a) $\dfrac{2}{5} = \dfrac{x}{15}$ b) $\dfrac{x}{10} = \dfrac{12}{15}$

Solution

a) **Step 1:** Find the cross products.

$$\frac{2}{5} \diagdown \frac{x}{15} \quad \begin{array}{l} 5 \cdot x = 5x \\ 2 \cdot 15 = 30 \end{array}$$

Step 2: Set the cross products equal to each other, and solve the equation.

$5x = 30$ Set the cross products equal to each other.

$\dfrac{5x}{5} = \dfrac{30}{5}$ Divide each side by 5.

$\dfrac{\overset{1}{\cancel{5}}x}{\cancel{5}} = \dfrac{30}{5}$ Divide out the common factor.

$x = 6$ Simplify.

406   CHAPTER 6   Ratios, Rates, and Proportions

www.mhhe.com/messersmith

Step 3: Check the solution in the original proportion, $\dfrac{2}{5} = \dfrac{x}{15}$, by checking to see whether the cross products are equal.

$$\dfrac{2}{5} \bowtie \dfrac{6}{15} \qquad \begin{array}{l} 5 \cdot 6 = 30 \\ \text{Substitute 6 for } x. \\ 2 \cdot 15 = 30 \end{array}$$

Since the cross products are equal, the solution of the proportion is $x = 6$.

 BE CAREFUL The solution of the equation is 6, *not* 30, the value of each cross product!

b) **Step 1:** Find the cross products.

$$\dfrac{x}{10} \bowtie \dfrac{12}{15} \qquad \begin{array}{l} 10 \cdot 12 = 120 \\ x \cdot 15 = x15 = 15x \quad \text{Commutative property} \end{array}$$

Step 2: Set the cross products equal to each other, and solve the equation.

$$120 = 15x \qquad \text{Set the cross products equal to each other.}$$

$$\dfrac{120}{15} = \dfrac{15x}{15} \qquad \text{Divide each side by 15.}$$

$$\dfrac{120}{15} = \dfrac{\overset{1}{\cancel{15}}x}{\underset{1}{\cancel{15}}} \qquad \text{Divide out the common factor.}$$

$$8 = x \qquad \text{Simplify.}$$

Step 3: The check is left to the student. The solution of $\dfrac{x}{10} = \dfrac{12}{15}$ is $x = 8$.

[YOU TRY 3]   Solve each proportion.

a) $\dfrac{4}{9} = \dfrac{x}{27}$ b) $\dfrac{x}{12} = \dfrac{6}{9}$

---

3   Solve a Proportion Containing Mixed Numbers or Decimals

Sometimes, proportions contain mixed numbers or decimals.

EXAMPLE 4   Solve each proportion.

a) $\dfrac{1\frac{2}{3}}{x} = \dfrac{8}{12}$ b) $\dfrac{0.2}{0.8} = \dfrac{3}{x}$

In-Class Example 4

Solve each proportion.

a) $\dfrac{1\frac{3}{5}}{x} = \dfrac{6}{10}$ b) $\dfrac{0.3}{0.9} = \dfrac{5}{x}$

Answer: a) $2\frac{2}{3}$ b) 15

Solution

a) **Step 1:** Find the cross products.

$$x \cdot 8 = x8 = 8x \quad \text{Commutative property}$$

$$1\frac{2}{3} \cdot 12 = \frac{5}{3} \cdot 12 = \frac{5}{{}_1\cancel{3}} \cdot \frac{\cancel{12}^4}{4} = \frac{20}{1} = 20$$

Step 2: Set the cross products equal to each other, and solve the equation.

$$8x = 20 \qquad \text{Set the cross products equal to each other.}$$

$$\frac{8x}{8} = \frac{20}{8} \qquad \text{Divide each side by 8.}$$

$$\frac{\overset{1}{\cancel{8}x}}{\underset{1}{\cancel{8}}} = \frac{20 \div 4}{8 \div 4} \qquad \text{Divide out the common factor.}$$

$$x = \frac{5}{2} = 2\frac{1}{2} \qquad \text{Simplify.}$$

We can write the solution either as an improper fraction or as a mixed number. Let's write it as a mixed number because there is a mixed number in the original proportion.

Step 3: Check the solution in the original proportion, $\dfrac{1\frac{2}{3}}{x} = \dfrac{8}{12}$, by checking to see whether the cross products are equal.

Substitute $2\frac{1}{2}$ for x.

$$2\frac{1}{2} \cdot 8 = \frac{5}{2} \cdot 8 = \frac{5}{{}_1\cancel{2}} \cdot \frac{\cancel{8}^4}{1} = \frac{20}{1} = 20$$

$$1\frac{2}{3} \cdot 12 = \frac{5}{3} \cdot 12 = \frac{5}{{}_1\cancel{3}} \cdot \frac{\cancel{12}^4}{1} = \frac{20}{1} = 20$$

Since the cross products are equal, the solution is $x = 2\frac{1}{2}$.

b) **Step 1:** Find the cross products.

$$0.8 \cdot 3 = 2.4$$
$$0.2 \cdot x = 0.2x$$

Step 2: Set the cross products equal to each other, and solve the equation.

$$2.4 = 0.2x \qquad \text{Set the cross products equal to each other.}$$

$$\frac{2.4}{0.2} = \frac{0.2x}{0.2} \qquad \text{Divide each side by 0.2.}$$

$$\frac{2.4}{0.2} = \frac{\cancel{0.2}x}{\cancel{0.2}} \qquad \text{Divide out the common factor.}$$

$$12 = x \qquad \text{Simplify.}$$

Step 3: The check is left to the student. The solution of $\dfrac{0.2}{0.8} = \dfrac{3}{x}$ is $x = 12$.

[YOU TRY 4] Solve each proportion.

a) $\dfrac{3\frac{1}{8}}{x} = \dfrac{20}{16}$ 　　b) $\dfrac{0.4}{0.6} = \dfrac{7}{x}$

W Hint

Be sure you have manually checked your answers first!

ANSWERS TO [YOU TRY] EXERCISES

1) a) 70　b) 28　　2) a) $x = 7$　b) $x = 9$　　3) a) $x = 12$　b) $x = 8$

4) a) $x = 2\frac{1}{2}$　b) $x = 10.5$

Using Technology

We can use a calculator to solve a proportion in the way we have already learned in this section. Or, we can use a shortcut, along with a calculator, to solve a proportion of the form $\dfrac{x}{b} = \dfrac{c}{d}$. To solve for x, we first find the product of b and c, and then divide by d.

Using this shortcut, we can solve $\dfrac{x}{7} = \dfrac{5.4}{6}$ by multiplying 7 and 5.4 and then dividing the product by 6: Enter $\boxed{7}\,\boxed{\times}\,\boxed{5}\,\boxed{.}\,\boxed{4}\,\boxed{\div}\,\boxed{6}\,\boxed{=}$ into the calculator. The display will show 6.3. Therefore, the solution is $x = 6.3$. Now, solve $\dfrac{x}{7} = \dfrac{5.4}{6}$ by hand. Did you get the same answer?

E Evaluate **6.4** Exercises 　　Do the exercises, and check your work.

*Additional answers can be found in the Answers to Exercises appendix.

Objective 1: Solve an Equation Using the Division Property of Equality

1) What does it mean to solve a proportion like $\dfrac{5}{9} = \dfrac{x}{63}$? To solve a proportion means to find the missing number that will make the proportion true.

2) What is a variable? It is a symbol, usually a letter, that is used to represent an unknown number.

3) Evaluate $2x$ when
   a) $x = 9$.　18
   b) $x = 6$.　12

4) Evaluate $9x$ when
   a) $x = 4$.　36
   b) $x = 10$.　90

5) Evaluate $4x$ when
   a) $x = 1$.　4
   b) $x = 12$.　48

6) Evaluate $10x$ when
   a) $x = 9$.　90
   b) $x = 2$.　20

7) Evaluate $11x$ when
   a) $x = 11$　121
   b) $x = 5$　55

8) Evaluate $7x$ when
   a) $x = 7$.　49
   b) $x = 6$.　42

9) Is $5x = 20$ an expression or an equation? Explain your answer. It is an equation because it contains an equal sign.

10) Explain the division property of equality. The division property of equality says that if we divide both sides of an equation by the same nonzero number, then we get an equivalent equation.

Solve each equation using the division property of equality.

11) $7x = 14$　$x = 2$
12) $4x = 44$　$x = 11$
13) $5x = 45$　$x = 9$
14) $8x = 56$　$x = 7$
15) $3x = 3$　$x = 1$
16) $10x = 10$　$x = 1$
17) $24 = 6x$　$x = 4$
18) $45 = 5x$　$x = 9$
19) $144 = 9x$　$x = 16$
20) $76 = 4x$　$x = 19$
21) $40x = 12$　$x = \dfrac{3}{10}$
22) $27x = 18$　$x = \dfrac{2}{3}$
23) $54 = 30x$　$x = \dfrac{9}{5}$
24) $56 = 21x$　$x = \dfrac{8}{3}$
25) $0.6x = 13.8$　$x = 23$
26) $0.4x = 5.2$　$x = 13$
27) $12 = 0.3x$　$x = 40$
28) $63 = 0.7x$　$x = 90$

Objective 2: Solve a Proportion

29) Explain how to solve a proportion.

30) Check the solution $x = 8$ in the proportion $\dfrac{4}{7} = \dfrac{x}{21}$ to determine whether it is the correct answer. Explain.

Solve each proportion, and check the answer using the cross products.

31) $\dfrac{x}{16} = \dfrac{1}{8}$ $x = 2$ 32) $\dfrac{x}{12} = \dfrac{1}{4}$ $x = 3$

33) $\dfrac{3}{7} = \dfrac{6}{x}$ $x = 14$ 34) $\dfrac{5}{12} = \dfrac{10}{x}$ $x = 24$

35) $\dfrac{1}{100} = \dfrac{x}{1000}$ $x = 10$ 36) $\dfrac{1}{100} = \dfrac{x}{10,000}$ $x = 100$

37) $\dfrac{6}{x} = \dfrac{4}{15}$ $x = \dfrac{45}{2}$ 38) $\dfrac{12}{x} = \dfrac{8}{5}$ $x = \dfrac{15}{2}$

39) $\dfrac{81}{6} = \dfrac{8}{x}$ $x = \dfrac{16}{27}$ 40) $\dfrac{57}{9} = \dfrac{14}{x}$ $x = \dfrac{42}{19}$

Objective 3: Solve a Proportion Containing Mixed Numbers or Decimals

Solve each proportion, and check the answer using the cross products.

41) $\dfrac{1\frac{4}{5}}{x} = \dfrac{9}{10}$ $x = 2$ 42) $\dfrac{2\frac{1}{4}}{x} = \dfrac{3}{8}$ $x = 6$

43) $\dfrac{1\frac{4}{9}}{5} = \dfrac{x}{3}$ $x = \dfrac{13}{15}$ 44) $\dfrac{3\frac{1}{4}}{10} = \dfrac{x}{2}$ $x = \dfrac{13}{20}$

45) $\dfrac{x}{5\frac{1}{2}} = \dfrac{7}{9}$ $x = 4\dfrac{5}{18}$ 46) $\dfrac{x}{4\frac{3}{8}} = \dfrac{3}{11}$ $x = 1\dfrac{17}{88}$

47) $\dfrac{0.5}{1.2} = \dfrac{0.7}{x}$ $x = 1.68$ 48) $\dfrac{0.4}{2.3} = \dfrac{0.6}{x}$ $x = 3.45$

49) $\dfrac{6}{x} = \dfrac{0.3}{5.2}$ $x = 104$ 50) $\dfrac{8}{x} = \dfrac{0.4}{6.1}$ $x = 122$

51) $\dfrac{1\frac{1}{6}}{x} = \dfrac{\frac{2}{5}}{1\frac{1}{2}}$ $x = 4\dfrac{3}{8}$ 52) $\dfrac{2\frac{1}{4}}{x} = \dfrac{\frac{2}{3}}{3\frac{1}{3}}$ $x = 11\dfrac{1}{4}$

53) $\dfrac{1\frac{1}{2}}{4} = \dfrac{2\frac{1}{3}}{x}$ $x = 6\dfrac{2}{9}$ 54) $\dfrac{4\frac{1}{4}}{6} = \dfrac{3\frac{2}{3}}{x}$ $x = 5\dfrac{3}{17}$

55) $\dfrac{x}{6\frac{1}{4}} = \dfrac{0.8}{1.5}$ $x = 3\dfrac{1}{3}$ 56) $\dfrac{x}{7\frac{1}{2}} = \dfrac{0.6}{2.5}$ $x = 1\dfrac{4}{5}$

57) $\dfrac{5}{2\frac{1}{3}} = \dfrac{x}{1.4}$ $x = 3$ 58) $\dfrac{4}{2\frac{1}{5}} = \dfrac{x}{5.5}$ $x = 10$

Mixed Exercises: Objectives 1–3

59) Evaluate $5x$ when

  a) $x = 11$. 55   b) $x = 6$. 30

60) Evaluate $8x$ when

  a) $x = 8$. 64   b) $x = 9$. 72

Solve.

61) $8x = 40$ $x = 5$ 62) $\dfrac{0.7}{1.2} = \dfrac{x}{6}$ $x = 3.5$

63) $\dfrac{x}{16} = \dfrac{9}{6}$ $x = 24$ 64) $9x = 63$ $x = 7$

65) $18 = 3x$ $x = 6$ 66) $\dfrac{35}{20} = \dfrac{x}{8}$ $x = 14$

67) $\dfrac{14}{9} = \dfrac{x}{1\frac{5}{7}}$ $x = 2\dfrac{2}{3}$ 68) $16 = 2x$ $x = 8$

69) $\dfrac{x}{2} = \dfrac{2.1}{3.5}$ $x = 1.2$ 70) $\dfrac{15}{4} = \dfrac{x}{3\frac{1}{3}}$ $x = 12\dfrac{1}{2}$

R Rethink

R1) There is another way to check whether your answer is correct after solving a proportion. Think of what it takes to compare fractions and what you know about common denominators to develop a new way to check your answer.

R2) Try this new method of checking your answer on a few of the exercises you just completed.

6.5 Solve Applied Problems Involving Proportions

What are your objectives for Section 6.5?	How can you accomplish each objective?
1 Solve Applied Problems Involving Proportions	• Use the Five Steps for Solving Applied Problems that you used previously, and add some details to Step 3 regarding proportions and cross multiplication. • Complete the given examples on your own. • Complete You Trys 1 and 2.

Read the explanations, follow the examples, take notes, and complete the You Trys.

1 Solve Applied Problems Involving Proportions

Proportions are used to solve many applied problems. Since a proportion is a statement that two ratios or rates are equal, look for the key words we learned in Sections 6.2 and 6.3 as well as some new ones: *in, per, for, from, on, out of, is to,* and *as*.

To solve an application involving a proportion, we will use the Five Steps for Solving Applied Problems that we first learned in Section 2.7.

Procedure Five Steps for Solving Applied Problems

Step 1: **Read** the problem carefully, more than once if necessary, until you understand it. Restate the problem in your own words. Draw a picture, if applicable. Identify what you are being asked to find.

Step 2: **Make a plan** for solving the problem. Underline important words that might help you solve the problem.

Step 3: **Solve** the problem using your plan and the information given. Look at the important words you have underlined.

Step 4: **State the answer** in a complete sentence.

Step 5: **Check** the answer.

In Step 2, we will use a variable to represent the unknown number.

EXAMPLE 1

In-Class Example 1

On a map of the United States, 1 inch represents 150 miles. If two cities are 2.5 inches apart on the map, what is the actual distance between the two cities?

Answer: 375 miles

On a map of the United States, 1 inch represents 120 miles. If two cities are 3.5 inches apart on the map, what is the actual distance between the two cities?

Solution

Step 1: **Read** the problem carefully, and restate it in your own words.

0   120 mi
1 in.

We can think of this problem as a proportion in this way:

1 in. *is to* 120 mi *as* 3.5 in. *is to* the actual distance.

We must find the actual distance between the two cities.

Step 2: **Make a plan.**

We are trying to find the actual distance between the two cities. Let's use the variable x to represent this distance.

x = the actual distance between the two cities

Plan: Write a proportion using x for the unknown quantity. We will write our rates in the form $\dfrac{\text{Number of inches}}{\text{Number of miles}}$ so that the numerators contain the same quantities and the denominators contain the same quantities:

$$\frac{1 \text{ in.}}{120 \text{ mi}} = \frac{3.5 \text{ in.}}{x}$$

1 in. *is to* 120 mi *as* 3.5 in. *is to* the actual distance, x.

Step 3: **Solve** the problem. We do not need the units when solving for x.

$$\begin{array}{l}\text{Number of inches} \rightarrow \dfrac{1 \text{ in.}}{120 \text{ mi}} = \dfrac{3.5 \text{ in.}}{x} \leftarrow \text{Number of inches} \\ \text{Number of miles} \rightarrow \quad\quad\quad\quad\quad\quad \leftarrow \text{Number of miles}\end{array}$$

$$\frac{1}{120} = \frac{3.5}{x} \qquad \text{Write the equation without the units.}$$

$$120 \cdot 3.5 = 1x \qquad \text{Find the cross products.}$$

$$420 = x \qquad \text{Solve the equation.}$$

Step 4: **State the answer** in a complete sentence.

3.5 in. represents 420 mi.

Step 5: **Check** the answer. Use the cross products to check $x = 420$ in the proportion $\dfrac{1}{120} = \dfrac{3.5}{x}$.

$$\frac{1}{120} \diagup\diagdown \frac{3.5}{420}$$

$120 \cdot 3.5 = 420$

Substitute 420 for x.

$1 \cdot 420 = 420$

The cross products are equal.

The answer is correct.

[YOU TRY 1]   If 4 granola bars cost \$4.76, find the cost of 6 granola bars.

 BE CAREFUL   Be sure you write the quantities in the right places in the proportion. The units in the numerators must be the same, and the units in the denominators must be the same.

EXAMPLE 2

According to the American Lung Association, approximately 7 out of 50 premature births are the result of smoking during pregnancy. At that rate, how many of a hospital's 292 premature births were due to smoking? Round the answer to the nearest whole number. (www.lungusa.org)

Solution

Step 1: **Read** the problem carefully, and restate it in your own words.

7 babies were born early because of smoking <u>out of</u> every 50 babies born early. How many babies were born early because of smoking <u>out of</u> 292 babies born early?

We can think of this problem as a proportion in this way:

7 babies *are to* 50 babies *as* how many babies *are to* 292 babies?

We must find the number of babies born early because of smoking out of a group of 292 who are born prematurely.

Step 2: **Make a plan.** We underlined important words in our restatement of the problem in Step 1.

Let's use the variable x to represent the number of babies born prematurely.

x = The number of babies born prematurely because of smoking out of 292 babies

Plan: Write a proportion using x for the unknown quantity. We will write our rates in the form $\dfrac{\text{Number born early due to smoking}}{\text{Total number born early}}$:

$$\begin{array}{l}\text{Number born early due} \\ \text{to smoking} \\ \text{Total number born early}\end{array} \begin{array}{l}\rightarrow \\ \rightarrow\end{array} \dfrac{7 \text{ babies}}{50 \text{ babies}} = \dfrac{x}{292 \text{ babies}} \begin{array}{l}\leftarrow \\ \leftarrow\end{array} \begin{array}{l}\text{Number born early due} \\ \text{to smoking} \\ \text{Total number born early}\end{array}$$

7 babies *are to* 50 babies *as* x *is to* 292 babies.

Step 3: **Solve** the problem. We do not need the units when solving for x.

$$\frac{7 \text{ babies}}{50 \text{ babies}} = \frac{x}{292 \text{ babies}}$$

$\dfrac{7}{50} = \dfrac{x}{292}$ Write the equation without the units.

$50x = 7 \cdot 292$ Find the cross products.

$50x = 2044$ Multiply.

$\dfrac{50x}{50} = \dfrac{2044}{50}$ Divide by 50.

$x = 40.88$ Perform the division.

$x \approx 41$ Round to the nearest whole number.

Step 4: **State the answer** in a complete sentence.

Approximately 41 babies out of 292 were born prematurely due to smoking.

Step 5: Check the answer. Use the cross products to check $x = 40.88$ in the proportion $\frac{7}{50} = \frac{x}{292}$.

$$\frac{7}{50} = \frac{40.88}{292}$$ Substitute 40.88 for x.

When we round 40.88 to the nearest whole number, we get 41. The answer is correct.

[**YOU TRY 2**]   A survey at Harrington High School revealed that 5 out of 8 of its seniors would be going away for college. How many of the 424 seniors were planning to go away for college?

ANSWERS TO [YOU TRY] EXERCISES

1) $7.14   2) 265

E Evaluate **6.5** Exercises   Do the exercises, and check your work.

*Additional answers can be found in the Answers to Exercises appendix.

Objective 1: Solve Applied Problems Involving Proportions

Solve each problem using a proportion. Be sure to keep the units organized.

1) On a highway map, 2 in. represents 140 mi. If two cities are 8.5 in. apart on the map, what is the actual distance between the two cities?   595 mi

2) In a scaled drawing, a 200-ft building is drawn 5 in. high. What is the actual height of a building that is drawn 3 in. high?   120 ft

3) If 120 g of frozen yogurt contains 12 g of fat, how much fat is in 200 g of frozen yogurt?   20 g

4) An 8-oz serving of Pepsi MAX contains 46 mg of caffeine. How much caffeine is in 20 oz of Pepsi MAX? (pepsiproductfacts.com)   115 mg

5) A high-speed train can travel 240 mi in 1.5 hr. At the same rate, how far can the train travel in 4 hr?   640 mi

6) On average, 5 gal of paint will cover 1750 sq ft of wall space. How many gallons of paint will be required to paint a home if the wall space is 1050 sq ft?   3 gal

7) If Gary earns $435.75 in 5 days, how much does he earn in 3 days? $261.45

8) If the cost to deliver 30 newspapers to a person's home is $48.00 dollars, what is the cost to deliver 8 newspapers? $12.80

9) In his pickup, Daryl can drive 224 mi on 14 gal of gas. How far could he drive on 20 gal?   320 mi

10) If a tortoise can walk 7 ft in 20 sec, how long would it take to walk 50 ft? Round to the nearest second.   143 sec

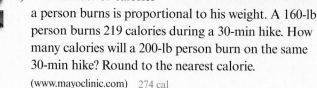
11) The number of calories a person burns is proportional to his weight. A 160-lb person burns 219 calories during a 30-min hike. How many calories will a 200-lb person burn on the same 30-min hike? Round to the nearest calorie. (www.mayoclinic.com)   274 cal

12) A recent study at Iowa State University found that 17 out of 20 American youths aged 8 to 18 who play video games show multiple signs of behavioral addiction. In a group of 260 youths in this age group, how many are expected to have this addiction? (www.iastate.edu)   221 youths

13) In November 2010, the U.S. Bureau of Labor Statistics reported that 9.8 out of 100 citizens were unemployed. In a group of 2500 citizens, how many were expected to be unemployed? (www.bls.gov)   245 citizens

14) At a campus election, it is expected that 7 out of 10 students will vote. On a campus of 12,318 students,

how many students are expected to vote? Round the answer to the nearest whole number. 8623 students

Use the floor plan shown for Exercises 15–22. One inch represents 4 feet on the plan.

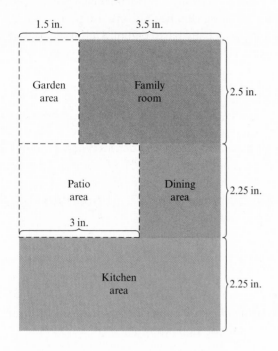

15) What are the actual length and width of the kitchen? length = 9 ft; width = 20 ft

16) What are the actual width and length of the dining area? length = 9 ft; width = 8 ft

17) What are the actual width and length of the family room? length = 14 ft; width = 10 ft

18) What are the actual width and length of the garden area? length = 10 ft; width = 6 ft

19) What are the actual width and length of the entire floor plan? length = 28 ft; width = 20 ft

20) What is the actual area of the patio area? 108 sq ft

21) What is the actual area of the entire floor plan? 560 sq ft

22) What is the combined area of the dining, family, and kitchen areas? 392 sq ft

Solve each problem using a proportion.

23) A nursing student observes an intravenous drip rate of 8 drops per 10 sec. How many drops should be observed in 1 min? 48 drops

24) Nadia teaches two classes, and each contains 35 students. If she grades the final exam at a rate of 15 min per exam, how many minutes will be required to grade all the finals? How many hours is this? 1050 min; 17.5 hr

25) To safely thaw a frozen turkey in the refrigerator takes 24 hr per every 4.5 lb. How many hours will it take to thaw a 15-lb turkey in this manner? (www.fsis.usda.gov) 80 hr

26) Suppose that a bicyclist pedals a bicycle at 40 revolutions per minute, resulting in a speed of 7 miles per hour. How fast will the bicyclist go if she pedals 60 revolutions per minute? 10.5 mph

27) At 2 P.M., Maria's shadow is 2 ft long, and she is 5 ft tall. If the flag pole casts a shadow that is 8.4 ft long, how tall is the flag pole? 21 ft

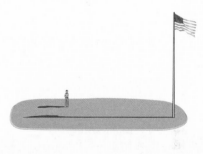

28) Refer to Exercise 27. At 5 P.M., Maria's shadow is 8 ft long. How long is the flag pole's shadow at this time? 33.6 ft

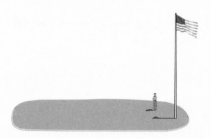

The standard wide-screen format ratio is 16:9, width to height. A new movie theatre is being constructed with four different screen sizes. Fill in the missing dimensions in the table.

	Width in feet	Height in feet
29)	32	18
30)	40	22.5
31)	64	36
32)	80	45

33) Rosa Vasquez won an election over her opponent by a ratio of 6:5. If her opponent received 2820 votes, how many did Rosa receive? 3384 votes

34) The ratio of women to men in a college physics lecture course is 4:17. Find the number of men in this course if it contains 32 women. 136 men

35) Suppose the gas to oil ratio for a two-stroke engine is 32:1. How much oil, in gallons, must be mixed with 8 gal of gasoline? If 1 gal equals 128 fl oz, how many ounces of oil must be added to 1 gal?   0.25 gal; 32 oz

36) A particular lawn mower requires a 40:1 gas to oil ratio. How much oil, in gallons, must be mixed with 2 gal of gasoline? If 1 gal equals 128 fl oz, how many ounces of oil must be added to the 2 gal?   0.05 gal; 6.4 oz

37) A high school wishes to have a student to teacher ratio of 22 to 1. If there are 2315 students, how many teachers are needed? Round to the nearest whole number.   105 teachers

38) If the ratio of cats to dogs at an animal shelter is 3 to 5 and there are 45 dogs at the shelter, how many cats are in the shelter?   27 cats

39) Approximately 9 out of 10 students believe that studying on a daily basis will improve one's grade. But of those who believe, only 1 out of 7 students study on a daily basis. Out of 8760 students, how many believe that studying on a daily basis will improve one's grade and do in fact study on a daily basis? Round to the nearest whole number.
1126 students

40) A school survey reveals that 4 out of 5 students eat at a fast-food restaurant every Friday after school. Only 1 out of 12 students who do this order a healthy food item from the menu. Out of 3850 students, how many students will go to a fast-food restaurant on Friday and order a healthy food item? Round to the nearest whole number.   257 students

R Rethink

R1) Did you remember to include units in your answers? Why is it important to include the units?

R2) Where have you previously encountered a ratio or rate that you could use to set up a proportion to solve for an unknown?

Group Activity – Ratios, Rates, and Proportions

Employees at Rapid Rental Cars record the "Beginning Odometer Reading" when a vehicle is rented out to a customer and the "Ending Odometer Reading" when that vehicle is returned. The table below lists the beginning and ending odometer readings, as well as the combined miles per gallon (mpg) for three different vehicles that were recently returned. (Note: The combined mpg is a weighted average of the miles per gallon that a car gets during city driving and the miles per gallon it gets during highway driving.)

Vehicle	Beginning Odometer Reading (miles)	Ending Odometer Reading (miles)	Combined mpg (miles per gallon)
2011 Honda Civic	5736	6227	29
2011 Nissan Maxima	11,032	11,518	27
2011 Chevy Malibu	7825	8714	26

(www.mpgbuddy.com/index.php)

1) Based on the data in the chart, use a proportion to estimate how many gallons of gas were used by the Honda during its rental period. Round to the nearest tenth if necessary.

2) Based on the data in the chart, use a proportion to estimate how many gallons of gas were used by the Nissan during its rental period. Round to the nearest tenth if necessary.

3) Based on the data in the chart, use a proportion to estimate how many gallons of gas were used by the Chevy during its rental period. Round to the nearest tenth if necessary.

4) You are going on a road trip from Salt Lake City to San Diego, and back. You decide to rent the Chevy Malibu from Rapid Rental Cars. You estimate that you will drive a total of 1600 mi on your trip. Use a proportion to determine how many gallons of gas you will use.

5) Before your trip, you need to stock up on a few travel items. For each pair of items below, determine the unit prices and then decide which option is the better buy.

Shampoo	Shaving Cream	Toothpaste
1.7 fl oz for $1.69	2.75 oz for $2.50	0.85 oz for $1.50
25.4 fl oz for $6.99	7 oz for $2.99	4 oz for $3.29

6) Explain why the unit rate for the 0.85-oz size of toothpaste is greater than its cost.

7) Your road map has a scale of $\frac{1}{4}$ inch per 10 miles. Use a proportion to determine the actual distance between Salt Lake City and San Diego if the two cities are $18\frac{3}{4}$ in. apart on the map.

8) At the end of your trip, your gas receipts show that you used a total of 71 gal of gas. How many miles did you actually drive on your trip? Is this more or less than the estimate of 1600 mi?

9) Do you think the mpg for city driving is more or less than the combined mpg for the Chevy Malibu? Explain.

Group Activity Answers

1) 16.9 gal   2) 18 gal   3) 34.2 gal   4) 61.5 gal

5)

$0.994/fl oz	$0.909/oz	$1.765/oz
$0.275/fl oz; better buy	$0.427/oz; better buy	$0.823/oz; better buy

6) Answers may vary. The price of $1.50 is for only 0.85 ounce, which is less than 1 full ounce. The unit rate, which is the cost for 1 full ounce, should be greater.

7) 750 mi

8) 1846 mi; this is more than the estimate.

9) Answers may vary. The city mpg will be less than the combined mpg. During city driving, there is a lot of stop-and-go traffic and idle time spent waiting at lights. Fuel is still being used to sit at a red light, but the car isn't covering any distance. This brings the mpg down. The highway mpg is higher because cars can drive faster on the highway, which means that they can cover more ground than they would in the city. The combined mpg is somewhere between the city and highway mpgs.

em POWER me The Right Approach to Homework

Let's face it: Homework has a bad reputation. Nonetheless, it is a fact of college life, and more importantly, it is an excellent opportunity to learn. Too many students sacrifice this opportunity either by not doing their homework, or, almost as harmfully, by allowing their negative attitudes to interfere with their performance.

To assess your own attitudes toward homework, consider each of the following statements. On a scale of 1 (Does not apply to me) to 5 (Strongly applies to me), mark how well each statement describes you.

_____ Usually I throw away my homework as soon as my instructor returns it.

_____ I put off my homework as long as possible.

_____ I don't write down my homework assignments; I just try to remember them.

_____ I like to have music and the TV on to keep me entertained while I'm doing homework.

_____ I often do my homework during class.

_____ I usually get so frustrated with homework that I just give up after a few questions.

_____ My goal with homework is to finish as quickly as possible, so that I can move on to something fun.

_____ I don't think I've ever completed a homework assignment early.

_____ I always keep my phone on while I'm doing my homework, in case anyone wants to talk.

_____ If there are homework problems I can't figure out, I just ask my friends to tell me the answers.

Find your average response to the statements. Do this by adding up all the numbers you wrote and dividing by 10. If your average is more than 4, it is likely that your feelings about homework are negatively impacting your performance. Remember, homework benefits you in the long run. It will help bring you closer to your educational and career goals. Make the most of your time doing homework by using the strategies described at the beginning of the chapter.

Chapter 6: Summary

Definition/Procedure	Example

6.1 Ratios

A **ratio** is a comparison of two quantities. It can compare numbers or measurements with the same units. Ratios can be written in several different ways. **(p. 383)**	The ratio of 5 to 9 can also be written as $$5:9 \quad \text{or} \quad \frac{5}{9}$$
Writing a Ratio in Lowest Terms When writing a ratio as a fraction in lowest terms, we divide out common units. **(p. 383)**	Write the ratio 4 ft to 10 ft as a fraction in lowest terms. $\dfrac{4 \text{ ft}}{10 \text{ ft}} = \dfrac{4}{10}$ Divide out common units. $= \dfrac{4 \div 2}{10 \div 2} = \dfrac{2}{5}$ Write the ratio in lowest terms.
If the units in a ratio are different, we must begin by changing one of the units so that it is the same as the other one. **(p. 387)**	Write the ratio as a fraction in lowest terms: 2 hr to 50 min. Change hours to minutes: 2 hr = 2 · 60 min = 120 min Then, the ratio of 2 hr to 50 min is $\dfrac{2 \text{ hr}}{50 \text{ min}} = \dfrac{120 \text{ min}}{50 \text{ min}} = \dfrac{120 \text{ min}}{50 \text{ min}} = \dfrac{120}{50} = \dfrac{12}{5}$

6.2 Rates

A **rate** compares quantities with different units. Rates are usually written in lowest terms. **(p. 392)**	Write the rate 190 mi in 4 hr as a fraction in lowest terms. $\dfrac{190 \text{ mi}}{4 \text{ hr}} = \dfrac{190 \text{ mi} \div 2}{4 \text{ hr} \div 2} = \dfrac{95 \text{ mi}}{2 \text{ hr}}$
Unit Rate A **unit rate** is a rate with a denominator of 1. **(p. 393)**	Find the unit rate: 376 mi on 16 gal $\dfrac{376 \text{ mi}}{16 \text{ gal}} = \dfrac{376 \text{ mi} \div 8}{16 \text{ gal} \div 8} = \dfrac{47 \text{ mi}}{2 \text{ gal}}$ Next, divide 47 by 2 to find the unit rate: $2)\overline{47.0}$ = 23.5 The unit rate is 23.5 mi/gal or 23.5 miles per gallon.
Unit Price and Best Buy The **unit price** of an item is the cost of the item per unit. We can use the unit price to figure out which item in a store gives us the most value for our money. This is called the **best buy**. Round answers to the thousandths place. **(p. 394)**	A grocery store sells an 8-oz container of cream cheese for $2.89 and a 12-oz container for $4.39. Which is the better buy? Find the unit price of each item. 8-oz container: $\dfrac{\$2.89}{8 \text{ oz}} \approx \$0.361$ per ounce 12-oz container: $\dfrac{\$4.39}{12 \text{ oz}} \approx \$0.366$ per ounce The 8-oz container has the lower unit price, so it is the better buy.

Definition/Procedure	Example

6.3 Proportions

A **proportion** is a statement that two ratios or two rates are equal. **(p. 398)**

Write the statement as a proportion:

1 in. is to 3 ft as 4 in. is to 12 ft.

$$\frac{1 \text{ in.}}{3 \text{ ft}} = \frac{4 \text{ in.}}{12 \text{ ft}}$$

Determining Whether a Proportion Is True or False by Writing the Ratios in Lowest Terms

One way to determine whether a proportion is true or false is by writing each ratio in lowest terms. **(p. 399)**

Determine whether each proportion is true or false by writing each ratio in lowest terms.

a) $\dfrac{24}{18} = \dfrac{12}{9}$ b) $\dfrac{2}{7} = \dfrac{14}{35}$

a) Write each fraction in lowest terms.

$$\frac{24}{18} = \frac{24 \div 6}{18 \div 6} = \frac{4}{3} \qquad \frac{12}{9} = \frac{12 \div 3}{9 \div 3} = \frac{4}{3}$$

Since each fraction simplifies to $\dfrac{4}{3}$, the proportion is true.

b) The fraction $\dfrac{2}{7}$ is already in lowest terms. Write $\dfrac{14}{35}$ in

lowest terms: $\dfrac{14}{35} = \dfrac{14 \div 7}{35 \div 7} = \dfrac{2}{5}$

Since $\dfrac{2}{7} \neq \dfrac{2}{5}$, the proportion is false.

Determining Whether a Proportion Is True or False Using Cross Products

Another way to determine whether a proportion is true or false is by finding the *cross products*. The **cross products** are the numbers we get when we *multiply along the diagonals* of the proportion.

Using Cross Products to Determine Whether a Proportion Is True or False

1) If the cross products in a proportion are equal, then the proportion is true.

2) If the cross products in a proportion are not equal, then the proportion is false. **(p. 400)**

Determine whether each proportion is true or false by finding the cross products.

a) $\dfrac{10}{15} = \dfrac{4}{6}$ b) $\dfrac{5.8}{3} = \dfrac{4.2}{2}$

a) Find the cross products.

$$\frac{10}{15} \diagup \frac{4}{6} \quad \begin{array}{l} 15 \cdot 4 = 60 \\ 10 \cdot 6 = 60 \end{array} \quad \begin{array}{l} \text{True. The cross} \\ \text{products are} \\ \text{equal.} \end{array}$$

The cross products are equal, so the proportion is true.

b) Find the cross products.

$$\frac{5.8}{3} \diagup \frac{4.2}{2} \quad \begin{array}{l} 3 \cdot 4.2 = 12.6 \\ 5.8 \cdot 2 = 11.6 \end{array} \quad \begin{array}{l} \text{False. The cross} \\ \text{products are } \textit{not} \\ \text{equal.} \end{array}$$

The cross products are *not* equal, so the proportion is false.

Definition/Procedure	Example

6.4 Solve Proportions

A **variable** is a symbol, usually a letter, used to represent an unknown number. When we put variables together with operation symbols like $+$, $-$, $\times$, and $\div$, we get an **expression.** For example, the expression $8x$ means $8 \cdot x$. The variable x represents a number. The value of the expression depends on the value of the variable. **(p. 404)**

Evaluate $3x$ when $x = 11$.

Evaluate $3x$ for $x = 11$:
$= 3(11)$ Substitute 11 for x.
$= 33$ Multiply.

When $x = 11$, $3x = 33$.

What Is an Equation?

When we set two expressions equal to each other, we get an **equation.** Therefore, an equation contains an $=$ sign, and an expression does not. **(p. 404)**

$5x$ is an expression. $5x = 20$ is an equation.

To **solve** an equation means to find the value of the variable that makes the equation true. The number that solves the equation is called the **solution. (p. 404)**

The equation $5x = 20$ means $5 \cdot x = 20$. The solution of the equation is $x = 4$ because $5 \cdot 4 = 20$.

Solving an Equation

We can solve an equation like $6x = 42$ using the *division property of equality*. This property says that if we divide both sides of an equation by the same nonzero number, then we get an equivalent equation. **(p. 405)**

Solve $6x = 42$.

$6x = 42$

$\dfrac{6x}{6} = \dfrac{42}{6}$ Divide each side by 6.

$\dfrac{\overset{1}{\cancel{6}}x}{\underset{1}{\cancel{6}}} = 7$ Divide out the common factor; $1x$ is the same as x.

$x = 7$ Simplify.

The solution is $x = 7$.

Solving a Proportion

If a proportion contains one variable, we use cross products and the division property of equality to find that missing value. This is called **solving the proportion.**

How to Solve a Proportion

Step 1: Find the cross products.

Step 2: Set the cross products equal to each other, and solve the equation.

Step 3: Check the solution by substituting it into the original proportion and finding the cross products. **(p. 406)**

Solve $\dfrac{3}{8} = \dfrac{x}{24}$.

Step 1: Find the cross products.

$$\frac{3}{8} \diagup\!\!\!\!\diagdown \frac{x}{24} \quad \begin{array}{l} 8 \cdot x = 8x \\ 3 \cdot 24 = 72 \end{array}$$

Step 2: Set the cross products equal to each other and solve the equation.

$8x = 72$ Set the cross products equal to each other.

$\dfrac{8x}{8} = \dfrac{72}{8}$ Divide each side by 8.

$\dfrac{\overset{1}{\cancel{8}}x}{\underset{1}{\cancel{8}}} = \dfrac{72}{8}$ Divide out the common factor.

$x = 9$ Simplify.

Step 3: Check the solution in the original proportion, $\dfrac{3}{8} = \dfrac{x}{24}$, by checking to see whether the cross products are equal.

$$\frac{3}{8} \diagup\!\!\!\!\diagdown \frac{9}{24} \quad \begin{array}{l} 8 \cdot 9 = 72 \\ 3 \cdot 24 = 72 \end{array} \quad \text{Substitute 9 for } x.$$

Since the cross products are equal, the solution is $x = 9$.

Definition/Procedure	Example

6.5 Solve Applied Problems Involving Proportions

We can solve many applied problems using proportions. Look for key words like *in, per, for, from, on, out of, is to,* and *as.*

Use the Five Steps for Solving Applied Problems that were first presented in Section 2.7.

Steps for Solving Applied Problems

Step 1: **Read** the problem carefully, more than once if necessary, until you understand it. Restate the problem in your own words. Draw a picture, if applicable. Identify what you are being asked to find.

Step 2: **Make a plan** for solving the problem. Underline important words that might help you solve the problem.

Step 3: **Solve** the problem using your plan and the information given. Look at the important words you have underlined.

Step 4: **State the answer** in a complete sentence.

Step 5: **Check** the answer. **(p. 411)**

In her hybrid car, Emilie can drive 336 mi on 8 gal of gas. How far can she drive on 12 gal?

Step 1: **Read** the problem carefully, and restate it in your own words.

We can think of this problem as a proportion in this way:

336 mi <u>is to</u> 8 gal <u>as</u> how many mi <u>is to</u> 12 gallons?

We must find the number of miles Emilie can drive on 12 gal of gas.

Step 2: **Make a plan.** We have underlined important words in our restatement of the problem in Step 1. Let x represent the quantity we are trying to find.

x = number of miles Emilie can drive on 12 gallons of gas

Plan: Write a proportion using x for the unknown quantity.

$$\frac{336 \text{ mi}}{8 \text{ gal}} = \frac{x}{12 \text{ gal}}$$

Step 3: **Solve** the problem. We do not need the units when solving for x.

$\dfrac{336}{8} = \dfrac{x}{12}$ Write the equation without the units.

$8x = 336 \cdot 12$ Find the cross products.

$8x = 4032$ Multiply.

$x = 504$ Divide by 8 to solve the equation.

Step 4: **State the answer** in a complete sentence.

Emilie can drive 504 mi on 12 gal of gas.

Step 5: **Check** the answer. Use the cross products to check $x = 504$ in the proportion. The check is left to the student.

Chapter 6: Review Exercises

*Additional answers can be found in the Answers to Exercises appendix.

(6.1)

1) What is a ratio?   A ratio compares two quantities with the same units.

2) The child to teacher ratio in the toddler room at a daycare is 4 to 1. What does this mean?   For every four children, there is one teacher.

Write each ratio as a fraction in lowest terms.

3) 175 yd to 300 yd $\dfrac{7}{12}$ 4) 60 oz to 160 oz $\dfrac{3}{8}$

5) \$1.25 to \$0.25 $\dfrac{5}{1}$ 6) 3.8 lb to 1.2 lb $\dfrac{19}{6}$

7) $\dfrac{5}{12}$ to $\dfrac{7}{16}$ $\dfrac{20}{21}$ 8) $2\dfrac{1}{4}$ to $1\dfrac{1}{2}$ $\dfrac{3}{2}$

9) 10 oz to 2 lb $\dfrac{5}{16}$ 10) 12 hr to 12 min $\dfrac{60}{1}$

The table shows lifetime theatre ticket sales for the top-grossing 3D movies. Use this information for Exercises 11–16.

Write each ratio as a fraction in lowest terms.

3D Movie Title	Lifetime Gross (Theatres)
Avatar (2009)	760 million
Toy Story 3 (2010)	410 million
Alice in Wonderland (2010)	330 million
Up (2010)	290 million
Despicable Me (2010)	250 million
Shrek Forever After (2010)	240 million
How to Train Your Dragon (2010)	220 million
Monsters vs. Aliens (2009)	200 million

(www.imbd.com)

11) What is the ratio that compares the number one 3D movie to the eighth best seller? $\frac{19}{5}$

12) What is the ratio that compares ticket sales for *Up* to ticket sales for *How to Train Your Dragon*? $\frac{29}{22}$

13) What is the ratio that compares the total ticket sales for *Up, Despicable Me,* and *How to Train Your Dragon* to ticket sales for *Avatar*? $\frac{1}{1}$

14) What is the ratio that compares the ticket sales for *Monsters vs. Aliens* to total ticket sales for *Up, Despicable Me, Shrek Forever After,* and *How to Train Your Dragon*? $\frac{1}{5}$

15) The gross earnings of which two movies give a ratio of 5 to 4? *Despicable Me* to *Monsters vs. Aliens*

16) The gross earnings of which two movies give a ratio of 11 to 8? *Alice in Wonderland* to *Shrek Forever After*

17) The year before a college football team went to a bowl game, the team sold 2800 season tickets. The year after the bowl game, they sold 4000 season tickets. Find the ratio of the increase in the number of tickets sold to the number sold before the bowl game. $\frac{3}{7}$

18) Write the ratio of the longest side to the shortest side.

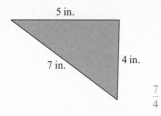

5 in.

7 in.   4 in.

$\frac{7}{4}$

(6.2)

19) What is the difference between a ratio and a rate?

Write each rate as a fraction in lowest terms.

20) 140 mi in 30 hr $\frac{14\ \text{mi}}{3\ \text{hr}}$

21) 2 cups for 6 servings $\frac{1\ \text{cup}}{3\ \text{servings}}$

22) $48 for 16 gal $\frac{\$3}{1\ \text{gal}}$

23) What is a unit rate? It is a rate with a denominator of 1.

24) Write the rate $\frac{\$15}{1\ \text{hr}}$ in two other ways. $15/hr or $15 per hour

Find each unit rate. Round the answer to the nearest hundredth where appropriate.

25) 180 text messages in 3 hr 60 text messages/hr

26) 384 desks for 12 classrooms 32 desks/classroom

27) $90 in 60 days $1.50/day

28) $131.25 in 15 hr $8.75/hr

29) Determine which package of paper napkins is the best buy, and give its unit price. 400-count; $0.012/napkin

Number of Napkins	Price
100	$1.49
250	$3.29
400	$4.99

30) Daryl drove his pickup truck 290 mi on 22.3 gal of gas. Find the vehicle's gas mileage to the nearest tenth. 13.0 mpg

31) A group of hikers in Yosemite National Park hiked the 14-mi round-trip trail to the top of Half-Dome and back. If it took $11\frac{1}{2}$ hr to do the hike, what is the group's average speed in miles per hour? Round the answer to the nearest tenth. 1.2 mph

32) Selena worked 24 hr and earned $468.00. Find her hourly wage. $19.50/hr

(6.3) Write each statement as a proportion.

33) 16 is to 14 as 24 is to 21. $\frac{16}{14} = \frac{24}{21}$

34) 9 mi is to 11 mi as 36 mi is to 44 mi. $\frac{9}{11} = \frac{36}{44}$

35) 350 cell phones is to 450 adults as 7 cell phones is to 9 adults. $\frac{350\ \text{cell phones}}{450\ \text{adults}} = \frac{7\ \text{cell phones}}{9\ \text{adults}}$

36) $80 is to 4 hr as $240 is to 12 hr. $\frac{\$80}{4\ \text{hr}} = \frac{\$240}{12\ \text{hr}}$

37) What are two ways to determine whether a proportion is true or false? 1) Write each ratio in lowest terms. 2) Find the cross products.

38) Explain how to use the cross products to determine whether a proportion is true or false. If the cross products are equal, then the proportion is true. If the cross products are not equal, then the proportion is false.

Determine whether each proportion is true or false by writing each ratio in lowest terms.

39) $\frac{28}{6} = \frac{42}{9}$ $\frac{14}{3} = \frac{14}{3}$; true 40) $\frac{30}{48} = \frac{16}{28}$ $\frac{5}{8} \neq \frac{4}{7}$; false

41) $\frac{120}{340} = \frac{200}{460}$ $\frac{6}{17} \neq \frac{10}{23}$; false 42) $\frac{225}{300} = \frac{63}{84}$ $\frac{3}{4} = \frac{3}{4}$; true

Determine whether each proportion is true or false by finding the cross products.

43) $\frac{14}{24} = \frac{4}{9}$ $126 \neq 96$; false 44) $\frac{1.4}{16} = \frac{1.8}{17}$ $23.8 \neq 28.8$; false

45) $\frac{5\frac{1}{4}}{6} = \frac{4\frac{1}{12}}{4\frac{2}{3}}$ $\frac{49}{2} = \frac{49}{2}$; true 46) $\frac{3\frac{1}{4}}{2.02} = \frac{4\frac{1}{2}}{3.04}$ $9.88 = 9.09$; false

47) a) Add $\frac{8}{9} + \frac{13}{15}$. $\frac{79}{45}$ or $1\frac{34}{45}$

   b) Determine whether the proportion $\frac{8}{9} = \frac{13}{15}$ is true or false.
   $120 \neq 117$; false

(6.4)

48) What is a variable?   It is a symbol, usually a letter, that is used to represent an unknown number.

49) Evaluate $12x$ when $x = 8$.   96

50) Evaluate $5x$ when $x = 3$.   15

Solve each equation using the division property of equality.

51) $2x = 18$ $x = 9$ 52) $8x = 88$ $x = 11$

53) $45 = 15x$ $x = 3$ 54) $6 = 1.2x$ $x = 5$

Solve each proportion, and check the answer using the cross products.

55) $\frac{4}{3} = \frac{x}{9}$ $x = 12$ 56) $\frac{5}{x} = \frac{11}{55}$ $x = 25$

57) $\frac{8}{15} = \frac{2}{x}$ $x = \frac{15}{4}$ 58) $\frac{x}{3} = \frac{63}{18}$ $x = \frac{21}{2}$

59) $\frac{x}{2\frac{1}{4}} = \frac{1\frac{2}{3}}{10}$ $x = \frac{3}{8}$ 60) $\frac{\frac{5}{9}}{3\frac{1}{3}} = \frac{\frac{5}{6}}{x}$ $x = 5$

61) $\frac{5.7}{x} = \frac{2.1}{1.4}$ $x = 3.8$ 62) $\frac{7}{4.5} = \frac{x}{3.6}$ $x = 5.6$

(6.5) Solve each problem using a proportion.

63) In an architectural drawing, a 300-ft-tall building is drawn 4 in. high. What is the actual height of a building that is drawn 6 in. high?   450 ft

64) On average, one tree produces nearly 260 lb of oxygen each year. How many pounds of oxygen will be produced by 12 trees in one year? (www.treesaregood.com)   3120 lb

65) A nursing student observes an intravenous drip rate of 10 drops per 12 sec. How many drops should be observed in 1 min?   50 drops

66) A university finds that, on average, 2 out of 9 of its students receive credit for English composition due to a high Advanced Placement test score. If the most recent freshman class contains 2548 students, approximately how many will receive credit for English composition through their AP tests? Round the answer to the nearest whole number.   566 students

Mixed Exercises: Sections 6.1–6.5

Write each ratio or rate as a fraction in lowest terms.

67) 27 books to 45 books $\frac{3}{5}$ 68) $5.50 to $2.50 $\frac{11}{5}$

69) 2850 ft in 90 sec $\frac{95 \text{ ft}}{3 \text{ sec}}$ 70) 18 hr to 2.5 days $\frac{3}{10}$

71) 4 yd to 6 ft $\frac{2}{1}$ 72) 420 mi on 24 gal $\frac{35 \text{ mi}}{2 \text{ gal}}$

Find each unit rate.

73) 224 miles in 3.5 hours   64 mi/hr   74) $31.50 for 6 people $5.25/person

Determine whether each proportion is true or false.

75) $\frac{5.5}{10} = \frac{4.2}{8}$ $44 \neq 42$; false 76) $\frac{96}{36} = \frac{112}{48}$ $\frac{8}{3} \neq \frac{7}{3}$; false

77) $\frac{16}{32} = \frac{4}{8}$ $128 = 128$; true 78) $\frac{1\frac{7}{8}}{3} = \frac{2\frac{1}{3}}{3\frac{11}{15}}$ $7 = 7$; true

Solve each proportion.

79) $\frac{4}{x} = \frac{11}{44}$ $x = 16$ 80) $\frac{5}{21} = \frac{x}{7}$ $x = \frac{5}{3}$

81) $\frac{x}{2\frac{1}{2}} = \frac{3\frac{1}{3}}{4}$ $x = 2\frac{1}{12}$ 82) $\frac{0.5}{0.4} = \frac{12.5}{x}$ $x = 10$

Solve each problem.

83) If the ratio of potato starch flour to tapioca flour in a gluten-free cookie recipe is 3 to 2, how much tapioca flour is used if the recipe calls for 1 cup of potato starch flour? $\frac{2}{3}$ cup

84) If Faviana slept a total of 511 hr over the past 10 weeks, what was her rate of sleep in hours per week?   51.1 hr/wk

85) The cost per unit at a local community college is raised from $48 per unit to $56 per unit. Find the ratio of the increase in cost to the original cost. $\frac{1}{6}$

86) If 80 grams of ice cream contains 10 grams of fat, how much fat is in 180 grams of ice cream?   22.5 grams

Chapter 6: Test

*Additional answers can be found in the Answers to Exercises appendix.

1) What is the difference between a ratio and a rate?
A ratio compares two quantities with the same units, but a rate compares quantities with different units.

Write each ratio as a fraction in lowest terms.

2) 63 points to 35 points $\frac{9}{5}$ 3) 24 in. to 3 ft $\frac{2}{3}$

4) 18 hr to 3 hr $\frac{6}{1}$

5) In 12 oz of yogurt, the ratio of cholesterol to protein is 10 g to 28 g. Write the ratio as a fraction in lowest terms, and explain what it means. $\frac{5}{14}$; for every 5 g of cholesterol in the yogurt, there are 14 g of protein.

6) Write the ratio of the longest side to the shortest side. $\frac{13}{5}$

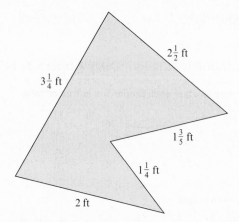

$2\frac{1}{2}$ ft

$3\frac{1}{4}$ ft

$1\frac{3}{5}$ ft

$1\frac{1}{4}$ ft

2 ft

7) A coffee stand raises the price of a 16-oz cup of coffee from \$1.25 to \$1.50. Find the ratio of the increase in price to the original price. $\frac{1}{5}$

Find each unit rate.

8) \$12.45 for 5 lb
\$2.49 per lb or \$2.49/lb

9) 170 mi in 4 hr
42.5 mi/hr or 42.5 mph

10) Thomas drove his motorcycle 5752 miles over the past year. What was his driving rate in miles per week? Round the answer to the nearest tenth. 110.6 mi/wk

11) A nursing student sets an intravenous drip rate at 1500 drops per 1/2 hour. What is the unit drip rate in drops per minute? 50 drops per minute

12) Determine which size of olive oil is the best buy, and give its unit price. 17 oz; \$0.482/oz

Size	Price
8 oz	\$3.99
17 oz	\$8.19
26 oz	\$12.69

13) Write the statement as a proportion. \$12 is to 9 lb as \$20 is to 15 lb. $\frac{\$12}{9\text{ lb}} = \frac{\$20}{15\text{ lb}}$

14) Determine whether each proportion is true or false.

a) $\frac{25}{35} = \frac{10}{14}$ true

b) $\frac{3\frac{1}{4}}{2} = \frac{9\frac{1}{2}}{6}$ false

15) Elsa multiplies $\frac{3}{10} \cdot \frac{4}{9}$ like this:

$$\frac{3}{10} \cdot \frac{4}{9} \quad \begin{array}{l} 10 \cdot 4 = 40 \\ 3 \cdot 9 = 27 \end{array} \quad \boxed{\frac{40}{27}}$$

Did she multiply these fractions correctly? Explain your answer. If Elsa's answer is wrong, find the correct answer.

16) Evaluate $6x$ when $x = 9$. 54

17) Solve $4x = 28$. $x = 7$

Solve each proportion. Check the answer using the cross products.

18) $\frac{5}{2} = \frac{x}{6}$ $x = 15$

19) $\frac{0.6}{0.18} = \frac{4}{x}$ $x = 1.2$

20) $\frac{2\frac{5}{8}}{x} = \frac{5}{8}$ $x = 4\frac{1}{5}$

Solve each problem using a proportion.

21) On an architectural drawing, 1 in. represents an actual length of 6 ft. How many inches long should an architect draw a wall that is 27 ft long? 4.5 in.

22) In a pharmacy, Dara reads that a medication is to be given to a patient at a rate of 2.7 mg for every 40 lb. How much medicine should be given to a patient weighing 140 lb? 9.45 mg

23) In 2008, approximately 20 out of 100 car accidents in the United States involved some type of distraction. In a county that had 40 accidents in 2008, how many involved driver distraction? (www.distraction.gov) 8 accidents

24) A 110-lb person burns approximately 88 calories performing high-impact aerobics for 10 min. At this rate, how many calories will be burned in 45 min? (www.mayoclinic.com) 396 cal

25) The ancient Greeks believed that the rectangle most pleasing to the eye, the golden rectangle, had sides in which the ratio of its length to its width was approximately 8 to 5. They erected many buildings using this golden ratio, including the Parthenon. The marble floor of a museum foyer is to be designed as a golden rectangle. Find the width of the foyer if the length will be 48 ft. 30 ft

Chapter 6: Cumulative Review for Chapters 1–6

*Additional answers can be found in the Answers to Exercises appendix.

Perform the indicated operations. Write all answers in lowest terms.

1) $\dfrac{8}{35} \div \dfrac{4}{21}$ $\dfrac{6}{5}$ or $1\dfrac{1}{5}$

2) $12 - 3.61$ 8.39

3) $577 + 38{,}914 + 4008 + 61$ $43{,}560$

4) $\begin{array}{r} 4073 \\ \times\ 809 \end{array}$ $3{,}295{,}057$

5) $\dfrac{7}{12} + \dfrac{3}{8}$ $\dfrac{23}{24}$

6) $2\dfrac{4}{5} \cdot 4\dfrac{1}{2}$ $\dfrac{63}{5}$ or $12\dfrac{3}{5}$

7) $5\dfrac{1}{6} - 2\dfrac{3}{4}$ $2\dfrac{5}{12}$

8) $7.84 \div 1.4$ 5.6

9) 65.7×0.03 1.971

10) $\dfrac{11}{15} - \dfrac{7}{10}$ $\dfrac{1}{30}$

11) $56{,}000{,}000 \div 10{,}000$ 5600

12) 4720×1000 $4{,}720{,}000$

13) $\sqrt{144} + 3(10 - 2) \div 6$ 16

14) $100 \div 4 + 2^3 \cdot 5 - (8 - 2)^2$ 29

For Exercises 15 and 16, round 174.8156 to the indicated place.

15) hundredths 174.82

16) tens 170

17) Write 0.64 as a fraction in lowest terms. $\dfrac{16}{25}$

18) Write as a ratio in lowest terms: 50 minutes to 2 hours $\dfrac{5}{12}$

19) Solve the proportion $\dfrac{x}{3} = \dfrac{15}{9}$. $x = 5$

20) Cantu records her gas purchases and odometer readings for each gas station visit. Complete the table below by finding the number of miles traveled and the gas mileage.

Date	Odometer Start	Odometer End	Miles Traveled	Gallons Purchased	Miles per Gallon
8/24	15,352.8	15,625.2	272.4	12.0	22.7
9/2	15,625.2	15,958.9	333.7	14.2	23.5
9/13	15,958.9	16,248.7	289.8	13.8	21.0
9/22	16,248.7	16,457.8	209.1	8.5	24.6

Solve each problem.

21) A sign in a clothing store says, "All merchandise is $\dfrac{1}{3}$ off."

A shirt with a regular price of \$44.99 is marked with a sale price of \$32.99. Is this correct? No. The price should be \$29.99.

22) Three friends go out to dinner and decide to split the bill evenly. Their dinner amounts to \$47.74, and they leave a \$9.50 tip. How much does each person owe? \$19.08

23) In 2009, California had the largest population at 36,961,664, while the least populated state, Wyoming, had a population of 544,270. How many more people lived in California? (www.census.gov) 36,417,394

24) In an area designated as a flood zone, approximately 5 out of 7 homeowners have flood insurance. If there are 1852 homes in this area, how many have flood insurance? Round the answer to the nearest whole number. 1323

25) The table shows the numbers of Americans, in millions, who did not have health insurance during the years 2004–2009. Find the mean, median, and mode. Round the answers to the nearest tenth of a million, if necessary. (www.census.gov) mean: 46.7 million; median: 46.1 million; mode: no mode

Year	2004	2005	2006	2007	2008	2009
Number of Uninsured Americans (in millions)	45.8	44.8	47.0	45.7	46.3	50.7

Measurement and Conversion

Math at Work:

Technical Writer

It's hard enough to understand how sophisticated electronics work. Now try explaining it to someone else. That challenge is the core of Mitch Kramer's job. As a technical writer at an electronics manufacturing company, Mitch writes how-to guides for the assembly and use of products as complicated as circuit boards and computer processors.

"My background is in computer information technology," Mitch says. "What I realized is that I had a unique ability to explain concepts to people in a way that made them clear. So I put that ability to work."

Mitch started out writing guides for the installation of televisions and other home electronics products and worked his way up to more complex writing. "People usually think of math and writing as separate activities," Mitch describes. "My career proves that they actually can go hand in hand."

Mitch's writing is included in all his company's products, helping clients across the United States and as far away as the United Kingdom and other European countries that use different measurement systems. Consequently, he needs to be familiar with conversions in order to clearly present concepts. For instance, he sometimes must convert inches and feet into centimeters and meters depending on the audience for whom he is writing.

In the end, though, he finds more similarities than differences in how to write clearly for different readers. "The beauty of math is that it is universal," Mitch says. "You just have to present it to people in a way that makes sense to them."

In this chapter, we explore a key component in sharing math across contexts (and continents!)—measurement and conversion. We also introduce some skills that will help you in your own writing, in class or on the job.

Many people consider math and writing to be wholly unrelated, but this is not the case. After all, you are reading a math *text*book right now. Further, nearly every profession that involves math also requires some writing, whether it is in the form of a lab report, a memo, or simply an email to colleagues. As a college student, you will also, of course, be asked to do a great deal of writing as you work toward your degree. The step-by-step skills below will help you write more successfully in any context.

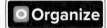

- Decide what your goals are for the piece of writing. Do you need to communicate an opinion? Explain a decision to a coworker?
- Do a *freewriting exercise* to help start your thinking: Write continuously on your topic, without stopping, for 5 to 10 minutes.

- Define the main point, or thesis, of your piece of writing. What is the core of what you want to say?
- Construct an outline. Think of this as the scaffold on which you will build your piece of writing.

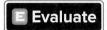

- Write your first draft. Do not let doubts get the better of you. The purpose of a first draft is to give you something to work with. Give yourself permission to be creative and make mistakes.
- Revise your first draft, asking yourself whether it accomplishes the goal you defined at the start of the process.
- Check your punctuation and spelling.

- Put yourself in the shoes of the person who will read the paper. How might he or she suggest changing the piece of writing?
- If you used anyone else's ideas in your writing, make sure you give them credit. Plagiarism could get you kicked out of school or fired!

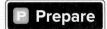

- Reconsider the message of your writing. Does it communicate what you want it to?

Chapter 7 POWER Plan

P Prepare

What are your goals for Chapter 7?

O Organize

How can you accomplish each goal? (Write in the steps you will take to succeed.)

1 Be prepared before and during class.

- _____
- _____
- _____
- _____

2 Understand the homework to the point where you could do it without needing any help or hints.

- _____
- _____
- _____

3 Use the P.O.W.E.R. framework to learn the steps of the writing process: *Becoming a Math Teacher to Reinforce Your Own Understanding.*

- _____
- _____
- _____

4 Write your own goal.
_____
_____

- _____
_____

What are your objectives for Chapter 7?	How can you accomplish each objective?
1 Learn how to use U.S. customary measurements and the metric system.	• Understand the relationships between the different ways to represent length, weight (mass), and capacity. • Be able to reproduce a chart that will help you convert between units. • Know how to correctly decide which unit would best describe a measurement.
2 Know how to convert units using multiplication and division or unit analysis.	• Understand that the procedure for multiplying or dividing to convert between units will work for U.S. customary measurements as well as for the metric system. • Understand unit fractions, and be able to apply the procedure for using unit analysis for both systems.
3 Know how to solve applied problems that involve measurements.	• Understand what you are being asked to find, and use the correct unit fractions. • Use the Five Steps for Solving Applied Problems, and add steps in the solving process that involve unit analysis.
4 Be able to convert between metric and U.S. customary measurements.	• Memorize the relationships between metric and U.S. customary measurements for length, weight (mass), and capacity. • Know how to use the formulas to convert between Fahrenheit and Celsius.
5 Write your own goal. _____	• _____ _____

E Evaluate	Complete the Chapter Review and Chapter Test. How did you do?	**R Rethink**	• After completing the emPOWERme exercise, explain the phrase "No one learns more about a topic than the teacher."
		• How can you use unit analysis to convert any measurement in both the U.S. customary and metric systems?
		• Which system of measurement do you find easier to use? Which system of measurement did you find easier to convert? Why?

7.1 Using U.S. Customary Measurements

P Prepare

O Organize

What are your objectives for Section 7.1?	**How can you accomplish each objective?**
1 Learn U.S. Customary Measurements	• Memorize the **Relationships Between U.S. Customary Measurements.** • Complete the given example on your own. • Complete You Try 1.
2 Use Multiplication or Division to Convert Between Units	• Write the procedure for **Using Multiplication or Division to Convert Between Units** in your own words, and add necessary intermediary steps after following the examples. • Complete the given example on your own. • Complete You Try 2.
3 Use Unit Analysis to Convert Between Units	• Write the definition of a *unit fraction* in your notes. • Write the equivalencies found in the table on p. 433 as unit fractions. • Write the procedure for **How to Convert Between Units Using Unit Analysis** in your own words. • Complete the given examples on your own. • Complete You Trys 3–6.
4 Solve Applied Problems Using Unit Analysis	• Use the Five Steps for Solving Applied Problems and add additional steps, as needed, from this section. • Complete the given examples on your own. • Complete You Trys 7 and 8.

 Read the explanations, follow the examples, take notes, and complete the You Trys.

1 Learn U.S. Customary Measurements

We use measurements every day: inches to measure the diagonal of a television screen, miles to measure the distance between two cities, quarts or gallons to measure a quantity of milk, pounds to measure our weight, and so on. Each of these is an example of a *U.S. customary measurement unit*. In the United States, we use **U.S. customary units** while most of the rest of the world uses the *metric system*. (The **metric system** uses units such as meters, liters, and grams. We will study the metric system in future sections.) In both systems, time is measured with the same units: seconds, minutes, hours, days, etc.

Sometimes, we must convert between different units like yards and feet. Therefore, we need to memorize the relationships between the units and their abbreviations given in the table here.

Relationships Between U.S. Customary Measurements

Length	Time
12 inches (in.) = 1 foot (ft)	60 seconds (sec) = 1 minute (min)
3 feet (ft) = 1 yard (yd)	60 minutes (min) = 1 hour (hr)
5280 feet (ft) = 1 mile (mi)	24 hours (hr) = 1 day
	7 days = 1 week (wk)
Capacity	**Weight**
8 fluid ounces (fl oz) = 1 cup (c)	16 ounces (oz) = 1 pound (lb)
2 cups (c) = 1 pint (pt)	2000 pounds (lb) = 1 ton
2 pints (pt) = 1 quart (qt)	
4 quarts (qt) = 1 gallon (gal)	

Let's practice using these basic relationships.

EXAMPLE 1

In-Class Example 1

Fill in the blank.
a) 1 hr = _____ min
b) _____ pt = 1 qt
c) 1 ft = _____ in.

Answer: a) 60 b) 2 c) 12

Fill in the blank.

a) 1 ft = _____ in.   1 ft = $\underline{12}$ in.

b) _____ wk = 1 yr $\underline{52}$ wk = 1 yr

c) 1 gal = _____ qt   1 gal = $\underline{4}$ qt

[YOU TRY 1]   Fill in the blank.

a) 1 yd = _____ ft   b) _____ lb = 1 ton   c) _____ c = 1 pt

Very often we have to convert between the units given in the table. A recipe, for example, might call for $2\frac{1}{2}$ cups of milk, but at the grocery store we buy milk in pints, quarts, or gallons. Do we buy a pint, a quart, or a gallon? Let's learn how to change from one U.S. unit to another. We can do this in two different ways: using multiplication or division, or using unit analysis.

2 Use Multiplication or Division to Convert Between Units

How do we know whether we multiply or divide to change units? Use these guidelines.

Procedure Use Multiplication or Division to Convert Between Units

1) When converting from a *larger unit* to a *smaller unit*, use *multiplication*.
2) When converting from a *smaller unit* to a *larger unit*, use *division*.

EXAMPLE 2

In-Class Example 2

Convert each measurement to the indicated unit.
a) 5 ft to inches
b) 4.5 days to hours
c) $3\frac{1}{2}$ c to pints
d) 4 oz to pounds

Answer: a) 60 in.
b) 108 hr
c) $1\frac{3}{4}$ pt or 1.75 pt
d) $\frac{1}{4}$ lb or 0.25 lb

Convert each measurement to the indicated unit.

a) 4 ft to inches

b) 1.5 days to hours

c) $2\frac{1}{2}$ c to pints

d) 12 oz to pounds

Solution

a) First, we need to know that 1 ft = 12 in. Next, notice that we are changing from a *larger unit,* feet, to a *smaller unit,* inches. So to change 4 ft to inches, we *multiply*.

$$4 \cdot 12 = 48 \text{ in.} \qquad \text{12 in. = 1 ft}$$

Therefore, 4 ft = 48 in.

b) Since we are asked to convert 1.5 days to hours, we need to know that 1 day = 24 hr. We are changing from a larger unit, *days,* to a smaller unit, *hours.* To change 1.5 days to hours, we will multiply.

$$1.5 \cdot 24 = 36 \qquad \text{24 hr = 1 day}$$

So, 1.5 days = 36 hr.

c) First ask yourself, *"How are cups and pints related?"* 2 c = 1 pt. This time we are asked to convert from a *smaller unit,* cups, to a *larger unit,* pints. Therefore, we will *divide*.

Change $2\frac{1}{2}$ to $\frac{5}{2}$.

$$2\frac{1}{2} \div 2 = \frac{5}{2} \div \frac{2}{1} = \frac{5}{2} \cdot \frac{1}{2} = \frac{5}{4} = 1\frac{1}{4} \text{ or } 1.25$$

Write 2 as $\frac{2}{1}$.　　Change division to multiplication by the reciprocal.

Therefore, $2\frac{1}{2}$ c = $1\frac{1}{4}$ pt or 1.25 pt.

d) To change 12 oz to pounds, we need to know that 16 oz = 1 lb. We are changing from the *smaller unit* of ounces to the *larger unit* of pounds, so we will *divide*.

$$12 \div 16 = \frac{12}{16} = \frac{12 \div 4}{16 \div 4} = \frac{3}{4} \text{ or } 0.75$$

Divide numerator and denominator by 4 to simplify the fraction.

Therefore, 12 oz $= \dfrac{3}{4}$ lb or 0.75 lb.

[YOU TRY 2] Convert each measurement to the indicated unit.

a) 8000 lb to tons

b) $1\dfrac{1}{2}$ qt to pints

c) 12 sec to minutes

d) 4.5 yd to feet

---

3 Use Unit Analysis to Convert Between Units

Another way to convert between units is to use *unit analysis*. This method is commonly used in chemistry, nursing, and other science courses. Recall from our work with ratios that we can divide out common units that appear in the numerator and denominator of a fraction. For example, we can write the ratio 9 feet to 12 feet as

$$\frac{9 \text{ ft}}{12 \text{ ft}} = \frac{9 \ \cancel{\text{ft}}}{12 \ \cancel{\text{ft}}} = \frac{3}{4} \qquad \text{Divide 9 and 12 by 3.}$$

because the units divide out. *In unit analysis, we divide out like units to help us convert between units and to guide us in performing the conversion correctly.*

Another concept we need to understand is that of a *unit fraction*. A **unit fraction** is a fraction that is equivalent to 1. The measurement equivalencies can be written as unit fractions. For example, we can think of the relationship 12 in. = 1 ft as the ratio 12 in. to 1 ft. Then, we can write the ratio

W Hint

Write the equivalencies as unit fractions.

$$\frac{12 \text{ in.}}{1 \text{ ft}} = \frac{12 \text{ in.}}{12 \text{ in.}} = \frac{\cancel{12 \text{ in.}}^{1}}{\cancel{12 \text{ in.}}_{1}} = \frac{1}{1} = 1$$

So, $\dfrac{12 \text{ in.}}{1 \text{ ft}}$ is a unit fraction because it is equal to 1. All of the equivalencies in the table on p. 433 can be written as unit fractions. To convert from one unit of measurement to another, we will multiply the measurement we are given by the appropriate unit fraction.

EXAMPLE 3

Use unit analysis to convert 36 in. to feet.

Solution

First, identify the units we are given and the units we want to get. Since we are given *inches* and we want to get *feet,* write down the relationship between inches and feet: 12 in. = 1 ft.

Next, multiply the measurement we are given, 36 in., by the unit fraction relating 12 in. and 1 ft *so that the inches divide out* and we will be left with feet.

$$36 \text{ in.} \cdot \frac{1 \text{ ft}}{12 \text{ in.}} = \frac{\overset{3}{\cancel{36 \text{ in.}}}}{1} \cdot \frac{1 \text{ ft}}{\underset{1}{\cancel{12 \text{ in.}}}} \qquad \text{Divide 36 and 12 by 12; divide out the unit of inches.}$$

$$= \frac{3 \text{ ft}}{1} \qquad \text{Multiply.}$$

$$= 3 \text{ ft} \qquad \text{Simplify.}$$

Therefore, 36 in. = 3 ft.

Let's summarize the steps for converting from one unit to another using unit analysis.

> **Procedure** How to Convert Between Units Using Unit Analysis
>
> **Step 1:** **Identify** the units given and the units we want to get. **Write down** the relationship between those units.
>
> **Step 2:** **Multiply** the given measurement by the unit fraction relating the unit given and the unit we want to get so that the given unit will divide out and leave us with the unit we want.

> **Note**
> The units tell us whether we are doing the conversion correctly. If the units do not divide out, then we are doing the problem incorrectly.

[YOU TRY 3] Use unit analysis to convert 120 min to hours.

EXAMPLE 4

Use unit analysis to convert each measurement to the indicated unit.

a) 5 wk to days   b) 7 pt to quarts

c) 1800 lb to tons   d) $5\frac{2}{3}$ yd to feet

Solution

a) **Step 1:** **Identify** the units given and the units we want to get. **Write down** the relationship between those units.

We are given *weeks* and want to convert to *days.* The relationship is

$$1 \text{ week} = 7 \text{ days}$$

Step 2: **Multiply** the given measurement by the unit fraction relating the unit given and the unit we want to get so that the given unit will divide out and leave us with the unit we want.

$$5 \text{ wk} \cdot \frac{7 \text{ days}}{1 \text{ wk}} = \frac{5 \text{ w\!k}}{1} \cdot \frac{7 \text{ days}}{1 \text{ w\!k}} \qquad \text{Divide out the unit of weeks.}$$

$$= \frac{35 \text{ days}}{1} \qquad \text{Multiply.}$$

$$= 35 \text{ days} \qquad \text{Simplify.}$$

So, 5 weeks = 35 days.

Note

If we had written the unit fraction with weeks in the numerator and days in the denominator, we would not have been able to divide out the units:

$5 \text{ wk} \cdot \dfrac{1 \text{ wk}}{7 \text{ days}}$. So, if you do not set up the problem correctly the first time, the units will let you know! In that case, try switching the numerator and denominator to see whether the units will divide out.

b) **Step 1:** **Identify** the units given and the units we want to get. **Write down** the relationship between those units.

We are given 7 *pints* and want to convert to *quarts*. The relationship is

$$2 \text{ pt} = 1 \text{ qt}$$

Step 2: **Multiply** the given measurement by the unit fraction relating the unit given and the unit we want to get so that the given unit will divide out and leave us with the unit we want.

Hint
Notice that we multiply when using unit fractions.

$$7 \text{ pt} \cdot \frac{1 \text{ qt}}{2 \text{ pt}} = \frac{7 \text{ p\!t}}{1} \cdot \frac{1 \text{ qt}}{2 \text{ p\!t}} \qquad \text{Divide out the unit of pints.}$$

$$= \frac{7 \text{ qt}}{2} \qquad \text{Multiply.}$$

$$= \frac{7}{2} \text{ qt} \qquad \text{Simplify.}$$

$$= 3\frac{1}{2} \text{ qt or } 3.5 \text{ qt} \qquad \text{Write the final answer as a mixed number or decimal.}$$

Therefore, $7 \text{ pt} = 3\dfrac{1}{2}$ qt or 3.5 qt.

c) **Step 1:** **Identify** the units given and the units we want to get. **Write down** the relationship between those units.

We are given 1800 *lb* and want to convert to *tons*. The relationship is

$$2000 \text{ lb} = 1 \text{ ton}$$

Step 2: **Multiply** the given measurement by the unit fraction relating the unit given and the unit we want to get so that the given unit will divide out and leave us with the unit we want.

$$1800 \text{ lb} \cdot \frac{1 \text{ ton}}{2000 \text{ lb}} = \frac{\overset{9}{\cancel{1800}} \text{ lb}}{1} \cdot \frac{1 \text{ ton}}{\underset{10}{\cancel{2000}} \text{ lb}}$$

Divide the numbers by 2000; divide out the unit of pounds.

$$= \frac{9 \text{ ton}}{10}$$

Multiply.

$$= \frac{9}{10} \text{ ton or } 0.9 \text{ ton}$$

Simplify.

Therefore, $1800 \text{ lb} = \dfrac{9}{10}$ ton or 0.9 ton.

d) ***Step 1:*** **Identify** the units given and the units we want to get. **Write down** the relationship between those units.

We are given $5\frac{2}{3}$ *yd* and want to convert to *feet.* The relationship is

$$1 \text{ yd} = 3 \text{ ft}$$

Step 2: **Multiply** the given measurement by the unit fraction relating the unit given and the unit we want to get so that the given unit will divide out and leave us with the unit we want.

$$5\frac{2}{3} \text{ yd} \cdot \frac{3 \text{ ft}}{1 \text{ yd}} = \frac{17}{3} \text{ yd} \cdot \frac{3 \text{ ft}}{1 \text{ yd}}$$

Change the mixed number to an improper fraction.

$$= \frac{17}{\underset{1}{\cancel{3}}} \text{ yd} \cdot \frac{\overset{1}{\cancel{3}} \text{ ft}}{1 \text{ yd}}$$

Divide out 3; divide out the unit of yards.

$$= \frac{17 \text{ ft}}{1}$$

Multiply.

$$= 17 \text{ ft}$$

Simplify.

So, $5\dfrac{2}{3} \text{ yd} = 17 \text{ ft}.$

[YOU TRY 4] Use unit analysis to convert each measurement to the indicated unit.

a) 3 lb to ounces   b) 9 c to pints

c) 48 min to hours   d) $2\dfrac{1}{4}$ mi to feet

Sometimes, we have to use more than one unit fraction to convert to the desired unit. This is often done in science classes.

Convert 96 in. to yards.

Solution

We are given *inches* and want to convert to *yards*. We will use two relationships to do this conversion. They are

$$12 \text{ in.} = 1 \text{ ft} \quad \text{and} \quad 3 \text{ ft} = 1 \text{ yd}$$

Use this unit fraction to change feet to yards.

$$\frac{\overset{8}{\cancel{96} \text{ in.}}}{1} \cdot \frac{1 \text{ ft}}{\cancel{12} \text{ in.}} \cdot \frac{1 \text{ yd}}{3 \text{ ft}} = \frac{8 \text{ yd}}{3} \quad \text{Multiply.}$$

Use this unit fraction to change inches to feet.

$$= \frac{8}{3} \text{ yd or } 2\frac{2}{3} \text{ yd}$$

[YOU TRY 5] Convert 1200 sec to hours.

EXAMPLE 6

Use unit analysis to convert 3 days to seconds.

Solution

We are given *days* and want to convert to *seconds*. The relationships are

$$1 \text{ day} = 24 \text{ hr} \quad 1 \text{ hr} = 60 \text{ min} \quad 1 \text{ min} = 60 \text{ sec}$$

We will do this conversion in a single step using more than one unit fraction.

Use this unit fraction to change hours to minutes.

$$\frac{3 \text{ days}}{1} \cdot \frac{24 \text{ hr}}{1 \text{ day}} \cdot \frac{60 \text{ min}}{1 \text{ hr}} \cdot \frac{60 \text{ sec}}{1 \text{ min}} \quad \text{Divide out the correct units.}$$

Use this unit fraction to change days to hours.

Finally, use this unit fraction to change minutes to seconds.

$$= \frac{259,200 \text{ sec}}{1} = 259,200 \text{ sec} \quad \text{Multiply and simplify.}$$

Therefore, 3 days = 259,200 sec.

[YOU TRY 6] Use unit analysis to convert 3 gal to cups.

4 Solve Applied Problems Using Unit Analysis

Unit analysis can be used to solve many different types of applied problems. We will use the steps for solving applied problems that we first learned in Section 2.7.

EXAMPLE 7

In-Class Example 7

Use Example 7.

Larry is a chef, and his company is catering a large party. One batch of cheese fondue uses $\frac{3}{4}$ cup heavy cream. If he needs to make 12 times that amount of cheese fondue, how many quarts of heavy cream does he need?

Solution

Step 1: **Read** the problem carefully, and restate it in your own words.

One batch of cheese fondue uses $\frac{3}{4}$ c heavy cream. We must determine the number of _quarts of heavy cream_ needed to make 12 batches of fondue.

Step 2: **Make a plan.** Let's underline important words in our restatement of the problem in Step 1.

Plan: First, multiply $\frac{3}{4}$ c by 12 to determine the number of cups of heavy cream needed. Then, change the number of cups to quarts.

Step 3: **Solve** the problem.

Total cups of heavy cream needed: $\dfrac{3}{4} c \cdot 12 = \dfrac{3}{4} c \cdot \dfrac{12}{1} = 9 c$

Change 9 _cups_ to _quarts_:

This unit fraction changes cups to pints.

$$\dfrac{9\,\cancel{c}}{1} \cdot \dfrac{1\,\cancel{pt}}{2\,\cancel{c}} \cdot \dfrac{1\,qt}{2\,\cancel{pt}} \qquad \text{Divide out the correct units.}$$

This unit fraction changes pints to quarts.

$$= \dfrac{9\,qt}{4} = \dfrac{9}{4}\,qt = 2\dfrac{1}{4}\,qt$$

Step 4: **State the answer** in a complete sentence.

Larry needs $2\dfrac{1}{4}$ qt heavy cream for the cheese fondue.

Step 5: **Check** the answer. Work backward. Change quarts to cups, then divide by 12.

$$2\dfrac{1}{4}\,qt = \dfrac{9}{4}\,qt \qquad \text{Change the mixed number to a fraction.}$$

$$\dfrac{9}{4}\,\cancel{qt} \cdot \dfrac{2\,\cancel{pt}}{1\,\cancel{qt}} \cdot \dfrac{2\,c}{1\,\cancel{pt}} \qquad \text{Divide out the correct factors and units.}$$

$$= 9 c$$

This 9 c heavy cream is for 12 batches of cheese fondue. Divide 9 by 12 to determine how many cups of heavy cream are used for one batch.

$$\frac{9\,c}{12} = \frac{9}{12}c = \frac{3}{4}c \text{ heavy cream}$$

This is the same as the amount stated in the original problem, so the answer is correct.

[YOU TRY 7] Julia's frozen lemonade recipe uses $\frac{2}{3}$ c orange juice. If she needs to make 6 times the amount of the recipe, how many quarts of orange juice will she need?

EXAMPLE 8

In-Class Example 8

Jamaal has to buy cinnamon at the grocery store. The label on the shelf for Brand A says that its unit cost is $1.39/oz. The label for Brand B says that the unit cost is $20.99/lb. Which is the better buy?

Answer: Brand B is the better buy because the unit cost of Brand A is $22.24/lb.

Kate has to buy paprika at the grocery store. The label on the shelf for Brand A says that its unit cost is $1.79/oz. The label for Brand B says that the unit cost is $22.59/lb. Which is the better buy?

Solution

Step 1: **Read** the problem carefully, and restate it in your own words.

Brand A costs $\underline{\$1.79/oz}$ and Brand B costs $\underline{\$22.59/lb}$. We must determine which brand is the $\underline{\text{better buy}}$.

Step 2: **Make a plan.** Underline important words in our restatement of the problem in Step 1.

The units on each unit cost must be the same in order to compare them. Therefore, we will change *ounces* to *pounds* in the unit cost of Brand A.

Plan: Use unit analysis to change the units on $1.79/oz to dollars/lb. Then, compare the unit costs to determine which is the better buy.

Step 3: **Solve** the problem.

Unit cost of Brand A in dollars/lb: $\dfrac{\$1.79}{\cancel{oz}} \cdot \dfrac{16 \, \cancel{oz}}{1 \text{ lb}} = \dfrac{\$28.64}{\text{lb}} = \$28.64/\text{lb}$

The unit cost of Brand B is $22.59/lb.

Step 4: **State the answer** in a complete sentence.

Brand B is the better buy because it has the lower unit cost.

Step 5: **Check** the answer. Work backward. The check is left to the student.

Note

We could have changed the units in the unit cost of Brand B from $22.59/lb to dollars/oz so that the units matched those of Brand A.

Using Technology

When using more than one unit fraction to convert to a desired unit, we can use a calculator to perform the required calculation. Suppose we wanted to convert 100 c to gallons. In this case, our expression of unit fractions would be

$$\frac{100\ c}{1} \cdot \frac{1\ pt}{2\ c} \cdot \frac{1\ qt}{2\ pt} \cdot \frac{1\ gal}{4\ qt}.$$

(Note: Because dividing or multiplying by 1 does not affect the final answer, we can disregard them in the calculation).

To perform the calculation with a calculator (disregarding the 1's) we enter $\boxed{1}\,\boxed{0}\,\boxed{0}\,\boxed{\div}\,\boxed{2}\,\boxed{\div}\,\boxed{2}\,\boxed{\div}\,\boxed{4}\,\boxed{=}$. The display will likely show 6.25. This means 100 c = 6.25 gal.

It is a common mistake to enter $\boxed{1}\,\boxed{0}\,\boxed{0}\,\boxed{\div}\,\boxed{2}\,\boxed{\times}\,\boxed{2}\,\boxed{\times}\,\boxed{4}\,\boxed{=}$ into the calculator for this problem. Why is this incorrect?

E Evaluate **7.1** Exercises   Do the exercises, and check your work.

Additional answers can be found in the Answers to Exercises appendix.

Objective 1: Learn U.S. Customary Measurements

In U.S. customary units,

1) name three units used to measure length.
Answers may vary.

2) name three units used to measure capacity.
Answers may vary.

3) what is the relationship between inches and feet?
12 in. = 1 ft

4) what is the relationship between ounces and pounds?
16 oz = 1 lb

Fill in the blank.

5) 1 min = __60__ sec; __60__ min = 1 hr

6) 1 day = __24__ hr; __60__ sec = 1 min

7) __3__ ft = 1 yd; __5280__ ft = 1 mi

8) __8__ fl oz = 1 c; 1 pt = __2__ c

9) __2__ pt = 1 qt; 1 c = __8__ fl oz

10) 1 ton = __2000__ lb; __16__ oz = 1 lb

Objective 2: Use Multiplication or Division to Convert Between Units

In U.S. customary units,

11) when do you use division to convert between units?
when you are converting from a smaller unit to a larger unit

12) when do you use multiplication to convert between units?   when you are converting from a larger unit to a smaller unit

Use multiplication or division to convert to the indicated unit.

13) 3 hr to minutes   180 min   14) 5 hr to minutes   300 min

15) 36 in. to feet   3 ft   16) 8 c to pints   4 pt

17) 6 qt to gallons $1\frac{1}{2}$ gal   18) 2 qt to gallons $\frac{1}{2}$ gal

19) 1500 lb to tons $\frac{3}{4}$ ton or 0.75 ton   20) 800 lb to tons $\frac{2}{5}$ ton or 0.4 ton

21) $2\frac{1}{2}$ hr to minutes   150 min   22) $3\frac{1}{2}$ lb to ounces   56 oz

23) $1\frac{3}{4}$ ft to inches 21 in. 24) $4\frac{2}{3}$ ft to inches 56 in.

25) 1.25 gal to quarts 5 qt 26) 2.75 days to hours 66 hr

27) 3.5 pt to quarts 1.75 qt or $1\frac{3}{4}$ qt 28) 6.5 pt to quarts 3.25 qt or $3\frac{1}{4}$ qt

29) A snow leopard can pounce on its prey from 45 feet away. How many yards is this? (www.sandiegozoo.com) 15 yd

30) A baby elephant can weigh up to $\frac{1}{8}$ ton at birth. How many pounds is this? (www.sandiegozoo.com) 250 lb

Objective 3: Use Unit Analysis to Convert Between Units

31) Write two different unit fractions for the relationship 60 min = 1 hr. $\frac{60\ min}{1\ hr}$ or $\frac{1\ hr}{60\ min}$

32) Write two different unit fractions for the relationship 3 ft = 1 yd. $\frac{3\ ft}{1\ yd}$ or $\frac{1\ yd}{3\ ft}$

33) What are the steps we use to convert between units using unit analysis?

34) To convert 4.2 min to seconds using unit analysis, Nisha sets up the problem this way:

$$4.2\ min \cdot \frac{1\ min}{60\ sec} = \frac{4.2\ min}{1} \cdot \frac{1\ min}{60\ sec}$$

   a) How do we know this is wrong? The units of minutes will not divide out.

   b) What is the correct way to set up this problem and why?

   c) Finish the correct work in part b) to convert 4.2 min to seconds. 252 sec

Use unit analysis to convert to the indicated unit.

35) 7 ft to inches 84 in. 36) 4 hr to minutes 240 min

37) 10 qt to pints 20 pt 38) 8 yd to feet 24 ft

39) 52 oz to pounds $3\frac{1}{4}$ lb or 3.25 lb 40) 5 c to pints $2\frac{1}{2}$ pt or 2.5 pt

41) $3\frac{1}{2}$ days to hours 84 hr 42) $4\frac{1}{3}$ yd to feet 13 ft

Use unit analysis to convert to the indicated unit.

43) 5 yd = ___15___ ft 44) 12 qt = ___24___ pt

45) 72 oz = ____ lb $4\frac{1}{2}$ or 4.5 46) 44 oz = ____ lb $2\frac{3}{4}$ or 2.75

47) 1.75 hr = ___105___ min 48) 3.25 hr = ___195___ min

49) $3\frac{1}{2}$ pt = ___7___ c 50) $5\frac{1}{2}$ pt = ___11___ c

51) $1\frac{1}{4}$ tons = ___2500___ lb 52) $2\frac{3}{4}$ tons = ___5500___ lb

53) 2640 ft = ____ mi $\frac{1}{2}$ or 0.5 54) 7920 ft = ____ mi $1\frac{1}{2}$ or 1.5

55) a) Convert 2 days to minutes in two separate steps, first by changing days to hours and then by changing hours to minutes. 2880 min

   b) Convert 2 days to minutes in a single step, using more than one unit fraction. 2880 min

56) a) Convert 2 hours to seconds in two separate steps, first by changing hours to minutes and then by changing minutes to seconds. 7200 sec

   b) Convert 2 hours to seconds in a single step, using more than one unit fraction. 7200 sec

Use more than one unit fraction to convert to the indicated unit.

57) 1 day = ____ sec 86,400 58) 2.5 days = ____ sec 216,000

59) 18 c = ___$4\frac{1}{2}$___ qt 60) 15 c = ___$3\frac{3}{4}$___ qt

61) 504 hr = ___3___ wk 62) 336 hr = ___2___ wk

63) 2.5 gal = ___40___ c 64) 1.25 gal = ___20___ c

65) 6600 yd = ___$3\frac{3}{4}$___ mi 66) 3740 yd = ___$2\frac{1}{8}$___ mi

Objective 4: Solve Applied Problems Using Unit Analysis

Solve each problem.

67) One batch of homemade vanilla ice cream uses $2\frac{1}{2}$ c half-and-half. How many pints of half-and-half are needed for four batches of ice cream? 5 pt

68) Irina will make buttermilk pancakes for her daughter's pajama party. She has to make six batches, and each batch uses $2\frac{1}{2}$ c buttermilk. How many pints of buttermilk should she buy? $7\frac{1}{2}$ pt or 7.5 pt

69) Melvina babysat four days in a row, 3.75 hr each time. Find the total number of minutes she babysat. 900 min

70) Susan is a restaurant manager and scheduled five employees to work 7.5 hr on Friday. Find the total number of minutes the employees worked. 2250 min

71) Mohsin purchased a 30-oz bag of dried Turkish figs for $11.40. What is the cost per pound? $6.08

72) Shufan bought an 8-oz jar of blackberry jam for $3.99. What is the cost per pound? $7.98

73) Roberto has to buy saltine crackers at the store. The label on the shelf for Brand A says that its unit cost is $3.19/lb. Brand B says that its unit cost is $0.18/oz. Which is the better buy?
Brand B is the better buy because its unit cost is $2.88/lb.

74) Jung-Su is having a dinner party and wants to make enough cheesecake for everyone. If he makes eight cheesecakes and each one uses $\frac{3}{4}$ c milk, how many quarts of milk should he buy? $1\frac{1}{2}$ qt or 1.5 qt

75) Valerie compares two brands of jars of pickles. Brand A sells for $0.19/oz while Brand B sells for $2.99/lb. Which is the better buy? Brand B is the better buy because the unit cost of Brand A is $3.04/lb.

76) Logan wants to buy the box of corn flakes with the lower unit cost. The label on the shelf for Brand A says that its unit cost is $0.31/oz, and the unit cost of Brand B is $5.09/lb. Which brand should Logan buy? He should buy Brand A because its unit cost is $4.96/lb.

77) When ladybugs fly, they flap their wings approximately 85 times per second. How many times does a ladybug flap its wings during a 5-minute flight? (www.sandiegozoo.com) 25,500 times

78) The Sony Bravia XBR HX909 3D HDTV offers a screen size that measures $4\frac{1}{3}$ ft diagonally. How many inches is this? (www.sonystyle.com) 52 in.

79) Joseph wants to line his garden with a fence that costs $2.25 per foot. Use the diagram below to calculate the total cost. $114.75

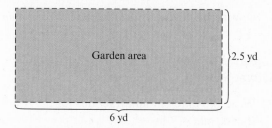

80) A high school wants to put a fence around its new football field. The length of the area that will be enclosed is 138 yd, and the width is 72 yd. If the fence costs $8.40 per foot, find the cost of the fence. $10,584.00

 **Rethink**

R1) Which process is easier to use: multiplication and division, or unit analysis?

R2) Why do you never have to "divide" when using unit analysis?

R3) Think of a situation where you needed to convert between U.S. customary units, and write an application problem similar to those you just solved.

7.2 The Metric System: Length

 Prepare

Organize

What are your objectives for Section 7.2?	How can you accomplish each objective?
1 Learn the Basic Units of Length	• Know what a *meter* represents by looking at the pictures of common objects, and understand the different associated prefixes. • Memorize the **Relationships Between Metric Units of Length.** • Complete the given examples on your own. • Complete You Trys 1 and 2.
2 Use Unit Fractions to Convert Between Units	• Use the same procedure for using unit fractions as done previously. • Complete the given example on your own. • Complete You Try 3.
3 Convert Between Units Using the Metric Conversion Chart	• Understand the *metric conversion chart,* and be able to reproduce it on your own. • Write the procedure for **How to Use the Metric Conversion Chart** in your own words. • Follow the example on your own. • Complete You Try 4.

W **Work**   Read the explanations, follow the examples, take notes, and complete the You Trys.

1   Learn the Basic Units of Length

Before the late 1700s, different countries used different units of measurement, which led to difficulties trading between countries. In the 1790s, the French Academy of Science developed a simpler system of measurement, based on multiples of 10, called the **metric system.** This system was adopted by almost all countries around the world. It made both measuring and trade easier. Although the United States still uses its own system of feet, cups, pounds, and so on, most scientific measurement in the United States is done in metric units.

 Note
The metric system is also called the *International System of Units,* or *SI* for short.

The basic unit of length in the metric system is the **meter.** A meter is about 39.37 inches long, so it is a little longer than a yard.

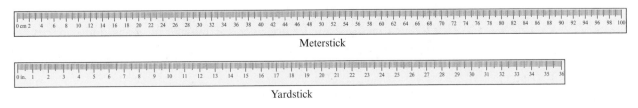

Meterstick

Yardstick

The other units of measurement in the decimal system are based on powers of 10. Because they are all related to the meter, these units are described by using a prefix on the word *meter*. The table shows the different units of measurement and their relationships to the meter.

Metric Units of Length

1 kilometer (km) = 1000 m
1 hectometer (hm) = 100 m
1 dekameter (dam) = 10 m
1 meter (m) = 1 m
1 decimeter (dm) = $\frac{1}{10}$ m or 0.1 m
1 centimeter (cm) = $\frac{1}{100}$ m or 0.01 m
1 millimeter (mm) = $\frac{1}{1000}$ m or 0.001 m

Note

The units used most often are kilometer, meter, centimeter, and millimeter.

We have already compared the length of a meter with the length of a yard. Here are some examples that will give you an idea of the lengths the metric units represent.

A dime is about 1 mm thick.

A USB plug is about 1 cm wide.

Distance is usually measured in kilometers.

A kilometer is about $\frac{2}{3}$ of a mile.

Height is usually measured in centimeters.

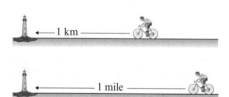

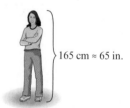

165 cm ≈ 65 in.

Note

These same metric prefixes are used for measuring mass and capacity, as we will see later in this chapter.

Now let's look closely at a meterstick to see how the meter, decimeter, centimeter, and millimeter are related.

The meterstick above shows us the following relationships:

Relationships Between Metric Units of Length

10 decimeters = 1 meter
100 centimeters = 1 meter
1000 millimeters = 1 meter
10 millimeters = 1 centimeter
10 centimeters = 1 decimeter

Let's practice deciding which metric unit is appropriate for measuring a particular length.

EXAMPLE 1

In-Class Example 1

Fill in the blank with the appropriate metric unit.
a) An e-reader is 18 _____ wide.
b) Farzan drives 24 _____ to work every day.
c) A fly is 6 _____ long.
d) Sarah's backyard garden is 4 _____ long.

Answer: a) 18 cm ≈ 7 in.
b) 24 km ≈ 15 mi
c) 6 mm ≈ 0.24 in.
d) 4 m ≈ 13 ft

Fill in the blank with the appropriate metric unit. Use km, m, cm, or mm.

a) A pen is 14 _____ long.

b) Gisele drives 8 _____ to work every day.

c) The lens of a camera on a phone is 3 _____ wide.

d) The length of a soccer field is 72 _____.

Solution

a) A pen is 14 <u>cm</u> long. (This is about 5.5 in.) Usually, we use centimeters instead of inches.

b) Gisele drives 8 <u>km</u> to work everyday. (8 km ≈ 5 mi) Kilometers are used instead of miles.

c) The lens of a camera on a phone is 3 <u>mm</u> wide. (3 mm ≈ 0.12 in.)

d) The length of a soccer field is 72 <u>m</u>. (This is about 78.74 yd.) Usually, we use meters instead of yards.

[YOU TRY 1]

Fill in the blank with the appropriate metric unit. Use km, m, cm, or mm.

a) The width of a bedroom is 4.5 _____.

b) A computer screen is 33 _____ wide.

c) Boston and New York City are approximately 306 _____ apart.

d) An ant is 5 _____ long.

EXAMPLE 2

In-Class Example 2

Use Example 2.

Find the length of the paper clip in the indicated unit.

a) mm   b) cm

Solution

a) Each of the smallest marks on the ruler is a millimeter. Each of the larger marks on the ruler is a centimeter. Remember, 1 cm = 10 mm, so we can begin by counting the 10 millimeters in each centimeter. Then, count the individual millimeters.

The length of the paper clip is 46 mm.

b) To measure the paper clip in centimeters, think of the ruler in terms of centimeters. Each of the larger marks on the ruler is a centimeter. Since it takes 10 mm to make a centimeter, each smaller mark, or millimeter, is $\frac{1}{10}$ cm or 0.1 cm. Count the 4 cm, then count the additional 6 mm or 0.6 cm.

The length of the paper clip is 4.6 cm.

[YOU TRY 2] Find the length of the nail clippers in the indicated unit.

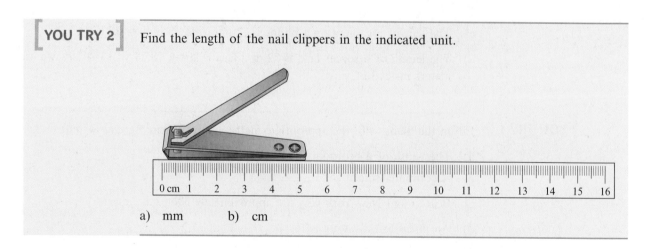

a) mm   b) cm

Often, measurements must be converted from one unit to another. We can do this by using unit fractions or by moving the decimal point. Let's use unit fractions first.

2 Use Unit Fractions to Convert Between Units

Since we know the relationships between the units of measurement in the metric system, we can write them as unit fractions to convert from one unit to another. We will use the unit fractions just as we did in Section 7.1.

In-Class Example 3

Use unit fractions to change to the indicated unit.
a) 52 km to m
b) 814 mm to m
c) 2.7 m to cm

Answer: a) 52,000 m
b) 0.814 m   c) 270 cm

Use unit fractions to change to the indicated unit.

a) 83 km to m   b) 162 mm to m   c) 1.5 m to cm

Solution

a) **Step 1:** **Identify** the units given and the units we want to get. **Write down** the relationship between those units.

   We are given *km* and want to convert to *m*. The relationship is

   $$1 \text{ km} = 1000 \text{ m}$$

   Step 2: **Multiply** the given measurement by the unit fraction relating the unit given and the unit we want to get so that the given unit will divide out and leave us with the unit we want.

   $$83 \text{ km} \cdot \frac{1000 \text{ m}}{1 \text{ km}} = \frac{83 \text{ km}}{1} \cdot \frac{1000 \text{ m}}{1 \text{ km}} \qquad \text{Divide out the unit of kilometers.}$$

   $$= \frac{83,000 \text{ m}}{1} \qquad \text{Multiply.}$$

   $$= 83,000 \text{ m} \qquad \text{Simplify.}$$

   So, 83 km = 83,000 m.

b) We are given 162 *mm* and want to convert to *m*. The relationship is

   $$1000 \text{ mm} = 1 \text{ m}$$

   Multiply the given measurement by the unit fraction so that millimeters divide out and meters remain.

   $$162 \text{ mm} \cdot \frac{1 \text{ m}}{1000 \text{ mm}} = \frac{162 \text{ mm}}{1} \cdot \frac{1 \text{ m}}{1000 \text{ mm}} \qquad \text{Divide out the unit of millimeters.}$$

   $$= \frac{162 \text{ m}}{1000} \qquad \text{Multiply.}$$

   $$= 0.162 \text{ m} \qquad \text{Simplify.}$$

   Therefore, 162 mm = 0.162 m. Notice that when we multiplied by the unit fraction, we did not divide out common factors of 162 and 1000. This is because we want to express the answer as a decimal.

c) We are given 1.5 *m* and want to convert to *cm*. The relationship is

$$1 \text{ m} = 100 \text{ cm}$$

Multiply the given measurement by the unit fraction so that meters divide out and centimeters remain.

$$1.5 \text{ m} \cdot \frac{100 \text{ cm}}{1 \text{ m}} = \frac{1.5 \text{ m̶}}{1} \cdot \frac{100 \text{ cm}}{1 \text{ m̶}}$$ Divide out the unit of meters.

$$= \frac{150 \text{ cm}}{1}$$ Multiply.

$$= 150 \text{ cm}$$ Simplify.

So, 1.5 m = 150 cm.

[YOU TRY 3] Use unit fractions to change to the indicated unit.

a) 962 cm to m   b) 8.3 m to mm   c) 174 mm to m

Another way to change from one unit to another is by moving the decimal point.

3 Convert Between Units Using the Metric Conversion Chart

The previous examples have shown that changing from one unit to another in the metric system involves multiplying or dividing by powers of 10. Therefore, we can convert between metric units by moving the decimal point. How do we know which way to move the decimal point to convert between units? We can use a *metric conversion chart*.

Metric Conversion Chart

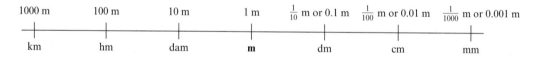

1000 m	100 m	10 m	1 m	$\frac{1}{10}$ m or 0.1 m	$\frac{1}{100}$ m or 0.01 m	$\frac{1}{1000}$ m or 0.001 m
km	hm	dam	**m**	dm	cm	mm

To make the chart, list the metric units from largest to smallest.

Procedure How to Use the Metric Conversion Chart

1) Find the unit that you are given.
2) Count the number of places you must move to go from the unit you are given to the unit you want to get.
3) Move the decimal point the same number of places and in the same direction that you did on the metric conversion chart.

Note

Moving the decimal point to the *right* is like multiplying by a power of 10.
Moving the decimal point to the *left* is like dividing by a power of 10.

EXAMPLE 4

Convert each measurement to the indicated unit.

a) 8.416 km to meters   b) 278.5 mm to meters

c) 9 m to centimeters   d) 120 mm to kilometers

Solution

a) Find km on the metric conversion chart. Since we have to change 8.416 km to meters, move *three places to the right* to get to m.

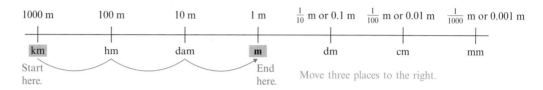

Since we moved *three places to the right* to get to m, move the decimal point *three places to the right* to change to meters.

$$8.416 \text{ km} = 8416 \text{ m}$$

Move the decimal point three places to the right.

Therefore, 8.416 km = 8416 m.

b) To change 278.5 mm to meters, find mm on the metric conversion chart. Move *three places to the left* to get to m.

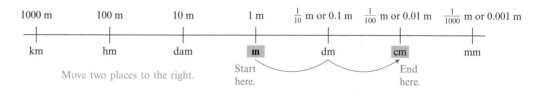

Since we moved *three places to the left* to get to m, move the decimal point *three places to the left* to change 278.5 mm to meters.

$$278.5 \text{ mm} = .2785 \text{ m}$$

Move the decimal point three places to the left.

So, 278.5 mm = 0.2785 m.

c) To change 9 m to centimeters, find m on the metric conversion chart. Move *two places to the right* to get to cm.

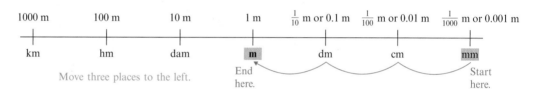

Put a decimal point at the end of the number 9. When you move the decimal point *two places to the right,* you must put in zeros as placeholders.

$$9. \text{ m} = 900 \text{ cm}$$ Put in zeros as placeholders.

Put the decimal point at   Move the decimal point two places
the end of the number.   to the right.

Therefore, 9 m = 900 cm.

d) To change 120 mm to kilometers, find mm on the metric conversion chart. Move *six places to the left* to get to km.

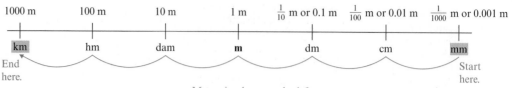

Move six places to the left.

Put a decimal point at the end of the number 120. When you move the decimal point *six places to the left,* you must put in zeros as placeholders.

$$120. \text{ m} = \underset{\sim}{000120} \text{ km} \qquad \text{Put in zeros as placeholders.}$$

Put the decimal point at the end of the number.　　Move the decimal point six places to the left.

So, 120 m = 0.000120 km or 0.00012 km.

YOU TRY 4   Convert each measurement to the indicated unit.

a) 72.9 cm to meters　　　b) 3.881 m to centimeters

c) 645 cm to kilometers　　d) 2 m to millimeters

ANSWERS TO YOU TRY EXERCISES

1) a) m b) cm c) km d) mm 　2) a) 53 mm b) 5.3 cm 　3) a) 9.62 m b) 8300 mm
c) 0.174 m 　4) a) 0.729 m b) 388.1 cm c) 0.00645 km d) 2000 mm

---

E Evaluate **7.2** Exercises   Do the exercises, and check your work.

*Additional answers can be found in the Answers to Exercises appendix.

Objective 1: Learn the Basic Units of Length
Use the meaning of metric prefixes to fill in the blanks.

1) *milli* means $\frac{1}{1000}$ so
   1 mm = $\frac{1}{1000}$ m

2) *deci* means $\frac{1}{10}$ so
   1 dm = $\frac{1}{10}$ m

3) *kilo* means 1000 so
   1 km = 1000 m

4) *hecto* means 100 so
   1 hm = 100 m

5) *centi* means $\frac{1}{100}$ so
   1 cm = $\frac{1}{100}$ m

6) *deka* means 10 so
   1 dam = 10 m

Use the ruler to find the measurements in Exercises 7–14.

7) The length of a dollar bill,

  a) in centimeters.   15.6 cm

  b) in millimeters.   156 mm

9) The diameter of a quarter,

  a) in millimeters.   24 mm

  b) in centimeters.   2.4 cm

8) The width of a dollar bill,

  a) in centimeters.   6.6 cm

  b) in millimeters.   66 mm

10) The diameter of a nickel,

  a) in millimeters.   21 mm

  b) in centimeters.   2.1 cm

11) Find the length of a cell phone, in centimeters.
Answers may vary.

12) Find the width of a driver's license, in millimeters.
Answers may vary.

13) Find the length of your pen or pencil, in centimeters.
Answers may vary.

14) Find the length of a key, in centimeters.
Answers may vary.

15) Arrange the following lengths in order from smallest to largest.

0.5 dm   3 cm   40 mm   0.06 m
3 cm   40 mm   0.5 dm   0.06 m

16) Arrange the following lengths in order from largest to smallest.

0.7 dm   80 mm   6 cm   0.05 m
80 mm   0.7 dm   6 cm   0.05 m

Fill in the most reasonable metric length unit. Choose from cm, km, m, and mm.

17) The textbook is 4 __cm__ thick.

18) The teacher is 1.7 __m__ tall.

19) The yardstick is approximately 0.9144 __m__ in length.

20) The diameter of a penny is approximately 19 __mm__.

21) The diameter of a dime is approximately 1.8 __cm__.

22) A CD-ROM disk has a thickness of 1.2 __mm__.

23) 65 mph is equivalent to approximately 104.6 __km__ per hour.

24) Joseph can run the 100-__m__ dash in 14.2 sec.

25) 10 ft per second is equivalent to approximately 3 __m__ per second.

26) Carol drives 19 __km__ to get to school.

Objective 2: Use Unit Fractions to Convert Between Units

Use unit fractions to change to the indicated unit.

27) 6 m to centimeters
600 cm

28) 4 m to millimeters
4000 mm

29) 3.8 m to millimeters
3800 mm

30) 1.25 m to centimeters
125 cm

31) 7300 m to kilometers
7.3 km

32) 300 m to kilometers
0.3 km

33) 250 mm to meters
0.25 m

34) 425 cm to meters
4.25 m

35) 18.2 m to kilometers
0.0182 km

36) 21.9 m to kilometers
0.0219 km

37) 13 dam to meters
130 m

38) 47 dam to meters
470 m

39) 2500 m to kilometers
2.5 km

40) 1800 m to kilometers
1.8 km

41) 342.8 dm to meters
34.28 m

42) 4.6 hm to meters
460 m

43) 0.75 cm to millimeters   7.5 mm

44) 342.8 dm to centimeters   3428 cm

Objective 3: Convert Between Units Using the Metric Conversion Chart

Metric Conversion Chart

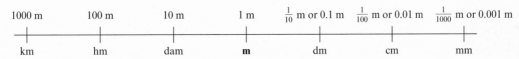

1000 m	100 m	10 m	1 m	$\frac{1}{10}$ m or 0.1 m	$\frac{1}{100}$ m or 0.01 m	$\frac{1}{1000}$ m or 0.001 m
km	hm	dam	**m**	dm	cm	mm

Use the metric conversion chart to convert each measurement to the indicated unit.

45) 15 m to centimeters
1500 cm

46) 64 m to decimeters
640 dm

47) 7.5 cm to millimeters
75 mm

48) 8.3 cm to millimeters
83 mm

49) 970 m to kilometers
0.97 km

50) 510 m to kilometers
0.51 km

51) 820 mm to meters
0.82 m

52) 475 cm to meters
4.75 m

53) 1600 cm to kilometers
0.016 km

54) 2400 mm to kilometers
0.0024 km

55) 8.6 cm to millimeters
86 mm

56) 11.7 cm to millimeters
117 mm

57) 3.49 km to meters
3490 m

58) 8.25 km to meters
8250 m

59) 2.34 m to decimeters
23.4 dm

60) 0.77 km to dekameters
77 dam

61) 43,000 cm to hectometers   4.3 hm

62) 26,000 dm to hectometers   26 hm

63) 9.44 km to millimeters   9,440,000 mm

64) 5.83 km to centimeters   583,000 cm

65) Arrange the following lengths in order from smallest to largest.

1.01 m   100 cm   1400 mm   12 dm
100 cm   1.01 m   12 dm   1400 mm

66) Arrange the following lengths in order from largest to smallest.

0.8 m   9.5 dm   75 cm   825 mm
9.5 dm   825 mm   0.8 m   75 cm

67) The system of blood vessels (arteries, veins, and capillaries) in the human body is over 96,000 km long. How many meters is this? (www.webmd.com)
96,000,000 m

68) The width of a balance beam used by female gymnasts is 10 cm. How many millimeters is this?
100 mm

69) American Veterinary Identification Devices (AVID) microchips measure 1.2 cm in length. Convert this number to millimeters. (www.avidplc.com) 12 mm

70) The average height of an adult female in the United States is 1.62 m. Convert the height to centimeters and millimeters. (National Center for Health Statistics) 162 cm; 1620 mm

Mixed Exercises: Objectives 1–3
Fill in the most reasonable metric length unit. Choose from cm, km, m, and mm.

71) The height of the door is 200 __cm__.

72) The width of the door is 760 __mm__.

73) A bicycle wheel has a radius of 0.8 __m__.

74) The length of a goldfish is 3 __cm__.

Convert to the indicated unit using either unit fractions or the metric conversion chart.

75) 340 cm to meters
3.4 m

76) 7 m to millimeters
7000 mm

77) 1.5 km to meters
1500 m

78) 86 cm to meters
0.86 m

 79) 20 km to centimeters
2,000,000 cm

80) 4310 mm to kilometers
0.00431 km

81) The Eiffel Tower in Paris is approximately 321 m tall. Change this number to centimeters.
(www.discoverfrance.net) 32,100 cm

82) A calculator is 7.2 cm wide. Change this number to millimeters. 72 mm

R Rethink

R1) What other common items are measured using a form of the meter?

R2) Compare converting the U.S. customary measurements to converting using the metric system. Which is easier to do? Why?

Here are some examples that will give you an idea of the size of a milliliter.

A box measuring 1 cm on each side has a volume of
1 cm · 1 cm · 1 cm = 1 cubic centimeter, and
1 cubic cm = 1 milliliter. **This box holds exactly 1 mL.**

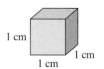

A teaspoon is about 5 mL.

A can of soda contains about 355 mL.

Let's practice deciding which metric unit is appropriate for measuring a particular capacity.

EXAMPLE 1

In-Class Example 1

Fill in the blank with the appropriate metric unit. Use mL or L.
a) A washing machine uses about 151 _____ of water.
b) A cup holds 350 _____ of coffee.

Answer:
a) L (151 L ≈ 40 gal)
b) mL (350 mL ≈ 1.5 c)

Fill in the blank with the appropriate metric unit. Use mL or L.

a) A dishwasher uses about 34 _____ of water.

b) A can contains 480 _____ of soup.

Solution

a) A dishwasher uses about 34 <u>L</u> of water. (This is about 9 gal.) We do not use mL because that would be a *very* small quantity.

b) A can contains 480 <u>mL</u> of soup. (480 mL ≈ 2 c) Liters would not make sense because 480 L ≈ 127 gal.

[YOU TRY 1]

Fill in the blank with the appropriate metric unit. Use mL or L.

a) The juice box holds 180 _____.

b) The car's tank holds 53 _____ of gas.

---

2 Convert Between Metric Units of Capacity

We learned two methods for converting between metric units of length: unit fractions and the metric conversion line. We can use those same methods to convert between metric units of capacity. Here is the metric conversion chart.

Metric Conversion Chart

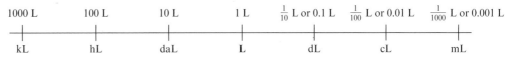

1000 L	100 L	10 L	1 L	$\frac{1}{10}$ L or 0.1 L	$\frac{1}{100}$ L or 0.01 L	$\frac{1}{1000}$ L or 0.001 L
kL	hL	daL	L	dL	cL	mL

Because we use milliliters often, you should remember that 1000 mL = 1 L.

Change to the indicated unit using unit fractions and using the metric conversion chart.

a) 1.4 L to milliliters   b)   250 mL to liters

Solution

a) **Unit fractions:** We are given *liters* and want to convert to *milliliters.* Use the relationship

$$1000 \text{ mL} = 1 \text{ L}$$

$$1.4 \text{ L} \cdot \frac{1000 \text{ mL}}{1 \text{ L}} = \frac{1.4 \cancel{L}}{1} \cdot \frac{1000 \text{ mL}}{1 \cancel{L}} \qquad \text{Divide out the unit of liters.}$$

$$= \frac{1400 \text{ mL}}{1} \qquad \text{Multiply.}$$

$$= 1400 \text{ mL} \qquad \text{Simplify.}$$

So, 1.4 L = 1400 mL.

Metric Conversion Chart:

Start at L on the metric conversion chart. To change from L to mL, we move *three places to the right*. Therefore, move the decimal point *three places to the right.*

$$1.4 \text{ L} = 1400. \text{ ml} \qquad \text{Put in zeros as placeholders.}$$

Move the decimal point three places to the right.

Therefore, 1.4 L = 1400 mL.

b) **Unit fractions:** We are given *milliliters* and want to convert to *liters.* Use the relationship

$$1000 \text{ mL} = 1 \text{ L}$$

$$250 \text{ mL} \cdot \frac{1 \text{ L}}{1000 \text{ mL}} = \frac{250 \cancel{\text{ mL}}}{1} \cdot \frac{1 \text{ L}}{1000 \cancel{\text{ mL}}} \qquad \text{Divide out the unit of milliliters.}$$

$$= \frac{250 \text{ L}}{1000} \qquad \text{Multiply.}$$

$$= 0.250 \text{ L} \qquad \text{Simplify.}$$

So, 250 mL = 0.250 L or 0.25 L.

Metric Conversion Chart:

Start at mL on the metric conversion chart. Move *three places to the left* to get from mL to L. Move the decimal point *three places to the left.*

$$250. \text{ mL} = .250 \text{ L}$$

Put the decimal point at the end of the number.   Move the decimal point three places to the left.

250 mL = 0.250 L or 0.25 L

[YOU TRY 2] Change to the indicated unit using unit fractions and using the metric conversion chart.

a) 120 mL to liters   b)   3.7 L to milliliters

---

3 Learn the Basic Units of Weight (Mass)

In the metric system, the basic unit of *mass* is the **gram.** Mass is commonly referred to as *weight,* but they are two different things. The **mass** of an object is the amount of matter in the object. The **weight** of an object is a measure of the force of gravity on an object. The farther we get from the center of the Earth, the less the pull of gravity. Therefore, an object on the surface of the Earth weighs more than if the object is far from the Earth. An astronaut, for example, is weightless in space but his or her mass is the same whether on Earth or in space.

In science classes, especially physics, it is important to understand the difference between mass and weight. If an object is on the Earth, the weight and mass of that object are the same. Therefore, we will use the word *weight.*

The abbreviation for gram is g. The gram is related to the metric length.

If each side of a box has a length of 1 cm, and we fill this tiny box with water, the weight of the water in the box is 1 gram.

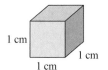

The weight of the water in this box is exactly 1 gram.

Here are some examples that will help you understand the measure of grams.

| A large paper clip weighs about 1 g. | A nickel weighs 5 g. | The iPhone 4S weighs 140 g. (www.apple.com) |

To describe larger and smaller units of weight (mass), use the same prefixes that are used for length and capacity. For example, 1 kilometer (km) = 1000 meters (m), 1 kiloliter (kL) = 1000 liters (L), and 1 kilogram (kg) = 1000 grams (g). *Kilo* means 1000. Here are other units of weight.

Metric Units of Weight

1 kilogram (kg) = 1000 g
1 hectogram (hg) = 100 g
1 dekagram (dag) = 10 g
1 gram (g) = 1 g
1 decigram (dg) = $\frac{1}{10}$ g or 0.1 g
1 centigram (cg) = $\frac{1}{100}$ g or 0.01 g
1 milligram (mg) = $\frac{1}{1000}$ g or 0.001 g

Note

The units used most often are kilogram, gram, and milligram.

In the metric system, kilograms are used instead of pounds. 1 kg ≈ 2.2 lb

Tom bought 1 kg of potatoes.

This newborn baby weighs 3.2 kg.

This man weighs 84 kg.

1 kg ≈ 2.2 lb

3.2 kg ≈ 7 lb

84 kg ≈ 185 lb

Milligrams are used to measure very small weights. For example, a certain multivitamin contains 60 mg of vitamin C.

Which metric unit of weight (mass) would we use in each case in Example 3?

EXAMPLE 3

In-Class Example 3

Fill in the blank with the appropriate metric unit. Use milligrams, grams, or kilograms.
a) Miguel's racing bike weighs 7.7 _____.
b) Meixiu's cell phone weighs 102 _____.
c) One package of ramen noodles contains 1660 _____ of sodium.

Answer:
a) kg (7.7 kg ≈ 17 lb)
b) g (102 g ≈ 3.6 oz)
c) mg (1660 mg ≈ 0.06 oz)

Fill in the blank with the appropriate metric unit. Use milligrams, grams, or kilograms.

a) A full-size pickup truck weighs about 4600 _____.

b) Tim bought an apple that weighed 170 _____.

c) A frozen diet dinner contains 650 _____ of sodium.

Solution

a) A full-size pickup truck weighs about 4600 kg. (This is about 10,141 lb.) The metric system uses kilograms instead of pounds.

b) Tim bought an apple that weighed 170 g. (170 g ≈ 6 oz) The unit of kg would be too large for an apple, and mg would be too small.

c) A frozen diet dinner contains 650 mg of sodium. (650 mg ≈ 0.02 oz) Milligrams are used to measure *very* small amounts.

Fill in the blank with the appropriate metric unit. Use milligrams, grams, or kilograms.

a) One packet of sugar substitute contains 1 _____.

b) One serving of canned spaghetti contains 450 _____ of potassium.

c) Melinda's laptop weighs 1.8 _____.

4 Convert Between Metric Units of Weight (Mass)

We can use unit fractions or the metric conversion chart to convert from one unit of weight (mass) to another.

Metric Conversion Chart

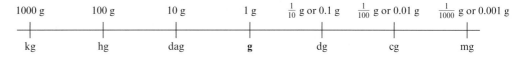

1000 g	100 g	10 g	1 g	$\frac{1}{10}$ g or 0.1 g	$\frac{1}{100}$ g or 0.01 g	$\frac{1}{1000}$ g or 0.001 g
kg	hg	dag	**g**	dg	cg	mg

Since we use grams, kilograms, and milligrams most often, remember the following relationships:

$$1 \text{ kg} = 1000 \text{ g} \qquad 1000 \text{ mg} = 1 \text{ g}$$

EXAMPLE 4

Change to the indicated unit using unit fractions and using the metric conversion chart.

a) Charise weighs 54 kg. Change kilograms to grams.

b) The chemist mixed 175 mg of sodium chloride with water. Change milligrams to grams.

Solution

a) **Unit fractions:** To change *kilograms* to *grams,* use the relationship 1 kg = 1000 g.

$$54 \text{ kg} \cdot \frac{1000 \text{ g}}{1 \text{ kg}} = \frac{54 \text{ kg}}{1} \cdot \frac{1000 \text{ g}}{1 \text{ kg}} \qquad \text{Divide out the unit of kilograms.}$$

$$= \frac{54,000 \text{ g}}{1} \qquad \text{Multiply.}$$

$$= 54,000 \text{ g} \qquad \text{Simplify.}$$

So, 54 kg = 54,000 g. (This is about 119 lb.)

Metric Conversion Chart:

Start at kg on the metric conversion chart and move *three places to the right* to get to g. Now, move the decimal point *three places to the right.*

$$54. \text{ kg} = 54000. \text{ g}$$

Put the decimal point at the end of the number.　　　Move the decimal point three places to the right.

So, 54 kg = 54,000 g.

b) **Unit fractions:** To change 175 mg to grams, use the relationship 1000 mg = 1 g.

$$175 \text{ mg} \cdot \frac{1 \text{ g}}{1000 \text{ mg}} = \frac{175 \text{ mg}}{1} \cdot \frac{1 \text{ g}}{1000 \text{ mg}} \qquad \text{Divide out the unit of milligrams.}$$

$$= \frac{175 \text{ g}}{1000} \qquad \text{Multiply.}$$

$$= 0.175 \text{ g} \qquad \text{Simplify.}$$

So, 175 mg = 0.175 g. (This is approximately 0.006 oz.)

Metric Conversion Chart:

Start at mg on the metric conversion chart and move *three places to the left* to get to g. Move the decimal point *three places to the left.*

$$175. \text{ mg} = .175 \text{ g}$$

Put the decimal point at the end of the number.   Move the decimal point three places to the left.

Therefore, 175 mg = 0.175 g.

[YOU TRY 4]

Change to the indicated unit using unit fractions and using the metric conversion chart.

a) The tablet contains 200 mg of ibuprofen. Change milligrams to grams.

b) The refrigerator weighs 91 kg. Change kilograms to grams.

---

5 Distinguish Between the Different Metric Units

Now that we have learned the metric units for length, capacity, and weight (mass), let's learn how to determine which metric unit should be used to measure certain quantities. Remember that the basic unit of measurement for length is *meter*, the basic unit of measurement for capacity is *liter*, and the basic unit of measurement for weight (mass) is *gram*.

EXAMPLE 5

Fill in the blank with the appropriate metric unit. Use m, mm, cm, km, L, mL, g, mg, or kg.

a) Trent bought a 1.5 -_____ carton of orange juice.

b) The CD case is 14 _____ wide.

c) The dog weighs 21 _____.

Solution

a) Trent bought a 1.5-L carton of orange juice. (This is about 0.4 gal.) To measure an amount of a liquid, we use a unit of capacity. Use liters instead of milliliters because milliliters would be too small: 1.5 mL ≈ 0.0004 gal.

b) The CD case is 14 cm wide. (14 cm ≈ 5.5 in.) Use centimeters because it is the appropriate unit of length. 14 km is too large (14 km ≈ 8.7 mi) and 14 mm is too small (14 mm ≈ 0.55 in.).

W Hint

Think of questions to ask yourself to help you decide which measurement to use.

c) The dog weighs 21 kg. (21 kg ≈ 46 lb.) The word *weighs* tells us to use a measurement for weight. Choose kilograms because both grams and milligrams are too small: 21 g ≈ 0.05 lb and 21 mg ≈ 0.00005 lb.

[YOU TRY 5] Fill in the blank with the appropriate metric unit. Use m, mm, cm, km, L, mL, g, mg, or kg.

a) The jar holds 35 _____ of basil leaves.

b) The bottle contains 240 _____ of cough syrup.

c) The distance from Minneapolis to Orlando is about 2526 _____.

ANSWERS TO [YOU TRY] EXERCISES

1) a) mL (180 mL ≈ 0.75 c)   b) L (53 L ≈ 14 gal)   2) a) 0.12 L (0.12 L ≈ 0.5 c)
b) 3700 mL (3700 mL ≈ 0.98 gal)   3) a) g (1 g ≈ 0.035 oz)   b) mg (450 mg ≈ 0.016 oz)
c) kg (1.8 kg ≈ 4 lb)   4) a) 0.2 g   b) 91,000 g   5) a) mg   b) mL   c) km

---

E Evaluate **7.3** Exercises   Do the exercises, and check your work.

*Additional answers can be found in the Answers to Exercises appendix.

Objective 1: Learn the Basic Units of Capacity

Fill in the blank with the appropriate metric unit.
Use milliliters or liters.

1) A teaspoon holds approximately 5 __mL__ of liquid.

2) A tablespoon holds approximately 14 __mL__ of liquid.

3) A can of soda pop contains 0.355 __L__ of soda pop.

4) A small cup of coffee contains 0.236 __L__ of coffee.

 5) An eye dropper delivers 0.05 __mL__ per drop.

6) A raindrop has a volume of 1 __mL__.

Determine whether the indicated quantity seems reasonable or unreasonable for each application. If it is unreasonable, specify whether it is too much or too little.

(24) 7) To create a bubble bath requires adding 10 L of bubble bath soap to a tub of warm water.   unreasonable; too much

8) Houng is going to make 6 servings of Vietnamese chicken noodle soup (Pho Ga). She needs to use 4½ mL of water to make this popular Vietnamese cuisine.   unreasonable; too little

9) An antacid tablet is dissolved in 120 mL of water.   reasonable

10) A patient was given 15 mL of cough syrup every four hours.   reasonable

11) When Bret washes his car, he uses approximately 450 mL of water.   unreasonable; too little

12) To help tired eyes, one should use 100 mL of saline solution eye drops twice a day.   unreasonable; too much

Objective 2: Convert Between Metric Units of Capacity

Change to the indicated unit using unit fractions and using the metric conversion chart.

 13) 325 mL to liters
0.325 L

14) 206 mL to liters
0.206 L

15) 4000 mL to liters   4 L   16) 5000 mL to liters   5 L

17) 7.1 L to milliliters   18) 3.4 L to milliliters
7100 mL   3400 mL

19) 0.06 L to milliliters   20) 0.01 L to milliliters
60 mL   10 mL

21) 35 mL to liters   0.035 L   22) 85 mL to liters   0.085 L

Objective 3: Learn the Basic Units of Weight (Mass)

Fill in the blank with the appropriate metric unit. Use milligrams, grams, or kilograms.

23) One grain of rice weighs 25 __mg__.

24) One grain of salt weighs 2 __mg__.

25) The large bag of wild bird seed weighs 9 __kg__.

26) David's laptop weighs 3125 __g__.

27) The weight of a computer mouse is 90 __g__.

28) A quarter weighs 5.67 __g__.

29) A dime weighs 2268 __mg__.

30) A penny weighs 2500 __mg__.

31) The bag of groceries weighs 3.7 __kg__.

32) The sign in an elevator says that it can carry at most 600 __kg__.

Determine whether the indicated quantity seems reasonable or unreasonable for each application. If it is unreasonable, specify whether it is *too much* or *too little*.

33) The average banana contains 465 mg of potassium.
reasonable

34) An orange contains approximately 70 mg of vitamin C.   reasonable

35) A recipe for four servings of chicken soup requires 1 kg of salt.   unreasonable; too much

36) To make 6 servings of sweet lemonade requires 200 mg of sugar.   unreasonable; too little

37) A recipe to make 40 chocolate chip cookies requires 200 g of chocolate chips.   reasonable

38) Sahar is planning to serve pita bread for her dinner guests. To make 16 pitas, she needs 750 g of flour.
reasonable

Objective 4: Convert Between Metric Units of Weight (Mass)

Change to the indicated unit using unit fractions and using the metric conversion chart.

39) 72 g to milligrams   40) 38 g to milligrams
72,000 g   38,000 g

41) 0.82 kg to grams   42) 0.79 kg to grams
820 g   790 g

43) 194 g to kilograms   44) 611 g to kilograms
0.194 kg   0.611 kg

45) 2.01 g to milligrams   46) 5.002 g to milligrams
2010 mg   5002 mg

47) $\frac{3}{4}$ kg to grams   750 g   48) $\frac{1}{4}$ kg to grams   250 g

Change to the indicated unit using unit fractions and using the metric conversion chart.

49) The patient receives 300 mg of medication every six hours. Change milligrams to grams.   0.3 g

50) The bag of dog food weighs 8 kg. Change kilograms to grams.   8000 g

51) A large egg weighs approximately 50 g. Change grams to milligrams.   50,000 mg

52) A lightweight running shoe weighs 361 g. Change grams to kilograms.   0.361 kg

53) Isaac's briefcase weighs 4.1 kg. Change kilograms to grams.   4100 g

54) A recipe for garam marsala uses 15 g of ginger powder. Change grams to milligrams.   15,000 mg

55) Juanita worked out with a kettlebell that weighed 3000 g. Change grams to kilograms.   3 kg

56) The kitten weighed 97,000 mg at birth. Change milligrams to grams.   97 g

Objective 5: Distinguish Between the Different Metric Units

Fill in the blank with the appropriate metric unit. Use m, mm, cm, km, L, mL, g, mg, or kg.

57) The height of a basketball hoop is approximately 3 __m__.

58) The car needed 1 __L__ of oil.

59) A hot dog weighs approximately 60 __g__.

60) A hamburger contains approximately 100 __mg__ of cholesterol.

61) Some mechanical pencils use lead that has a diameter of 0.7 __mm__.

62) A handheld eraser has a length of approximately 6 __cm__.

63) One gallon is approximately 3.785 __L__.

64) One tablespoon of liquid is approximately 14 __mL__.

65) Joseph drives his car to work a distance of 23 __km__ every day.

66) The track around the football field measures 400 __m__.

Mixed Exercises

Determine whether the indicated quantity seems reasonable or unreasonable for each application. If it is unreasonable, specify whether it is too much or too little.

67) The diameter of a regulation table tennis ball is approximately 44 mm.   reasonable

68) Martin takes 200 mg of vitamin C on a daily basis.   reasonable

69) Agneza fills her car's gas tank with 16 mL of gasoline.   unreasonable; too little

70) The driveway is 3.7 km wide.   unreasonable; too much

Change to the indicated unit.

71) 340 mL to liters   72) 2 km to meters
    0.34 L   2000 m

73) 9.1 g to milligrams   74) 6000 g to kilograms
    9100 mg   6 kg

75) $15\frac{1}{2}$ m to kilometers   76) $\frac{1}{2}$ L to milliliters
    0.0155 km   500 mL

77) A communications satellite weighs about 315 kg. Change kilograms to grams.   315,000 g

78) A dining room table is 160 cm long. Change centimeters to meters.   1.6 m

R Rethink

R1) Describe steps you can take to check your answers for the exercises.

R2) Can you explain to a friend the quickest way to convert metric units? What would you tell her?

7.4 Solve Applied Problems Involving Metric Units

P Prepare

O Organize

What are your objectives for Section 7.4?	How can you accomplish each objective?
1 Perform Operations with Metric Units	• Create a procedure for performing operations on numbers with different metric units. • Complete the given examples on your own. • Complete You Trys 1 and 2.
2 Solve Applied Problems Involving Metric Units	• Use the Five Steps for Solving Applied Problems, and add any additional steps needed. • Complete the given examples on your own. • Complete You Trys 3–5.

 **Work**   **Read the explanations, follow the examples, take notes, and complete the You Trys.**

1 Perform Operations with Metric Units

To solve some applications, we have to add, subtract, multiply, or divide numbers with metric units. For example, 4.6 kg + 2.1 kg = 6.7 kg. Because the units are the same, we add the numbers and keep the units of kg. However, if these units are not the same, we may have to express them with the same units before performing the operations.

EXAMPLE 1

In-Class Example 1

Add 3 m + 82 cm.

Answer: 3.82 m or 382 cm

Add 2 m + 31 cm.

Solution

The units are not the same, so we have to convert one of the units so that it is the same as the other. We can convert to either meters or centimeters using the metric conversion chart or unit fractions. Let's use the relationship between meters and centimeters to move the decimal point.

Express each measurement in meters.	Express each measurement in centimeters.
31 cm = 0.31 m Change centimeters to meters.	2 m = 200 cm Change meters to centimeters.
Now, add the measurements.	Now, add the measurements.
2 m + 31 cm = 2 m + 0.31 m = 2.31 m	2 m + 31 cm = 200 cm + 31 cm = 231 cm

> **W Hint**
> Is it easier for you to understand what 2.31 m represents or what 231 cm represents?

The answer can be expressed either way: 2 m + 31 cm = 2.31 m or 231 cm.

> **[YOU TRY 1]**   Add 4 m + 742 mm.

EXAMPLE 2

In-Class Example 2

Divide 54 L by 6.

Answer: 9 L

Divide 36 L by 4.

Solution

Only one number is a unit of measurement. This problem means *divide 36 L into four equal parts.* We just divide 36 by 4, and keep the units of L.

$$36 \text{ L} \div 4 = 9 \text{ L}$$

> **[YOU TRY 2]**   Multiply 7 g by 8.

---

2 Solve Applied Problems Involving Metric Units

As we did to solve other applications, we will use the steps introduced in Section 2.7 to solve applied problems involving metric units.

EXAMPLE 3

In-Class Example 3

Rhonda has a chain that is 1 m 30 cm long. She cuts off a piece that is 75 cm long. Find the length of chain remaining, in centimeters.

Answer: 55 cm

Latrice has a piece of fabric that is 1 m 20 cm long. She cuts off a piece that is 85 cm long. Find the length of fabric remaining, in centimeters.

Solution

Step 1: **Read** the problem carefully, and restate it in your own words.

A piece of fabric is <u>1 m 20 cm long</u>, and <u>Latrice cuts off a piece that is 85 cm long</u>. We have to <u>find the length of the fabric that remains, in centimeters</u>.

Step 2: **Make a plan.** Let's underline important words in our restatement of the problem in Step 1.

Because Latrice cuts off an 85-cm piece of fabric, we have to *subtract* that from the total length of 1 m 20 cm. The units are not the same, so convert 1 m 20 cm to centimeters since we are asked to express the answer in centimeters.

Plan: Change 1 m 20 cm to centimeters. Then, subtract 85 cm from that measurement.

Step 3: **Solve** the problem.

Change 1 m 20 cm to centimeters.	Subtract 85 cm from 120 cm.
1 m 20 cm = 100 cm + 20 cm = 120 cm	$\begin{array}{r} {\scriptstyle 11\ 10} \\ \cancel{1}\ \cancel{2}\ \cancel{0} \\ -\quad 8\ 5 \\ \hline 3\ 5 \end{array}$ 120 cm − 85 cm = 35 cm

Step 4: **State the answer** in a complete sentence.

35 cm of fabric remains.

Step 5: **Check** the answer. Work backward.

Amount of fabric remaining + Amount of fabric cut off = Original length of fabric

$$35 \text{ cm} \quad + \quad 85 \text{ cm} \quad = \quad 120 \text{ cm}$$

We can think of 120 cm as 100 cm + 20 cm = 1 m + 20 cm. This is the same as the original length of fabric stated in the problem.

[YOU TRY 3] A carton of orange juice contains 1 L 450 mL. If Zach uses 600 mL, how many milliliters of orange juice is left in the carton?

When we are working with problems involving money, round answers to the nearest cent.

EXAMPLE 4

In-Class Example 4

At the deli, pancetta costs $26.99/kg. Maria needs 250 g for a recipe. How much will the pancetta cost?

Answer: $6.75

At the deli, prosciutto costs $48.99/kg. Giovanni needs 120 g for a chicken saltimbocca recipe. How much will the prosciutto cost?

Solution

Step 1: **Read** the problem carefully, and restate it in your own words.

Giovanni has to buy <u>120 g</u> of prosciutto. It costs <u>$48.99/kg</u>. <u>We must determine how much the prosciutto will cost</u>.

Step 2: **Make a plan.** Underline important words in our restatement of the problem in Step 1.

The $48.99 *per* kilogram, is the *unit cost* of the prosciutto. To find the cost of 120 g of prosciutto, we have to multiply the unit cost by the amount of prosciutto Giovanni is buying. *First*, however, we have to change 120 g to kilograms so that the units are the same.

Plan: Change 120 g to kilograms. Then, multiply that number by the unit cost, $48.99/kg, to find the cost of the prosciutto.

Step 3: **Solve** the problem.

To change 120 g to kilograms, use either unit fractions or the metric conversion chart. We will use unit fractions. Then, use unit fractions to find the cost.

Change 120 g to kilograms.	Find the cost of the prosciutto.
$\dfrac{120 \text{ g}}{1} \cdot \dfrac{1 \text{ kg}}{1000 \text{ g}} = \dfrac{120 \text{ kg}}{1000} = 0.120 \text{ kg} = 0.12 \text{ kg}$	Multiply the amount of prosciutto by the unit cost. $\dfrac{0.12 \text{ kg}}{1} \cdot \dfrac{\$48.99}{\text{kg}} = \$5.8788 \approx \$5.88$

Step 4: **State the answer** in a complete sentence.

Giovanni spent $5.88 for 120 g of prosciutto.

Step 5: **Check** the answer. Work backward. Divide $5.88 by 0.12 kg to get the unit cost. $5.88 ÷ 0.12 kg = $49.00/kg. This is close to the given unit cost of $48.99/kg. The difference is due to the rounding of the cost of the prosciutto in Step 3.

[YOU TRY 4]

In the bulk foods section of the grocery store, lentils cost $3.49/kg. If Devyani buys 640 g, how much does she pay?

EXAMPLE 5

In-Class Example 5

On a production line, 360 L of maple syrup is divided evenly into 500 bottles. How many milliliters of syrup is in each bottle?

Answer: 720 mL

On a production line, 280 L of shampoo is divided evenly into 800 bottles. How many milliliters of shampoo is in each bottle?

Solution

Step 1: **Read** the problem carefully, and restate it in your own words.

<u>280 L</u> of shampoo is <u>divided evenly into 800 bottles</u>. We must <u>determine the number of milliliters of shampoo in each bottle</u>.

Step 2: **Make a plan.** Underline important words in our restatement of the problem in Step 1.

Plan: First, change 280 L to milliliters since the answer should be in milliliters. Then, divide the total amount of shampoo produced by 800.

Step 3: **Solve** the problem.

To change 280 L to milliliters, use either unit fractions or the metric conversion chart. Using the relationship between liters and milliliters, move the decimal point in 280 L three places to the right to change to milliliters:

$$280 \text{ L} = 280{,}000 \text{ mL}$$

Divide 280,000 mL by 800 to determine the number of milliliters of shampoo in each bottle:

$$800\overline{)280{,}000}^{\,350}$$

Step 4: **State the answer** in a complete sentence.

Each bottle will contain 350 mL of shampoo.

Step 5: **Check** the answer. Work backward.

If 800 bottles each contain 350 mL of shampoo, then the total amount of shampoo is 800 · 350 mL = 280,000 mL. Changing from milliliters to liters, we get 280 L.

[YOU TRY 5] Twenty kilograms of granola is packaged evenly into 50 bags. How many grams of granola are in each bag?

ANSWERS TO [YOU TRY] EXERCISES

1) 4.742 m or 4742 mm   2) 56 g   3) 850 mL   4) $2.23   5) 400 g

---

E Evaluate **7.4** Exercises   Do the exercises, and check your work.

*Additional answers can be found in the Answers to Exercises appendix.

Objective 1: Perform Operations with Metric Units

Perform the indicated operation.

1) 3 m + 55 cm
   3.55 m or 355 cm

2) 9 m + 23 cm
   9.23 m or 923 cm

3) 2.4 kg + 160 g
   2.56 kg or 2560 g

4) 1.3 kg + 420 g
   1.72 kg or 1720 g

5) 0.8 L + 619 mL
   1.419 L or 1419 mL

6) 0.7 L + 525 mL
   1.225 L or 1225 mL

7) 1.75 m + 32 cm
   2.07 m or 207 cm

8) 4.64 m + 72 cm
   5.36 m or 536 cm

9) 0.27 m + 57 cm
   0.84 m or 84 cm

10) 0.38 m + 49 cm
    0.87 m or 87 cm

11) 2.25 kg − 455 g
    1.795 kg or 1795 g

12) 0.68 kg − 325 g
    0.355 kg or 355 g

13) 0.75 L − 75 mL
    0.675 L or 675 mL

14) 0.13 L − 13 mL
    0.117 L or 117 mL

15) 2.5 g + 300 mg
    2.8 g or 2800 mg

16) 3.5 cm + 50 mm
    8.5 cm or 85 mm

17) Divide 24 L by 8.
    3 L

18) Divide 30 g by 5.
    6 g

19) Divide 750 mL by 3.
    250 mL

20) Divide 900 cm by 6.
    150 cm

21) Divide 4.8 m by 12.
    0.4 m

22) Divide 9.6 m by 16.
    0.6 m

23) Multiply 14 cm by 8.
    112 cm

24) Multiply 32 cm by 7.
    224 cm

25) Multiply 1.77 g by 9.
    15.93 g

26) Multiply 5.18 g by 4.
    20.72 g

27) Divide 9 kg by 2.
    4.5 kg

28) Divide 14 km by 4.
    3.5 km

29) Divide 0.612 kg by 18.
    0.034 kg

30) Divide 0.552 kg by 24.
    0.023 kg

31) Multiply 0.05 mL by 60. 3 mL

32) Multiply 0.05 mL by 80. 4 mL

33) Multiply 355 cm by 6. 2130 cm

34) Multiply 720 mm by 4. 2880 mm

35) Multiply 0.048 km by 5. 0.24 km

36) Multiply 0.025 kg by 6. 0.15 kg

Objective 2: Solve Applied Problems Involving Metric Units

Solve each problem.

37) Tanhoa measured a length of wood and found it to be 1 m 4 cm long. If he cuts off 32 cm, what is the length of the remaining board, in centimeters? 72 cm

38) If Corina cuts off 70 cm from a piece of fabric measuring 1 m 50 cm in length, how long is the remaining piece, in centimeters? 80 cm

39) White cheddar cheese costs $34.75/kg. Angelique needs 350 g for an au gratin potato recipe. Find the cost of the cheese. $12.16

40) Luke bought 600 g of chocolates for his girlfriend for Valentine's Day. If the chocolates cost $39.99/kg, how much did he pay? $24.00

41) A home soda maker can make a total of 60 L of soda. If Yuka plans to make 200 bottles containing the same amount of soda, how many milliliters will be in each bottle? 300 mL

42) Ninety kilograms of rice is divided evenly into 120 bags. How many grams of rice are in each bag? 750 g

43) If the weight of toothpaste applied to a toothbrush is 430 mg, approximately how many brushes can you get from a 170-g tube of toothpaste? 395 brushes

44) A can of soda contains approximately 355 mL. The volume of four 2-L bottles of soda has the same volume as how many cans? Round the answer to the nearest tenth. 22.5 cans

45) If the average rate of human hair growth is 12 mm per month, approximately how many years will it take to grow hair that is 1 meter in length? Round the answer to the nearest year. (http://emedicine.medscape.com/article/837994-overview) 7 yr

46) How many drops of solution are in a 0.5-L container if each drop is 0.05 mL? 10,000 drops

47) A patient is prescribed a total of 560 mg of medication to be taken twice a day over a 4-day period. How much should each dosage be? 70 mg

48) A patient is prescribed a total of 315 mg of medication to be taken three times a day over a 1-week period. How much should each dosage be? 15 mg

49) An eye drop bottle contains 15 mL of saline solution. If you put one drop of solution in each eye every day, how many days will it take to empty the bottle? Assume each drop is 0.05 mL. 150 days

50) Abigail's new lipstick container weighed 18.5 g (including the cap). After putting on lipstick 30 times, the lipstick container weighed 18.2 g (including the cap). What is the weight of one application, in mg? 10 mg

51) A drug prescription of 45 pills costs $427.95. If each pill contains 3 mg of medication, what is the cost per milligram? $3.17/mg

52) A drug prescription of 60 pills costs $326.40. If each pill contains 4 mg of medication, what is the cost per milligram? $1.36/mg

Mixed Exercises: Objectives 1 and 2

Perform the indicated operation.

53) Multiply 118 mL by 15. 1770 mL or 1.77 L

54) 1.85 L + 216 mL 2.066 L or 2066 mL

55) 1.65 kg − 980 g 0.67 kg or 670 g

56) Divide 6.3 m by 7. 0.9 m or 90 cm

57) 0.5 cm + 50 mm 5.5 cm or 55 mm

58) 0.35 kg − 35 g 0.315 kg or 315 g

59) Divide 1.2 m by 4. 0.3 m or 30 cm

60) 4.7 cm + 47 mm 9.4 cm or 94 mm

Solve each problem.

61) Charlotte's lip gloss costs $5.10 for 10.2 mL. If each application uses 0.06 mL, what is the cost per application? $0.03 per application

62) A 25.5-mL bottle of Jerry's favorite cologne costs $38.00. Each stroke of the spray applicator delivers 0.15 mL of cologne. If he paid $27.20 for the bottle, what is the cost of each spray? $0.16 per spray

Use the table for Exercises 63–68.

12-oz Beverage or as Noted	Caffeine Amount (milligrams)
Red Bull (8.2 oz)	80.0
Jolt	71.2
Pepsi One	55.5
Mountain Dew	55.0
Dr. Pepper	41.0

(National Soft Drink Association)

63) Which has more caffeine, a four-pack of Red Bull or a six-pack of Pepsi One? a six-pack of Pepsi One

64) Which has more caffeine, two Jolts or four Dr. Peppers? four Dr. Peppers

65) If Rene drinks two cans of Red Bull per day, how many grams of caffeine does he receive each week? 1.12 g

66) If Maurice drinks two cans of Mountain Dew per day, how many grams of caffeine does he receive each week? 0.77 g

67) How many grams of caffeine are in a six-pack of Pepsi One cans? 0.333 g

68) How many grams of caffeine are in a four-pack of 8.2-oz Red Bull cans? 0.32 g

R Rethink

R1) Think back on the main objectives involving metric units. Write a paragraph describing what makes the metric system easy to use.

R2) Which objectives do you still need to master?

7.5 Metric–U.S. Customary Conversions and Temperature

What are your objectives for Section 7.5?	How can you accomplish each objective?
1 Convert Between U.S. Customary and Metric Units	• Understand the **Relationships Between U.S. Customary Units and Metric Units.** • Use unit fractions to convert between units. • Complete the given examples on your own. • Complete You Trys 1 and 2.
2 Understand the Relationship Between the Fahrenheit and Celsius Scales	• Learn the *freezing and boiling points of water.* • Use your basic knowledge relating Celsius and Fahrenheit to answer questions relating to temperature. • Complete the given example on your own. • Complete You Try 3.
3 Convert Between Fahrenheit and Celsius Units	• Learn the **Procedure for Converting Between Fahrenheit and Celsius Temperatures.** • Complete the given examples on your own. • Complete You Trys 4 and 5.

W Work

Read the explanations, follow the examples, take notes, and complete the You Trys.

1 Convert Between U.S. Customary and Metric Units

Even though we use the U.S. customary system of measurement, we still come across metric units in the United States. In sports, for example, a track-and-field athlete might compete in a 400-m race. How long is this in yards? A pharmacist might mix 50 mg of antibiotic in a solution for a patient in a hospital. How many ounces is this?

We can use the following relationships to convert between U.S. customary units and metric units.

Relationships Between U.S. Customary Units and Metric Units

Length	Capacity	Weight (Mass)
1 inch = 2.54 centimeters	1 cup ≈ 236.59 milliliters	1 ounce ≈ 28.35 grams
1 foot ≈ 0.30 meter	1 quart ≈ 0.95 liter	1 pound ≈ 0.45 kilogram
1 yard ≈ 0.91 meter	1 gallon ≈ 3.79 liters	
1 mile ≈ 1.61 kilometers		

We will use unit fractions to convert between the two measurement systems. This method is one that is used often in nursing and science courses as well.

EXAMPLE 1

As of January 2011, Michael Johnson of the United States was the world record holder in the 400-m race. Convert 400 m to yards. Round the answer to the nearest tenth.

In-Class Example 1

As of January 2011, Usain Bolt of Jamaica was the world record holder in the 200-m race. Convert 200-m to yards. Round the answer to the nearest tenth.

Answer: 219.8 yd

Solution

First, identify the units we are given and the units we want to get. Since we are given *meters* and we want to convert to *yards*, write down the relationship between meters and yards: 1 yd ≈ 0.91 m.

Next, multiply the measurement we are given, 400 m, by the unit fraction relating yards and meters so that the meters divide out and we will be left with yards.

$$400 \text{ m} \cdot \frac{1 \text{ yd}}{0.91 \text{ m}} = \frac{400 \text{ m}}{1} \cdot \frac{1 \text{ yd}}{0.91 \text{ m}} \qquad \text{Divide out the unit of meters.}$$

$$= \frac{400 \text{ yd}}{0.91} \qquad \text{Multiply.}$$

$$\approx 439.6 \text{ yd} \qquad \text{Simplify.}$$

400 m ≈ 439.6 yd. Therefore, a 400-meter race is approximately 439.6 yd.

[YOU TRY 1] A marathon is, officially, 42.195 km. Convert this number to miles. Round the answer to the nearest tenth.

BE CAREFUL Look at Example 1. If we had tried to multiply 400 m by the unit fraction relating meters and yards as $\frac{400 \text{ m}}{1} \cdot \frac{0.91 \text{ m}}{1 \text{ yd}}$, the units of meters would not divide out. That's how we know this is the wrong way to do this problem! If this happens the first time you try to convert between units, don't panic. Write the unit fraction the other way to see whether the correct units will divide out.

Let's convert between other units.

EXAMPLE 2

In-Class Example 2

Convert to the indicated unit. Round the answer to the nearest tenth, if necessary.
a) A carrot soup recipe uses 2.5 c of vegetable stock. Convert this number to milliliters.
b) A handheld leaf blower weighs 4 kg. Convert this number to pounds.
c) Diana bought a 20-in. LCD monitor for her computer. Convert this number to centimeters.

Answer: a) 2.5 c ≈ 591.5 mL
b) 4 kg ≈ 8.9 lb
c) 20 in. = 50.8 cm

 Hint

Write out the example as you are reading it.

Convert to the indicated unit. Round the answer to the nearest tenth, if necessary.

a) Kevin makes a green cleaning solution by mixing 1.5 c of vinegar with water. Convert this number to milliliters.

b) A recipe calls for 2 kg of beef stew meat. Convert this number to pounds.

c) Huong wants to buy a 50-in. plasma television. Convert this number to centimeters.

Solution

a) We are given 1.5 *cups* and want to convert to *milliliters*. The relationship is

$$1 \text{ cup} \approx 236.59 \text{ mL}$$

Multiply the given measurement of 1.5 c by the unit fraction relating cups and milliliters so that *cups* will divide out and leave us with milliliters.

$$1.5 \text{ c} \cdot \frac{236.59 \text{ mL}}{1 \text{ c}} = \frac{1.5 \cancel{c}}{1} \cdot \frac{236.59 \text{ mL}}{1 \cancel{c}} \qquad \text{Divide out the unit of cups.}$$

$$= \frac{354.885 \text{ mL}}{1} \qquad \text{Multiply.}$$

$$= 354.885 \text{ mL} \qquad \text{Simplify.}$$

$$\approx 354.9 \text{ mL} \qquad \text{Round to the nearest tenth.}$$

So, 1.5 c vinegar ≈ 354.9 mL.

b) We are given *kilograms* and want to convert to *pounds*. The relationship is

$$1 \text{ lb} \approx 0.45 \text{ kg}$$

Multiply 2 kg by the unit fraction relating kilograms and pounds so that kilograms will divide out and leave us with pounds.

$$2 \text{ kg} \cdot \frac{1 \text{ lb}}{0.45 \text{ kg}} = \frac{2 \cancel{\text{kg}}}{1} \cdot \frac{1 \text{ lb}}{0.45 \cancel{\text{kg}}} \qquad \text{Divide out the unit of kilograms.}$$

$$= \frac{2 \text{ lb}}{0.45} \qquad \text{Multiply.}$$

$$\approx 4.4 \text{ lb} \qquad \text{Divide.}$$

Therefore, 2 kg of beef ≈ 4.4 lb.

c) We are given *inches* and want to convert to *centimeters*. The relationship is

$$1 \text{ inch} = 2.54 \text{ cm}$$

Because this is an *exact* conversion, we use = instead of ≈.

Multiply 50 in. by the unit fraction relating inches and centimeters so that inches will divide out and leave us with centimeters.

$$50 \text{ in.} \cdot \frac{2.54 \text{ cm}}{1 \text{ in.}} = \frac{50 \cancel{\text{in.}}}{1} \cdot \frac{2.54 \text{ cm}}{1 \cancel{\text{in.}}} \qquad \text{Divide out the unit of inches.}$$

$$= \frac{127 \text{ cm}}{1} \qquad \text{Multiply.}$$

$$= 127 \text{ cm} \qquad \text{Simplify.}$$

Therefore, 50 in. = 127 cm.

[YOU TRY 2] Convert to the indicated unit. Round the answer to the nearest tenth, if necessary.

a) An art teacher mixes 3.5 c of water with some flour to make plaster of Paris. Convert this number to milliliters.

b) Anastasia is 152.4 cm tall. Convert this number to inches.

c) A box contains 9 oz of fruit snacks. Convert this number to grams.

2 Understand the Relationship Between the Fahrenheit and Celsius Scales

In the United States, we use the Fahrenheit scale to measure temperature. In most of the rest of the world, the Celsius scale is used. (Science courses, even in the United States, usually use the Celsius scale.) To get a feel for how these two measures of temperature are related, let's look at some widely known Fahrenheit temperatures and give their Celsius equivalents.

Relationships Between Fahrenheit and Celsius

Freezing Point of Water		Boiling Point of Water	
In Degrees Fahrenheit	In Degrees Celsius	In Degrees Fahrenheit	In Degrees Celsius
32°F	0°C	212°F	100°C

Note

The symbol ° represents degrees. We read 32°F as "32 degrees Fahrenheit," and we read 100°C as "100 degrees Celsius."

Here are some other temperatures that might help you understand how the Fahrenheit and Celsius scales are related.

The average high temperature in Miami in July is 91°F. This is approximately 33°C. (www.weather.com)

This thermometer compares Fahrenheit and Celsius temperatures.

The temperature inside a refrigerator should be at most 40°F. This is approximately 4°C. (www.usda.gov)

EXAMPLE 3

In-Class Example 3

Determine which Celsius temperature is appropriate for the situation.
a) The temperature in a freezer should be at most ____. Choose from −18°C, 5°C, and 32°C. (www.usda.gov)
b) A comfortable household temperature is ____. Choose from 21°C, 50°C, and 68°C.

Answer:
a) −18°C (−18°C ≈ 0°F)
b) 21°C (21°C ≈ 70°F)

Determine which Celsius temperature is appropriate for the situation.

a) The average low temperature in Fairbanks, Alaska, in February is ____. Choose from −28°C, 10°C, and 28°C. (www.weather.com)

b) A comfortable household temperature is ____. Choose from 21°C, 50°C, and 68°C.

Solution

a) The average low temperature in Fairbanks, Alaska, in February is −28°C. This is the only reasonable answer because −28°C ≈ −18°F. The other two choices do not make sense because 10°C = 50°F and 28°C ≈ 82°F.

b) A comfortable household temperature is 21°C. This is approximately 70°F. The other temperatures are too hot: 50°C = 122°F and 68°C ≈ 154°F.

[YOU TRY 3] Determine which Celsius temperature is appropriate for the situation.

a) The oven temperature to bake a cake might be ____. Choose from 30°C, 180°C, and 350°C.

b) The average low temperature in Denver, Colorado, in January is about ____. Choose from −9°C, 15°C, and 22°C. (www.weather.com)

3 Convert Between Fahrenheit and Celsius Units

To convert between Fahrenheit temperature and Celsius temperature, we can use these formulas.

Hint

Be sure you learn these formulas!

Procedure How to Convert Between Fahrenheit and Celsius Temperatures

Changing from °F to °C	Changing from °C to °F
$C = \dfrac{5(F - 32)}{9}$	$F = \dfrac{9C}{5} + 32$
To change a Fahrenheit temperature (F) to Celsius (C):	To change a Celsius temperature (C) to Fahrenheit (F):
1) **Substitute** the Fahrenheit temperature for F in the formula.	1) **Substitute** the Celsius temperature for C in the formula.
2) **Evaluate** the expression using the order of operations.	2) **Evaluate** the expression using the order of operations.
3) **Round** the answer to the nearest degree, if necessary.	3) **Round** the answer to the nearest degree, if necessary.

EXAMPLE 4

Convert 77°F to Celsius.

In-Class Example 4

Convert 86°F to Celsius.

Answer: 30°C

Solution

To change from degrees Fahrenheit to Celsius, use $C = \dfrac{5(F - 32)}{9}$.

$$C = \frac{5(F - 32)}{9}$$

$$C = \frac{5(77 - 32)}{9} \qquad \text{Substitute 77 for } F.$$

$$C = \frac{5(45)}{9} \qquad \text{First, perform subtraction inside parentheses.}$$

$$C = \frac{5(\overset{5}{45})}{\underset{1}{9}} \qquad \text{Divide 9 out of the numerator and denominator.}$$

$$C = 25 \qquad \text{Multiply.}$$

Therefore, 77°F = 25°C.

[YOU TRY 4] Convert 41°F to Celsius.

EXAMPLE 5 Convert 7°C to Fahrenheit.

In-Class Example 5

Convert 3°C to Fahrenheit.

Answer: 3°C ≈ 37°F

Solution

To change from degrees Celsius to Fahrenheit, use $F = \dfrac{9C}{5} + 32$.

$$F = \frac{9C}{5} + 32$$

$$F = \frac{9(7)}{5} + 32 \qquad \text{Substitute 5 for } C.$$

$$F = \frac{63}{5} + 32 \qquad \text{First, multiply in the numerator.}$$

$$F = 12.6 + 32 \qquad \text{Divide 63 by 5.}$$

$$F = 44.6 \qquad \text{Add.}$$

Round the answer to the nearest degree: 44.6°F ≈ 45°F.
    Therefore, 7°C ≈ 45°F.

[YOU TRY 5] Convert 17°C to Fahrenheit.

ANSWERS TO [YOU TRY] EXERCISES

1) 26.2 mi   2) a) 3.5 c ≈ 828.1 mL   b) 152.4 cm = 60 in.   c) 9 oz ≈ 255.2 g
3) a) 180°C (180°C = 356°F)   b) −9°C (−9°C ≈ 16°F)   4) 5°C   5) 17°C ≈ 63°F

Fahrenheit to Celsius

When converting 91°F to Celsius, we use the formula $C = \dfrac{5(F - 32)}{9}$ and replace F with 91. This gives us the equation $C = \dfrac{5(91 - 32)}{9}$. Using a calculator to find the value of the right-hand side of the equation, we must follow the order of operations. In this case, we first simplify the expression in the parentheses, then multiply by 5, and then divide by 9. Enter $(\boxed{9}\,\boxed{1}\,\boxed{-}\,\boxed{3}\,\boxed{2})\,\boxed{\times}\,\boxed{5}\,\boxed{\div}\,\boxed{9}\,\boxed{=}$ into the calculator.

The display will likely show 32.77777777. Rounding to the nearest tenth, we get 32.8. This means 91°F ≈ 32.8°C.

Celsius to Fahrenheit

When converting 18°C to Fahrenheit, we use the formula $F = \dfrac{9C}{5} + 32$ and replace C with 18. This gives us the equation $F = \dfrac{9(18)}{5} + 32$. Using a calculator to find the value of the right-hand side of the equation, we must follow the order of operations. In this case, we first multiply 9 by 18, then divide by 5, and then add 32. We now enter $\boxed{9}\,\boxed{\times}\,\boxed{1}\,\boxed{8}\,\boxed{\div}\,\boxed{5}\,\boxed{+}\,\boxed{3}\,\boxed{2}\,\boxed{=}$ into the calculator.

The display will show 64.4. This means 18°C = 64.4°F.

E Evaluate 7.5 Exercises   Do the exercises, and check your work.

*Additional answers can be found in the Answers to Exercises appendix.

Objective 1: Convert Between U.S. Customary and Metric Units

Convert to the indicated unit. Round the answer to the nearest tenth, if necessary. Use the table on p. 472.

1) 50 ft to meters   15 m
2) 100 yd to meters   91 m

3) 200 yd to meters   182 m
4) 100 ft to meters   30 m

5) 2 c to milliliters   473.2 mL
6) 3 gal to liters   11.4 L

7) 4 kg to pounds   8.9 lb
8) 150 g to ounces   5.3 oz

9) 70 cm to inches   27.6 in.
10) 120 km to miles   74.5 mi

11) $6\frac{1}{2}$ qt to liters   6.2 L
12) 2.4 gal to liters   9.1 L

13) 40 mi to kilometers   64.4 km
14) 7 in. to centimeters   17.8 cm

15) 18 cm to inches   7.1 in.
16) 130 km to miles   80.7 mi

17) 63 kg to pounds   140 lb
18) 470 g to ounces   16.6 oz

19) 12.6 oz to grams   357.2 g
20) $23\frac{3}{4}$ lb to kilograms   10.7 kg

21) 11 L to gallons   2.9 gal
22) 7 L to quarts   7.4 qt

23) 39 m to yards   42.9 yd
24) 15 m to feet   50 ft

For Exercises 25–28, convert to the indicated metric unit:

a) using the values in the table on p. 472 to get an approximation of the equivalent metric unit.

b) using the exact relationships of 1 ft = 12 in., 1 yd = 36 in., 1 in. = 2.54 cm, and 100 cm = 1 m.

25) 10 ft to meters
   a) 10 ft ≈ 3 m   b) 10 ft = 3.048 m
26) 18 ft to meters
   a) 18 ft ≈ 5.4 m   b) 18 ft = 5.4864 m

27) 50 yd to meters
   a) 50 yd ≈ 45.50 m   b) 50 yd = 45.72 m
28) 1 yd to meters
   a) 1 yd ≈ 0.91 m
   b) 1 yd = 0.9144 m

Solve each problem.

29) The average length of goldfish ranges from 2 to 18 inches, depending on the variety. Find the length, in centimeters, of an 18-in. goldfish. (www.petco.com)   45.72 cm

30) Marcia measures the length of her walking stride and finds it to be 26 in. How many centimeters is this?   66.04 cm

31) A 9-kg bag of cat litter weighs approximately how many pounds?   20 lb

32) A bag of dry dog food is available in a 15.5-lb bag. Approximately how many kilograms is this?   7 kg

33) A dishwasher earns an Energy Star rating if it uses less than 5.8 gal of water per cycle. Does a dishwasher that uses 21 L of water per cycle qualify? (www.energystar.gov)   yes

34) Mehdi's luggage weighs 23 kg. If the airline charges an additional $25 to check a piece of luggage that weighs over 50 lb, will he have to pay the extra money for his bag?   yes

35) To conserve water, Mark installs a new, ultralow-flow toilet in his home that uses 6 L of water per flush. The old toilet uses 3.5 gal of water per flush. How much water, in gallons, does the new toilet save per flush? Round the answer to the nearest tenth.   1.9 gal per flush

36) Janet's top-loading washing machine uses 28 gal of water to wash a medium-sized load while Trisha's front-loading machine uses 50 L. Which machine uses less water, and by how much, in gallons? Round the answer to the nearest tenth.
Trisha's machine uses approximately 14.8 gallons less water.

37) Jeremy searches a field with a metal detector and finds a pure gold nugget weighing 18.7 g. If the price of gold is $925.00 per ounce, how much is the nugget worth? $610.14

38) Ysela's wedding band contains 8.4 g of platinum. If the price of platinum is $1713.00 per ounce, how much is the platinum content worth? $507.56

Objective 2: Understand the Relationship Between the Fahrenheit and Celsius Scales

Determine which Celsius temperature is appropriate for the situation.

39) On a snowy day, the temperature outdoors is ___−4°C__. Choose from −4°C, 8°C, and 30°C.

40) Hot cocoa is best served at __46°C__. Choose from 10°C, 46°C, and 100°C.

41) To bake a casserole, the oven temperature might be __200°C__. Choose from 30°C, 200°C, and 375°C.

42) A hot tub might have a water temperature of __35°C__. Choose from 10°C, 35°C, and 80°C.

43) If the outdoor temperature is 29°C, choose clothing best suited for this temperature. Choose from a T-shirt and shorts, jeans and sweater, heavy coat and gloves.   T-shirt and shorts

44) Is a temperature change of 10°C equal to a temperature change of 38°F? Explain your answer.
No; Answers may vary.

Objective 3: Convert Between Fahrenheit and Celsius Units

Use the formula $C = \dfrac{5(F - 32)}{9}$.

45) Explain how to change a temperature from °F to °C.

46) Explain how to change a temperature from °C to °F.
Use the formula $F = \dfrac{9C}{5} + 32$.

Perform the following temperature conversions. Round to the nearest degree.

47) 41°F to Celsius   5°C   48) 95°F to Celsius   35°C

49) 82°F to Celsius   28°C   50) 34°F to Celsius   1°C

51) 104°F to Celsius   40°C   52) 45°F to Celsius   7°C

53) 72°F to Celsius   22°C   54) 61°F to Celsius   16°C

55) 20°C to Fahrenheit   68°F   56) 85°C to Fahrenheit   185°F

57) 73°C to Fahrenheit   163°F   58) 6°C to Fahrenheit   43°F

59) 25°C to Fahrenheit   77°F   60) 55°C to Fahrenheit   131°F

61) 9°C to Fahrenheit   48°F   62) 2°C to Fahrenheit   36°F

Mixed Exercises: Objectives 1–3

Convert to the indicated unit. Round the answer to the nearest tenth, if necessary.

63) 75 ft to meters   22.5 m   64) 12 gal to liters   45.5 L

65) $14\dfrac{1}{5}$ oz to grams   402.6 g   66) 6.5 in. to centimeters   16.5 cm

67) 9 L to quarts   9.5 qt   68) 58 kg to pounds   128.9 lb

69) 500 mL to cups   2.1 c   70) 200 km to miles   124.2 mi

71) Silvia rode her bike 15 mi on the boardwalk at the beach. How many kilometers did she ride? Round to the nearest tenth.   24.2 km

72) The length of Gabriella's walking stride is 26 in. How many centimeters is this?   66.04 cm

73) A cool air-conditioned room might have a temperature of __20°C__. Choose from 20°C, 40°C, and 66°C.

74) A person with a high fever might have a temperature of __39°C__. Choose from 39°C, 99°C, and 102°C.

75) Convert 52°F to Celsius. Round to the nearest degree.   11°C

76) Convert 26°C to Fahrenheit. Round to the nearest degree.   79°F

77) The highest temperature ever recorded on Earth was 57.8°C in El Azizia, Libya, in 1922. What is this temperature in Fahrenheit? Round to the nearest degree. (www.ncdc.noaa.gov)   136°F

78) The highest temperature ever recorded in Antarctica was 59°F in 1974. What is this temperature in Celsius? Round to the nearest degree. (www.ncdc.noaa.gov)   15°C

R Rethink

R1) If you had to use one relationship between U.S. customary units and metric units for each of the following, which would you pick and why? length, capacity, weight

R2) If you memorized only one of the formulas for converting between Fahrenheit and Celsius, how could you derive the other formula?

Group Activity – Measurement and Conversion

Activity 1: Measurement

A. Match each object listed on the left with the most appropriate measurement from the list on the right. [Hint: Think about whether the object is measuring a length, capacity, or weight (mass).]

1) The thickness of a dime	a. 1827.35 km
2) The weight of a peanut	b. 136 g
3) The amount of water in a swimming pool	c. 6.4 cm
4) The amount of water in a raindrop	d. 0.98 m
5) The length of your little finger	e. 30,000 mg
6) The width of a twin bed	f. 0.5 mL
7) The weight of an apple	g. 2 L
8) The distance between Los Angeles and Seattle	h. 68.22 kL
9) The weight of a compact car	i. 1700 kg
10) The amount of soda in a soda bottle	j. 1.35 mm

B. Use the measurements in A. to answer the following questions.

1) Convert the measurement for the weight of a compact car to grams. What do you notice about the numerical part of your answer?

2) Convert the measurement for the thickness of a dime to centimeters. What do you notice about the numerical part of your answer?

3) Convert the measurement for the amount of water in a raindrop to deciliters. What do you notice about the numerical part of your answer?

4) Convert the measurement for the width of a twin bed to centimeters. What do you notice about the numerical part of your answer?

5) Convert the measurement for the amount of water in a swimming pool to liters. What do you notice about the numerical part of your answer?

6) Describe any patterns that you notice after answering the five questions above.

Activity 2: Conversions

- Work in groups of two or three.
- Name something that could be measured by each metric measurement listed below (make sure you state whether it is a length, capacity, or weight).
- Convert each metric measurement to an appropriate U.S. customary measurement.
- Determine whether your original answer was reasonable.
- If your first answer was not reasonable, name something that is more appropriate.
- The first one has been done for you.

1) 6.75 kg: The weight of a computer monitor

2) 90.96 L

3) 28.65 m

4) 350 g

5) 2.8 kg

Group Activity Answers

Activity 1 Answers

A. 1) j   2) e   3) h   4) f   5) c   6) d   7) b   8) a   9) i   10) g

B. 1) 1700 kg = 1,700,000 g. The numerical part of the answer increased.

    2) 1.35 mm = 0.135 cm. The numerical part of the answer decreased.

    3) 0.5 mL = 0.005 dL. The numerical part of the answer decreased.

    4) 0.98 m = 98 cm. The numerical part of the answer increased.

    5) 68.22 kL = 68,220 L. The numerical part of the answer increased.

    6) Answers will vary. Possible answer: When we convert a larger unit to a smaller unit, the numerical part of the answer gets larger. When we convert a smaller unit to a larger unit, the numerical part of the answer gets smaller. When we convert from a larger unit to a smaller unit, we multiply to get our answer. When we convert from a smaller unit to a larger unit, we divide to get our answer.

Activity 2 Answers

1) The weight of a computer monitor (6.75 kg is about 15 pounds)

2) Possible answer: The amount of water in a bathtub: 90.96 L ≈ 24 gal

3) Possible answer: The length of a basketball court: 28.65 m ≈ 95.5 ft

4) Possible answer: The weight of a cell phone: 350 g ≈ 12.35 oz

5) Possible answer: The weight of a textbook: 2.8 kg ≈ 6.2 lb

Compare your answers with the answers of another group. Were your answers similar in length, capacity, and weight?

---

em **POWER** me   Becoming a Math Teacher to Reinforce Your Own Understanding

One of the best ways to learn new material is to explain it to another person. Putting ideas into words reinforces your understanding. This is as true for math as it is for any subject. This exercise will help you master mathematical skills by teaching them to someone else.

1. **Pick a math skill from this book.** It's best to select a skill that you are relatively comfortable with, but not one you feel you know so well that you don't need any additional practice.

2. **Select an audience.** Who would benefit from learning this mathematical skill? Maybe you have a friend in construction who would be helped by understanding the techniques of measurement conversion. Maybe a family member who likes to cook would find it easier to change serving sizes in recipes if he or she knew more about fractions.

3. **Write a brief description of the skill you have chosen, including at least three sample problems.**

4. **Share what you wrote with the person you selected,** and discuss the mathematical skill with him or her. Ask what he or she understands and what is still unclear. Answering the questions will also help you master your topic.

After performing this exercise, do you feel more confident using the math skill you helped teach? Do you think this process would help you learn other topics?

Chapter 7: Summary

Definition/Procedure	Example

7.1 Using U.S. Customary Measurements

The relationships between U.S. Customary units can be found on p. 433.

12 in. = 1 ft   4 qt = 1 gal   16 oz = 1 lb

Using Multiplication or Division to Convert Between Units

1) When converting from a *larger unit* to a *smaller unit,* use *multiplication.*

2) When converting from a *smaller unit* to a *larger unit,* use *division.* **(p. 434)**

Convert 1.5 gal to quarts.

Since we are going from a larger unit to a smaller unit, we will multiply.

$$1.5 \text{ gal} \cdot 4 = 6 \text{ qt} \qquad 4 \text{ qt} = 1 \text{ gal}$$

So, 1.5 gal = 6 qt.

Unit Fractions

A **unit fraction** is a fraction that is equivalent to 1. We can write measurement equivalencies as unit fractions. **(p. 435)**

We can write 12 in. = 1 ft as the unit fraction

$$\frac{12 \text{ in.}}{1 \text{ ft}} \text{ or } \frac{1 \text{ ft}}{12 \text{ in.}}.$$

Using Unit Analysis to Convert Between Units

To convert from one unit of measurement to another, we multiply the measurement we are given by the appropriate unit fraction. **(p. 436)**

Use unit analysis to convert 54 in. to feet.

$$54 \text{ in.} \cdot \frac{1 \text{ ft}}{12 \text{ in.}} = \frac{\overset{9}{\cancel{54 \text{ in.}}}}{1} \cdot \frac{1 \text{ ft}}{\underset{2}{\cancel{12 \text{ in.}}}}$$

Divide 54 and 12 by 6; divide out the unit of inches.

$$= \frac{9 \text{ ft}}{2}$$

Multiply.

$$= \frac{9}{2} \text{ ft}$$

Simplify.

$$= 4\frac{1}{2} \text{ ft or 4.5 ft}$$

Write the final answer as a mixed number or decimal.

7.2 The Metric System: Length

The Metric System

The **metric system** is based on multiples of 10. The basic unit of length is the **meter.** A meter is about 39.37 in. long, so it is a little longer than a yard. **(p. 445)**

Meterstick

Yardstick

Since the metric units of length are related to the meter, the units are described by using a prefix on the word *meter.*

The measurements on the left allow us to state these additional relationships:

Metric Units of Length

1 kilometer (km) = 1000 m

1 hectometer (hm) = 100 m

1 dekameter (dam) = 10 m

1 meter (m) = 1 m

1 decimeter (dm) = $\frac{1}{10}$ m or 0.1 m

1 centimeter (cm) = $\frac{1}{100}$ m or 0.01 m

1 millimeter (mm) = $\frac{1}{1000}$ m or 0.001 m

The units used most often are kilometer, meter, centimeter, and millimeter. **(p. 446)**

Additional Relationships Between Metric Units of Length

10 decimeters = 1 meter

100 centimeters = 1 meter

1000 millimeters = 1 meter

10 millimeters = 1 centimeter

10 centimeters = 1 decimeter

Definition/Procedure	Example
Use Unit Fractions to Convert Between Units We can use unit fractions and the relationships between metric units to convert from one unit to another. **(p. 449)**	Use unit fractions to convert 27 km to meters. $27 \text{ km} \cdot \dfrac{1000 \text{ m}}{1 \text{ km}} = \dfrac{27 \cancel{\text{ km}}}{1} \cdot \dfrac{1000 \text{ m}}{1 \cancel{\text{ km}}}$ Divide out the unit of kilometers. $= \dfrac{27{,}000 \text{ m}}{1}$ Multiply. $= 27{,}000 \text{ m}$ Simplify. Therefore, 27 km = 27,000 m.
Use the Metric Conversion Chart to Convert Between Units This is how to use the metric conversion chart to convert from one unit to another: 1) Find the unit that you are given. 2) Count the number of places you must move to go from the unit you are given to the unit you want to get. 3) Move the decimal point the same number of places and in the same direction that you did on the metric conversion chart. **(p. 450)**	Use the metric conversion chart to change 45 cm to meters. Find cm on the chart. Since we move *two places to the left* to reach m, we move the decimal point in 45 cm *two places to the left* to change to meters. Remember that the whole number 45 can be written with a decimal point to the right of the 5. $$45. \text{ cm} = .45 \text{ m}$$ Put the decimal point at the end of the number. Move the decimal point two places to the left. So, 45 cm = 0.45 m.

7.3 The Metric System: Capacity and Weight (Mass)

Units of Capacity Units of capacity measure quantities of liquids. In the United States, we use units such as quarts and gallons. In the metric system, the basic unit of capacity is the **liter,** abbreviated as L. A liter is a little more than a quart. **(p. 455)**	
To describe larger and smaller units of capacity in the metric system, we use the same prefixes on *liter* that we used for *meter* to describe length. The units used most often are liter and milliliter. **(p. 456)**	1 kiloliter (kL) = 1000 liters (L) 1000 milliliters (mL) = 1 liter (L)

Definition/Procedure	Example
Converting Between Metric Units of Capacity We can use unit fractions or the metric conversion chart to convert between metric units of capacity. **(p. 457)**	Change 350 mL to liters using a) a unit fraction and b) the metric conversion chart. a) To use a unit fraction, we use the relationship 1000 mL = 1 L. $$350 \text{ mL} \cdot \frac{1 \text{ L}}{1000 \text{ mL}} = \frac{350 \text{ mL}}{1} \cdot \frac{1 \text{ L}}{1000 \text{ mL}} \quad \text{Divide out the unit of milliliters.}$$ $$= \frac{350 \text{ L}}{1000} \quad \text{Multiply.}$$ $$= 0.350 \text{ L} \quad \text{Simplify.}$$ So, 350 mL = 0.350 L or 0.35 L. b) We can also use the metric conversion chart. Start at mL on the metric conversion chart. Move *three places to the left* to get from mL to L. Move the decimal point *three places to the left.* 350. mL = .350 L Put the decimal point at the end of the number. Move the decimal point three places to the left. So, 350 mL = 0.350 L or 0.35 L.
Units of Weight (Mass) In the metric system, the basic unit of mass is the **gram,** abbreviated as g. If an object is on the Earth, the weight and mass of that object are the same. So, we will use the word *weight.* **(p. 459)**	A penny weighs approximately 2.5 g. (www.usmint.gov)
To describe larger and smaller units of weight (mass) in the metric system, we use the same prefixes on *grams* that we used for *meter* to describe length. The units used most often are kilogram, gram, and milligram. **(p. 459)**	1 kilogram (kg) = 1000 grams (g) 1000 milligrams (mg) = 1 gram (g)
Converting Between Metric Units of Weight (Mass) We can use unit fractions or the metric conversion chart to convert between metric units of weight (mass). **(p. 461)**	Change 4.8 kg to grams using a) a unit fraction and b) the metric conversion chart. a) To use a unit fraction, we use the relationship 1 kg = 1000 g. $$4.8 \text{ kg} \cdot \frac{1000 \text{ g}}{1 \text{ kg}} = \frac{4.8 \text{ kg}}{1} \cdot \frac{1000 \text{ g}}{1 \text{ kg}} \quad \text{Divide out the unit of kilograms.}$$ $$= \frac{4800 \text{ g}}{1} \quad \text{Multiply.}$$ $$= 4800 \text{ g} \quad \text{Simplify.}$$ So, 4.8 kg = 4800 g. b) We can also use the metric conversion chart. Start at kg on the metric conversion chart. Move *three places to the right* to get from kg to g. Move the decimal point *three places to the right.* 4.8 kg = 4800. g Move the decimal point three places to the right. 4.8 kg = 4800 g

Definition/Procedure	Example

7.4 Solve Applied Problems Involving Metric Units

Perform Operations with Metric Units

We can add, subtract, multiply, and divide numbers with metric units. Sometimes, it is necessary to express the numbers with the same units before performing the operations. **(p. 466)**

Add 3 m + 215 mm.

The units are not the same, so we will convert one of the units so that it is the same as the other.

Express each measurement in meters.	Express each measurement in millimeters.
215 mm = 0.215 m	3 m = 3000 mm
Now, add the measurements.	Now, add the measurements.
3 m + 215 mm = 3 m + 0.215 m = 3.215 m	3 m + 215 mm = 3000 mm + 215 mm = 3215 mm

Solve an Applied Problem Involving Metric Units

We can use the problem-solving steps introduced in Section 2.7 to solve applications involving metric units. **(p. 466)**

The instructions on a 140-mL bottle of prescription cough medicine say to take 10 mL of the medicine two times per day until it is gone. How many days will the medicine last?

Step 1: **Read** the problem carefully, and restate it in your own words.

A bottle contains a total of 140 mL of medicine. The dosage is 10 mL twice a day. We must determine how many days the medicine will last.

Step 2: **Make a plan.** Underline important words in our restatement of the problem in Step 1.

Plan: First, determine how much medicine is taken per day. Then, divide the total amount of medicine, 140 mL, by the amount of medicine taken each day.

Step 3: **Solve** the problem.

Since the dosage is 10 mL twice a day, the total amount of medicine taken each day is 10 mL · 2 = 20 mL.

Divide 140 mL by 20 mL to determine the number of days the medicine will last: $\dfrac{140 \text{ mL}}{20 \text{ mL}} = 7$

Step 4: **State the answer** in a complete sentence.

The medicine will last 7 days.

Step 5: **Check** the answer. The check is left to the student.

Definition/Procedure	Example

7.5 Metric–U.S. Customary Conversions and Temperature

We can convert between U.S. customary and metric units. **(p. 472)**

Relationships Between U.S. Customary Units and Metric Units

Length

1 in. = 2.54 cm	1 yd ≈ 0.91 m
1 ft ≈ 0.30 m	1 mi ≈ 1.61 km

Capacity

1 cup ≈ 236.59 mL	1 gal ≈ 3.79 L
1 qt ≈ 0.95 L	

Weight (Mass)

1 oz ≈ 28.35 g	1 lb ≈ 0.45 kg

We can use unit fractions to convert between the two measurement systems. **(p. 473)**

Change 20 in. to cm.

Identify the relationship between inches and centimeters:

$$1 \text{ in.} = 2.54 \text{ cm}$$

Multiply the given measurement of 20 in. by the unit fraction relating inches and centimeters so that *inches* will divide out and leave us with centimeters.

$$20 \text{ in.} \cdot \frac{2.54 \text{ cm}}{1 \text{ in.}} = \frac{20 \text{ in.}}{1} \cdot \frac{2.54 \text{ cm}}{1 \text{ in.}} \quad \text{Divide out the unit of inches.}$$

$$= \frac{50.8 \text{ cm}}{1} \quad \text{Multiply.}$$

$$= 50.8 \text{ cm} \quad \text{Simplify.}$$

Therefore, 20 in. = 50.8 cm.

Changing from °F to °C

$$C = \frac{5(F - 32)}{9}$$

To change a Fahrenheit temperature (F) to Celsius (C):

1) **Substitute** the Fahrenheit temperature for *F* in the formula.

2) **Evaluate** the expression using the order of operations.

3) **Round** the answer to the nearest degree, if necessary. **(p. 476)**

Convert 95°F to Celsius.

$$C = \frac{5(F - 32)}{9}$$

$$C = \frac{5(95 - 32)}{9} \quad \text{Substitute 95 for } F.$$

$$C = \frac{5(63)}{9} \quad \text{Perform subtraction inside parentheses.}$$

$$C = \frac{5(63)^7}{9^1} \quad \text{Divide 9 out of the numerator and denominator.}$$

$$C = 35 \quad \text{Multiply.}$$

Therefore, 95°F = 35°C.

Changing from °C to °F

$$F = \frac{9C}{5} + 32$$

To change a Celsius temperature (C) to Fahrenheit (F):

1) **Substitute** the Celsius temperature for *C* in the formula.

2) **Evaluate** the expression using the order of operations.

3) **Round** the answer to the nearest degree, if necessary. **(p. 476)**

Convert 11°C to Fahrenheit.

$$F = \frac{9C}{5} + 32$$

$$F = \frac{9(11)}{5} + 32 \quad \text{Substitute 11 for } C.$$

$$F = \frac{99}{5} + 32 \quad \text{Multiply in the numerator.}$$

$$F = 19.8 + 32 \quad \text{Divide 99 by 5.}$$

$$F = 51.8 \quad \text{Add.}$$

Round the answer to the nearest degree: 51.8°F ≈ 52°F.

Therefore, 11°C ≈ 52°F.

Chapter 7: Review Exercises

*Additional answers can be found in the Answers to Exercises appendix.

(7.1) Fill in the blank.

1) ___3___ ft = 1 yd

2) 1 pt = ___2___ c

3) 1 lb = ___16___ oz

4) ___60___ min = 1 hr

5) To convert from seconds to minutes, do we use multiplication or division? Explain your answer. Use division because we are converting from a smaller unit to a larger unit.

6) To convert from feet to inches, do we use multiplication or division? Explain your answer. Use multiplication because we are converting from a larger unit to a smaller unit.

Use multiplication or division to convert to the indicated unit.

7) 10 qt to gallons $2\frac{1}{2}$ gal or 2.5 gal

8) 52 oz to pounds $3\frac{1}{4}$ lb or 3.25 lb

9) $1\frac{1}{4}$ days to hours 30 hr

10) 3.5 ft to inches 42 in.

Use unit analysis to convert to the indicated unit.

11) 7 min to seconds 420 sec

12) 81 in. to feet $6\frac{3}{4}$ ft or 6.75 ft

13) 5 pt to quarts $2\frac{1}{2}$ qt or 2.5 qt

14) 4.6 hr to minutes 276 min

15) $6\frac{2}{3}$ yd to feet 20 ft

16) 630 in. to yards $17\frac{1}{2}$ yd or 17.5 yd

Solve each problem.

17) Vlad is comparing two brands of hot dogs. The label for Brand A says that its unit cost is $3.49/lb. The unit cost for Brand B is $0.24/oz. Which is the better buy? Brand A; the unit cost of Brand B in dollars/pound is $3.84/lb.

18) It takes Helen 20 min to crochet each square for an afghan. How many hours will it take for her to make the 96 squares she needs for the blanket? 32 hr

(7.2) Fill in the blank.

19) 1 m = ___100___ cm

20) 1 km = ___1000___ m

21) ___1000___ mm = 1 m

22) ___10___ mm = 1 cm

For Exercises 23 and 24, determine which unit of metric length would be most appropriate for each situation. Choose from m, mm, cm, and km.

23) The distance between New York City and Los Angeles km

24) The length of a key cm

Use unit fractions to change to the indicated unit.

25) 631 mm to meters 0.631 m

26) 892 m to kilometers 0.892 km

27) 1.2 km to meters 1200 m

28) 5.75 m to centimeters 575 cm

Use the metric conversion chart to change to the indicated unit.

29) 7 m to centimeters 700 cm

30) 4 m to millimeters 4000 mm

31) 96.5 mm to meters 0.0965 m

32) 28.3 m to kilometers 0.0283 km

33) 0.8 km to centimeters 80,000 cm

34) 0.7 km to millimeters 700,000 mm

(7.3) For Exercises 35–38, determine which unit of metric unit of capacity would be more appropriate for each situation. Choose from mL and L.

35) The amount of gas it takes to fill a car's tank L

36) The amount of water used to do dishes in the kitchen sink L

37) The amount of milk in a baby bottle mL

38) The amount of soup in a can mL

Use unit fractions to convert to the indicated unit.

39) 3.25 L to milliliters 3250 mL

40) 4.75 L to milliliters 4750 mL

41) 140 mL to liters 0.14 L

42) 290 mL to liters 0.29 L

Use the metric conversion chart to change to the indicated unit.

43) 630 mL to liters 0.63 L

44) 850 mL to liters 0.85 L

45) 2 L to milliliters 2000 mL

46) 9 mL to milliliters 9000 mL

Fill in the blank.

47) ___1000___ g = 1 kg

48) 1000 mg = ___1___ g

For Exercises 49–52, fill in the blank with mg, g, or kg.

49) The tablet contains 200 ___mg___ of ibuprofen.

50) A female elephant can weigh about 3500 ___kg___.

51) Jada's backpack weighs 4 ___kg___.

52) The strawberry weighed 23 ___g___.

Use unit fractions to convert to the indicated unit.

53) 82 mg to grams 0.082 g

54) 61 mg to grams 0.061 g

55) 13 kg to grams 13,000 g

56) 22 kg to grams 22,000 g

57) $4\frac{1}{2}$ g to milligrams 4500 mg

58) 7.9 g to milligrams 7900 mg

Use the metric conversion chart to change to the indicated unit.

59) 9750 g to kilograms
9.75 kg

60) 8140 g to kilograms
8.14 kg

61) 0.02 kg to milligrams
20,000 mg

62) 0.06 kg to milligrams
60,000 mg

(7.4) Perform the indicated operation.

63) Divide 48 g by 8.   6 g

64) Multiply 0.05 mL by 4.
0.2 mL

65) 7 m + 47 cm
7.47 m or 747 cm

66) 0.09 g − 37 mg
0.053 g or 53 mg

Solve each problem.

67) If Ruby cuts off 85 cm from a piece of fabric measuring 2 m 50 cm in length, how long is the remaining piece, in centimeters?   165 cm

68) Danny cuts a metal pipe measuring 1 m 80 cm into three equal lengths. Find the length of each piece, in centimeters.   60 cm

69) Masa harina costs about $3.98/kg. Lupita's tortilla recipe uses 250 g of the flour and makes about 15 tortillas. If she wants to make 120 tortillas so that she can share them with friends and family, find the cost of the masa harina. $7.96

70) Davida's 50-mL pump spray perfume bottle delivers 0.1 mL of her favorite perfume per stroke. If she applies the perfume twice a day, how many days will the bottle last?   250 days

(7.5) For Exercises 71–78, convert to the indicated unit.

71) During the 2010–2011 season, the year the Green Bay Packers won Super Bowl XLV, quarterback Aaron Rodgers threw for 3922 yd. Convert this number to meters. Round to the nearest meter. (www.packers.com)   3569 m

72) According to the *Guinness World Records,* the world's tallest man was about 2.7 m tall. Convert this number to feet. (www.guinnessworldrecords.com)   9 ft

73) Ralph caught a lake trout that weighed 11 kg. Convert this number to pounds. Round to the nearest tenth.   24.4 lb

74) A 5-minute shower uses about 12.5 gal of water. Convert this number to liters. Round to the nearest tenth.   47.4 L

75) The builder installed a 190-liter water heater in a new home. Convert this number to gallons. Round to the nearest gallon.   50 gal

76) A bakery ordered a 22.5-kg sack of Swiss pastry flour. Convert this number to pounds.   50 lb

77) Crystal's cell phone is 4 in. long. Convert this number to centimeters. Round to the nearest tenth.   10.2 cm

78) The driving distance between Little Rock, AR, and Nashville, TN, is about 350 mi. Convert this number to kilometers. Round to the nearest kilometer.   564 km

Determine which Celsius temperature is appropriate for the situation.

79) Water freezes at ___0°C___. Choose from 0°C, 10°C, and 32°C.

80) The high temperature on a summer day in Hawaii might be ___31°C___. Choose from 5°C, 84°C, and 31°C.

Perform the following temperature conversions. Round to the nearest degree, if necessary.

81) Convert 50°F to Celsius.   10°C

82) Convert 86°F to Celsius.   30°C

83) Convert 79°F to Celsius.   26°C

84) Convert 37°F to Celsius.   3°C

85) Convert 5°C to Fahrenheit.   41°F

86) Convert 65°C to Fahrenheit.   149°F

87) Convert 132°C to Fahrenheit.   270°F

88) Convert 19°C to Fahrenheit.   66°F

Mixed Exercises

Fill in the blank with the appropriate metric unit. Choose from mm, cm, m, km, mL, L, mg, g, and kg.

89) The diameter of a DVD is 120 ___mm___.

90) The glass contains 350 ___mL___ of orange juice.

91) Heinrich's car weighs 1620 ___kg___.

92) Tina's bedroom is 4.5 ___m___ wide.

93) The aquarium in Celina's house holds 75 ___L___ of water.

94) A kitten weighs about 100 ___g___ at birth. (http://veterinarymedicine.dvm360.com)

Convert to the indicated unit.

95) 2.25 L to milliliters
2250 mL

96) 0.6 kg to grams   600 g

97) 48 cm to meters   0.48 m

98) 1294 mm to meters   1.294 m

99) $5\frac{1}{3}$ min to seconds
320 sec

100) $2\frac{3}{4}$ days to hours
66 hr

101) 5800 mg to kilograms
0.0058 kg

102) 1.7 km to millimeters
1,700,000 mm

Perform the indicated operation.

103) 89 cm − 52 mm
83.8 cm or 838 mm

104) Divide 20 L by 4.
5 L

105) Multiply 0.6 kg by 7.
4.2 kg

106) 2 g + 85 mg
2.085 g or 2085 mg

Convert to the indicated unit. Round the answer to the nearest tenth, if necessary.

107) 160 km to miles 99.4 mi

108) 80 g to ounces 2.8 oz

109) 6 qt to liters 5.7 L

110) 2 c to milliliters 473.2 mL

111) 9.8 kg to pounds
21.8 lb

112) $6\frac{1}{2}$ in. to centimeters
16.5 cm

Perform the following temperature conversions. Round to the nearest degree, if necessary.

113) Convert 22°C to Fahrenheit. 72°F

114) Convert 59°F to Celsius. 15°C

Solve each problem.

115) Marilyn needs to buy 110 g of pepperoni for a pizza, and the pepperoni costs $22.00/kg. How much will Marilyn pay for the pepperoni? $2.42

116) Neda has a length of ribbon that is 1 m 60 cm long. If she cuts off 75 cm, how much ribbon is left, in centimeters?
85 cm

Chapter 7:   Test

*Additional answers can be found in the Answers to Exercises appendix.

Fill in the blank.

1) __4__ qt = 1 gal

2) 1 min = __60__ sec

Convert to the indicated unit.

3) 21 ft to yards 7 yd

4) 6 pt to quarts 3 qt

5) 24 oz to pounds $1\frac{1}{2}$ lb or 1.5 lb

6) $4\frac{2}{3}$ ft to inches 56 in.

7) 3.5 days to minutes 5040 min

Fill in the blank with the appropriate metric unit. Choose from mm, cm, m, km, mL, L, mg, g, and kg.

8) The mechanic put 1.5 __L__ of oil in the car's engine.

9) Sonya is 7 years old and 112 __cm__ tall.

10) Christopher weighs 79 __kg__.

11) The diameter of a quarter is 24 __mm__.

12) The bottle contains 475 __mL__ of salad dressing.

13) The cookie weighs about 8 __g__.

14) The traffic light is 8.5 __m__ tall.

Convert to the indicated unit.

15) 250 mg to grams 0.25 g

16) 7.3 m to centimeters 730 cm

17) 62 mL to liters 0.062 L

18) $2\frac{1}{2}$ kg to grams 2500 g

19) 19.35 cm to millimeters 193.5 mm

20) 800,000 mm to kilometers 0.8 km

21) Add 3 kg + 45 g. 3.045 kg or 3045 g

Determine which Celsius temperature is appropriate for the situation.

22) The temperature when Sven shoveled snow could have been __−7°C__. Choose from 23°C, 11°C, and −7°C.

23) The temperature when Monique drove her convertible with the top down could have been __26°C__. Choose from 26°C, 68°C, and 80°C.

Convert to the indicated unit. Round the answer to the nearest tenth, if necessary.

24) 50 in. to centimeters   25) 6 kg to pounds   13.3 lb
    127 cm
26) 320 km to miles   198.8 mi   27) 14.8 gal to liters   56.1 L

28) $1\frac{1}{2}$ cups to milliliters   354.9 mL

Perform the following temperature conversions. Round to the nearest degree, if necessary.

29) 77°F to Celsius   25°C   30) 4°C to Fahrenheit   39°F

Solve each problem.

31) PVC pipe costs $2.48 per foot. Find the cost of 54 in. of this pipe. $11.16

32) If your hair grows about 12 mm per month, how long would it take to grow 6 cm?   5 months

33) At an Asian market, dried shrimp costs $33.80/kg. Oki needs 1 lb of the shrimp for a stir fry recipe. How much will she pay for the shrimp? $15.21

34) Parvesh has a piece of plastic landscape edging that is 5 m long. If he cuts off 72 cm, find the length of edging remaining, in meters.   4.28 m

35) A patient is prescribed 2100 mg of diclofenac for arthritis. The instructions say to take one tablet twice a day for two weeks. How much diclofenac is in each tablet?   75 mg

Chapter 7:   Cumulative Review for Chapters 1–7

*Additional answers can be found in the Answers to Exercises appendix.

1) What is the difference between a digit and a number?

2) Write 8,031,207 in words.
   eight million, thirty-one thousand, two hundred seven

3) Write *six hundred four thousand nine* using digits.
   604,009

4) Explain, in your own words, how to determine whether a whole number is divisible by 3.
   A number is divisible by 3 if the sum of its digits is divisible by 3.

5) Determine whether each number is divisible by 2, 3, 5, and/or 10.

   a) 290   2, 5, 10   b) 16,425   3, 5

Perform the indicated operations. Write all answers in lowest terms.

6) $\frac{7}{8} - \frac{2}{3}$ $\frac{5}{24}$ 7) 413.6 − 257.92   155.68

8) 1323 ÷ 27   49   9) 0.0882 × 1000   88.2

10) 59 + 2085 + 647 + 18,996   21,787

11) $\frac{14}{27} \cdot \frac{15}{28}$ $\frac{5}{18}$ 12) $3\frac{5}{9} \div 3\frac{1}{3}$ $1\frac{1}{15}$

13) $120 \div 8 + 2^4 - \sqrt{49}$ 24   14) $\frac{54}{6} + 4[12^2 - 3(1 + 5)^2]$ 153

15) 1.44 ÷ 32   0.045

16) Write $\frac{54}{96}$ in lowest terms. $\frac{9}{16}$

17) Write 0.083 in words.   eighty-three thousandths

18) What is the difference between a ratio and a rate?

19) The ratio of full-time faculty to part-time faculty in a math department is 20 to 70. Write this ratio as a fraction in lowest terms, and explain what it means.
    $\frac{2}{7}$; for every 2 full-time faculty members, there are 7 part-time faculty members.

20) Convert 74 g to mg.   74,000 mg

21) Convert 63°F to Celsius. Round to the nearest degree.   17°C

Solve each problem.

22) The distance between home plate and first base on a baseball diamond is 90 ft. Approximately how many meters is this? Use 1 ft ≈ 0.30 m.   27 m

23) A cookie recipe uses $2\frac{1}{2}$ c flour and makes 36 cookies. If Lisa wants to make 54 cookies, how much flour will she need? $3\frac{3}{4}$ c

24) Four friends went on a road trip. Kaveh spent $96.70 on food and $270.18 on entertainment; the four friends evenly split the hotel bill of $673.64 and the $172.00 spent on gasoline. How much did Kaveh spend on this trip? $578.29

25) Adenuga ran 400 m in 48 seconds. What was his speed in meters per minute?   500 m/min

Percents

Math at Work:

Environmental Inspector

Vikki Chun grew up loving the outdoors. Now, she makes her living protecting it. Vikki works as an environmental inspector for her town, ensuring that local businesses and residents comply with environmental regulations.

"A lot of my work takes place in the field," Vikki says. "I visit offices, factories, even private residences, and perform inspections to confirm everyone is doing their part to keep our environment clean."

Another component of Vikki's job is convincing others of the importance of environmental protection. She often speaks before community boards or to business leaders, making her case for green initiatives. She finds that her skills with math help her not only when she's performing sophisticated soil or water tests, but also when she is giving a speech. "Numbers have a big impact when you are talking to a group," describes Vikki. "If I explain that recycling just 5% more waste can lead to a 20% or 30% reduction in the growth of our town's landfill, it allows people to really understand the scope of the issues I'm talking about."

You'll learn about working with percentages in this chapter, as well as get some advice on speaking in public.

Surveys find that most people are more afraid of public speaking than of dying! Clearly, there is something about standing up in front of a crowd that makes many of us nervous. Yet even if you find the idea of an oral presentation or a wedding toast terrifying, you can learn to cope with these emotions and make public speaking a strength. Start by studying the skills presented below.

- Define what it is you want to say. What is the core message you want your audience to take away from your remarks?
- Consider the audience to whom you are speaking. This will help you strike the appropriate tone.

- Create note cards you can refer to during your speech. Don't write down word for word what you will say, and don't try to memorize everything. Give yourself enough reminders to guide you through the speech.
- Create visuals such as charts, graphs, or slides. Such visuals are particularly important if you will be discussing mathematical results or concepts.
- Practice your presentation until you feel comfortable with it.

- To manage any stage fright, take a series of long, slow breaths in the minutes before you start to speak. Visualize yourself giving your speech successfully, and imagine the feeling of relief you'll feel afterward.
- As you give your talk, speak clearly and slowly, and stand straight and tall.
- Make eye contact with your audience members to keep them engaged. Don't bury your face in your notes.

- Talk to people who heard you speak, and get their feedback. Ask them to be honest in their evaluations!

- Ask yourself whether you successfully communicated the core message you defined at the start of this process.

Chapter 8 ⓟⓞⓦⓔⓡ Plan

🅟 Prepare	**🅞 Organize**
What are your goals for Chapter 8?	**How can you accomplish each goal? (Write in the steps you will take to succeed.)**
1 Be prepared before and during class.	• _____ • _____ • _____ • _____
2 Understand the homework to the point where you could do it without needing any help or hints.	• _____ • _____ • _____
3 Use the P.O.W.E.R. framework to learn how to prepare for a speech: *What's Your Level of Self-Consciousness?*	• _____ • _____ • _____
4 Write your own goal. _____ _____	• _____
What are your objectives for Chapter 8?	**How can you accomplish each objective?**
1 Understand percents, and be able to convert between percents, fractions, and decimals.	• Understand what a percent represents and how it compares to a fraction or decimal. • Understand the procedures that allow you to convert between percents and decimals. • Determine standard procedures to convert more complex percents to decimals or fractions. • Know three different methods to write a fraction as a percent.
2 Know how to compute percents of a number, and solve applied problems involving percents by using an equation.	• Be able to mentally find percents that are multiples of 5, 10, or 100. • Understand what you are being asked to find, and use the correct formula. • Modify and apply the Five Steps for Solving Applied Problems to solve application problems that contain percents.
3 Know how to compute common percents by using formulas.	• Understand the formulas and procedures for *sales tax, commission, sale price,* and *percent increase/decrease.* • Know how to use the correct formula with the Five Steps for Solving Applied Problems.
4 Learn how to find simple interest and compound interest.	• Understand the definitions of *interest, simple interest, principal,* and *compound interest.* • Learn the formulas to compute simple interest and compound interest.
5 Write your own goal. _____ _____	• _____

	W **Work**	Read Sections 8.1–8.8, and complete the exercises.
E **Evaluate** Complete the Chapter Review and Chapter Test. How did you do?	R **Rethink**	• After completing the emPOWERme exercise, what steps can you take to become a better public speaker?
	• How can you use your ability to mentally compute percents to help you multiply and divide larger numbers in your head? How can you use it to help you double-check your answers on an exam or quiz?	

8.1 Introduction to Percent

P Prepare

O Organize

What are your objectives for Section 8.1?	How can you accomplish each objective?
1 Understand the Meaning of Percent	• Know the definition of a *percent*. • Be able to write a sentence that describes a percentage. • Complete the given examples on your own. • Complete You Trys 1 and 2.
2 Relate Percents to Fractions and Decimals	• Recognize how to write a percent as a fraction and/or a decimal. • Complete the given example on your own. • Complete You Try 3.
3 Change Percents to Decimals	• Write the procedure for **Changing a Percent to a Decimal** in your own words. • Complete the given example on your own. • Complete You Try 4.
4 Change Decimals to Percents	• Write the procedure for **Changing a Decimal to a Percent** in your own words. • Complete the given example on your own. • Complete You Try 5.

 **Work**   **Read the explanations, follow the examples, take notes, and complete the You Trys.**

1 Understand the Meaning of Percent

Percents are everywhere: 75% of people under the age of 30 in the United States use Facebook, or the unemployment rate in the United States is 9%. These are just a couple of ways percents are used. But what does percent mean?

Definition

Percent means *out of 100*.

Let's think about the meaning of each percent in the first paragraph.

75% of people under the age of 30 in the United States use Facebook means that in the United States, 75 out of 100 people under the age of 30 use Facebook. *The unemployment rate in the United States is 9%* means that 9 out of every 100 people in the United States are unemployed.

We can think about percentages (percents) with a picture.

The figure to the right is divided into 100 squares of equal size, and 23 of them are shaded. Therefore, 23 *out of* 100 squares are shaded, or 23% of the squares are shaded.

EXAMPLE 1

In-Class Example 1

Explain the meaning of the following statement: *15% of teenagers who are texters send over 6000 text messages each month.* (pewresearch.org)

Answer:
15 out of every 100 teenagers who text send over 6000 text messages each month.

Explain the meaning of the following statement: *Approximately 79% of full-time undergraduates received financial aid during the 2007–2008 academic year.* (nces.ed.gov)

Solution

79% means 79 *out of* 100, so the statement means that approximately 79 out of 100 undergraduates received financial aid in the 2007–2008 academic year.

[**YOU TRY 1**] Explain the meaning of the following statement: *In 2008, approximately 70% of married women with children under 18 were working outside the home.* (www.census.gov)

EXAMPLE 2

In-Class Example 2

Rewrite the statement using a percent: *A study found that 85 out of 100 adult drivers always wear a seat belt.* (www.cdc.gov)

Answer:
A study found that 85% of adult drivers always wear a seat belt.

Rewrite the statement using a percent: *In 2008, approximately 3 out of every 100 employers in the United States allowed employees to work some of their hours at home.* (www.census.gov)

Solution

Percent means *out of 100*, so 3 *out of* 100 is the same as 3%. We can rewrite the statement as follows: *In 2008, approximately 3% of employers in the United States allowed employees to work some of their hours at home.*

[YOU TRY 2] Rewrite the statement using a percent: *In 2007, 63 out of 100 male high school juniors played on at least one sports team.* (www.census.gov)

2 Relate Percents to Fractions and Decimals

In Section 6.5, we learned that we could write an expression like *3 out of 8* as the fraction $\frac{3}{8}$. Because percent means *out of 100*, we can write a percent as a fraction. In Example 1, because 79% means *79 out of 100*, we can write 79% as $\frac{79}{100}$. And, because fractions can be written as decimals, we can write percents as decimals as well:

$$79\% = \frac{79}{100} = 0.79$$

EXAMPLE 3

In-Class Example 3

Write each percent as a fraction and then as a decimal.
a) 59%   b) 3%

Answer:

a) $\frac{59}{100}$; 0.59

b) $\frac{3}{100}$; 0.03

Write each percent as a fraction and then as a decimal.

a)   83%   b)   7%

Solution

a)   Because 83% means 83 out of 100, we write

$$83\% = \frac{83}{100} = 0.83$$

b)   Because 7% means 7 out of 100, write

$$7\% = \frac{7}{100} = 0.07$$

[YOU TRY 3] Write each percent as a fraction and then as a decimal.

a)   61%   b)   9%

We will learn more about percents and fractions in Section 8.2.

3 Change Percents to Decimals

We can change percents directly to decimals by remembering that when we divide a number by 100, we move the decimal point two places to the left. For example,

$$\frac{31}{100} = 31 \div 100 = 0.31$$

Let's use this method to change a percent to a decimal.

Procedure How to Change a Percent to a Decimal

1) Remove the percent symbol.
2) Move the decimal point two places to the left.

EXAMPLE 4

In-Class Example 4

Write each percent as a decimal.
a) 75% b) 8% c) 0.9%
d) 100% e) 433%

Answer:
a) 0.75 b) 0.08 c) 0.009
d) 1 e) 4.33

Write each percent as a decimal.

a) 25%   b) 4%   c) 0.7%   d) 100%   e) 316%

Solution

a) $25\% = 25.\%$ Put the decimal point at the end of the number.
    $= 0.25$ Remove the percent symbol, and move the decimal point two places to the left.

b) $4\% = 4.\%$ Put the decimal point at the end of the number.
    $= 0.04$ Remove the percent symbol, and move the decimal point two places to the left.

c) $0.7\% = 0.007$ Remove the percent symbol, and move the decimal point two places to the left.

d) $100\% = 100.\%$ Put the decimal point at the end of the number.
    $= 1.00$ Remove the percent symbol, and move the decimal point two places to the left.
    $= 1$

e) $316\% = 316.\%$ Put the decimal point at the end of the number.
    $= 3.16$ Remove the percent symbol, and move the decimal point two places to the left.

Note

1) We see in Example 4d that 100% = 1.
2) Example 4e shows that 316% = 3.16, a number that is greater than 1.

In general, we can say that a percent greater than 100 is equivalent to a decimal number greater than 1.

YOU TRY 4   Write each percent as a decimal.

a) 48%   b) 6%   c) 0.5%   d) 120%   e) 500%

---

4 Change Decimals to Percents

If we remember the relationship between a decimal and a fraction, we can then write the decimal as a percent. For example, 0.74 = 74% because

$$0.74 = \frac{74}{100} = 74\%$$

So, to change 0.74 to 74%, we moved the decimal point two places to the right and put the percent symbol at the end of the number.

Procedure How to Change a Decimal to a Percent

1) Move the decimal point two places to the right.
2) Put the percent symbol at the end of the number.

EXAMPLE 5

Write each decimal as a percent.

a) 0.99   b) 0.0085   c) 4.13   d) 1.5   e) 2

Solution

a) $0.99 = 99.$ Move the decimal point two places to the right.

   $= 99\%$ Put the % symbol at the end of the number.
                    Remove the decimal point from the end of the number.

b) $0.0085 = 0.85$ Move the decimal point two places to the right.

   $= 0.85\%$ Put the % symbol at the end of the number.

c) $4.13 = 413.$ Move the decimal point two places to the right.

   $= 413\%$ Put the % symbol at the end of the number.
                    Remove the decimal point from the end of the number.

d) $1.5 = 150.$ Move the decimal point two places to the right.

   $= 150\%$ Put the % symbol at the end of the number.
                    Remove the decimal point from the end of the number.

e) $2 = 2.$ Put the decimal point at the end of the number.

   $= 200.$ Move the decimal point two places to the right.

   $= 200\%$ Put the % symbol at the end of the number.
                    Remove the decimal point from the end of the number.

Note

1) Examples 5a and b show that a number less than 1 is a percent less than 100.

2) Examples 5c, d, and e show that a number greater than 1 is a percent greater than 100.

3) We saw in Example 4d that 1 = 100%.

[YOU TRY 5]

Write each decimal as a percent.

a) 0.62   b) 0.0047   c) 8.95   d) 2.7   e) 4

ANSWERS TO [YOU TRY] EXERCISES

1) In 2008, approximately 70 out of every 100 married women with children under 18 were working outside the home.

2) In 2007, 63% of male high school juniors played on at least one sports team.

3) a) $\frac{61}{100}$; 0.61 b) $\frac{9}{100}$; 0.09   4) a) 0.48 b) 0.06 c) 0.005 d) 1.2 e) 5

5) a) 62% b) 0.47% c) 895% d) 270% e) 400%

Using Technology

When using a calculator to change a decimal to a percent, we multiply the decimal by 100 and put the % symbol at the end of the number. To convert 0.38 to a percent, we enter $\boxed{.}\boxed{3}\boxed{8}\boxed{\times}\boxed{1}\boxed{0}\boxed{0}\boxed{=}$ into the calculator. The display screen will likely show 38. as the result. Finally, we remove the decimal and write 38% for our final answer.

E Evaluate **8.1** Exercises   Do the exercises, and check your work.

*Additional answers can be found in the Answers to Exercises appendix.

Objective 1: Understand the Meaning of Percent

Explain the meaning of each statement.

1) 23% of students who consume media approximately 3 hours per day earn mostly C grades or lower. (www.zdnet.com)

2) As of 2009, 30% of American women aged 25 and older obtained a bachelor's degree or more. (www.census.gov)

3) 52% of Americans have listened to online radio. (www.edisonresearch.com/internet_studies.php)

4) 48% of all Americans have a profile on one or more social networking websites. (Arbitron Internet and Multimedia Study)

5) Approximately 44% of all online videos are being viewed in the workplace. (The Nielsen Company)

6) 67% of U.S. middle school students spend less than 1 hour each day on math homework. (Raytheon Middle School Student Media Consumption Study)

Rewrite each statement using a percent.

7) In 2007–2008, approximately 18 out of 100 public school principals reported that their school required students to wear a uniform. (nces.ed.gov)

8) In 2007–2008, 76 out of 100 public school teachers were female. (nces.ed.gov)

9) In 2009, 26 out of 100 veterans were aged 25 and older with at least a bachelor's degree. (factfinder.census.gov)

10) In 2008, 9 out of 100 New Orleans residents aged 5 and older spoke a language other than English at home. (2008 American Community Survey)

11) As of September 2008, 14 out of 100 members of the armed forces were women. (www.census.gov)

12) Twenty-six out of 100 Americans read news on mobile devices. (pewresearch.org)

Objective 2: Relate Percents to Fractions and Decimals

Write each percent as a fraction and a decimal.

13) 67% $\frac{67}{100} = 0.67$ 14) 43% $\frac{43}{100} = 0.43$

15) 59% $\frac{59}{100} = 0.59$ 16) 97% $\frac{97}{100} = 0.97$

17) 1% $\frac{1}{100} = 0.01$ 18) 9% $\frac{9}{100} = 0.09$

19) 10% $\frac{10}{100} = 0.10$ 20) 50% $\frac{50}{100} = 0.50$

Objective 3: Change Percents to Decimals

21) Explain how to change a percent to a decimal by moving the decimal point.   Remove the percent symbol, then move the decimal point two places to the left.

22) Is this statement true or false? 3.4% = 340   false; 3.4% = 0.034

Write each percent as a decimal by moving the decimal point.

23) 72%   0.72   24) 68%   0.68

25) 33%   0.33   26) 24%   0.24

27) 8%   0.08   28) 3%   0.03

29) 5%   0.05   30) 6%   0.06

31) 45.2%   0.452   32) 13.5%   0.135

33) 2.8% 0.028

34) 6.7% 0.067

35) 0.4% 0.004

36) 0.1% 0.001

37) 200% 2

38) 400% 4

39) 300% 3

40) 700% 7

41) 150% 1.5

42) 140% 1.4

43) 406% 4.06

44) 209% 2.09

45) 0.25% 0.0025

46) 0.91% 0.0091

47) 0.01% 0.0001

48) 0.07% 0.0007

49) 53.08% 0.5308

50) 41.03% 0.4103

51) Any percent greater than 100% is greater than what decimal number? 1

52) Any percent less than 100% is less than what decimal number? 1

Objective 4: Change Decimals to Percents

53) Explain how to change a decimal to a percent.

54) Is this statement true or false? If a decimal number is greater than 1, then when it is changed to a percent, it will be greater than 100%. True

Write each decimal as a percent.

55) 0.82 82%

56) 0.59 59%

57) 0.08 8%

58) 0.09 9%

59) 0.7 70%

60) 0.4 40%

61) 0.175 17.5%

62) 0.285 28.5%

63) 0.462 46.2%

64) 0.943 94.3%

65) 0.0125 1.25%

66) 0.0672 6.72%

67) 8.6 860%

68) 1.7 170%

69) 6 600%

70) 9 900%

71) 10 1000%

72) 25 2500%

Mixed Exercises: Objectives 1, 3, and 4

For Exercises 73–76, read the graph to get the answer as a percent, then change the percent to a decimal.

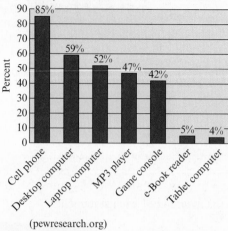

Gadget Ownership, 2010
% of American adults who own each device

(pewresearch.org)

73) In 2010, what percent of American adults owned an MP3 player? 47% = 0.47

74) In 2010, what percent of American adults owned a laptop computer? 52% = 0.52

75) In 2010, what percent of American adults owned an e-book reader? 5% = 0.05

76) In 2010, what percent of American adults owned a tablet computer? 4% = 0.04

Write each decimal as a percent and each percent as a decimal.

77) In 2010, Asian or Pacific Islander students were 0.3712 of the undergraduate student body at the University of California, Los Angeles. (www.admissions.ucla.edu/campusprofile.htm) 37.12%

78) The sales tax in Los Angeles, California, is 0.095. 9.5%

79) The state unemployment rate in North Dakota for December 2010 was 3.8%. (www.bls.gov) 0.038

80) The annual percentage rate on a credit card is 14.99%. 0.1499

R Rethink

R1) Before you began working on this exercise set, how confident were you when working with percents? Do you feel more confident now?

R2) How often do you encounter percents every day? If you had to explain to a friend why a good understanding of percents is important, what would you say?

8.2 Percents and Fractions

P Prepare | O Organize

What are your objectives for Section 8.2?	How can you accomplish each objective?
1 Write Percents as Fractions in Lowest Terms	• Create a step-by-step procedure for writing percents as fractions in lowest terms. • Complete the given examples on your own. • Complete You Trys 1 and 2.
2 Write Percents Containing Decimals or Fractions as Fractions in Lowest Terms	• Know the two different techniques for writing a percent that contains a decimal as a fraction. • Write a statement that explains how to change a percent that contains a fraction to a fraction. • Complete the given examples on your own. • Complete You Trys 3–5.
3 Write Fractions as Percents	• Know how to write a fraction as a percent by finding an equivalent fraction with a denominator of 100, using long division, and using a proportion. • Complete the given examples on your own. • Complete You Trys 6–9.

W Work   **Read the explanations, follow the examples, take notes, and complete the You Trys.**

1   Write Percents as Fractions in Lowest Terms

When we change a percent to a fraction, we usually write it in lowest terms.

EXAMPLE 1

In-Class Example 1

Use Example 1.

Write each percent as a fraction in lowest terms.

a) 25%   b) 50%   c) 75%

Solution

a) $25\% = \dfrac{25}{100} = \dfrac{25 \div 25}{100 \div 25} = \dfrac{1}{4}$ Divide numerator and denominator by 25.

b) $50\% = \dfrac{50}{100} = \dfrac{50 \div 50}{100 \div 50} = \dfrac{1}{2}$ Divide numerator and denominator by 50.

c) $75\% = \dfrac{75}{100} = \dfrac{75 \div 25}{100 \div 25} = \dfrac{3}{4}$ Divide numerator and denominator by 25.

Note

We see and use 25%, 50%, and 75% often, so you should remember that

$25\% = \dfrac{1}{4}$, $50\% = \dfrac{1}{2}$, and $75\% = \dfrac{3}{4}$.

[YOU TRY 1] Write each percent as a fraction in lowest terms.

a) 30%   b) 55%   c) 81%

EXAMPLE 2

Write each percent as a fraction or mixed number in lowest terms.

a) 64%   b) 120%

In-Class Example 2

Write each percent as a fraction or mixed number in lowest terms.
a) 54% b) 160%

Answer:

a) $\dfrac{27}{50}$ b) $\dfrac{8}{5}$ or $1\dfrac{3}{5}$

Solution

a) $64\% = \dfrac{64}{100} = \dfrac{64 \div 4}{100 \div 4} = \dfrac{16}{25}$ Divide numerator and denominator by 4.

b) $120\% = \dfrac{120}{100} = \dfrac{120 \div 20}{100 \div 20}$ Divide numerator and denominator by 20.

$= \dfrac{6}{5}$ Perform the division.

$= 1\dfrac{1}{5}$ Write as a mixed number.

So, $120\% = \dfrac{6}{5}$ or $1\dfrac{1}{5}$.

W Hint

Use this note to help develop a procedure for writing percents as fractions in lowest terms.

Note

1) A percent *less than* 100% will be a fraction *less than* 1.
2) A percent *greater than* 100% will be a fraction (or mixed number) *greater than* 1.
3) 100% = 1

[YOU TRY 2] Write each percent as a fraction or mixed number in lowest terms.

a) 88%   b) 190%

---

2 Write Percents Containing Decimals or Fractions as Fractions in Lowest Terms

Some percents contain decimals. We will learn two ways to change a percent like 16.5% to a fraction in lowest terms. One method is to first change the percent to a decimal, and then change the decimal to a fraction.

EXAMPLE 3

Write 16.5% as a fraction in lowest terms by first writing 16.5% as a decimal.

In-Class Example 3

Write 29.6% as a fraction in lowest terms by first writing 29.6% as a decimal.

Answer: $\dfrac{37}{125}$

Solution

First, change 16.5% to a decimal: $16.5\% = 0.165$

Next, change the decimal to a fraction: $0.165 = \dfrac{165}{1000}$ ← denominator of 1000

↑ thousandths place

Now, simplify $\dfrac{165}{1000}$: $\dfrac{165}{1000} = \dfrac{165 \div 5}{1000 \div 5} = \dfrac{33}{200}$

Therefore, $16.5\% = \dfrac{33}{200}$.

[YOU TRY 3]

Write 72.4% as a fraction in lowest terms by first writing 72.4% as a decimal.

Another way to change 16.5% to a fraction in lowest terms is to first write it as a fraction with a denominator of 100.

EXAMPLE 4

Write 16.5% as a fraction in lowest terms by first writing it as a fraction with a denominator of 100.

In-Class Example 4

Write 29.6% as a fraction in lowest terms by first writing it as a fraction with a denominator of 100.

Answer: $\dfrac{37}{125}$

Solution

$$16.5\% = \dfrac{16.5}{100}$$

A fraction is *not* in lowest terms if it contains a decimal. Therefore, the next step is to eliminate the decimal from the fraction.

Because the digit farthest to the right in 16.5 is in the tenths place, multiplying 16.5 by 10 will move the decimal point to the end of the number.

$$16.5 \cdot 10 = 165$$

If we multiply the numerator of $\dfrac{16.5}{100}$ by 10, we must multiply the denominator by 10 so that we do not change the value of the fraction:

$$\dfrac{16.5}{100} \cdot \dfrac{10}{10} = \dfrac{165}{1000}$$

Now, simplify $\dfrac{165}{1000}$: $\dfrac{165}{1000} = \dfrac{165 \div 5}{1000 \div 5} = \dfrac{33}{200}$

Therefore, $16.5\% = \dfrac{33}{200}$. The result is the same no matter which method is used.

[YOU TRY 4]

Write 72.4% as a fraction in lowest terms by first writing it as a fraction with a denominator of 100.

If a percent contains a fraction, like $33\frac{1}{3}\%$, we can change it to a fraction by first writing $33\frac{1}{3}$ over 100.

EXAMPLE 5

In-Class Example 5

Use Example 5.

Write $33\frac{1}{3}\%$ as a fraction in lowest terms.

Solution

Begin by writing $33\frac{1}{3}\%$ as a fraction with a denominator of 100: $33\frac{1}{3}\% = \dfrac{33\frac{1}{3}}{100}$.

This fraction may look complicated, but remember that a fraction is another way to represent a division problem. So, we can write

$$\frac{33\frac{1}{3}}{100} = 33\frac{1}{3} \div 100 = \frac{100}{3} \div 100 = \frac{\overset{1}{\cancel{100}}}{3} \cdot \frac{1}{\underset{1}{\cancel{100}}} = \frac{1}{3}$$

Change the mixed number to an improper fraction.

W Hint

How would you describe the quickest way to do Example 5?

Therefore, $33\frac{1}{3}\% = \dfrac{1}{3}$.

[YOU TRY 5]

Write $66\frac{2}{3}\%$ as a fraction in lowest terms.

3 Write Fractions as Percents

We can use several different methods to write a fraction as a percent. Because percent means *out of 100,* one way is to start by writing the given fraction as a fraction with a denominator of 100.

EXAMPLE 6

In-Class Example 6

Write $\dfrac{14}{25}$ as a percent by first writing it as a fraction with a denominator of 100.

Answer: 56%

Write $\dfrac{4}{5}$ as a percent by first writing it as a fraction with a denominator of 100.

Solution

To write $\dfrac{4}{5}$ with a denominator of 100, multiply the fraction by $\dfrac{20}{20}$.

$$\frac{4}{5} \cdot \frac{20}{20} = \frac{80}{100} = 80\%$$

This means *80 out of 100* or *80%.*

W Hint

When do you think this would be the quickest method to use?

So, $\dfrac{4}{5} = 80\%$.

YOU TRY 6 Write $\dfrac{19}{50}$ as a percent by first writing it as a fraction with a denominator of 100.

We can also change a fraction to a percent using long division.

EXAMPLE 7

In-Class Example 7

Write $\dfrac{1}{8}$ as a percent using long division.

Answer: 12.5%

Write $\dfrac{7}{8}$ as a percent using long division.

Solution

Use long division to change $\dfrac{7}{8}$ to a decimal, then change the decimal to a percent.

$$\begin{array}{r} .875 \\ 8\overline{)7.000} \end{array}$$

Therefore, $\dfrac{7}{8} = 0.875 = 87.5\%$.

YOU TRY 7

Write $\dfrac{9}{25}$ as a percent using long division.

A third way to write a fraction as a percent is to use a proportion.

EXAMPLE 8

In-Class Example 8

Use a proportion to change each fraction to a percent.

a) $\dfrac{5}{8}$ b) $\dfrac{31}{20}$

Answer: a) 62.5% b) 155%

W Hint

Would it be helpful to create a procedure in your notes to outline these steps?

Use a proportion to change each fraction to a percent.

a) $\dfrac{3}{8}$ b) $\dfrac{27}{25}$

Solution

a) Remember, percent means *out of 100*. To change $\dfrac{3}{8}$ to a percent, we can think of this problem as the proportion "3 is to 8 as what number is to 100?" Write this statement as the proportion $\dfrac{3}{8} = \dfrac{x}{100}$, where x is the percent.

Solve the equation for x by setting the cross products equal to each other.

$$8 \cdot x = 8x$$
$$\dfrac{3}{8} \underset{\diagup\diagdown}{} \dfrac{x}{100}$$
$$3 \cdot 100 = 300$$

$$8x = 300$$

$$\dfrac{8x}{8} = \dfrac{300}{8} \qquad \text{Divide each side by 8.}$$

$$\dfrac{\overset{1}{\cancel{8}}x}{\underset{1}{\cancel{8}}} = 37.5 \qquad \text{Divide out the common factor; } 1x \text{ is the same as } x.$$

$$x = 37.5 \qquad \text{Simplify.}$$

Therefore, $\dfrac{3}{8} = \dfrac{37.5}{100}$. So, $\dfrac{3}{8} = 37.5\%$. We can also think of 37.5% as $37\dfrac{1}{2}\%$.

b) Set up the proportion $\dfrac{27}{25} = \dfrac{x}{100}$, where x is the percent. Solve the equation.

$$25 \cdot x = 25x$$

$$\dfrac{27}{25} \diagtimes \dfrac{x}{100}$$

$$27 \cdot 100 = 2700$$

$$25x = 2700$$

$$\dfrac{25x}{25} = \dfrac{2700}{25} \qquad \text{Divide each side by 25.}$$

$$\dfrac{\overset{1}{\cancel{25}}x}{\underset{1}{\cancel{25}}} = 108 \qquad \text{Divide out the common factor; } 1x \text{ is the same as } x.$$

$$x = 108$$

Therefore, $\dfrac{27}{25} = \dfrac{108}{100} = 108\%$.

[YOU TRY 8] Use a proportion to change each fraction to a percent.

a) $\dfrac{7}{8}$ b) $\dfrac{12}{5}$

EXAMPLE 9

In-Class Example 9

Use Example 9.

Use a proportion to change $\dfrac{5}{6}$ to a percent. Give the exact answer, and also round the answer to the nearest tenth of a percent.

Solution

Set up the proportion $\dfrac{5}{6} = \dfrac{x}{100}$, where x is the percent. Solve the equation.

$$6 \cdot x = 6x$$

$$\dfrac{5}{6} \diagtimes \dfrac{x}{100}$$

$$5 \cdot 100 = 500$$

$$6x = 500$$

$$\dfrac{6x}{6} = \dfrac{500}{6} \qquad \text{Divide each side by 6.}$$

$$\dfrac{\overset{1}{\cancel{6}}x}{\underset{1}{\cancel{6}}} = 83.\overline{3} \qquad \text{Divide out the common factor; } 1x \text{ is the same as } x.$$

$$x = 83.\overline{3}$$

To find the *exact* answer, we write $\dfrac{5}{6} = \dfrac{83.\overline{3}}{100} = 83.\overline{3}\%$.

We can *round to the nearest tenth of a percent* by first rounding $83.\overline{3}$ to 83.3. Then, $\dfrac{5}{6} \approx \dfrac{83.3}{100} = 83.3\%$.

Note

When we solve the equation in Example 9, if we change $\dfrac{500}{6}$ to the mixed

number $83\dfrac{1}{3}$, then we can also say that $\dfrac{5}{6} = 83\dfrac{1}{3}\%$.

[YOU TRY 9]

Use a proportion to change $\dfrac{4}{9}$ to a percent. Give the exact answer, and also round

the answer to the nearest tenth of a percent.

Summary Writing a Fraction as a Percent

We can write a fraction as a percent using one of these methods:

1) Write the fraction with a denominator of 100.

2) Use long division to change the fraction to a decimal, then change the decimal to a percent.

3) Use a proportion.

ANSWERS TO [YOU TRY] EXERCISES

1) a) $\dfrac{3}{10}$ b) $\dfrac{11}{20}$ c) $\dfrac{81}{100}$ 2) a) $\dfrac{22}{25}$ b) $\dfrac{19}{10}$ or $1\dfrac{9}{10}$ 3) $\dfrac{181}{250}$ 4) $\dfrac{181}{250}$ 5) $\dfrac{2}{3}$

6) 38%   7) 36%   8) a) 87.5% b) 240%   9) exact: $44.\overline{4}\%$; rounded: 44.4%

Using Technology

We can use a calculator to change a fraction to a percent. For example, to

convert $\dfrac{7}{9}$ to a percent, we enter $\boxed{7}\ \boxed{\div}\ \boxed{9}\ \boxed{\times}\ \boxed{1}\ \boxed{0}\ \boxed{0}\ \boxed{=}$ into the calculator.

(Multiplying by 100 is the same as moving the decimal point two places to the right.) The display screen will likely show 77.77778 for the result. This means that the exact answer is $77.\overline{7}\%$. If we are asked to round our answer to the *nearest tenth of a percent,* we would write 77.8% for our final answer.

*Additional answers can be found in the Answers to Exercises appendix.

Objective 1: Write Percents as Fractions in Lowest Terms

Write each percent as a fraction or mixed number in lowest terms.

1) 20% $\frac{1}{5}$

2) 90% $\frac{9}{10}$

3) 10% $\frac{1}{10}$

4) 40% $\frac{2}{5}$

5) 85% $\frac{17}{20}$

6) 16% $\frac{4}{25}$

7) 67% $\frac{67}{100}$

8) 51% $\frac{51}{100}$

9) 2% $\frac{1}{50}$

10) 4% $\frac{1}{25}$

11) 160% $1\frac{3}{5}$

12) 150% $1\frac{1}{2}$

13) 275% $2\frac{3}{4}$

14) 225% $2\frac{1}{4}$

Objective 2: Write Percents Containing Decimals or Fractions as Fractions in Lowest Terms

Write each percent as a fraction in lowest terms by first writing the percent as a decimal.

15) 47% $0.47 = \frac{47}{100}$

16) 13% $0.13 = \frac{13}{100}$

17) 52% $0.52 = \frac{13}{25}$

18) 64% $0.64 = \frac{16}{25}$

19) 12.5% $0.125 = \frac{1}{8}$

20) 37.5% $0.375 = \frac{3}{8}$

21) 22.5% $0.225 = \frac{9}{40}$

22) 17.5% $0.175 = \frac{7}{40}$

23) 8.4% $0.084 = \frac{21}{250}$

24) 7.6% $0.076 = \frac{19}{250}$

25) 0.3% $0.003 = \frac{3}{1000}$

26) 0.9% $0.009 = \frac{9}{1000}$

27) 0.5% $0.005 = \frac{1}{200}$

28) 0.2% $0.002 = \frac{1}{500}$

29) 93.75% $0.9375 = \frac{15}{16}$

30) 56.25% $0.5625 = \frac{9}{16}$

Write each percent as a fraction in lowest terms by first writing it as a fraction with a denominator of 100.

31) 80.5% $\frac{161}{200}$

32) 51.2% $\frac{64}{125}$

33) 9.9% $\frac{99}{1000}$

34) 4.3% $\frac{43}{1000}$

35) 1.58% $\frac{79}{5000}$

36) 2.94% $\frac{147}{5000}$

37) 0.4% $\frac{1}{250}$

38) 0.6% $\frac{3}{500}$

39) Do you prefer to use the method in Exercises 15–30 or the method in Exercises 31–38 to change a percent to a decimal? Why?   Answers may vary.

40) When George writes 11.9% as a fraction, he gets a final answer of $\frac{11.9}{100}$. Is this correct? Explain.

This is not the final answer because a fraction is not in lowest terms if it contains a decimal. The final answer should be $\frac{119}{1000}$.

Write each percent as a fraction in lowest terms.

41) $62\frac{1}{2}$% $\frac{5}{8}$

42) $87\frac{1}{2}$% $\frac{7}{8}$

43) $6\frac{1}{4}$% $\frac{1}{16}$

44) $81\frac{1}{4}$% $\frac{13}{16}$

45) $83\frac{1}{3}$% $\frac{5}{6}$

46) $6\frac{2}{3}$% $\frac{1}{15}$

47) $25\frac{4}{5}$% $\frac{129}{500}$

48) $51\frac{2}{5}$% $\frac{257}{500}$

Objective 3: Write Fractions as Percents

Write the fraction as a percent by first writing it as a fraction with a denominator of 100.

49) $\frac{7}{10}$ $\frac{70}{100} = 70\%$

50) $\frac{1}{10}$ $\frac{10}{100} = 10\%$

51) $\frac{3}{4}$ $\frac{75}{100} = 75\%$

52) $\frac{2}{5}$ $\frac{40}{100} = 40\%$

53) $\frac{21}{25}$ $\frac{84}{100} = 84\%$

54) $\frac{33}{50}$ $\frac{66}{100} = 66\%$

55) $\frac{1}{20}$ $\frac{5}{100} = 5\%$

56) $\frac{1}{25}$ $\frac{4}{100} = 4\%$

57) $\frac{49}{50}$ $\frac{98}{100} = 98\%$

58) $\frac{17}{20}$ $\frac{85}{100} = 85\%$

59) $\frac{31}{10}$ $\frac{310}{100} = 310\%$

60) $\frac{23}{10}$ $\frac{230}{100} = 230\%$

61) $\frac{6}{5}$ $\frac{120}{100} = 120\%$

62) $\frac{7}{4}$ $\frac{175}{100} = 175\%$

Write the fraction as a percent using long division.

63) $\frac{5}{8}$ 62.5%

64) $\frac{3}{8}$ 37.5%

65) $\frac{12}{25}$ 48%

66) $\frac{3}{20}$ 15%

67) $\frac{9}{5}$ 180%

68) $\frac{27}{25}$ 108%

69) $\frac{1}{16}$ 6.25%

70) $\frac{13}{16}$ 81.25%

Use a proportion to change the fraction to a percent.

24 71) $\frac{3}{25}$ 12%

72) $\frac{9}{20}$ 45%

73) $\frac{13}{20}$ 65%

74) $\frac{24}{25}$ 96%

75) $\frac{7}{40}$ 17.5%

76) $\frac{3}{40}$ 7.5%

77) $\frac{13}{8}$ 162.5%

78) $\frac{9}{8}$ 112.5%

Use a proportion to change the fraction to a percent. Give the exact answer, and also round the answer to the nearest tenth of a percent.

79) $\frac{2}{3}$
exact: $66.\overline{6}\%$; rounded: 66.7%

80) $\frac{1}{3}$
exact: $33.\overline{3}\%$; rounded: 33.3%

81) $\frac{1}{9}$
exact: $11.\overline{1}\%$; rounded: 11.1%

82) $\frac{8}{9}$
exact: $88.\overline{8}\%$; rounded: 88.9%

83) $\frac{5}{12}$
exact: $41.6\overline{6}\%$; rounded: 41.7%

84) $\frac{7}{12}$
exact: $58.\overline{3}\%$; rounded: 58.3%

85) $\frac{11}{6}$
exact: $183.\overline{3}\%$; rounded: 183.3%

86) $\frac{7}{6}$
exact: $116.\overline{6}\%$; rounded: 116.7%

87) Name three methods for writing a fraction as a percent.

88) Which method do you prefer for writing a fraction as a percent? Why?   Answers may vary.

Mixed Exercises: Objectives 1–3
Solve each problem. Write your answer as a fraction in lowest terms, as a decimal, and as a percent.

89) A calculus class started the semester with 50 students and ended with 42 students. What portion of the students who started the class finished it?

90) The current polar bear population is about 25,000, and approximately 15,000 of them live in Canada. What portion of the polar bear population lives in Canada? (www.worldwildlifefund.org)

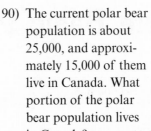

91) A Banana Nut Bread Clif Bar contains 9 g of protein. The recommended daily allowance of protein is 50 g. What portion of the recommended daily allowance of protein is in the Clif bar? (www.clifbar.com)

92) A soccer team won 9 of its 16 soccer games. What portion of the games did the team win?

Write each percent as a fraction or mixed number in lowest terms.

93) 8% $\frac{2}{25}$

94) 145% $1\frac{9}{20}$

Write each number as a percent.

95) 2   200%

96) 0.079   7.9%

97) $1\frac{4}{5}$ 180%

98) $\frac{13}{4}$ 325%

Write each percent as a decimal.

99) 92%   0.92

100) 5.1%   0.051

101) $17\frac{1}{2}\%$ 0.175

102) 180%   1.8

R Rethink

R1) Why is it important to be able to write a percent as a fraction or decimal?

R2) Explain how your knowledge of decimals and fractions helped you complete the exercises.

R3) Find the solution for Exercise 65 using all three methods. Then, compare and contrast the methods. What do you see that is similar?

8.3 Compute Basic Percents Mentally

P Prepare

O Organize

What are your objectives for Section 8.3?	How can you accomplish each objective?
1 Find 10% of a Number	• Write the procedure for **Finding 10% of a Number** in your own words. • Complete the given examples on your own. • Complete You Trys 1 and 2.
2 Compute Percents That Are Multiples of 10	• Write the procedure for **Finding Percents That Are Multiples of 10** in your own words. • Complete the given examples on your own. • Complete You Trys 3–5.
3 Find and Use 5% of a Number	• Write the procedure for **Finding 5% of a Number** in your own words. • Understand how to combine Objectives 2 and 3. • Complete the given examples on your own. • Complete You Trys 6–8.
4 Perform Computations with Multiples of 100%	• Write the procedure for **Performing Computations with Multiples of 100%** in your own words. • Complete the given example on your own. • Complete You Try 9.
5 Solve Applications Containing Basic Percentages	• Use the Five Steps for Solving Applied Problems, and add additional steps needed from this section. • Complete the given examples on your own. • Complete You Trys 10 and 11.

W Work

Read the explanations, follow the examples, take notes, and complete the You Trys.

We use percents every day. We may want to buy a purse that is marked down 20% or leave a 15% tip at a restaurant. These computations can be done "in our heads." Let's begin by finding 10% of a number mentally.

1 Find 10% of a Number

EXAMPLE 1

Find:

a) $\frac{1}{10}$ of 40   b) 10% of 40

Solution

a) To find $\frac{1}{10}$ *of* 40, we multiply: $\frac{1}{10} \cdot 40 = \frac{1}{10} \cdot \frac{40}{1} = \frac{4}{1} = 4$

We learned in earlier chapters that, in a problem like this, *of* means multiply.

b) As in part a), the *of* in 10% *of* 40 means multiply. First, we can change 10% to a decimal or a fraction. Let's change 10% to a decimal.

$$10\% = \frac{10}{100} = \frac{1}{10} = 0.1$$

So, to find 10% of 40 we multiply $0.1 \cdot 40. = 4$.

To multiply a number by 0.1, move the decimal point one place to the left.

Notice that this is the same as the result in a) because $\frac{1}{10}$ and 10% are equivalent.

Note

Recall from our study of decimals that to multiply a number by 0.1, we move the decimal point one place to the left as in part b) of Example 1: $0.1 \cdot 40 = 4$. This fact is very important and will allow us to mentally compute percents that are multiples of 10.

[YOU TRY 1] Find:

a) $\frac{1}{10}$ of 80   b) 10% of 80

Procedure How to Find 10% of a Number

To find 10% of a number, locate the decimal point in the number and move it one place to the left.

Example: 10% of 50. = 5

| EXAMPLE 2 |

Find:

In-Class Example 2

Find: a) 10% of 50
b) 10% of 8300
c) 10% of 37

Answer:
a) 5   b) 830   c) 3.7

a) 10% of 90   b) 10% of 3500   c) 10% of 78

Solution

a) To find 10% of 90, locate the decimal point in 90 and move it one place to the left: 10% of 90. = 9

b) To find 10% of 3500, locate the decimal point in 3500 and move it one place to the left: 10% of 3500. = 350

c) To find 10% of 78, locate the decimal point in 78 and move it one place to the left: 10% of 78. = 7.8

[YOU TRY 2] Find:

a) 10% of 70   b) 10% of 5100   c) 10% of 16

2 Compute Percents That Are Multiples of 10

Now that we know how to find 10% of a number, let's use that information to find percents that are multiples of 10, like 20%, 30%, 40%, etc.

EXAMPLE 3

In-Class Example 3

Find: a) 20% of 60
b) 30% of 60

Answer: a) 12 b) 18

Find:

a) 20% of 40   b) 30% of 40

Solution

a) 20% *of* 40 means 0.20 · 40 or 0.2 · 40.

$$\begin{array}{r} 4\,0 \\ \times\ 0.2 \\ \hline 8.0 \end{array}$$

20% of 40 = 8

b) 30% *of* 40 means 0.30 · 40 or 0.3 · 40.

$$\begin{array}{r} 4\,0 \\ \times\ 0.3 \\ \hline 1\,2.0 \end{array}$$

30% of 40 = 12

[YOU TRY 3]

Find:

a) 20% of 80   b) 30% of 80

Do you see a pattern? Let's compare both parts of Example 3 to 10% of 40 in Example 1b.

10% of 40 = 4	10% of 40 = 4
20% of 40 = 8	30% of 40 = 12

Procedure How to Find Percents That Are Multiples of 10

If we know the value of 10% of a number,

1) find 20% of the number by multiplying the value by 2;
2) find 30% of the number by multiplying the value by 3;
3) find 40% of the number by multiplying the value by 4;

and so on.

If we learn these rules, we can do many percentage calculations in our heads. For example, if we want to know how much money we will save if an item is on sale or if we want to compute the amount of a tip, we can use what we learn here.

EXAMPLE 4

In-Class Example 4

Find 80% of 60.

Answer: 48

Find 70% of 40.

Solution

In Example 1, we found that 10% of 40 = 4. Therefore, 70% of 40 = 7 · 4 = 28.

[YOU TRY 4]   Find 70% of 80.

EXAMPLE 5

In-Class Example 5

Find: a) 70% of 30
b) 90% of 400
c) 20% of 15

Answer: a) 21 b) 360
c) 3

Find:

a) 60% of 80   b) 90% of 500   c) 20% of 35

Solution

a) To find 60% of 80, first find 10% of 80. Then, multiply the result by 6.

$$10\% \text{ of } 80. = 8$$
$$60\% \text{ of } 80 = 6 \cdot 8 = 48$$

b) To find 90% of 500, first find 10% of 500. Then, multiply the result by 9.

$$10\% \text{ of } 500. = 50$$
$$90\% \text{ of } 500 = 9 \cdot 50 = 450$$

W Hint

Make up a percent problem on your own, and explain to someone how to compute it mentally.

c) To find 20% of 35, first find 10% of 35. Then, multiply the result by 2.

$$10\% \text{ of } 35. = 3.5$$
$$20\% \text{ of } 35 = 2 \cdot 3.5 = 7$$

[YOU TRY 5]   Find:

a) 80% of 50   b) 40% of 700   c) 20% of 41

---

3 Find and Use 5% of a Number

If we know what 10% of a number equals, then how can we find 5% of the number? We will use the same reasoning that we have used throughout this section. For example, we know that 10% of 40 = 4. What is 5% of 40?

5% is *half* of 10%

$$10\% \text{ of } 40 = 4$$
$$5\% \text{ of } 40 = \frac{1}{2} \cdot 4 = 2$$

Multiply 4 by $\frac{1}{2}$.

Therefore, 5% of 40 = 2. Remember that multiplying a number by $\frac{1}{2}$ is the same as dividing the number by 2.

Procedure How to Find 5% of a Number

If we know the value of 10% of a number, then 5% of the number is *half* of that value.

Example: Since 10% of 140 = 14, 5% of 140 = $\frac{1}{2} \cdot 14 = 7$.

EXAMPLE 6

In-Class Example 6

Find: a) 5% of 180
b) 5% of 32

Answer:
a) 9   b) 1.6

Find:

a)   5% of 160   b)   5% of 34

Solution

a)   First, find 10% of 160. Then, find 5% of 160 by finding $\frac{1}{2}$ of that result.

5% is half of 10%
$\left\{ \begin{array}{l} 10\% \text{ of } 160 = 16 \\ 5\% \text{ of } 160 = \frac{1}{2} \cdot 16 = 8 \end{array} \right.$

Multiply 16 by $\frac{1}{2}$.

b)   First, find 10% of 34. Then, find 5% of 34 by finding $\frac{1}{2}$ of that result.

5% is half of 10%
$\left\{ \begin{array}{l} 10\% \text{ of } 34 = 3.4 \\ 5\% \text{ of } 34 = \frac{1}{2} \cdot 3.4 = 3.4 \div 2 = 1.7 \end{array} \right.$

Multiply 3.4 by $\frac{1}{2}$.

[YOU TRY 6]   Find:

a)   5% of 220   b)   5% of 62

Using what we have learned, how can we find 15% of a number?

EXAMPLE 7

In-Class Example 7

Find 15% of 80.

Answer: 12

Find 15% of 60.

Solution

To find 15% of 60, find 10% of 60 and 5% of 60, and then add the results.

$$10\% \text{ of } 60 = 6 \qquad\qquad 5\% \text{ of } 60 = 3$$

$$\begin{aligned} 15\% \text{ of } 60 &= 10\% \text{ of } 60 + 5\% \text{ of } 60 \\ &= \quad 6 \quad + \quad 3 \qquad\text{\small 5\% of 60 is 3 since } \tfrac{1}{2} \text{ of 6 is 3.} \\ &= 9 \end{aligned}$$

Therefore, 15% of 60 = 9.

[YOU TRY 7]   Find 15% of 40.

We can use the same reasoning to find other percentages.

EXAMPLE 8

Find 35% of 120.

Solution

We want to think of 35% of 120 as 30% of 120 + 5% of 120. We need to know 10% of 120 to find these values.

$$10\% \text{ of } 120 = 12, \text{ so } 30\% \text{ of } 120 = 36 \text{ and } 5\% \text{ of } 120 = 6$$

$$35\% \text{ of } 120 = 30\% \text{ of } 120 + 5\% \text{ of } 120$$
$$= \quad 36 \quad + \quad 6$$
$$= 42$$

So, 35% of 120 = 42.

W Hint

Write a new procedure to help you complete exercises similar to Example 8.

[YOU TRY 8]   Find 45% of 20.

Note

In Example 7, we could have found 15% of 60 another way. Since 5% of 60 = 3, then 15% of 60 = 3 · 5% of 60 = 3 · 3 = 9. Likewise, in Example 8, we could have found 35% of 120 another way. Since 5% of 120 = 6, then 35% of 120 = 7 · 5% of 120 = 7 · 6 = 42.

4   Perform Computations with Multiples of 100%

Earlier in this chapter, we learned that 100% = 1. Additionally, we can change other percents to decimal numbers by moving the decimal point in the percent: 200% = 2, 300% = 3, and so on.

If we remember that 100% = 1, 200% = 2, 300% = 3, etc., we can often perform calculations with multiples of 100% "in our heads."

Procedure Perform Computations with Multiples of 100%

100% *of* a number equals the number. To find 200% *of* a number, multiply the number by 2, to find 300% *of* a number, multiply the number by 3, and so on.

EXAMPLE 9

Find:

a) 100% of 79   b) 200% of 300   c) 400% of 8

Solution

a) 100% of 79 means 1 · 79 = 79.

b) 200% of 300 means 2 · 300 = 600.

c) 400% of 8 means 4 · 8 = 32.

Find:

a) 100% of 53   b) 300% of 400   c) 600% of 7

5 Solve Applications Containing Basic Percentages

One way we use percentages is to compute a tip.

EXAMPLE 10

In-Class Example 10

A restaurant bill is $16.00. If Bashir wants to leave a 15% tip, find the amount of the tip and the total amount of money he will pay.

Answer:

tip: $2.40; total amount: $18.40

A restaurant bill is $28.00. If Charlie wants to leave a 15% tip, find the amount of the tip and the total amount of money Charlie will pay.

Solution

Step 1: **Read** the problem carefully, and restate it in your own words.

Charlie wants to leave <u>15% of $28.00</u> as a tip. We have to <u>find the amount of the tip and the total amount Charlie will pay</u>.

Step 2: **Make a plan.** Let's underline important words in our restatement of the problem in Step 1.

Plan: To find the amount of the tip, compute 15% of $28.00. Then, add the tip to the $28.00 to determine the total amount Charlie will pay.

Step 3: **Solve** the problem.

First, find the amount of the tip, 15% *of* $28.00.

$$15\% \text{ of } \$28.00 = 10\% \text{ of } \$28.00 + 5\% \text{ of } \$28.00$$
$$= \quad \$2.80 \quad + \quad \$1.40 \qquad 5\% \text{ of } \$28.00 = \$1.40 \text{ since } \frac{1}{2} \text{ of } \$2.80 = \$1.40.$$
$$= \$4.20$$

The tip is $4.20.

Now, find the total amount Charlie will pay.

$$\text{Total amount Charlie will pay} = \text{Amount of the bill} + \text{Amount of the tip}$$
$$= \quad \$28.00 \quad + \quad \$4.20$$
$$= \$32.20$$

Step 4: **State the answer** in a complete sentence.

The amount of the tip is $4.20, and the total amount Charlie will pay is $32.20.

Step 5: **Check** the answer. Double-check the calculations to be sure all of the arithmetic is correct.

15% of $28.00 = $2.80 + $1.40 = $4.20.

Total amount of bill = $28.00 + $4.20 = $32.20.

The answer is correct.

[YOU TRY 10] Siddhani wants to leave a 15% tip on the $24.00 restaurant bill. Find the amount of the tip and the final amount she pays.

When we are shopping, we often see signs like "Save 20%!" or "Everything is 30% off!" How do we know whether we are paying the correct amount when we get to the cash registers? (Cash registers DO make mistakes sometimes!) This is when it is very helpful for us to know how to perform mental calculations with percentages. And whether we are figuring out how much money we will save in a store or computing a tip, rounding the numbers we are working with can give us a ballpark figure of how much we are saving or how much we should leave as a tip.

EXAMPLE 11

In-Class Example 11

A sign in a store says that all yoga gear is 20% off the regular price. Armine likes a yoga mat with a regular price of $39.95. Approximately how much money will she save if she buys this mat, and what is the sale price?

Answer:
approximate amount of the discount: $8.00; approximate sale price: $32.00

A sign in a store says that all purses are 20% off. Ting likes a purse with a regular price of $49.95. Approximately how much money will she save if she buys this purse, and what is the sale price?

Solution

Step 1: **Read** the problem carefully, and restate it in your own words.

Ting wants to buy a purse with a <u>regular price of $49.95</u>. It is <u>on sale for 20% off of the regular price.</u>

We have to <u>determine, approximately, the amount of the discount and the sale price of the purse.</u>

Step 2: **Make a plan.** Let's underline important words in our restatement of the problem in Step 1.

Plan: Round $49.95 to $50.00 to make the number easier to work with. Find the approximate amount of the discount: 20% of $50.00. Then, subtract that amount from $50.00 to determine the approximate sale price of the purse.

Step 3: **Solve** the problem.

Approximate amount of the discount: 20% of $50.00 = 2 · $5.00 = $10.00

Now, find the approximate sale price of the purse.

$$\text{Sale price} = \text{Original price} - \text{Amount of discount}$$
$$= \quad \$50.00 \quad - \quad \$10.00$$
$$= \$40.00$$

Step 4: **State the answer** in a complete sentence.

Ting will save approximately $10.00, and the sale price will be about $40.00.

Step 5: **Check** the answer. Double-check the calculations to be sure all the arithmetic is correct.

Approximate amount of the discount: 20% of $50.00 = $10.00

Approximate sale price of the purse = $50.00 − $10.00 = $40.00

(The exact amount of the discount, 20% of $49.95, is $9.99. The exact sale price is $39.96. Our approximations are very close.)

E Evaluate **8.3** Exercises   Do the exercises, and check your work.

*Additional answers can be found in the Answers to Exercises appendix.

Objective 1: Find 10% of a Number

1) Find:

a) $\dfrac{1}{10}$ of 60   6

b) 10% of 60   6

2) Find:

a) $\dfrac{1}{10}$ of 50   5

b) 10% of 50   5

3) Find:

a) $\dfrac{1}{10}$ of 320   32

b) 10% of 320   32

4) Find:

a) $\dfrac{1}{10}$ of 470   47

b) 10% of 470   47

5) Find:

a) $\dfrac{1}{10}$ of 3650   365

b) 10% of 3650   365

6) Find:

a) $\dfrac{1}{10}$ of 2370   237

b) 10% of 2370   237

7) Explain how to find 10% of a number "in your head."   Locate the decimal point in the number, and move it one place to the left.

8) Why do $\dfrac{1}{10}$ of a number and 10% of the same number give the same result?   If you change $\dfrac{1}{10}$ to a percent, you will get 10%.

Find 10% of each of the following numbers "in your head."

9) 70   7

10) 90   9

11) 410   41

12) 850   85

13) 600   60

14) 200   20

15) 1000   100

16) 4000   400

 17) 3870   387

18) 5440   544

19) 23   2.3

20) 76   7.6

21) 5   0.5

22) 8   0.8

Objective 2: Compute Percents That Are Multiples of 10

23) Explain how to find 20% of a number "in your head."   Find 10% of the number, then multiply by 2.

24) Explain how to find 30% of a number "in your head."   Find 10% of the number, then multiply by 3.

Find each of the following percentages "in your head."

25) a) 10% of 60   6
    b) 20% of 60   12
    c) 70% of 60   42

26) a) 10% of 20   2
    b) 20% of 20   4
    c) 90% of 20   18

27) a) 10% of 70   7
    b) 30% of 70   21
    c) 80% of 70   56

28) a) 10% of 10   1
    b) 30% of 10   3
    c) 40% of 10   4

29) a) 30% of 200   60
    b) 70% of 200   140

30) a) 20% of 100   20
    b) 80% of 100   80

31) a) 20% of 800   160
    b) 50% of 800   400

32) a) 40% of 600   240
    b) 90% of 600   540

33) a) 60% of 110   66
    b) 40% of 110   44

34) a) 70% of 120   84
    b) 30% of 120   36

35) a) 10% of 31   3.1
    b) 20% of 31   6.2

36) a) 10% of 42   4.2
    b) 20% of 42   8.4

Objective 3: Find and Use 5% of a Number

37) Explain how to find 5% of a number "in your head."   Find 10% of the number, then multiply that result by $\dfrac{1}{2}$, or divide the result by 2.

38) Explain how to find 15% of a number "in your head."   Find 10% of the number, find 5% of the number, then add those results.

Find 5% of each of the following numbers "in your head."

39) 80   4

40) 20   1

41) 120   6

42) 140   7

43) 500   25

44) 300   15

45) 400   20

46) 600   30

47) 68   3.4

48) 84   4.2

49) 22   1.1

50) 46   2.3

Find each of the following percentages "in your head."

51) a) 10% of 60   6

b) 5% of 60   3

c) 15% of 60   9

52) a) 10% of 80   8

b) 5% of 80   4

c) 15% of 80   12

53) a) 10% of 200   20

b) 5% of 200   10

c) 15% of 200   30

54) a) 10% of 400   40

b) 5% of 400   20

c) 15% of 400   60

55) a) 10% of 180   18

b) 5% of 180   9

c) 15% of 180   27

56) a) 10% of 120   12

b) 5% of 120   6

c) 15% of 120   18

Find 15% of each of the following numbers.

57) 20   3

58) 40   6

59) 800   120

60) 600   90

61) 440   66

62) 320   48

63) 500   75

64) 900   135

65) 4000   600

66) 6000   900

67) 88   13.2

68) 66   9.9

Find each of the following percentages "in your head."

69) 45% of 80   36

70) 35% of 40   14

71) 35% of 60   21

72) 45% of 20   9

73) 25% of 200   50

74) 25% of 600   150

75) 75% of 120   90

76) 55% of 120   66

Objective 4: Perform Computations with Multiples of 100%

Find each of the following percentages "in your head."

77) a) 100% of 35   35

b) 200% of 35   70

78) a) 100% of 23   23

b) 200% of 23   46

79) a) 300% of 5   15

b) 500% of 5   25

80) a) 400% of 7   28

b) 900% of 7   63

81) a) 400% of 30   120

b) 600% of 30   180

82) a) 300% of 80   240

b) 700% of 80   560

83) a) 700% of 200   1400

b) 200% of 200   400

84) a) 600% of 500   3000

b) 500% of 200   1000

Objective 5: Solve Applications Containing Basic Percentages

Solve each problem.

85) A restaurant bill is $24.00. If Joan wants to leave a 15% tip, find the amount of the tip and the total amount of money she will pay. $3.60; $27.60

86) Antonio wants to leave a 15% tip on his $8.00 restaurant bill. Find the amount of the tip and the final amount he pays. $1.20; $9.20

87) Habib wants to leave a 15% tip on his $18.00 restaurant bill. Find the amount of the tip and the final amount he pays. $2.70; $20.70

88) A restaurant bill is $32.00. If Georgette wants to leave a 15% tip, find the amount of the tip and the total amount of money Georgette will pay. $4.80; $36.80

89) Dawn gets a manicure and a pedicure for $60. If she wants to leave a 15% tip, find the amount of the tip and the total amount of money she will pay. $9.00; $69.00

90) Yesla gets a haircut, color treatment, and a deep conditioning hair treatment. She wants to leave a 15% tip. If the total cost for these services is $80.00, find the amount of the tip and the final amount she pays. $12.00; $92.00

91) Between flights, Russ gets a shoe shine in the airport terminal for $8.00. If Russ wants to leave a 20% tip, find the amount of the tip and the total amount of money he will pay. $1.60; $9.60

92) Kimberly's gardener charges her $35.00 a month for weekly landscape service. If she wants to include a 20% tip with the monthly payment, find the amount of the tip and her final monthly payment. $7.00; $42.00

93) Rene's weekly pool service costs $54.00 per month. If he wants to include a 5% tip with the monthly payment, find the amount of the tip and his final monthly payment. $2.70; $56.70

94) Philip hires a tree trimming service to trim and shape a tree on his property. The service costs $180.00. If he wants to include a 5% tip with the cost, find the amount of the tip and the final cost. $9.00; $189.00

Solve each problem by first rounding the regular price of the item to the nearest dollar.

95) Kelly finds a dress marked 20% off its regular price of $69.95. Approximately how much money will she save if she buys the dress, and what is the approximate sale price? $14.00; $56.00

96) Stella finds a pair of leather boots marked 30% off their regular price of $119.95. Approximately how much money will she save if she buys the boots, and what is the approximate sale price? $36.00; $84.00

97) Amir and his wife Anna like a refrigerator for their new home that is marked 25% off its regular price of $679.95. Approximately how much money will they save if they buy the refrigerator, and what is the approximate sale price? $170.00; $510.00

98) Duyen sees that her favorite jeans are marked 40% off their regular price of $59.95. Approximately how much money will she save if she buys the jeans, and what is the approximate sale price?
$24.00; $36.00

99) Daryl finds an MP3 player marked 20% off its regular price of $29.95. Approximately how much money will he save if he buys the MP3 player, and what is the approximate sale price? $6.00; $24.00

100) Ely's favorite running shoes are marked 30% off their regular $89.95 price. Approximately how much money will he save if he buys the shoes, and what is the approximate sale price? $27.00; $63.00

R Rethink

R1) How could you use the techniques you learned about percents to help you with multiplication and division of other numbers?

R2) The next time you are buying something on sale or you are computing a tip, do you feel confident that you could use what you have learned here to estimate how much money you will save or how much tip you should leave?

R3) How would you explain the methods learned here to a friend?

8.4 Use an Equation to Solve Percent Problems

What are your objectives for Section 8.4?	How can you accomplish each objective?
1 Find the Percent of a Number Using Multiplication	• Write your own procedure for **Finding a Percent of a Number Using Multiplication.** • Complete the given examples on your own. • Complete You Trys 1 and 2.
2 Use an Equation to Find the Number	• Use the first paragraph of this section to write a procedure. • Complete the given examples on your own. • Complete You Trys 3 and 4.
3 Use an Equation to Find the Percentage	• Follow Example 5 to create a procedure for **Using an Equation to Find the Percentage.** • Complete You Try 5.

W Work

Read the explanations, follow the examples, take notes, and complete the You Trys.

At the beginning of Section 8.3, we learned that a statement like *10% of 40* means we multiply $0.1 \cdot 40 = 4$. We also did this calculation mentally: 10% of 40 = 4.

We computed percents like 10%, 15%, 20%, 25%, 100%, and 200% mentally because it is not too complicated to work with multiples of 5% and 10%. But what if we have to find 63% of 84? How should we find this?

1 Find the Percent of a Number Using Multiplication

EXAMPLE 1

In-Class Example 1

Find: a) 39% of 78
b) 6.8% of 900

Answer:
a) 30.42 b) 61.2

W Hint
What would be a quick way to determine whether you were close to the correct answer?

Find:

a) 63% of 84   b) 9.5% of 700

Solution

a) The *of* in 63% *of* 84 means multiply. Change 63% to a decimal, then multiply.

$$63\% \text{ of } 84 = 0.63 \cdot 84 = 52.92$$

b) To find 9.5% *of* 700, change 9.5% to a decimal, then multiply.

$$9.5\% \text{ of } 700 = 0.095 \cdot 700 = 66.5$$

[YOU TRY 1] Find:

a) 47% of 92   b) 3.2% of 180

Many real-world problems involve computations containing percents.

In 2010, a female pharmacist earned 83.2% of what a male earned for doing the same job. If a male pharmacist earned $108,000 in 2010, how much did his female colleague earn? (www.bls.gov)

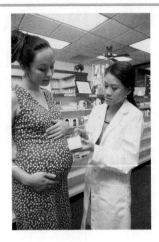

Solution

Step 1: **Read** the problem carefully, and restate it in your own words.

In 2010, a <u>male pharmacist earned $108,000</u>. His <u>female colleague earned 83.2% *of*</u> this amount. We must <u>determine how much the female colleague earned</u>.

Step 2: **Make a plan.** Let's underline important words in our restatement of the problem in Step 1.

We can also think of the problem statement as *a female pharmacist earned 83.2% of $108,000.*

Plan: Find 83.2% of $108,000.

Step 3: **Solve** the problem.

$$83.2\% \text{ of } \$108,000 = 0.832 \cdot \$108,000 = \$89,856$$

Step 4: **State the answer** in a complete sentence.

The female pharmacist earned $89,856.

Step 5: **Check** the answer. Double-check the calculations to be sure all of the arithmetic is correct.

$$83.2\% \text{ of } \$108,000 = 0.832 \cdot \$108,000 = \$89,856$$

The answer is correct.

[YOU TRY 2] The number of people who watched the Oscars telecast in 2011 was about 90.2% of the number who watched in 2010. If approximately 41,700,000 people watched the Oscars in 2010, how many watched in 2011? (www.ibtimes.com)

---

2 Use an Equation to Find the Number

We can also use an equation to solve problems like those in Examples 1 and 2 as well as to solve other problems involving percents. To do this, we will first write a statement or question in English and use that to write a mathematical equation. Read the statement slowly and carefully, and think about what the words mean in terms of math.

EXAMPLE 3

 Hint

Sometimes it is helpful to have an estimate of what the answer should be close to. For instance, what would 30% of 400 be?

Use an equation to find:

a) 29% of 400   b) 130% of 92

Solution

a) Let's think of finding 29% of 400 as the question, "What is 29% of 400?" Remember from Section 6.5 (applications involving proportions) that we can use a variable, x, to represent the unknown quantity. Therefore,

$$x = \text{the unknown quantity, 29\% of 400}$$

Write the question in English, understand its meaning in terms of math, and write an equation.

English:	What	is	29%	of	400?
Meaning:	What number	equals	29%	times	400?
	↓	↓	↓	↓	↓
Equation:	x	$=$	0.29	$\cdot$	400

The equation is $x = 0.29 \cdot 400$. Solve the equation.

$$x = 116 \qquad \text{Multiply.}$$

Therefore, 116 is 29% of 400.

b) Think of 130% of 92 as "What is 130% of 92?" Let x represent the unknown quantity.

$$x = \text{the unknown quantity, 130\% of 92}$$

Write the question in English, understand its meaning in terms of math, and write an equation.

English:	What	is	130%	of	92?
Meaning:	What number	equals	130%	times	92?
	↓	↓	↓	↓	↓
Equation:	x	$=$	1.30	$\cdot$	92

The equation is $x = 1.3 \cdot 92$. Solve the equation.

$$x = 119.6 \qquad \text{Multiply.}$$

Therefore, 119.6 is 130% of 92. Notice that because 130% is greater than 100%, the answer is greater than 92.

YOU TRY 3

Use an equation to find:

a) 72% of 600   b) 160% of 34

We can use an equation to find other quantities involving percentages.

EXAMPLE 4

Use an equation to solve each problem.

a) 7 is 10% of what number?   b) $3\frac{1}{2}\%$ of what number is 56?

Use an equation to solve
each problem.
a) 8 is 10% of what number?
b) $4\frac{1}{2}$% of what number is 54?

Answer: a) 80   b) 1200

Solution

a) Let x represent the unknown value.

$$x = \text{the number}$$

Write the question in English, understand its meaning in terms of math, and write an equation.

English:	7	is	10%	of	what number?
Meaning:	7	equals	10%	times	what number?
	↓	↓	↓	↓	↓
Equation:	7	=	0.1	·	x

The equation is $7 = 0.1 \cdot x$. Solve it.

$$7 = 0.1x \qquad \text{Write the equation without the multiplication symbol.}$$

$$\frac{7}{0.1} = \frac{0.1x}{0.1} \qquad \text{Divide both sides by 0.1 to get } x \text{ by itself.}$$

$$70 = x \qquad \text{Perform the division.}$$

Therefore, 7 is 10% of 70. We can check the answer by finding 10% of 70.

$$10\% \text{ of } 70 = 7 \quad ✓$$

The answer is correct.

b) Let x represent the unknown value.

$$x = \text{the number}$$

Write the question in English, understand its meaning in terms of math, and write an equation.

English:	$3\frac{1}{2}$%	of	what number	is	56?
Meaning:	3.5%	times	what number	equals	56?
	↓	↓	↓	↓	↓
Equation:	0.035	·	x	=	56

The equation is $0.035 \cdot x = 56$. Solve it.

$$0.035x = 56 \qquad \text{Write the equation without the multiplication symbol.}$$

$$\frac{0.035x}{0.035} = \frac{56}{0.035} \qquad \text{Divide both sides by 0.035 to get } x \text{ by itself.}$$

$$x = 1600 \qquad \text{Perform the division.}$$

Therefore, $3\frac{1}{2}$% of 1600 is 56. Check the answer by multiplying.

$$3\frac{1}{2}\% \text{ of } 1600 = 3.5\% \text{ of } 1600 = 0.035 \cdot 1600 = 56 \quad ✓$$

The answer is correct.

[**YOU TRY 4**]   Use an equation to solve each problem.

a)   12 is 20% of what number?   b) $7\frac{1}{2}$% of what number is 105?

3 Use an Equation to Find the Percentage

Sometimes we are asked to find a percentage. We can use an equation to do this, too.

Use an equation to solve each problem.

a) 20 is what percent of 80?   b) What percent of 3500 is 7?

c) What percent of 40 is 64?

Solution

a) We will solve these problems like we solved the problems in Examples 3 and 4. What is the unknown quantity? It is a percent. Let x represent the percent.

$$x = \text{the percent}$$

Write the question in English, understand its meaning in terms of math, and write an equation.

English:	20	is	what percent	of	80?
Meaning:	20	equals	what percent	times	80?
	↓	↓	↓	↓	↓
Equation:	20	=	x	·	80

The equation is $20 = x \cdot 80$. The commutative property says we can also write $x \cdot 80$ as $80 \cdot x$. So, we can think of the equation as $20 = 80 \cdot x$ or $20 = 80x$. Solve this equation.

$$20 = 80x$$

$$\frac{20}{80} = \frac{80x}{80} \qquad \text{Divide both sides by 80 to get } x \text{ by itself.}$$

$$0.25 = x \qquad \text{Perform the division.}$$

The final answer is *not* 0.25 because x represents a percent. The last step is to change 0.25 to a percent.

$$0.25 = 25\% \qquad \text{Change 0.25 to a percent.}$$

Therefore, 20 is 25% of 80. We can check the answer using multiplication.

$$25\% \text{ of } 80 = 0.25 \cdot 80 = 20$$

The answer is correct.

 BE CAREFUL When you are asked to find a percent, the value that you get for x is *not* the final answer. You must change that number to a percent.

We could have solved $20 = 80x$ by simplifying the fraction $\dfrac{20}{80}$ like this:

$$20 = 80x$$

$$\dfrac{20}{80} = \dfrac{80x}{80}$$ Divide both sides by 80 to get x by itself.

$$\dfrac{1}{4} = x$$ Simplify the fraction to solve for x.

Then, rewrite $\dfrac{1}{4}$ as a percent: $\dfrac{1}{4} = 25\%$. Either method will give us the same result.

b) To determine *what percent of 3500 is 7*, first let x represent the unknown quantity, the percent.

$$x = \text{the percent}$$

Write the question in English, understand its meaning in terms of math, and write an equation.

English:	what percent	of	3500	is	7?
Meaning:	what percent	times	3500	equals	7?
	↓	↓	↓	↓	↓
Equation:	x	·	3500	=	7

The equation is $x \cdot 3500 = 7$, or $3500x = 7$. Solve this equation.

$$3500x = 7$$

$$\dfrac{3500x}{3500} = \dfrac{7}{3500}$$ Divide both sides by 3500 to get x by itself.

$$x = 0.002$$ Perform the division.

Change 0.002 to a percent: $0.002 = 0.2\%$ $\left(\text{Because } 0.2 = \dfrac{2}{10} = \dfrac{1}{5}, \text{ the answer may also be written as } \dfrac{1}{5}\%.\right)$

Therefore, 7 is 0.2% of 3500.

c) In *what percent of 40 is 64*, the unknown quantity is the percent. Let the variable represent this unknown.

$$x = \text{the percent}$$

Write the question in English, understand its meaning in terms of math, and write an equation.

English:	what percent	of	40	is	64?
Meaning:	what percent	times	40	equals	64?
	↓	↓	↓	↓	↓
Equation:	x	·	40	=	64

The equation is $x \cdot 40 = 64$. The commutative property lets us think of the equation as $40x = 64$. Solve $40x = 64$.

$$40x = 64$$

$$\frac{40x}{40} = \frac{64}{40} \qquad \text{Divide both sides by 40 to get } x \text{ by itself.}$$

$$x = 1.6 \qquad \text{Perform the division.}$$

Change 1.6 to a percent: $1.6 = 160\%$

Therefore, 64 is 160% of 40. Since 64 is greater than 40, it makes sense that the percentage is greater than 100.

[YOU TRY 5] Use an equation to solve each problem.

a) 40 is what percent of 5000?   b) What percent of 1800 is 153?

c) What percent of 90 is 117?

ANSWERS TO [YOU TRY] EXERCISES

1) a) 43.24 b) 5.76   2) 37,613,400 people   3) a) 432 b) 54.4   4) a) 60 b) 1400
5) a) 0.8% b) 8.5% c) 130%

Using Technology

We can use a calculator to solve problems involving percent. But first we must learn how to construct and solve equations for these problems.

Suppose we wanted to know, for example, what percent of 2500 is 75? First, set up an equation using x to represent the unknown quantity, and do the calculation by hand. Be sure to write down all the steps so you can understand the order in which the numbers and operations are entered into the calculator. Once you have completed the calculation by hand, enter $\boxed{7}\boxed{5}\boxed{\div}\boxed{2}\boxed{5}\boxed{0}\boxed{0}\boxed{\times}\boxed{1}\boxed{0}\boxed{0}\boxed{=}$ into the calculator. The display will likely show 3, as the result. Because we calculated a percent, we remove the decimal point and write our final answer as 3%. Therefore 3% of 2500 is 75.

Did you get the right answer by hand? Do you understand the order in which the numbers and operations were entered into the calculator?

E Evaluate **8.4** Exercises   Do the exercises, and check your work.

*Additional answers can be found in the Answers to Exercises appendix.

Objective 1: Find the Percent of a Number Using Multiplication

Find the percent using multiplication.

1) 57% of 63 35.91

2) 29% of 39 11.31

3) 76% of 161 122.36

4) 93% of 157 146.01

5) 6.1% of 300 18.3

6) 8.2% of 800 65.6

7) 1.9% of 420 7.98

8) 4.5% of 540 24.3

9) 52.4% of 3600 1886.4

10) 81.7% of 2200 1797.4

11) 126% of 95 119.7

12) 165% of 72 118.8

Solve each problem.

13) In 2001, white females earned 73.4% of what white males earned working similar jobs. If a white male earned $45,000 in 2001, what amount did a white female earn working a similar job? (www.census.gov)
$33,030

14) In 2007, an American middle school district reported that 23% of its students admitted to posting something online about another person to make others laugh. If the school district has 1963 middle school students, approximately how many students admitted to this form of cyberbullying? (www.cyberbullying.us) 451 students

15) The percent of private industry employees who had nonfatal workplace injuries and illnesses in 2009 was 3.6%. If a private industry employer has 250 workers, how many employees are expected to have a nonfatal workplace injury? (www.bls.gov) 9

16) Approximately 81% of all American households own a computer. Out of 275,000 American households, approximately how many own a computer? (www.leichtmanresearch.com) 222,750 households

17) A bank loan officer recommends that a young couple put 15% down on a new home costing $275,000. What is the amount of the recommended down payment? $41,250

18) Sharon's weekly salary is $2490.00, and 27% of this amount is withheld for taxes. How much of her weekly salary is withheld for taxes? $672.30

19) At a community college, approximately 57% of the students are female. If the college has 10,400 students, how many students are female? 5928

20) The L.A. Galaxy soccer team won 60% of its games during the 2010 season. The team played a total of 30 games. How many games did the team win in 2010? (http://mlssoccer.com/standings) 18 games

21) Approximately 61% of households in the United States have at least one high-definition television. Out of 450,000 U.S. households, approximately how many have a high-definition television? (www.leichtmanresearch.com) 274,500 households

22) In 2010, 20.7% of married couples had a wife who earned at least $5000 more than the husband. Out of 2000 married couples, how many wives were expected to earn at least $5000 more than the husband in 2010? (www.census.gov) 414

23) In 2007, 80% of American home owners were 65 and older. Out of 250,000 American home owners, how many are expected to have been 65 and older in 2007? (www.census.gov) 200,000

24) Between 2006 and 2010, 11% of American children aged 11–17 repeated a grade in school. In a school district with 7500 students aged 11–17, how many are expected to have repeated a grade between 2006 and 2010? (www.census.gov) 825

Objective 2: Use an Equation to Find the Number

Use an equation to find each number.

25) 20% of 70 14

26) 30% of 60 18

27) 64% of 800 512

28) 43% of 900 387

29) 58% of 200 116

30) 79% of 500 395

31) 0.6% of 150 0.9

32) 0.4% of 140 0.56

33) 170% of 13 22.1

34) 190% of 18 34.2

35) 250% of 57 142.5

36) 230% of 96 220.8

Use an equation to solve each problem.

37) Find 90% of 150 problems. 135 problems

38) Find 30% of 40 cars. 12 cars

39) Find 55% of 700 computers. 385 computers

40) Find 85% of 20 dogs. 17 dogs

41) Find 0.5% of 1200 coupons. 6 coupons

42) Find 0.3% of 9000 cats. 27 cats

43) Find 120% of 620 textbooks. 744 textbooks

44) Find 110% of 470 in. 517 in.

Use an equation to solve each problem.

45) 6 is 30% of what number? 20

46) 12 is 40% of what number? 30

47) 78 is 65% of what number? 120

48) 24 is 15% of what number? 160

49) 75% of what number is 300? 400

50) 62% of what number is 186? 300

51) 160% of what number is 72? 45

52) 180% of what number is 63? 35

53) $5\frac{1}{2}\%$ of what number is 110?   2000

54) $6\frac{1}{2}\%$ of what number is 143?   2200

55) 555 is $92\frac{1}{2}\%$ of what number?   600

56) 322 is $80\frac{1}{2}\%$ of what number?   400

Objective 3: Use an Equation to Find the Percentage

Use an equation to solve each problem.

57) 24 is what percent of 40?   60%

58) 18 is what percent of 60?   30%

59) 27 is what percent of 60?   45%

60) 28 is what percent of 80?   35%

61) What percent of 400 is 108?   27%

62) What percent of 300 is 222?   74%

63) 170 is what percent of 5000?   3.4%

64) 688 is what percent of 8000?   8.6%

65) 323 is what percent of 3400?   9.5%

66) 90 is what percent of 7500?   1.2%

67) What percent of 135 is 162?   120%

68) What percent of 102 is 153?   150%

69) What percent of 700 is 4.9?   0.7%

70) What percent of 900 is 3.6?   0.4%

Mixed Exercises: Objectives 1–3

Solve each problem.

71) What is 17% of 90?   15.3

72) What percent of 2500 is 130?   5.2%

73) $7\frac{1}{2}\%$ of what number is 225?   3000

74) What is 83.5% of 4800 flowers?   4008 flowers

75) 40 is what percent of 250?   16%

76) 85% of what number is 221?   260

77) Find 53.1% of $8610. $4571.91

78) What percent of 135 is 162?   120%

79) Approximately 25% of Gulf War II–era veterans reported having a service-connected disability in July 2010. Out of 7500 Gulf War II–era veterans, approximately how many reported a service-connected disability in July 2010? (www.bls.gov)   1875

80) In December 2010, insurance benefit costs were 8% of a private-industry employee's total earnings. If a private industry employee earned $4500 in December 2010, what was the employee's cost for insurance benefits? (www.bls.gov) $360

R Rethink

R1) Write a procedure that can help you check your answers using estimation.

R2) Which objectives do you still need to work on to master?

8.5 Solve Applications Involving Percents

 **Prepare**

 **Organize**

What are your objectives for Section 8.5?	How can you accomplish each objective?
1 Use an Equation to Solve an Applied Problem	• Write the Five Steps for Solving Applied Problems, and add a new component about using variables in Step 2. • Complete the given examples on your own. • Complete You Trys 1–3.
2 Use a Proportion to Find a Percent	• Use the Five Steps for Solving Applied Problems, and add a new component explaining how to set up the correct proportion. • Complete the given example on your own. • Complete You Try 4.

W **Work**

Read the explanations, follow the examples, take notes, and complete the You Trys.

1 Use an Equation to Solve an Applied Problem

In the previous section, we practiced using equations to solve basic percent problems. Now, we will use equations to solve applications involving percents. We will use the five-step problem-solving process we have been using throughout the book, but we will add a new component: In Step 2, we will define the variable that will be used in the equation. Then we will write a statement or question in English and write a mathematical equation.

EXAMPLE 1

In-Class Example 1

Use an equation to solve the problem.

One week, Kiara sent 32 text messages to her mom. If this is 8% of all the texts she sent that week, find the total number of texts Kiara sent that week.

Answer: 400 text messages

Use an equation to solve the problem.

When Monika gets her paycheck every two weeks, she deposits 5% of her take-home pay into her savings account. If she puts $60 into her savings account every two weeks, how much is her take-home pay?

Solution

Step 1: **Read** the problem carefully, and restate it in your own words.

Monika puts $60 into her savings account every two weeks, and this <u>is 5% of her take-home pay</u>. We must <u>find her take-home pay</u>.

Step 2: **Make a plan.** Let's underline important words in our restatement of the problem in Step 1.

We can also think of the statement above as *$60 is 5% of her take-home pay. Find her take-home pay.*

Plan: Since we are trying to find Monika's take-home pay, that will be what *x* represents.

$$x = \text{Monika's take-home pay}$$

The equation will come from the statement *$60 is 5% of her take-home pay.* Write the statement in English; then write an equation and solve it.

Step 3: **Solve** the problem.

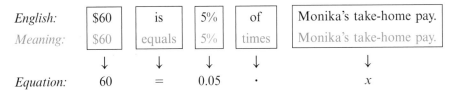

English:	$60	is	5%	of	Monika's take-home pay.
Meaning:	$60	equals	5%	times	Monika's take-home pay.

	↓	↓	↓	↓	↓
Equation:	60	=	0.05	·	x

The equation is $60 = 0.05x$. Solve the equation.

$$60 = 0.05x$$

$$\frac{60}{0.05} = \frac{0.05x}{0.05} \qquad \text{Divide both sides by 0.05 to get } x \text{ by itself.}$$

$$x = 1200 \qquad \text{Perform the division.}$$

Step 4: **State the answer** in a complete sentence.

Monika's take-home pay is $1200.

Step 5: **Check** the answer. We have found that $60 is 5% of $1200. Find 5% of $1200 to see if it equals $60.

$$5\% \text{ of } \$1200 = 0.05 \cdot \$1200 = \$60 \quad ✓$$

The answer is correct.

[YOU TRY 1] Use an equation to solve the problem.

Daryl's car payment is 7% of his monthly salary. Determine how much Daryl earns each month if his car payment is $210 per month.

EXAMPLE 2

In-Class Example 2

Use an equation to solve the problem.

According to AARP, more men are going to spas than ever before. If a spa has 164 regular clients and approximately 35% of them are men, how many of the regular clients are men? (www.aarp.org)

Answer: 57

Use an equation to solve the problem.

During the 2010–2011 academic year, the University of Texas at Austin had 38,420 undergraduate students. Approximately 19.4% of them were Hispanic. How many undergrads were Hispanic? (www.dailytexanonline.com)

Solution

Step 1: **Read** the problem carefully, and restate it in your own words.

Approximately 19.4% of the 38,420 undergraduates were Hispanic. Determine how many undergrads were Hispanic.

Step 2: **Make a plan.** Underline the important words in our restatement of the problem in Step 1.

We can also think of the problem as *19.4% of 38,420 undergraduates were Hispanic. Find the number of Hispanic undergrads.*

Plan: Since we are trying to find the number of Hispanic undergraduate students, that will be what *x* represents.

$$x = \text{the number of Hispanic undergraduates}$$

The equation will come from the statement *19.4% of 38,420 undergraduates were Hispanic.* Write the statement in English; then write an equation and solve it.

Step 3: **Solve** the problem.

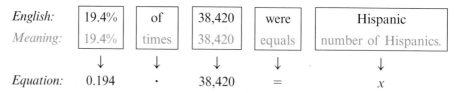

English:	19.4%	of	38,420	were	Hispanic
Meaning:	19.4%	times	38,420	equals	number of Hispanics.
Equation:	0.194	·	38,420	=	x

The equation is $0.194 \cdot 38{,}420 = x$. Solve the equation.

$$0.194 \cdot 38{,}420 = x$$
$$7453.48 = x \qquad \text{Multiply.}$$

Because we are finding the number of students, we should round to the nearest whole number: $7453.48 \approx 7453$.

Step 4: **State the answer** in a complete sentence.

In 2010–2011, approximately 7453 undergraduates were Hispanic.

Step 5: **Check** the answer. When we solved the equation in Step 3, we found that 19.4% of 38,420 = 7453.48, which we rounded to 7453. Double-check the arithmetic to see that this is the correct answer.

[YOU TRY 2] Use an equation to solve the problem.

At the 2010 Winter Olympics in Vancouver, Canada, the United States won 37 medals. Approximately 24.3% of them were gold medals. How many gold medals did American athletes win? (www.olympic.org)

We can use an equation to find a percentage.

EXAMPLE 3 Use an equation to solve the problem.

In 2010, 14 out of 35 automakers installed oil life monitoring systems in their cars to let drivers know when an oil change is needed. What percent of the automakers used this system? What percent did not use this system? (www.edmunds.com)

Solution

Step 1: **Read** the problem carefully, and restate it in your own words.

In 2010, <u>14 out of 35 automakers</u> installed oil life monitoring systems in their cars. <u>We must determine what percent of automakers this is</u>. <u>We must also determine what percent did *not* use this system.</u>

In-Class Example 3

Use an equation to solve the problem.

Nineteen out of the 20 Smithsonian Institutions have free admission. What percent have free admission? What percent do not have free admission? (www.si.edu)

Answer: 95% have free admission; 5% do not have free admission

Step 2: Make a plan. Underline the important words in our restatement of the problem in Step 1.

We can think of the first part of the problem as *14 automakers is what percent of 35 automakers?*

Plan: Let x = the percent. Write the statement in English; then write an equation and solve it.

After we determine the percent that *did* use the oil life monitoring system, we will find the number that did *not* install the system.

Step 3: Solve the problem. First, find the percent that *did* install the monitoring system:

English:	14 automakers	is	what percent	of	35 automakers?
Meaning:	14 automakers	equals	what percent	times	35 automakers?

	↓	↓	↓	↓	↓
Equation:	14	=	x	·	35

The equation is $14 = x \cdot 35$. We can rewrite it as $14 = 35x$. Solve this equation.

$$14 = 35x$$

$$\frac{14}{35} = \frac{35x}{35} \qquad \text{Divide both sides by 35 to solve for } x.$$

$$0.4 = x \qquad \text{Perform the division.}$$

Because x represents a percent, change 0.4 to a percent: $0.4 = 40\%$.

So, 40% of the automakers installed the oil life monitoring system. To determine the percent that did not, subtract 40% from 100% since 100% equals all the automakers: $100\% - 40\% = 60\%$.

Step 4: State the answer in a complete sentence.

In 2010, 40% of automakers installed oil life monitoring systems and 60% did not.

Step 5: Check the answer. To determine the number that installed the system, find 40% of 35: 40% of $35 = 0.4 \cdot 35 = 14$. The number that did not install the system is 60% of $35 = 0.6 \cdot 35 = 21$. Add $14 + 21 = 35$, the total number of automakers. The answer is correct.

[**YOU TRY 3**]

Use an equation to solve the problem.

A college cheerleading squad has 20 members, and 17 of them were gymnasts before they went to college. What percent of the cheerleaders were gymnasts? What percent were not gymnasts?

2 Use a Proportion to Find a Percent

Recall that percents can be written as fractions. For example, $31\% = \dfrac{31}{100}$, which can be thought of as a ratio, 31 out of 100. Because a proportion is a statement that two ratios or rates are equal, we can also use proportions to find a percent.

EXAMPLE 4

Use a proportion to solve the problem.

Statistics show that about 7 out of 50 Las Vegas tourists are from foreign countries. What percent of the tourists are from outside the United States? (www.lasvegassun.com)

Solution

Step 1: **Read** the problem carefully, and restate it in your own words.

7 tourists <u>out of</u> every 50 tourists are from foreign countries. <u>What percent of Las Vegas tourists are from foreign countries?</u>

Step 2: **Make a plan.** Let's underline important words in our restatement of the problem in Step 1.

We can write *7 foreign tourists out of 50 total tourists* as the rate, or fraction, $\frac{7}{50}$. If we write this fraction with a denominator of 100, **the numerator will be the percent** since percent means *out of 100*. We can do this by writing a proportion. Think of the stated problem as

7 foreign tourists *are to* 50 total tourists *as* how many foreign tourists *are to* 100 total tourists?

Let x = the number of foreign tourists out of 100 tourists, or **the percent**.

Plan: Write a proportion using x for the percent. We will write our rates in the form $\dfrac{\text{number of foreign tourists}}{\text{total number of tourists}}$ so that the numerators contain the same quantities and the denominators contain the same quantities:

$$\text{foreign tourists} \rightarrow \frac{7 \text{ foreign tourists}}{50 \text{ total tourists}} = \frac{x}{100 \text{ total tourists}} \leftarrow \text{foreign tourists}$$
$$\text{total tourists} \rightarrow \qquad\qquad\qquad\qquad\qquad\qquad \leftarrow \text{total tourists}$$

7 foreign tourists *are to* 50 total tourists *as* x foreign tourists *are to* 100 total tourists.

Step 3: **Solve** the problem. We do not need the units when solving for x.

$$\frac{7}{50} = \frac{x}{100} \qquad \text{Write the equation without the units.}$$

$$50x = 7 \cdot 100 \qquad \text{Find the cross products.}$$

$$50x = 700 \qquad \text{Multiply.}$$

$$\frac{50x}{50} = \frac{700}{50} \qquad \text{Divide by 50.}$$

$$x = 14 \qquad \text{Perform the division.}$$

Finding that $x = 14$ means that $\frac{7}{50} = \frac{14}{100}$, and $\frac{14}{100} = 14\%$.

Step 4: **State the answer** in a complete sentence.

Therefore, 14% of Las Vegas tourists are from foreign countries.

Step 5: Check the answer. Use the cross products to check $x = 14$ in the proportion $\dfrac{7}{50} = \dfrac{x}{100}$.

$$\dfrac{7}{50} \diagdown\!\!\!\!\diagup \dfrac{14}{100}$$

$50 \cdot 14 = 700$

Substitute 14 for x.

$7 \cdot 100 = 700$

The cross products are equal, so the answer is correct.

[YOU TRY 4] Use a proportion to solve the problem.

A study done by the Centers for Disease Control and Prevention found that 8 out of 25 births in the United States in 2007 were by Cesarean section. What percent of U.S. births in 2007 were by C-section? (www.cdc.gov)

Note

We could have solved Example 3 using a proportion. Let x = the number of automakers out of 100 that have installed oil life monitoring systems in their cars. This is the same as the **percent**. Then, we can write the proportion $\dfrac{14}{35} = \dfrac{x}{100}$, and solve for x. We get $x = 40$. Therefore, $\dfrac{14}{35} = \dfrac{40}{100}$, and $\dfrac{40}{100} = 40\%$.

ANSWERS TO [YOU TRY] EXERCISES

1) $3000   2) 9   3) 85% were gymnasts; 15% were not gymnasts   4) 32%

E Evaluate **8.5** Exercises   Do the exercises, and check your work.

*Additional answers can be found in the Answers to Exercises appendix.

Objective 1: Use an Equation to Solve an Applied Problem

Use an equation to solve each problem.

1) Kathy owns a small business and sets aside 7% of her weekly sales to pay her monthly utility bill. If she set aside $84 for utilities, what was her weekly sales amount? $1200

2) A small liberal arts college has 2300 students enrolled. If 55% of the students are female, how many male students are enrolled in the college?   1035 males

3) In 2010, 23% of American firms reported that they were charging their employees more for health insurance. Out of 2500 American firms, how many are expected to have raised their health insurance premiums? (The Kaiser Family Foundation)   575

4) In a survey conducted with viewers of the popular television show *ER*, 32% said they received information that helped them make choices about their own family's health care. Out of 12,000 viewers, how many are expected to make health care choices based on watching the show? (The Kaiser Family Foundation; Survey of *ER* viewers)   3840

---

5) In 2010, approximately 11% of American elementary through high school students enrolled in private school. Out of a population of 23,000 American elementary through high school students, how many are expected to enroll in nonprivate schools?
(U.S. National Center for Education Statistics) 20,470

6) Watermelon is 91% water. How many pounds of an 8-lb watermelon is not water? 0.72 lb

The table below represents the percent of Americans aged 55–64 in 2006 that were medically uninsured. Use these data for Exercises 7–10.

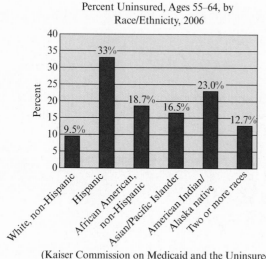

Percent Uninsured, Ages 55–64, by Race/Ethnicity, 2006

(Kaiser Commission on Medicaid and the Uninsured)

7) In a sample population of 13,500 Hispanics aged 55–64, how many were expected to have been uninsured in 2006? 4455

8) In a sample population of 8000 Asian/Pacific Islanders aged 55–64, how many were expected to have been uninsured in 2006? 1320

9) In a sample population of 15,000 white non-Hispanics, how many were expected to have been insured in 2006? 13,575

10) In a sample population of 18,000 African American, non-Hispanics, how many were expected to have been insured in 2006? 14,634

The table below compares the attitudes of adults 18 and older to teenagers' attitudes with regard to cell phone usage. Use these data for Exercises 11–16.

Adult vs. Teen Attitudes Toward Cell Phone Usage

	% Who Agree	
	Adults	Teens
I feel safer because I can always use my cell phone to get help.	91	93
I like that my cell phone makes it easy to arrange plans with other people.	88	84
I think it's rude when someone repeatedly interrupts a conversation or meeting to check their cell phone.	86	n/a
I get irritated when a call or text on my cell phone interrupts me.	42	48
When I am bored, I use my cell phone to entertain myself.	39	69

(Pew Research Center's Internet & American Life Project, April 29–May 30, 2010)

11) When comparing two equally-sized groups of 1500 adults and teens, how many more teens are expected to use a cell phone to entertain themselves when they are bored? 450

12) When comparing two equally-sized groups of 1200 adults and teens, how many more adults are expected to like that their cell phone makes it easy to arrange plans with other people? 48

13) In a group of 750 adults, how many are expected to think that it's rude when someone repeatedly interrupts a conversation or meeting to check their cell phone? 645

14) In a large lecture hall containing 300 adult students, how many of these students are expected to use their cell phone for entertainment if they become bored? 117

15) In a group of 200 teens, how many are expected *not* to feel safer because they can always use their cell phone to get help? 14

16) In a classroom of 25 teens, how many do *not* like that their cell phone makes it easy to arrange plans with other people? 4

Use an equation to solve each problem.

17) Hector's parents sent 84 text messages last month. This is 20% of the total recorded on the bill. How many total text messages did the family send last month?   420

18) Janice bought a coupon book and has already used 33 of them. If this is 60% of all the coupons, how many coupons were in the book?   55

19) During a weeklong clearance sale, a bike store sold 30% of its inventory, which amounted to 75 bicycles. How many bikes did the store have in stock?   250

20) A salesperson earned a commission of $144 one week. If his commission rate is 12%, find the value of the merchandise he sold. $1200

21) Five percent of the units in an apartment building are vacant. If there are six empty apartments, find the total number of units in the apartment building.   120

22) Alex got 12 questions correct on his math quiz, for a grade of 80%. How many questions were on the quiz?   15

23) A high school basketball varsity team includes three sophomores. If there are 15 players on the team, what percent of the team were sophomores? What percent were not sophomores?   20%; 80%

24) Steve decides to take a mountain bike ride on a 36-mile-loop trail. When his mountain bike mileage gauge indicates that he has traveled 27 miles, what percent of the trail has he traveled? What percent of the trail remains?   75%; 25%

25) Susan has $240 deducted from her weekly $1200 salary to pay for child care. What percent of Susan's salary is deducted for child care? What percent is not?   20%; 80%

26) Lorena has $54 deducted from her $450 weekly salary to pay for car pool transportation to work. What percent is deducted for the car pool? What percent is not?   12%; 88%

27) In a math class of 40 students, five students received an A for the letter grade at the end of the semester. What percent of students received an A for their letter grade? What percent did not?   12.5%; 87.5%

28) In a large auditorium with 500 seats, 36 seats were reserved for VIP guests. What percent of the seating was reserved for VIP guests? What percent was not?   7.2%; 92.8%

29) Approximately 2 out of 5 American adult workers regularly work more than 40 hours per week. What percent is this? (www.expedia.com)   40%

30) In 2008, 6 out of 25 American adult workers checked work email or voice mail while on vacation. What percent is this? (www.expedia.com)   24%

Objective 2: Use a Proportion to Find a Percent

Use a proportion to solve each problem.

31) 70 freshmen is what percent of 280 freshmen?   25%

32) 94 births is what percent of 470 births?   20%

33) 92 mL is what percent of 400 mL?   23%

34) 42 kg is what percent of 120 kg?   35%

35) 2 weeks is what percent of 14 days?   100%

36) 1 day is what percent of 48 hr?   50%

37) 350 mL is what percent of 1.75 L?   20%

38) 1 L is what percent of 1250 mL?   80%

39) In January 2011, a study by the Bureau of Transportation Statistics found that 19 out of 25 flights arrived on time. What percent of flights were on time? (www.bts.gov)   76%

40) The results of a 2005 study by the National Center for Education Statistics found that 19 out of 20 secondary schools had rooms with Internet access. What percent of secondary schools had Internet access in 2005? (nces.ed.gov)   95%

41) In 2009, a study found that 17 out of 50 employed U.S. adults did not take all the vacation days they receive each year. What percent is this? (www.expedia.com)   34%

42) When American families travel on vacation, they spend, on average, 11 out of every 25 dollars on transportation. What percent of the family vacation budget is spent on transportation? (www.bls.gov)   44%

43) In 2007–2008, 16 out of 25 American public school teachers were female. What percent of American public school teachers were female in 2007–2008? (nces.ed.gov)   64%

44) The U.S. Postal Service is one of the leading employers of minorities. In 2009, approximately 2 out of 5 of its employees were a minority. What percent of U.S. Postal employees were minorities in 2009? (U.S. Postal Service) 40%

45) In 2005, 4 out of 25 U.S. female military officers were African American. What percent of U.S. female military officers were African American? (www.prb.org) 16%

46) A human brain weighing 1400 g contains approximately 980 g of water. What percent of the human brain weight is water? (ga.water.usgs.gov) 70%

47) In 2009, 61 ATV-related fatalities involved children under the age of 16. Of these 61 fatalities, 29 involved children under the age of 12. What percent of the 61 fatalities involved children under the age of 12? Round the answer to the nearest tenth of a percent. (U.S. Consumer Product Safety Commission) 47.5%

48) Doctors recommend that adults get 8 hours of sleep per day. What percent of one day is 8 hours? Round the answer to the nearest tenth of a percent. (www.mayoclinic.com) 33.3%

49) In a classroom of 40 students, six students were absent. What percentage of the students were present? 85%

50) On the first day of classes, a math professor has two seats open in her class of 40 students. With two seats open, what percent of the class is filled? 95%

51) A coed softball team of 12 players has three females. What percentage of the team is male? 75%

52) The Department of Health and Human Services recommends that adults get at least 30 minutes of exercise per day. What percent of one day is 30 minutes? Round your answer to the nearest tenth of a percent. (www.hhs.gov) 2.1%

Mixed Exercises: Objectives 1 and 2
Solve each problem.

53) At a college basketball game, 16% of the tickets sold were to the visiting team. If 14,200 tickets were sold, how many were sold to the visitors? 2272

54) A school computer lab has 55 laptop computers for students to check out. If 44 computers are currently checked out, what percentage of the 55 laptop computers is still available for checkout? 20%

55) After a recent flood, 144 people spent the night at a Red Cross shelter. If 25% of the total number of cots were still available, how many cots were in the shelter? 192

56) Popular belief says that adults should drink eight 8-oz glasses of water per day. According to the Mayo Clinic, this is actually about 61.5% of the recommended daily amount for men. How much water should men drink each day? Round to the nearest whole number. (www.mayoclinic.com) 104 oz

57) 50 cm is what percent of 2 m? 25%

58) 205 days is what percent of 250 days? 82%

59) If 28 out of 32 chemistry students plan to take a physics course, what percent do not think they will take physics? 12.5%

60) A survey of 2500 people revealed that 63% of them would take a train to work if they had commuter rail service in their town. How many people said they would like to ride a train to work? 1575

R1) Think of a situation where you needed to determine a percent or a percent of a number. Write a problem similar to the exercises presented, and solve it.

R2) The Five Steps for Solving Applied Problems have worked for many different sections. How could you use them to help you in other courses?

Putting It All Together

What are your objectives?	How can you accomplish each objective?
1 Review the Concepts of Sections 8.1–8.5	• Be sure that you can apply the objectives you have learned in the previous sections. • If you are not confident about a certain example, go back to the section that gives more explanation. • Be sure to note the summaries and the procedures to refresh your memory on topics already covered. • Complete the given examples on your own. • Complete all the You Trys.

W Work

Read the explanations, follow the examples, take notes, and complete the You Trys.

1 Review the Concepts of Sections 8.1–8.5

In Section 8.1, we said that percent means *out of 100*. Therefore, we can write a percent like 58% as $58\% = \dfrac{58}{100} = 0.58$ or $58\% = \dfrac{58}{100} = \dfrac{29}{50}$. We can change a percent to a fraction with a denominator of 100, and then write it as a decimal or as a fraction in lowest terms.

We can also change a percent to a decimal by moving the decimal point two places to the left and removing the percent symbol.

EXAMPLE 1

In-Class Example 1

Write each percent as a decimal.
a) 72.4% b) 0.5% c) 318%

Answer:
a) 0.724 b) 0.005 c) 3.18

Write each percent as a decimal.

a) 16% b) 0.3% c) 225%

Solution

a) $16\% = 16.\% = 0.16$ b) $0.3\% = 0.003$

c) $225\% = 225.\% = 2.25$

Note

A percent greater than 100 is equivalent to a decimal number greater than 1.

[YOU TRY 1] Write each percent as a decimal.

a) 47% b) 130% c) 6.8%

To change a decimal to a percent, we move the decimal point two places to the right and then put the percent symbol at the end of the number.

EXAMPLE 2

Write each decimal as a percent.

a) 0.73   b) 0.09   c) 1

Solution

a) $0.73 = 73\%$ b) $0.09 = 9\%$ c) $1 = 1. = 100\%$

⌐ Put a decimal point
at the end of the number.

YOU TRY 2

Write each decimal as a percent.

a) 0.008   b) 4   c) 0.51

There are three different ways to change a fraction to a percent.

EXAMPLE 3

Change each fraction to a percent.

a) $\dfrac{5}{8}$ b) $\dfrac{13}{20}$ c) $\dfrac{7}{6}$

Solution

a) Since the denominator, 8, does not divide evenly into 100, we will *not* write this fraction with a denominator of 100. To change $\dfrac{5}{8}$ to a percent, we should use either long division or a proportion. Let's use **long division.**

$$8\overline{)5.000} \quad .625$$

Therefore, $\dfrac{5}{8} = 0.625 = 62.5\%$ or $62\dfrac{1}{2}\%$.

b) Look at the denominator of $\dfrac{13}{20}$. If we multiply 20 by 5, we will get a denominator of 100. Therefore, we will change $\dfrac{13}{20}$ to a percent by **writing the fraction with a denominator of 100.**

$$\dfrac{13}{20} = \dfrac{13}{20} \cdot \dfrac{5}{5} = \dfrac{65}{100} = 65\% \qquad \text{So, } \dfrac{13}{20} = 65\%.$$

c) The denominator of 6 does not divide evenly into 100, so we will not try to write $\dfrac{7}{6}$ with a denominator of 100. We could use either long division or a proportion.

Let's **use a proportion.** Set up the proportion $\dfrac{7}{6} = \dfrac{x}{100}$, where x is the percent, and solve for x.

$$\dfrac{7}{6} \diagdown \dfrac{x}{100} \qquad \begin{array}{l} 6 \cdot x = 6x \\ 7 \cdot 100 = 700 \end{array}$$

$$6x = 700$$

$$\dfrac{6x}{6} = \dfrac{700}{6} \qquad \text{Divide each side by 6.}$$

$$\dfrac{\overset{1}{6}x}{\underset{1}{6}} = 116.\overline{6} \qquad \text{Divide out the common factor; } 1x \text{ is the same as } x.$$

$$x = 116.\overline{6} \qquad \text{Simplify.}$$

So, $\dfrac{7}{6} = \dfrac{116.\overline{6}}{100} = 116.\overline{6}\%$. If we change $\dfrac{700}{6}$ to the mixed number $116\dfrac{2}{3}$, then we can also see that $\dfrac{7}{6} = 116\dfrac{2}{3}\%$.

$\left[\ \textbf{YOU TRY 3}\ \right]$ Change each fraction to a percent.

a) $\dfrac{22}{25}$ b) $\dfrac{5}{12}$ c) $\dfrac{9}{16}$

In Section 8.3, we learned how to compute percentages of some numbers mentally. Recall that to find 10% of a number, we move the decimal point in that number one place to the left. We can also find percents that are multiples of 10.

EXAMPLE 4

 Hint

In your own words, summarize how to find percents that are multiples of 10%.

Perform each of the calculations mentally.

a) 10% of 120   b) 40% of 120   c) 5% of 120   d) 45% of 120

Solution

a) 10% of 120 = 12   Move the decimal point one place to the left.

b) In part a), we found that 10% of 120 = 12. To find 40% of 120, multiply that result by 4.

$$10\% \text{ of } 120 = 12$$
$$40\% \text{ of } 120 = 4 \cdot 12 = 48$$

40% of 120 = 48

c) Because 10% of 120 is 12, 5% of 120 is $\dfrac{1}{2}$ of that result.

$$10\% \text{ of } 120 = 12$$

5% is half of 10% $\Bigg($

$$5\% \text{ of } 120 = \dfrac{1}{2} \cdot 12 = 6$$

5% of 120 = 6

d) We want to think of 45% of 120 as 40% of 120 + 5% of 120.

$$45\% \text{ of } 120 = 40\% \text{ of } 120 + 5\% \text{ of } 120$$
$$= \quad 48 \quad + \quad 6$$
$$= 54$$

So, 45% of 120 = 54.

$\left[\ \textbf{YOU TRY 4}\ \right]$ Find:

a) 10% of 60   b) 60% of 60   c) 5% of 60   d) 65% of 60

We can use these types of mental calculations when we leave a tip at a restaurant or when we buy something on sale.

To solve a problem such as *find 87% of 195,* we multiply because the *of* indicates multiplication:

$$87\% \text{ of } 195 = 0.87 \cdot 195 = 169.65$$

Sometimes, however, it is helpful to use an equation to solve a problem involving percents.

EXAMPLE 5

Use an equation to solve each problem.

a) 160% of what number is 384?   b)   27 is what percent of 36?

In-Class Example 5

Use an equation to solve each problem.
a) 150% of what number is 270?
b) 91 is what percent of 140?

Answer:
a) 180   b) 65%

Solution

a) Let x represent the unknown value: $x =$ the number

Write the question in English, understand its meaning in terms of math, and write an equation.

English:	160%	of	what number	is	384?
Meaning:	160%	times	what number	equals	384?
	↓	↓	↓	↓	↓
Equation:	1.6	·	x	=	384

The equation is $1.6 \cdot x = 384$. Solve this equation.

$1.6x = 384$ Write the equation without the multiplication symbol.

$\dfrac{1.6x}{1.6} = \dfrac{384}{1.6}$ Divide both sides by 1.6 to get x by itself.

$x = 240$ Perform the division.

Therefore, 160% of 240 is 384.

b) Begin by letting x represent the unknown quantity: $x =$ the percent

Write the question in English, understand its meaning in terms of math, and write an equation.

English:	27	is	what percent	of	36?
Meaning:	27	equals	what number	times	36?
	↓	↓	↓	↓	↓
Equation:	27	=	x	·	36

The equation is $27 = x \cdot 36$, which we can also write as $27 = 36x$.

$27 = 36x$

$\dfrac{27}{36} = \dfrac{36x}{36}$ Divide both sides by 36 to get x by itself.

$0.75 = x$ Perform the division.

Change 0.75 to a percent: $0.75 = 75\%$. Therefore, 27 is 75% of 36. We can check the answer using multiplication.

$$75\% \text{ of } 36 = 0.75 \cdot 36 = 27 \quad ✓$$

[YOU TRY 5] Use an equation to solve each problem.

a)   153 is what percent of 180?   b)   8% of what number is 120?

ANSWERS TO [YOU TRY] EXERCISES

1) a) 0.47   b) 1.3   c) 0.068   2) a) 0.8%   b) 400%   c) 51%

3) a) 88%   b) 41.$\overline{6}$% or $41\frac{2}{3}$%   c) 56.25% or $56\frac{1}{4}$%   4) a) 6   b) 36   c) 3   d) 39

5) a) 85%   b) 1500

Putting It All Together Exercises

E Evaluate   Do the exercises, and check your work.

*Additional answers can be found in the Answers to Exercises appendix.

Objective 1: Review the Concepts of Sections 8.1–8.5

Write each percent as a decimal.

1) a) 96%   0.96   b) 0.02%   0.0002

c) $4\frac{1}{2}$%   0.045

2) a) 172%   1.72   b) $\frac{3}{5}$%   0.006

c) 23.8%   0.238

Write each percent as a fraction or mixed number in lowest terms.

3) a) 8% $\frac{2}{25}$ b) $\frac{3}{4}$% $\frac{3}{400}$

c) 250% $\frac{5}{2}$ or $2\frac{1}{2}$

4) a) 31% $\frac{31}{100}$ b) $18\frac{1}{3}$% $\frac{11}{60}$

c) 50.2% $\frac{251}{500}$

Write each number as a percent.

5) a) 0.413   41.3%   b) $\frac{17}{25}$ 68%

c) $\frac{2}{3}$ 66.$\overline{6}$% or $66\frac{2}{3}$%   d) $3\frac{1}{4}$ 325%

6) a) 2   200%   b) $\frac{9}{8}$ 112.5%

c) 0.003   0.3%   d) $\frac{9}{20}$ 45%

In Exercises 7–14, perform the calculations mentally.

7) Find:

a) 10% of 20   2   b) 5% of 20   1

c) 30% of 20   6   d) 35% of 20   7

8) Find:

a) 10% of 40   4   b) 5% of 40   2

c) 70% of 40   28   d) 75% of 40   30

9) Find 80% of 70.   56   10) Find 60% of 90.   54

11) Find 45% of 60.   27   12) Find 95% of 30.   28.5

13) Find 400% of 9.   36   14) Find 300% of 50.   150

15) Find 16% of 89.   14.24   16) Find 3.8% of 5600.   212.8

17) Find $72\frac{1}{4}$% of 9000.   6502.5   18) Find 0.5% of 700.   3.5

In Exercises 19–22, solve each problem by doing the calculations in your head.

19) A video game has a regular price of $59.89, and it is on sale for 15% off. Find the approximate amount of the discount and the sale price. $9.00; $51.00

20) A box of diapers has a regular price of $23.99, and it is on sale for 10% off. Find the approximate amount of the discount and the sale price. $2.40; $21.60

21) Leah leaves a 20% tip on an $18.00 restaurant bill. Find the amount of the tip and the total amount Leah pays the server. $3.60; $21.60

22) Marcus' restaurant bill is $40.17, and he wants to leave a 15% tip. Round the bill to the nearest dollar, and compute the tip based upon that amount. How much tip will he leave, and how much does he owe if he adds this tip to the original amount he owes? $6.00; $46.17

Use an equation to solve each problem.

24) 23) 7% of what number is 10.5?   150

24) What is 38% of 4000?   1520

25) 108 is what percent of 90?   120%

26) 664.3 is 91% of what number?   730

27) What is $23\frac{1}{2}$% of 8200?   1927

28) What percent of 175 is 28?   16%

Use an equation to solve each problem.

29) A study shows that 3.2% of American adults are vegetarians. If the American adult population is about 228,125,000, how many adults are vegetarians? (www.vegetariantimes.com)   7,300,000

30) A study showed that, in 2009, approximately 1 out of 6 Americans did not have health insurance. What percent of Americans did not have health insurance? (www.usatoday.com)   16.6%

31) A poll revealed that 62% of women between the ages of 18 and 54 look up ex-boyfriends online. If 1054 women admitted to looking up their ex-boyfriends, how many women were surveyed? (http://mobilelink.elle.com)   1700

32) A bag of candy-covered chocolates contained 9 yellow candies. If this is approximately 17.3% of the total, how many candies were in the bag? Round to the nearest whole number.   52

24) 33) Through 2010, the New York Yankees had won 27 World Series titles, more than any other team. Find the percentage of titles won by the Yankees given that there had been 105 World Series until that time. Round to the nearest tenth of a percent. (mlb.mlb.com)   25.7%

34) A survey done by the Pew Research Center showed that about 22% of adults used Twitter or a social networking site to get information about the 2010 midterm elections. Given that 2257 adults were surveyed, how many used a social networking site to learn about the elections in 2010? (pewresearch.org)   497

R Rethink

R1) Which topics do you still need to master before moving to the next section?

8.6 More Applications with Percents

P Prepare

O Organize

What are your objectives for Section 8.6?	How can you accomplish each objective?
1 Compute Sales Tax	• Learn the formula to compute **Sales Tax,** and add it to the Five Steps for Solving Applied Problems. • Complete the given examples on your own. • Complete You Trys 1 and 2.
2 Compute Commissions	• Learn the formula to compute **Amount of Commission,** and add it to the Five Steps for Solving Applied Problems. • Complete the given examples on your own. • Complete You Trys 3 and 4.
3 Find a Sale Price	• Learn the formula to compute **Amount of Discount and Sale Price,** and add it to the Five Steps for Solving Applied Problems. • Complete the given example on your own. • Complete You Try 5.
4 Find Percent Increase and Decrease	• Write the procedure for **Finding a Percent Increase or Decrease** in your own words, and add it to the Five Steps for Solving Applied Problems. • Complete the given examples on your own. • Complete You Trys 6 and 7.

 **W Work**   **Read the explanations, follow the examples, take notes, and complete the You Trys.**

In this section, we will learn how to solve more everyday problems involving percents: sales tax, commissions, sale price, and percent increase and decrease.

1 Compute Sales Tax

When we buy something, we often pay *sales tax*. **Sales tax** is a percent of the cost of a purchase. Cities, states, and even countries charge sales tax to help fund their governments. We can use this formula to find the amount of sales tax on an item.

> **Formula** Sales Tax
>
> Amount of sales tax = Rate of tax · Cost of item
>
> The rate of tax is usually given as a percent. To use it in the formula, *change the percent to a decimal.*

We will use the five-step problem solving process to solve these applications.

EXAMPLE 1

In-Class Example 1

A pair of shoes costs $59.99. If the sales tax rate is 6%, find the amount of the tax and the total cost of the shoes.

Answer: amount of tax: $3.60; total cost: $63.59

A pair of jeans costs $39.99. If the sales tax rate is 7%, find the amount of the tax and the total cost of the jeans.

Solution

Step 1: **Read** the problem carefully, and restate it in your own words.

The <u>price of the jeans is $39.99</u>, plus <u>there is a 7% sales tax.</u> <u>We must determine how much is paid in sales tax and also find the total cost of the jeans.</u>

Step 2: **Make a plan.** Let's underline important words in our restatement of the problem in Step 1.

Plan: First, use the formula to find the amount of the sales tax. Then, add that amount to the price of the jeans to find the total cost.

Step 3: **Solve** the problem.

Change the sales tax rate from a percent to a decimal: 7% = 0.07

Amount of sales tax = Rate of tax · Cost of item

Amount of sales tax =   0.07   ·   39.99

= $2.7993 ≈ $2.80   Round to the nearest cent.

Find the total cost of the jeans.

Total cost of the jeans = Price of the jeans + Amount of sales tax

Total cost of the jeans = $39.99   + $2.80

= $42.79

Step 4: **State the answer** in a complete sentence.

The amount of sales tax is $2.80. The total cost of the jeans is $42.79.

Step 5: **Check** the answer. Double-check the calculations to be sure all the arithmetic is correct.

Amount of tax = 0.07 · $39.99 = $2.7993 ≈ $2.80. Then the total cost of the jeans is $39.99 + $2.80 = $42.79.   ✓

The answer is correct.

[YOU TRY 1]   A digital camera costs $189.99. If the sales tax rate is 8%, find the amount of the sales tax and the total cost of the camera.

We can use the sales tax formula to find any quantity in the formula that we do not know.

A price tag shows that a laptop computer costs $1200. The sales tax on the computer is $102. What is the sales tax rate?

Solution

Step 1: **Read** the problem carefully, and restate it in your own words.

A laptop costs $1200 and the sales tax is $102. We must find the rate of the sales tax.

Step 2: **Make a plan.** Let's underline important words in our restatement of the problem in Step 1.

Plan: Use the formula

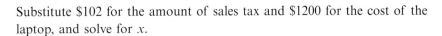

Amount of sales tax = Rate of tax · Cost of item

Since we are trying to find the rate of tax, choose a variable to represent that part of the formula.

$$x = \text{rate of tax}$$

Substitute $102 for the amount of sales tax and $1200 for the cost of the laptop, and solve for x.

Step 3: **Solve** the problem.

Amount of sales tax = Rate of tax · Cost of item
$$\$102 \qquad = \qquad x \quad \cdot \quad \$1200$$

Solve the equation.

$$102 = x \cdot 1200$$
$$\frac{102}{1200} = \frac{x \cdot 1200}{1200} \qquad \text{Divide both sides by 1200.}$$
$$0.085 = x \qquad \text{Perform the division.}$$

Change the decimal to a percent: $0.085 = 8.5\%$

Step 4: **State the answer** in a complete sentence.

The sales tax rate is 8.5%.

Step 5: **Check** the answer.

Find 8.5% of $1200 to see whether the sales tax is $102.

$$0.085 \cdot \$1200 = \$102 \quad ✓$$

The answer is correct.

[YOU TRY 2] An engagement ring costs $3600 before tax. If the sales tax is $189, what is the rate of the sales tax?

2 Compute Commissions

Salespeople and real estate agents are often paid on *commission*. That is, the amount of money they earn, their **commission,** is a percent *of* total sales. (As in other percent problems we have studied so far, the word *of* indicates multiplication.) The formula for computing commission is similar to the formula used to find the amount of sales tax.

Formula Amount of Commission

Amount of commission = Rate of commission · Amount of sales

The rate of commission is usually given as a percent. To use it in the formula, *change the percent to a decimal.*

EXAMPLE 3

In-Class Example 3

Ludmilla sells medical supplies to hospitals and earns 9.5% in commissions. If she sold $870,000 worth of medical supplies last year, find the amount of Ludmilla's commission.

Answer: $82,650

Vinny sells advertising space on websites, and his commission rate is 7.5%. This month his advertising sales total $35,800. Find the amount of his commission.

Solution

Step 1: **Read** the problem carefully, and restate it in your own words.

Vinny's <u>sales total $35,800</u>, and <u>he earns 7.5% commission</u>. We must <u>find the amount of his commission</u>.

Step 2: **Make a plan.** Let's underline important words in our restatement of the problem in Step 1.

Plan: Use the formula to find the amount of the commission.

Step 3: **Solve** the problem.

Change the rate of commission from a percent to a decimal: 7.5% = 0.075

Amount of commission = Rate of commission · Amount of sales

Amount of commission =   0.075   · $35,800

= $2685

Step 4: **State the answer** in a complete sentence.

Vinny's commission is $2685.

Step 5: **Check** the answer. Double-check the calculations to be sure all the arithmetic is correct.

Amount of commission = 0.075 · $35,800 = $2685 ✓

The answer is correct.

[YOU TRY 3] A real estate agent earns a 6% commission on a home that sold for $174,000. How much did the agent earn for selling this house?

We can use the formula to find the rate of commission.

EXAMPLE 4

 Hint

Remember to **write down** what the variable represents!

Last month, Vanitra earned a commission of $520 for selling $13,000 worth of appliances. What is her rate of commission?

Solution

Step 1: **Read** the problem carefully, and restate it in your own words.

Vanitra sold <u>$13,000 worth of appliances</u> and her <u>commission was $520</u>. We must <u>find her rate of commission</u>.

Step 2: **Make a plan.** Let's underline important words in our restatement of the problem in Step 1.

Plan: Use the formula

$$\text{Amount of commission} = \text{Rate of commission} \cdot \text{Amount of sales}$$

Since we are trying to find the rate of commission, choose a variable to represent that part of the formula.

$$x = \text{rate of commission}$$

Substitute $520 for the amount of commission and $13,000 for the amount of sales, and solve for x.

Step 3: **Solve** the problem.

$$\text{Amount of commission} = \text{Rate of commission} \cdot \text{Amount of sales}$$
$$\$520 \quad = \quad x \quad \cdot \quad \$13,000$$

Solve the equation.

$$520 = x \cdot 13,000$$
$$\frac{520}{13,000} = \frac{x \cdot 13,000}{13,000} \qquad \text{Divide both sides by 13,000.}$$
$$0.04 = x \qquad \text{Perform the division.}$$

Change the decimal to a percent: $0.04 = 4\%$

Step 4: **State the answer** in a complete sentence.

The rate of commission is 4%.

Step 5: **Check** the answer.

Find 4% of $13,000 to see whether the commission is $520.

$$0.04 \cdot \$13,000 = \$520 \quad \checkmark$$

The answer is correct.

[YOU TRY 4] One month, a salesman sold $19,800 worth of furniture. If his commission was $990, what was his rate of commission?

---

3 Find a Sale Price

In Section 8.3, we learned how to find or approximate the sale price of an item when the numbers were easy to work with. We will look at more problems here. Let's review the process we used to find the amount of the discount and then the sale price.

> **Formulas** Amount of Discount and Sale Price
>
> Amount of discount = Rate of discount · Original price
>
> Sale price = Original price − Amount of discount
>
> The rate of discount is usually given as a percent. To use it in the formula, change the percent to a decimal.

EXAMPLE 5

In-Class Example 5

The original price of a toboggan is $150. At the end of the winter, it is on sale for 33% off. What is the sale price of the toboggan?

Answer: $100.50

The original price of a winter coat is $120. At the end of the winter season, the coat is on sale for 33% off. What is the sale price of the coat?

Solution

Step 1: **Read** the problem carefully, and restate it in your own words.

The regular price of a coat is $120, and it is 33% off. We must find the sale price of the coat.

Step 2: **Make a plan.** Let's underline important words in our restatement of the problem in Step 1.

Plan: Use the formula to find the amount of the discount. Then, subtract the discount from the original price to find the sale price of the coat.

Step 3: **Solve** the problem.

Change the percent to a decimal: 33% = 0.33

Amount of discount = Rate of discount · Original price

Amount of discount =   0.33   · $120

= $39.60

Now, find the sale price of the coat.

Sale price = Original price − Amount of discount

Sale price = $120   − $39.60

= $80.40

Step 4: **State the answer** in a complete sentence.

The sale price of the coat is $80.40.

Step 5: **Check** the answer. Double-check the calculations to be sure all the arithmetic is correct.

Amount of discount = 0.33 · $120 = $39.60

Sale price = $120 − $39.60 = $80.40 ✓

The answer is correct.

The original price of a gas grill is $549. At the end of the summer, it is 35% off. Find the sale price of the grill.

4 Find Percent Increase and Decrease

One way to describe an increase or decrease in a number is with a percentage. We call this a **percent change.** Specifically, if a quantity increases, we can find the **percent increase** in the quantity. If a quantity decreases, we can find the **percent decrease** in the quantity.

> **Procedure** How to Find Percent Increase or Decrease
>
> 1) First, **find the amount of the increase or decrease** by subtracting the smaller number from the larger number.
>
> 2) Then, **use a proportion** to find the percent increase or decrease.
>
> $$\frac{\text{Amount of increase or decrease}}{\text{Original amount}} = \frac{\text{Percent increase or decrease}}{100}$$

W Hint

You will subtract to find the amount of the increase *or* the amount of the decrease.

EXAMPLE 6

In 1990, a town had a population of 3000. In 2010, its population had grown to 6600. Find the percent increase in the population from 1990 to 2010.

In-Class Example 6

Last summer, Farzana's driving time to work was 20 minutes. This summer, it takes 42 minutes because of road construction. Find the percent increase in Farzana's commuting time.

Answer: 110%

Solution

Step 1: Read the problem carefully, and restate it in your own words.

The population of a town grew from <u>3000 in 1990 to 6600 in 2010</u>. We must <u>find the percent increase in the population from 1990 to 2010</u>.

Step 2: Make a plan. Underline important words in our restatement of the problem in Step 1.

This is a *percent increase* problem because the population increased from 1990 to 2010.

Plan: Find the amount of the increase, then use a proportion to find the percent increase. Let $x =$ the percent increase.

Step 3: Solve the problem.

First, find the *amount* of the increase: $6600 - 3000 = 3600$.

The original amount in the formula is 3000, the population in the earlier year. Set up a proportion.

$$\text{Amount of increase} \rightarrow \frac{3600}{3000} = \frac{x}{100} \leftarrow \text{Percent increase}$$
$$\text{Original amount} \rightarrow$$

Solve the proportion using cross products.

$$\frac{3600}{3000} \underset{\displaystyle 100}{\overset{\displaystyle x}{\diagdown}} \begin{array}{l} 3000 \cdot x = 3000x \\ 3600 \cdot 100 = 360,000 \end{array}$$

$3000x = 360,000$ Set the cross products equal to each other.

$\dfrac{3000x}{3000} = \dfrac{360,000}{3000}$ Divide both sides by 3000.

$x = 120$ Perform the division.

The percent increase is 120%.

Step 4: **State the answer** in a complete sentence.

The population increased by 120% from 1990 to 2010. This answer makes sense because the *amount* of the increase, 3600, is more than the original population of 3000.

Step 5: **Check** the answer.

The amount of the increase was 120% of 3000 = 1.2 · 3000 = 3600.

Then, the population in 2010 was 3000 + 3600 = 6600. ✓

The answer is correct.

$\Big[$ **YOU TRY 6** $\Big]$ Five years ago, a start-up company had 15 employees. Now it has 39. Find the percent increase in the number of employees.

In a *percent decrease* application, we will see a *decrease* in a quantity.

EXAMPLE 7

In-Class Example 7

In 1990, 492,000 people worked in textile mills in the United States. In 2009, that number was 126,000. Find the percent decrease in the number of people working in textile mills. Round the answer to the nearest tenth of a percent. (www.census.gov)

Answer: 74.4%

In 2000, Americans smoked a total of 430 billion cigarettes. In 2006, that number was 380 billion. Find the percent decrease in the number of cigarettes smoked. Round the answer to the nearest tenth of a percent. (www.cdc.gov)

Solution

Step 1: **Read** the problem carefully, and restate it in your own words.

The number of cigarettes smoked fell from 430 billion in 2000 to 380 billion in 2006. We must find the percent decrease in the number of cigarettes smoked.

Step 2: **Make a plan.** Underline the important words in our restatement of the problem in Step 1.

This is a *percent decrease* problem because the number of cigarettes *decreased* from 2000 to 2006.

Plan: Find the amount of the decrease, then find the percent decrease using a proportion.

Let x = the percent decrease.

Step 3: **Solve** the problem.

First, find the *amount* of the decrease: 430 billion − 380 billion = 50 billion

The original amount in the formula is 430 billion, the number of cigarettes smoked in the earlier year. **Set up a proportion.** We can leave out the unit of billions since they are the same in the number of cigarettes in both years.

Amount of decrease → $\dfrac{50}{430} = \dfrac{x}{100}$ ← Percent decrease
Original amount →

Solve the proportion using cross products.

$\dfrac{50}{430} \diagdown \dfrac{x}{100}$ $430 \cdot x = 430x$
$50 \cdot 100 = 5000$

$430x = 5000$ Set the cross products equal to each other.

$\dfrac{430x}{430} = \dfrac{5000}{430}$ Divide both sides by 430.

$x \approx 11.6$ Round the quotient to the nearest tenth.

The percent decrease is approximately 11.6%.

Step 4: **State the answer** in a complete sentence.

The number of cigarettes smoked by Americans decreased by approximately 11.6% from 2000 to 2006.

Step 5: **Check** the answer.

The amount of the decrease was approximately 11.6% of 430 billion: $0.116 \cdot 430$ billion $= 49.88$ billion.

Then, the number of cigarettes smoked in 2006 was approximately 430 billion $- 49.88$ billion $= 380.12$ billion. This is close to the number given in the problem, 380 million. The difference is due to rounding to the tenth of a percent.

The answer is correct.

[**YOU TRY 7**]   In 1990, 17,695,000 people had manufacturing jobs in the United States. That number fell to 11,883,000 in 2009. Find the percent decrease in the number of Americans working in manufacturing. (www.census.gov)

ANSWERS TO [**YOU TRY**] **EXERCISES**

1) amount of tax: $15.20; total cost: $205.19   2) 5.25%   3) $10,440   4) 5%   5) $356.85
6) 160%   7) 32.8%

Using Technology

Simple arithmetic calculators often have a percent key that can be used to quickly calculate the sales price of an item. The percent key is generally labeled $\boxed{\%}$. Suppose the original price of a cookware set is $150. During a clearance sale, the cookware is on sale for 35% off. To find the sale price of the cookware, we enter $\boxed{1}\boxed{5}\boxed{0}\boxed{-}\boxed{3}\boxed{5}\boxed{\%}$ into the calculator. The display will likely show 97.5 as the result. This means that the sale price of the cookware is $97.50.

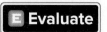

*Additional answers can be found in the Answers to Exercises appendix.

Objective 1: Compute Sales Tax
Solve each problem.

 1) A pair of tennis shoes costs $55. If the sales tax rate is 6%, find the amount of the tax and the total cost of the shoes. $3.30; $58.30

2) An office supply store sells software to make personal business cards for $32. If the sales tax rate is 5%, find the amount of the tax and the total cost of the software. $1.60; $33.60

3) A price tag shows that a wireless telephone system costs $78. If the sales tax rate is 8%, find the amount of the tax and the total cost of the phone system.
$6.24; $84.24

4) A price tag shows that a portable DVD player costs $56. If the sales tax rate is 7%, find the amount of the tax and the total cost of the DVD player.
$3.92; $59.92

5) A 4-GB memory stick costs $4. If the sales tax rate is 7.75%, find the amount of the tax and the total cost of the memory stick. $0.31; $4.31

6) A gel ink ballpoint pen and pencil set costs $8. If the sales tax rate is 8.25%, find the amount of the tax and the total cost of the set. $0.66; $8.66

7) The price of a pay-as-you-go cell phone is $75. If the sales tax rate is 7.8%, find the amount of the tax and the total cost of the set. $5.85; $80.85

8) The sales tax rate for an online purchase of a four-person tableware set was 8.5%. If the purchase price was $32, find the amount of the tax and the total cost of the set. $2.72; $34.72

9) A microwave oven is on sale for $54. Find the amount of the tax and the total cost of the microwave if the sales tax rate is 7%. $3.78; $57.78

10) A package of four avocados costs $7.50. Find the amount of the tax and the total cost of the avocados if the sales tax rate is 6%. $0.45; $7.95

Find each sales tax rate.

11) A picture frame sold for $12, and the amount of the sales tax was $0.96. What was the sales tax rate?   8%

12) A computer monitor sells for $110, and the sales tax is $9.90. What is the sales tax rate?   9%

13) A six-pack of soft pastels costs $26. Hailey also pays $1.17 for sales tax. What is the sales tax rate?
4.5%

14) A two-day sale is offering a cookware set for $140. If the sales tax amount for the purchase is $11.62, what is the sales tax rate?   8.3%

15) A sweater costs $79.99 plus $6.76 in sales tax. What is the sales tax rate? Round the answer to the nearest hundredth of a percent.   8.45%

16) Suppose the regular price of headphones is $39.99. If the sales tax amount is $3.54, what is the sales tax rate? Round the answer to the nearest hundredth of a percent.   8.85%

17) Janessa's total bill for a dress was $91.77, which included $7.77 for sales tax. What was the sales tax rate?   9.25%

18) A coffeemaker costs $64.71, including the sales tax. If the tax was $4.71, what was the sales tax rate?
7.85%

19) Lance paid $1363.20 for a road bike, including tax. Find the sales tax rate if the amount of the tax was $83.20.   6.5%

20) The cost of a new desktop computer, including tax, is $1446.24. If $66.24 of this is sales tax, what is the sales tax rate?   4.8%

Objective 2: Compute Commissions
Solve each problem.

21) How much commission will a real estate agent earn on a sale of a $425,000 home if the agent is paid 3.5% commission on the selling price? $14,875

22) A cosmetics salesperson is paid a 12.5% rate on beauty products she sells from her home. Find her commission if she sold $1650 worth of products.
$206.25

23) Edina receives 4% commission for finding customers who want the exterior of their homes painted. If she finds two customers who will each pay $3500 for the job, what is Edina's total commission? $280

24) Randy is paid 3% commission to find homeowners who want to have their roofs replaced. If he arranges two jobs, each costing $8500, how much commission does Randy earn for the two jobs? $510

25) A Caribbean vacation property sales agent receives 5% commission for each property she sells. If she sells three $150,000 condos, how much commission does she earn? $22,500

26) Suzanne earns 6% commission at an electronics warehouse store. How much commission will Suzanne earn on the sale of three HD televisions each worth $1250? $225

27) A shoe salesman sold 14 pairs of shoes, giving him total sales of $950 for the day. If he received a commission of $114, what is his commission rate? 12%

28) Junji received a commission check for $1020 for his monthly sales of $6800. What is his commission rate? 15%

29) A medical equipment salesperson sold six refurbished ultrasound machines to local hospitals for $3000 each, earning a commission of $2880. What is the salesperson's commission rate? 16%

30) A dental X-ray machine salesperson sold five $1800 machines. If the salesperson received a $1260 commission check for the sales, what is her commission rate? 14%

31) Joanna sells cleaning supplies as a door-to-door salesperson working on a commission. If she received a commission check for $293.75 for selling $2350 worth of cleaning supplies, what is her commission rate? 12.5%

32) A pawn shop salesperson made $343.65 commission for selling $2370 worth of pawned merchandise. What is his commission rate? 14.5%

Objective 3: Find a Sale Price
Solve each problem.

33) A pair of leather gloves that regularly sells for $54 is marked 30% off. What is the sale price of the gloves? $37.80

34) A handbag that regularly sells for $180 is marked 40% off. What is the sale price of the handbag? $108

35) An outlet store is selling a designer dress that regularly sells for $235 at 35% off. What is the sale price of the dress? $152.75

36) A ski outlet store is selling its ski boots at 45% off. If the boots regularly sell for $240, what is the sale price? $132

37) A pet groomer has a 25%-off weekend special on a pet grooming package for large dogs, which includes a flea-killing shampoo and a hand-cut trim. What is the sale price if the package normally costs $90? $67.50

38) The regular price of a graphite fishing pole is $86. What is the sale price if the fishing pole is marked 35% off? $55.90

39) A caterer offers a 25% discount per guest to wedding parties serving over 200 guests. The regular price per guest is $12.00. If Sandra hires the caterer to serve 250 guests at her wedding reception, what is the total cost to serve all 250 guests? $2250

40) A 20% group discount rate is given to groups larger than 20 people attending a play. If the tickets regularly sell for $45 per person, what is the discounted price for a group of 30 people to attend the play? $1080

41) The regular price of a raincoat is $79.99, and it is on sale for 25% off. Find the total cost of the raincoat if the sales tax rate is 7.5%. $64.49

42) During an end-of-the-year clearance sale, a department store is selling its most popular pair of jeans at 60% off. If the regular price of the jeans is $124.99, find the total cost if the sales tax rate is 8.5%. $54.25

43) During a Memorial Day sale, a retailer sells bedroom sets at 35% off. If a bedroom set regularly sells for $1259.99, find the total cost if the sales tax rate is 9%. $892.70

44) An office supply store sells a computer desk for $349.99. If the desk is marked 40% off, find the total cost if the sales tax rate is 9.5%. $229.94

Objective 4: Find Percent Increase and Decrease

Solve each problem.

45) It took $40 for Stephanie to fill her tank with gas four months ago. Today, it takes $50 to fill her tank. Find the percent increase in price.   25%

46) Anthony scored 60% on his first math exam. He was determined to do better on his second math exam by studying more. His hard work paid off, and he scored 96%. Find the percent increase in the exam score.
60%

47) Almost 50 years ago, a U.S. postage stamp cost 4 cents. In 2011, it cost 44 cents. Find the percent increase in price. (www.usps.com)   1000%

48) When Tatiana first bought her Japanese maple tree, it was 2 ft high. It is now 9 ft high. Find the percent increase in height.   350%

49) Sebastian bought a 4-GB flash drive two years ago for $50. Today he bought one for $8. Find the percent decrease in price.   84%

50) Cinta bought her first car four years ago for $15,000. Today she purchased a new car, and the dealership gave her $1500 for her old car. Find the percent decrease in the value of Cinta's first car.   90%

51) The number of American adults newly diagnosed with diabetes in 2008 was 1,728,000. In 2009, it increased to 1,812,000 adults. Find the percent increase in the number of American adults diagnosed with diabetes. Round the answer to the nearest tenth of a percent. (www.cdc.gov)   4.9%

52) In 1896, the first modern Olympics in Athens had 14 teams. In 2008, the Summer Olympics in Beijing had 204 teams. Find the percent increase in the number of teams participating in the Olympics. Round the answer to the nearest tenth of a percent. (www.olympic.org)   1357.1%

53) The median sale price of new homes in the United States in 2007 was $313,600. In 2010, it was $272,200. Find the percent decrease in price. Round the answer to the nearest tenth of a percent. (www.census.gov)   13.2%

54) The average sale price of new American homes in 2007 was $247,900. In 2010, it was $222,600. Find the percent decrease in price. Round the answer to the nearest tenth of a percent. (www.census.gov)   10.2%

55) In 2002, Christina was 3 ft 4 in. tall. Ten years later, she was 5 ft 10 in. tall. Find the percent increase in height.   75%

56) Anthony discovered the shoes he wore as a toddler in his parents' attic. As a toddler, his feet were approximately 56 mm long. His feet are now 19.6 cm long. Find the percent increase in length.   250%

Mixed Exercises: Objectives 1–4

57) Sophie is a jewelry sales representative who is paid 12.5% commission on her weekly sales. If her weekly sales totaled $3800, what was the amount of her commission? $475

58) Tadas sometimes rides his bike to work, adding 40 minutes to his commute time. It takes Tadas 10 minutes to get to work if he travels by car. Find the percent decrease in commute time when Tadas drives his car to work.   75%

59) A table saw with a price tag of $180 is marked 33% off. What is the sale price for the table saw? $120.60

60) Adam is a fitness machine sales representative who is paid on commission. If he received a commission of $238 on an elliptical machine he sold for $2800, what was Adam's commission rate?   8.5%

61) The sales tax amount for a new wireless router is $3.90. If the router costs $60, what is the sales tax rate?   6.5%

62) A price tag shows that a skateboard costs $80. Find the amount of the sales tax and the total cost of the skateboard if the sales tax rate is 5.25%.

$4.20; $84.20

63) In 2009, Subway had 31,812 stores worldwide. In 2010, they had 33,959 stores. Find the percent increase in the number of Subway stores. Round the answer to the nearest tenth of a percent. (www.qsrweb.com)   6.7%

64) A washer-dryer pair regularly sells for $1250. During a Memorial Day sales event, the pair is marked down by 40% off. What is the sale price for the washer dryer pair? $750

R Rethink

R1) Are computing sales tax and finding the amount of commission similar? If so, how?

R2) How can you use the objectives you just mastered every day?

R3) Could you explain to a friend how to use percents to solve application problems?

8.7 Simple Interest

P Prepare

O Organize

What are your objectives for Section 8.7?	How can you accomplish each objective?
1 Compute Simple Interest	• Know the definitions of *interest, simple interest,* and *principal.* • Learn the formula for finding **Simple Interest.** • Be sure to notice the subtle differences between the examples, as they get a bit more complex with each one. • Complete the given examples on your own. • Complete You Trys 1–4.
2 Compute the Original Amount Plus Interest	• Write a procedure for computing the original amount plus interest. • Complete the given examples on your own. • Complete You Trys 5 and 6.

W Work

Read the explanations, follow the examples, take notes, and complete the You Trys.

1 Compute Simple Interest

Why do banks pay us interest when we deposit money in a bank account? Why do *we* pay interest when we borrow money? What *is* interest? Let's look at two examples.

> Kelly has a savings account containing $4700. The bank pays Kelly *interest*, or a *fee*, to use her money to loan to other people and businesses.
>
> Omar wants to borrow $12,000 from his credit union to buy a car. The credit union will loan him the money, but it will charge him *interest*, or a *fee*, to borrow this money. In the end, Omar will owe the credit union more than the $12,000 that he borrowed.

Interest is a fee paid for borrowing money. Banks pay interest to customers who deposit money in savings accounts for using their money to loan to people and businesses. This is why people earn interest on bank accounts. Likewise, when we borrow money from banks, credit unions, and credit card companies, we pay them interest. Often, interest is computed as a percentage of the money borrowed for a given length of time.

There are different ways to compute interest. In this section, we will learn about *simple interest*. **Simple interest** is calculated based on the original amount of money borrowed. The original amount of money borrowed is called the **principal.**

Here is the formula for computing simple interest.

Formula Simple Interest

$$\text{Interest} = \text{Principal} \cdot \text{Rate} \cdot \text{Time}$$
$$I = P \cdot R \cdot T$$

P = the principal. This is the original amount of money borrowed or the original amount of money in a bank account.

R = the interest rate. It is usually given as a percent. **We must change it to a decimal when we use it in the equation.**

T = the time, *in years*, that the money will be borrowed or the length of time an amount of money is in an account.

 When using the formula $I = P \cdot R \cdot T$:

1) the interest rate *must* be in decimal form.

2) the time *must* be in years.

EXAMPLE 1

Saori borrows $1200 for 1 year at an interest rate of 7%. Find the interest.

Solution

Use the formula $I = P \cdot R \cdot T$.

The principal, P, is the amount of money borrowed: $P = \$1200$.

The interest rate, R, is 7%. Change this to a decimal: $R = 0.07$.

The time, T, is the length of the loan, 1 year: $T = 1$.

$$I = \quad P \cdot R \cdot T$$
$$I = (1200)(0.07)(1) \qquad \text{Substitute the values.}$$
$$I = 84 \qquad \text{Multiply.}$$

The interest is $84.

[YOU TRY 1] Gao borrows $1400 for 1 year at an interest rate of 5%. Find the interest.

EXAMPLE 2

In-Class Example 2

Spiro deposits $2000 into an account earning 4% interest for $3\frac{1}{2}$ years. How much interest will he earn?

Answer: $280

W Hint

Be sure to notice the subtle differences between the examples, as they get a bit more complex with each one.

Ted deposits $5000 into an account earning 3% interest for $2\frac{1}{2}$ years. How much interest will he earn?

Solution

Use the formula $I = P \cdot R \cdot T$.

$$P = \$5000 \qquad R = 0.03 \qquad T = 2\frac{1}{2} \text{ or } 2.5$$
$$\uparrow$$
$$\text{Change 3\% to a decimal.}$$

$$I = \quad P \cdot R \cdot T$$
$$I = (5000)(0.03)(2.5) \qquad \text{Substitute the values.}$$
$$I = 375 \qquad \text{Multiply.}$$

Ted will earn $375 in interest.

[YOU TRY 2] Devorah deposits $3000 into an account earning 5% interest for $1\frac{1}{2}$ years. How much interest will she earn?

Remember, when you substitute the time in the formula, it **must** be in years.

EXAMPLE 3

In-Class Example 3

Write each time in terms of years.
a) 7 months   b) 26 weeks

Answer:

a) $\frac{7}{12}$ yr   b) $\frac{1}{2}$ yr

Write each time in terms of years.

a) 5 months   b) 13 weeks

Solution

a) We will use unit fractions to change 5 months to years.

$$5 \text{ months} \cdot \frac{1 \text{ yr}}{12 \text{ months}} = \frac{5 \text{ months}}{1} \cdot \frac{1 \text{ yr}}{12 \text{ months}} \qquad \text{Divide out the unit of months.}$$

$$= \frac{5 \text{ yr}}{12} \qquad \text{Multiply.}$$

$$= \frac{5}{12} \text{ yr} \qquad \text{Simplify.}$$

Because the units will always divide out in this way, **we can change from months to years by writing the number of months over 12.** Simplify, if possible.

Example: $5 \text{ months} = \dfrac{5}{12} \text{ yr}$

b) Let's use unit fractions to change 13 weeks to years.

$$13 \text{ weeks} \cdot \frac{1 \text{ yr}}{52 \text{ weeks}} = \frac{13 \; \cancel{\text{weeks}}}{1} \cdot \frac{1 \text{ yr}}{52 \; \cancel{\text{weeks}}} \qquad \text{Divide out the unit of weeks.}$$

$$= \frac{13 \text{ yr}}{52} \qquad \text{Multiply.}$$

$$= \frac{13}{52} \text{ yr or } \frac{1}{4} \text{ yr} \qquad \text{Simplify.}$$

Note

Because the units will always divide out in this way, **we can change from weeks to years by writing the number of weeks over 52.** Simplify, if possible.

Example: $13 \text{ weeks} = \dfrac{13}{52} \text{ yr or } \dfrac{1}{4} \text{ yr}$

[YOU TRY 3] Write each time in terms of years.

a) 11 months   b) 40 weeks

EXAMPLE 4

In-Class Example 4

Nick borrows $680 for 9 months at $5\frac{1}{2}$% interest. How much interest will he owe?

Answer: $28.05

Arkady borrows $960 for 3 months at $6\frac{1}{2}$% interest. How much interest will he owe?

Solution

Change the interest rate to a decimal: $R = 6\dfrac{1}{2}\% = 6.5\% = 0.065$

Rewrite the time, T, in terms of years: $3 \text{ months} = \dfrac{3}{12} \text{ yr} = \dfrac{1}{4} \text{ yr}$

Identify P, R, and T:

$$P = \$960 \qquad R = 0.065 \qquad T = \frac{1}{4}$$

$$I = \; P \; \cdot \; R \; \cdot \; T$$

$$I = (960)(0.065)\left(\frac{1}{4}\right) \qquad \text{Substitute the values.}$$

$$I = (62.4)\left(\frac{1}{4}\right) \qquad \text{Multiply the first two numbers.}$$

$$I = 15.60$$

Arkady will owe $15.60 in interest.

Celia borrows $450 at $7\frac{1}{2}$% interest for 4 months. How much interest will she owe?

2 Compute the Original Amount Plus Interest

To determine the *total* amount of money that must be paid back on a loan or to determine the *total* amount of money in a bank account after being paid interest, we must add the interest to the original amount borrowed or deposited in an account.

EXAMPLE 5

In-Class Example 5

Nikeesha deposited $3450 into an account at 3% interest for 18 months. How much will be in her account after this time?

Answer: $3605.25

Freija deposited $2850 into an account at 5% interest for 18 months. How much will be in her account after this time?

Solution

First, find the amount of interest Freija will earn.

Change 18 months to years: $18 \text{ months} = \frac{18}{12} \text{ yr} = \frac{3}{2} \text{ yr or } 1.5 \text{ yr}$

Use $I = P \cdot R \cdot T$.

$$P = \$2850 \qquad R = 0.05 \qquad T = 1.5$$
$$\uparrow$$
Change the percent to a decimal.

$$I = P \cdot R \cdot T$$
$$I = (2850)(0.05)(1.5) \qquad \text{Substitute the values.}$$
$$I = 213.75 \qquad \text{Multiply.}$$

Freija will earn $213.75 in interest.

Add $213.75 to the amount deposited to determine the total amount in the account after 18 months.

$$\text{Total amount} = \text{Amount deposited} + \text{Amount of interest}$$
$$= \qquad \$2850 \qquad + \qquad \$213.75$$
$$= \$3063.75$$

After 18 months, Freija will have $3063.75 in her account.

Javier deposited $5720 into an account for 30 months at 6% interest. How much money will be in his account after this time?

In the beginning of the section, we said that if Omar borrows $12,000 to buy a car, he will pay interest on that money. Let's determine the total amount he will owe for borrowing that money.

EXAMPLE 6

In-Class Example 6

Aidan borrows $11,000 at $4\frac{3}{4}$% interest for 4 years from his credit union to buy a new car. Determine the total amount of money he will owe.

Answer: $13,090

Omar borrows $12,000 at $4\frac{3}{4}$% interest for 5 years from his credit union to buy a car. Determine the total amount of money he will owe.

Solution

First, find the amount of interest Omar will owe.

Change $4\frac{3}{4}$% to a decimal: $4\frac{3}{4}$% = 4.75% = 0.0475

Use $I = P \cdot R \cdot T$.

$$P = \$12,000 \qquad R = 0.0475 \qquad T = 5$$
$$I = \quad P \ \cdot \ R \ \cdot \ T$$
$$I = (12,000)(0.0475)(5) = 2850$$

The interest is $2850.

Add $2850 to the amount Omar borrowed to determine the total amount of money he will owe.

$$\text{Total amount owed} = \text{Amount borrowed} + \text{Amount of interest}$$
$$= \qquad \$12,000 \qquad + \qquad \$2850$$
$$= \$14,850$$

Omar will owe $14,850.

[YOU TRY 6]

Maria borrows $14,000 at $5\frac{1}{4}$% interest for 6 years for a new car. Determine the total amount of money she will owe.

ANSWERS TO [YOU TRY] **EXERCISES**

1) $70   2) $225   3) a) $\frac{11}{12}$ yr   b) $\frac{10}{13}$ yr   4) $11.25   5) $6578   6) $18,410

Using Technology

We can use a calculator to quickly calculate I where $I = (960)(0.065)\left(\dfrac{1}{4}\right)$. To calculate $(960)(0.065)\left(\dfrac{1}{4}\right)$, we enter $\boxed{9}\,\boxed{6}\,\boxed{0}\,\boxed{\times}\,\boxed{.}\,\boxed{0}\,\boxed{6}\,\boxed{5}\,\boxed{\div}\,\boxed{4}\,\boxed{=}$ into the calculator. The display will likely show 15.6 for the result. Since we are dealing with money, we will round to the nearest hundredth and write our final answer as $15.60 for the value of I.

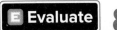
*Additional answers can be found in the Answers to Exercises appendix.

Objective 1: Compute Simple Interest

Solve each problem.

1) Marshall borrows $1600 for 1 year at an interest rate of 6%. Find the interest. $96

2) Donnell borrows $900 for 1 year at an interest rate of 5%. Find the interest. $45

3) Bret borrows $1400 for 2 years at an interest rate of 4%. Find the interest. $112

4) Carrie borrows $800 for 2 years at an interest rate of 8%. Find the interest. $128

5) Marlene borrowed $1500 at a high interest rate of 18%. Find the amount of interest after 1 year. $270

6) Anming borrowed $2500 at a high interest rate of 16%. Find the amount of interest after 1 year. $400

7) If Gustavo borrowed $1580 from a lender who charges 4.25% interest, how much interest does Gustavo owe after 4 years? $268.60

8) If a person borrows $1750 from a lender who charges 3.75% interest, how much interest does the person owe after 4 years? $262.50

9) Zachary deposits $6000 into an account earning 4% interest for $3\frac{1}{2}$ years. How much interest will he earn?
$840

10) Kashif deposits $3000 into an account earning 6% interest for $2\frac{1}{4}$ years. How much interest will he earn?
$405

Write each time in terms of years.

11) 7 months $\frac{7}{12}$ yr

12) 1 month $\frac{1}{12}$ yr

13) 2 months $\frac{1}{6}$ yr

14) 9 months $\frac{3}{4}$ yr

15) 8 months $\frac{2}{3}$ yr

16) 6 months $\frac{1}{2}$ yr

17) 26 weeks $\frac{1}{2}$ yr

18) 10 weeks $\frac{5}{26}$ yr

19) 39 weeks $\frac{3}{4}$ yr

20) 4 weeks $\frac{1}{13}$ yr

21) 18 months $\frac{3}{2}$ yr or 1.5 yr

22) 15 months $\frac{5}{4}$ yr or 1.25 yr

23) 28 months $\frac{7}{3}$ yr

24) 22 months $\frac{11}{6}$ yr

25) 65 weeks $\frac{5}{4}$ yr or 1.25 yr

26) 78 weeks $\frac{3}{2}$ yr or 1.5 yr

27) Noor borrows $6000 for 10 months at 4% interest. How much interest will she owe? $200

28) Raymond borrows $2000 for 3 months at a 5% interest rate. How much interest will he owe? $25

29) How much interest will Gentry owe if he borrows $1040 for 10 weeks at a 2.5% interest rate? $5

30) How much interest will Dobrila owe if she borrows $2600 for 30 weeks at a 3.5% interest rate? $52.50

31) If Tyler borrowed $1950 for 40 weeks at $5\frac{3}{4}$% interest, how much interest did he owe? $86.25

32) If Caroline borrowed $1200 for 13 weeks at a $4\frac{1}{4}$% interest rate, how much interest will she owe? $12.75

33) If Yasmeen borrows $15,000 for 48 months at $3\frac{1}{2}$% interest, how much interest will she owe? $2100

34) If Aleksos borrows $18,000 for 60 months at a $5\frac{1}{2}$% interest rate, how much interest will he owe? $4950

Objective 2: Compute the Original Amount Plus Interest

Solve each simple interest problem.

35) A bank loaned Baharah $1500 at an interest rate of 8%. If she wants to pay back the loan in 6 months, how much does Baharah pay back to the bank including interest? $1560

36) Wade took out an emergency student loan for $900 at an interest rate of 4.5%. If Wade wants to pay back the loan in 3 months, how much does he pay back to the lender, including interest? $910.13

37) A bank loaned Roger $2000 at an interest rate of 6.5%. If he wants to pay back the loan in 15 months, how much does he pay back to the bank, including interest? $2162.50

38) Sonia took out a personal loan for $700 at an interest rate of 5.5%. If Sonia wants to pay back the loan in 18 months, how much does she pay back to the lender, including interest? $757.75

39) Rene puts $3000 into a savings account at a 4% interest rate. How much is in the account after two years? $3240

40) Sukhon decides to invest $5000 in an account that pays 3.5% interest. If she does not withdraw any money, how much is in the account after 5 years?
$5875

41) Tanya borrows $14,000 at $5\frac{3}{4}$% interest for 3 years for home improvements. Determine the total amount of money she will owe. $16,415

42) David borrows $2500 to pay for a new engine for his car. How much does he owe if he plans to pay the loan back in 2 years at an interest rate of $6\frac{1}{4}\%$?
$2812.50

43) A bank loaned Tessa $4500 at an interest rate of $3\frac{3}{4}\%$. If her payment plan is over 3 years, how much does she owe? $5006.25

44) Cleveland borrowed $1500 from a lender charging $5\frac{1}{4}\%$ interest. How much does Cleveland owe if he plans to pay the loan back in 2 years? $1657.50

45) If Ryan takes out a loan for $5200 and plans to pay it back in 15 weeks, how much does he owe if the interest rate is $4\frac{3}{4}\%$? $5271.25

46) If Nicoleta borrows $2600 from a lender charging $5\frac{3}{4}\%$ interest, how much does she owe if she plans to pay back the loan in 20 weeks? $2657.50

47) Naoto borrows money for some unexpected car repairs. He will take out an emergency loan for $624 at $6\frac{1}{4}\%$ interest and plans to pay off the loan in 10 weeks. How much will he owe? $631.50

48) Jaabir needs a new refrigerator for his home. He finds one he likes for $780. If he borrows the amount at 7% interest, how much does Jaabir owe if he plans to pay off the loan in 25 weeks? $806.25

49) Fredericka is going to put a $2000 down payment on a new car costing $14,000. If the finance company charges 4.5% interest, how much does Fredericka owe, and what is her monthly payment if she chooses one of the following three payment plans?

a) a 3-yr loan
$13,620; $378.33

b) a 4-yr loan
$14,160; $295.00

c) a 5-yr loan $14,700; $245.00

d) How much does Fredericka save if she pays off the loan in 3 years instead of 5 years? $1080

50) Jeremy wants to buy a new truck costing $24,000 and makes a $4000 down payment. If the finance company charges 3.5% interest, how much does Jeremy owe, and what is his monthly payment if he chooses one of the following three payment plans?

a) a 3-yr loan $22,100; $613.89

b) a 4-yr loan $22,800; $475.00

c) a 5-yr loan $23,500; $391.67

d) How much does Jeremy save if he pays off the loan in 3 years instead of 5 years? $1400

51) Paavo takes out a home improvement loan for $30,000 at an interest rate of 5.5%. How much does he owe, and what is his monthly payment if he chooses one of the following three payment plans?

a) A 5-yr loan $38,250; $637.50

b) A 6-yr loan $39,900; $554.17

c) A 7-yr loan $41,550; $494.64

d) How much does Paavo save if he pays off the loan in 5 years instead of 7 years? $3300.00

52) Clara needs to take out a student loan for $20,000 at an interest rate of 4.5%. Once she graduates, how much does Clara owe, and what is her monthly payment if she chooses one of the following three payment plans?

a) A 4-yr loan $23,600; $491.67

b) A 5-yr loan $24,500; $408.33

c) A 6-yr loan $25,400; $352.78

d) How much does Clara save if she pays off the loan in 4 years instead of 6 years? $1800

R Rethink

R1) How will you think differently about the way you borrow money? (Think about your student loans or credit cards.)

R2) How will you think differently about the way you save money? (Think about your savings account.)

8.8 Compound Interest

What are your objectives for Section 8.8?	How can you accomplish each objective?
1 Understand Compound Interest	• Know the definitions of *compound interest* and *compounded annually.* • Understand the process of finding compound interest using $I = P \cdot R \cdot T$. • Complete the given example on your own. • Complete You Try 1.
2 Use a Table to Evaluate $A = P(1 + R)^T$	• Follow the explanation to understand how the formula for **Interest Compounded Annually** is derived. • Learn the formula for computing **Interest Compounded Annually,** and be able to use the table provided. • Complete the given examples on your own. • Complete You Trys 2 and 3.
3 Use a Calculator to Evaluate $A = P(1 + R)^T$	• Enter the interest rate as a decimal in your calculator. • Complete the given example on your own. • Complete You Try 4.
4 Compute Other Compound Amounts	• Learn the formula for computing **Compound Interest.** • Complete the given example on your own. • Complete You Try 5.

W Work   Read the explanations, follow the examples, take notes, and complete the You Trys.

1 Understand Compound Interest

In the previous section, we learned that simple interest is computed only on the original principal. In this section, we will learn about another type of interest: *compound interest.*

> **Definition**
>
> **Compound interest** is interest that is paid on the original principal *plus* the interest that has already been paid.

Compound interest is computed by repeatedly applying the simple interest formula, $I = P \cdot R \cdot T$. For example, interest may be computed at the end of each year that the money is in an account so that the principal is different each year. In this case, we say that interest is **compounded annually.** Let's look at an example that compares simple interest and compound interest.

EXAMPLE 1

Maya deposits $1000 into an account for 3 years at 4% interest.

a) Determine the amount of interest if she earns *simple interest* for 3 years. Then, find the total amount in her account after 3 years.

b) Determine the amount of interest she earns if the interest is *compounded annually* for 3 years. That is, determine the total amount of interest Maya earns after 3 years if the interest is computed and added to her account at the end of each year. Then, find the total amount in her account after 3 years.

c) Will the amount of money in her account after 3 years be different if the interest is computed differently? Explain your answer.

Solution

a) If Maya deposits $1000 for 3 years at 4% into a *simple interest* account, use $I = P \cdot R \cdot T$ *once* to find the amount of interest she will earn.

$$P = 1000 \qquad R = 4\% = 0.04 \qquad T = 3$$
$$I = P \cdot R \cdot T$$
$$I = (1000)(0.04)(3) \qquad \text{Substitute the values.}$$
$$I = 120 \qquad \text{Multiply.}$$

Maya will earn $120 in interest. After 3 years, her account balance will be $1000 + $120 = $1120.

b) If the interest is *compounded annually* for 3 years, then at the end of each year we apply the simple interest formula to determine how much interest was earned that year.

In Year 1, the principal is $1000. Compute the interest earned *this* year using the simple interest formula.

	Principal	Interest Earned Use $I = P \cdot R \cdot T$	Total Amount in Account at the End of Year 1
Year 1	$1000	$I = (\$1000)(0.04)(1) = \$40$	$1000 + $40 = $1040

Year 2 has a *new principal* of $1040. We compute the interest for one year on this amount using the simple interest formula.

	Principal	Interest Earned Use $I = P \cdot R \cdot T$	Total Amount in Account at the End of Year 2
Year 2	$1040	$I = (\$1040)(0.04)(1) = \$41.60$	$1040 + $41.60 = $1081.60

Year 3 has a *new principal* of $1081.60. We compute the interest for one year on this amount using the simple interest formula.

	Principal	Interest Earned Use $I = P \cdot R \cdot T$	Total Amount in Account at the End of Year 3
Year 3	$1081.60	$I = (\$1081.60)(0.04)(1) = \$43.26$	$1081.60 + $43.26 = $1124.86

After 3 years, Maya will have a total of $1124.86 in her account. The total amount of interest she will earn is $40 + $41.60 + $43.26 = $124.86. We can also determine the amount of interest this way: $1124.86 − $1000 = $124.86.

 Hint

How long would it take to find compound interest over 20 years using this process?

 Note

This example shows how the interest is computed on a different principal each year. This is why it is called *compound* interest.

c) If interest is compounded annually for 3 years, Maya will earn $4.86 more than if she earned simple interest: $1124.86 − $1120 = $4.86.

[YOU TRY 1]

Tara deposits $2000 into an account for 3 years at 6% interest.

a) Determine the amount of interest if she earns *simple interest* for 3 years. Then, find the total amount in her account after 3 years.

b) Determine the amount of interest she earns if the interest is *compounded annually* for 3 years. Then, find the total amount in her account after 3 years.

c) Will the amount of money in her account after 3 years be different if the interest is computed differently? Explain your answer.

2 Use a Table to Evaluate $A = P(1 + R)^T$

In Example 1b), we found the total amount in the compound interest account after 3 years by using the simple interest formula three times. It is also true that the amount of money in the account at the end of each year is 100% + 4% = 104% of the principal. So, we can think of the compound interest problem in Example 1b) like this:

At the end of Year 1: Amount in account = ($1000)(1.04) = $1040

<u>1 factor of 1.04</u>

At the end of Year 2: Amount in account = ($1000)(1.04)(1.04) = ($1000)(1.04)² = $1081.60

<u>2 factors of 1.04</u>

At the end of Year 3: Amount in account = ($1000)(1.04)(1.04)(1.04) = ($1000)(1.04)³ = $1124.86

<u>3 factors of 1.04</u>

This is the same as the result in Example 1b. Do you notice a pattern in the calculations we just performed?

Amount in the account at the end of Year 1 = ($1000)(1.04)¹

Amount in the account at the end of Year 2 = ($1000)(1.04)²

Amount in the account at the end of Year 3 = ($1000)(1.04)³

This pattern suggests the following formula.

Formula Interest Compounded Annually

Let A = the total amount in an account after T years. Use this formula to find the value of A when interest is compounded annually:

$$A = P(1 + R)^T$$

P = the principal and R = the interest rate in decimal form.

We can find A using either an annual compound interest table or a calculator. Let's use the table first. When we use a table to find A in $A = P(1 + R)^T$, we look up the value of the *compound interest factor*. The **compound interest factor** is the value of $(1 + R)^T$.

Note

When we use the table, we leave the interest rate, R, as a percent.

EXAMPLE 2

In-Class Example 2

Use Example 2.

Use the annual compound interest table to solve this problem.

Laura invests $9000 for 4 years at 6.5% compounded annually.

a) How much will she have in her account after 4 years?

b) How much interest will Laura earn?

Solution

a) Use the formula $A = P(1 + R)^T$. We must find A when

$$P = 9000 \qquad R = 6.5\% \qquad T = 4$$

Use the table in Appendix A.6 to find the value of $(1 + R)^T$ when $R = 6.5\%$ and $T = 4$. Here are a few lines from the table:

Interest Compounded Annually Value of $(1 + R)^T$

Years	4%	4.5%	5%	5.5%	6%	6.5%
1	1.04	1.045	1.05	1.055	1.06	1.065
2	1.0816	1.0920	1.1025	1.1130	1.1236	1.1342
3	1.1249	1.1412	1.1576	1.1742	1.1910	1.2079
4	1.1699	1.1925	1.2155	1.2388	1.2625	1.2865
5	1.2167	1.2462	1.2763	1.3070	1.3382	1.3701

W Hint

Using this table will make the computation much easier.

Find the interest rate of 6.5% at the top of the table. Go down that column until you get to the row for Year 4. The number in that box is 1.2865. (Use *all* of the digits; do not round this number!) This is the compound interest factor. In the compound interest formula, $A = P(1 + R)^T$, replace $(1 + R)^T$ with 1.2865.

$$A = P(1 + R)^T$$
$$A = 9000(1.2865) \qquad \text{$P = 9000$ and $(1 + R)^T = 1.2865$}$$
$$A = 11{,}578.50 \qquad \text{Multiply.}$$

After 4 years, Laura will have $11,578.50 in her account.

b) To determine the amount of interest Laura will earn, subtract the amount she invested from the amount in the account after 4 years.

$$\text{Amount of interest} = \$11{,}578.50 - \$9000 = \$2578.50$$

Laura will earn $2578.50 in interest.

[YOU TRY 2] Use the annual compound interest table to solve this problem.

Ahmad invests $6400 for 5 years at 4.5% interest compounded annually.

a) How much will he have in his account after 4 years?

b) How much interest will Ahmad earn?

EXAMPLE 3

In-Class Example 3

Use the annual compound interest table to solve this problem.

Jeff deposits $14,500 into an account for 8 years at 6% interest compounded annually. How much money will be in his account after this time? How much interest will he earn?

Answer:
$23,110.10; $8610.10

Use the annual compound interest table to solve this problem.

Ignacio deposits $12,500 into an account for 10 years at 7% interest compounded annually. How much money will be in his account after this time? How much interest will he earn?

Solution

Use the table in Appendix A.6 to find the value of $(1 + R)^T$ when $R = 7\%$ and $T = 10$.

Find the interest rate of 7% at the top of the table. Go down that column until you get to the row for Year 10. The number in that box is 1.9672. (Remember, do not round this number!) This is the compound interest factor. In the compound interest formula $A = P(1 + R)^T$, replace $(1 + R)^T$ with 1.9672.

$$A = P(1 + R)^T$$
$$A = 12{,}500(1.9672) \qquad P = 12{,}500 \text{ and } (1 + R)^T = 1.9672$$
$$A = 24{,}590 \qquad \text{Multiply.}$$

After 10 years, Ignacio will have $24,590 in his account. Find the amount of interest he will earn.

$$\text{Amount of interest} = \$24{,}590 - \$12{,}500 = \$12{,}090$$

He will earn $12,090 in interest.

[YOU TRY 3] Use the annual compound interest table to solve this problem.

Latoya deposits $16,200 into an account for 9 years at 8% interest compounded annually. How much will be in her account after this time? How much interest will she earn?

3 Use a Calculator to Evaluate $A = P(1 + R)^T$

If you are allowed to use a calculator in this class, then you can use it to find A in the formula $A = P(1 + R)^T$.

Note

When you use a calculator to find A in the formula $A = P(1 + R)^T$, you must write the interest rate, R, in decimal form.

EXAMPLE 4

Use a calculator to solve this problem.

Steve invests $6000 at 3% interest compounded annually for 5 years. Find the amount of money in his account after 5 years.

Solution

Use $A = P(1 + R)^T$. We want to find A, the total amount after 5 years.

$$P = 6000 \qquad R = 3\% = 0.03 \qquad T = 5$$

$A = P(1 + R)^T$

$A = 6000(1 + 0.03)^5$ $P = 6000$, $R = 0.03$, and $T = 5$

$A = 6000(1.03)^5$ Add inside the parentheses.

$A = \$6955.64$ Evaluate on a calculator. Round to the nearest cent.

After 5 years, the account will contain $6955.64.

Using Technology

To calculate A, where $A = 6000(1.03)^5$, using a calculator, we will need to use the exponent function key. In most cases, the exponent function key is labeled $\boxed{y^x}$ or $\boxed{\wedge}$. To calculate $6000(1.03)^5$ following the order of operations, we enter $\boxed{1}\boxed{.}\boxed{0}$ $\boxed{3}\boxed{y^x}\boxed{5}\boxed{=}\boxed{\times}\boxed{6}\boxed{0}\boxed{0}\boxed{0}\boxed{=}$ into the calculator. The display will likely show 6955.64444 for the result. Because we are dealing with money, we will round to the nearest hundredth and write our final answer as $6955.64 for the value of A.

    Note: If your calculator does not have an exponent key, you may be able to perform the operation by entering the following into your calculator:

$\boxed{1}\boxed{.}\boxed{0}\boxed{3}\boxed{\times}\boxed{=}\boxed{=}\boxed{=}\boxed{=}\boxed{\times}\boxed{6}\boxed{0}\boxed{0}\boxed{0}\boxed{=}$

[YOU TRY 4] Use a calculator to solve this problem.

Dimos invests $10,000 at 5% interest compounded annually for 7 years. Find the amount of money in the account after this time.

4 Compute Other Compound Amounts

Interest can be compounded more often than every year. It can be compounded

Semiannually	Quarterly	Monthly	Weekly	Daily
2 times per year	**4** times per year	**12** times per year	**52** times per year	**365** times per year (some banks use 360)

We can use a single formula to find the amount in an account when interest is compounded in these ways.

Formula Compound Interest

Let A = the total amount in an account after T years. Use this formula to find the value of A when interest is compounded more than one time per year:

$$A = P\left(1 + \frac{R}{n}\right)^{n \cdot T}$$

P = the principal, R = the interest rate in decimal form, and n = the number of times interest is compounded each year.

EXAMPLE 5

In-Class Example 5

Jenny invests $5600 at $4\frac{1}{2}$% interest for 3 years compounded quarterly.
a) Find the amount of money in her account after 3 years.
b) How much interest did Jenny earn?

Answer: a) $6404.58
b) $804.58

Divya invests $8300 at $5\frac{1}{2}$% interest for 6 years compounded quarterly.

a) Find the amount of money in her account after 6 years.

b) How much interest did Divya earn?

Solution

a) Use $A = P\left(1 + \frac{R}{n}\right)^{n \cdot T}$. We have to find A, the total amount in Divya's account after 6 years. Because interest is **compounded quarterly,** or **4** times per year, $n = 4$. Identify all the values that we will use in the formula, substitute them into the formula, and use a calculator to evaluate.

$$P = 6000 \qquad R = 5\frac{1}{2}\% = 5.5\% = 0.055 \qquad T = 6 \qquad n = 4$$

Compounded quarterly means 4 times per year.

$$A = P\left(1 + \frac{R}{n}\right)^{n \cdot T}$$

$$A = 8300\left(1 + \frac{0.055}{4}\right)^{4 \cdot 6} \qquad \text{Substitute the values.}$$

$$A = 8300(1 + 0.01375)^{24} \qquad \text{Divide } \frac{0.055}{4} \text{ and multiply } 4 \cdot 6.$$

$$A = 8300(1.01375)^{24} \qquad \text{Add inside the parentheses.}$$

$$A = 11{,}519.11 \qquad \text{Evaluate.}$$

After 6 years, the account will contain $11,519.11.

b) Interest earned = $11,519.11 − $8300 = $3219.11

Using Technology

To calculate A, where $A = 8300(1.01375)^{24}$, using a calculator, we will need to use the exponent function key. In most cases, the exponent function key is labeled $\boxed{y^x}$ or $\boxed{\wedge}$. To calculate $8300(1.01375)^{24}$ following the order of operations, we enter $\boxed{1}\boxed{.}\boxed{0}\boxed{1}\boxed{3}\boxed{7}\boxed{5}\boxed{y^x}\boxed{2}\boxed{4}\boxed{=}\boxed{\times}\boxed{8}\boxed{3}\boxed{0}\boxed{0}\boxed{=}$. The display will likely show 11519.10947 for the result. Because we are dealing with money, we will round to the nearest hundredth and write our final answer as $11,519.11 for the value of A.

[YOU TRY 5]

Matt invests $7800 at $6\frac{1}{2}\%$ interest for 5 years compounded monthly. Find the amount of money in the account after 5 years, and determine the amount of interest Matt earned.

ANSWERS TO [YOU TRY] EXERCISES

1) a) $360; $2360   b) $382.03; $2382.03   c) If the interest is compounded yearly, Tara will have $22.03 more in her account than if interest were computed as simple interest.
2) a) $7975.68   b) $1575.68   3) $32,383.80; $16,183.80   4) $14,071
5) total amount: $10,785.98; amount of interest: $2985.98

E Evaluate   **8.8** Exercises   Do the exercises, and check your work.

*Additional answers can be found in the Answers to Exercises appendix.

Objective 1: Understand Compound Interest

Answer the following questions.

 1) Romero deposits $1000 into an account for 2 years at 5% interest.

  a) Determine the amount of interest if he earns *simple interest* for 2 years. Then, find the total amount in his account after 2 years.
interest: $100; total: $1,100

  b) Determine the amount of interest he earns if the interest is *compounded annually* for 2 years. Then, find the total amount in his account after 2 years.
interest: $102.50; total: $1102.50

  c) Will the amount of money in his account after 2 years be different if the interest is computed differently? Explain your answer.

2) Alnira deposits $6000 into an account for 2 years at 6% interest.

  a) Determine the amount of interest if she earns *simple interest* for 2 years. Then, find the total amount in her account after 2 years.
interest: $720; total: $6720

  b) Determine the amount of interest she earns if the interest is *compounded annually* for 2 years. Then, find the total amount in her account after 2 years.   interest: $741.60; total: $6741.60

  c) Will the amount of money in her account after 2 years be different if the interest is computed differently? Explain your answer.

3) Chau deposits $5000 into an account for 3 years at 3% interest.

  a) Determine the amount of interest if he earns *simple interest* for 3 years. Then, find the total amount in his account after 3 years.
interest: $450; total: $5450

  b) Determine the amount of interest he earns if the interest is *compounded annually* for 3 years. Then, find the total amount in his account after 3 years.
interest: $463.64; total: $5463.64

  c) Will the amount of money in his account after 3 years be different if the interest is computed differently? Explain your answer.
If interest is compounded annually, Chau will earn $13.64 more than if it is computed as simple interest.

4) Grace deposits $3000 into an account for 3 years at 4% interest.

   a) Determine the amount of interest if she earns *simple interest* for 3 years. Then, find the total amount in her account after 3 years.
interest: $360; total: $3360

   b) Determine the amount of interest she earns if the interest is *compounded annually* for 3 years. Then, find the total amount in her account after 3 years.
interest: $374.59; total: $3374.59

   c) Will the amount of money in her account after 3 years be different if the interest is computed differently? Explain your answer.

5) Athena deposits $2000 into an account for 2 years at 3% interest.

   a) Determine the amount of interest if she earns *simple interest* for 2 years. Then, find the total amount in her account after 2 years.
interest: $120; total: $2120

   b) Determine the amount of interest she earns if the interest is *compounded annually* for 2 years. Then, find the total amount in her account after 2 years.
interest: $121.80; total: $2121.80

   c) Will the amount of money in her account after 2 years be different if the interest is computed differently? Explain your answer.

6) Tyrone deposits $4000 into an account for 2 years at 4% interest.

   a) Determine the amount of interest if he earns *simple interest* for 2 years. Then, find the total amount in his account after 2 years.
interest: $320; total: $4320

   b) Determine the amount of interest he earns if the interest is *compounded annually* for 2 years. Then, find the total amount in his account after 2 years.
interest: $326.40; total: $4326.40

   c) Will the amount of money in his account after 2 years be different if the interest is computed differently? Explain your answer.

Objective 2: Use a Table to Evaluate $A = P(1 + R)^T$

Use the annual compound interest table to solve these problems.

7) Mayumie deposits $8400 into an account for 6 years at 5% interest compounded annually. How much will be in her account after this time? How much interest will she earn?   total: $11,256.84; interest: $2856.84

8) Leon deposits $7500 into an account for 8 years at 6% interest compounded annually. How much will be in his account after this time? How much interest will he earn?   total: $11,953.50; interest: $4453.50

9) Lorenzo deposits $10,000 into an account for 12 years at 8% interest compounded annually. How much will be in his account after this time? How much interest will he earn?   total: $25,182; interest: $15,182

10) Lan deposits $14,000 into an account for 11 years at 6% interest compounded annually. How much will be in her account after this time? How much interest will she earn?   total: $26,576.20; interest: $12,576.20

11) Gloriana deposits $17,500 into an account for 10 years at 5.5% interest compounded annually. How much will be in her account after this time? How much interest will she earn?   total: $29,891.75; interest: $12,391.75

12) Garth deposits $22,500 into an account for 8 years at 4.5% interest compounded annually. How much will be in his account after this time? How much interest will he earn?   total: $31,997.25; interest: $9497.25

13) Eduardo deposits $25,000 into an account for 8 years at 4.5% interest compounded annually. How much will be in his account after this time? How much interest will he earn?   total: $35,552.50; interest: $10,552.50

14) Alejandra deposits $35,000 into an account for 12 years at 4.5% interest compounded annually. How much will be in her account after this time? How much interest will she earn?   total: $59,356.50; interest: $24,356.50

Objective 3: Use a Calculator to Evaluate $A = P(1 + R)^T$

Use a calculator to solve these problems.

15) Thao invests $7000 at 4% interest compounded annually for 8 years. Find the amount of money in the account after this time. $9579.98

16) Felipe invests $12,000 at 6% interest compounded annually for 6 years. Find the amount of money in the account after this time. $17,022.23

17) Cora invests $15,500 at 4.5% interest compounded annually for 10 years. Find the amount of money in the account after this time. $24,071.03

18) Pyotr invests $16,500 at 5.5% interest compounded annually for 12 years. Find the amount of money in the account after this time. $31,369.92

19) Alison invests $11,500 at 5.25% interest compounded annually for 9 years. Find the amount of money in the account after this time, and determine how much interest she earned.
total: $18,226.23; interest: $6726.23

20) Tiana invests $13,500 at 6.25% interest compounded annually for 11 years. Find the amount of money in the account after this time, and determine how much interest she earned.   total: $26,299.78; interest: $12,799.78

21) Mike invests $22,000 at 6.75% interest compounded annually for 20 years. Find the amount of money in the account after this time, and determine how much interest he earned.   total: $81,241.95; interest: $59,241.95

22) Roger invests $31,000 at 7.25% interest compounded annually for 15 years. Find the amount of money in the account after this time, and determine the amount of interest he earned.   total: $88,577.05; interest: $57,577.05

23) Hannah borrows $5000 for 3 years at 4% interest compounded annually. Find the total amount of money she will have to repay and the amount of interest she owes.   total: $5624.32; interest: $624.32

24) Farshad borrows $8000 for 4 years at 5% interest compounded annually. Find the total amount of money he will have to repay and the amount of interest he owes.   total: $9724.05; interest: $1724.05

Objective 4: Compute Other Compound Amounts
Use a calculator to solve these problems.

25) Herman invests $6400 at 5.5% interest for 7 years compounded quarterly. Find the amount of money in the account after 7 years, and determine the amount of interest Herman earned.
total: $9380.89; interest: $2980.89

26) Raffi invests $7200 at 4.5% interest for 9 years compounded quarterly. Find the amount of money in the account after 9 years, and determine the amount of interest he earned.   total: $10,770.60; interest: $3570.60

27) Peggy invests $8400 at $6\frac{1}{2}$% interest for 10 years compounded semiannually. Find the amount of money in the account after 10 years, and determine the amount of interest she earned.
total: $15,925.04; interest: $7525.04

28) Jesse invests $5900 at $7\frac{1}{2}$% interest for 12 years compounded semiannually. Find the amount of money in the account after 12 years, and determine the amount of interest Jesse earned.
total: $14,274.69; interest: $8374.69

29) Alejandro invests $12,000 at 5.75% interest for 6 years compounded monthly. Find the amount of money in the account after 6 years, and determine the amount of interest Alejandro earned.
total: $16,929.92; interest: $4929.92

30) Vivian invests $8200 at 6.75% interest for 8 years compounded monthly. Find the amount of money in the account after 5 years, and determine the amount of interest she earned.
total: $14,049.98; interest: $5849.98

31) Lauren invests $14,000 at 3% interest for 5 years compounded weekly. Find the amount of money in the account after 5 years, and determine the amount of interest Lauren earned.   total: $16,264.98; interest: $2264.98

32) Olaf invests $5700 at 4% interest for 6 years compounded weekly. Find the amount of money in the account after 6 years, and determine the amount of interest he earned.   total: $7245.45; interest: $1545.45

33) Parwana deposits $21,450 into a savings account that pays $4\frac{3}{4}$% interest compounded daily. Find the amount of money in the account after 7 years, and determine the amount of interest she will earn.
total: $29,910.30; interest: $8460.30

34) Joseph and Kayla sell their home and make a profit of $28,750. They decide to invest it in a savings account that pays $4\frac{1}{4}$% interest compounded monthly. Find the amount of money in the account after 4 years, and determine the amount of interest Joseph and Kayla will earn.
total: $34,067.28; interest: $5317.28

35) Samantha finds a high-interest savings account at a local bank paying $7\frac{1}{4}$% interest compounded weekly. The bank requires that the money be deposited for 10 years to earn the high interest rate. If Samantha deposits $31,540 into the account, find the amount of money in the account after 10 years, and determine the amount of interest Samantha earned.   total: $65,088.74; interest: $33,548.74

36) Christian borrowed $37,650 from the family fortune to open a small business. He plans to repay the loan at the end of 4 years at $6\frac{3}{4}$% interest compounded monthly. Find the total amount Christian must repay. How much interest does he pay?
total: $49,282.86; interest: $11,632.86

37) Bob and Irma deposit their life savings of $275,000 into a savings account that pays 4.5% interest compounded monthly. If they leave the money in the account for 30 years, how much money will they have in the account? How much interest will they earn?   total: $1,058,116.96; interest: $783,116.96

38) Jennifer received an inheritance in the amount of $145,000. She decides to place it all into a savings account that pays 4.75% interest compounded monthly. If she leaves the money in the account for 15 years, how much money will she have in the account? How much interest will she earn?
total: $295,251.43; interest: $150,251.43

39) Alex finances $16,500 to buy a work truck. If the lender provides him with a 5-year loan at 3.75% interest compounded monthly, how much does Alex owe? Also find the amount of interest he will pay the lender.   owe: $19,896.98; interest: $3396.98

40) Dagmar borrows $19,800 from her bank to buy a new car. If she gets a 6-year loan at 4.75% interest compounded monthly, how much does Dagmar owe? How much interest will she pay the bank?
owe: $26,314.48; interest: $6514.48

R Rethink

R1) If you could memorize only one formula for compound interest, which one would you memorize and why?

R2) Now that you have completed these exercises, think about how you would like the interest to be computed if you were to invest money.

Group Activity – Percents

Students should work in groups of two or three to complete this activity.

At Ernie's Electronics, employees earn a base salary of $500 per week, plus a 5% commission rate on all sales. Suppose you work at Ernie's Electronics. Answer the following questions about your earnings.

1) Last week, you sold $5800 worth of merchandise. How much did you earn in commission last week (try to calculate this mentally)?

2) How much was your *gross pay* for last week? Hint: *Gross pay* refers to your weekly pay before taxes are deducted.

3) Approximately 7% of your weekly pay is deducted for government taxes. What was your *net pay* for last week? Hint: *Net pay* refers to the amount of money that you receive after taxes are deducted. This is also known as your *take-home pay*.

4) Last week, you bought an iPod, which cost $245.99. The sales tax rate was 6.6%. What was the total cost of the iPod (round to the nearest cent)?

5) What percentage of last week's *net pay* was the total cost of the iPod (round to the nearest tenth of a percent)?

6) After working at Ernie's Electronics for several months, you were able to save $1500. You want to put your savings into an interest-bearing account. Your bank has three options: **Option A:** $3\frac{1}{4}\%$ interest rate, simple interest; **Option B:** 3.15% interest rate, compounded annually; **Option C:** 3% interest rate, compounded monthly. Predict which account will generate the greatest account balance after 5 years. Then, calculate the total account balance after 5 years for each option. Was your prediction correct?

Group Activity Answers

1) $290   2) $790   3) $734.70   4) $262.23   5) 35.7%
6) Student predictions will vary. Option A: $1743.75; Option B: $1751.61; Option C: $1742.43

em POWER me What's Your Level of Self-Consciousness?

One of the main reasons people feel nervous when speaking in public is their self-consciousness. To explore your own level of self-consciousness, choose the phrase from the following rating scale that is closest to your feelings about each statement below.

0 = Extremely uncharacteristic
1 = Generally uncharacteristic
2 = Equally characteristic and uncharacteristic
3 = Generally characteristic
4 = Extremely characteristic

1. I'm concerned about my style of doing things. _____

2. I'm concerned about the way I present myself. _____

3. I'm self-conscious about the way I look. _____

4. I usually worry about making a good impression. _____

5. One of the last things I do before I leave the house is look in the mirror. _____

6. I'm concerned about what other people think of me. _____

7. I'm usually aware of my appearance. _____

Scoring: Add up the numbers to get a total score. If you score below 16, you are unusually low in self-consciousness, and public speaking should be less of a burden for you than it is for most other people. If you score between 16 and 22, you have a medium level of self-consciousness. Public speaking is not necessarily easy for you, but it does not provoke too many fears. If you score above 22, your level of self-consciousness is relatively high. Public speaking is likely to be particularly challenging for you.

_____

Scale items are adapted from A. Fenigstein, A. Scheier, and A. Buss. (1975). Public and private self-consciousness, assessment and theory. *Journal of Consulting and Clinical Psychology, 43,* Table 1, p. 324.

Chapter 8:   Summary

Definition/Procedure	Example

8.1 Introduction to Percent

Percent means *out of 100*. **(p. 497)**

Explain the meaning of the statement. *In 2008, approximately 23% of men in the United States smoked cigarettes.* (www.americanheart.org)

23% means 23 *out of* 100, so the statement means that approximately 23 out of 100 men in the United States smoked cigarettes in 2008.

Because percent means *out of 100,* we can write a percent as a fraction, and because fractions can be written as decimals, we can also write percents as decimals. **(p. 498)**

Write 57% as a fraction and then as a decimal.

Since 57% means 57 out of 100, we write

$$57\% = \frac{57}{100} = 0.57$$

How to Change a Percent to a Decimal

1) Remove the percent symbol.

2) Move the decimal point two places to the left. **(p. 499)**

Write 21% as a decimal.

$21\% = 21.\%$ Put the decimal point at the end of the number.

$= 0.21$ Remove the percent symbol, and move the decimal point two places to the left.

How to Change a Decimal to a Percent

1) Move the decimal point two places to the right.

2) Put the percent symbol at the end of the number. **(p. 500)**

Write 0.43 as a percent.

$0.43 = 43.$ Move the decimal point two places to the right.

$= 43\%$ Put the % symbol at the end of the number. Remove the decimal point from the end of the number.

8.2 Percents and Fractions

When we change a percent to a fraction, we usually write it in lowest terms. **(p. 503)**

Write 40% as a fraction in lowest terms.

$$40\% = \frac{40}{100}$$

$$= \frac{40 \div 20}{100 \div 20} = \frac{2}{5}$$ Divide numerator and denominator by 20.

Write Percents Containing Decimals or Fractions as Fractions in Lowest Terms

One method for changing a percent to a fraction is to first change the percent to a decimal, and then change the decimal to a fraction. **(p. 504)**

Write 22.5% as a fraction in lowest terms by first writing 22.5% as a decimal.

First, change 22.5% to a decimal: $22.5\% = 0.225$

Next, change the decimal to a fraction and simplify.

$$0.225 = \frac{225}{1000} = \frac{225 \div 25}{1000 \div 25} = \frac{9}{40}$$

Therefore, $22.5\% = \frac{9}{40}$.

Definition/Procedure	Example
Another way to change a percent to a fraction in lowest terms is to first write it as a fraction with a denominator of 100. **(p. 505)**	Write 22.5% as a fraction in lowest terms by first writing it as a fraction with a denominator of 100. $$22.5\% = \frac{22.5}{100}$$ The next step is to eliminate the decimal from the fraction. $$\frac{22.5}{100} \cdot \frac{10}{10} = \frac{225}{1000}$$ Now, simplify $\frac{225}{1000}$: $\quad \frac{225}{1000} = \frac{225 \div 25}{1000 \div 25} = \frac{9}{40}$ Therefore, $22.5\% = \frac{9}{40}$.

Write Fractions as Percents
We can use several different methods to write a fraction as a percent.

1) Since percent means *out of 100,* one way is to start by writing the given fraction as a fraction with a denominator of 100. **(p. 506)**

1) Write $\frac{3}{5}$ as a percent by first writing it as a fraction with a denominator of 100.

Multiply the fraction by $\frac{20}{20}$.

$$\frac{3}{5} \cdot \frac{20}{20} = \frac{60}{100} = 60\% \qquad \text{So, } \frac{3}{5} = 60\%.$$

2) We can also change a fraction to a percent using long division. **(p. 507)**

2) Write $\frac{1}{8}$ as a percent using long division.

$$8\overline{)1.000}^{\,0.125} \quad \text{Therefore, } \frac{1}{8} = 0.125 = 12.5\%.$$

3) A third way to write a fraction as a percent is to use a proportion. **(p. 507)**

3) Use a proportion to change $\frac{3}{25}$ to a percent.

We want to write $\frac{3}{25}$ with a denominator of 100. Set up the proportion $\frac{3}{25} = \frac{x}{100}$, where x is the percent, and solve for x.

$$\frac{3}{25} \diagdown\mkern-18mu\diagup \frac{x}{100} \qquad \begin{array}{l} 25 \cdot x = 25x \\[4pt] 3 \cdot 100 = 300 \end{array}$$

$$25x = 300$$

$$\frac{25x}{25} = \frac{300}{25} \qquad \text{Divide each side by 25.}$$

$$\frac{\overset{1}{\cancel{25}}x}{\underset{1}{\cancel{25}}} = 12 \qquad \text{Divide out the common factor.}$$

$$x = 12 \qquad \text{Simplify.}$$

Therefore, $\frac{3}{25} = \frac{12}{100}$. So, $\frac{3}{25} = 12\%$.

Definition/Procedure	Example

8.3 Compute Basic Percents Mentally

How to Find 10% of a Number
To find 10% of a number, locate the decimal point in the number and move it one place to the left. **(p. 513)**

Find 10% of 875.

To find 10% of 875, locate the decimal point in 875 and move it one place to the left. 10% of 875. = 87.5

How to Find Percents That Are Multiples of 10
If we know the value of 10% of a number,

1) find 20% of the number by multiplying the value by 2

2) find 30% of the number by multiplying the value by 3

3) find 40% of the number by multiplying the value by 4

and so on. **(p. 514)**

Find 30% of 70.

To find 30% of 70, first find 10% of 70. Then, multiply the result by 3.

$$10\% \text{ of } 70 = 7$$
$$30\% \text{ of } 70 = 3 \cdot 7 = 21$$

How to Find 5% of a Number
Find the value of 10% of a number, and then multiply that value by $\frac{1}{2}$. **(p. 515)**

Find 5% of 64.

First, find 10% of 64. Then, find 5% of 64 by finding $\frac{1}{2}$ of that result.

$$10\% \text{ of } 64 = 6.4$$
$$5\% \text{ of } 64 = \frac{1}{2} \cdot 6.4 = 3.2$$

How to Find Percents That Are Multiples of Five, but Not Multiples of 10

1) Split the percentage into the greatest multiple of 10% and the remaining 5%, and find those percentages.

2) Add the results. **(p. 516)**

Find 25% of 240.

To find 25% of 240, find 20% of 240 and 5% of 240 and then add the results.

10% of 240 = 24 so 20% of 240 = 48 and 5% of 240 = 12
25% of 240 = 20% of 240 + 5% of 240
$$= \quad 48 \quad + \quad 12$$
$$= 60$$

Perform Computations with Multiples of 100%
100% *of* a number equals the number. To find 200% *of* a number, multiply the number by 2, to find 300% *of* a number, multiply the number by 3, and so on. **(p. 517)**

Find 500% of 43.

500% of 43 means $5 \cdot 43 = 215$.

Solve Applications Containing Basic Percentages

Step 1: **Read** the problem carefully, and restate it in your own words.

Step 2: **Make a plan.** Underline important words in our restatement of the problem in Step 1.

Step 3: **Solve** the problem.

Step 4: **State the answer** in a complete sentence.

Step 5: **Check** the answer. Double-check the calculations to be sure all the arithmetic is correct. **(p. 518)**

A restaurant bill at Karma is $34.00. If Deena wants to leave a 20% tip, find the amount of the tip and the total amount of money Deena will pay.

Step 1: **Read** the problem carefully, and restate it in your own words.

Deena wants to leave 20% of $34.00 as a tip. We have to find the amount of the tip and the total amount Deena will pay.

Step 2: **Make a plan.** Let's underline important words in our restatement of the problem in Step 1.

Plan: To find the amount of the tip, compute 20% of $34.00. Then, add the tip to the $34.00 to determine the total amount Deena will pay.

Definition/Procedure	Example
	Step 3: **Solve** the problem.
	First, find the amount of the tip, 20% *of* $34.00.
	20% of $34.00 = 2 · $3.40 = $6.80 The tip is $6.80.
	Now, find the total amount Deena will pay.
	Total paid = Amount of the bill + Amount of the tip
	= $34.00 + $6.80
	= $40.80
	Step 4: **State the answer** in a complete sentence.
	The amount of the tip is $6.80, and the total amount Deena will pay is $40.80.
	Step 5: **Check** the answer. Double-check the calculations to be sure all the arithmetic is correct.
	20% of $34.00 = $6.80
	Total amount of bill = $34.00 + $6.80 = $40.80 ✓
	The answer is correct.

8.4 Use an Equation to Solve Percent Problems

Find the Percent of a Number Using Multiplication by first changing the percent to a decimal and then multiplying. **(p. 523)**	Find 33% of 55.
	The *of* in 33% of 55 means multiply. Change 33% to a decimal, then multiply.
	33% of 55 = 0.33 · 55 = 18.15
Use an Equation to Find the Number	Use an equation to find 33% of 55.
We will first write a statement or question in English and use that to write a mathematical equation. Read the statement slowly and carefully, and think about what the words mean in terms of math. **(p. 524)**	Let's think of finding 33% of 55 as the question, "What is 33% of 55?"
	Let x = the unknown quantity, 33% of 55.
	Write the question in English, understand its meaning in terms of math, and write an equation.

English: | What | is | 33% | of | 55? |
Meaning: | What | equals | 33% | times | 55? |

$$\downarrow \qquad \downarrow \qquad \downarrow \qquad \downarrow \qquad \downarrow$$

Equation: x =   0.33   ·   55

The equation is $x = 0.33 \cdot 55$. Solve the equation.

$$x = 18.15 \qquad \text{Multiply.}$$

Therefore, 18.15 is 33% of 55.

Definition/Procedure	Example
We can also use an equation to find other quantities involving percentages. **(p. 525)**	Use an equation to solve the following problem. 4 is 20% of what number? Let x represent the unknown value. x = the number Write the question in English, understand its meaning in terms of math, and write an equation. *English:* 4 | is | 20% | of | what number? *Meaning:* 4 | equals | 20% | times | what number? *Equation:* 4 = 0.2 · x The equation is $4 = 0.2 \cdot x$. Solve it. $4 = 0.2x$ Write the equation without the multiplication symbol. $\dfrac{4}{0.2} = \dfrac{0.2x}{0.2}$ Divide both sides by 0.2 to get x by itself. $20 = x$ Perform the division. Therefore, 4 is 20% of 20. We can check the answer by finding 20% of 20: 20% of 20 = 4 ✓ The answer is correct.
Use an Equation to Find the Percentage We will first write a statement or question in English and use that to write a mathematical equation. Read the statement slowly and carefully, and think about what the words mean in terms of math. **(p. 527)**	33 is what percent of 150? What is the unknown quantity? It is a percent. Let x = the percent. Write the question in English, understand its meaning in terms of math, and write an equation. *English:* 33 | is | what percent | of | 150? *Meaning:* 33 | equals | what percent | times | 150? *Equation:* 33 = x · 150 The equation is $30 = x \cdot 150$. The commutative property says we can also write $x \cdot 150$ as $150 \cdot x$. So, we can think of the equation as $33 = 150 \cdot x$ or $33 = 150x$. Solve this equation. $33 = 150x$ $\dfrac{33}{150} = \dfrac{150x}{150}$ Divide both sides by 150 to get x by itself. $0.22 = x$ Perform the division. The final answer is not 0.22 because x represents a percent. The last step is to change 0.22 to a percent. $0.22 = 22\%$ Change 0.22 to a percent. Therefore, 33 is 22% of 150. We can check the answer using multiplication. 22% of $150 = 0.22 \cdot 150 = 33$ ✓ The answer is correct.

BE CAREFUL When you are asked to find a percent, the value that you get for x is *not* the final answer. You must change that number to a percent.

Definition/Procedure	Example

8.5 Solve Applications Involving Percents

Use an Equation to Solve an Applied Problem

Step 1: **Read** the problem carefully, and restate it in your own words.

Step 2: **Make a plan.** Underline important words in our restatement of the problem in Step 1.

Define the variable that will be used in the equation. Then write a statement or question in English. Write a mathematical equation.

Step 3: **Solve** the problem.

Step 4: **State the answer** in a complete sentence.

Step 5: **Check** the answer. Double-check the calculations to be sure all the arithmetic is correct. **(p. 532)**

Use an equation to solve the problem.

Mitchell spends 8% of his yearly salary on food every year. If he spent $7000 on food last year, how much money did he make that year?

Solution

Step 1: **Read** the problem carefully, and restate it in your own words.

Mitchell spends <u>$7000</u> on food every year, and this is <u>8% of his annual salary</u>. We must <u>find his salary for the year.</u>

Step 2: **Make a plan.** Underline the important words in our restatement of the problem in Step 1.

We can also think of the statement above as *$7000 is 8% of his annual salary. Find his annual salary.*

Plan: Since we are trying to find Mitchell's annual salary, that will be what x represents.

Let x = Mitchell's annual salary.

The equation will come from the statement *$7000 is 8% of his annual salary.* Write out the statement in English, then write an equation and solve it.

Step 3: **Solve** the problem.

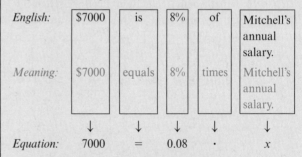

English:	$7000	is	8%	of	Mitchell's annual salary.
Meaning:	$7000	equals	8%	times	Mitchell's annual salary.
Equation:	7000	=	0.08	·	x

The equation is $7000 = 0.08x$.

$$7000 = 0.08x$$

$$\frac{7000}{0.08} = \frac{0.08x}{0.08} \qquad \text{Divide both sides by 0.08 to solve for } x.$$

$$87,500 = x \qquad \text{Perform the division.}$$

Step 4: **State the answer** in a complete sentence.

Mitchell's annual salary is $87,500.

Step 5: **Check** the answer. We have found that $7000 is 8% of $87,500. Find 8% of $87,500 to see whether it equals $7000.

$$8\% \text{ of } \$87,500 = 0.08 \cdot \$87,500 = \$7000 \quad ✓$$

The answer is correct.

Definition/Procedure	Example

Use a Proportion to Find a Percent

Recall that percents can be written as fractions, and since a proportion is a statement that two ratios or rates are equal, we can also use proportions to find a percent.

Step 1: **Read** the problem carefully, and restate it in your own words.

Step 2: **Make a plan.** Underline important words in our restatement of the problem in Step 1.

Step 3: **Solve** the problem.

Step 4: **State the answer** in a complete sentence.

Step 5: **Check** the answer. Double-check the calculations to be sure all the arithmetic is correct. **(p. 535)**

Use a proportion to solve the problem.

At a local coffee shop, 6 out of every 40 drinks served are decaffeinated. What percent of the drinks served are decaffeinated?

Solution

Step 1: **Read** the problem carefully, and restate it in your own words.

6 drinks <u>out of</u> every 40 drinks are decaffeinated. <u>What percent of the drinks are decaffeinated</u>?

Step 2: **Make a plan.** Let's underline important words in our restatement of the problem in Step 1.

We can write *6 decaffeinated drinks out of 40 total drinks* as the rate, or fraction, $\frac{6}{40}$. If we write this fraction with a denominator of 100, **the numerator will be the percent** since percent means *out of 100*. We can do this by writing a proportion. Think of the stated problem as *6 decaffeinated drinks <u>are to</u> 40 total drinks <u>as</u> how many decaffeinated drinks <u>are to</u> 100 total drinks?*

Let x = the number of decaffeinated drinks out of 100 drinks, or **the percent.**

Plan: Write a proportion using x for the percent. We will write our rates in the form $\frac{\text{number of decaffeinated drinks}}{\text{total number of drinks}}$ so that the numerators contain the same quantities and the denominators contain the same quantities:

$$\frac{6 \text{ decaffeinated drinks}}{40 \text{ total drinks}} = \frac{x}{100 \text{ total drinks}}$$

Step 3: **Solve** the problem. We do not need the units when solving for x.

$$\frac{6}{40} \diagdown \frac{x}{100}$$

$40 \cdot x = 40x$ Write the equation without the units.
$6 \cdot 100 = 600$

$40x = 6 \cdot 100$ Find the cross products.

$40x = 600$ Multiply.

$\dfrac{40x}{40} = \dfrac{600}{40}$ Divide by 40.

$x = 15$ Perform the division.

Finding that $x = 15$ means that $\frac{6}{40} = \frac{15}{100}$, and $\frac{15}{100} = 15\%$.

Definition/Procedure	Example
	Step 4: **State the answer** in a complete sentence. Therefore, 15% of drinks served are decaffeinated. *Step 5:* **Check** the answer. Use the cross products to check $x = 15$ in the proportion $\frac{6}{40} = \frac{x}{100}$. $$\frac{6}{40} = \frac{15}{100} \quad \text{Substitute 15 for } x.$$ The cross products are equal, so the answer is correct.

8.6 More Applications with Percents

Compute Sales Tax

Amount of sales tax = Rate of tax · Cost of item

Step 1: **Read** the problem carefully, and restate it in your own words.

Step 2: **Make a plan.** Underline important words in our restatement of the problem in Step 1.

Step 3: **Solve** the problem.

Step 4: **State the answer** in a complete sentence.

Step 5: **Check** the answer. Double-check the calculations to be sure all the arithmetic is correct. **(p. 547)**

A pair of sandals costs $29.99. If the sales tax rate is 9%, find the amount of tax and the total cost of the sandals.

Solution

Step 1: **Read** the problem carefully, and restate it in your own words.

The price of the sandals is $29.99, and there is a 9% sales tax. We must determine how much is paid in sales tax and also find the total cost of the sandals.

Step 2: **Make a plan.** Let's underline important words in our restatement of the problem in Step 1.

Plan: First, use the formula to find the amount of the sales tax. Then, add that amount to the price of the sandals to find the total cost.

Step 3: **Solve** the problem.

Change the sales tax rate from a percent to a decimal: 9% = 0.09

Amount of sales tax = Rate of tax · Cost of item
Amount of sales tax =   0.09   · $29.99
                     = $2.6991
                     ≈ $2.70   Round to the nearest cent.

Find the total cost of the sandals.

$$\frac{\text{Total cost of}}{\text{the sandals}} = \frac{\text{Price of}}{\text{the sandals}} + \frac{\text{Amount of}}{\text{sales tax}}$$

Total cost of = $29.99 + $2.70
the sandals
             = $32.69

Step 4: **State the answer** in a complete sentence.

The amount of sales tax is $2.70. The total cost of the sandals is $32.69.

Step 5: **Check** the answer. Double-check the calculations to be sure all the arithmetic is correct.

Amount of tax = 0.09 · $29.99 = $2.6991 ≈ $2.70. Then the total cost of the sandals is $29.99 + $2.70 = $32.69. ✓

The answer is correct.

Definition/Procedure	Example
Compute Commissions $$\text{Amount of commission} = \text{Rate of commission} \cdot \text{Amount of sales}$$ **Step 1:** **Read** the problem carefully, and restate it in your own words. **Step 2:** **Make a plan.** Underline important words in our restatement of the problem in Step 1. Use the formula to find the missing information. **Step 3:** **Solve** the problem. The rate of commission is usually given as a percent. To use it in the formula, *change the percent to a decimal.* **Step 4:** **State the answer** in a complete sentence. **Step 5:** **Check** the answer. Double-check the calculations to be sure all the arithmetic is correct. **(p. 550)**	Everett is a salesman at a furniture store, and his commission rate is 9.5%. Today he sold $4800 worth of furniture. Find the amount of his commission. **Solution** **Step 1:** **Read** the problem carefully, and restate it in your own words. Everett's <u>sales total $4800</u>, and <u>he earns 9.5% commission</u>. We must <u>find the amount of his commission</u>. **Step 2:** **Make a plan.** Let's underline important words in our restatement of the problem in Step 1. *Plan:* Use the formula to find the amount of the commission. **Step 3:** **Solve** the problem. Change the rate of commission from a percent to a decimal: 9.5% = 0.095 $$\text{Commission} = \frac{\text{Rate of commission}}{} \cdot \text{Amount of sales}$$ $$\text{Commission} = 0.095 \cdot \$4800$$ $$= \$456$$ **Step 4:** **State the answer** in a complete sentence. Everett's commission is $456. **Step 5:** **Check** the answer. Double-check the calculations to be sure all the arithmetic is correct. Amount of commission = $0.095 \cdot \$4800 = \$456$. ✓ The answer is correct.

8.7 Simple Interest

Interest is a fee paid for borrowing money. **Simple interest** is calculated on the original amount of money borrowed. The original amount of money borrowed is called the **principal**. To find the simple interest earned, use this formula. $$\text{Interest} = \text{Principal} \cdot \text{Rate} \cdot \text{Time}$$ $$I = P \cdot R \cdot T$$ P = the principal. This is the original amount of money borrowed or the original amount of money in a bank account. R = the interest rate. It is usually given as a percent. **We must change it to a decimal when we use it in the equation.** T = the time, *in years,* that the money will be borrowed or the amount of time an amount of money is in an account. **(p. 560)**	Zoe borrows $2800 for 2 years at 7% simple interest. How much interest will she owe? $$P = \$2800 \qquad R = 7\% = 0.07 \qquad T = 2$$ $$I = P \cdot R \cdot T$$ $$I = (2800)(0.07)(2) \qquad \text{Substitute the values.}$$ $$I = 392 \qquad \text{Multiply.}$$ Zoe will owe $392 in interest.

Definition/Procedure	Example

8.8 Compound Interest

Compute Interest Compounded Annually

Compound interest is interest that is paid on the original principal *plus* the interest that has already been paid.

When interest is computed at the end of each year, we say that the interest is **compounded annually.**

Interest Compounded Annually

Let A = the total amount in an account after T years. Use this formula to find the value of A when interest is compounded annually:

$$A = P(1 + R)^T$$

P = the principal and R = the interest rate in decimal form.

We can find A using the table in Appendix A.6, or we can use a calculator. **(p. 567)**

Deshawn invests $16,000 at 4.5% interest compounded annually for 5 years. How much money will be in the account after 5 years?

   If we use the table, we find the value of $(1 + R)^T$ when $R = 4.5\%$ and $T = 5$. We get 1.2462. In the compound interest formula with $P = 16,000$, replace $(1 + R)^T$ with 1.2462.

$$A = P(1 + R)^T$$
$$A = 16,000(1.2462) \qquad P = 16,000 \text{ and } (1 + R)^T = 1.2462$$
$$A = 19,939.2 \qquad \text{Multiply.}$$

   We can also use a calculator to find A. If a calculator is used, remember to write R as a decimal.

   After 5 years, the account will contain $19,939.20.

Compute Other Compound Amounts

If interest is computed more than once per year, we can use this formula to find the amount of money in the account after T years.

Compound Interest

Let A = the total amount in an account after T years. Use this formula to find the value of A when interest is compounded more than one time per year:

$$A = P\left(1 + \frac{R}{n}\right)^{n \cdot T}$$

P = the principal, R = the interest rate in decimal form, and n = the number of times interest is compounded each year.

Use a calculator to find A. **(p. 573)**

Norah invests $7000 at 6% interest compounded monthly for 3 years. Find the amount of interest in her account after 3 years and the amount of interest Norah will earn.

We will use a calculator.

$$P = \$7000 \qquad R = 6\% = 0.06 \qquad T = 3 \qquad n = 12$$

$$A = P\left(1 + \frac{R}{n}\right)^{n \cdot T} \qquad \begin{array}{l}\text{Compounded monthly} \\ \text{means 12 times per year.}\end{array}$$

$$A = 7000\left(1 + \frac{0.06}{12}\right)^{12 \cdot 3} \qquad \text{Substitute the values.}$$

$$A = 7000(1 + 0.005)^{36} \qquad \text{Divide } \frac{0.06}{12} \text{ and multiply } 12 \cdot 3.$$

$$A \approx 8376.76 \qquad \begin{array}{l}\text{Evaluate. Round to the} \\ \text{nearest cent.}\end{array}$$

Norah will have $8376.76 in her account. The amount of interest she will earn is $8376.76 − $7000 = $1376.76.

Chapter 8:   Review Exercises

*Additional answers can be found in the Answers to Exercises appendix.

(8.1) Answer the following questions.

1) Rewrite the statement using a percent. *In 2009, 59 out of 100 American females aged 16 and older participated in the labor force.* (www.census.gov)   In 2009, 59% of American females aged 16 and older participated in the labor force.

2) Explain the meaning of the statement. *In December 2009, 59% of TV viewers used the Internet while also watching TV.* (The Nielsen Company)
59% means 59 out of 100, so the statement means that in December 2009, 59 out of 100 TV viewers used the Internet while also watching TV.

3) Rewrite the statement using a percent. *In 2009, 92 out of 100 veterans were 25 years and older with at least a high school diploma.* (factfinder.census.gov)

4) Rewrite the statement using a percent. *Thirty-four out of one hundred Americans rank watching TV as their top favorite media activity.* (Deloitte's State of the Media Democracy Survey)
34% of all Americans rank watching TV as their top favorite media activity.

Write each percent as a fraction and a decimal.

5) 14% $\dfrac{14}{100} = 0.14$

6) 18% $\dfrac{18}{100} = 0.18$

7) 34% $\dfrac{34}{100} = 0.34$

8) 31% $\dfrac{31}{100} = 0.31$

Write each percent as a decimal.

9) 0.35%   0.0035

10) 0.47%   0.0047

11) 201%   2.01

12) 305%   3.05

Write each decimal as a percent and each percent as a decimal.

13) In 2010, residents of Illinois were 0.91 of the entire student body at Northern Illinois University. (www.niu.edu/about/fastfacts.shtml)   91%

14) The sales tax in Chicago, Illinois, is 0.0975.   9.75%

15) The state unemployment rate in Nevada for December 2010 was 14.5%. (www.bls.gov/lau)   0.145

16) The interest rate for a car loan is 3.25%.   0.0325

(8.2) Write each percent as a fraction or mixed number in lowest terms.

17) 23% $\dfrac{23}{100}$

18) 77% $\dfrac{77}{100}$

19) 210% $2\dfrac{1}{10}$

20) 370% $3\dfrac{7}{10}$

Write each percent as a fraction in lowest terms by first writing the percent as a decimal.

21) 42.5% $0.425 = \dfrac{17}{40}$

22) 57.5% $0.575 = \dfrac{23}{40}$

23) 43.75% $0.4375 = \dfrac{7}{16}$

24) 68.75% $0.6875 = \dfrac{11}{16}$

Write each percent as a fraction in lowest terms.

25) $26\dfrac{2}{3}\%$ $\dfrac{4}{15}$

26) $53\dfrac{1}{3}\%$ $\dfrac{8}{15}$

Write the fraction as a percent by first writing it as a fraction with a denominator of 100.

27) $\dfrac{11}{20}$ $\dfrac{55}{100} = 55\%$

28) $\dfrac{11}{50}$ $\dfrac{22}{100} = 22\%$

29) $\dfrac{49}{50}$ $\dfrac{98}{100} = 98\%$

30) $\dfrac{11}{25}$ $\dfrac{44}{100} = 44\%$

Write the fraction as a percent using long division.

31) $\dfrac{5}{8}$ 62.5%

32) $\dfrac{1}{16}$ 6.25%

33) $\dfrac{12}{5}$ 240%

34) $\dfrac{7}{4}$ 175%

(8.3)

35) First find 10% of 70, then find the following.

   a) 60% of 70   42

   b) 90% of 70   63

   c) 20% of 70   14

36) First find 10% of 30, then find the following.

   a) 60% of 30   18

   b) 90% of 30   27

   c) 30% of 30   9

37) Find:

   a) 90% of 140   126

   b) 70% of 140   98

38) Find:

   a) 60% of 60   36

   b) 20% of 60   12

39) Find:

   a) 15% of 130   19.5

   b) 15% of 72   10.8

40) Find:

   a) 15% of 150   22.5

   b) 15% of 24   3.6

41) Find:

   a) 100% of 49   49

   b) 200% of 38   76

42) Find:

   a) 200% of 157   314

   b) 400% of 34   136

43) An electronics warehouse store is having a one-day 35% off sale on its big-screen 3D televisions that regularly sell for $1799. If a buyer purchases the television on the day of the sale, approximately how much money will the buyer save, and what is the approximate sale price? $630; $1170

44) A home improvement store is having a 35% off clearance sale on its large-capacity steam washer-dryer sets that regularly sell for $1899. Approximately how much money will a buyer save during the clearance sale, and what is the approximate clearance price? $665; $1235

(8.4) Find the percent using multiplication.

45) Find:

   a) 72% of 44   31.68

   b) 6.7% of 500   33.5

46) Find:

   a) 28% of 36   10.08

   b) 3.5% of 700   24.5

47) Find:

   a) 24% of 132   31.68

   b) 1.8% of 240   4.32

48) Find:

   a) 36% of 152   54.72

   b) 3.1% of 360   11.16

49) A bank loan officer recommends that a young couple put 20% down on a new home costing $325,000. What is the amount of the recommended down payment? $65,000

50) At a local community college, approximately 43% of the students are male. If the college has 9500 students, how many students are female?   5415

51) Use an equation to solve each problem.

   a) 16 is 8% of what number?   200

   b) 15% of what number is 75?   500

   c) $4\frac{1}{2}$% of what number is 90?   2000

52) Use an equation to solve each problem.

   a) 28 is 14% of what number?   200

   b) 37% of what number is 148?   400

   c) $4\frac{1}{2}$% of what number is 135?   3000

53) Use an equation to solve each problem.

   a) 70 is 20% of what number?   350

   b) 13% of what number is 117?   900

   c) $8\frac{1}{2}$% of what number is 204?   2400

54) Use an equation to solve each problem.

   a) 48 is 6% of what number?   800

   b) 63% of what number is 504?   800

   c) $8\frac{1}{2}$% of what number is 136?   1600

(8.5) Solve each problem.

55) In a class of 40 math students, 24 students claimed that they did not spend enough time over the weekend preparing for the exam. What percent of students did not spend enough time over the weekend preparing for the exam? What percent did?   60%; 40%

56) Maria races in a triathlon that requires her to swim 0.5 mile, bike 7 miles, and then run 2.5 miles. What percent of the race is swimming? What percent of the race is biking? What percent of the race is running?   5%; 70%; 25%

57) About 1 in 5 employed adults reported that they've canceled or postponed vacation plans because of work. What percent is this?
   (www.expedia.com; 2009 Vacation Deprivation Survey)   20%

58) Sylvia decides to give $450 from her $3000 savings account to the Red Cross to help people in need. What percent of her savings did she give to the Red Cross? What percent of her savings did she keep?   15%; 85%

Use a proportion to solve the problem.

59) A coed soccer team of 20 players has eight females on the team. What is the percentage of males on the team?   60%

60) During basketball practice, Joseph makes 52 out of 80 free throws. What percent of free throw attempts does Joseph miss?   35%

Find the percent using a proportion.

61) 80 cm is what percent of 2 m?   40%

62) 0.3 m is what percent of 120 cm?   25%

63) 6 ft is what percent of 1 yd?   200%

64) 36 in. is what percent of 1 yd?   100%

65) 2 qt is what percent of 1 gal?   50%

66) 1 c is what percent of 1 qt?   25%

67) 500 mL is what percent of 0.25 L?   200%

68) 2 L is what percent of 1250 mL?   160%

(8.6) Solve each problem.

69) A price tag shows that a computer printer costs $86. If the sales tax rate is 8%, find the amount of tax and the total cost of the computer printer. $6.88; $92.88

70) Carly finds a paper shredder for her home business that costs $57. If the sales tax rate is 7%, find the amount of tax and the total cost of the paper shredder. $3.99; $60.99

71) If the sales tax amount was $11.40 for a purchase of $150, what was the sales tax rate?   7.6%

72) Jeremy paid $1.62 in sales tax on a package of blank compact disks with a list price of $18. What is the tax rate?   9%

73) A salesperson for an office furniture store is paid a commission rate of 6%. If he sells $12,500 worth of office furniture, how much commission does he earn? $750

74) Shelly sells $6560 worth of jewelry in one week. What is the amount of her commission check for her weekly sales if she is paid 8% commission? $524.80

75) A desktop computer that regularly sells for $1350 is marked 40% off. What is the sale price of the desktop computer? $810

76) During a holiday sale, the first 50 customers get a 60% discount on one item in the department store. If Tanomo is one of the first 50 customers and she finds a dress costing $120, what is the sale price for her dress? $48

77) Randy bought a Les Paul custom guitar in 1987 for $900. Today it is worth $3150. Find the percent increase in the price.   250%

78) In Fall 2011, a professor taught 300 students. In Fall 2012, she had 348 students. Find the percent increase in the number of students.   16%

79) Ramona sometimes rides the bus to work to help save the environment. It takes 1 hour 30 minutes when she rides the bus. When she takes her car, it takes 45 minutes to get to work. Find the percent decrease in time for Ramona's commute to work when she uses the car.   50%

80) In the past, Mike's heating bill during the winter months averaged $150. This year he replaced his windows with dual-pane, energy-saving windows, and his average heating bill during the winter dropped to $90. Find the percent decrease in Mike's heating bill.   40%

(8.7) Solve each problem.

81) Julia borrowed $1200 at a high interest rate of 16%. Find the amount of interest after 1 year. $192

82) Jamal borrowed $2500 at an interest rate of 6%. Find the amount of interest after 2 years. $300

83) If Andy borrowed $1600 from a lender who charges 3.75% interest, how much interest does Andy owe after 2 years? $120

84) If a person borrows $2500 from a lender who charges 4.25% interest, how much interest does the person owe after 3 years? $318.75

85) Write each in terms of years.

   a) 13 months $\frac{13}{12}$ yr   b) 39 weeks $\frac{3}{4}$ yr

86) Write each in terms of years.

   a) 5 months $\frac{5}{12}$ yr   b) 3 weeks $\frac{3}{52}$ yr

87) How much interest will Josephine owe if she borrows $960 for 10 weeks at a $2\frac{3}{4}$% interest rate? $5.08

88) How much interest will Russell owe if he borrows $2200 for 30 months at a $5\frac{1}{4}$% interest rate? $288.75

89) Glenda took out a personal loan for $900 at an interest rate of 4.2%. If Glenda wants to pay back the loan in 18 months, how much does she pay back to the lender, including interest? $956.70

90) Brad puts $4000 into a savings account at a 5.25% interest rate. How much is in the account after 3 years? $4630

91) Capri is going to put a $3000 down payment on a new car costing $18,000. If the finance company charges 3.5% interest, how much does Capri owe and what is her monthly payment if she chooses one of the following three payment plans?

   a) a 3-yr loan
      $16,575; $460.42
   b) a 4-yr loan
      $17,100; $356.25
   c) a 5-yr loan
      $17,625; $293.75
   d) How much does Capri save if she pays off the loan in 3 years instead of 5 years? $1050

92) April is going to put a $3500 down payment on a new car costing $19,500. If the finance company charges 2.5% interest, how much does April owe and what is her monthly payment if she chooses one of the following three payment plans?

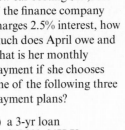

   a) a 3-yr loan
      $17,200; $477.78
   b) a 4-yr loan
      $17,600; $366.67
   c) a 5-yr loan
      $18,000; $300
   d) How much does April save if she pays off the loan in 3 years instead of 5 years? $800

(8.8)

93) Ahmed deposits $6000 into an account for 3 years at 4% interest.

   a) Determine the amount of interest if he earns *simple interest* for 3 years. Then, find the total amount in his account after 3 years.   interest: $720; total: $6720

   b) Determine the amount of interest he earns if the interest is *compounded annually* for 3 years. Then, find the total amount in his account after 3 years.   interest: $749.18; total: $6749.18

   c) Will the amount of money in his account after 3 years be different if the interest is computed differently? Explain your answer.   If interest is compounded annually, Ahmed will earn $29.18 more than if it is computed as simple interest.

94) Tina deposits $5000 into an account for 4 years at 5% interest.

   a) Determine the amount of interest if she earns *simple interest* for 4 years. Then, find the total amount in her account after 3 years.   interest: $1000; total: $6000

   b) Determine the amount of interest she earns if the interest is *compounded annually* for 4 years. Then, find the total amount in her account after 4 years.   interest: $1077.53; total: $6077.53

   c) Will the amount of money in her account after 4 years be different if the interest is computed differently? Explain your answer.   If interest is compounded annually, Tina will earn $77.53 more than if it is computed as simple interest.

95) Shufan invests $6700 at $4\frac{3}{4}$% for 8 years compounded weekly. Find the amount of money in the account after 8 years, and also determine the amount of interest Shufan earned.   total: $9795.61; interest: $3095.61

96) Wade and Carol deposit their inheritance of $325,000 into a savings account that pays 5.25% compounded monthly. If they leave the money in the account for 15 years, how much money will they have in the account? How much interest will they earn?   total: $713,089.92; interest: $388,089.92

Chapter 8:   Test

*Additional answers can be found in the Answers to Exercises appendix.

1) What does *percent* mean?   out of 100

Write each percent as a decimal and as a fraction in lowest terms.

2) 45%   0.45; $\frac{9}{20}$

3) 0.7%   0.007; $\frac{7}{1000}$

4) 6%   0.06; $\frac{3}{50}$

5) 14.8%   0.148; $\frac{37}{250}$

Write each number as a percent.

6) 0.6   60%

7) 0.0924   9.24%

8) $\frac{4}{5}$ 80%

9) $\frac{7}{8}$ 87.5%

10) $3\frac{1}{2}$ 350%

11) 2   200%

12) a) Explain how to compute 10% of 40 "in your head." Then, find 10% of 40.

   b) Find 80% of 40.   32

   c) Find 5% of 40.   2

   d) Find 85% of 40.   34

13) Find 300% of 15.   45

14) A restaurant bill is $38. If Liz wants to leave a 20% tip, determine the amount of the tip and the total amount of money she would pay. $7.60; $45.60

15) The original price of a pair of boots is $60. Now, they are on sale for 30% off. What is the sale price of the boots? $42

16) Find 27.3% of 480.   131.04

Solve each problem using an equation.

17) 35% of what number is 280?   800

18) 360 is what percent of 4000?   9%

Solve each problem.

19) Vernon's mortgage payment is 20% of his monthly income. If his mortgage payment is $1280, how much does he make each month? $6400

20) A dining room set costs $2478 plus a sales tax of $7\frac{1}{2}$%. What is the total cost of the dining room set, including sales tax? $2663.85

21) A survey in early 2011 revealed that 27 out of 50 Americans aged 25–39 drink coffee daily. What percent of Americans drink coffee every day?   54%

22) When Soldier Field in Chicago opened in 1924, its seating capacity was 74,000. When the new Soldier Field opened in 2003, its new seating capacity was 61,500. Find the percent decrease in the seating capacity. Round the answer to the nearest tenth of a percent. (www.stadiumsofprofootball.com)   16.9%

23) Keiko borrows $9000 for 4 years at 4.5% simple interest. How much interest will she owe on this loan? $1620

24) Paul deposits $5000 for 9 months into an account paying 3% interest. How much money will be in the account after 9 months? $5112.50

25) Trisha deposits $8000 at 7% interest compounded annually in a college fund for her son. The money will remain in the account for 10 years.

   a) How much will be in the college fund after 10 years? $15,737.21

   b) How much interest did Trisha earn? $7737.21

Chapter 8:   Cumulative Review for Chapters 1–8

*Additional answers can be found in the Answers to Exercises appendix.

1) Rewrite 30 + 17 using the commutative property.   17 + 30

2) Round 19,483,350 to the nearest hundred thousand.
   19,500,000

3) The following pictograph shows the preferred sport in a high school classroom. Use the pictograph to answer the following exercises.

Favorite Sports

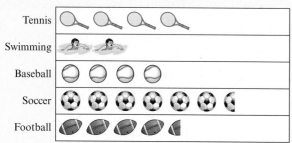

Each picture represents 2 students.

a) Find the number of students who prefer baseball.   8

b) How many students are in the class?   42

c) Which sport is most popular among these students? How many students prefer this sport?   soccer; 13

d) Which sport is least popular?   swimming

e) How many fewer students prefer swimming than football?   5

f) How many more students prefer football to baseball?   1

4) Write 4 · 4 · 4 · 4 · 4 using an exponent. 4^5

Perform the indicated operations. Write all answers in lowest terms.

5) 4100×0.065 266.5

6) $\frac{8}{9} \div 10$ $\frac{4}{45}$

7) $\$32 - \$17.79$ $\$14.21$

8) $\frac{3}{10} + \frac{1}{4} + \frac{5}{8}$ $\frac{47}{40}$ or $1\frac{7}{40}$

9) $16\overline{)12{,}848}$ 803

10) $72 - 18 \div 6 + 5^3 \cdot \sqrt{121}$ 1444

11) $7.8 \div 0.03$ 260

12) Write as a decimal number: *one and seven hundredths*.   1.07

13) Write the ratio of 8 ft to 4 yd. $\frac{2}{3}$

14) Solve the proportion $\frac{x}{16} = \frac{17\frac{1}{2}}{28}$. $x = 10$

15) Change 500 mL to liters.   0.5 L

16) Convert 2 wk to hours.   336 hr

17) When he played with the Houston Rockets, Yao Ming's height was listed as 7 ft 6 in., and his weight was 310 lb. Find his height in centimeters and his weight in kilograms. Use 1 in. = 2.54 cm and 1 lb ≈ 0.45 kg. (www.nba.com)
height: 228.6 cm; weight: 139.5 kg

18) Write 70.5% as a fraction in lowest terms. $\frac{141}{200}$

19) Write 1.8 as a percent.   180%

20) Find 90% of 60.   54

21) Solve using an equation: 29.4 is 30% of what number?   98

Solve each problem.

22) An airline survey revealed that 11 out of 20 passengers do not check their luggage. On a flight with 148 passengers, how many carried all their luggage onto the plane? Round to the nearest person.   81 people

23) Manuela spent $263.24 on food for Thanksgiving dinner for her whole family. This was $145.89 more than her grocery bill the week before. How much did Manuela spend on groceries the week before Thanksgiving? $117.35

24) Manuela's stuffing recipe uses $3\frac{1}{2}$ c of chicken broth and feeds 10 people. If she will be feeding 25 people and wants to make enough stuffing for everyone, how much chicken broth will she need? $8\frac{3}{4}$ c

25) Concertgoers were asked to bring canned goods to donate to a food pantry. If 15,400 people attended the concert and 62% of them brought at least one item, how many people donated canned goods for the food pantry?   9548 people

Geometry

Math at Work:

Interior Designer

Jamie Callum walks into a room and sees possibilities. She immediately starts imagining pictures on the walls, rugs across the floor, lights hanging from the ceiling. As an interior designer, her job, in her words, "is to make spaces comfortable, beautiful, and functional."

Jamie grew up reading fashion and architecture magazines. What she never expected, however, was how much math interior design would require. "I couldn't do my job without geometry," Jamie explains. "I have to account for the angles of walls, the perimeters of rooms, and which furniture should be parallel and perpendicular to the walls. Math helps me bring my creative ideas to life." Jamie's combination of mathematical skill and creative inspiration has enabled her to design the interiors of homes, restaurants, and offices.

Interior design, Jamie explains, is ultimately a series of decisions. "Every room is like a blank page," she describes. "You have to choose how to fill that page. When I started my career, it was hard for me to make up my mind. With experience, I've become much more decisive—and successful."

In this chapter, we will explore geometry, the math of angles, lines, and shapes. We'll also discuss some ways to improve decision making.

All of us face important decisions in our lives at one time or another. How can we make the *right* decisions? How do we know which among various options is the best one to pick? The techniques below can help improve the quality of your decision making, whether you are choosing where to live, what to major in, or simply what to eat for dinner.

 **Prepare**

- Identify your goals. What do you seek to accomplish in making this decision?

 **Organize**

- Develop a list of choices, and assess each of your alternatives. Think through the outcomes that might result from each potential choice and the likelihoods of these outcomes.
- Compare your choices and their possible results. Ask yourself: Which choice will bring the most positive, and the most likely, outcomes?

 **Work**

- If you are still unsure what to choose, give the decision time. You might think of new options, or gain a fresh perspective on your choices.
- Another option if you can't make up your mind: Flip a coin. This might sound crazy, but the real power of the coin toss comes in helping you discover your true feelings. If you flip a coin and are disappointed with the outcome, that is a major clue as to what you should do.
- Carry out your decision. There is no point thinking through your options and making a choice unless you follow through on it!

Evaluate

- Consider whether the actual outcomes of your decision match what you anticipated.
- Think about changing your mind. Admitting a decision was wrong can sometimes be the best course of action.

Rethink

- Periodically take stock of your larger goals. Are the choices you are making taking you to a place you want to be?
- Be sensitive to changes in your priorities, and be open to rethinking your decisions accordingly.

Chapter 9 POWER Plan

What are your goals for Chapter 9?	How can you accomplish each goal? (Write in the steps you will take to succeed.)
1 Be prepared before and during class.	• _____ • _____ • _____ • _____
2 Understand the homework to the point where you could do it without needing any help or hints.	• _____ • _____ • _____
3 Use the P.O.W.E.R. framework to learn how to make decisions: *Exercise Your Problem-Solving Skills.*	• _____ • _____ • _____
4 Write your own goal. _____ _____	• _____

What are your objectives for Chapter 9?	How can you accomplish each objective?
1 Understand the basic components of geometry.	• Know the definitions of lines, segments, rays, different types of angles, and parallel and perpendicular lines. • Be able to find missing angle measures by using the definitions of complementary, supplementary, congruent, and vertical angles.
2 Be able to find perimeter (circumference) and area as well as classify various types of geometric figures.	• Know the definitions of a rectangle, square, triangle, circle, parallelogram, and trapezoid. • Find missing measures of different figures. • Identify different types of triangles. • Understand what π represents. • Use the formulas to find the perimeter and area of a rectangle, square, triangle, circle, parallelogram, and trapezoid.
3 Be able to compute the volume of different geometric figures.	• Use the formulas to find the volume of a rectangular solid, sphere, hemisphere, cylinder, cone, and pyramid.
4 Learn how to compute square roots, use the Pythagorean theorem, and compare similar triangles.	• Memorize the Pythagorean theorem, and be able to find an unknown side of a right triangle. • Understand how to compare similar triangles, and be able to write a proportion to find a missing length.
5 Write your own goal. _____ _____	• _____

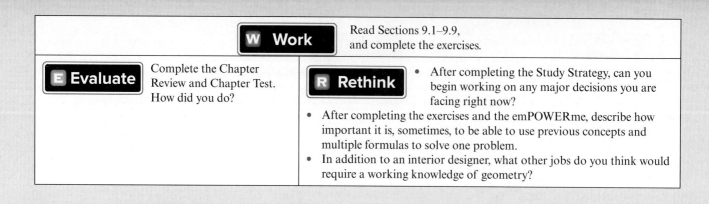

	W Work	Read Sections 9.1–9.9, and complete the exercises.

E Evaluate	Complete the Chapter Review and Chapter Test. How did you do?	R Rethink	• After completing the Study Strategy, can you begin working on any major decisions you are facing right now?
			• After completing the exercises and the emPOWERme, describe how important it is, sometimes, to be able to use previous concepts and multiple formulas to solve one problem.
			• In addition to an interior designer, what other jobs do you think would require a working knowledge of geometry?

9.1 Introduction to Geometry

P Prepare   ## O Organize

What are your objectives for Section 9.1?	How can you accomplish each objective?
1 Identify Lines, Line Segments, and Rays	• Write the definitions of *space, plane, point, line, line segment,* and *ray* in your notes with an example next to each. • Complete the given example on your own. • Complete You Try 1.
2 Identify and Classify Angles	• Learn the different parts that make up an *angle* such as *rays* and *vertex,* and understand the different ways to name an angle using ∠. • Understand what a *degree* represents. • Memorize the definitions of an *acute angle, right angle, obtuse angle,* and a *straight angle.* • Complete the given examples on your own. • Complete You Trys 2 and 3.
3 Identify Parallel and Perpendicular Lines	• Draw examples and write the definitions of *intersecting lines, parallel lines,* and *perpendicular lines* in your notes. • Complete the given example on your own. • Complete You Try 4.

W Work   Read the explanations, follow the examples, take notes, and complete the You Trys.

Thousands of years ago, the Egyptians developed techniques to measure the amount of land a person owned. They used this information to collect taxes. Later, the Greeks formalized this process of measurement into a branch of mathematics we call **geometry**. The word *geometry* comes from the Greek words for "earth measurement."

Today, geometry is used in many different ways. We use geometry when we do home improvement projects, buy carpeting, or work in the garden. And it is used by people in different careers like interior design, air traffic control, science, construction, and many more.

In this chapter, we will learn some basics of geometry beginning with some terms.

1 Identify Lines, Line Segments, and Rays

Space is an unlimited, three-dimensional expanse. The Earth is an example of an object in space. A **plane** is a flat surface that continues indefinitely. A floor is part of a plane, as is a wall or a piece of paper. The most basic concept in geometry is a *point*. A **point** is a location in space with no length, width, or height. A point is represented by a dot, and we usually name a point with a capital letter. For example, here is point P.

$\bullet\ P$

Point P

A **line** is a straight set of points that continues forever in two directions. When we draw a line through two points, we draw arrows at the ends to show that the line never ends. We name the line using any two points on the line and put the notation $\longleftrightarrow$ above the letters to indicate that it is a line. We can also name a line with a lowercase letter. For example, here is line PQ or $\overleftrightarrow{PQ}$ or line l.

line PQ or $\overleftrightarrow{PQ}$ or line l

A **line segment** is a piece of a line with two endpoints. We name a line segment using its two endpoints. For example, this line segment with endpoints A and B can be named $\overline{AB}$ or $\overline{BA}$.

The name of this line segment is $\overline{AB}$ or $\overline{BA}$.

A **ray** is a part of a line. It has one endpoint and continues forever in the other direction. *We name a ray using the endpoint first and any other point on the ray.* Here is ray RT, which we write as $\overrightarrow{RT}$.

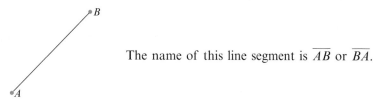

Ray RT or $\overrightarrow{RT}$

EXAMPLE 1

In-Class Example 1

Identify each figure as a line, a line segment, or a ray. Then, name it using the correct notation.

a) *A* •

B •

b)

• *Y*

• *X*

c) •———————•
   P   *Q*

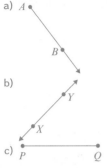

Answer: a) ray; $\overrightarrow{AB}$
b) line; $\overleftrightarrow{XY}$ or $\overleftrightarrow{YX}$
c) line segment; $\overline{PQ}$ or $\overline{QP}$

Identify each figure as a line, a line segment, or a ray. Then, name it using the correct notation.

a)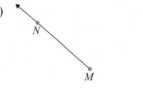
N

M

b)
A •

B •

c) •———————•
   X   *Y*

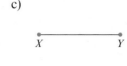

Solution

a) This figure has *one* endpoint and an arrowhead on the other end indicating that it goes on forever in that direction. **This is a ray.** Write its name as $\overrightarrow{MN}$. (Notice that the *M must* come first because it is the endpoint of the ray.)

b) This figure is straight and continues forever in both directions. **This is a line.** Write its name as $\overleftrightarrow{AB}$ or $\overleftrightarrow{BA}$.

c) This figure is straight with two endpoints. **This is a line segment.** Write its name as $\overline{XY}$ or $\overline{YX}$.

[YOU TRY 1] Identify each figure as a line, a line segment, or a ray. Then name it using the correct notation.

a) *C* •
   |
   |
   |
   D •

b) *G*

   H •

c)
   N
   M

---

2 Identify and Classify Angles

If we join two rays at their endpoints, we get an **angle**. The **vertex** of the angle is the common endpoint. This angle is formed by joining rays $\overrightarrow{BA}$ and $\overrightarrow{BC}$.

An angle is denoted by the symbol $\angle$. We can name this angle in different ways:

Put the vertex in the middle	Using only the vertex	Using the number label given to the angle
$\angle ABC$ or $\angle CBA$	$\angle B$	$\angle 1$

Note

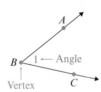

Sometimes two or more angles share the same vertex. In this case, we do **not** name the angle using only the vertex.

EXAMPLE 2

Name each of the numbered angles in this figure in two different ways.

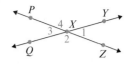

Solution

W Hint

How many different rays, line segments, and lines are represented in this example?

First, notice that X is the vertex of *all* the angles. So, **we cannot use just the vertex to name any of the angles in this figure.**

We can give each of the angles the following names:

$\angle 1$: $\angle YXZ$ or $\angle ZXY$ $\angle 2$: $\angle ZXQ$ or $\angle QXZ$

$\angle 3$: $\angle PXQ$ or $\angle QXP$ $\angle 4$: $\angle PXY$ or $\angle YXP$

[**YOU TRY 2**]

Name each of the numbered angles in this figure in two different ways.

In-Class Example 2

Name each of the numbered angles in this figure in two different ways.

Answer:

$\angle 1$: $\angle BAC$ or $\angle CAB$
$\angle 2$: $\angle CAD$ or $\angle DAC$
$\angle 3$: $\angle EAD$ or $\angle DAE$
$\angle 4$: $\angle EAB$ or $\angle BAE$

Angles can be different sizes. In Example 2, $\angle 1$ is smaller than $\angle 2$. We can measure the size of an angle using **degrees.** The symbol for degrees is $°$. For example, if the measure of an angle is 45 degrees, we write $45°$. Let's look at a circle to understand the sizes of degree measures.

If we start at a ray and go all the way around the circle, we have moved $360°$. We say that a circle contains $360°$.

If we start at a ray and form an angle halfway around a circle, the angle measure is $180°$. A **straight angle** is an angle whose measure is $180°$.

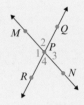

The angle formed by moving a quarter of the way around a circle has a measure of $90°$. A **right angle** is an angle whose measure is $90°$. (It may also be called a *square angle*.) A right angle is denoted with a small square at the vertex:

A right angle has a measure of $90°$.

Definition

1) An **acute angle** is an angle whose measure is greater than 0° and less than 90°.

Examples:

2) A **right angle** is an angle whose measure is 90°.

Examples:

3) An **obtuse angle** is an angle whose measure is greater than 90° and less than 180°.

Examples:

4) A **straight angle** is an angle whose measure is 180°.

Examples:

Note

Angles can also be measured in radians. This topic is studied in future math courses.

EXAMPLE 3

In-Class Example 3

Use Example 3.

Classify each angle as acute, right, obtuse, or straight.

a)
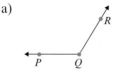

b)
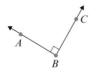

c)

d)

Solution

a) The measure of ∠*PQR* is greater than 90° and less than 180°. It is an **obtuse angle.**

b) The small square inside the angle tells us that its measure is *exactly* 90°. ∠*ABC* is a **right angle.**

c) The measure of ∠*YXZ* is less than 90°, so it is an **acute angle.**

d) The measure of ∠*T* is 180°, so it is a **straight angle.**

Classify each angle as acute, right, obtuse, or straight.

a)   b) R S T c) Y Z d) A

Note

The measure of an angle is denoted by m∠. For example, in Example 3b, the measure of ∠ABC is 90°. We write this as m∠ABC = 90°.

3 Identify Parallel and Perpendicular Lines

At the beginning of this section, we said that a plane is a flat surface that continues indefinitely. A surface like a piece of paper is part of a plane.

Two lines that cross each other are called **intersecting lines.**

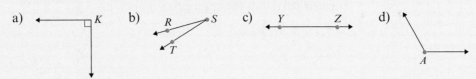

Lines l and k *intersect* at point A.

Parallel lines are lines in the same plane that do *not* intersect. The symbol ‖ means "is parallel to."

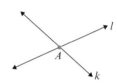

Lines x and y do *not* intersect. They are *parallel*. We can write $x \parallel y$.

Perpendicular lines intersect at right angles. The symbol ⊥ means "is perpendicular to."

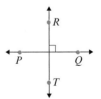

Lines $\overleftrightarrow{PQ}$ and $\overleftrightarrow{RT}$ intersect at right angles. They are *perpendicular*. We can write $\overleftrightarrow{PQ} \perp \overleftrightarrow{RT}$.

EXAMPLE 4

In-Class Example 4

Classify each pair of lines as parallel, perpendicular, or neither. If they are parallel or perpendicular, use the appropriate notation.

a)

b)

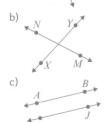

c)

Answer:
a) $a \perp b$ b) neither
c) $\overleftrightarrow{AB} \parallel \overleftrightarrow{HJ}$

Classify each pair of lines as parallel, perpendicular, or neither. If they are parallel or perpendicular, use the appropriate notation.

a)

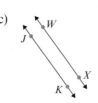

b)

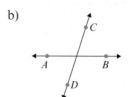

c)

Solution

a) Lines m and n meet at right angles, so they are perpendicular. Write $m \perp n$.

b) Lines $\overleftrightarrow{AB}$ and $\overleftrightarrow{CD}$ intersect but not at right angles. They are neither parallel nor perpendicular.

c) Lines $\overleftrightarrow{JK}$ and $\overleftrightarrow{WX}$ do *not* intersect, so they are parallel. Write $\overleftrightarrow{JK} \parallel \overleftrightarrow{WX}$.

YOU TRY 4

Classify each pair of lines as parallel, perpendicular, or neither. If they are parallel or perpendicular, use the appropriate notation.

a)

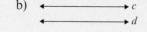

b)

c)

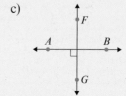

Note

Even if two lines or rays *look like* they intersect at right angles, we cannot assume they are right angles unless the angle is denoted with the square.

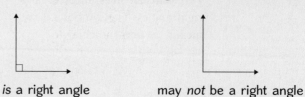

is a right angle   may *not* be a right angle

ANSWERS TO YOU TRY **EXERCISES**

1) a) line segment; $\overline{CD}$ or $\overline{DC}$ b) ray; $\overrightarrow{HG}$ c) line; $\overleftrightarrow{MN}$ or $\overleftrightarrow{NM}$
2) $\angle 1$: $\angle RPM$ or $\angle MPR$; $\angle 2$: $\angle MPQ$ or $\angle QPM$; $\angle 3$: $\angle QPN$ or $\angle NPQ$; $\angle 4$: $\angle RPN$ or $\angle NPR$
3) a) right b) acute c) straight d) obtuse
4) a) neither b) $c \parallel d$ c) $\overleftrightarrow{AB} \perp \overleftrightarrow{FG}$

E Evaluate 9.1 Exercises

Do the exercises, and check your work.

*Additional answers can be found in the Answers to Exercises appendix.

Objective 1: Identify Lines, Line Segments, and Rays

1) Explain the difference between a line segment and a ray. Answers may vary.

2) Draw a picture of a vertical ray pointing downward. Name the ray. Answers may vary.

Identify each figure as a line, line segment, or a ray. Then name it using the correct notation.

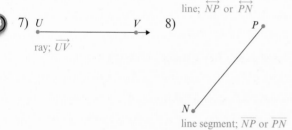

3) line; $\overleftrightarrow{TU}$ or $\overleftrightarrow{UT}$

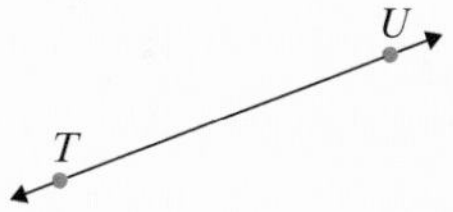

4) ray; $\overrightarrow{NM}$

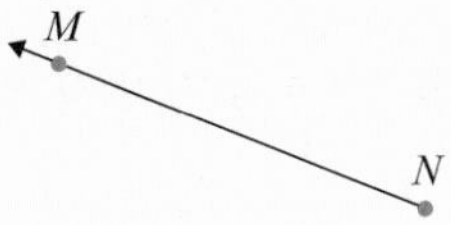

5)

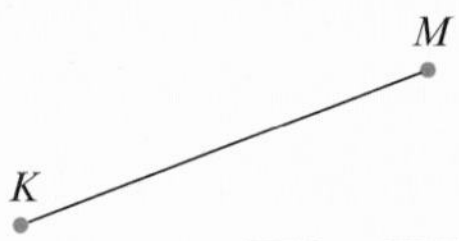

line segment; $\overline{KM}$ or $\overline{MK}$

6)

line; $\overleftrightarrow{NP}$ or $\overleftrightarrow{PN}$

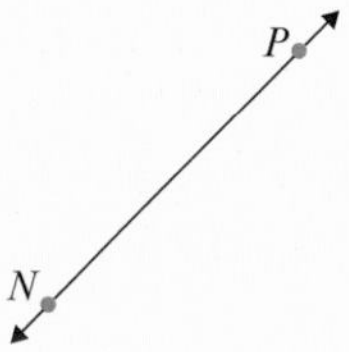

7)

ray; $\overrightarrow{UV}$

8)

line segment; $\overline{NP}$ or $\overline{PN}$

9)

ray; $\overrightarrow{KJ}$

10)

line; $\overleftrightarrow{YZ}$ or $\overleftrightarrow{ZY}$

11) Draw a line named $\overleftrightarrow{CT}$. Answers may vary.

12) Draw a ray named $\overrightarrow{RD}$. Answers may vary.

Objective 2: Identify and Classify Angles

13) What is an obtuse angle?
An obtuse angle has a measure greater than 90° and less than 180°.

14) What is an acute angle?
An acute angle has a measure less than 90°.

15) What is a right angle, and how is it indicated when an angle is drawn? A right angle has a measure of exactly 90°, and it is indicated by a small square in the angle.

16) What kind of angle has a measure of 180°?
a straight angle

Name each of the numbered angles in the figures in two different ways.

17)

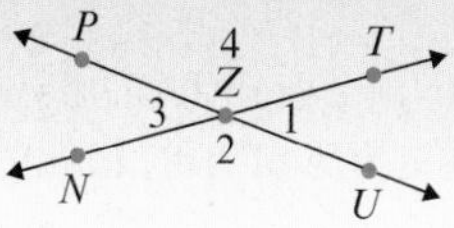

18)

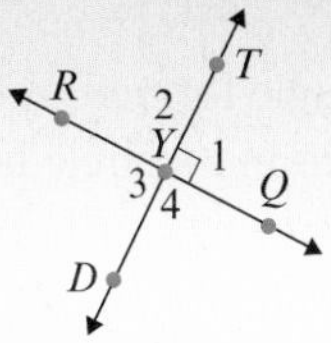

19)

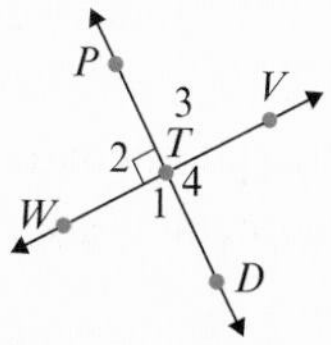

20)

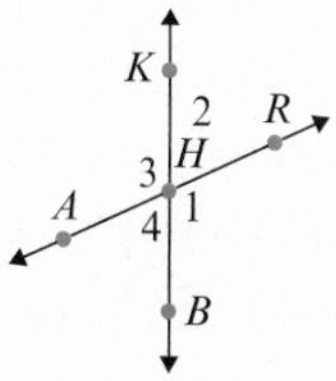

21)

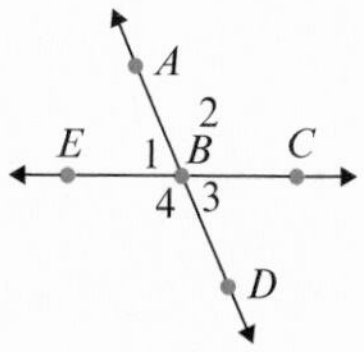

22)

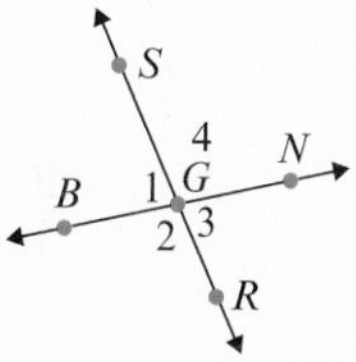

Classify each angle as acute, right, obtuse, or straight.

23) acute

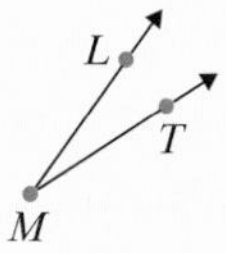

24) right

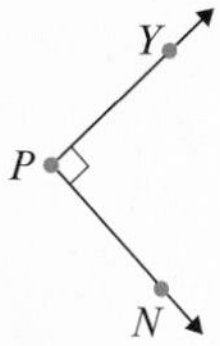

25) obtuse

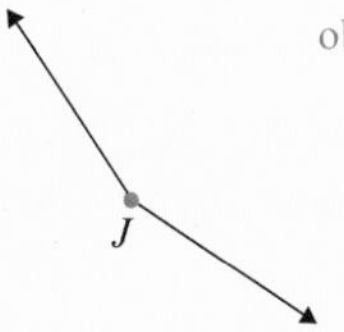

26) acute

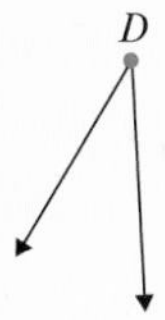

27)

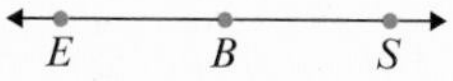

straight

28) obtuse

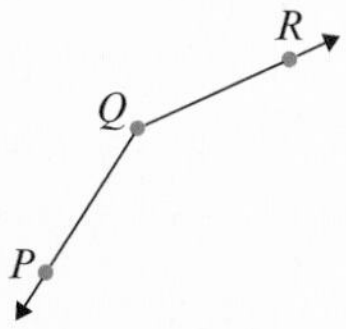

29) right

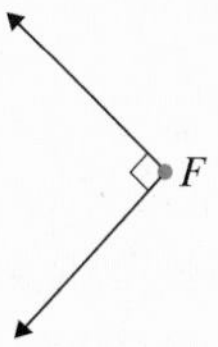

30)

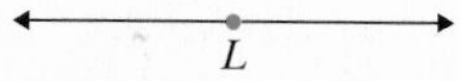

straight

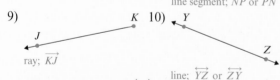

31) Draw an obtuse angle named ∠*TNW*.
   Answers may vary.
32) Draw a right angle named ∠*AYC*.
   Answers may vary.
33) The angle formed by moving one-third of the way around a circle has a measure of how many degrees?   120°

34) The angle formed by moving one-eighth of the way around a circle has a measure of how many degrees?   45°

Objective 3: Identify Parallel and Perpendicular Lines

Classify each pair of lines as parallel, perpendicular, or neither. If they are parallel or perpendicular, use the appropriate notation.

35)
parallel; $\overleftrightarrow{GK} \parallel \overleftrightarrow{LP}$

36)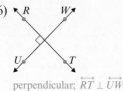
perpendicular; $\overleftrightarrow{RT} \perp \overleftrightarrow{UW}$

37)
neither

38)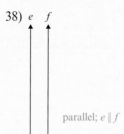
parallel; $e \parallel f$

39)
perpendicular; $c \perp d$

40)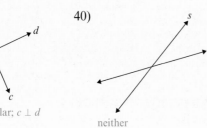
neither

Mixed Exercises: Objectives 1–3

Classify each angle as acute, right, obtuse, or straight.

41) 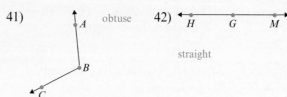 obtuse

42) straight

43) 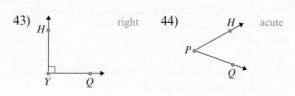 right

44) 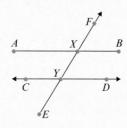 acute

Use the figure for Exercises 45–54.

45) Identify the ray in the figure. $\overrightarrow{EF}$

46) Identify the line segment in the figure. $\overline{AB}$ or $\overline{BA}$

Answer *true* or *false* for Exercises 47–54.

47) ∠*BXF* is an acute angle.   true

48) ∠*DYE* is an obtuse angle.   true

49) $\overline{AB} \parallel \overrightarrow{EF}$ false

50) $\overleftrightarrow{CD} \perp \overline{AB}$ false

51) m∠*EYD* is greater than m∠*CYE*.   true

52) m∠*AXF* is less than m∠*BXF*.   false

53) m∠*AXY* could be 116°.   false

54) m∠*XYD* could be 77°.   true

R Rethink

R1) After completing the exercises, do you understand all the definitions? Could you explain them to a friend?

R2) If a circle were divided into only 100 degrees instead of 360 degrees, how many degrees would represent a right angle and a straight angle?

9.2 Angles

P Prepare

O Organize

What are your objectives for Section 9.2?	How can you accomplish each objective?
1 Understand Complementary and Supplementary Angles	• Write the definition of *complementary angles* in your own words, and draw examples. • Write the definition of *supplementary angles* in your own words, and draw examples. • Complete the given examples on your own. • Complete You Trys 1–3.
2 Understand Congruent and Vertical Angles	• Write the definition of *congruent angles* in your own words, and draw examples. • Write the definition of *vertical angles* in your own words, and draw examples. • Write the definition of *adjacent angles* in your own words, and draw examples. • Complete the given examples on your own. • Complete You Trys 4–8.

W Work

Read the explanations, follow the examples, take notes, and complete the You Trys.

In this section, we will learn more about angles and their relationships. Let's begin with complementary and supplementary angles.

1 Understand Complementary and Supplementary Angles

Definition

Two angles are **complementary angles** if their measures add to 90°.

Example:

$\angle A$ and $\angle B$ are complementary angles
because $m\angle A + m\angle B = 70° + 20° = 90°$.

We say that $\angle A$ and $\angle B$ are *complements* of each other.

W Hint

Can you write a procedure for finding the complement of an angle in your notes?

In the definition box, $\angle A$ and $\angle B$ are complementary because $70° + 20° = 90°$. But, it is also true that $90° - 70° = 20°$ and $90° - 20° = 70°$. So, if we know the measure

$$\underset{m\angle A \quad m\angle B}{\uparrow \qquad \uparrow} \qquad \underset{m\angle B \quad m\angle A}{\uparrow \qquad \uparrow}$$

of one angle and want to find its complement, we subtract the measure of the given angle from 90°.

EXAMPLE 1

If m∠R = 31°, find the measure of its complement.

Solution

To find the measure of the complement of ∠R, subtract 31° from 90°:
$$90° − 31° = 59°$$
The measure of the complement of ∠R is 59°.

Check by adding:

$$m∠R + \text{Measure of its complement} = 31° + 59° = 90°. \checkmark$$

[**YOU TRY 1**] If m∠Z = 16°, find the measure of its complement.

We use a special term for two angles whose sum is 180°.

Definition

Two angles are **supplementary angles** if their measures add to 180°.

Example:

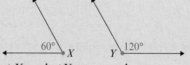

∠X and ∠Y are supplementary angles
because m∠X + m∠Y = 60° + 120° = 180°.

We say that ∠X and ∠Y are *supplements* of each other.

In the definition box for supplementary angles, ∠X and ∠Y are supplementary because
60° + 120° = 180°. It is also true that 180° − 60° = 120° and 180° − 120° = 60°. So, if
$$\begin{array}{cccc} \uparrow & \uparrow & \uparrow & \uparrow \\ m∠X & m∠Y & m∠Y & m∠X \end{array}$$
we know the measure of one angle and we want to find its supplement, we subtract
the measure of the given angle from 180°.

W Hint

Can you write a procedure
for finding the supplement
of an angle in your notes?

EXAMPLE 2

If m∠C = 114°, find the measure of its supplement.

Solution

To find the measure of the supplement of ∠C, subtract 114° from 180°:
$$180° − 114° = 66°$$
The measure of the supplement of ∠C is 66°.

Check by adding:

$$m∠C + \text{Measure of its supplement} = 114° + 66° = 180°. \checkmark$$

We can think about complementary and supplementary angles in another way.

EXAMPLE 3   Find each missing angle measure.

In-Class Example 3

Find each missing angle measure.

a) ∠MNP is a right angle.
    Find m∠x.

b) ∠XYZ is a straight angle.
    Find m∠a.

Answer:
a) m∠x = 11°
b) m∠a = 143°

a)   ∠PQR is a right angle.
     Find m∠x.

b)   ∠ABC is a straight angle.
     Find m∠y.

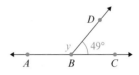

Solution

a)   Because ∠PQR is a right angle, its measure is 90°. The figure shows that
     m∠TQR + m∠x = 90°. (That is, ∠TQR and ∠x are *complementary* angles.)
     To find m∠x, subtract 68° from 90°:

$$90° - m∠TQR = m∠x$$
$$90° - 68° = 22°$$
$$m∠x = 22°$$

b)   Because ∠ABC is a straight angle, its measure is 180°. The figure shows that
     m∠y + m∠DBC = 180°. (That is, ∠y and ∠DBC are *supplementary* angles.)
     To find m∠y, subtract 49° from 180°:

$$180° - m∠DBC = m∠y$$
$$180° - 49° = 131°$$
$$m∠y = 131°$$

[YOU TRY 3]   Find each missing angle measure.

a)   ∠CDF is a right angle.
     Find m∠n.

b)   ∠RTV is a straight angle.
     Find m∠w.

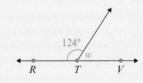

Definition

Two angles are **congruent angles** if their measures are the same.

Example:

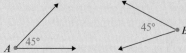

∠A and ∠B are *congruent angles* because their angle measures are the same.

We can also say that ∠A and ∠B are *congruent*. We can write this as ∠A ≅ ∠B. Read this as "Angle *A is congruent to* angle *B*." The symbol ≅ means "is congruent to."

When two lines intersect, four angles are formed.

Definition

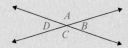

Vertical angles are the angles opposite each other—the angles that do not share a common side.

Example: ∠A and ∠C are vertical angles.

∠D and ∠B are vertical angles.

Vertical angles are congruent. That is, their angle measures are the same.

Example: ∠A ≅ ∠C and ∠D ≅ ∠B

> **W Hint**
>
> Would it be helpful to make notes on the example?

EXAMPLE 4

In-Class Example 4

Identify the vertical angles, and make a statement about their congruence.

Answer: ∠Q and ∠N are vertical angles; ∠Q ≅ ∠N. ∠M and ∠P are vertical angles; ∠M ≅ ∠P.

Identify the vertical angles, and make a statement about their congruence.

Solution

∠W and ∠Y are vertical angles. Therefore, ∠W ≅ ∠Y. (∠W is congruent to ∠Y.)

∠X and ∠Z are vertical angles. Therefore, ∠X ≅ ∠Z. (∠X is congruent to ∠Z.)

Identify the vertical angles, and make a statement about their congruence.

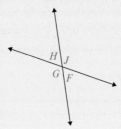

We can use what we know about vertical angles to find missing angle measures.

EXAMPLE 5

Find m∠QPT and m∠QPR.

In-Class Example 5

Find m∠EAB and m∠BAC.

Answer: m∠EAB = 75°;
m∠BAC = 105°

Solution

Begin by identifying the vertical angles because *vertical angles have the same measure.*

∠QPT and ∠RPS are vertical angles. Since
m∠RPS = 57°, m∠QPT = 57°.

∠QPR and ∠TPS are vertical angles. Since
m∠TPS = 123°, m∠QPR = 123°.

Find m∠QWY and m∠ZWY.

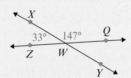

Two angles that share a common side also have a special relationship.

Definition

Adjacent angles are angles that share a common side and a common vertex.

Example: ∠A and ∠B are adjacent angles.   ∠B and ∠C are adjacent angles.

∠C and ∠D are adjacent angles.   ∠D and ∠A are adjacent angles.

Note

When angles are formed with two intersecting lines as pictured in the definition box, the measures of adjacent angles add up to 180°. (Can you see that two adjacent angles form a straight angle?)

EXAMPLE 6

Identify the adjacent angles.

Answer: ∠L and ∠M;
∠M and ∠N;
∠N and ∠K;
∠K and ∠L

Solution

∠S and ∠T are adjacent angles.   ∠T and ∠U are adjacent angles.

∠U and ∠R are adjacent angles.   ∠R and ∠S are adjacent angles.

[YOU TRY 6]   Identify the adjacent angles.

Now let's find some angle measures based on what we have learned about vertical and adjacent angles.

EXAMPLE 7

Answer: m∠X = 133°;
m∠Y = 47°;
m∠Z = 133°

Find the measures of angles A, B, and C.

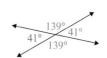

Solution

Look for any relationship between the 41° angle and *any other angle*: **The 41° angle and ∠B are vertical angles, so they have the same angle measure.**

$$m\angle B = 41°$$

What is the relationship between the 41° angle and ∠A? They are not only adjacent angles, but *they also form a straight angle*. Therefore, **the sum of their measures is 180°.**

$$41° + m\angle A = 180° \quad \text{or} \quad 180° - 41° = m\angle A = 139°$$

$$m\angle A = 139°$$

∠A and ∠C are vertical angles, so m∠A = m∠C.

$$m\angle C = 139°$$

We can fill in the missing angle measures:

Find the measures of angles *T*, *V*, and *W*.

EXAMPLE 8

Find each missing angle measure.

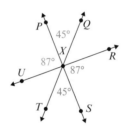

In-Class Example 8

Find each missing angle measure.

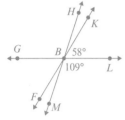

Answer:
m∠*FBM* = 13°;
m∠*FBG* = 58°;
m∠*GBH* = 109°;
m∠*HBK* = 13°

Solution

Begin by finding the vertical angles because they are congruent.

∠*RXS* ≅ ∠*UXP* so m∠*RXS* = m∠*UXP*

m∠*UXP* = 87°

∠*TXS* ≅ ∠*PXQ* so m∠*TXS* = m∠*PXQ*

m∠*PXQ* = 45°

Fill in these angle measures:

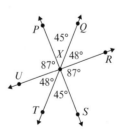

∠*TXQ* is a straight angle, so its measure is 180°.

Therefore, m∠*TXU* + m∠*UXP* + m∠*PXQ* = 180°. To find m∠*TXU*, add the measures of ∠*UXP* and ∠*PXQ*, then subtract from 180°.

m∠*UXP* + m∠*PXQ* = 87° + 45° = 132°

Then, **m∠*TXU* = 180° − 132° = 48°.**

∠*TXU* and ∠*QXR* are vertical angles, so their measures are the same:
m∠*QXR* = 48°.

Fill in all the missing angle measures.

Find each missing angle measure.

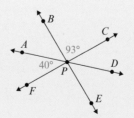

E Evaluate **9.2** Exercises   Do the exercises, and check your work.

*Additional answers can be found in the Answers to Exercises appendix.

Objective 1: Understand Complementary and Supplementary Angles

1) What are supplementary angles?
   Supplementary angles have measures that sum to 180°.
2) What are complementary angles?
   Complementary angles have measures that sum to 90°.

Find the measure of the complement of each of the given angles.

 3) m∠V = 61°   29°   4) m∠Y = 19°   71°

5) m∠Q = 23°   67°   6) m∠H = 38°   52°

7) m∠K = 7°   83°   8) m∠T = 46°   44°

Find the measure of the supplement of each of the given angles.

9) m∠C = 103°   77°   10) m∠X = 166°   14°

 11) m∠J = 54°   126°   12) m∠U = 21°   159°

13) m∠B = 117°   63°   14) m∠D = 8°   172°

Find the missing angle measure.

15) ∠ATB is a right angle. Find m∠b.

16) ∠ZXV is a right angle. Find m∠a.

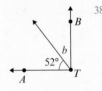

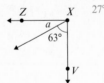

17) ∠BGN is a straight angle. Find m∠z.
138°

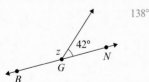

18) ∠RYQ is a straight angle. Find m∠a.
165°

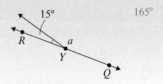

19) ∠ATB is a right angle. Find m∠y.

20) ∠KMR is a right angle. Find m∠n.   75°

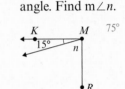

21) ∠WTV is a straight angle. Find m∠x.

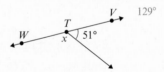

22) ∠KZD is a straight angle. Find m∠y.   22°

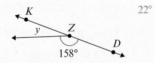

23) ∠JZE is a right angle.   56°

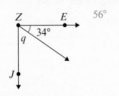

24) ∠CWQ is a straight angle.   123°

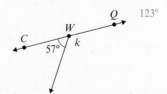

25) The measure of the supplement of an acute angle is *always, sometimes,* or *never* an obtuse angle.   always

26) The measure of the complement of an acute angle is *always, sometimes,* or *never* an obtuse angle.   never

Objective 2: Understand Congruent and Vertical Angles

27) What does it mean if two angles are congruent?
Their angle measures are the same.

28) Use the correct notation to write "∠*T* is congruent to ∠*K*."   ∠*T* ≅ ∠*K*

29) What do we know about the measures of vertical angles?   Their angle measures are the same.

30) What is the difference between vertical angles and adjacent angles?   Answers may vary.

Identify the vertical angles, and make a statement about their congruence.

31)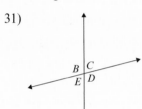
∠*B* and ∠*D* are vertical angles; therefore, ∠*B* ≅ ∠*D*.
∠*C* and ∠*E* are vertical angles; therefore, ∠*C* ≅ ∠*E*.

32)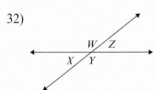
∠*W* and ∠*Y* are vertical angles; therefore, ∠*W* ≅ ∠*Y*.
∠*X* and ∠*Z* are vertical angles; therefore, ∠*X* ≅ ∠*Z*.

33)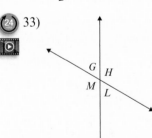
∠*G* and ∠*L* are vertical angles; therefore, ∠*G* ≅ ∠*L*.
∠*M* and ∠*H* are vertical angles; therefore, ∠*M* ≅ ∠*H*.

Find the measures of the indicated angles.

34) ∠*SRN* and ∠*BRN*   35) ∠*TJQ* and ∠*DJQ*

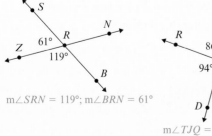

m∠*SRN* = 119°; m∠*BRN* = 61°

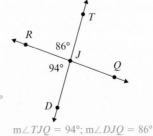

m∠*TJQ* = 94°; m∠*DJQ* = 86°

36) ∠*PQN* and ∠*PQV*   37) ∠*ADF* and ∠*FDB*

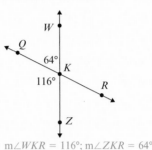

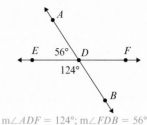

m∠*PQN* = 37°; m∠*PQV* = 143°

m∠*ADF* = 124°; m∠*FDB* = 56°

38) ∠*WKR* and ∠*ZKR*

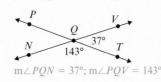

m∠*WKR* = 116°; m∠*ZKR* = 64°

Identify the adjacent angles.

39)   40)

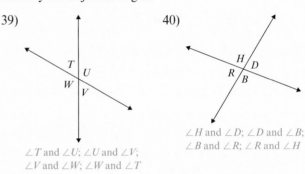

∠*T* and ∠*U*; ∠*U* and ∠*V*;
∠*V* and ∠*W*; ∠*W* and ∠*T*

∠*H* and ∠*D*; ∠*D* and ∠*B*;
∠*B* and ∠*R*; ∠*R* and ∠*H*

41) Draw two intersecting lines with vertical angles *P* and *R*.   Answers may vary.

42) Draw two intersecting lines with adjacent angles *G* and *H*.   Answers may vary.

43) Find the measures of angles *A*, *C*, and *F*.

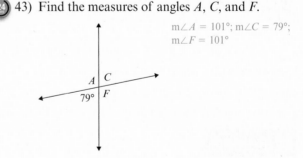

m∠*A* = 101°; m∠*C* = 79°;
m∠*F* = 101°

44) Find the measures of angles *K*, *M*, and *P*.

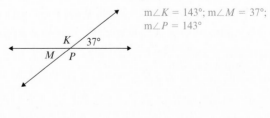

m∠*K* = 143°; m∠*M* = 37°;
m∠*P* = 143°

45) Find the measures of angles *T*, *U*, and *V*.

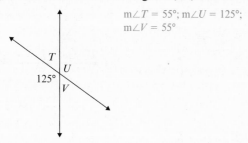

m∠*T* = 55°; m∠*U* = 125°;
m∠*V* = 55°

46) Find the measures of angles *H*, *D*, and *B*.

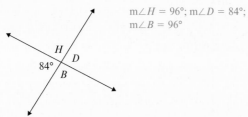

m∠*H* = 96°; m∠*D* = 84°;
m∠*B* = 96°

Find each missing angle measure.

 47)

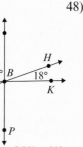

m∠*FBH* = 71°; m∠*PBK* = 91°;
m∠*PBQ* = 71°; m∠*QBD* = 18°

48)

m∠*BXL* = 31°; m∠*LXJ* = 110°;
m∠*JXH* = 39°; m∠*DXC* = 110°

49)

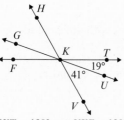

m∠*HKT* = 120°; m∠*VKF* = 120°;
m∠*FKG* = 19°; m∠*GKH* = 41°

50)

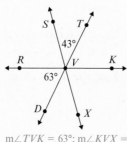

m∠*TVK* = 63°; m∠*KVX* = 74°;
m∠*DVX* = 43°; m∠*RVS* = 74°

51) When two lines intersect, four angles are formed. When three lines intersect at the same point, six angles are formed. How many angles are formed when five lines intersect at the same point, and what is the sum of the measures of all the angles?
10 angles; 360°

52) What angle is congruent to its complement?   45°

Mixed Exercises: Objectives 1 and 2
Identify the vertical angles and make a statement about their congruence.

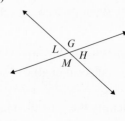 53)

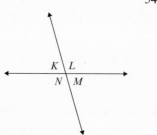

54)

55) If m∠*G* = 32°, find the measure of its supplement.
148°

56) If m∠*R* = 74°, find the measure of its complement.
16°

57) Find each missing angle measure.

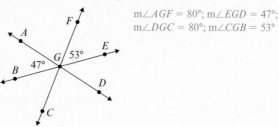

m∠*AGF* = 80°; m∠*EGD* = 47°;
m∠*DGC* = 80°; m∠*CGB* = 53°

58) Find the measure of angles *F*, *G*, and *H*.

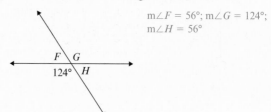

m∠*F* = 56°; m∠*G* = 124°;
m∠*H* = 56°

R Rethink

R1) Look at Exercises 57 and 58. What is the sum of the measures of all the angles? What conclusion can you draw to quickly check your work on similar problems?

R2) What other conclusions were you able to draw after completing this section?

9.3 Rectangles and Squares

What are your objectives for Section 9.3?	How can you accomplish each objective?
1 Find the Perimeter and Area of a Rectangle	• Write the definition of a *rectangle* in your own words, draw an example, and note its main characteristics. • Write the formula for determining the **Perimeter of a Rectangle** in your notes. • Write the formula for determining the **Area of a Rectangle** in your notes. • Complete the given examples on your own. • Complete You Trys 1–4.
2 Find the Perimeter and Area of a Square	• Write the definition of a *square* in your own words, draw an example, and note its main characteristics. • Write the formula for determining the **Perimeter of a Square** in your notes. • Write the formula for determining the **Area of a Square** in your notes. • Complete the given example on your own. • Complete You Try 5.
3 Find the Perimeter and Area of an Irregular Figure	• After following the examples, write your procedures for finding the perimeter and area of an irregular figure. • Complete the given example on your own. • Complete You Try 6.

W Work   **Read the explanations, follow the examples, take notes, and complete the You Trys.**

We have worked with rectangles in previous sections. Let's review some of those facts here.

1   Find the Perimeter and Area of a Rectangle

Definition

A **rectangle** is a four-sided figure containing four right angles.

Here are other important characteristics of a rectangle.

1) The opposite sides are parallel and congruent (the same length).

2) The longer side of a rectangle is called the **length,** often abbreviated l. The shorter side is called the **width,** often abbreviated w.

3) We can use a small square to indicate that a four-sided figure has 90° angles. We can do this in a couple of ways.

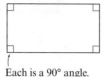

Each is a 90° angle.

If the sides are parallel and *one* 90° angle is indicated, then the other angles also measure 90°.

In Section 1.3, we said that the **perimeter** of a figure is the distance around the figure. So, if we are given a rectangle with length *l* and width *w*, we can use the following formulas to find its perimeter. Perimeter is often denoted by *P*.

W Hint

Is there another way to think about this formula?

Formula Perimeter of a Rectangle

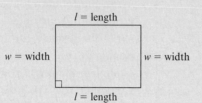

l = length

w = width   *w* = width

l = length

We can find the perimeter, *P*, of a rectangle using one of the following formulas:

1) $P = 2 \cdot \text{length} + 2 \cdot \text{width}$ or

2) $P = 2 \cdot l + 2 \cdot w$

EXAMPLE 1

Find the perimeter of the rectangle.

In-Class Example 1

Find the perimeter of the rectangle.

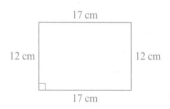

17 cm

12 cm   12 cm

17 cm

Answer: 58 cm

14 cm

9 cm   9 cm

14 cm

Solution

Identify the length, *l*, and the width, *w*. Then, use the formula $P = 2 \cdot l + 2 \cdot w$.

$l = 14$ cm, $w = 9$ cm

$P = 2 \cdot l + 2 \cdot w$
$P = 2 \cdot 14 \text{ cm} + 2 \cdot 9 \text{ cm}$ Substitute the values for *l* and *w*.
$P = 28 \text{ cm} + 18 \text{ cm}$ Multiply.
$P = 46 \text{ cm}$ Add.

The perimeter of the rectangle is 46 cm. We would get the same result if we just added the lengths of the sides: $P = 14 \text{ cm} + 9 \text{ cm} + 14 \text{ cm} + 9 \text{ cm} = 46 \text{ cm}$.

Find the perimeter of the rectangle.

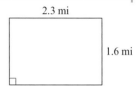

5 mm

21 mm

Let's use perimeter to solve an application.

EXAMPLE 2

In-Class Example 2

Use Example 2.

A trolley carries tourists around a city, and its route is in the shape of a rectangle. How far does the trolley drive in one complete route?

2.3 mi

1.6 mi

Solution

The trolley route is in the shape of a rectangle, and we are asked to find how far the trolley drives during one complete route. Since the trolley is driving *around* the outside of a rectangle, this is a *perimeter* problem.

Identify length and width: $l = 2.3$ mi, $w = 1.6$ mi

Use the formula $P = 2 \cdot l + 2 \cdot w$ to find the perimeter, P.

$P = 2 \cdot l + 2 \cdot w$

$P = 2 \cdot 2.3 \text{ mi} + 2 \cdot 1.6 \text{ mi}$ Substitute the values for l and w.

$P = 4.6 \text{ mi} + 3.2 \text{ mi}$ Multiply.

$P = 7.8 \text{ mi}$ Add.

The trolley goes 7.8 mi during one complete route.

[YOU TRY 2]

Deepa's jogging route is in the shape of a rectangle. How far does she jog in one complete route?

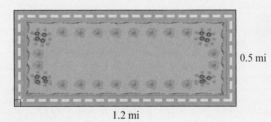

0.5 mi

1.2 mi

We first learned about the *area* of a figure in Section 3.6. The **area** of a figure is the size of the region enclosed in the figure.

For example, if we have a rug that is 8 ft long and 5 ft wide, the amount of surface that it covers is the *area* of the rug.

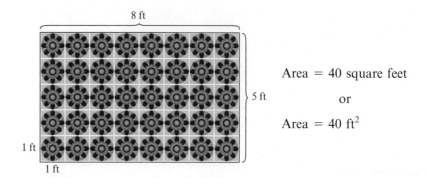

Area = 40 square feet

or

Area = 40 ft²

Each square inside this rectangle has a length and width of 1 foot. The area of each *square* is 1 *square* foot. This can be abbreviated as 1 ft².

How many squares are inside this rectangular rug? There are 40 squares. Therefore, the area of the rectangular rug is 40 *square* feet or 40 ft².

We can also find the area of a rectangle by multiplying its length and width.

Formula Area of a Rectangle

We can find the area, A, of a rectangle using this formula:

l = length

w = width

Area = length · width   or
$A = l \cdot w$

The units for area are *square* units like square feet (ft²), square inches (in²), square meters, (m²), etc.

We can apply the area formula to find the area of the rug pictured above: $A = l \cdot w = 8 \text{ ft} \cdot 5 \text{ ft} = 40 \text{ ft}^2$.

EXAMPLE 3

Find the area of the rectangle.

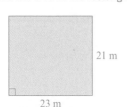
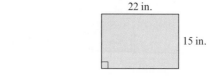

22 in.

15 in.

Solution

Identify the length and width: $l = 22$ in., $w = 15$ in.
Use the formula $A = l \cdot w$.

$$A = l \cdot w$$
$$A = 22 \text{ in.} \cdot 15 \text{ in.} \quad \text{Substitute the values for } l \text{ and } w.$$
$$A = 330 \text{ in}^2 \quad \text{Multiply.}$$

The area of the rectangle is 330 in².

Find the area of the rectangle.

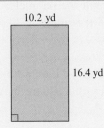

10.2 yd

16.4 yd

EXAMPLE 4

In-Class Example 4

Tam wants to buy carpet for her rectangular living room, which measures 16 ft by $12\frac{1}{2}$ ft. How much carpet will she need?

Answer: 200 ft^2

Dimitri buys a rectangular plot of land to build a house. The lot measures $23\frac{1}{2}$ m by 40 m. What is the area of the lot?

Solution

Draw and label a rectangle to represent the land.

Identify the length and width: $l = 40$ m,

$w = 23\frac{1}{2}$ m

40 m

$23\frac{1}{2}$ m

Use the formula $A = l \cdot w$.

$A = l \cdot w$

$A = 40 \text{ m} \cdot 23\frac{1}{2} \text{ m}$ Substitute the values for l and w.

$A = 40 \text{ m} \cdot \dfrac{47}{2} \text{ m}$ Change the mixed number to an improper fraction.

$A = 940 \text{ m}^2$ Multiply.

The area of the lot is 940 m^2.

[YOU TRY 4]

A rectangular truck bed liner is 1.8 m long and 1.1 m wide. Find the area of the liner.

---

2 Find the Perimeter and Area of a Square

Definition

A **square** is a rectangle with all four sides of equal length.

Example:

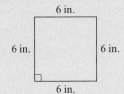

6 in.

6 in.   6 in.

6 in.

To find the perimeter of the square in the definition box, we can add the lengths of all of the sides:

$$P = 6 \text{ in.} + 6 \text{ in.} + 6 \text{ in.} + 6 \text{ in.} = 24 \text{ in.}$$

Notice that we have added the length of a side *four times*. So, we can find the perimeter of a square by multiplying the length of a side by 4.

Formula Perimeter of a Square

The **perimeter**, P, of a square with side length s can be found using one of these formulas:

$$\text{Perimeter} = \text{side} + \text{side} + \text{side} + \text{side} \quad \text{or}$$
$$P = 4 \cdot \text{side} \quad \text{or}$$
$$P = 4 \cdot s$$

We find the area of a square by multiplying length times width, but since those values are the same, we can use one of the following formulas.

Formula Area of a Square

The **area**, A, of a square with side length s can be found using one of these formulas:

$$\text{Area} = \text{side} \cdot \text{side} \quad \text{or}$$
$$A = s \cdot s \quad \text{or}$$
$$A = s^2$$

The units for area are *square* units.

EXAMPLE 5

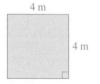
For the square pictured here, find a) its perimeter and b) its area.

7 cm

7 cm

Solution

a)   Identify the side length, s: $s = 7$ cm

Use the formula $P = 4 \cdot s$ or add up all the side lengths.

Formula	*Add side lengths*
$P = 4 \cdot s$	$P = \text{side} + \text{side} + \text{side} + \text{side}$
$P = 4 \cdot 7 \text{ cm}$	$P = 7 \text{ cm} + 7 \text{ cm} + 7 \text{ cm} + 7 \text{ cm}$
$P = 28 \text{ cm}$	$P = 28 \text{ cm}$

The perimeter is 28 cm. We get the same result using either method.

b)   The side length is $s = 7$ cm. Use one of the formulas to find the area.

$A = \text{side} \cdot \text{side}$	or	$A = s^2$
$A = 7 \text{ cm} \cdot 7 \text{ cm}$		$A = (7 \text{ cm})^2$
$A = 49 \text{ cm}^2$		$A = 49 \text{ cm}^2$

The area is 49 cm^2, and we get the same answer using either formula.

3 Find the Perimeter and Area of an Irregular Figure

Sometimes, we are asked to find the perimeter and area of a figure that consists of other figures put together. In this case, we must try to break down the figure into shapes that we know.

Remember that the perimeter of a figure is the distance *around* the figure, while the area of a figure is the size of the region enclosed in the figure.

EXAMPLE 6

In-Class Example 6

For the figure pictured here, find a) its perimeter and b) its area.

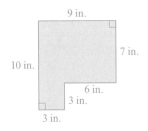

9 in.

10 in.

7 in.

6 in.

3 in.

3 in.

Answer:
a) 38 in.   b) 72 in²

Hint

Write explanations, in your own words, of how to find the perimeter and area of an irregularly-shaped figure.

For the figure pictured here, find a) its perimeter and b) its area.

14 in.

11 in.

16 in.

9 in.

5 in.

5 in.

Solution

a) The **perimeter** is the distance around the figure, so add up the lengths of all the sides.

$P = 14 \text{ in.} + 11 \text{ in.} + 9 \text{ in.} + 5 \text{ in.} + 5 \text{ in.} + 16 \text{ in.}$
$P = 60 \text{ in.}$

The perimeter is 60 in.

b) The **area** is the size of the region enclosed in the figure. Let's break up this figure into two regions: a rectangle and a square.

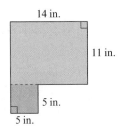

14 in.

11 in.

5 in.

5 in.

Total area = Area of rectangle + Area of square
$$= \quad l \cdot w \quad + \quad s^2$$
$$= 14 \text{ in.} \cdot 11 \text{ in.} \quad + \quad (5 \text{ in.})^2$$
$$= 154 \text{ in}^2 \quad + \quad 25 \text{ in}^2$$
$$= 179 \text{ in}^2$$

The area of the figure is 179 in².

[**YOU TRY 6**] For the figure pictured here, find
a) its perimeter and b) its area.

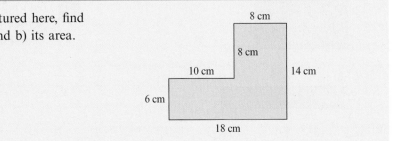

8 cm

8 cm

10 cm

14 cm

6 cm

18 cm

Using Technology

We can use a calculator to help us find the perimeter and area of a rectangle with length 6.5 cm and width 2.8 cm. Recall that $P = 2 \cdot l + 2 \cdot w$. Because we must follow the order of operations, we may need to instruct the calculator to perform multiplication before addition using the parenthesis keys. So to find the perimeter, we enter [(] [2] [×] [6] [.] [5] [)] [+] [(] [2] [×] [2] [.] [8] [)] [=] into the calculator. The display screen will show [1] [8] [.] [6] for the result. This means that the perimeter is equal to 18.6 cm. To find the area, we simply multiply the length times the width. Therefore, we enter [6] [.] [5] [×] [2] [.] [8] [=] into the calculator. The display screen will show 18.2 for the result. This means that the area is 18.2 cm².

E Evaluate 9.3 Exercises

Do the exercises, and check your work.

*Additional answers can be found in the Answers to Exercises appendix.

Objective 1: Find the Perimeter and Area of a Rectangle

1) In your own words, define *perimeter of a rectangle*. Then, state the formula for finding the perimeter.
   It is the distance around the rectangle. $P = 2 \cdot l + 2 \cdot w$

2) In your own words, define *area of a rectangle*. Then, state the formula.
   It is the size of the region enclosed by the rectangle. $A = l \cdot w$

Find the perimeter and area of the given rectangle.

3)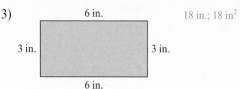
6 in.
3 in.   3 in.
6 in.
18 in.; 18 in²

4)
9 ft
7 ft
32 ft; 63 ft²

5)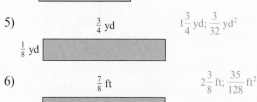
$\frac{3}{4}$ yd
$\frac{1}{8}$ yd
$1\frac{3}{4}$ yd; $\frac{3}{32}$ yd²

6)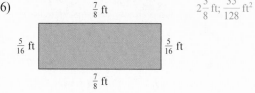
$\frac{7}{8}$ ft
$\frac{5}{16}$ ft $\frac{5}{16}$ ft
$\frac{7}{8}$ ft
$2\frac{3}{8}$ ft; $\frac{35}{128}$ ft²

7)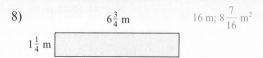
6$\frac{1}{2}$ in.
3$\frac{1}{2}$ in.
20 in.; $22\frac{3}{4}$ in²

8)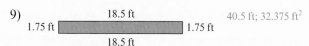
6$\frac{3}{4}$ m
1$\frac{1}{4}$ m
16 m; $8\frac{7}{16}$ m²

9)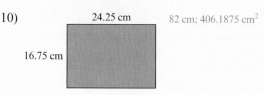
18.5 ft
1.75 ft   1.75 ft
18.5 ft
40.5 ft; 32.375 ft²

10) 24.25 cm
16.75 cm
82 cm; 406.1875 cm²

11) A regulation bowling lane is 60 ft long from the foul line to the head pin and 41.5 in. wide. Find the perimeter and area of this portion of the lane in units of inches. (United States Bowling Congress)
1523 in.; 29,880 in²

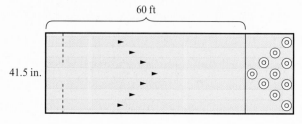
60 ft
41.5 in.

12) Steve's bike route is in the shape of a rectangle. How far does he ride his bike if he rides through his full route? 14.6 km

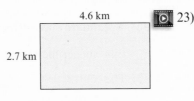
4.6 km
2.7 km

13) Ogechi's rose garden is 13.25 ft long and 1.5 ft wide. What length of decorative fencing does she need to line the perimeter of the garden? 29.5 ft

13.25 ft
1.5 ft

14) Higinio wants to make eight cloth place mats for his dining table. Using the dimensions for one place mat shown in the figure at right, what is the combined area of all eight place mats? 1920 in²

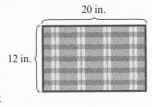
20 in.
12 in.

15) Suppose a rectangle has a perimeter of 20 ft. If the rectangle has a length of 8 ft, what is its width? 2 ft

16) What is the sum of the measures of all the angles inside a rectangle? 360°

Objective 2: Find the Perimeter and Area of a Square

17) Suppose a square has a perimeter of 10 ft. What is its side length? 2.5 ft or $2\frac{1}{2}$ ft

18) Answer *true* or *false*. If the area of a square is 16 m², its side length is 8 m. false

Find the perimeter and area of the given square.

19)
12 cm
12 cm
48 cm; 144 cm²

20)
17 in.
17 in.
68 in.; 289 in²

21)
$\frac{3}{5}$ m
$\frac{3}{5}$ m
$\frac{3}{5}$ m
$\frac{3}{5}$ m
$2\frac{2}{5}$ m; $\frac{9}{25}$ m²

22)
7.8 yd
7.8 yd
7.8 yd
7.8 yd
31.2 yd; 60.84 yd²

23)
4.6 mm
4.6 mm
18.4 mm; 21.16 mm²

24)
$\frac{11}{16}$ ft
$\frac{11}{16}$ ft
$2\frac{3}{4}$ ft; $\frac{121}{256}$ ft²

25)
$1\frac{3}{8}$ m
$1\frac{3}{8}$ m
$5\frac{1}{2}$ m; $1\frac{57}{64}$ m²

26)
$\frac{5}{6}$ yd
$\frac{5}{6}$ yd
$3\frac{1}{3}$ yd; $\frac{25}{36}$ yd²

27) A square has an area of 25 ft². What is the length of each side of the square? 5 ft

28) The perimeter of a square is 34 mm. How long is each side of the square? $\frac{17}{2}$ mm or $8\frac{1}{2}$ mm

Objective 3: Find the Perimeter and Area of an Irregular Figure

Find the perimeter and the area of each figure.

29)
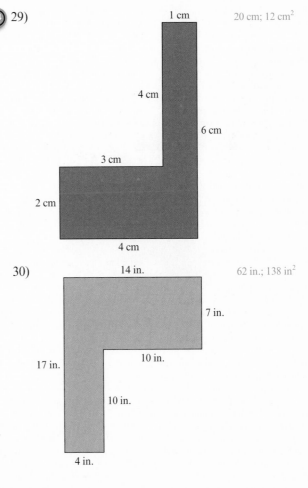
1 cm
4 cm
6 cm
3 cm
2 cm
4 cm
20 cm; 12 cm²

30)
14 in.
7 in.
10 in.
17 in.
10 in.
4 in.
62 in.; 138 in²

31)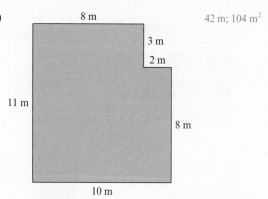

8 m   42 m; 104 m²

3 m

2 m

11 m

8 m

10 m

32)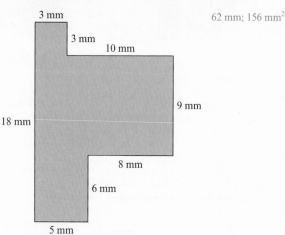

3 mm   62 mm; 156 mm²

3 mm

10 mm

9 mm

18 mm

8 mm

6 mm

5 mm

33)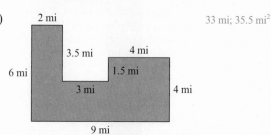

2 mi   33 mi; 35.5 mi²

3.5 mi   4 mi

6 mi   1.5 mi

3 mi   4 mi

9 mi

34)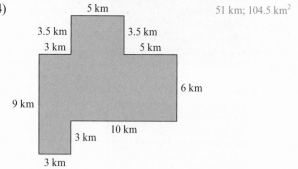

5 km   51 km; 104.5 km²

3.5 km   3.5 km

3 km   5 km

6 km

9 km

3 km   10 km

3 km

Solve each problem.

35) A regulation football field is 120 yd long and $53\frac{1}{3}$ yd wide. Find the perimeter and the area of the field. (www.nfl.com) $346\frac{2}{3}$ yd; 6400 yd²

36) A standard sheet of paper measures $8\frac{1}{2}$ in. by 11 in. Find its perimeter and area.   39 in.; $93\frac{1}{2}$ in²

37) The central processing unit (CPU) is responsible for handling all instructions and basic calculations it receives from hardware components and software programs within a computer system. The CPU square package connects to the motherboard via a socket. Find the total area of the CPU square package if one side length is 37.5 mm. (www.intel.com)   1406.25 mm²

38) The HTC EVO™ 3D phone has a total area of 13 in². If its length is 5 in., what is the phone's width? (www.htc.com)   2.6 in.

39) Mr. and Mrs. Miller want to have the kitchen floor finished with ceramic tile. A local tile company charges $8.25 per square foot to install the tile they have chosen. If their kitchen floor measures 10 ft by 12 ft, what is the total cost to have the tile installed? $990

40) The Mejias' living room floor is shown in the diagram. If the cost of installing new carpet and padding is $6.25 per square foot, what is the total cost? $1025

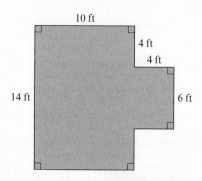

10 ft

4 ft

4 ft

14 ft

6 ft

41) The area of a baseball infield within the baselines is a square with a side length of 90 ft. Find the area within the baselines. How far must a baseball player travel when he hits a home run? (www.mlb.com)   8100 ft²; 360 ft

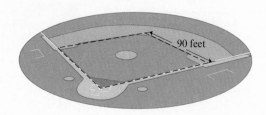

90 feet

42) Mackenzie has 22 ft of decorative fencing to line her rectangular flower garden. If her garden must have a width of 4 ft, what will the length of her garden have to be to use all 22 ft of fencing?   7 ft

43) A walking area surrounding the pool in the diagram below is going to be refinished with a nonslip surface. If it costs $17.50 per square foot to install the surface, what is the total cost? $1890

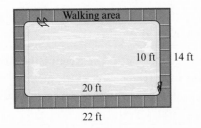

44) Mr. and Mrs. Anh want to install wood flooring and carpet in an area of their home as shown in the diagram below. Installation costs are $5.75 per square foot for carpet and $6.25 per square foot for the wood flooring. What is the total cost for the installation of both? $1128

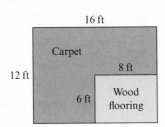

Mixed Exercises: Objectives 1–3

Sketch the described area, and then find the area and perimeter of the figure.

45) A rectangle that is 6 cm by 4 cm
area = 24 cm^2; perimeter = 20 cm

46) A square with a 6-in. side length
area = 36 in^2; perimeter = 24 in.

Find the perimeter and the area of the given figure. In Exercises 49 and 50, you must first find the missing length.

47)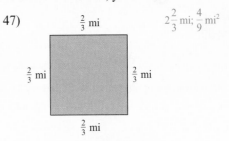
$2\frac{2}{3}$ mi; $\frac{4}{9}$ mi^2

48)
15 in.; 14.0625 in^2

49)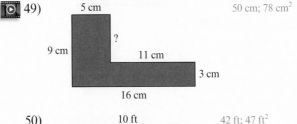
50 cm; 78 cm^2

50)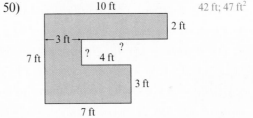
42 ft; 47 ft^2

Solve each problem.

51) Cailen is an artist and wants to frame one of her paintings by herself. The frame she chooses costs $1.19 per inch. Find the cost of the frame if the painting is 1.75 ft by 2.5 ft. $121.38

52) Frank will replace the broken glass in his back door with a rectangular piece of glass that costs $2.79 per square foot. If he needs a piece of glass that is 21 in. by 36 in., find the cost of the glass. $14.65

R Rethink

R1) Revisit Exercises 29–31, and think of another way to find the total area using subtraction. Describe what you did to find the area.

R2) Describe how a good knowledge of common squares and multiplication has helped you with this section.

9.4 Triangles

P Prepare

O Organize

What are your objectives for Section 9.4?	How can you accomplish each objective?
1 Find the Perimeter and Area of a Triangle	• Write the definition of a *triangle* in your own words, draw an example, and note its main characteristics. • Know how to find the perimeter of a triangle. • Write the formula for determining the **Area of a Triangle** in your notes. • Complete the given examples on your own. • Complete You Trys 1–3.
2 Find Angle Measures in a Triangle	• Write the property for **The Sum of the Angle Measures in a Triangle** in your notes. • Complete the given example on your own. • Complete You Try 4.
3 Classify Triangles	• Learn the three different classifications of triangles by their angles: *acute triangle, right triangle,* and *obtuse triangle.* • Learn the three different classifications of triangles by their sides: *equilateral triangle, isosceles triangle,* and *scalene triangle.* • Complete the given examples on your own. • Complete You Trys 5 and 6.

W Work

Read the explanations, follow the examples, take notes, and complete the You Trys.

In this section, we will learn about triangles.

1 Find the Perimeter and Area of a Triangle

> ### Definition
>
> A **triangle** is a closed figure with exactly three sides.
>
> Example:
>
>

As with other figures, the perimeter of a triangle is the distance around the triangle. To find the perimeter, we add the lengths of the three sides.

EXAMPLE 1

Find the perimeter of this triangle.

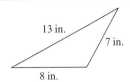

13 in.

7 in.

8 in.

Solution

$P = 13$ in. $+ 7$ in. $+ 8$ in. $= 28$ in.

[YOU TRY 1] Find the perimeter of this triangle.

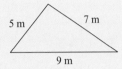

5 m

7 m

9 m

In-Class Example 1

Find the perimeter of this triangle.

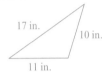

17 in.

10 in.

11 in.

Answer: 38 in.

To find the *area* of a triangle, we use the following formula. (The derivation of the area formula is given in Appendix A.5.)

Formula Area of a Triangle

The **area**, A, of a triangle is

$$\text{Area} = \frac{1}{2} \cdot \text{base} \cdot \text{height} \quad \text{or}$$

$$A = \frac{1}{2} \cdot b \cdot h \quad \text{or}$$

$$A = 0.5 \cdot b \cdot h$$

where $b =$ the length of the base and $h =$ the height.

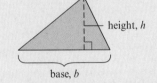

height, h

base, b

BE CAREFUL The *base* of the triangle is always the side of the triangle that forms the right angle with the height. The height is not always labeled inside the triangle.

Examples:

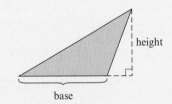

height

base

height

base

EXAMPLE 2

Find the area of each triangle.

a)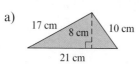

b)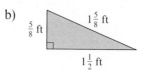

c)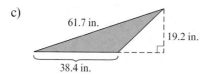

Solution

a) Identify the base, b, and height, h. Remember, the base is the side that forms the right angle with the height.

$$b = 21 \text{ cm} \qquad h = 8 \text{ cm}$$

(We do not need the lengths 17 cm and 10 cm.)

$$A = \frac{1}{2} \cdot b \cdot h$$

$$A = \frac{1}{2} \cdot 21 \text{ cm} \cdot \overset{4}{\underset{1}{8}} \text{ cm} \qquad \text{Substitute the values, and divide out 2.}$$

$$A = 84 \text{ cm}^2 \qquad \text{Multiply.}$$

The area is 84 cm^2. Remember to use *square* units for area.

b) Identify the base, b, and height, h: $\quad b = 1\frac{1}{2} \text{ ft}, \quad h = \frac{5}{8} \text{ ft}$

$$A = \frac{1}{2} \cdot b \cdot h$$

$$A = \frac{1}{2} \cdot 1\frac{1}{2} \text{ ft} \cdot \frac{5}{8} \text{ ft} \qquad \text{Substitute the values.}$$

$$A = \frac{1}{2} \cdot \frac{3}{2} \text{ ft} \cdot \frac{5}{8} \text{ ft} \qquad \text{Change the mixed number to a fraction.}$$

$$A = \frac{15}{32} \text{ ft}^2 \qquad \text{Multiply.}$$

The area is $\frac{15}{32}$ ft^2.

c) In this triangle, the base must be extended with a dotted line to find the height. (The base is *still* the base of the actual triangle.)

Identify the base, b, and the height, h: $\quad b = 38.4$ in. and $h = 19.2$ in.

Because the numbers are decimals, we will use the area formula with the decimal for $\frac{1}{2}$, $A = 0.5 \cdot b \cdot h$.

$$A = 0.5 \cdot b \cdot h$$

$$A = 0.5 \cdot 38.4 \text{ in.} \cdot 19.2 \text{ in.} \qquad \text{Substitute the values.}$$

$$A = 368.64 \text{ in}^2 \qquad \text{Multiply.}$$

The area is 368.64 in^2.

[YOU TRY 2] Find the area of each triangle.

a)

37 in.   12 in.   13 in.

40 in.

b)

$2\frac{1}{2}$ m

$2\frac{5}{6}$ m $1\frac{1}{3}$ m

c)

34.7 cm

73.5 cm

29.5 cm

52.6 cm

Let's put together what we know about triangles and rectangles to solve a problem.

EXAMPLE 3

Find the area of the shaded region.

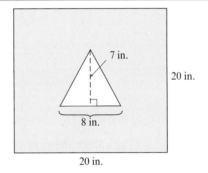

7 in.

20 in.

8 in.

20 in.

In-Class Example 3

Find the area of the shaded region.

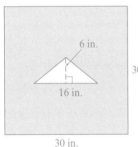

6 in.

30 in.

16 in.

30 in.

Answer: 852 in²

Solution

The area of the shaded region is the area of the square *minus* the area of the triangle.

Square

Length of a side, $s = 20$ in.

$A = s^2 = (20 \text{ in.})^2 = 400 \text{ in}^2$

Triangle

$b = 8$ in. and $h = 7$ in.

$A = \frac{1}{2} \cdot b \cdot h = \frac{1}{2} \cdot 8 \text{ in.} \cdot 7 \text{ in.} = 28 \text{ in}^2$

$$\begin{array}{rcl} \text{Area of the} \\ \text{shaded region} & = & \text{Area of} \\ & & \text{the square} \end{array} - \begin{array}{c} \text{Area of} \\ \text{the triangle} \end{array}$$

$= 400 \text{ in}^2 \quad - \quad 28 \text{ in}^2$

$= 372 \text{ in}^2$

The area of the shaded region is 372 in².

[YOU TRY 3] Find the area of the shaded region.

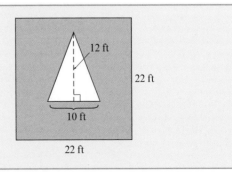

12 ft

22 ft

10 ft

22 ft

Next we will learn about angle measures in a triangle.

2 Find Angle Measures in a Triangle

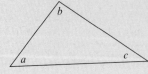
> **W Hint**
>
> Find 90 − 37. How could that help you with triangles that have a right angle?

We can use this fact to find missing angle measures in a triangle.

EXAMPLE 4

In-Class Example 4

Find m∠x in each triangle.

a)

b)

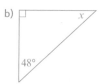

Answer: a) 119° b) 42°

Find m∠x in each triangle.

a)

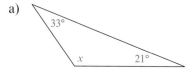

b)

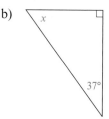

Solution

a) Since the measures of all the angles in a triangle add up to 180°, we find m∠x by subtracting:

$$m\angle x = 180° - 33° - 21° = 126°$$

b) It may look like only one angle is labeled (37°), but remember that the angle marked with the small square is a *right* angle, so its measure is 90°.

$$m\angle x = 180° - 37° - 90° = 53°$$

↑   ↑

All of the   The measure of
angles add   the right angle
to 180°.

[**YOU TRY 4**] Find m∠x in each triangle.

a)

b)

3 Classify Triangles

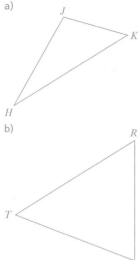
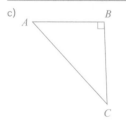
We can classify triangles by the measures of their angles and by the lengths of their sides.

Definition

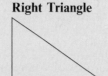

Acute Triangle

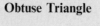

Right Triangle

Obtuse Triangle

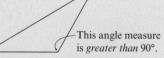

This angle measure is *greater than* 90°.

An **acute triangle** is one in which all three angles are acute. (All three angles measure *less than* 90°.)

A **right triangle** contains one *right*, or 90°, angle.

An **obtuse triangle** contains one *obtuse* angle. (The measure of an obtuse angle is *greater than* 90°.)

EXAMPLE 5

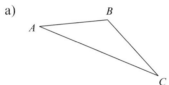
Classify each triangle as acute, right, or obtuse.

a)

b)

c)

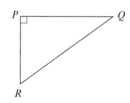

Solution

a)   This is an *obtuse triangle* because $\angle B$ is an obtuse angle. ($m\angle B$ is *greater than* 90°.)

b)   This is an *acute triangle* because each angle is acute. (The measure of each angle is *less than* 90°.)

c)   This is a *right triangle* because $\angle P$ is a right angle. ($m\angle P = 90°$)

[YOU TRY 5]

Classify each triangle as acute, right, or obtuse.

a)

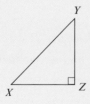

b)

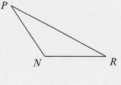

c)

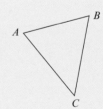

Definition

Equilateral Triangle   **Isosceles Triangle**   **Scalene Triangle**

An **equilateral triangle** has *three* sides of equal length.

An **isosceles triangle** has *two* sides of equal length.

A **scalene triangle** has *no* sides of equal length.

When the sides of triangles are the same length, we mark them with a hash mark like this: |

In-Class Example 6

Classify each triangle as equilateral, isosceles, or scalene.

a)
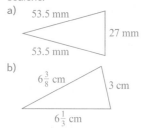

b)

c)

Answer:
a) isosceles   b) scalene
c) equilateral

EXAMPLE 6

Classify each triangle as equilateral, isosceles, or scalene.

a)
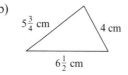

b)

c)

Solution

a)   This is an *isosceles triangle* because two of the sides are the same length.

b)   This is a *scalene triangle* because no sides are the same length.

c)   What do you notice about the lengths of the sides? *All sides are the same length.* This is an *equilateral triangle.*

[YOU TRY 6]

Classify each triangle as equilateral, isosceles, or scalene.

a)
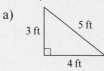

b)
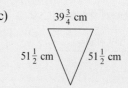

c)

Note

Each angle in an equilateral triangle has a measure of 60°.

ANSWERS TO [YOU TRY] EXERCISES

1) 21 m   2) a) 240 in^2 b) $1\frac{2}{3}$ m^2 c) 775.85 cm^2 3) 424 ft^2 4) a) 67°   b) 25°

5) a) right   b) obtuse   c) acute   6) a) scalene   b) equilateral   c) isosceles

---

E Evaluate **9.4** Exercises   Do the exercises, and check your work.

*Additional answers can be found in the Answers to Exercises appendix.

Objective 1: Find the Perimeter and Area of a Triangle

1) What is the formula for the area of a triangle?

2) How do you identify the base of a triangle?
It is the side of the triangle that forms a right angle with the height.

Find the perimeter and area of the given triangle.

3)
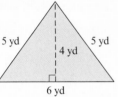
5 yd   4 yd   5 yd
6 yd
16 yd; 12 yd^2

4)
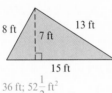
8 ft   7 ft   13 ft
15 ft
36 ft; $52\frac{1}{2}$ ft^2

5)
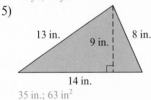
13 in.   9 in.   8 in.
14 in.
35 in.; 63 in^2

6)
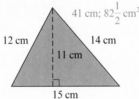
12 cm   11 cm   14 cm
15 cm
41 cm; $82\frac{1}{2}$ cm^2
14 m; $5\frac{5}{8}$ m^2

7)
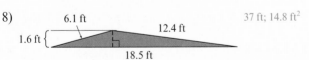
$6\frac{1}{2}$ m $2\frac{1}{2}$ m $2\frac{1}{4}$ m
5 m

8)
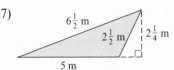
6.1 ft   12.4 ft
1.6 ft
18.5 ft
37 ft; 14.8 ft^2

9)
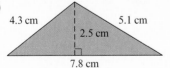
4.3 cm   2.5 cm   5.1 cm
7.8 cm
17.2 cm; 9.75 cm^2

10)
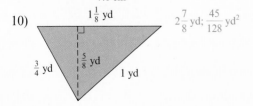
$1\frac{1}{8}$ yd
$\frac{3}{4}$ yd $\frac{5}{8}$ yd   1 yd
$2\frac{7}{8}$ yd; $\frac{45}{128}$ yd^2

Find the area of the shaded region.

11)
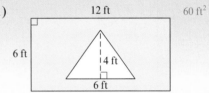
12 ft   60 ft^2
6 ft   4 ft
6 ft

12)
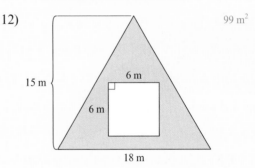
99 m^2
15 m   6 m   6 m
18 m

Find the area of the *unshaded* region in each figure.

13)
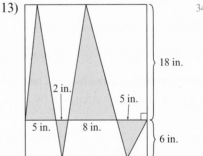
342 in^2
2 in.   5 in.   18 in.
5 in.   8 in.   6 in.

14)
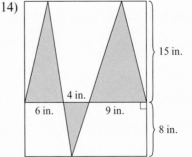
308.5 in^2
15 in.
4 in.
6 in.   9 in.   8 in.

Find the perimeter and the area of each figure.

24
15)

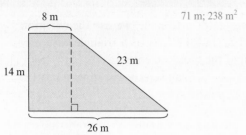

71 m; 238 m²

16)

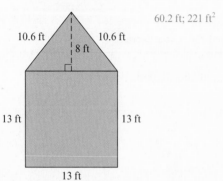

60.2 ft; 221 ft²

17)

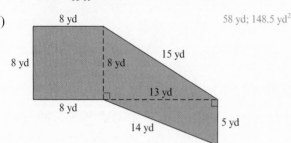

58 yd; 148.5 yd²

18)

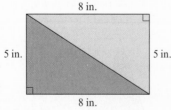

54 in.; 96 in²

19) Find the area of each triangle in the figure. Then, find the area of the rectangle that is formed by both triangles. What do you notice?

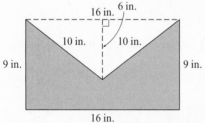

20 in²; 20 in²; 40 in²; The sum of the areas of the two triangles equals the area of the rectangle.

20) How many different triangles can you find in the figure below?

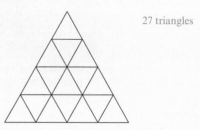

27 triangles

Objective 2: Find Angle Measures in a Triangle

21) The measures of all the angles of a triangle add up to what number?   180°

22) Answer *true* or *false*. A triangle can have two right angles.   false

Find m∠x in each triangle.

23)

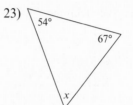

m∠x = 59°

24)

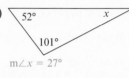

m∠x = 27°

25)

m∠x = 36°

26)

m∠x = 20°

27)

m∠x = 13°

28)

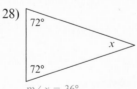

m∠x = 36°

29)

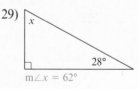

m∠x = 62°

30)

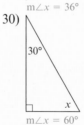

m∠x = 60°

Objective 3: Classify Triangles

31) What is an acute triangle?
    a triangle with three acute angles

32) What is an obtuse triangle?
    a triangle with an obtuse angle

33) What is a scalene triangle?
    a triangle with three sides of different lengths

34) What is an equilateral triangle?
    a triangle with all sides of the same length

Classify each triangle as acute, right, or obtuse.

35) 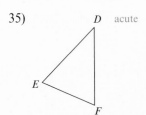 acute

36) 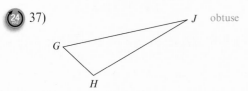 obtuse

37) 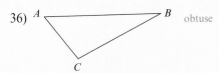 obtuse

38) 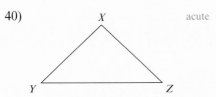 right   39) 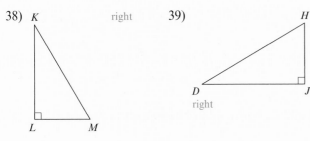 right

40) 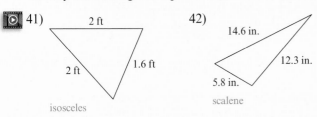 acute

Classify each triangle as equilateral, isosceles, or scalene.

41)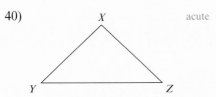
2 ft
2 ft   1.6 ft
isosceles

42)
14.6 in.
12.3 in.
5.8 in.
scalene

43)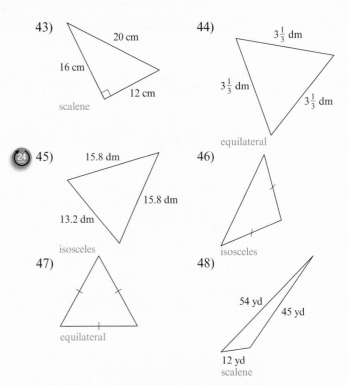
20 cm
16 cm
12 cm
scalene

44)
$3\frac{1}{3}$ dm
$3\frac{1}{3}$ dm
$3\frac{1}{3}$ dm
equilateral

45)
15.8 dm
15.8 dm
13.2 dm
isosceles

46)
isosceles

47)
equilateral

48)
54 yd
45 yd
12 yd
scalene

For Exercises 49–52, answer *true* or *false*.

49) A triangle can have two obtuse angles.   false

50) Each of the angles in an equilateral triangle has a measure of 60°.   true

51) Every equilateral triangle has three acute angles.   true

52) A right triangle can have an obtuse angle.   false

Solve each problem.

53) A hexagonal gazebo rooftop is made using equally-sized triangles. Use the picture to calculate the total area of the rooftop.

(Note: A hexagon is a six-sided figure.)

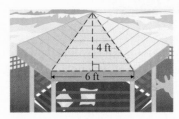
4 ft
6 ft

72 ft²

54) Find the area of the front side of the gingerbread house below.

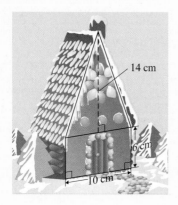

14 cm

6 cm

10 cm

130 cm²

55) A community center wishes to have its courtyard area covered with natural stone pavers. If the installation cost is $12 per square foot, use the diagram below to determine the total cost.

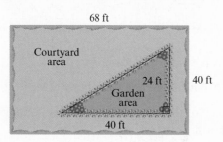

68 ft

Courtyard area

24 ft   40 ft

Garden area

40 ft

$26,880

56) Shirley buys a piece of remnant fabric that is triangular in shape with a base of length 2 yd and a height measuring $\frac{1}{2}$ yd. If the fabric sells for $4.50 per square yard, how much does Shirley pay for the remnant fabric? $2.25

57) The 3rd POWER 312 speaker cabinet is triangular in shape and is an innovative approach to guitar amplification. Each individual cabinet is approximately 0.86 m along the base and 0.76 m in height. Using these dimensions, find the front surface area of the four-speaker cabinet system shown below. (www.3rdpower.com)

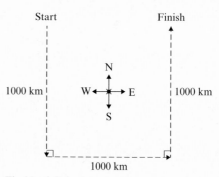

1.3072 m²

58) Where on the planet can you travel the rectangular path shown below and end up at the same place you started? (Hint: The curvature of the Earth bends the path such that you start and finish at the same point.) How does this problem relate to a triangle?

Start   Finish

N

1000 km   W ← → E   1000 km

S

1000 km

The North Pole; Answers may vary.

R Rethink

R1) Can a triangle have more than one obtuse or right angle? Why or why not? Draw some triangles to help you reach your conclusion.

R2) How do the lengths of the sides of a triangle compare with the sizes of the angles in the triangle?

9.5 Parallelograms and Trapezoids

P Prepare

What are your objectives for Section 9.5?	How can you accomplish each objective?
1 Find the Perimeter and Area of a Parallelogram	• Write the definition of a *parallelogram* in your own words, draw an example, and note its main characteristics. • Know how to find the perimeter of a parallelogram. • Write the formula for determining the **Area of a Parallelogram** in your notes. • Complete the given examples on your own. • Complete You Trys 1–3.
2 Find the Perimeter and Area of a Trapezoid	• Write the definition of a *trapezoid* in your own words, draw an example, and note its main characteristics. • Know how to find the perimeter of a trapezoid. • Write the formula for determining the **Area of a Trapezoid** in your notes. • Complete the given examples on your own. • Complete You Trys 4–6.

O Organize

W Work

Read the explanations, follow the examples, take notes, and complete the You Trys.

The next geometric figures we will learn about are parallelograms and trapezoids. Let's discuss parallelograms first.

1 Find the Perimeter and Area of a Parallelogram

Definition

A **parallelogram** is a four-sided figure whose opposite sides are parallel and the same length.

Here are two examples of parallelograms.

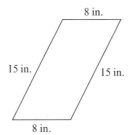

The opposite sides are the same length, and they are parallel.

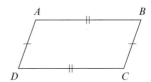

$\overline{AD} \parallel \overline{BC}$ ($\overline{AD}$ is parallel to $\overline{BC}$)

and

$\overline{AB} \parallel \overline{DC}$ ($\overline{AB}$ is parallel to $\overline{DC}$)

Opposite sides are the same length, as indicated by the hash marks "|" and "‖".

Find the perimeter of the
parallelogram.

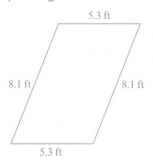

5.3 ft

8.1 ft   8.1 ft

5.3 ft

Answer: 26.8 ft

Note

Rectangles and squares are also parallelograms.

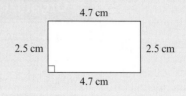

4.7 cm

2.5 cm   2.5 cm

4.7 cm

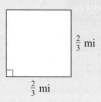

$\frac{2}{3}$ mi

$\frac{2}{3}$ mi

How do we find the perimeter of a parallelogram? Add the lengths of the four sides.

EXAMPLE 1

Find the perimeter of the parallelogram.

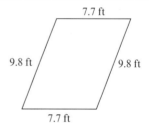

7.7 ft

9.8 ft   9.8 ft

7.7 ft

Solution

$P = 7.7 \text{ ft} + 9.8 \text{ ft} + 7.7 \text{ ft} + 9.8 \text{ ft} = 35 \text{ ft}$

[YOU TRY 1] Find the perimeter of the parallelogram.

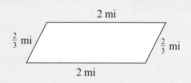

2 mi

$\frac{2}{3}$ mi $\frac{2}{3}$ mi

2 mi

We can use this formula to find the area of a parallelogram. (The derivation of the area formula is given in Appendix A.5.)

Formula Area of a Parallelogram

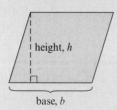

height, h

base, b

The area, A, of a parallelogram is

$$\text{Area} = \text{base} \cdot \text{height} \qquad \text{or}$$
$$A = b \cdot h$$

where b = the length of the base and h = the height. Notice that the base is the side that forms a right angle with the height.

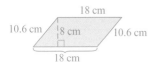
Find the area of the parallelogram.

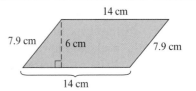

Solution

Area = base · height, so identify the base and height. Remember, the base is the side that forms the right angle with the height.

$$b = 14 \text{ cm} \qquad h = 6 \text{ cm}$$

(We do not need the 7.9 cm to find the area.)

$$A = b \cdot h$$
$$A = 14 \text{ cm} \cdot 6 \text{ cm} \qquad \text{Substitute the values.}$$
$$A = 84 \text{ cm}^2 \qquad \text{Multiply.}$$

The area of the parallelogram is 84 cm².

[YOU TRY 2] Find the area of the parallelogram.

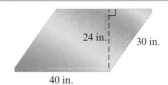

A piece of sheet metal in the shape of the given parallelogram costs $0.02 per square inch to produce. How much does it cost to produce this piece of sheet metal?

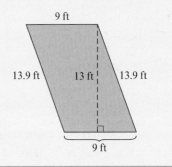

Solution

The cost of producing the piece of sheet metal is $0.02 per *square inch*. *Square inches* are units of *area,* so first we must find the area of the sheet metal.

Identify the base and the height: $b = 40$ in. and $h = 24$ in.

$$A = b \cdot h = 40 \text{ in.} \cdot 24 \text{ in.} = 960 \text{ in}^2$$

To find the cost of the sheet metal, multiply the area and the cost per square inch.

$$\text{Cost} = \text{Area} \cdot \text{Cost per square inch}$$
$$= 960 \text{ in}^2 \cdot \frac{\$0.02}{\text{in}^2} \qquad \text{Write the cost per square inch as a fraction.}$$
$$= \frac{960 \text{ in}^2}{1} \cdot \frac{\$0.02}{\text{in}^2} \qquad \text{Divide out the units.}$$
$$= \$19.20 \qquad \text{Multiply.}$$

The cost of producing this sheet metal is $19.20. Notice that the units of in² divide out and leave us with a unit of dollars, the correct unit for cost.

[YOU TRY 3] A jewelry maker will use a piece of metal in the shape of this parallelogram to make a medallion for a necklace. The metal costs $0.03 per square centimeter. What is the cost of the metal?

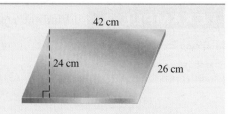

42 cm

24 cm

26 cm

2 Find the Perimeter and Area of a Trapezoid

Definition

A **trapezoid** is a four-sided figure with exactly one pair of parallel sides.

Here are some examples of trapezoids.

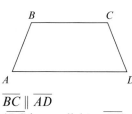

$\overline{BC} \parallel \overline{AD}$
($\overline{BC}$ is parallel to $\overline{AD}$)

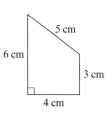

The sides of length 6 cm and 3 cm are parallel.

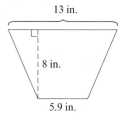

The sides of length 13 in. and 5.9 in. are parallel.

Note

The opposite sides of a trapezoid do *not* have to be the same length.

To find the perimeter of a trapezoid, we add the lengths of the four sides. To find the *area* of a trapezoid, use this formula:

Formula Area of a Trapezoid

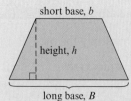

short base, b

height, h

long base, B

The area, A, of a trapezoid is

$$A = \frac{1}{2} \cdot \text{height} \cdot (\text{short base} + \text{long base}) \quad \text{or}$$

$$A = \frac{1}{2} \cdot h \cdot (b + B) \quad \text{or}$$

$$A = 0.5 \cdot h \cdot (b + B)$$

where h = the height, b = the length of the short base, and B = the length of the long base.

The bases are always the parallel sides.

EXAMPLE 4

Find the perimeter and area of each trapezoid.

a)

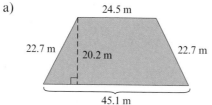

b)

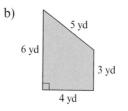

Solution

a) *Perimeter:* The perimeter is the distance around the figure, so add the lengths of the sides. (Do not add the 20.2 m because it is the height of the trapezoid and not a side.)

$$P = 24.5 \text{ m} + 22.7 \text{ m} + 45.1 \text{ m} + 22.7 \text{ m} = 115 \text{ m}$$

The perimeter is 115 m.

Area: Because the lengths contain decimal numbers, we will use the formula for the area of a trapezoid that contains the decimal:

$$A = 0.5 \cdot h \cdot (b + B)$$

where h = height, b = short base, and B = long base. Identify h, b, and B. *The bases are the parallel sides.*

$$h = 20.2 \text{ m} \qquad b = 24.5 \text{ m} \qquad B = 45.1 \text{ m}$$

(We do *not* need either of the 22.7 m sides.)

$A = 0.5 \cdot h \cdot (b + B)$

$A = 0.5 \cdot 20.2 \text{ m} \cdot (24.5 \text{ m} + 45.1 \text{ m})$ Substitute the values.

$A = 0.5 \cdot 20.2 \text{ m} \cdot (69.6 \text{ m})$ Add within the parentheses.

$A = 702.96 \text{ m}^2$ Multiply.

The area is 702.96 m^2.

b) *Perimeter:* $P = 5 \text{ yd} + 3 \text{ yd} + 4 \text{ yd} + 6 \text{ yd} = 18 \text{ yd}$

Area: We will use the formula $A = \dfrac{1}{2} \cdot h \cdot (b + B)$, and identify h, b, and B.

The parallel sides are 6 yd and 3 yd, so those are the bases.

$$b = 3 \text{ yd} \qquad \text{and} \qquad B = 6 \text{ yd}$$

Short base   Long base

What is h? $h = 4$ yd. Notice that this segment forms a right angle with each base.

$A = \dfrac{1}{2} \cdot h \cdot (b + B)$

$A = \dfrac{1}{2} \cdot 4 \text{ yd} \cdot (3 \text{ yd} + 6 \text{ yd})$ Substitute the values.

$A = \dfrac{1}{2} \cdot 4 \text{ yd} \cdot (9 \text{ yd})$ Add within the parentheses.

$A = 18 \text{ yd}^2$ Divide out 2, then multiply.

The area is 18 yd^2.

> **W Hint**
>
> Are the bases of a trapezoid always on the top and bottom?

[YOU TRY 4] Find the perimeter and area of each trapezoid.

a)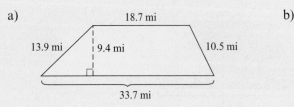

18.7 mi

13.9 mi 9.4 mi 10.5 mi

33.7 mi

b)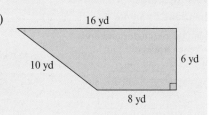

16 yd

10 yd 6 yd

8 yd

BE CAREFUL Example 4b shows us that the height of the trapezoid is *not* always vertical.

EXAMPLE 5

In-Class Example 5

Use Example 5.

A flower bed is in the shape of the trapezoid shown in Example 4b. If the garden is to be enclosed with decorative edging that costs $2.39/ft, find the cost of the edging.

Solution

The flower bed will be *enclosed* with the edging. This means the edging will go *around* the flower bed. *We will use the perimeter of the trapezoid to determine the cost of the edging.*

In Example 4b, we found that the perimeter of the figure is 18 *yd*. The unit cost of the edging, however, is $2.39/*ft*.

Because the units of length are different, we must change 18 *yd to feet:*

$$18 \text{ yd} \cdot \frac{3 \text{ ft}}{1 \text{ yd}} = 54 \text{ ft}$$

To find the cost of the edging, multiply 54 ft and the unit cost, $2.39/ft.

$$\text{Cost} = 54 \text{ ft} \cdot \frac{\$2.39}{\text{ft}}$$ Write the unit cost as a fraction, and divide out the units of feet.

$$\text{Cost} = \$129.06$$ Multiply.

The cost of the edging is $129.06.

[YOU TRY 5] A parking lot for bikes is in the shape of the trapezoid shown in You Try 4b. If the lot is to be enclosed with a fence that costs $8.99/ft, find the cost of the fence.

Let's look at one more area problem.

EXAMPLE 6 Find the area of this figure.

 Hint

Could you break up this figure into more than two pieces to find its area?

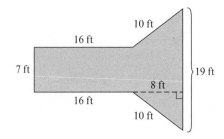

10 ft

16 ft

7 ft 19 ft

8 ft

16 ft

10 ft

In-Class Example 6

Find the area of this figure.

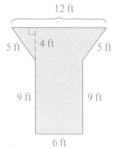

Answer: 90 ft^2

Solution

Break up the figure into two parts: a rectangle and a trapezoid. Then,

Total area = Area of rectangle + Area of trapezoid

Let's draw each figure separately and compute each area.

Rectangle

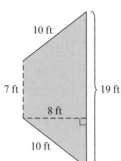

Area of a Rectangle

$A = l \cdot w$

$A = 16 \text{ ft} \cdot 7 \text{ ft} = 112 \text{ ft}^2$

Trapezoid

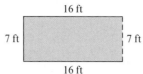

Area of a Trapezoid

$A = \dfrac{1}{2} \cdot h \cdot (b + B)$

$A = \dfrac{1}{2} \cdot 8 \text{ ft} \cdot (7 \text{ ft} + 19 \text{ ft})$ Substitute the values.

$A = \dfrac{1}{2} \cdot 8 \text{ ft} \cdot (26 \text{ ft})$ Add in the parentheses.

$A = 104 \text{ ft}^2$ Multiply.

Total area = Area of rectangle + Area of trapezoid

Total area =   112 ft^2 +   104 ft^2

Total area =   216 ft^2

[YOU TRY 6] Find the area of this figure.

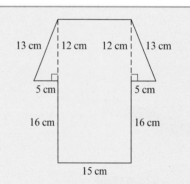

ANSWERS TO [YOU TRY] EXERCISES

1) $5\dfrac{1}{3}$ mi   2) 117 ft^2 3) $30.24

4) a) $P = 76.8$ mi; $A = 246.28$ mi^2 b) $P = 40$ yd; $A = 72$ yd^2

5) $1078.80   6) 480 cm^2

*Additional answers can be found in the Answers to Exercises appendix.

Objective 1: Find the Perimeter and Area of a Parallelogram

1) Make a drawing showing how to form a rectangle and a parallelogram using two identically-sized right triangles.

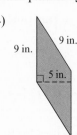

2) What is the formula for the area of a parallelogram?
Area = base · height or $A = b \cdot h$

Find the perimeter and area of each parallelogram.

3)
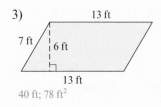
13 ft
7 ft
6 ft
13 ft
40 ft; 78 ft^2

4)
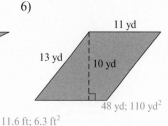
9 in.
9 in.
5 in.
36 in.; 45 in^2

5)
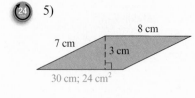
8 cm
7 cm
3 cm
30 cm; 24 cm^2

6)
11 yd
13 yd
10 yd
48 yd; 110 yd^2

7)
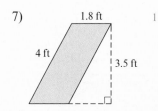
1.8 ft
4 ft
3.5 ft
11.6 ft; 6.3 ft^2

8)
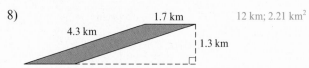
1.7 km
4.3 km
1.3 km
12 km; 2.21 km^2

9)
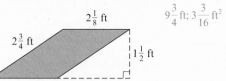
$2\frac{1}{8}$ ft
$2\frac{3}{4}$ ft
$1\frac{1}{2}$ ft
$9\frac{3}{4}$ ft; $3\frac{3}{16}$ ft^2

10)
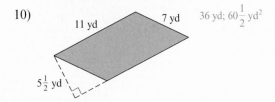
11 yd   7 yd
$5\frac{1}{2}$ yd
36 yd; $60\frac{1}{2}$ yd^2

11) A parallelogram with no right angles *always,* *sometimes,* or *never* has two acute angles and two obtuse angles.   always

12) In your own words, explain why the rectangle and the parallelogram below have the same area.

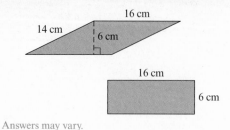
16 cm
14 cm   6 cm
16 cm
6 cm

Answers may vary.

Solve each problem.

13) Husna will sew together pieces of fabric shaped as parallelograms to make a comforter. Each piece will have the shape shown here. What is the total area of the comforter if she uses 160 pieces?   1620 in^2

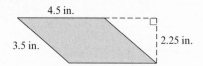
4.5 in.
3.5 in.   2.25 in.

14) Maarten has a swimming pool shaped as the parallelogram shown in the figure. For the winter months, he is having a custom winter cover made at a cost of $12 per square meter. What is the total cost of the cover?
$648

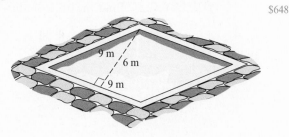
9 m
6 m
9 m

Objective 2: Find the Perimeter and Area of a Trapezoid

15) Write three forms of the formula for the area of a trapezoid.

16) How do you know which sides of the trapezoid are the bases?
They are the sides that make 90° angles with the height.

Find the perimeter and area of each trapezoid.

17) 48 cm; 117 cm²

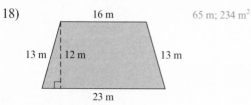

8 cm
10 cm
9 cm
12 cm
18 cm

18) 65 m; 234 m²

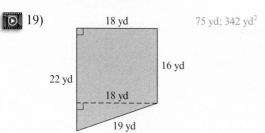

16 m
13 m   12 m   13 m
23 m

19) 75 yd; 342 yd²

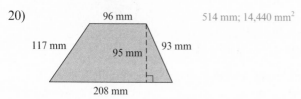

18 yd
16 yd
22 yd
18 yd
19 yd

20) 514 mm; 14,440 mm²

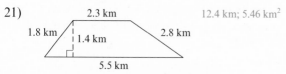

96 mm
117 mm   95 mm   93 mm
208 mm

21) 12.4 km; 5.46 km²

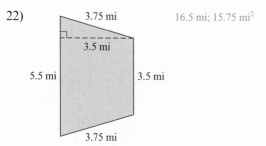

2.3 km
1.8 km   1.4 km   2.8 km
5.5 km

22) 16.5 mi; 15.75 mi²

3.75 mi
3.5 mi
5.5 mi   3.5 mi
3.75 mi

23)

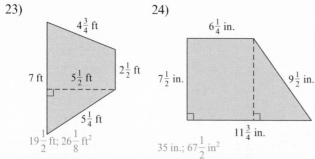

$4\frac{3}{4}$ ft
7 ft $5\frac{1}{2}$ ft $2\frac{1}{2}$ ft
$5\frac{1}{4}$ ft
$19\frac{1}{2}$ ft; $26\frac{1}{8}$ ft²

24)

$6\frac{1}{4}$ in.
$7\frac{1}{2}$ in. $9\frac{1}{2}$ in.
$11\frac{3}{4}$ in.
35 in.; $67\frac{1}{2}$ in²

For Exercises 25 and 26, answer *always, sometimes,* or *never.*

25) The bases of a trapezoid are the same length.   never

26) A trapezoid with no right angles has four acute angles.
never

Solve each problem.

27) Jerome, who is 3 years old, drew a family portrait on a sheet of paper shaped like a trapezoid. His parents want to have a custom frame built for the picture, at a cost of $0.45 per inch. What is the cost to build the custom frame for Jerome's picture? $22.50

12 in.
9 in.   9 in.
20 in.

28) Mrs. Saldivar wants to install a chain-link fence around her pet area in the backyard. The area is shaped like a trapezoid with one side up against the wall of the home. (The side by the wall is the same length as the opposite side.) If the fence costs $8.50 per foot to install, how much will it cost to enclose the pet area? $399.50

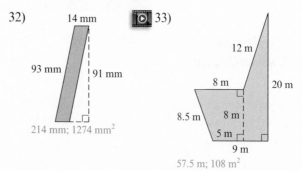

18 ft
8 ft
Pet area
21 ft

Mixed Exercises: Objectives 1 and 2
Find the perimeter and the area of each figure.

29) $13\frac{3}{10}$ cm; $3\frac{1}{4}$ cm²

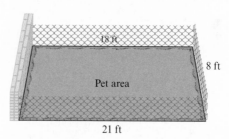

$3\frac{1}{4}$ cm
$3\frac{2}{5}$ cm   1 cm

30) 30.6 dm; 41 dm²

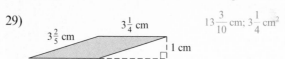

7.4 dm
4.5 dm   4 dm   5.6 dm
13.1 dm

31) 53 ft; 74.25 ft²

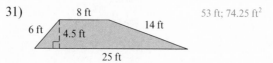

8 ft
6 ft   4.5 ft   14 ft
25 ft

32)

14 mm
93 mm   91 mm
214 mm; 1274 mm²

33)

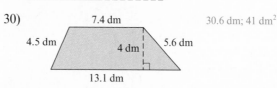

12 m
8 m   20 m
8.5 m   8 m
5 m
9 m
57.5 m; 108 m²

34)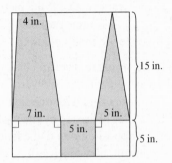

24 in.; 24 in²

3 in.   5 in.

4 in.

5 in.   3 in.

4 in.

35) Find the area of the shaded region.   145 in²

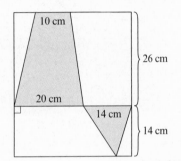

4 in.

15 in.

7 in.   5 in.

5 in.

5 in.

36) Find the area of the *unshaded* region.   872 cm²

10 cm

26 cm

20 cm

14 cm

14 cm

37) A construction worker needs to calculate the exact area of the irregular walkway shown in the figure. Using only four horizontal lines, how can he partition the walkway forming only parallelograms and trapezoids to make the calculation?

Walkway

38) Suppose the construction worker in Exercise 37 wanted to use only vertical lines. Using only two vertical lines, how can he partition the walkway forming trapezoids, triangles, and only one parallelogram?

Walkway

39) Mr. and Mrs. Szabo are having a new driveway installed at a cost of $40.50 per square meter. The driveway is represented by the shaded region in the figure. What is the total cost for the new driveway?
$6885

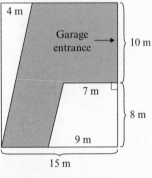

4 m

Garage entrance

10 m

7 m

8 m

9 m

15 m

40) The entranceway to the Green family home will be paved with red brick at a cost of $12 per square foot including installation. The entranceway is represented by the shaded area below. What is the total cost? $528

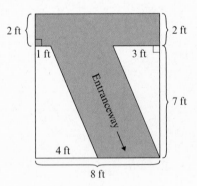

2 ft   2 ft

1 ft   3 ft

7 ft

Entranceway

4 ft

8 ft

R1) After completing Exercises 1–12, what conclusions can you draw about parallelograms and rectangles?

R2) What objects do you encounter that are a combination of some of the geometric shapes we have studied so far in this chapter?

9.6 Circles

 **P Prepare**	**O Organize**
What are your objectives for Section 9.6?	**How can you accomplish each objective?**
1 Find the Radius and Diameter of a Circle	• Write the definition of a *circle* in your own words, draw an example, and note its main characteristics. • Understand what a *radius* and a *diameter* are. • Write the formula for determining the **Diameter and Radius of a Circle** in your notes. • Complete the given examples on your own. • Complete You Trys 1 and 2.
2 Find the Circumference of a Circle and Understand What π Represents	• Write the definition of *circumference* in your own words. • Write the definition of π in your own words. • Understand the decimal and fractional **Approximations of π.** • Write the formula for determining the **Circumference of a Circle** in your notes. • Complete the given examples on your own. • Complete You Trys 3 and 4.
3 Find the Area of a Circle	• Understand how the area of a circle is derived from using information known about a parallelogram. • Write the formula for determining the **Area of a Circle** in your notes. • Write the definition of a *semicircle* in your notes. • Complete the given examples on your own. • Complete You Trys 5–8.

W Work   Read the explanations, follow the examples, take notes, and complete the You Trys.

1   Find the Radius and Diameter of a Circle

Definition

A **circle** is a two-dimensional, or flat, figure in which all points are the same distance from the fixed center point.

Example: Each point on this circle is the same distance from the center.

(Continued)

The **radius,** *r*, is the distance from the center of the circle to any point on the circle.

The **diameter,** *d*, is the distance across the circle passing through the center.

Notice that the diameter is *twice* the length of the radius. (We can also say that the radius is half the length of the diameter.)

W Hint

If you memorize only one of the formulas, you can use it to find the other value.

Formula Diameter and Radius of a Circle

1) diameter = 2 · radius   or $d = 2 \cdot r$

2) radius = $\dfrac{\text{diameter}}{2}$ or $r = \dfrac{d}{2}$

EXAMPLE 1

In-Class Example 1

Find the diameter of a circle with a radius of 5 in.

Answer: 10 in.

Find the diameter of a circle with a radius of 3 in.

Solution

The diameter is *two times* the radius.

$$d = 2 \cdot r$$
$$d = 2 \cdot 3 \text{ in.} \qquad \text{Substitute the value.}$$
$$d = 6 \text{ in.}$$

[YOU TRY 1] Find the diameter of a circle with a radius of 11 m.

EXAMPLE 2 Find the radius of a circle with a diameter of 15 cm.

Solution

The radius is *half* the diameter.

$$r = \frac{d}{2}$$

$$r = \frac{15 \text{ cm}}{2} \qquad \text{Substitute the value.}$$

$$r = \frac{15}{2} \text{ cm or } 7\frac{1}{2} \text{ cm or } 7.5 \text{ cm}$$

We can write the answer in any of these forms.

[**YOU TRY 2**] Find the radius of a circle with a diameter of 21 in.

2 Find the Circumference of a Circle and Understand What π Represents

We know that the perimeter of a figure is the distance around the figure. This is true for circles as well. The perimeter of a circle, however, has a special name. It is called the *circumference*.

Definition

The **circumference** of a circle is the distance around the circle. (The circumference is the *perimeter* of the circle.) It is usually abbreviated with C.

Let's look at several circles of different sizes and do some calculations.

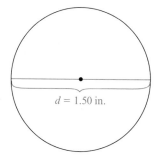

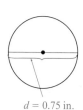

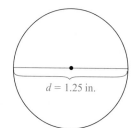

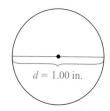

diameter = 1.50 in.
Circumference
$C \approx 4.71$ in.
$\dfrac{C}{d} = \dfrac{4.71 \text{ in.}}{1.50 \text{ in.}} = 3.14$

diameter = 0.75 in.
Circumference
$C \approx 2.36$ in.
$\dfrac{C}{d} = \dfrac{2.36 \text{ in.}}{0.75 \text{ in.}} = 3.14\overline{6}$

diameter = 1.25 in.
Circumference
$C \approx 3.93$ in.
$\dfrac{C}{d} = \dfrac{3.93 \text{ in.}}{1.25 \text{ in.}} = 3.144$

diameter = 1.00 in.
Circumference
$C \approx 3.14$ in.
$\dfrac{C}{d} = \dfrac{3.14 \text{ in.}}{1.00 \text{ in.}} = 3.14$

Even though the circles are different sizes, whenever we divide the circumference of a circle by its diameter, we *always* get a number that is close to 3.14. This is *not a coincidence*. *The circumference of a circle divided by its diameter is always the same value, and that value is called π (pi).*

Definition

π is the ratio of any circle's circumference to its diameter. That is, $\pi = \dfrac{C}{d}$. (π is the Greek letter pi and is read as "pie.")

There is no exact decimal equivalent of π. An approximate decimal value is $\pi \approx$ 3.14159265, but it is most common to approximate π as 3.14 or as the fraction $\dfrac{22}{7}$.

Property Approximations for π

$$\pi \approx 3.14 \quad \text{and} \quad \pi \approx \frac{22}{7}$$

Because these are *approximate* values, calculations using π will give *approximate* answers. Therefore, we should use the $\approx$ symbol instead of $=$.

We use π to find the circumference of a circle.

Formula Circumference of a Circle

1) Circumference = π · diameter   or
   $$C = \pi \cdot d$$
   Because $d = 2 \cdot$ radius, we can also write $C = \pi \cdot 2 \cdot$ radius   or

2) Circumference = 2 · π · radius   or
   $$C = 2 \cdot \pi \cdot r$$

Note
Remember, because the *circumference* of a circle is the same as the *perimeter* of a circle, the units for circumference are linear units like ft, cm, in., etc. They are *not* square units.

EXAMPLE 3

Find the circumference of each circle. Give the *exact* value and an *approximate* value using $\pi \approx 3.14$.

a)

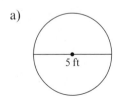

5 ft

b)

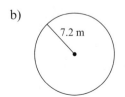

7.2 m

In-Class Example 3

Find the circumference of each circle. Give the *exact* value and an *approximate* value using $\pi \approx 3.14$.

a)

9 ft

b)

5.6 m

Answer:

a) exact: 9π ft;
   approximation: 28.26 ft
b) exact: 11.2π m;
   approximation: 35.168 m

Solution

a) Are we given the diameter or the radius of this circle? We are given that the *diameter* = 5 ft. So, use the formula containing the diameter.

$$C = \pi \cdot d$$
$$C = \pi \cdot 5 \text{ ft} \qquad \text{Substitute the diameter.}$$
$$C = 5\pi \text{ ft} \qquad \text{This is the } exact \text{ value.}$$

(We usually write π between the number and the units.) To find an *approximate* value for the circumference, substitute 3.14 for π and multiply.

$$C \approx 5(3.14) \text{ ft} \qquad \text{Substitute 3.14 for } \pi.$$
$$C \approx 15.7 \text{ ft} \qquad \text{Multiply.}$$

The circumference is *exactly* 5π ft. The *approximate* value is 15.7 ft.

(Notice that we write 5π ft *without* a multiplication symbol.)

b) We are given that the *radius* = 7.2 m. Use the formula containing the radius.

$$C = 2 \cdot \pi \cdot r$$
$$C = 2 \cdot \pi \cdot (7.2 \text{ m}) \qquad \text{Substitute the radius.}$$
$$C = 14.4\pi \text{ m} \qquad \text{Multiply.}$$

The circumference is *exactly* equal to 14.4π m. Find the *approximation* of the circumference by substituting 3.14 for π.

$$C \approx 14.4(3.14) \text{ m} \qquad \text{Substitute 3.14 for } \pi.$$
$$C \approx 45.216 \text{ m} \qquad \text{Multiply.}$$

The circumference is *approximately* equal to 45.216 m.

[YOU TRY 3] Find the circumference of each circle. Give the exact value and an approximate value using $\pi \approx 3.14$.

a)

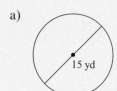

15 yd

b)

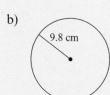

9.8 cm

EXAMPLE 4

Find the circumference of the circle. Give the exact value and an approximate value using $\pi \approx \dfrac{22}{7}$.

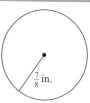

$\frac{7}{8}$ in.

In-Class Example 4

Find the circumference of the circle. Give the exact value and an approximate value using $\pi \approx \dfrac{22}{7}$.

$\frac{7}{12}$ in.

Answer:

exact: $\dfrac{7}{6}\pi$ in.; approximation:
$\dfrac{11}{3}$ in. or $3\dfrac{2}{3}$ in. or $3.\overline{6}$ in.

Solution

We are given the *radius* of this circle, so we will use the formula containing the radius.

$$C = 2 \cdot \pi \cdot r$$
$$C = 2 \cdot \pi \cdot \frac{7}{8} \text{ in.} \qquad \text{Substitute the radius.}$$
$$C = \frac{\overset{1}{2}}{1} \cdot \pi \cdot \frac{7}{\underset{4}{8}} \text{ in.} \qquad \text{Divide out 2.}$$
$$C = \frac{7}{4}\pi \text{ in.} \qquad \text{Multiply.}$$

Exact value of the circumference: $C = \dfrac{7}{4}\pi$ in. Find an *approximate* value of the circumference by substituting $\dfrac{22}{7}$ for π.

$$C \approx \frac{7}{4}\left(\frac{22}{7}\right) \text{ in.} \qquad\qquad \text{Substitute } \tfrac{22}{7} \text{ for } \pi.$$

$$C \approx \frac{\overset{1}{7}}{\underset{2}{4}}\left(\frac{\overset{11}{22}}{\underset{1}{7}}\right) \text{ in.} \qquad\qquad \text{Divide out common factors.}$$

$$C \approx \frac{11}{2} \text{ in. or } 5\frac{1}{2} \text{ in. or 5.5 in.} \qquad \text{Multiply.}$$

The *approximation* of the circumference is $C \approx \dfrac{11}{2}$ in. or $5\dfrac{1}{2}$ in. or 5.5 in.

[YOU TRY 4] Find the circumference of the circle. Give the exact value and an approximate value using $\pi \approx \dfrac{22}{7}$.

---

3 Find the Area of a Circle

We can understand where the formula for the area of a circle comes from if we relate it to the area of a parallelogram. Let's begin by cutting a circle in half and then dividing it into pie-shaped pieces.

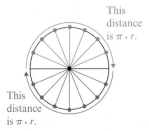

Since the distance around a whole circle is $2 \cdot \pi \cdot r$, the distance around *half* the circle (or the *semicircle*) is $\dfrac{1}{2} \cdot 2 \cdot \pi \cdot r$ or $\pi \cdot r$.

If we cut out the pie-shaped pieces and put them together as seen here, we get a figure that is approximately a parallelogram with **base $= \pi \cdot r$** and **height $= r$.**

The formula for the area of a parallelogram is Area $=$ base $\cdot$ height. Use this formula to find the area of the parallelogram that was formed from the circle.

$$
\begin{array}{ll}
\text{Area} = \text{base} \cdot \text{height} & \text{Area of a parallelogram} \\
\text{Area} = \pi \cdot r \cdot r & \text{Substitute for base and height.} \\
\text{Area} = \pi \cdot r^2 & \text{Multiply; } r \cdot r = r^2
\end{array}
$$

This is the formula for the area of a circle.

Formula Area of a Circle

The **area**, A, of a circle with radius r is

$$A = \pi \cdot r^2$$

Remember that we use *square units* for area.

EXAMPLE 5

In-Class Example 5

Find the area of a circle with a radius of 2.5 mi. Give an exact value and an approximation using $\pi \approx 3.14$.

2.5 mi

Answer:
exact: 6.25π mi^2;
approximation: 19.625 mi^2

Find the area of a circle with a radius of 1.5 mi. Give an exact value and an approximation using $\pi \approx 3.14$.

Solution

If we are not given a picture, it can be helpful if we sketch the circle.

1.5 mi

Use the area formula with $r = 1.5$ mi.

$A = \pi \cdot r^2$ Area formula
$A = \pi \cdot (1.5 \text{ mi})^2$ Substitute 1.5 mi for r.
$A = \pi \cdot 2.25 \text{ mi}^2$ $(1.5 \text{ mi})^2 = 1.5 \text{ mi} \cdot 1.5 \text{ mi} = 2.25 \text{ mi}^2$
$A = 2.25\pi \text{ mi}^2$ Use the commutative property to rewrite the answer.

The exact area is 2.25π mi^2.

Find the *approximate* area by substituting 3.14 for π.

$A \approx 2.25(3.14) \text{ mi}^2$ Substitute 3.14 for π.
$A \approx 7.065 \text{ mi}^2$ Multiply.

The area is approximately 7.065 mi^2.

$\begin{bmatrix} \textbf{YOU TRY 5} \end{bmatrix}$ Find the area of a circle with a radius of 70 mm. Give an exact value and an approximation using $\pi \approx 3.14$.

Remember, we must know the *radius* to find the area of a circle.

EXAMPLE 6

In-Class Example 6

Use Example 6.

Find the area of a circle with a diameter of 20 cm. Give an exact value and an approximation using $\pi \approx 3.14$.

Solution

Let's sketch the circle and label it with the information we are given.

20 cm

We can see from our drawing that the *diameter* is 20 cm, but we need the *radius*.

The radius is *half* the diameter, so $r = \dfrac{d}{2} = \dfrac{20 \text{ cm}}{2} = 10$ cm. Use $r = 10$ cm in the area formula.

$$A = \pi \cdot r^2 \qquad \text{Area formula}$$
$$A = \pi \cdot (10 \text{ cm})^2 \qquad \text{Substitute 10 cm for } r.$$
$$A = \pi \cdot 100 \text{ cm}^2 \qquad (10 \text{ cm})^2 = 10 \text{ cm} \cdot 10 \text{ cm} = 100 \text{ cm}^2$$
$$A = 100\pi \text{ cm}^2 \qquad \text{Use the commutative property.}$$

The area of the circle is *exactly* 100π cm². Substitute 3.14 for π to find the approximate area.

$$A \approx 100(3.14) \text{ cm}^2 \qquad \text{Substitute 3.14 for } \pi.$$
$$A \approx 314 \text{ cm}^2 \qquad \text{Multiply.}$$

The area of the circle is *approximately* 314 cm².

[**YOU TRY 6**] Find the area of a circle with a diameter of 200 yd. Give an exact value and an approximation using $\pi \approx 3.14$.

Note

If you are working with geometric figures and a picture is *not* given in the problem, it can be helpful to draw a picture and label it with the information in the problem. Sometimes, looking at a *picture* can help us to better understand what is happening in the problem so that we can solve it.

A **semicircle** is half a circle. To find the area of a semicircle, we use the formula for the area of a circle and divide by 2.

EXAMPLE 7

In-Class Example 7

Find the area of this semicircle. Give the exact value and an approximation using 3.14 for π.

18 in.

Answer:
exact: 162π in²;
approximation: 508.68 in²

Hint

Would it be helpful to write a procedure for finding the area of a semicircle?

Find the area of this semicircle. Give the exact value and an approximation using 3.14 for π.

16 in.

Solution

First, we will find the area of a *whole* circle that has a radius of 16 in. Then, we will divide by 2 since a semicircle is *half* a circle.

Whole Circle

$$A = \pi \cdot r^2$$
$$A = \pi \cdot (16 \text{ in.})^2 \qquad \text{Substitute 16 in. for } r.$$
$$A = 256\pi \text{ in}^2 \qquad (16 \text{ in.})^2 = 16 \text{ in.} \cdot 16 \text{ in.} = 256 \text{ in}^2$$

Divide by 2 to find the area of the semicircle.

Semicircle

$$A = \frac{\text{Area of whole circle}}{2} = \frac{256\pi \text{ in}^2}{2} = 128\pi \text{ in}^2$$

The *exact* area of the semicircle is 128π in². To find the *approximate* area, substitute 3.14 for π.

$$A \approx 128(3.14) \text{ in}^2 \qquad \text{Substitute 3.14 for } \pi.$$
$$A \approx 401.92 \text{ in}^2 \qquad \text{Multiply.}$$

[**YOU TRY 7**]

Find the area of the semicircle. Give the exact value and an approximation using 3.14 for π.

24 cm

We can use what we have learned about circles to solve problems.

EXAMPLE 8

In-Class Example 8

Eva will have a circular rug custom made, at a cost of $18.29/ft². If the diameter of the rug is 6 ft, what is the cost of the rug? Use 3.14 for π.

Answer: $516.88

Tiffany wants a custom teak table made for her dining room. The tabletop will be a circle with a diameter of 4 ft. If the wood for the tabletop costs $4.20/ft², find the total cost of the wood. Use 3.14 for π.

Solution

Let's draw and label a picture first.

$d = 4$ ft

We need to determine the *amount* of wood that is needed to make the tabletop. *This is the area.* Since $A = \pi \cdot r^2$, we need to know the *radius* of the table.

The diameter = 4 ft, so the radius = $\dfrac{4 \text{ ft}}{2}$ = 2 ft.

$$A = \pi \cdot r^2 \qquad \text{Area of a circle}$$
$$A = \pi \cdot (2 \text{ ft})^2 \qquad \text{Substitute 2 ft for } r.$$
$$A = 4\pi \text{ ft}^2 \qquad (2 \text{ ft})^2 = 2 \text{ ft} \cdot 2 \text{ ft} = 4 \text{ ft}^2$$
$$A \approx 4(3.14) \text{ ft}^2 \qquad \pi \approx 3.14$$
$$A \approx 12.56 \text{ ft}^2 \qquad \text{Multiply.}$$

To find the total cost of the wood, multiply the area and the unit cost of the wood.

$$\text{Cost} = 12.56 \text{ ft}^2 \cdot \frac{\$4.20}{\text{ft}^2} = \$52.752$$

Round the answer to the nearest cent: $52.75

The cost of the wood for the tabletop is $52.75.

[**YOU TRY 8**]

Esteban will make a cover for the circular swimming pool in his backyard. How much will it cost if the material for the cover costs $0.09/ft² and the diameter of the cover will be 22 ft? Use 3.14 for π.

Using Technology

We can use a calculator to help us calculate the area of a circle using the formula $A = \pi r^2$. Remember that we must perform the exponent operation before we multiply. To instruct the calculator to do this, we must use the parenthesis keys.

Suppose we have a circle with radius 3 m. We can approximate the area using either $\pi \approx 3.14$ or $\pi \approx \frac{22}{7}$. If we approximate the area using $\pi \approx 3.14$, we enter ③.①④⨯(③ y^x ②)= into the calculator. The display screen will show 28.26. This means that the area is approximately 28.26 m^2.

If we approximate the area using $\pi \approx \frac{22}{7}$, we enter ②②÷⑦⨯ (③ y^x ②)= into the calculator. The display screen will show 28.285714. Rounded to the nearest hundredth, the area is approximately 28.29 m^2.

E Evaluate **9.6** Exercises   Do the exercises, and check your work.

*Additional answers can be found in the Answers to Exercises appendix.

Objective 1: Find the Radius and Diameter of a Circle

1) What is the difference between the radius and the diameter of a circle?

2) How are the radius and diameter of a circle related?
   The radius is half the diameter. The diameter is twice the radius.

Find the diameter of the circle.

3) 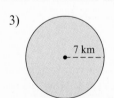 7 km   14 km

4) 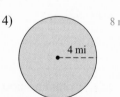 4 mi   8 mi

5) 1.6 m   3.2 m

6)  1.8 mm   3.6 mm

7) 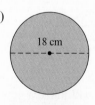 $\frac{3}{4}$ in. $\frac{3}{2}$ in. or $1\frac{1}{2}$ in.

8) $\frac{2}{5}$ cm $\frac{4}{5}$ cm

Find the radius of the circle.

9) 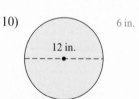 18 cm   9 cm

10) 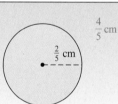 12 in.   6 in.

11) 1.1 m   0.55 m

12) 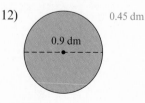 0.9 dm   0.45 dm

13)
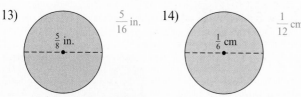
$\frac{5}{8}$ in. $\frac{5}{16}$ in.

14)
$\frac{1}{6}$ cm $\frac{1}{12}$ cm

15)
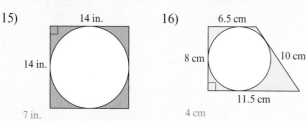
14 in.
14 in.
7 in.

16)
6.5 cm
8 cm   10 cm
11.5 cm
4 cm

Objective 2: Find the Circumference of a Circle and Understand What π Represents

17) What do we call the perimeter of a circle?
the circumference

18) Where does the number π come from? What are the two values we can use for the approximation of π?

19) If we are given the diameter of a circle, what formula should we use to find the circumference? $C = \pi \cdot d$

20) If we are given the radius of a circle, what formula should we use to find the circumference?
$C = 2 \cdot \pi \cdot r$

Find the circumference of each circle. Give the *exact* value and an *approximate* value using $\pi \approx 3.14$.

21)
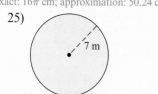
5 in.
exact: 10π in.; approximation: 31.4 in.

22)
4 yd
exact: 8π yd; approximation: 25.12 yd

(24) 23)
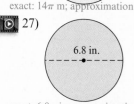
8 cm
exact: 16π cm; approximation: 50.24 cm

24)
6 ft
exact: 12π ft; approximation: 37.68 ft

25)
7 m
exact: 14π m; approximation: 43.96 m

26)
11 cm
exact: 22π cm; approximation: 69.08 cm

27)
6.8 in.
exact: 6.8π in.; approximation: 21.352 in.

28)
3.5 yd
exact: 3.5π yd; approximation: 10.99 yd

29)
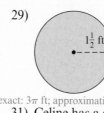
$1\frac{1}{2}$ ft
exact: 3π ft; approximation: 9.42 ft

30)
$2\frac{2}{5}$ ft
exact: $4\frac{4}{5}\pi$ ft; approximation: 15.072 ft

31) Celine has a garden shaped as a semicircle. Use the figure to calculate the exact and approximate perimeter of the garden. Use $\pi \approx 3.14$.

4 m

exact: $4 + 2\pi$ m; approximation: 10.28 m

32) A Little League baseball field has a shape equivalent to one-fourth of a circle. Use the figure to calculate the exact and approximate perimeter of the field shown in the figure. Use $\pi \approx 3.14$.

100 yd   100 yd
exact: $50\pi + 200$ yd; approximation: 357 yd

Find the circumference of each circle. Give the *exact* value and an *approximate* value using $\pi \approx \frac{22}{7}$.

33)
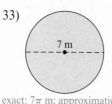
7 m
exact: 7π m; approximation: 22 m

34)
5 cm

(24) 35)
$\frac{7}{9}$ in.

36)
$\frac{1}{4}$ mi

37)
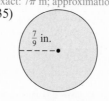
$\frac{14}{15}$ cm

38)
$\frac{7}{10}$ mm

39) We now know that π is the ratio of a circle's circumference to its diameter or $\pi = \frac{C}{d}$. We also learned that $\pi \approx \frac{22}{7}$. Does this mean that we can create a circle with a circumference of 22 in. and a diameter of 7 in.? Write an explanation of your answer.   No; answers may vary.

40) Suppose you have a circle of radius 7 cm. If you double the radius, by how much does the circumference increase? Use $\pi \approx \dfrac{22}{7}$.

The circumference doubles from 44 cm to 88 cm.

Objective 3: Find the Area of a Circle

41) What is the formula for the area of a circle? $A = \pi \cdot r^2$

42) How do you find the area of a semicircle?
Find the area of the whole circle with the given radius or diameter, and then divide by 2.

Find the area of the given circle. Give the *exact* value and an *approximate* value using $\pi \approx 3.14$.

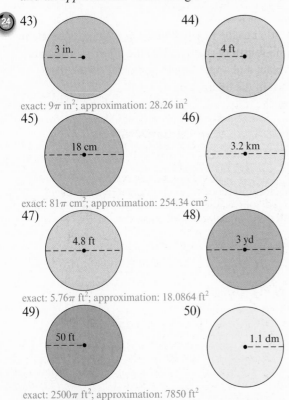

43)

44)

3 in.

4 ft

exact: 9π in^2; approximation: 28.26 in^2

45)

46)

18 cm

3.2 km

exact: 81π cm^2; approximation: 254.34 cm^2

47)

48)

4.8 ft

3 yd

exact: 5.76π ft^2; approximation: 18.0864 ft^2

49)

50)

50 ft

1.1 dm

exact: 2500π ft^2; approximation: 7850 ft^2

Find the area of the semicircle. Give the *exact* value and an *approximate* value using $\pi \approx 3.14$.

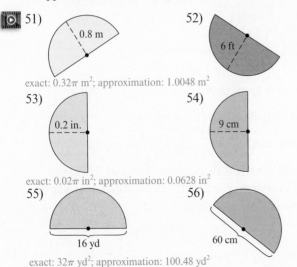

51)

52)

0.8 m

6 ft

exact: 0.32π m^2; approximation: 1.0048 m^2

53)

54)

0.2 in.

9 cm

exact: 0.02π in^2; approximation: 0.0628 in^2

55)

56)

16 yd

60 cm

exact: 32π yd^2; approximation: 100.48 yd^2

Mixed Exercises: Objectives 1–3
Solve each problem. Use $\pi \approx 3.14$.

57) The General Sherman Tree in Sequoia National Park is the largest tree (by volume) in the world. The maximum diameter at its base is 36.5 ft. What is the circumference of the tree at this diameter? Using an average arm span of a human being as 67 in., estimate the number of people required to make a human chain around the tree. (www.nps.gov)
114.61 ft; approximately 21 humans

58) What is the difference in the perimeter of an 8-in.-diameter circle and a 12-in.-diameter circle? 12.56 in.

59) Ji-Min needs to replace a circular window having a diameter of 5 ft. She decides to use double-strength glass costing $3 per square foot. Find the total cost for the glass. $58.88

60) The Johnsons have a round, 8-ft-diameter pool that needs a new custom-fit insulated cover. If the cover costs $4.50 per square foot, what is the total cost? $226.08

61) The playground pictured here is having rubber flooring installed to help protect children against injuries from falls. If the cost, including installation, is $8.00 per square foot, what is the total cost of installing the surface? $6672

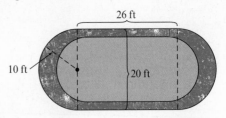

26 ft

10 ft

20 ft

62) A playing field will have sod installed at a cost of $0.50 per square foot. In addition, the field will have a fence installed around its perimeter for $5.00 per foot. Find the combined cost for both jobs. $7284

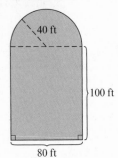

40 ft

100 ft

80 ft

63) Thaddeus wants to cover an area around a pond with natural slate stone. If the cost of the slate is $6.50 per square foot, how much will it cost to surround the pond? $979.68

Slate stone
Pond
8 ft
4 ft

64) Mario's famous large 16-in.-diameter sausage and mushroom pizza costs $16.00. Approximate the cost per square inch of Mario's pizza. $0.08 per square inch

Find the area and circumference of each circle. Give the *exact* value and an *approximate* value using $\pi \approx 3.14$.

65)
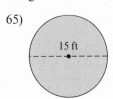
15 ft

Area: exact: 56.25π ft^2;
approximation: 176.625 ft^2
Circumference: exact: 15π ft;
approximation: 47.1 ft

66)
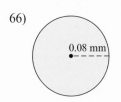
0.08 mm

Area: exact: 0.0064π mm^2;
approximation: 0.020096 mm^2
Circumference: exact: 0.16π mm;
approximation: 0.5024 mm

 67) Marla needs to fence in an area of her yard that has a shape equivalent to three-fourths of an entire circle. What length of fence does she need to completely enclose this region? Use 3.14 for π.   40.26 m

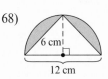
6 m

Find the area of the shaded region. Use 3.14 for π.

68)
6 cm
12 cm
20.52 cm^2

69) The Motorola Talkabout® MR350R two-way radio set has a maximum range of 35 mi under ideal conditions. Under these conditions, what is the broadcast area for an individual radio? Do one calculation using $\dfrac{22}{7}$ for π and another using 3.14 for π. Are the answers the same? Why or why not? (www.motorola.com)

70) A community college radio station can broadcast a radio signal 40 mi in all directions. Find the size of the broadcast area. Use 3.14 for π.   5024 mi^2

R Rethink

R1) When would it be better to use the fractional representation of π instead of the decimal representation of π?

R2) Were there any exercises you got wrong or did not know how to do? If so, circle them or write them on your paper and ask your instructor for help.

9.7 Volume

P Prepare

O Organize

What are your objectives for Section 9.7?	How can you accomplish each objective?
1 Find the Volume of a Rectangular Solid	• Write the definition of *volume* in your own words, and draw a few examples. • Write the formula for determining the **Volume of a Rectangular Solid** in your notes. • Complete the given example on your own. • Complete You Try 1.
2 Find the Volume of a Sphere	• Write the definition of a *sphere* in your own words, and draw an example. • Write the formula for determining the **Volume of a Sphere** in your notes. • Write the definition of a *hemisphere* in your own words. • Complete the given examples on your own. • Complete You Trys 2–4.
3 Find the Volume of a Cylinder	• Write the definition of a *right circular cylinder* in your own words. • Write the formula for determining the **Volume of a Cylinder** in your notes. • Complete the given example on your own. • Complete You Try 5.
4 Find the Volume of a Cone and a Pyramid	• Write the definitions of a *cone* and a *pyramid* in your own words. • Write the formula for determining the **Volume of a Cone** in your notes. • Write the formula for determining the **Volume of a Rectangular Pyramid** in your notes. • Complete the given examples on your own. • Complete You Trys 6 and 7.

Read the explanations, follow the examples, take notes, and complete the You Trys.

Until now, we have worked with two-dimensional figures; that is, we have worked with figures in a *flat* plane, such as rectangles, triangles, and circles. A rectangle, for example, has the two dimensions of length and width.

1 Find the Volume of a Rectangular Solid

In this section, we will learn about three-dimensional (or solid) objects like a rectangular solid, a sphere, and a cylinder. (A rectangular solid, or a *box,* has the three dimensions of length, width, and height.)

We have found the *area* of two-dimensional figures, and now we will find the *volume* of some three-dimensional objects.

Definition

The **volume** of a three-dimensional object is a measure of the amount of space occupied by the object or the amount of space inside the object. Volume is measured in *cubic* units.

Here are two examples of cubic units used to measure volume.

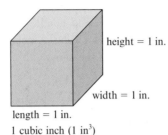

height = 1 in.

width = 1 in.

length = 1 in.

1 cubic inch (1 in³)

height = 1 cm

width = 1 cm

length = 1 cm

1 cubic centimeter (1 cm³)

If we say that the volume of this box is 18 cm³, it means that we can fit 18 of the 1-cm³ boxes inside this larger box.

Let's begin finding volumes of solid objects (or *solids*) with a familiar shape: a box. A **rectangular solid** is a box-like shape with dimensions of length, width, and height.

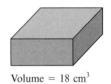

Volume = 18 cm³

Formula Volume of a Rectangular Solid

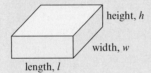

height, h

width, w

length, l

The **volume,** *V*, of a rectangular solid with length *l*, width *w*, and height *h* is

$$\text{Volume} = \text{length} \cdot \text{width} \cdot \text{height} \qquad \text{or}$$
$$V = l \cdot w \cdot h$$

Use *cubic units* to measure volume.

Note

Remember that an exponent represents repeated multiplication. For example, $2 \cdot 2 \cdot 2 = 2^3$; the exponent 3 means that 2 is being multiplied by itself 3 times. Multiplying units works the same way. For example, $\text{cm} \cdot \text{cm} \cdot \text{cm} = \text{cm}^3$.

EXAMPLE 1

Find the volume of each box.

a)

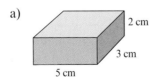

2 cm

3 cm

5 cm

b)

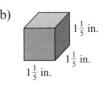

$1\frac{1}{5}$ in.

$1\frac{1}{5}$ in.

$1\frac{1}{5}$ in.

Find the volume of each box.
a)

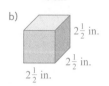

2 cm

4 cm

6 cm

b)

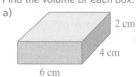

$2\frac{1}{2}$ in.

$2\frac{1}{2}$ in.

$2\frac{1}{2}$ in.

Answer:
a) 48 cm³

b) $\frac{125}{8}$ in³ or $15\frac{5}{8}$ in³ or

15.625 in³

Solution

a) Identify length, width, and height.

$$l = 5 \text{ cm}, w = 3 \text{ cm}, h = 2 \text{ cm}$$

Use the volume formula.

$$V = l \cdot w \cdot h$$
$$V = 5 \text{ cm} \cdot 3 \text{ cm} \cdot 2 \text{ cm} \qquad \text{Substitute the values.}$$
$$V = 30 \text{ cm}^3 \qquad\qquad \text{cm} \cdot \text{cm} \cdot \text{cm} = \text{cm}^3$$

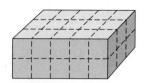

This box will hold 30 of the 1-cm³ boxes or 30 cm³.

b) Notice that the length, width, and height of this box are the same. This is a special type of rectangular solid; it is a *cube*. A **cube** is a rectangular solid in which the length, width, and height are the same.

$$V = l \cdot w \cdot h$$

$$V = 1\frac{1}{5} \text{ in.} \cdot 1\frac{1}{5} \text{ in.} \cdot 1\frac{1}{5} \text{ in.} \qquad \text{Substitute the values.}$$

$$V = \frac{6}{5} \text{ in.} \cdot \frac{6}{5} \text{ in.} \cdot \frac{6}{5} \text{ in.} \qquad \text{Change the mixed numbers to improper fractions.}$$

$$V = \frac{216}{125} \text{ in}^3 \qquad \text{Multiply.}$$

The volume is $\frac{216}{125}$ in³ or $1\frac{91}{125}$ in³ or 1.728 in³. All of these answers are equivalent.

$\left[\text{ YOU TRY 1 }\right]$ Find the volume of each box.

a)

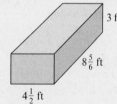

3 ft

$8\frac{5}{6}$ ft

$4\frac{1}{2}$ ft

b)

5 m

5 m

5 m

Note

Since all sides of a **cube** are the same length, we can also label the length of each side as *s* and write the formula for its volume like this:

s

s

s

$$\text{Volume} = s \cdot s \cdot s \qquad \text{or}$$
$$V = s^3$$

2 Find the Volume of a Sphere

A **sphere** is a round, three-dimensional object like a basketball or the Earth. The radius of a sphere is the distance from the center to the edge of the sphere.

Formula Volume of a Sphere

The **volume**, V, of a sphere with radius r is

$$\text{Volume} = \frac{4}{3} \cdot \pi \cdot (\text{radius})^3 \qquad \text{or}$$

$$V = \frac{4}{3} \cdot \pi \cdot r^3$$

EXAMPLE 2

In-Class Example 2

Use Example 2.

Find the volume of a sphere with radius 3 ft. Give an exact value and an approximation using $\frac{22}{7}$ for π.

Solution

Use the volume formula with $r = 3$ ft.

$$V = \frac{4}{3} \cdot \pi \cdot r^3$$

$$V = \frac{4}{3} \cdot \pi \cdot (3 \text{ ft})^3 \qquad \text{Substitute 3 ft for } r.$$

$$V = \frac{4}{3} \cdot \pi \cdot 27 \text{ ft}^3 \qquad (3 \text{ ft})^3 = 3 \text{ ft} \cdot 3 \text{ ft} \cdot 3 \text{ ft} = 27 \text{ ft}^3$$

$$V = \frac{4}{3} \cdot \pi \cdot \frac{\overset{9}{27} \text{ ft}^3}{1} \qquad \text{Divide 3 and 27 by 3.}$$

$$V = 36\pi \text{ ft}^3 \qquad \text{Multiply.}$$

The *exact* volume is 36π ft^3.

To find an approximation, substitute $\frac{22}{7}$ for π.

$$V \approx 36\left(\frac{22}{7}\right) \text{ ft}^3 \qquad \text{Substitute } \frac{22}{7} \text{ for } \pi.$$

$$V \approx \frac{792}{7} \text{ ft}^3 \qquad \text{Multiply.}$$

The volume is approximately $\frac{792}{7}$ ft^3 or $113\frac{1}{7}$ ft^3 or 113.14 ft^3, rounded to the nearest hundredth.

[YOU TRY 2]

Find the volume of a sphere with radius 6 m. Give an exact value and an approximation using $\frac{22}{7}$ for π.

Note

Remember to use the symbol $\approx$ when *approximating* the volume.

EXAMPLE 3

In-Class Example 3

Use Example 3.

Find the volume of a sphere with radius $\frac{1}{2}$ m. Give an exact value and an approximation to the nearest hundredth. Use 3.14 for π.

Solution

Use the volume formula with $r = \frac{1}{2}$ m.

$$V = \frac{4}{3} \cdot \pi \cdot r^3$$

$$V = \frac{4}{3} \cdot \pi \cdot \left(\frac{1}{2} \text{ m}\right)^3 \qquad \text{Substitute } \frac{1}{2} \text{ m for } r.$$

$$V = \frac{4}{3} \cdot \pi \cdot \frac{1}{8} \text{ m}^3 \qquad \left(\frac{1}{2} \text{ m}\right)^3 = \frac{1}{2} \text{ m} \cdot \frac{1}{2} \text{ m} \cdot \frac{1}{2} \text{ m} = \frac{1}{8} \text{ m}^3$$

$$V = \frac{\overset{1}{4}}{3} \cdot \pi \cdot \frac{1}{\underset{2}{8}} \text{ m}^3 \qquad \text{Divide 4 and 8 by 4.}$$

$$V = \frac{1}{6} \pi \text{ m}^3 \qquad \text{Multiply.}$$

The *exact* volume is $\frac{1}{6} \pi \text{ m}^3$.

Substitute 3.14 for π to find an approximation.

$$V \approx \frac{1}{6}(3.14) \text{ m}^3 \qquad \text{Substitute 3.14 for } \pi.$$

$$V \approx \frac{1}{6}\left(\frac{3.14}{1}\right) \text{ m}^3 \approx \frac{3.14}{6} \text{ m}^3 \approx 0.52 \text{ m}^3$$

The volume of the sphere is *approximately* 0.52 m³.

$\left[\text{YOU TRY 3}\right]$

Find the volume of a sphere with radius $\frac{1}{4}$ in. Give an exact value and an approximation to the nearest hundredth. Use 3.14 for π.

A **hemisphere** is half a sphere. To find the volume of a hemisphere, find the volume of a *whole* sphere with the same radius and divide by 2 or *multiply* by $\frac{1}{2}$.

EXAMPLE 4

A hemisphere has a radius of 10 cm. Find its exact volume and an approximation to the nearest hundredth. Use 3.14 for π.

In-Class Example 4

A hemisphere has a radius of 5 cm. Find its exact volume and an approximation to the nearest hundredth. Use 3.14 for π.

Answer: exact: $\dfrac{250}{3}\pi$ cm^3;

approximation: $\dfrac{785}{3}$ cm^3 or

$261\dfrac{2}{3}$ cm^3 or 261.67 cm^3

Solution

First, we will find the volume of a *whole* sphere that has a radius of 10 cm. Then, we will divide by 2.

Whole Sphere

$$V = \frac{4}{3} \cdot \pi \cdot r^3$$

$$V = \frac{4}{3} \cdot \pi \cdot (10 \text{ cm})^3 \qquad \text{Substitute 10 cm for } r.$$

$$V = \frac{4}{3} \cdot \pi \cdot 1000 \text{ m}^3 \qquad (10 \text{ cm})^3 = 1000 \text{ cm}^3$$

$$V = \frac{4000}{3}\pi \text{ cm}^3 \qquad \text{Multiply.}$$

Since a *hemisphere* is $\dfrac{1}{2}$ a sphere, multiply the volume of the sphere by $\dfrac{1}{2}$ to find the volume of the hemisphere.

Hemisphere

$$V = \frac{1}{2} \cdot \frac{4000}{3}\pi \text{ cm}^3 \qquad \text{Multiply the volume of the whole sphere by } \frac{1}{2}.$$

$$V = \frac{1}{2} \cdot \frac{\overset{2000}{4000}}{3}\pi \text{ cm}^3 = \frac{2000}{3}\pi \text{ cm}^3$$

The *exact* volume of the hemisphere is $\dfrac{2000}{3}\pi$ cm^3. To find the *approximate* volume, substitute 3.14 for π.

$$V \approx \frac{2000}{3}(3.14) \text{ cm}^3 \qquad \text{Substitute 3.14 for } \pi.$$

$$V \approx \frac{2000}{3}\left(\frac{3.14}{1}\right) \text{ cm}^3 \approx \frac{6280}{3} \text{ cm}^3 \qquad \text{Multiply.}$$

The volume of the hemisphere is *approximately* $\dfrac{6280}{3}$ cm^3 or $2093\dfrac{1}{3}$ cm^3 or 2093.33 cm^3.

[YOU TRY 4] A hemisphere has a radius of 15 ft. Find its exact volume and an approximation to the nearest hundredth. Use 3.14 for π.

3 Find the Volume of a Cylinder

Definition

A **right circular cylinder** is a three-dimensional object in which the two ends are circles that form right angles with the sides.

Examples:

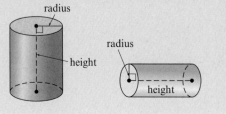

A soup can is an example of a cylinder, as is a hockey puck. To find the volume of a cylinder, we use the following formula.

Formula Volume of a Cylinder

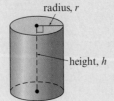

radius, *r*

height, *h*

The **volume,** *V*, of a right circular cylinder with radius *r* and height *h* is

$$\text{Volume} = \pi \cdot (\text{radius})^2 \cdot \text{height} \quad \text{or}$$

$$V = \pi \cdot r^2 \cdot h$$

EXAMPLE 5

In-Class Example 5

Use Example 5.

A hockey puck is 3 in. in diameter, and it is 1 in. thick. Find the exact volume of the hockey puck and the approximate volume to the nearest hundredth. Use 3.14 for π.

3 in.

1 in.

Solution

 Hint

Do you see a relationship between the volume of a cylinder and a formula you learned before?

The formula for the volume of a cylinder is $V = \pi \cdot r^2 \cdot h$. The height of the hockey puck, *h*, is 1 in. But, we are given the diameter, *not* the radius. How do we find the radius?

$$\text{radius} = \frac{\text{diameter}}{2} = \frac{3 \text{ in.}}{2} = 1.5 \text{ in.}$$

Find the volume of the hockey puck using *r* = 1.5 in. and *h* = 1 in.

$$V = \pi \cdot r^2 \cdot h$$
$$V = \pi \cdot (1.5 \text{ in.})^2 \cdot (1 \text{ in.}) \qquad \text{Substitute the values.}$$
$$V = \pi \cdot 2.25 \text{ in}^2 \cdot 1 \text{ in.} \qquad (1.5 \text{ in.})^2 = 2.25 \text{ in}^2$$
$$V = 2.25\pi \text{ in}^3 \qquad \text{Multiply.}$$

The volume of the hockey puck is exactly 2.25π in^3. Find the approximate value by substituting 3.14 for π.

$$V \approx 2.25(3.14) \text{ in}^3 \approx 7.065 \text{ in}^3 \approx 7.07 \text{ in}^3$$

The volume of the hockey puck is *approximately* 7.07 in^3.

[YOU TRY 5] Find the volume of this can. Give the exact value and an approximation to the nearest hundredth. Use 3.14 for π.

3 in.

4 in.

4 Find the Volume of a Cone and a Pyramid

The last objects for which we will find the volume are a cone and a rectangular pyramid. A *rectangular* pyramid is a pyramid with a rectangular (or square) base.

Cone

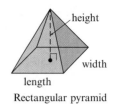

Rectangular pyramid

> ### Note
>
> In future math courses, you may study pyramids with other kinds of bases, such as triangles or hexagons (a six-sided figure).

> ### Formula Volume of a Cone
>
> The **volume**, V, of a cone with a base of radius r and height h is
>
> $$\text{Volume} = \frac{1}{3} \cdot \pi \cdot (\text{radius})^2 \cdot \text{height} \qquad \text{or}$$
>
> $$V = \frac{1}{3} \cdot \pi \cdot r^2 \cdot h$$

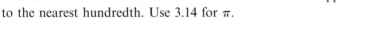

EXAMPLE 6

Find the volume of the cone. Give the exact value and an approximation to the nearest hundredth. Use 3.14 for π.

Solution

Identify the radius and height: $r = 2$ m, $h = 3$ m. Use the volume formula.

$$V = \frac{1}{3} \cdot \pi \cdot r^2 \cdot h$$

$$V = \frac{1}{3} \cdot \pi \cdot (2 \text{ m})^2 \cdot 3 \text{ m} \qquad \text{Substitute the values.}$$

$$V = \frac{1}{3} \cdot \pi \cdot 4 \text{ m}^2 \cdot 3 \text{ m} \qquad (2 \text{ m})^2 = 4 \text{ m}^2$$

$$V = \frac{1}{3} \cdot \pi \cdot 4 \text{ m}^2 \cdot \overset{1}{3} \text{ m} \qquad \text{Divide out 3.}$$

$$V = 4\pi \text{ m}^3 \qquad \text{Multiply.}$$

The volume is *exactly* 4π m³.

Substitute 3.14 for π to find the approximate volume.

$$V \approx 4(3.14) \text{ m}^3 \approx 12.56 \text{ m}^3$$

The volume is *approximately* 12.56 m³.

Find the volume of the cone. Give an exact value and an approximation to the nearest hundredth. Use 3.14 for π.

Note

The formula for the volume of a cone, $V = \dfrac{1}{3} \cdot \pi \cdot r^2 \cdot h$, can also be thought of as $V = \dfrac{1}{3} \cdot A \cdot h$ where $A = \pi \cdot r^2$, the area of the base of the cone.

The volume of a pyramid equals one-third of the area of the base *times* the height of the pyramid.

Formula Volume of a Rectangular Pyramid

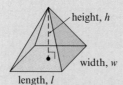

height, *h*

width, *w*

length, *l*

The **volume**, V, of a rectangular pyramid with height h, and a base of length l and width w is

$$\text{Volume} = \frac{1}{3} \cdot \text{length} \cdot \text{width} \cdot \text{height} \quad \text{or}$$

$$V = \frac{1}{3} \cdot l \cdot w \cdot h$$

Because $l \cdot w$ equals the *area* of the base, we can also think of the volume formula as $V = \dfrac{1}{3} \cdot A \cdot h$, where $A = l \cdot w$, the area of the base of the pyramid.

EXAMPLE 7

In-Class Example 7

Find the volume of the pyramid with the given dimensions.

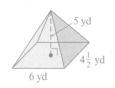

5 yd

$4\frac{1}{2}$ yd

6 yd

Answer: 45 yd³

Find the volume of the pyramid with the given dimensions.

Solution

Identify the values.

$$l = 8 \text{ yd} \qquad w = 6\frac{1}{2} \text{ yd} \qquad h = 12 \text{ yd}$$

12 yd

$6\frac{1}{2}$ yd

8 yd

Use the formula.

$$V = \frac{1}{3} \cdot l \cdot w \cdot h$$

$$V = \frac{1}{3} \cdot 8 \text{ yd} \cdot 6\frac{1}{2} \text{ yd} \cdot 12 \text{ yd} \qquad \text{Substitute the values.}$$

$$V = \frac{1}{3} \cdot \frac{8}{1} \text{ yd} \cdot \frac{13}{2} \text{ yd} \cdot \frac{12}{1} \text{ yd} \qquad \text{Write the numbers as fractions.}$$

$$V = \frac{1}{\overset{}{3}} \cdot \frac{8}{1} \text{ yd} \cdot \frac{13}{\underset{1}{2}} \text{ yd} \cdot \frac{\overset{4}{12}}{1} \text{ yd} \qquad \text{Divide out common factors.}$$

$$V = 208 \text{ yd}^3 \qquad \text{Multiply.}$$

YOU TRY 7   Find the volume of the pyramid with the given dimensions.

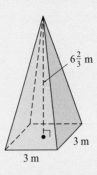

$6\frac{2}{3}$ m

3 m

3 m

ANSWERS TO [**YOU TRY**] **EXERCISES**

1) a) $\dfrac{477}{4}$ ft³ or $119\dfrac{1}{4}$ ft³ or 119.25 ft³   b) 125 m³

2) exact: 288π m³; approximation: $\dfrac{6336}{7}$ m³ or $905\dfrac{1}{7}$ m³ or 905.14 m³

3) exact: $\dfrac{1}{48}\pi$ in³; approximation: 0.07 in³   4) exact: 2250π ft³; approximation: 7065 ft³

5) exact: 9π in³; approximation: 28.26 in³   6) exact: 32π in³; approximation: 100.48 in³   7) 20 m³

Using Technology

We can use a calculator to help us calculate the volume of a sphere using the formula $V = \dfrac{4}{3}\pi r^3$. Remember that we must perform the exponent operation before we divide or multiply. To instruct the calculator to do this, we must use the parenthesis keys.

    Suppose we have a sphere with radius 2 ft. Use $\pi \approx 3.14$. To find the volume, enter $\boxed{4}\,\boxed{\div}\,\boxed{3}\,\boxed{\times}\,\boxed{3}\,\boxed{.}\,\boxed{1}\,\boxed{4}\,\boxed{\times}\,\boxed{(}\,\boxed{2}\,\boxed{y^x}\,\boxed{3}\,\boxed{)}\,\boxed{=}$ into the calculator. The display screen will show 33.4933333 for the result. Rounded to the nearest hundredth, the volume is approximately 33.49 ft³.

E Evaluate   **9.7**   Exercises   Do the exercises, and check your work.

*Additional answers can be found in the Answers to Exercises appendix.

Objective 1: Find the Volume of a Rectangular Solid

1) Write the formula that represents the volume of a rectangular solid with length *l*, width *w*, and height *h*. $V = l \cdot w \cdot h$

2) When can you call a rectangular solid a cube?
when all the side lengths are equal

Find the volume of each rectangular solid.

3)

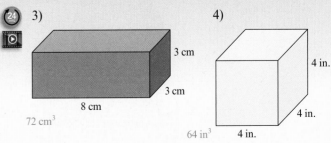

3 cm

3 cm

8 cm

72 cm³

4)

4 in.

4 in.

4 in.

64 in³

5)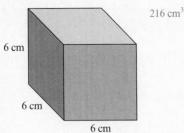

216 cm³

6 cm
6 cm
6 cm

6)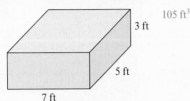

105 ft³

3 ft
5 ft
7 ft

7)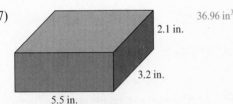

36.96 in³

2.1 in.
3.2 in.
5.5 in.

8)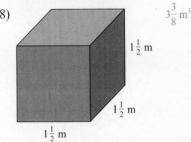

$3\frac{3}{8}$ m³

$1\frac{1}{2}$ m
$1\frac{1}{2}$ m
$1\frac{1}{2}$ m

Objective 2: Find the Volume of a Sphere

9) Write the formula that represents the volume of a sphere with radius r. $V = \frac{4}{3}\pi r^3$

10) Because a hemisphere is half a sphere, what is the formula for the volume of a hemisphere with radius r? $V = \frac{2}{3}\pi r^3$

Find the volume of each sphere. Give an exact answer and an approximation using the indicated value for π. Round the approximation to the nearest hundredth.

11) Use 3.14 for π.

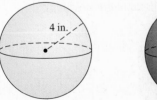

4 in.

exact: $\frac{256}{3}\pi$ in³;
approximation: 267.95 in³

12) Use 3.14 for π.

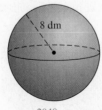

8 dm

exact: $\frac{2048}{3}\pi$ dm³;
approximation: 2143.57 dm³

13) Use $\frac{22}{7}$ for π.

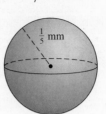

$\frac{1}{5}$ mm

14) Use $\frac{22}{7}$ for π.

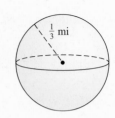

$\frac{1}{3}$ mi

15) Use 3.14 for π.

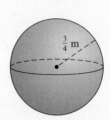

$\frac{3}{4}$ m

16) Use $\frac{22}{7}$ for π.

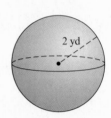

2 yd

Find the volume of each hemisphere. Give an exact answer and an approximation using the indicated value for π. Round the approximation to the nearest hundredth.

17) Use $\frac{22}{7}$ for π.

1 ft

18) Use 3.14 for π.

6 mm

exact: 144π mm³; approximation: 452.16 mm³

19) Use 3.14 for π.

4 in.

20) Use $\frac{22}{7}$ for π.

2 in.

exact: $\frac{128}{3}\pi$ in³; approximation: 133.97 in³

Objective 3: Find the Volume of a Cylinder

21) Write down the equation that represents the volume of a right circular cylinder with radius r and height h. $V = \pi r^2 h$

22) If you double the height of a right circular cylinder and keep the radius the same, by what factor does the volume change? by a factor of 2

Find the volume of each right circular cylinder. Give an exact value and an approximation using the indicated value for π.

23) Use 3.14 for π.

0.2 m

exact: 1.25π m³; approximation:3.925 m³

24) Use 3.14 for π.

4 in.

1.5 in

25) Use $\frac{22}{7}$ for π. Round to the nearest hundredth.

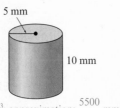

5 mm

10 mm

exact: 250π mm³; approximation: $\frac{5500}{7}$ mm³ $\approx$ 785.71 mm³

26) Use $\frac{22}{7}$ for π. Round to the nearest hundredth.

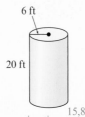

6 ft

20 ft

exact: 720π ft³; approximation: $\frac{15,840}{7}$ ft³ $\approx$ 2262.86 ft³

27) Use 3.14 for π.

28) Use $\frac{22}{7}$ for π.

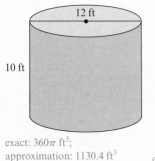

12 ft

10 ft

6 cm

7 cm

exact: 360π ft³;
approximation: 1130.4 ft³

exact: 63π cm³;
approximation: 198 cm³

Objective 4: Find the Volume of a Cone and a Pyramid

29) Write down the formula that represents the volume of a cone with a base of radius r and height h. $V = \frac{1}{3}\pi r^2 h$

30) Write down the formula that represents the volume of a pyramid with a base of length l and width w and that has height h. $V = \frac{1}{3} \cdot l \cdot w \cdot h$

Find the volume of each cone. Give an exact value and an approximation using $\pi = 3.14$.

31)

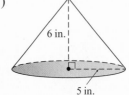

6 in.

5 in.

exact: 50π in³;
approximation: 157 in³

32)

exact: 18π ft³;
approximation:
56.52 ft³

6 ft

3 ft

33)

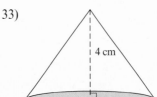

4 cm

3 cm

exact: 12π cm³;
approximation: 37.68 cm³

34)

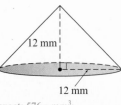

12 mm

12 mm

exact: 576π mm³;
approximation: 1808.64 mm³

Find the volume of the pyramid with the given dimensions.

35)

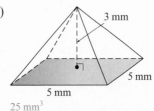

3 mm

5 mm

5 mm

25 mm³

36)

64 ft³

12 ft

4 ft

4 ft

37)

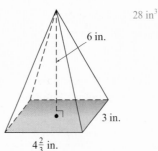

28 in³

6 in.

3 in.

$4\frac{2}{3}$ in.

38)

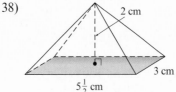

2 cm

11 cm³

3 cm

$5\frac{1}{2}$ cm

Mixed Exercises: Objectives 1–4

Find the exact volume of each solid. Use $\pi \approx 3.14$, if required, to also approximate the volume to the nearest hundredth.

39)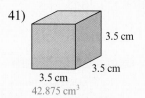

2 in. 5 in.

exact: 20π in³;
approximation: 62.8 in³

40)

7 m

$\frac{112}{3}$ m³ or $37\frac{1}{3}$ m³

4 m

4 m

41)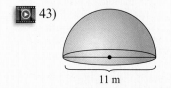

3.5 cm

3.5 cm

3.5 cm

42.875 cm³

42)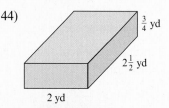

6 ft

2.5 ft

43)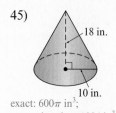

11 m

44)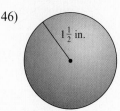

$\frac{3}{4}$ yd

$2\frac{1}{2}$ yd

2 yd

45)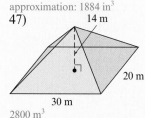

18 in.

10 in.

exact: 600π in³;
approximation: 1884 in³

46)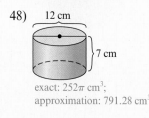

$1\frac{1}{2}$ in.

47)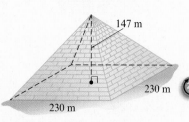

14 m

20 m

30 m

2800 m³

48)

12 cm

7 cm

exact: 252π cm³;
approximation: 791.28 cm³

Solve each problem. Use $\pi \approx 3.14$ if required, to approximate the volume to the nearest hundredth.

49) The Great Pyramid of Giza is the world's largest pyramid. The base of the pyramid has four side lengths all approximately equal to 230 m. The height of the pyramid is approximately 147 m. Calculate the volume of the Great Pyramid of Giza using these dimensions. (www.nationalgeographic.com) 2,592,100 m³

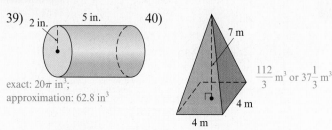

147 m

230 m

230 m

50) The radius of the Earth is approximately 4000 mi. Using this dimension, calculate the circumference of the Earth. (nssdc.gsfc.nasa.gov) 25,120 mi

51) The *BOSE*® Acoustimass® 3 speaker system has 2 cube speakers and an Acoustimass® module. The cube speakers measure 4 in. by 3 in. by 3 in. high. The Acoustimass® module measures 12.5 in. by 7.5 in. by 14 in. high. Find the combined volume of the speaker system. (www.bose.com) 1384.5 in³

52) Ethanol is an alcohol that is currently blended into 50% of the nation's fuel supply. The primary source for ethanol is corn, which is sometimes stored in a corn silo shaped like a right circular cylinder. If the silo has a diameter of 40 ft and a height of 160 ft, what is its volume? (www.afdc.energy.gov) 200,960 ft³

53) A waffle cone maker lets you make your own waffle cone having a diameter of approximately 3 in. and a height of approximately 8 in. Using these dimensions, find the volume of the waffle cone. 18.84 in³

54) The Epcot Center geodesic sphere has a diameter of approximately 50 m. What is the volume of the sphere rounded to the nearest cubic meter? 65,417 m³

55) A seventeenth-century cannonball found at Charles Fort in Kinsale, Ireland, has a diameter of 15.5 cm. Find the volume of the cannonball. (Information on display at Charles Fort) 1948.83 cm³

56) A dime is 1.35 mm thick, and its diameter is approximately 18 mm. What is the volume of a dime? (www.usmint.gov) 343.36 mm³

57) The Millers' farm has a corn storage silo shaped as a right circular cylinder with a hemispherical top. If the cylinder has a diameter of 6 m and a height of 40 m, find the volume of the silo. 1186.92 m³

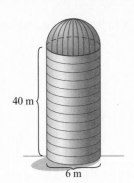

40 m

6 m

58) Savannah will make fruit punch for a family reunion. She will use a large punch bowl in the shape of a hemisphere with a diameter measuring 48 cm. What is the volume of the bowl? To the nearest liter, how much punch will it take to completely fill the bowl? (Note: 1 cm³ = 1 mL)

28,938.24 cm³; 29 L

R Rethink

R1) Which formulas do you find easier to use and why?

R2) Which two formulas would you need to use to find the volume of ice cream in a waffle cone,

assuming that the cone is completely full and that there is one round scoop on the top?

9.8 Square Roots and the Pythagorean Theorem

P Prepare

O Organize

What are your objectives for Section 9.8?	How can you accomplish each objective?
1 Approximate Square Roots	• Refresh your memory on **The First 12 Perfect Square Roots,** and write them in your notes. • Write a procedure for approximating a square root by following Example 1. • Complete You Try 1.
2 Find an Unknown Length in a Right Triangle	• Write the definition of a *hypotenuse* and *legs* of a right triangle in your notes. • Understand and memorize the **Pythagorean Theorem.** • Write the formula for **Finding an Unknown Side of a Right Triangle** in your notes. • Complete the given example on your own. • Complete You Try 2.
3 Apply the Pythagorean Theorem	• Be able to identify when a word problem requires use of the Pythagorean theorem. • Complete the given example on your own. • Complete You Try 3.

W Work

Read the explanations, follow the examples, take notes, and complete the You Trys.

In Section 2.6, we first learned how to find the square root of a number. For example,

$$\sqrt{9} = 3 \qquad \text{because} \qquad 3^2 = 9$$

We can represent this geometrically with a square.

3 in.

3 in.

Area = 3 in. · 3 in. = 9 in²

We say that 9 is a *perfect square* and that $\sqrt{9}$ is a *perfect square root* because $\sqrt{9} = 3$. Here is a list of the first 12 perfect square roots.

Summary The First 12 Perfect Square Roots

$\sqrt{1} = 1$	$\sqrt{16} = 4$	$\sqrt{49} = 7$	$\sqrt{100} = 10$
$\sqrt{4} = 2$	$\sqrt{25} = 5$	$\sqrt{64} = 8$	$\sqrt{121} = 11$
$\sqrt{9} = 3$	$\sqrt{36} = 6$	$\sqrt{81} = 9$	$\sqrt{144} = 12$

Note: $\sqrt{0} = 0$

---

1 Approximate Square Roots

If a number is *not* a perfect square, its square root will *not* be a whole number. We can approximate its value using perfect squares that we *do* know.

EXAMPLE 1

In-Class Example 1

Approximate each square root to the nearest tenth, and plot it on a number line.
a) $\sqrt{7}$ b) $\sqrt{34}$

Answer:
a) 2.6

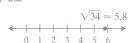
$\sqrt{7} \approx 2.6$

0 1 2 3 4 5

b) 5.8

$\sqrt{34} \approx 5.8$

0 1 2 3 4 5 6

Approximate each square root to the nearest tenth, and plot it on a number line.

a) $\sqrt{5}$ b) $\sqrt{22}$

Solution

a) The number 5 is *not* a perfect square. Let's ask ourselves two questions:

1) What is the largest perfect square that is *less than* 5?   **4**

2) What is the smallest perfect square that is *greater than* 5?   **9**

Listing these numbers from smallest to largest, we get

4   5   9
↑   ↑
Perfect square   Perfect square
$\sqrt{4} = 2$ $\sqrt{9} = 3$

Because 5 *is between* 4 and 9, $\sqrt{5}$ *is between* $\sqrt{4}$ and $\sqrt{9}$. In order from smallest to largest, we get

$$\sqrt{4} = 2 \qquad \sqrt{5} = ? \qquad \sqrt{9} = 3$$

$\sqrt{5}$ must be between 2 and 3. Because 5 is closer to 4 than to 9, $\sqrt{5}$ will be closer to $\sqrt{4}$ than to $\sqrt{9}$. So, $\sqrt{5}$ will be closer to 2 than to 3. Let's see whether 2.2 is a good approximation of $\sqrt{5}$.

If $\sqrt{5} \approx 2.2$, then $(2.2)^2 \approx 5$.

$$(2.2)^2 = 2.2 \times 2.2 = 4.84 \qquad \text{Close to 5 but } \textit{less than 5}$$

Let's see whether 2.3 is a *better* approximation of $\sqrt{5}$.
If $\sqrt{5} \approx 2.3$, then $(2.3)^2 \approx 5$.

$$(2.3)^2 = 2.3 \times 2.3 = 5.29 \qquad \text{Close to 5 but } \textit{more than 5}$$

Since 4.84 is closer to 5 than 5.29, the better approximation is 2.2.

$$\sqrt{5} \approx 2.2$$

b) The number 22 is *not* a perfect square. Ask ourselves,

   1) What is the largest perfect square that is *less than* 22? **16**

   2) What is the smallest perfect square that is *greater than* 22? **25**

List the numbers from smallest to largest.

16	22	25
↑		↑
Perfect square		Perfect square
$\sqrt{16} = 4$		$\sqrt{25} = 5$

Because 22 *is between* 16 and 25, $\sqrt{22}$ *is between* $\sqrt{16}$ and $\sqrt{25}$. In order from smallest to largest, we get

$$\sqrt{16} = 4 \qquad \sqrt{22} = ? \qquad \sqrt{25} = 5$$

$\sqrt{22}$ *is between* 4 and 5. Because 22 is closer to 25 than to 16, $\sqrt{22}$ will be closer to 5 than to 4. Let's try 4.6 as an approximation of $\sqrt{22}$.

If $\sqrt{22} \approx 4.6$, then $(4.6)^2 \approx 22$.

$$(4.6)^2 = 4.6 \times 4.6 = 21.16 \qquad \text{Close to 22 but } \textit{less than 22}$$

Let's see whether 4.7 is a better approximation.

If $\sqrt{22} \approx 4.7$, then $(4.7)^2 \approx 22$.

$$(4.7)^2 = 4.7 \times 4.7 = 22.09 \qquad \text{This is closer to 22 than the other approximation.}$$

Therefore, $\sqrt{22} \approx 4.7$.

$$\sqrt{22} \approx 4.7$$

[YOU TRY 1] Approximate each square root to the nearest tenth, and plot it on a number line.

a) $\sqrt{13}$ b) $\sqrt{59}$

We can use a calculator to approximate square roots.

A regular or scientific calculator will have a $\sqrt{}$ key or $\sqrt{x}$ key. To approximate $\sqrt{5}$ and $\sqrt{22}$ from Example 1 on a calculator, follow the steps here. Depending on your calculator, you may not have to press the $=$ key.

To find $\sqrt{5}$, press 5 $\sqrt{x}$. Answer: 2.236067977
Round this to 2.2.
To find $\sqrt{22}$, press 22 $\sqrt{x}$. Answer: 4.69041576
Round this to 4.7.

The long answer that the calculator gives us is also an approximation.

2 Find an Unknown Length in a Right Triangle

We have learned that a right triangle contains a right, or 90°, angle. Right triangles have special properties that other triangles do not. We can label a right triangle as shown in the figure.

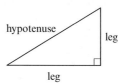

The side opposite the right angle is the longest side of the triangle and is called the **hypotenuse.** The other two sides are called the **legs.** The *Pythagorean theorem* states a relationship between the lengths of the sides of a right triangle.

Property Pythagorean Theorem

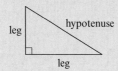

For any **right** triangle,

$$(\text{leg})^2 + (\text{leg})^2 = (\text{hypotenuse})^2$$

We can use the Pythagorean theorem to find an unknown side of a right triangle. From the Pythagorean theorem, we get these two formulas.

Formulas Finding an Unknown Side of a Right Triangle

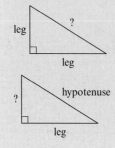

1) To find the **hypotenuse** of a right triangle, use this formula:

$$\text{hypotenuse} = \sqrt{(\text{leg})^2 + (\text{leg})^2}$$

2) To find a **leg** of a right triangle, use this formula:

$$\text{leg} = \sqrt{(\text{hypotenuse})^2 - (\text{known leg})^2}$$

The Pythagorean theorem and the given formulas apply *only* to **right** triangles.

EXAMPLE 2

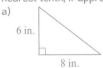
Find the length of the missing side. Give the exact answer and the answer to the nearest tenth, if appropriate.

a)

3 in.
4 in.

b)

11 cm   8 cm

Solution

a) First ask yourself, "*Which part of the right triangle is unknown?*" The side *across from* the right angle is unknown, and that is the *hypotenuse*. Use the formula for finding the hypotenuse.

$$\text{hypotenuse} = \sqrt{(\text{leg})^2 + (\text{leg})^2}$$

$$= \sqrt{(3)^2 + (4)^2} \qquad \text{Substitute the values for the legs.}$$

$$= \sqrt{9 + 16} \qquad 3^2 = 9; \ 4^2 = 16$$

$$= \sqrt{25} \qquad \text{Add.}$$

$$= 5 \qquad \text{Evaluate } \sqrt{25}.$$

The length of the hypotenuse is 5 in.

b) Ask yourself, "*Which part of the right triangle is unknown?*" The unknown side is *next to* the right angle, so it is a *leg*. Use the formula for finding an unknown leg.

$$\text{leg} = \sqrt{(\text{hypotenuse})^2 - (\text{known leg})^2}$$

Identify the hypotenuse and the leg. Remember, the hypotenuse is the side *across from* the right angle.

$$\text{hypotenuse} = 11 \text{ cm} \qquad \text{leg} = 8 \text{ cm}$$

$$\text{leg} = \sqrt{(\text{hypotenuse})^2 - (\text{known leg})^2}$$

$$\text{leg} = \sqrt{(11)^2 - (8)^2} \qquad \text{Substitute the values for the hypotenuse and leg.}$$

$$= \sqrt{121 - 64} \qquad 11^2 = 121; \ 8^2 = 64$$

$$= \sqrt{57} \qquad \text{Subtract.}$$

$$\approx 7.5 \qquad \text{Round to the nearest tenth.}$$

The length of the leg is *exactly* $\sqrt{57}$ cm, and it is *approximately* 7.5 cm.

[YOU TRY 2]

Find the length of the missing side. Give the exact answer and the answer to the nearest tenth, if appropriate.

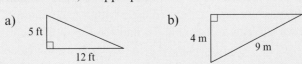

a)
5 ft
12 ft

b)
4 m
9 m

---

3 Apply the Pythagorean Theorem

The Pythagorean theorem can be used in many ways.

EXAMPLE 3

In-Class Example 3

Use Example 3.

A wire is attached to the top of a pole as shown here. Find the length of the wire.

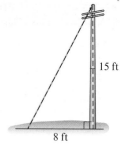

15 ft

8 ft

Solution

Notice that the pole, the wire, and the ground form a right triangle. Ask yourself, "*Which part of the triangle is unknown?*" The unknown side is *across from* the right angle, so this is the *hypotenuse*. Use the formula for finding the hypotenuse.

$$\text{hypotenuse} = \sqrt{(\text{leg})^2 + (\text{leg})^2}$$

$$= \sqrt{(8)^2 + (15)^2} \qquad \text{Substitute the values of the legs.}$$

$$= \sqrt{64 + 225} \qquad 8^2 = 64;\ 15^2 = 225$$

$$= \sqrt{289} \qquad \text{Add.}$$

$$= 17 \qquad \sqrt{289} = 17$$

The wire is 17 ft long.

[YOU TRY 3]

A computer screen is 13 in. long and 8 in. wide. Find the exact length of the diagonal and the approximation to the nearest tenth.

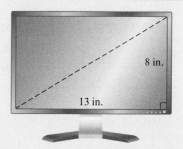

8 in.

13 in.

ANSWERS TO [YOU TRY] EXERCISES

1) a) 3.6; $\sqrt{13} \approx 3.6$

+—+—+—+—+—●—+—+
0 1 2 3 4 5

b) 7.7; $\sqrt{59} \approx 7.7$

+—+—+—+—+—+—+—+—●—+
0 1 2 3 4 5 6 7 8 9

2) a) 13 ft   b) exact: $\sqrt{65}$ m; approximation: 8.1 m   3) exact: $\sqrt{233}$ in.; approximation: 15.3 in.

Using Technology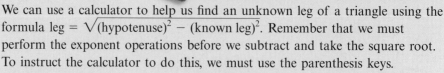

We can use a calculator to help us find an unknown leg of a triangle using the formula $\text{leg} = \sqrt{(\text{hypotenuse})^2 - (\text{known leg})^2}$. Remember that we must perform the exponent operations before we subtract and take the square root. To instruct the calculator to do this, we must use the parenthesis keys.

Suppose we have a right triangle with a hypotenuse of length 13 mm and a known leg length of 5 mm. To find the length of the missing leg, we enter $\boxed{1}\,\boxed{3}\,\boxed{y^x}\,\boxed{2}\,\boxed{=}\,\boxed{-}\,\boxed{(}\,\boxed{5}\,\boxed{y^x}\,\boxed{2}\,\boxed{)}\,\boxed{=}\,\boxed{\sqrt{\ }}$ into the calculator. The display screen will show 12 for the result. This means that the length of the unknown leg is 12 mm.

*Additional answers can be found in the Answers to Exercises appendix.

Objective 1: Approximate Square Roots

1) Write down the first four perfect squares and their square roots.   perfect squares: 1, 4, 9, 16; their square roots: 1, 2, 3, 4

2) What makes a number a perfect square?   It is the square of a whole number.

Approximate each square root to the nearest tenth and plot it on a number line.

3) $\sqrt{2}$ 0 1 2 3 4 5 $\sqrt{2} \approx 1.4$ 0 1 2 3 4 5

4) $\sqrt{3}$ 0 1 2 3 4 5 $\sqrt{3} \approx 1.7$ 0 1 2 3 4 5

5) $\sqrt{8}$ 0 1 2 3 4 5 $\sqrt{8} \approx 2.8$ 0 1 2 3 4 5

6) $\sqrt{6}$ 0 1 2 3 4 5 $\sqrt{6} \approx 2.4$ 0 1 2 3 4 5

7) $\sqrt{20}$ 0 1 2 3 4 5 $\sqrt{20} \approx 4.5$ 0 1 2 3 4 5

8) $\sqrt{12}$ 0 1 2 3 4 5 $\sqrt{12} \approx 3.5$ 0 1 2 3 4 5

9) $\sqrt{10}$ 0 1 2 3 4 5 $\sqrt{10} \approx 3.2$ 0 1 2 3 4 5

10) $\sqrt{27}$ 0 1 2 3 4 5 6 $\sqrt{27} \approx 5.2$ 0 1 2 3 4 5 6

11) $\sqrt{45}$ 4 5 6 7 8 9 $\sqrt{45} \approx 6.7$ 4 5 6 7 8 9

12) $\sqrt{66}$ 4 5 6 7 8 9 $\sqrt{66} \approx 8.1$ 4 5 6 7 8 9

Use a calculator and its square root key to approximate the following square roots to the nearest thousandth.

13) $\sqrt{20}$ 4.472

14) $\sqrt{12}$ 3.464

15) $\sqrt{45}$ 6.708

16) $\sqrt{66}$ 8.124

17) $\sqrt{157}$ 12.530

18) $\sqrt{300}$ 17.321

Objective 2: Find an Unknown Length in a Right Triangle

19) Write the formula to find the leg of a right triangle.   unknown leg $= \sqrt{(\text{hypotenuse})^2 - (\text{known leg})^2}$

20) Write the formula to find the hypotenuse of a right triangle.   hypotenuse $= \sqrt{(\text{leg})^2 + (\text{leg})^2}$

Find the length of the missing side. Give the exact answer and the answer to the nearest tenth if appropriate.

21) 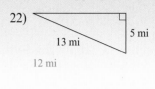   3 km   4 km   5 km

22) 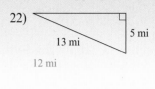   13 mi   5 mi   12 mi

23) 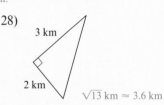   5 ft   6 ft $\sqrt{11}$ ft ≈ 3.3 ft

24) 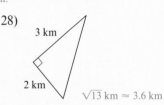   3 m $\sqrt{40}$ m ≈ 6.3 m   7 m

25) 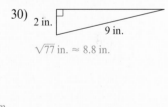   6 in.   8 in.   10 in.

26) 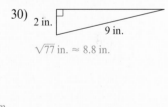   12 dm   5 dm   13 dm

27) 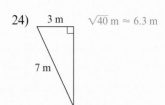   3 mi   5 mi $\sqrt{34}$ mi ≈ 5.8 mi

28) 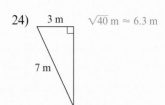   3 km   2 km $\sqrt{13}$ km ≈ 3.6 km

29) 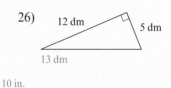   4 cm   10 cm $\sqrt{84}$ cm ≈ 9.2 cm

30) 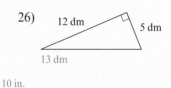   2 in.   9 in. $\sqrt{77}$ in. ≈ 8.8 in.

31) 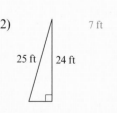   16 cm   12 cm   20 cm

32) 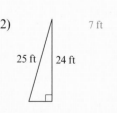   7 ft   25 ft   24 ft

Use a calculator to find the unknown side length. Approximate your answer to the nearest thousandth.

33)   2.53 km   2.831 km   1.27 km

34)   10.5 yd   6.3 yd   12.245 yd

35)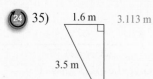

1.6 m   3.113 m

3.5 m

36)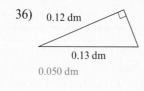

0.12 dm

0.13 dm

0.050 dm

Objective 3: Apply the Pythagorean Theorem

37) Does the Pythagorean theorem apply to any type of triangle?   No, it applies only to right triangles.

38) Answer *true or false*: $\sqrt{3^2 + 4^2} = 3 + 4$.   false

Solve each problem. Give the exact answer and an answer approximated to the nearest tenth, if appropriate.

39) Trang flies his kite using 20 m of kite string. How high above Trang is his kite when he uses all 20 m of his kite string and he is standing 15 m away from directly below the kite? $\sqrt{175}$ m ≈ 13.2 m

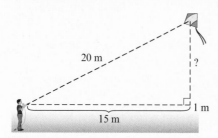

20 m   ?

15 m   1 m

40) A flat-screen TV is 38 in. wide and 13 in. high. Find the length of the diagonal. $\sqrt{1613}$ in. ≈ 40.2 in.

41) In the middle of a baseball game, a player tried to steal second base. The catcher threw the ball from home base to second base in time to get the player out. How far did the catcher have to throw the ball? $\sqrt{16,200}$ ft ≈ 127.3 ft

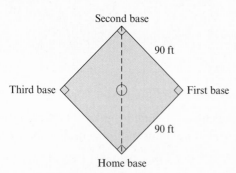

Second base

90 ft

Third base   First base

90 ft

Home base

42) Find the height of an equilateral triangle with side lengths of 6 dm. Give both the exact height and an approximation rounded to the nearest tenth.
$\sqrt{27}$ dm ≈ 5.2 dm

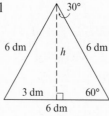

30°

6 dm h 6 dm

3 dm   60°

6 dm

43) Ethan and Trevin have a tin-can phone with a string of length 9 yd. In order for the phone to work, the string has to be tight. If Ethan is in a tree house 4 yd off the ground, how far does Trevin have to be from the base of the tree to make the phone work? Assume Ethan and Trevin are the same height. $\sqrt{65}$ yd ≈ 8.1 yd

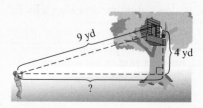

9 yd   4 yd

?

44) During a rescue exercise, a ladder truck parks 15 m from the base of a building. The truck must place its ladder at a fourth-story window, 15 m above the base of the ladder. How far should the ladder be extended to reach the window? $\sqrt{450}$ m ≈ 21.2 m

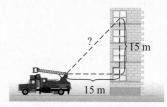

?   15 m

15 m

Mixed Exercises: Objectives 1–3

Approximate each square root to the nearest tenth and plot it on a number line.

45) $\sqrt{15}$

0 1 2 3 4 5

$\sqrt{15}$ ≈ 3.9

0 1 2 3 4 5

46) $\sqrt{32}$

1 2 3 4 5 6

$\sqrt{32}$ ≈ 5.7

1 2 3 4 5 6

Use a calculator and its square root key to approximate the following square roots to the nearest thousandth.

47) $\sqrt{17}$ 4.123

48) $\sqrt{59}$ 7.681

Find the length of the missing side. Give the exact answer and the answer to the nearest tenth, if appropriate.

49)
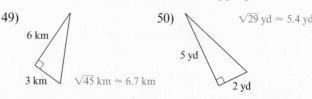

6 km

3 km $\sqrt{45}$ km ≈ 6.7 km

50) $\sqrt{29}$ yd ≈ 5.4 yd

5 yd

2 yd

51) 2 ft

5 ft

$\sqrt{21}$ ft ≈ 4.6 ft

52)
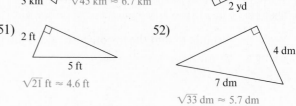

4 dm

7 dm

$\sqrt{33}$ dm ≈ 5.7 dm

Use a calculator to find the unknown side length.
Approximate your answer to the nearest thousandth.

53)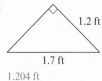

1.2 ft

1.7 ft

1.204 ft

54)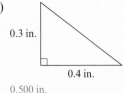

0.3 in.

0.4 in.

0.500 in.

Solve each problem. Give the exact answer and an answer
approximated to the nearest tenth, if appropriate.

 55) A ladder 13 ft long is leaning
against a wall, forming a right
triangle. The bottom of the ladder
is 5 ft away from the wall. How far
off the ground does the top of the
ladder touch the wall?   12 ft

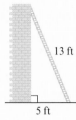

13 ft

5 ft

56) A news helicopter travels directly from the news
station to a warehouse fire in a neighboring city.
The news van leaves the same location but must
travel a rectangular path through city blocks to get
to the fire. The van first travels 7 km south and then
3 km east. How much further than the helicopter
did the news van travel to get to the scene of the
fire? $(10 - \sqrt{58})$ km ≈ 2.4 km

R1) After completing these exercises and taking a
closer look at Exercise 41, what general statement
could you make about a diagonal of a square?
How could you find the length of a diagonal?

R2) When solving applications involving geometry,
explain how you begin to solve the problem.

9.9 Similar Triangles

P Prepare

O Organize

What are your objectives for Section 9.9?	How can you accomplish each objective?
1 Find Unknown Lengths in Similar Triangles	• Understand how the angles and sides of similar triangles are marked. • Write the definitions of *corresponding angles* and *corresponding sides* in your own words. • Write the definition of *similar triangles* in your own words. • Write a procedure for finding an unknown length in similar triangles. • Complete the given examples on your own. • Complete You Trys 1–3.
2 Solve Applied Problems Involving Similar Triangles	• Use the five-step process to solve similar triangles applications. • Complete the given example on your own. • Complete You Try 4.

Read the explanations, follow the examples, take notes, and complete the You Trys.

1 Find Unknown Lengths in Similar Triangles

Look at these triangles:

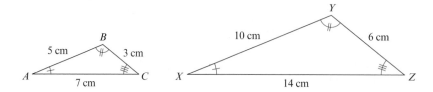

They are the same *shape,* but they are not the same size. We can also say something about their angles:

$m\angle A = m\angle X$ which is indicated by ⊢

$m\angle B = m\angle Y$ which is indicated by ⊬

$m\angle C = m\angle Z$ which is indicated by ⊯

The angles with the same measure are called **corresponding angles.** The sides opposite the corresponding angles are called the **corresponding sides.** Although corresponding angles have the same measure, corresponding sides are *not* necessarily the same length.

Corresponding Angles	Corresponding Sides
$\angle A$ and $\angle X$	$\overline{BC}$ and $\overline{YZ}$
$\angle B$ and $\angle Y$	$\overline{AC}$ and $\overline{XZ}$
$\angle C$ and $\angle Z$	$\overline{AB}$ and $\overline{XY}$

Triangles like these are called *similar triangles.*

Definition

Similar triangles have the same shape, the measures of their corresponding angles are the same, and the lengths of their corresponding sides are proportional.

Notice that, above, each side in the larger triangle is twice the length of the corresponding side in the smaller triangle. This is what we mean when we say that corresponding sides are proportional: *The ratios of the lengths of corresponding sides of the triangles are the same.* We use this fact to find a missing side length in similar triangles.

EXAMPLE 1

Find the unknown length in the larger of these two similar triangles.

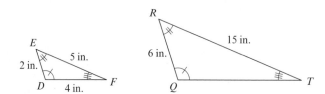

Find the unknown length in
the larger of these two
similar triangles.

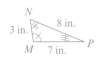

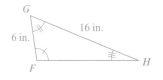

Answer: 14 in.

Solution

We can find the missing length, $\overline{QT}$, just by thinking about how the sides of the first triangle are related to the sides of the second triangle.

Corresponding Sides	Lengths of Those Sides
$\overline{DE}$ and $\overline{QR}$	2 in. and 6 in.
$\overline{EF}$ and $\overline{RT}$	5 in. and 15 in.

How are the corresponding sides related? **The sides in the larger triangle are 3 times the length of the corresponding sides in the smaller triangle.**

So, the length of side $\overline{QT}$ is 3 *times* the length of $\overline{DF}$.

$$\text{Length of } \overline{QT} = 3 \cdot \text{length of } \overline{DF}$$
$$= 3 \cdot (4 \text{ in.}) \qquad \text{Substitute the value.}$$
$$= 12 \text{ in.} \qquad \text{Multiply.}$$

[YOU TRY 1] Find the unknown length in the larger of these two similar triangles.

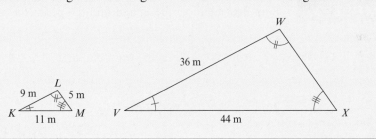

If we cannot figure out the relationship between the sides just by looking at the lengths of the sides, then we can use a proportion. Let's solve Example 1 using a proportion.

EXAMPLE 2

In-Class Example 2

Use a proportion to find the
unknown length in In-Class
Example 1.

Answer: 14 in.

Use a proportion to find the unknown length in Example 1.

Solution

Label the unknown length x.

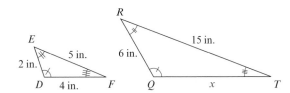

Choose either of the two corresponding side pairs that we know; let's choose 2 in. and 6 in. The corresponding sides that include the side we do not know are 4 in. and x.

The ratios of the corresponding sides are equal, so we can set up a proportion. Read it as

$$\text{Corresponding sides} \Big\langle \frac{2}{6} = \frac{4}{x} \Big\rangle \text{Corresponding sides}$$

2 is to 6 as 4 is to x.

Our proportion is $\frac{2}{6} = \frac{4}{x}$. Set the cross products equal to each other, and solve.

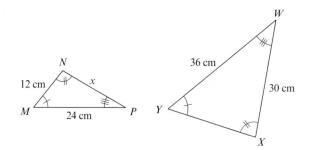

$$6 \cdot 4 = 24$$
$$2 \cdot x = 2x$$

$2x = 24$ Set the cross products equal to each other.

$\dfrac{2x}{2} = \dfrac{24}{2}$ Divide by 2.

$x = 12$ Simplify.

The length of the missing side is 12 in. This is the same result we obtained in Example 1.

W Hint

Could this example be solved by setting up a different proportion?

[YOU TRY 2]   Use a proportion to find the unknown length in You Try 1.

Sometimes, you must look at the triangles carefully to recognize the corresponding sides.

EXAMPLE 3

Find the length of side x, and find the perimeter of the smaller of these similar triangles.

In-Class Example 3

Find the length of side x, and find the perimeter of the smaller of these similar triangles.

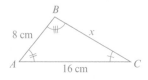

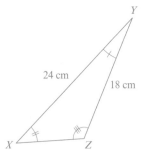

Answer: $x = 12$ cm; perimeter = 36 cm

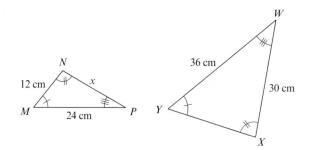

Solution

These triangles are not positioned in the same way. Let's redraw the second triangle so that we can identify the corresponding sides more easily.

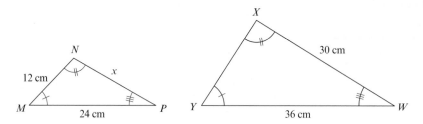

Identify two corresponding sides that we *do* know: 24 cm and 36 cm

Identify the corresponding sides that include the side we must find: x and 30 cm

Write a proportion:

Corresponding sides $\left< \dfrac{24}{36} = \dfrac{x}{30} \right>$ Corresponding sides

24 is to 36 as x is to 30.

Set the cross products equal to each other, and solve.

$$\frac{24}{36} \diagdown \frac{x}{30} \qquad 36 \cdot x = 36x$$
$$24 \cdot 30 = 720$$

$$36x = 720 \qquad \text{Set the cross products equal to each other.}$$

$$\frac{36x}{36} = \frac{720}{36} \qquad \text{Divide by 36.}$$

$$x = 20 \qquad \text{Simplify.}$$

The length of the missing side is 20 cm. Now, we can find the perimeter of the smaller triangle.

$$\text{Perimeter} = 12 \text{ cm} + 20 \text{ cm} + 24 \text{ cm} = 56 \text{ cm}$$

[YOU TRY 3] Find the length of side *x*, and find the perimeter of the smaller of these similar triangles.

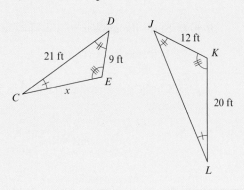

2 Solve Applied Problems Involving Similar Triangles

In-Class Example 4

A statue is 8 ft tall, and it casts a shadow that is 10 ft long. At the same time, a tree nearby casts a shadow that is 55 ft long. How tall is the tree?

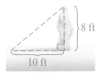

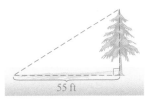

Answer: The tree is 44 ft tall.

Many applications involve similar triangles. Let's use the five-step process to solve this problem.

EXAMPLE 4 Josh is 6 ft tall, and he casts a shadow that is 8 ft long. At the same time, a tree nearby casts a shadow that is 60 ft long. How tall is the tree?

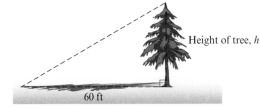

Solution

Step 1: Read the problem carefully, and restate it in your own words.

Josh's shadow is 8 ft long, and he is 6 ft tall. The tree's shadow is 60 ft long. How tall is the tree?

Step 2: **Make a plan.** These are similar triangles, so we can write a proportion.

8 ft and 60 ft are corresponding sides. 6 ft and *x* are corresponding sides.

$$\text{Corresponding sides} \left\langle \frac{8}{60} = \frac{6}{h} \right\rangle \text{Corresponding sides}$$

8 is to 60 as 6 is to *h*.

Step 3: **Solve** the problem.

$$\frac{8}{60} \times \frac{6}{h} \quad \begin{array}{l} 60 \cdot 6 = 360 \\ 8 \cdot h = 8h \end{array}$$

$$360 = 8h \qquad \text{Set the cross products equal.}$$

$$\frac{360}{8} = \frac{8h}{8} \qquad \text{Divide by 8.}$$

$$45 = h \qquad \text{Simplify.}$$

Step 4: **State the answer** in a complete sentence.

The tree is 45 ft tall.

Step 5: **Check** the answer. Check that the ratios of the corresponding sides are the same.

$$\text{Corresponding sides} \left\langle \frac{8}{60} = \frac{8 \div 4}{60 \div 4} = \frac{2}{15} \right.$$

$$\text{Corresponding sides} \left\langle \frac{6}{45} = \frac{6 \div 3}{45 \div 3} = \frac{2}{15} \right.$$

The ratios are the same, so the answer is correct.

[**YOU TRY 4**] A girl is 4 ft tall and casts a shadow that is 6 ft long. At the same time, a telephone pole casts a shadow that is 27 ft long. How tall is the pole?

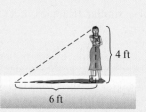

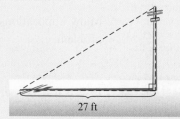

ANSWERS TO [**YOU TRY**] **EXERCISES**

1) 20 m   2) 20 m   3) *x* = 15 ft; perimeter = 45 ft   4) The pole is 18 ft tall.

---

*Additional answers can be found in the Answers to Exercises appendix.

Objective 1: Find Unknown Lengths in Similar Triangles

1) Write the definition of similar triangles and then look up the definition of the word *similar* in a dictionary. Compare the two definitions.

2) What does it mean when we say that corresponding sides are proportional?   It means that the ratios of the lengths of corresponding sides of a triangle are the same.

3) Are all equilateral triangles similar? In your own words, explain why or why not.   yes; answers may vary

4) Are all right triangles similar? In your own words, explain why or why not.   no; answers may vary

Write the corresponding angles and the corresponding sides for each pair of similar triangles.

5)
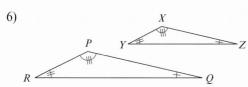

6)
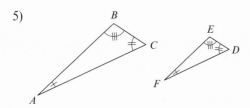

7)
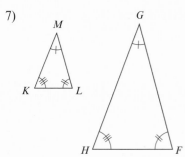

8)
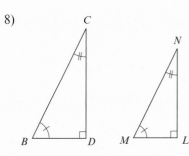

9)
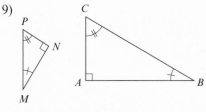

10)
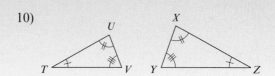

Find the unknown length in the larger of each pair of similar triangles; then, find its perimeter.

11)
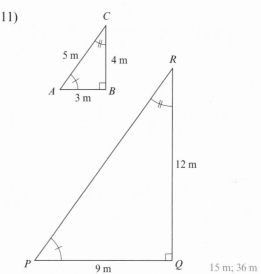
15 m; 36 m

12)
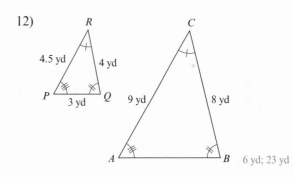
6 yd; 23 yd

13)
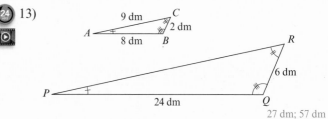
27 dm; 57 dm

14)
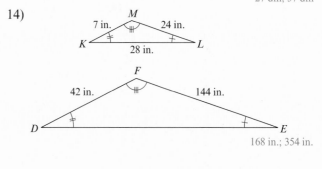
168 in.; 354 in.

15)

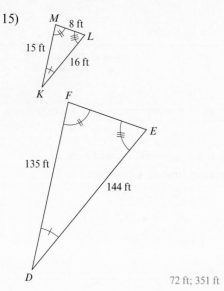

72 ft; 351 ft

16)

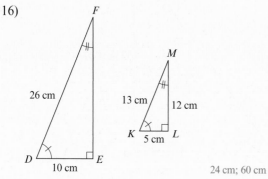

24 cm; 60 cm

17)

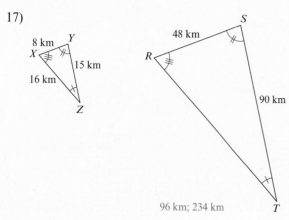

96 km; 234 km

18)

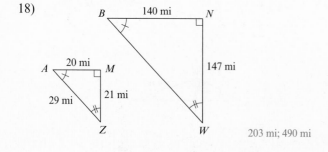

203 mi; 490 mi

Use a proportion to find the unknown length labeled *x*. Then, find the perimeter of the triangle with the unknown side length labeled *x*.

19)

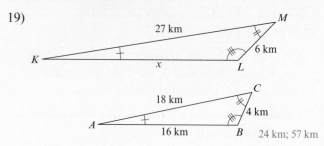

24 km; 57 km

20)

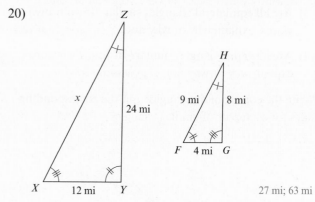

27 mi; 63 mi

21)

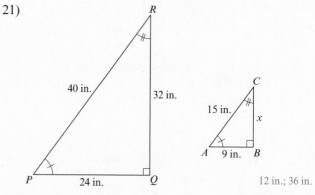

12 in.; 36 in.

22)

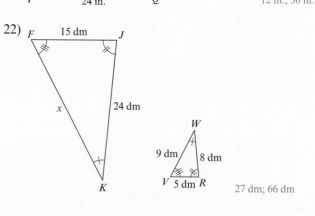

27 dm; 66 dm

23)

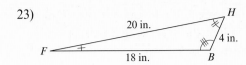

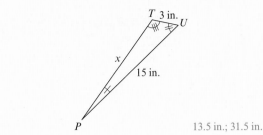

13.5 in.; 31.5 in.

24)

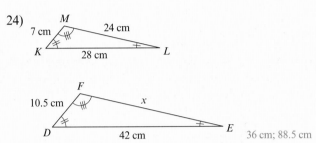

36 cm; 88.5 cm

24 25)

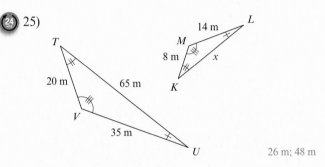

26 m; 48 m

26)

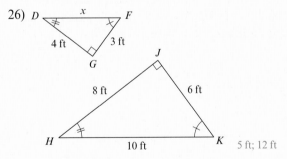

5 ft; 12 ft

Objective 2: Solve Applied Problems Involving Similar Triangles

Solve each problem.

27) A college had a ribbon-cutting ceremony for its new Math and Science building, and the school's band was asked to participate. To find the height of the building, a math student measured the shadows cast by the new building and the drum major's baton. The shadow of the 3.5-ft baton was 4 ft. The

shadow of the new building was 52 ft. Find the height of the building.   45.5 ft

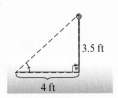
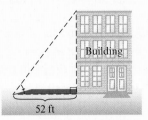

28) The height of a tree can be found by lining up the top of the tree with the top of a 2-m stick. Use similar triangles to find the height of the tree.   16 m

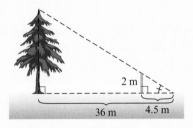

○ 29) Maria is 5 ft tall, and she casts a shadow that is 2 ft long. At the same time, a flagpole casts a shadow that is 8.4 ft long. How tall is the flagpole?   21 ft

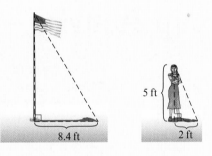

30) Refer to Exercise 29. Later in the day, Maria's shadow is 8 feet long. How long is the flagpole's shadow at this time?   33.6 ft

24 31) The height of a statue can be found by comparing its shadow to a shadow cast by a 1.5-m stick at the same time of day. Suppose a statue casts a 5-m shadow on the ground while the stick casts a 2-m shadow. Find the height of the statue.   3.75 m

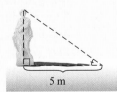

32) Jaromir and Bogdan are on opposite sides of a river and want to calculate its width. On one side of the river, Jaromir places a marker at point A. On the other side, Bogdan places a marker at point B, creating line segment $\overline{AB}$. Next, Bogdan marks off line segment $\overline{CD}$, intersecting segment $\overline{AB}$ at point M, forming two similar right triangles as shown in the figure to the right. Note that point D is directly across the river from point A. With his tape measure, Bogdan finds the length of segments $\overline{CM}$, $\overline{MD}$, and $\overline{BC}$ to be 3 ft, 6 ft, and 5 ft, respectively. Find the width of the river using Bogdan's measurements.   10 ft

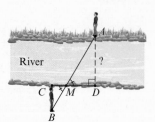

R1) When wouldn't be a good time of day to try your own experiment similar to Exercise 29. Why?

R2) Which objectives do you still need to master? Do you need to review material from previous sections or chapters to get up to speed?

Group Activity – Geometry

The Buyer family recently purchased a foreclosed home at a real estate auction. The Buyers got a great deal on the price of the home, but the home needs many repairs. The Buyers decide to install new floor molding (baseboards) in the living room. The rectangular living room is 24 ft long and 15 ft wide. The floor plan of the room is shown below.

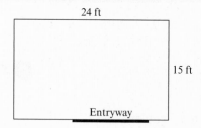

1) Mr. and Mrs. Buyer are going to a home improvement store to purchase the floor molding for the living room. They each estimated the amount of floor molding that is needed (ignoring the entryway for now). Mr. Buyer thinks that they will need 360 ft of molding, and Mrs. Buyer thinks they will need 78 ft of molding. Which estimate is correct? Give reasons to support your answer.

2) Describe in your own words how to determine the perimeter of a rectangle if you know the length and width.

3) Calculate the amount of floor molding required for all six of the rooms in the table below.

ROOM	LENGTH	WIDTH	CALCULATIONS: $2l + 2w = P$	PERIMETER
Living	24 ft	15 ft	$2(24) + 2(15) = 48 + 30 = 78$	78 ft
Dining	16 ft	12 ft		
Family	30 ft	16 ft		
Bedroom 1	18 ft	15 ft		
Bedroom 2	14 ft	14 ft		
Bedroom 3	13 ft	13 ft		

4) In the rooms above, there is a total of 4 entryways and 3 doorways. Each entryway is 7 ft wide, and each doorway is 3 ft wide. Accounting for the space in the entryways and doorways, how much molding is needed for all six rooms?

5) The type of floor molding that the Buyers chose is sold in lengths of 12 ft for $2.50 each. How many lengths will they have to buy? What will the total cost be?

Group Activity Answers

1) Mrs. Buyer is correct. She calculated the perimeter of the room, and Mr. Buyer calculated the area of the room. The floor molding covers the distance around the room so the formula for perimeter should be used.

2) Answers may vary.

3)

ROOM	LENGTH	WIDTH	CALCULATIONS: $2l + 2w = P$	PERIMETER
Living	24 ft	15 ft	$2(24) + 2(15) = 48 + 30 = 78$	78 ft
Dining	16 ft	12 ft	$2(16) + 2(12) = 32 + 24 = 56$	56 ft
Family	30 ft	16 ft	$2(30) + 2(16) = 60 + 32 = 92$	92 ft
Bedroom 1	18 ft	15 ft	$2(18) + 2(15) = 36 + 30 = 66$	66 ft
Bedroom 2	14 ft	14 ft	$2(14) + 2(14) = 28 + 28 = 56$	56 ft
Bedroom 3	13 ft	13 ft	$2(13) + 2(13) = 26 + 26 = 52$	52 ft

4) 363 ft

5) 31 lengths; $77.50

In math class, many problems use a single formula and have clear answers: How many degrees is this angle? What is the volume of this cone? Outside of class, of course, problems can be much trickier. Indeed, when it comes to decision making, sometimes the real issue is not picking the right option, but rather thinking of any options at all!

Try to solve these problems. In some cases, you will need to apply the math skills you've learned so far in this course. To help you devise solutions, a hint regarding the best approach to use is included after each problem.

1. One cold, dark, and rainy night, a college student has a flat tire on a deserted stretch of country road. He pulls onto the shoulder to change it. After removing the four lug nuts and placing them into the hubcap, he removes the flat tire and takes his spare out of the trunk. As he is moving the spare tire into position, his hand slips and he upsets the hubcap with the lug nuts, which tumble off into the night where he can't find them. What should he do? (Hint: Instead of asking how he might find the lug nuts, reword the problem and ask where else he might find lug nuts.)

2. Cheryl, who is a construction worker, is paving a walk, and she needs to add water quickly to the concrete she has just poured. She reaches for her pail to get water from a spigot in the front of the house, but suddenly realizes the pail has a large rust hole in it and cannot be used. As the concrete dries prematurely, she fumbles through her toolbox for tools and materials with which to repair the pail. She finds many tools, but nothing that would serve to patch the pail. The house is locked, and no one is home. What should she do? (Hint: When is a pail not a pail?)

3. A caterpillar has to climb up the muddy wall of a well that is 12 ft deep. Each day, the caterpillar advances 4 ft, but each night as he sleeps, he slips back 2 ft. How many days will it take him to get out? (Hint: Draw it.)

After working to solve these problems, consider these questions: Which problems were the easiest to solve, and which were more difficult? Why? Were the hints helpful? Do you think there was more than one solution to any of the problems? Did your initial assumptions about the problem help or hinder your efforts to solve it?

emPOWERme Answers

1. Remove one lug nut from each of the other three tires on the car, and use these three to attach the spare tire. This will hold until four more lug nuts can be purchased.
2. Dump the tools out of the toolbox, and use it as a pail.
3. Five days; on the fifth day the caterpillar will reach the top and will not have to slide down again.

Adapted from Halpern, D.F. (1996). *Thought and Knowledge: An Introduction to Critical Thinking* (3rd ed.). Mahwah, NJ: Erlbaum; and Bransford, J.D. & Stein, B.S. (1993). *The Ideal Problem Solver* (2nd ed.). New York: W.H. Freeman.

Chapter 9:   Summary

Definition/Procedure	Example

9.1 Introduction to Geometry

Identify Lines, Line Segments, and Rays

Space is an unlimited, three-dimensional expanse.

A **plane** is a flat surface that continues indefinitely.

A **point** is a location in space with no length, width, or height.

A **line** is a straight set of points that continues forever in two directions.

A **line segment** is a piece of a line with two endpoints.

A **ray** is a part of a line that has one endpoint and that continues forever in the other direction. **(p. 599)**

Identify each figure as a line, a line segment, or a ray. Then, name it using correct notation.

a)   b)   c)

Solution

a) This figure is straight with two endpoints. **This is a line segment.** Write its name as $\overline{RT}$ or $\overline{TR}$.

b) This figure is straight and continues forever in both directions. **This is a line.** Write its name as $\overleftrightarrow{YZ}$ or $\overleftrightarrow{ZY}$.

c) This figure has *one* endpoint and an arrowhead on the other end indicating it goes on forever in that direction. **This is a ray.** Write its name as $\overrightarrow{CA}$. (Notice that the C *must* come first because it is the endpoint of the ray.)

Identifying Angles

If we join two rays at their endpoints, we get an **angle.** The **vertex** of the angle is the common endpoint. An angle is denoted by the symbol ∠. **(p. 600)**

Name each of the angles in this figure in two different ways.

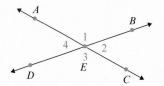

Solution

First, notice that *E* is the vertex of all the angles. So, we cannot use just the vertex to name any of the angles in this figure.

We can give each of the angles the following names:

∠1: ∠*AEB* or ∠*BEA*
∠2: ∠*BEC* or ∠*CEB*
∠3: ∠*CED* or ∠*DEC*
∠4: ∠*DEA* or ∠*AED*

Classifying Angles

We measure the size of an angle using **degrees.** The symbol for degrees is °.

An **acute angle** is an angle whose measure is greater than 0° and less than 90°.

A **right angle** is an angle whose measure is 90°.

An **obtuse angle** is an angle whose measure is greater than 90° and less than 180°.

A **straight angle** is an angle whose measure is 180°. **(p. 601)**

Classify each angle as acute, right, obtuse, or straight.

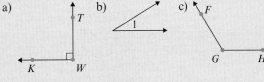

Solution

a) The small square inside the angle tells us that its measure is exactly 90°. ∠*KWT* is a *right* angle.

b) The measure of ∠1 is less than 90°, so it is an *acute* angle.

c) The measure of ∠*FGH* is greater than 90° and less than 180°. It is an *obtuse* angle.

d) The measure of ∠*V* is 180°, so it is a *straight* angle.

Definition/Procedure	Example
Identifying Parallel and Perpendicular Lines Two lines that cross each other are called **intersecting lines.** **Parallel lines** are lines in the same plane that do *not* intersect. The symbol ∥ means "is parallel to." **Perpendicular lines** intersect at right angles. The symbol ⊥ means "is perpendicular to." **(p. 603)**	Classify each pair of lines as parallel, perpendicular, or neither. If they are parallel or perpendicular, use the appropriate notation. a) 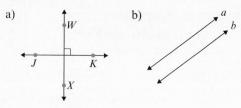 b) c) **Solution** a) Lines $\overleftrightarrow{JK}$ and $\overleftrightarrow{WX}$ meet at right angles, so they are perpendicular. Write $\overleftrightarrow{JK} \perp \overleftrightarrow{WX}$. b) Lines a and b do not intersect, so they are parallel. Write $a \parallel b$. c) Lines $\overleftrightarrow{MN}$ and $\overleftrightarrow{OP}$ intersect but not at right angles. They are neither parallel nor perpendicular.

9.2 Angles

Complementary Angles Two angles are **complementary angles** if their measures add to 90°. **(p. 607)**	If m∠B = 67°, find the measure of its complement. To find the *complement* of ∠B, subtract 67° from 90°: 90° − 67° = 23°. The measure of the complement of ∠B is 23°.
Supplementary Angles Two angles are **supplementary angles** if their measures add to 180°. **(p. 608)**	If m∠R = 95°, find the measure of its supplement. To find the *supplement* of ∠R, subtract 95° from 180°: 180° − 95° = 85°. The measure of the supplement of ∠R is 85°.
Congruent Angles Two angles are **congruent angles** if their measures are the same. **(p. 610)**	∠A and ∠B are *congruent angles* because their angle measures are the same. 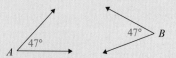
Vertical and Adjacent Angles When two lines intersect, **vertical angles** are the angles opposite each other, the angles that do not share a common side. Vertical angles are congruent. That is, their angle measures are the same. **Adjacent angles** are angles that share a common side and a common vertex. **(p. 610)**	Identify the vertical and adjacent angles, and find the missing angle measures. **Vertical Angles** ∠WMZ and ∠XMY, ∠XMW and ∠YMZ

Definition/Procedure	Example

Adjacent Angles

$\angle WMZ$ and $\angle YMZ$, $\angle WMZ$ and $\angle XMW$

$\angle XMW$ and $\angle XMY$, $\angle XMY$ and $\angle YMZ$

$m\angle XMY = 119°$

$m\angle YMZ = m\angle XMW = 180° - 119° = 61°$

9.3 Rectangles and Squares

Rectangles

A **rectangle** is a four-sided figure containing four right angles.

The opposite sides are parallel and congruent.

The longer side of a rectangle is called the length, l. The shorter side is called the width, w.

A small square indicates that the rectangle has four 90° angles. **(p. 617)**

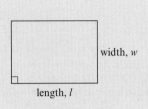

width, w

length, l

Perimeter of a Rectangle

The **perimeter** of a figure is the distance around the figure.

We can find the perimeter, P, of a rectangle using one of the following formulas:

1) $P = 2 \cdot \text{length} + 2 \cdot \text{width}$ or

2) $P = 2 \cdot l + 2 \cdot w$ **(p. 618)**

Find the perimeter of the rectangle.

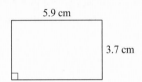

5.9 cm

3.7 cm

$P = 2 \cdot l + 2 \cdot w$

$P = 2 \cdot 5.9 \text{ cm} + 2 \cdot 3.7 \text{ cm}$ Substitute the values.

$P = 11.8 \text{ cm} + 7.4 \text{ cm}$ Multiply.

$P = 19.2 \text{ cm}$ Add.

Area of a Rectangle

The **area** of a rectangle is the size of the region enclosed in the figure.

We can find the area, A, of a rectangle using this formula:

$Area = \text{length} \cdot \text{width}$ or

$A = l \cdot w$

The units for area are *square* units. **(p. 620)**

Find the area of the rectangle above.

$A = l \cdot w$

$A = 5.9 \text{ cm} \cdot 3.7 \text{ cm}$ Substitute the values.

$A = 21.83 \text{ cm}^2$ Multiply.

Perimeter and Area of a Square

A **square** is a rectangle with all four sides of equal length.

The **perimeter,** P, of a square with side length s can be found using one of these formulas:

1) $\text{Perimeter} = \text{side} + \text{side} + \text{side} + \text{side}$

2) $P = 4 \cdot \text{side}$

3) $P = 4 \cdot s$

The **area,** A, of a square with side length s can be found using one of these formulas:

1) $\text{Area} = \text{side} \cdot \text{side}$

2) $A = s \cdot s$

3) $A = s^2$

(p. 621)

Find a) the area and b) the perimeter of this square.

$\frac{1}{2}$ ft

$\frac{1}{2}$ ft

a) Use $P = 4 \cdot s$.

$P = 4 \cdot \frac{1}{2} \text{ ft}$ Substitute the length of the side.

$P = 2 \text{ ft}$ Multiply.

b) Use $A = s^2$.

$A = \left(\frac{1}{2} \text{ ft}\right)^2$ Substitute the length of the side.

$A = \frac{1}{4} \text{ ft}^2$

Definition/Procedure	Example

9.4 Triangles

Perimeter and Area of a Triangle
A **triangle** is a closed figure with exactly three sides.

The **perimeter** of a triangle is the distance around the triangle.

The **area**, A, of a triangle is

1) Area = $\frac{1}{2}$ · base · height   or

2) $A = \frac{1}{2} \cdot b \cdot h$ or

3) $A = 0.5 \cdot b \cdot h$

where b = the length of the base and h = the height. **(p. 628)**

Find a) the perimeter and b) the area of this triangle.

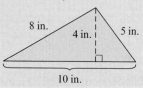

a) To find the perimeter, add the lengths of the sides of the triangle.

$$P = 8 \text{ in.} + 5 \text{ in.} + 10 \text{ in.} = 23 \text{ in.}$$

b) To find the area, we will use $A = \frac{1}{2} \cdot b \cdot h$.

$A = \frac{1}{2} \cdot 10 \text{ in.} \cdot 4 \text{ in.}$ Substitute the values.

$A = 20 \text{ in}^2$ Multiply.

The Sum of the Angle Measures in a Triangle
The measures of the angles in a triangle add up to 180°. **(p. 632)**

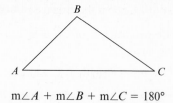

$$\text{m}\angle A + \text{m}\angle B + \text{m}\angle C = 180°$$

Classifying Triangles
An **acute triangle** is one in which all three angles are acute.

Acute triangle:

A **right triangle** contains one *right*, or 90°, angle.

Right triangle:

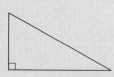

An **obtuse triangle** contains one *obtuse* angle.

Obtuse triangle:

An **equilateral triangle** has *three* sides of equal length.

Equilateral triangle:

An **isosceles triangle** has *two* sides of equal length.

Isosceles triangle:

A **scalene triangle** has *no* sides of equal length. **(p. 633)**

Scalene triangle:

Definition/Procedure	Example

9.5 Parallelograms and Trapezoids

Area of a Parallelogram

A **parallelogram** is a four-sided figure whose opposite sides are parallel and the same length.

The area, A, of a parallelogram is

$$\text{Area} = \text{base} \cdot \text{height} \quad \text{or}$$
$$A = b \cdot h$$

where b = the length of the base and h = the height. The base is the side that forms a right angle with the height. **(p. 639)**

Find the area of the parallelogram.

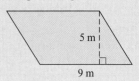

$A = b \cdot h$
$A = 9\text{ m} \cdot 5\text{ m}$ Substitute the values.
$A = 45\text{ m}^2$ Multiply.

Area of a Trapezoid

A **trapezoid** is a four-sided figure with exactly one pair of parallel sides.

The area, A, of a trapezoid is

$$A = \frac{1}{2} \cdot \text{height} \cdot (\text{short base} + \text{long base}) \quad \text{or}$$

$$A = \frac{1}{2} \cdot h \cdot (b + B) \quad \text{or}$$

$$A = 0.5 \cdot h \cdot (b + B)$$

where h = the height, b = the length of the short base, and B = the length of the long base.

The bases are always the parallel sides. (p. 640)

Find the area of the trapezoid.

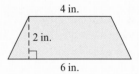

$A = \frac{1}{2} \cdot h \cdot (b + B)$

$A = \frac{1}{2} \cdot 2\text{ in.} \cdot (4\text{ in.} + 6\text{ in.})$ Substitute the values.

$A = \frac{1}{2} \cdot 2\text{ in.} \cdot (10\text{ in.})$ Add inside the parentheses.

$A = 10\text{ in}^2$ Multiply.

9.6 Circles

Radius and Diameter of a Circle

A **circle** is a two-dimensional, or flat, figure in which all points are the same distance from the fixed center point.

The **radius**, r, is the distance from the center of the circle to any point on the circle.

The **diameter**, d, is the distance across the circle passing through the center.

The diameter and the radius are related in this way:

1) Diameter = $2 \cdot$ Radius   or $d = 2 \cdot r$

2) Radius = $\dfrac{\text{Diameter}}{2}$ or $r = \dfrac{d}{2}$

(p. 649)

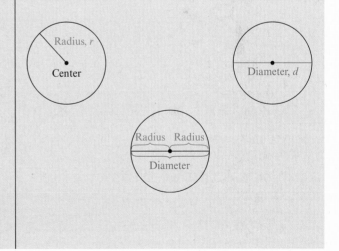

Definition/Procedure	Example

What is π?

π is the ratio of the circle's circumference to its diameter. That is, $\pi = \dfrac{C}{d}$. (π is the Greek letter pi and is read as "pie.")

There is no exact, decimal equivalent of π. An approximate decimal value is $\pi = 3.14159265$, but we usually use one of the following approximations for π.

$$\pi \approx 3.14 \quad \text{and} \quad \pi \approx \frac{22}{7}$$

Because these are *approximate* values, calculations using π will give *approximate* answers. Therefore, we should use the $\approx$ symbol instead of $=$. **(p. 652)**

This is how the value of π is computed.

If we measure the distance around the circle, its circumference, we get approximately 3.14 in.

$$\frac{\text{circumference}}{\text{diameter}} \approx \frac{3.14 \text{ in.}}{1 \text{ in.}} = 3.14$$
$$\pi \approx 3.14$$

Circumference of a Circle

The **circumference** of a circle is the distance around the circle. (The circumference is the *perimeter* of the circle.) It is usually abbreviated with C.

These are formulas for the circumference of a circle.

1) Circumference = $\pi \cdot$ diameter   or
$$C = \pi \cdot d$$

Because $d = 2 \cdot$ radius, we can also write
$C = \pi \cdot 2 \cdot$ radius

2) Circumference = $2 \cdot \pi \cdot$ radius   or
$$C = 2 \cdot \pi \cdot r$$

(p. 652)

Find the circumference of this circle. Give the *exact* value and an *approximate* value using $\pi \approx \dfrac{22}{7}$.

14 cm

We are given the diameter, so we will use the formula containing the diameter of the circle.

$$C = \pi \cdot d$$
$$C = \pi \cdot 14 \text{ cm} \quad \text{Substitute the diameter.}$$
$$C = 14\pi \text{ cm} \quad \text{This is the } exact \text{ value.}$$

To find the *approximate* circumference, substitute $\dfrac{22}{7}$ for π.

$$C \approx 14\left(\frac{22}{7}\right) \text{cm} \quad \text{Substitute } \frac{22}{7} \text{ for } \pi.$$
$$C \approx 44 \text{ cm} \quad \text{Multiply.}$$

The *circumference* is exactly 14π cm, and it is *approximately* 44 cm.

Area of a Circle

The **area**, A, of a circle with radius r is
$$A = \pi \cdot r^2$$
(p. 654)

Find the area of the circle above. Give the *exact* value and an *approximate* value using 3.14 for π.

In the circle above, we are given the diameter. To use the area formula, we need to find the radius.

$$r = \frac{d}{2} = \frac{14 \text{ cm}}{2} = 7 \text{ cm} \quad \text{radius} = 7 \text{ cm}$$
$$A = \pi r^2$$
$$A = \pi (7 \text{ cm})^2 \quad \text{Substitute the value of the radius.}$$
$$A = 49\pi \text{ cm}^2 \quad \text{Evaluate the exponent.}$$

The *exact* area is 49π cm^2.

This time, we will substitute 3.14 for π to *approximate* the area.

$$A \approx 49\pi \text{ cm}^2$$
$$A \approx 49(3.14) \text{ cm}^2 \quad \text{Substitute 3.14 for } \pi.$$
$$A \approx 153.86 \text{ cm}^2 \quad \text{Multiply.}$$

The area is *approximately* 153.86 cm^2.

Definition/Procedure	Example

9.7 Volume

The **volume** of a three-dimensional object is a measure of the amount of space occupied by the object or the amount of space inside the object.

Volume is measured in *cubic* units, the number of *cubic* units it takes to fill the object. **(p. 663)**

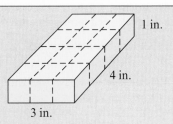

If we say that the volume of this box is 12 in^3, it means that we can fit *twelve* 1-in^3 boxes inside this larger box.

Volume of a Rectangular Solid

A **rectangular solid** is a box-like shape with dimensions of length, width, and height.

The **volume**, V, of a rectangular solid (or box) with length l, width w, and height h is

$$\text{Volume} = \text{length} \cdot \text{width} \cdot \text{height} \quad \text{or}$$
$$V = l \cdot w \cdot h$$

A **cube** is a rectangular solid in which all sides are the same length. The volume of a cube with side length s is

$$\text{Volume} = s \cdot s \cdot s \quad \text{or}$$
$$V = s^3$$

(p. 663)

Find the volume of this box.

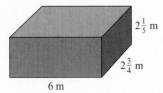

$$V = l \cdot w \cdot h$$
$$V = 6 \text{ m} \cdot 2\tfrac{3}{4} \text{ m} \cdot 2\tfrac{1}{5} \text{ m} \qquad \text{Substitute the values.}$$
$$V = 6 \text{ m} \cdot \frac{11}{4} \text{ m} \cdot \frac{11}{5} \text{ m} \qquad \text{Change to improper fractions.}$$
$$V = \frac{363}{10} \text{ m}^3 \text{ or } 36\tfrac{3}{10} \text{ m}^3 \text{ or } 36.3 \text{ m}^3 \qquad \text{Multiply.}$$

We can express our answer in any of these ways.

Volume of a Sphere

A **sphere** is a round, three-dimensional object like a basketball or the Earth. The radius of a sphere is the distance from the center to the edge of the sphere.

The **volume**, V, of a sphere with radius r is

$$\text{Volume} = \frac{4}{3} \cdot \pi \cdot (\text{radius})^3 \quad \text{or}$$
$$V = \frac{4}{3} \cdot \pi \cdot r^3$$

(p. 665)

Find the volume of a sphere with radius 3 m. Give an exact value and an approximation using $\frac{22}{7}$ for π.

$$V = \frac{4}{3} \cdot \pi \cdot r^3$$
$$V = \frac{4}{3} \cdot \pi \cdot (3 \text{ m})^3 \qquad \text{Substitute 3 m for } r.$$
$$V = \frac{4}{3} \cdot \pi \cdot 27 \text{ m}^3 \qquad \begin{array}{l}(3 \text{ m})^3 = 3 \text{ m} \cdot 3 \text{ m} \cdot 3 \text{ m} \\ = 27 \text{ m}^3 \end{array}$$
$$V = \frac{4}{\underset{1}{3}} \cdot \pi \cdot \frac{\overset{9}{27} \text{ m}^3}{1} \qquad \text{Divide 3 and 27 by 3.}$$
$$V = 36\pi \text{ m}^3 \qquad \text{Multiply.}$$

The *exact* volume is 36π m^3. To find an approximation, substitute $\frac{22}{7}$ for π.

$$V \approx 36\left(\frac{22}{7}\right) \text{ m}^3 \qquad \text{Substitute } \frac{22}{7} \text{ for } \pi.$$
$$V \approx \frac{792}{7} \text{ m}^3 \qquad \text{Multiply.}$$

The volume is approximately $\frac{792}{7}$ m^3 or $113\tfrac{1}{7}$ m^3 or 113.14 m^3, rounded to the nearest hundredth.

Definition/Procedure	**Example**

Volume of a Right Circular Cylinder

A **right circular cylinder** is a three-dimensional object in which the two ends are circles that form right angles with the sides.

The **volume,** V, of a right circular cylinder with radius r and height h is

$$\text{Volume} = \pi \cdot (\text{radius})^2 \cdot \text{height} \quad \text{or}$$
$$V = \pi \cdot r^2 \cdot h$$

(p. 667)

A can of tomato paste has a radius of 2.5 cm and is 8 cm tall. Approximate the volume of the can using $\pi \approx 3.14$.

$V = \pi \cdot r^2 \cdot h$	
$V = \pi \cdot (2.5 \text{ cm})^2 \cdot (8 \text{ cm})$	Substitute the values.
$V = \pi \cdot 6.25 \text{ cm}^2 \cdot 8 \text{ cm}$	$(2.5 \text{ cm})^2 = 6.25 \text{ cm}^2$
$V = 50\pi \text{ cm}^3$	Multiply.
$V \approx 50(3.14) \text{ cm}^3$	Substitute 3.14 for π.
$V \approx 157 \text{ cm}^3$	Multiply.

Volume of a Cone

The **volume,** V, of a cone with a base of radius r and height h is

$$\text{Volume} = \frac{1}{3} \cdot \pi \cdot (\text{radius})^2 \cdot \text{height} \quad \text{or}$$

$$V = \frac{1}{3} \cdot \pi \cdot r^2 \cdot h$$

The formula for the volume of a cone, $V = \frac{1}{3} \cdot \pi \cdot r^2 \cdot h$, can also be thought of as $V = \frac{1}{3} \cdot A \cdot h$, where $A = \pi \cdot r^2$, the area of the base of the cone. **(p. 669)**

Find the exact volume of the cone with radius 6 ft and height 8 ft.

$V = \frac{1}{3} \cdot \pi \cdot r^2 \cdot h$	
$V = \frac{1}{3} \cdot \pi \cdot (6 \text{ ft})^2 \cdot 8 \text{ ft}$	Substitute the values.
$V = \frac{1}{3} \cdot \pi \cdot 36 \text{ ft}^2 \cdot 8 \text{ ft}$	$(6 \text{ ft})^2 = 36 \text{ ft}^2$
$V = 96\pi \text{ ft}^3$	Multiply.

Volume of a Rectangular Pyramid

The **volume,** V, of a rectangular pyramid with height h, and a base of length l and width w is

$$\text{Volume} = \frac{1}{3} \cdot \text{length} \cdot \text{width} \cdot \text{height} \quad \text{or}$$

$$V = \frac{1}{3} \cdot l \cdot w \cdot h$$

Because $l \cdot w$ equals the *area* of the base, we can also think of the volume formula as $V = \frac{1}{3} \cdot A \cdot h$, where $A = l \cdot w$, the area of the base of the pyramid. **(p. 670)**

Find the volume of the pyramid with the given dimensions.

$V = \frac{1}{3} \cdot l \cdot w \cdot h$	
$V = \frac{1}{3} \cdot 3 \text{ yd} \cdot 1 \text{ yd} \cdot 2 \text{ yd}$	Substitute the values.
$V = 2 \text{ yd}^3$	Multiply.

9.8 Square Roots and the Pythagorean Theorem

Perfect Squares and Square Roots

A number such as 16 is a **perfect square** because it is the square of a whole number: $16 = 4^2$.

We also say that $\sqrt{16}$ is a **perfect square root** because $\sqrt{16} = 4$. **(p. 676)**

The First 12 Perfect Square Roots

$\sqrt{1} = 1$	$\sqrt{16} = 4$	$\sqrt{49} = 7$	$\sqrt{100} = 10$
$\sqrt{4} = 2$	$\sqrt{25} = 5$	$\sqrt{64} = 8$	$\sqrt{121} = 11$
$\sqrt{9} = 3$	$\sqrt{36} = 6$	$\sqrt{81} = 9$	$\sqrt{144} = 12$

Note: $\sqrt{0} = 0$

Definition/Procedure	Example

Characteristics of Right Triangles
Right triangles have special properties that other triangles do not.

The side opposite the right angle is the longest side of the triangle and is called the **hypotenuse**. The other two sides are called the **legs**. (p. 678)

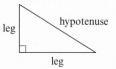

The Pythagorean Theorem
The **Pythagorean theorem** states the following relationship between the lengths of the sides of a right triangle.

For any **right** triangle,

$$(\text{leg})^2 + (\text{leg})^2 = (\text{hypotenuse})^2$$

The Pythagorean theorem applies **only** to right triangles. (p. 678)

$$(3 \text{ in.})^2 + (4 \text{ in.})^2 \stackrel{?}{=} (5 \text{ in.})^2$$
$$9 \text{ in}^2 + 16 \text{ in}^2 = 25 \text{ in}^2 \checkmark$$

Finding an Unknown Side of a Right Triangle
1) To find the **hypotenuse** of a right triangle, use this formula:

$$\text{hypotenuse} = \sqrt{(\text{leg})^2 + (\text{leg})^2}$$

2) To find a **leg** of a right triangle, use this formula:

$$\text{leg} = \sqrt{(\text{hypotenuse})^2 - (\text{known leg})^2}$$

(p. 678)

Find the length of the missing side. Give the exact answer and the answer to the nearest tenth.

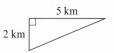

First ask yourself, "*Which part of the right triangle is unknown?*" The side *across from* the right angle is unknown, and that is the *hypotenuse*. Use the formula for finding the hypotenuse.

$$\begin{aligned}
\text{hypotenuse} &= \sqrt{(\text{leg})^2 + (\text{leg})^2} \\
&= \sqrt{(5)^2 + (2)^2} \quad \text{Substitute the values.} \\
&= \sqrt{25 + 4} \quad 5^2 = 25; 2^2 = 4 \\
&= \sqrt{29} \quad \text{Add.}
\end{aligned}$$

The length of the hypotenuse is exactly $\sqrt{29}$ km.

$$\sqrt{29} \approx 5.4 \quad \text{Approximate by hand or using a calculator}$$

The length of the hypotenuse is approximately $\sqrt{29} \approx 5.4$ km.

9.9 Similar Triangles

The angles with the same measure are called **corresponding angles.**

The sides opposite the corresponding angles are called the **corresponding sides.**

Although corresponding angles have the same measure, corresponding sides are *not* necessarily the same length.

Similar triangles have the same shape, the measures of their corresponding angles are the same, and the lengths of their corresponding sides are proportional. (p. 684)

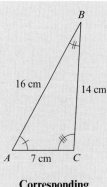

Corresponding Angles	Corresponding Sides
$\angle A$ and $\angle X$	$\overline{BC}$ and $\overline{YZ}$
$\angle B$ and $\angle Y$	$\overline{AC}$ and $\overline{XZ}$
$\angle C$ and $\angle Z$	$\overline{AB}$ and $\overline{XY}$

These are similar triangles. The ratio of the corresponding sides of the first triangle to those of the second triangle is $\frac{2}{1}$.

Definition/Procedure	Example
Finding the Length of an Unknown Side in Similar Triangles We can use a proportion to find the length of an unknown side in similar triangles. **(p. 685)**	Use a proportion to find the unknown length, *x*. 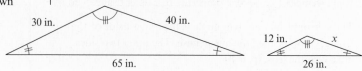

Choose *either* of the two corresponding side pairs that we know; let's choose 30 in. and 12 in. The corresponding sides that include the side we do not know are 40 in. and *x*. *The ratios of the corresponding sides are equal, so we can set up a proportion and solve for x.*

$$\begin{array}{c} 12 \cdot 40 = 480 \\ \dfrac{30}{12} \diagdown \dfrac{40}{x} \qquad \text{Set up the proportion.} \\ 30 \cdot x = 30x \end{array}$$

$$30x = 480 \qquad \begin{array}{l}\text{Set the cross products}\\\text{equal to each other.}\end{array}$$

$$\frac{30x}{30} = \frac{480}{30} \qquad \text{Divide by 30.}$$

$$x = 16 \qquad \text{Simplify.}$$

The unknown length is 16 in.

Chapter 9:   Review Exercises

*Additional answers can be found in the Answers to Exercises appendix.

(9.1) Name each of the numbered angles in the figures in two different ways.

1)

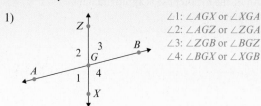

∠1: ∠AGX or ∠XGA
∠2: ∠AGZ or ∠ZGA
∠3: ∠ZGB or ∠BGZ
∠4: ∠BGX or ∠XGB

2)

∠1: ∠RQM or ∠MQR
∠2: ∠MQS or ∠SQM
∠3: ∠LQS or ∠SQL
∠4: ∠RQL or ∠LQR

Classify each angle as acute, right, obtuse, or straight.

3) straight

4) obtuse   5) acute

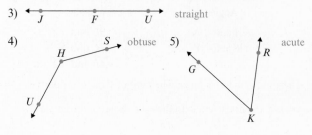

6) 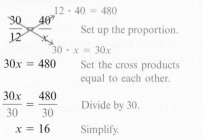 right

Classify each pair of lines as parallel, perpendicular, or neither. If they are parallel or perpendicular, use the appropriate notation.

7) neither   8) parallel; $\overleftrightarrow{AB} \parallel \overleftrightarrow{CD}$

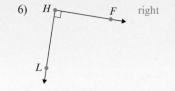

9) 10) neither

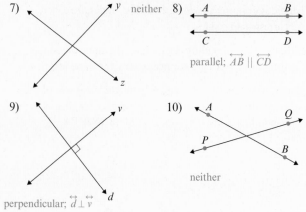

perpendicular; $\overleftrightarrow{d} \perp \overleftrightarrow{v}$

(9.2) Find the measure of the complement of each of the given angles.

11) m∠V = 47°   43°   12) m∠Y = 56°   34°

Find the measure of the supplement of each of the given angles.

13) m∠C = 106°   74°   14) m∠X = 23°   157°

Find the missing angle measure.

15) ∠DNA is a right angle.   16) ∠ABD is a straight angle.
    Find m∠r.   18°   Find m∠d.   97°

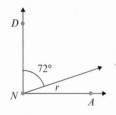

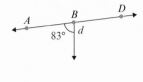

17) ∠ZXV is a straight   18) ∠EZJ is a right angle.
    angle. Find m∠p.   44°   Find m∠q.   56°

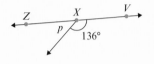

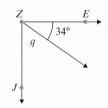

19) Find the measures of   20) Find the measures of
    angles N, T, and Z.   angles 1, 2, and 3.

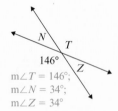

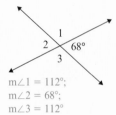

m∠T = 146°;   m∠1 = 112°;
m∠N = 34°;   m∠2 = 68°;
m∠Z = 34°   m∠3 = 112°

(9.3) Find the perimeter and area of each rectangle.

21)   36 cm; 80 cm²

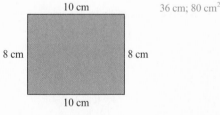

22)   4¼ in.   6 7/12 in.; 9 11/12 in²

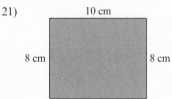

2⅓ in.

Find the perimeter and area of each square.

23)   1.35 ft   5.4 ft; 1.8225 ft²

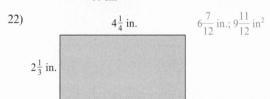

1.35 ft   1.35 ft

1.35 ft

24)   28 mm   112 mm; 784 mm²

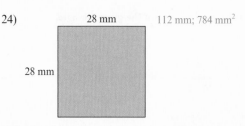

28 mm

Find the perimeter and the area of the given figure. Note that you must first find the missing lengths.

25)   10 cm   56 cm; 96 cm²

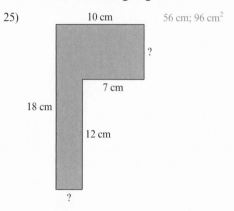

26)   2 ft   52 ft; 60 ft²

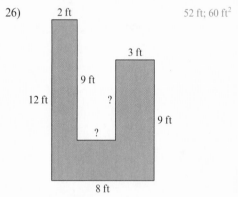

Solve each problem.

27) Regulation soccer fields vary in size depending on age and skill level. What is the difference between the areas of the two soccer fields shown below?   4600 yd²

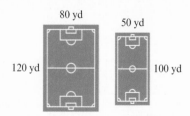

28) A 3 × 3 Rubik's cube has a side length of approximately 2.25 in. Find the combined area of all six faces of the cube.
    30.375 in²

(9.4) Find the perimeter and area of the given triangle.

29) 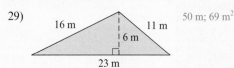   50 m; 69 m²

30) 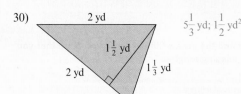 $5\frac{1}{3}$ yd; $1\frac{1}{2}$ yd²

31) 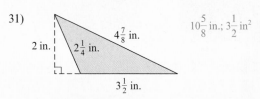 $10\frac{5}{8}$ in.; $3\frac{1}{2}$ in²

32) 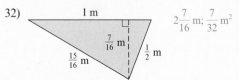 $2\frac{7}{16}$ m; $\frac{7}{32}$ m²

33) Find the area of the shaded region.   379 ft²

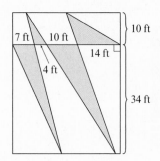

34) Find the area of the unshaded region.   69 m²

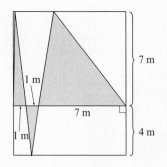

Find m∠x in each triangle.

35) 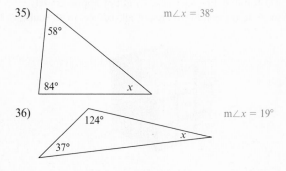   m∠x = 38°

36)   m∠x = 19°

Classify each triangle as acute, right, or obtuse.

37) 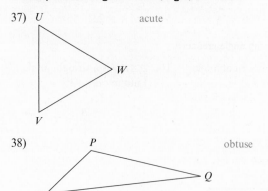   acute

38)   obtuse

Classify each triangle as equilateral, isosceles, or scalene.

39) 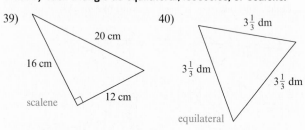   scalene

40)   equilateral

(9.5) Find the perimeter and area of the given parallelogram.

41)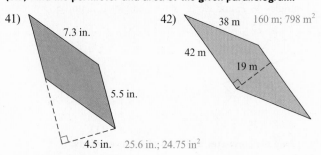

42)   160 m; 798 m²

25.6 in.; 24.75 in²

Find the perimeter and area of the given trapezoid.

43)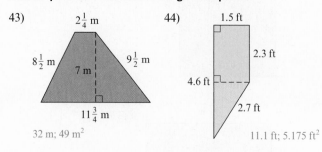

44)

32 m; 49 m²   11.1 ft; 5.175 ft²

Solve each problem.

45) Mr. and Mrs. Nguyen have a reflecting pond in their backyard with an irregular shape shown in the figure below. They hire a monthly service at a cost of $0.60 per square foot to maintain the pond. What is the cost of the Nguyens' monthly service? $100.80

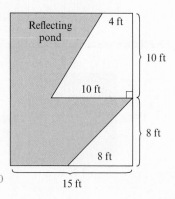

46) The entranceway to a newly renovated hotel is going to be paved with natural stone costing $126 per square meter for the installation. The entranceway is represented by the shaded area below. What is the total cost for the new entranceway? $27,216

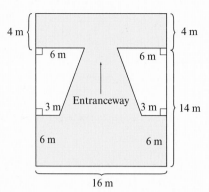

4 m
6 m   6 m
3 m   Entranceway   3 m   14 m
6 m   6 m
16 m

(9.6) Find the diameter of each circle.

47)   11.6 cm   48)   4.8 km

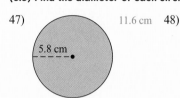
5.8 cm

2.4 km

Find the radius of each circle.

49)   0.6 ft   50)   6.5 in.

1.2 ft

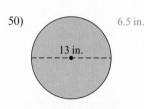
13 in.

Find the area of each circle. Give the *exact* value and an *approximate* value using $\pi \approx 3.14$. Round the approximation to the nearest hundredth.

51)   52)

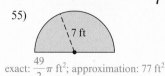
$1\frac{1}{2}$ m

exact: $\frac{9}{4}\pi$ m²;
approximation: 7.07 m²

1.2 ft

exact: 1.44π ft²;
approximation: 4.52 ft²

Find the circumference of each circle. Give the *exact* value and an *approximate* value using $\pi \approx 3.14$. Round the approximation to the nearest hundredth.

53)   54)

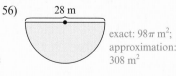
13 mm

exact: 13π mm;
approximation: 40.82 mm

$\frac{7}{10}$ ft

exact: $\frac{7}{10}\pi$ ft;
approximation: 2.20 ft

Find the area of the semicircle. Give the *exact* value and an *approximate* value using $\pi \approx \frac{22}{7}$.

55)   56)   28 m

7 ft

exact: $\frac{49}{2}\pi$ ft²; approximation: 77 ft²

exact: 98π m²;
approximation: 308 m²

Find the area of the shaded region. Round your answer to the nearest hundredth. Use $\pi \approx 3.14$.

57)

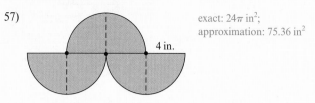
4 in.

exact: 24π in²;
approximation: 75.36 in²

(9.7) Find the volume of each box.

58)

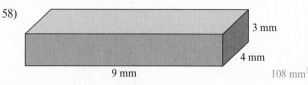
3 mm
4 mm
9 mm   108 mm³

59)

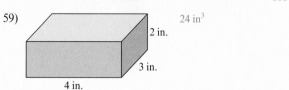
2 in.
3 in.
4 in.   24 in³

60)

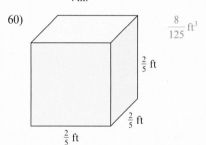
$\frac{2}{5}$ ft
$\frac{2}{5}$ ft
$\frac{2}{5}$ ft
$\frac{8}{125}$ ft³

61)

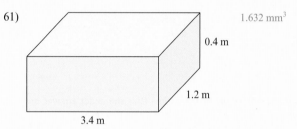
0.4 m
1.2 m
3.4 m   1.632 mm³

Find the volume of each solid. Give an exact and an approximate answer using $\pi \approx 3.14$. Round the approximation to the nearest hundredth.

62)   63)

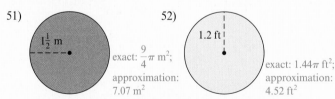
30 cm

exact:
36,000π cm³;
approximation:
113,040.00 cm³

0.6 dm

exact:
0.288π dm³;
approximation:
0.90 dm³

64)   65)   2 in.

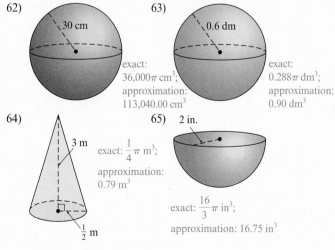
3 m

exact: $\frac{1}{4}\pi$ m³;
approximation:
0.79 m³

$\frac{1}{2}$ m

exact: $\frac{16}{3}\pi$ in³;
approximation: 16.75 in³

66)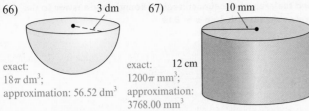
3 dm

exact:
18π dm^3;
approximation: 56.52 dm^3

67)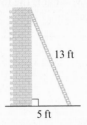
10 mm

12 cm

exact:
1200π mm^3;
approximation:
3768.00 mm^3

68)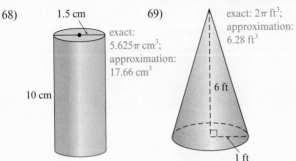
1.5 cm

10 cm

exact:
5.625π cm^3;
approximation:
17.66 cm^3

69)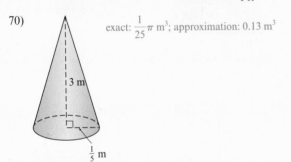
6 ft

1 ft

exact: 2π ft^3;
approximation:
6.28 ft^3

70)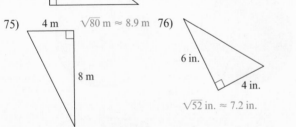
3 m

$\frac{1}{5}$ m

exact: $\frac{1}{25}\pi$ m^3; approximation: 0.13 m^3

(9.8) Approximate each square root to the nearest tenth and plot it on a number line.

71) $\sqrt{32}$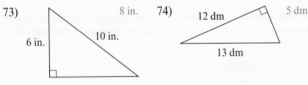
1 2 3 4 5 6

$\sqrt{32} \approx 5.7$
1 2 3 4 5 6

72) $\sqrt{50}$
4 5 6 7 8 9

$\sqrt{50} \approx 7.1$
4 5 6 7 8 9

Find the length of the missing side. Give the exact answer and the answer to the nearest tenth, if appropriate.

73)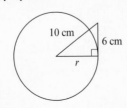
8 in.
6 in. 10 in.

74)
12 dm 5 dm
13 dm

75)
4 m $\sqrt{80}$ m $\approx$ 8.9 m
8 m

76)
6 in.
4 in.
$\sqrt{52}$ in. $\approx$ 7.2 in.

Solve each problem. Give the exact answer and an approximate answer to the nearest tenth, if appropriate.

77) Find the area of the circle.
Use $\pi \approx 3.14$.
64π cm$^2 \approx 201.0$ cm^2

10 cm
6 cm
r

78) A ladder 13 feet long is leaning against a wall, forming a right triangle. The bottom of the ladder is 5 feet away from the wall. Find the area of the formed triangle. 30 ft^2

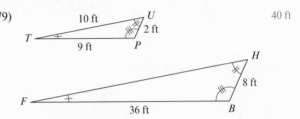
13 ft

5 ft

(9.9) Find the unknown length in the larger of each pair of similar triangles.

79)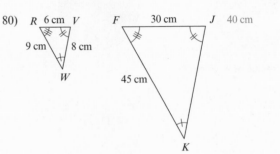
10 ft
T 2 ft
9 ft P
U
40 ft

H
8 ft
F
36 ft B

80)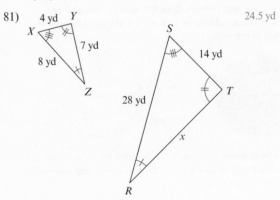
R 6 cm V
9 cm 8 cm
W

F 30 cm J 40 cm
45 cm
K

Use a proportion to find the unknown length labeled x.

81)
4 yd Y
X
7 yd
8 yd
Z
24.5 yd

S
14 yd
28 yd T
x
R

82)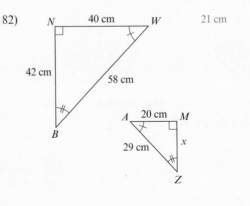
N 40 cm W
42 cm
58 cm
B
21 cm

A 20 cm M
29 cm x
Z

Solve each problem.

83) The height of a rocket can be found by comparing its shadow to a shadow cast by a 1.5-m stick at the same time of day. Suppose a rocket casts a 112-m shadow on the ground while the stick casts a 4-m shadow. Find the height of the rocket by writing a proportion and solving it.   42 m

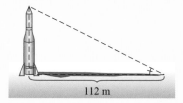

84) Refer to the previous exercise. Suppose at the same time, a tree nearby casts a 16-m shadow on the ground. How tall is the tree?   6 m

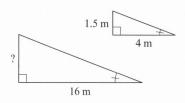

Mixed Exercises

Find m∠x in each triangle.

85)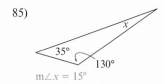

m∠x = 15°

86)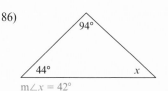

m∠x = 42°

Classify each triangle as equilateral, isosceles, or scalene.

87)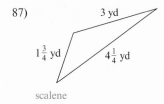

scalene

88)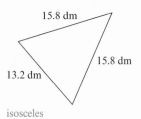

isosceles

Use the figure below for Exercises 89–92.

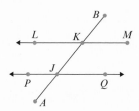

89) Identify the ray in the figure. $\overrightarrow{ML}$

90) Identify the line segment in the figure. $\overline{AB}$ or $\overline{BA}$

Answer *true* or *false* for Exercises 91–92.

91) ∠PJK is an acute angle.   false

92) ∠MKJ is an obtuse angle.   true

Solve each problem. Give the exact answer and the answer to the nearest tenth, if appropriate.

93) Mr. and Mrs. Fraser want to install wood flooring on their rectangular living room floor that measures 20 ft by 14 ft. If the installation charge is $5.50 per square foot, what is the total installation charge? $1540

94) Suppose a rectangle has a perimeter of 30 ft. If the rectangle has a length of 6 ft, what is its width?   9 ft

95) The base of a pyramid is a square with a side length of 50 ft. If the height of the pyramid is 42 ft, find the volume of the pyramid.   35,000 ft³

96) A television screen is 20 in. long and 12 in. wide. Find the exact length of the diagonal and an approximation to the nearest tenth. $\sqrt{544}$ in. ≈ 23.3 in.

Find the area of the figure.

97)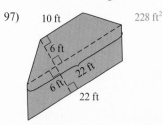

228 ft²

98) Find the perimeter of the figure. Give the *exact* value and an *approximate* value using $\pi \approx 3.14$.

exact: $(15\pi + 50)$ ft; approximation: 97.1 ft

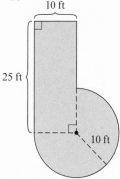

Find each missing angle measure.

99)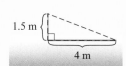

m∠ABC = 106°; m∠KBE = 42°;
m∠HBG = 32°; m∠ABK = 32°

100)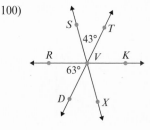

m∠TVK = 63°; m∠KVX = 74°;
m∠DVX = 43°; m∠RVS = 74°

Find the unknown length in the larger of these two similar triangles.

101)

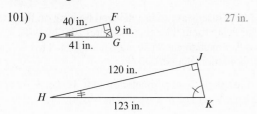

40 in. *F*   27 in.

D   9 in.

41 in. *G*

120 in. *J*

H   123 in. *K*

102)   *L*   35 mm

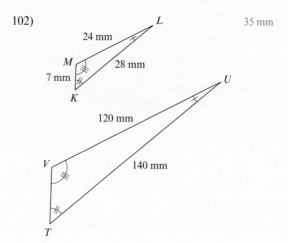

24 mm

M   28 mm

7 mm

K

U

120 mm

V   140 mm

T

Chapter 9: Test

Additional answers can be found in the Answers to Exercises appendix.

1) Identify each figure as a line, line segment, or ray, and name it using the correct notation.

a)   *K*

   N   ray; $\overrightarrow{NK}$

b)   *G*

   F   line; $\overleftrightarrow{FG}$ or $\overleftrightarrow{GF}$

c)   *A*

   R   line segment; $\overline{AR}$ or $\overline{RA}$

2) a) What does it mean if two lines are perpendicular?
         They intersect at 90° angles.
   b) What does it mean if two lines are parallel?
        They never intersect.

3) Find

   a) the supplement of 21°.   159°

   b) the complement of 21°.   69°

4) What is the difference between an acute angle and an obtuse angle?   An acute angle has a measure less than 90°, but the measure of an obtuse angle is greater than 90° and less than 180°.

5) $\angle ABC$ is a right angle.
Find m$\angle XBC$.   17°

   A

     X

   73°

   B   *C*

6) Find each missing angle measure.

m$\angle RAT$ = _____   m$\angle WAX$ = _____
m$\angle TAW$ = _____   m$\angle YAZ$ = _____
m$\angle RAT$ = 29°; m$\angle WAX$ = 87°;
m$\angle TAW$ = 64°; m$\angle YAZ$ = 64°

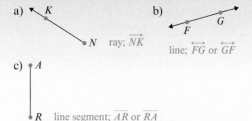

X   29°   *Y*

A

Z

W   87°

T   *R*

For Exercises 7–10,

   a) identify the figure.

   b) find the area.

   c) find the perimeter.

7)

12 cm   10 cm

   8 cm

   15 cm

a) triangle   b) 60 cm²   c) 37 cm

8)

12 in.

9 in.

14 in.

13 in.

a) trapezoid   b) 138 in²   c) 48 in.

9)

$5\frac{1}{2}$ ft

$7\frac{2}{3}$ ft

10)

9.4 m

4.7 m   6.1 m

a) parallelogram
b) 44.18 m²   c) 31 m

11) The angles in a triangle add up to how many degrees?   180°

For Exercises 12 and 13,

   a) classify the triangle as acute, obtuse, or right.

   b) classify the triangle as equilateral, isosceles, or scalene.

   c) find m$\angle x$.

12)

39°

120°   *x*

a) obtuse   b) scalene   c) 21°

13)

3 yd

3 yd

   x $\sqrt{18}$ yd

a) right   b) isosceles   c) 45°

14) For this figure, find

   a) the area.   78 ft²

   b) the perimeter.   44 ft

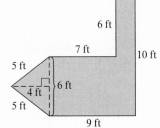

15) What term do we use for the perimeter of a circle?
   circumference

For Exercises 16 and 17, find

a) the area.

b) the circumference.

Give the exact value and an approximation using 3.14 for π. Round the approximation to the nearest hundredth, where appropriate.

16)
   10 in.

17)
   18 cm

18) Find the approximate area of the shaded region using $\frac{22}{7}$ for π.   42 km²

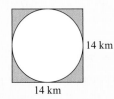
14 km
14 km

For Exercises 19–21,

a) identify the figure.

b) find the volume of the solid.

Give the exact value and, where appropriate, an approximate value rounded to the nearest hundredth using 3.14 for π.

19)
   3 ft

20)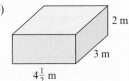
   2 m
   3 m
   $4\frac{1}{2}$ m

   a) rectangular solid or box   b) 27 m³

21)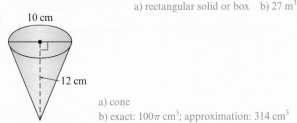
   10 cm
   12 cm

   a) cone
   b) exact: 100π cm³; approximation: 314 cm³

22) Approximate $\sqrt{41}$ to the nearest tenth and plot it on a number line.

   6.4; $\sqrt{41} \approx 6.4$

23) Can the Pythagorean theorem be used to find the lengths of the sides of any kind of triangle? Explain your answer.
   No. The Pythagorean theorem can be used only with right triangles.

In Exercises 24 and 25, find the length of the missing side. Give the exact value and, where appropriate, an approximation to the nearest tenth.

24)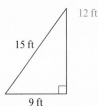
   12 ft
   15 ft
   9 ft

25)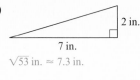
   2 in.
   7 in.
   $\sqrt{53}$ in. $\approx$ 7.3 in.

26) Given these two similar triangles, find the length of the side labeled x.   10 km

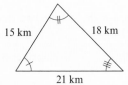
   x
   12 km
   14 km
   15 km
   18 km
   21 km

Solve each problem. Where appropriate, use 3.14 for π.

27) A town's park district will install a flower garden in the shape shown here. It will be enclosed by decorative fencing that costs $18.99/ft. Find the cost of the fence. $607.68

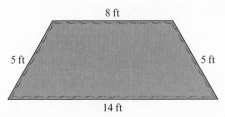
   8 ft
   5 ft
   5 ft
   14 ft

28) Romeo brings a 13-ft ladder to Juliet's window. He places the bottom of the ladder 5 ft from her house, and the top of the ladder rests at the bottom of her window. Find the height of Juliet's window.
   12 ft

   13 ft
   5 ft

29) Sierra is printing out an essay on paper that measures 8.5 in. by 11 in. She sets the top and bottom margins at 1 in. and the left and right margins at 1.25 in. Find the area of the region on the paper available for print.   54 in²

30) A Tootsie Roll is in the shape of a cylinder. It is 21 mm long, and its diameter is 10 mm. What is the volume of the Tootsie Roll?   1648.5 mm³

*Additional answers can be found in the Answers to Exercises appendix.

Perform the indicated operations.

1) $4006 + 73 + 9 + 98,995$ 103,083

2) $3050 - 3(125) + \sqrt{(3)^2 + (4)^2}$ 2680

3) $\begin{array}{r} 908 \\ \times\, 437 \end{array}$ 396,796   4) $48 \cdot \dfrac{7}{18}$ $\dfrac{56}{3}$ or $18\dfrac{2}{3}$

5) $3\dfrac{3}{4} \div 5\dfrac{5}{8}$ $\dfrac{2}{3}$ 6) $\dfrac{5}{6} - \dfrac{7}{12} + \dfrac{3}{8}$ $\dfrac{5}{8}$

7) $51.3 - 4.206$ 47.094   8) 71.4×9.305 664.377

9) $5.238 \div 0.06$ 87.3

10) Approximate the location of $\dfrac{11}{8}$ on the number line.

0 1 2 3 4

11) Write $\dfrac{2100}{2520}$ in lowest terms. $\dfrac{5}{6}$

12) Arrange these numbers from smallest to largest.

$$\dfrac{7}{8},\, 0.75,\, \dfrac{5}{16},\, 0.5 \qquad \dfrac{5}{16},\, 0.5,\, 0.75,\, \dfrac{7}{8}$$

13) Write the ratio of 18 in. to 2 ft. $\dfrac{3}{4}$

14) Change 5400 seconds to hours.   1.5 hr

15) Change 3 km to m.   3000 m

16) Write 0.39 as a percent.   39%

17) Find 70% of 80.   56

18) Find the supplement of 54°.   126°

19) Find the volume of the cone. Give an exact value and an approximation using $\pi \approx 3.14$.

exact: 112π m³; approximation: 351.68 m³

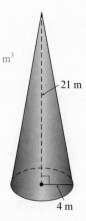

21 m

4 m

20) Find the area of the shaded region. Use 3.14 for π.   297 in²

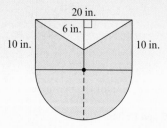

20 in.

6 in.

10 in.   10 in.

21) Use a proportion to find the unknown length labeled x. Then find the perimeter of the triangle with the unknown side length labeled x.   20 ft; 97.5 ft

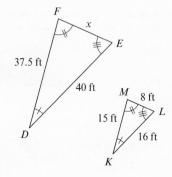

F

x

E

37.5 ft

40 ft

M 8 ft

15 ft L

D

16 ft

K

Solve each problem.

22) On average, 5 gal of paint will cover 1750 sq ft of wall space. How many gallons of paint will be required to paint a home if the wall space is 1050 sq ft?   3 gal

23) When Vinh was in the fifth grade, it took him 1 min 40 sec to make it through his playground's obstacle course. In the seventh grade, he could run the same course in 1 min 7 sec. Find the percent decrease in time it took Vinh to run the course in the seventh grade.   33%

24) Olga's paycheck, before deductions, is $480.00. From this, $21.60 is taken out for health insurance. What percent of her paycheck goes to health insurance?   4.5%

25) After completely charging her laptop's battery, Jenny used her laptop computer for 90 min. If her laptop now indicates that she has $\dfrac{3}{4}$ battery life remaining, how long can Jenny's laptop run on a fully charged battery?   360 min

Signed Numbers

Math at Work:

Loan Officer

If you want to own a home, Mariano Marquez is a good person to talk to. As a loan officer for a bank, his job is to help people obtain a mortgage loan to buy a house. "I think we all share the dream of owning the roof over our head," says Mariano. "I try to make that happen for people."

In assisting his customers, Mariano gathers all their financial data—including their savings, their income, their credit card debt, and any outstanding loans they might hold—to create a picture of where they stand in terms of money. He uses this to determine what sort of mortgage loan they can afford. "There's a lot of sophisticated math that goes into my work," Mariano explains. "But on a basic level, it's a matter of adding up all the projected income people have and subtracting their projected expenses. If the resulting number is positive, we can move forward; if the number is negative, we have a problem."

Mariano has a piece of advice for any future homebuyers: Get a handle on your finances early. "Even people in college should keep track of how they spend," Mariano says. "You'd be surprised at how easy it is to save a little bit of money each month." Of course, the more you have saved up, the easier it is to get a mortgage, or any other kind of loan.

We explore signed numbers in this chapter—including the positive and negative numbers Mariano refers to. We also introduce some financial literacy skills that you can start using right away.

 **Study Strategies** Beginning Financial Literacy

Particularly for busy college students, it is easy to lose track of how you are spending your money on a daily, weekly, and monthly basis. Unfortunately, spending this way can lead to credit card debt, overdrawn accounts, and other financial woes. The good news is that there are some simple skills you can apply to create a budget that will help put you in the driver's seat of your financial life.

- Identify your financial goals. Do you want to save for a big purchase? Pay off your student loans or credit card debt? Simply avoid debt in the first place?

- Track how you spend your money. For a week, write down *every* purchase you make in a small notebook that is always with you. This will help you understand how much you spend on small, daily purchases.
- Make a list of everything you know you will need to spend money on in the year ahead: tuition, rent, car insurance, and so on.
- Make a list of all your income for the year ahead, such as wages and financial aid.

- Make a budget by adding up all your sources of income and then everything you spend money on.
- If you find your costs are greater than your income, find ways to reduce your spending.
- Also consider ways to earn extra income, perhaps by taking on a part-time job, if your schedule permits it.

- Review where you stand financially each month, and adjust your budget accordingly. For example, make sure your estimates for how much you will spend on food or entertainment match what you actually spend.

- Reconsider your financial goals. Given how much money you make and how much you spend, are your goals realistic?
- Be on the lookout for issues that might create budget chaos, such as credit cards with interest rates that spike after a certain amount of time.

Chapter 10 $\boxed{\text{P O W E R}}$ Plan

P Prepare

What are your goals for Chapter 10?	O Organize — How can you accomplish each goal? (Write in the steps you will take to succeed.)
1 Be prepared before and during class.	• _____ • _____ • _____ • _____
2 Understand the homework to the point where you could do it without needing any help or hints.	• _____ • _____ • _____
3 Use the P.O.W.E.R. framework to learn beginning financial literacy: *Discover Your Personal Financial Philosophy.*	• _____ • _____ • _____
4 Write your own goal. _____ _____	• _____ _____

What are your objectives for Chapter 10?	How can you accomplish each objective?
1 Learn the basics of signed numbers.	• Understand the symbols presented in Section 10.1, and know how to compare them. • Realize that absolute values will help you find opposites.
2 Discover how to add and subtract signed numbers.	• Recognize the similarities between addition and subtraction on the number line. • Know how to decide whether the sum or difference will be negative or positive. • Watch the exercise videos for extra help if you get stuck on a certain problem.
3 Learn how to multiply and divide signed numbers.	• Know the procedures for multiplying or dividing numbers with the same or different signs. • Know why a negative fraction can be written in three different ways.
4 Apply the order of operations.	• Know what parentheses mean with regard to signed numbers and exponents. • Be able to recite the order of operations without hesitation. (Use **P**lease **E**xcuse **M**y **D**ear **A**unt **S**ally for help.)
5 Write your own goal. _____ _____	• _____ _____

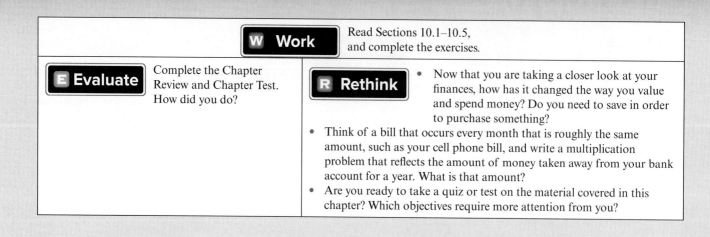

W Work Read Sections 10.1–10.5, and complete the exercises.

E Evaluate Complete the Chapter Review and Chapter Test. How did you do?

R Rethink

- Now that you are taking a closer look at your finances, how has it changed the way you value and spend money? Do you need to save in order to purchase something?
- Think of a bill that occurs every month that is roughly the same amount, such as your cell phone bill, and write a multiplication problem that reflects the amount of money taken away from your bank account for a year. What is that amount?
- Are you ready to take a quiz or test on the material covered in this chapter? Which objectives require more attention from you?

10.1 Introduction to Signed Numbers

P Prepare

O Organize

What are your objectives for Section 10.1?	How can you accomplish each objective?
1 Understand Signed Numbers	• Write the definitions of *positive number* and *negative number* in your own words using the symbols < and >. • Summarize the procedure for **Writing Signed Numbers.** • Complete the given example on your own. • Complete You Try 1.
2 Compare Signed Numbers	• Follow Examples 2 and 3, and create a procedure you can follow to compare signed numbers. • Complete You Trys 2 and 3.
3 Evaluate Expressions Involving Absolute Value	• Write the definition and property of the *absolute value of a number* in your own words. • Complete the given example on your own. • Complete You Try 4.
4 Find the Opposite of a Number	• Write the definition of *opposites* in your own words. • Complete the given examples on your own. • Complete You Trys 5 and 6.

W Work Read the explanations, follow the examples, take notes, and complete the You Trys.

1 Understand Signed Numbers

Until this point, we have worked with *positive numbers* and zero.

Definition

A **positive number** is a number greater than zero.

On a number line, positive numbers are to the *right* of 0. Some numbers, however, are *less than* zero. These are called *negative numbers*.

Definition

A **negative number** is a number less than zero. To indicate that a number is negative, we put a negative sign, $-$, in front of it.

   Example: -16 is read as "negative sixteen."

Here are some examples of how we use negative numbers.

Statement	Use a negative number
9 degrees below zero	$-9°$
A golf score of 4 under par	-4
A loss of $281	$-\$281$

Because numbers get smaller as we move to the *left* on a number line, negative numbers are to the *left* of zero. (Zero separates the negative numbers from the positive numbers, and zero is neither positive nor negative.)

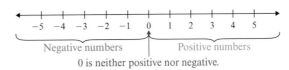

0 is neither positive nor negative.

Positive numbers, negative numbers, and zero are also called **signed numbers.**

Procedure Writing Signed Numbers

1) A *negative* number is written with a negative sign in front of it. For example, -8 is "negative eight."
2) A *positive* number can be written with a "+" sign in front of it. For example, $+13$ is "positive thirteen."
3) If a number does *not* have a sign in front of it, the number is assumed to be positive. For example, 25 is "positive twenty-five" or just "twenty-five."

Next, let's graph some signed numbers on a number line. Remember that negative numbers are to the *left* of 0.

EXAMPLE 1

Graph each pair of numbers on a number line.

a) 5, −3

b) $\frac{1}{2}$, $-\frac{1}{2}$

c) $2\frac{1}{3}$, $-4\frac{2}{3}$

d) 1.25, −3.25

Solution

a)

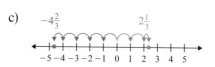

−3 is 3 units to   The number 5 is 5
the *left* of 0.   units to the *right* of 0.

b)

−3 is 3 units to the left of 0.

$-\frac{1}{2}$ is $\frac{1}{2}$ unit to the $\frac{1}{2}$ is $\frac{1}{2}$ unit to the
left of 0.   *right* of 0.

c)

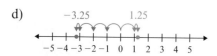

To graph $-4\frac{2}{3}$, move $2\frac{1}{3}$ is to the *right* of 0.

4 units to the *left*
of 0, then move another
$\frac{2}{3}$ unit to the *left*.

d)

To graph −3.25, move   1.25 is to the *right* of 0.
3 units to the *left* of 0,
then move another 0.25
unit to the left.

[YOU TRY 1]

Graph each pair of numbers on a number line.

a) 3, −4

b) $\frac{3}{4}$, $-\frac{3}{4}$

c) $1\frac{1}{2}$, $-3\frac{1}{2}$

d) 4.75, −2.75

---

2 Compare Signed Numbers

Remember that numbers get *smaller* as we move to the *left* on a number line and that numbers get *larger* as we move to the *right* on a number line. We can use the *less than* symbol, <, and the *greater than* symbol, >, to compare signed numbers.

For example, we can compare the numbers 1 and 4 in two ways.

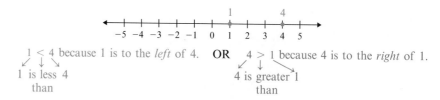

1 < 4 because 1 is to the *left* of 4.   OR   4 > 1 because 4 is to the *right* of 1.

1 is less 4   4 is greater 1
   than   than

EXAMPLE 2

Fill in the blank with < or > to compare each pair of numbers. Look at the number line to help you, if necessary.

a) 7 _____ 3

b) −6 _____ −1

c) −5 _____ −8

d) 2 _____ −4

e) −3 _____ 0

←+−+−+−+−+−+−+−+−+−+−+−+−+−+−+−+→
−8−7−6−5−4−3−2−1 0 1 2 3 4 5 6 7 8

Solution

a) $7 > 3$ because 7 is to the *right* of 3 on the number line.

b) $-6 < -1$ because -6 is to the *left* of -1 on the number line.

c) $-5 > -8$ because -5 is to the *right* of -8.

d) $2 > -4$ because 2 is to the *right* of -4.

e) $-3 < 0$ because -3 is to the *left* of 0.

[**YOU TRY 2**] Fill in the blank with $<$ or $>$ to compare each pair of numbers. Look at the number line in Example 2 to help you, if necessary.

a) -1 ____ -4 b) 5 ____ 8 c) -6 ____ 2

d) 0 ____ -7 e) -8 ____ -3

Be careful when comparing fractions and decimals. Graph the numbers to accurately compare them.

EXAMPLE 3

In-Class Example 3

Graph each pair of numbers on a number line, then fill in the blank with $<$ or $>$ to compare the numbers.

a) $-\dfrac{1}{4}$ ____ $-\dfrac{2}{3}$

b) $-3\dfrac{4}{5}$ ____ $-3\dfrac{1}{2}$

c) -2.7 ____ -2.3

Answer:

a) $>$

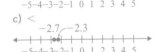

b) $<$

c) $<$

Graph each pair of numbers on a number line, then fill in the blank with $<$ or $>$ to compare the numbers.

a) $-\dfrac{1}{3}$ ____ $-\dfrac{3}{4}$ b) $-2\dfrac{7}{8}$ ____ $-2\dfrac{1}{2}$ c) -3.6 ____ -3.2

Solution

a) Draw a number line, and graph each number:

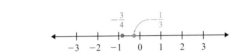

$-\dfrac{1}{3} > -\dfrac{3}{4}$ since $-\dfrac{1}{3}$ is to the *right* of $-\dfrac{3}{4}$.

b)

$-2\dfrac{7}{8} < -2\dfrac{1}{2}$ because $-2\dfrac{7}{8}$ is to the *left* of $-2\dfrac{1}{2}$.

c)

$-3.6 < -3.2$ because -3.6 is to the *left* of -3.2.

[**YOU TRY 3**] Graph each pair of numbers on a number line, then fill in the blank with $<$ or $>$ to compare the numbers.

a) $-\dfrac{5}{8}$ ____ $-\dfrac{1}{6}$ b) $-1\dfrac{1}{4}$ ____ $-1\dfrac{2}{3}$ c) -4.5 ____ -4.1

---

3 Evaluate Expressions Involving Absolute Value

The concept of *absolute value* is one that is used often in mathematics. What *is* absolute value?

> ### Definition
> The **absolute value** of a number is the distance of the number from 0.

The absolute value of a number tells us the *distance* between that number and 0 on a number line, *not* which side of 0 the number is on. Therefore, the absolute value of a number is never negative.

> ### Property Absolute Value of a Number
>
> 1) The absolute value of a number is the *distance* between that number and 0 on a number line, and distance is *not* negative. Therefore, *the absolute value of a number is never negative.*
>
> 2) The absolute value of a number is denoted by two vertical bars. For example, we read $|4|$ as "the absolute value of 4."
>
>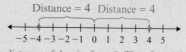
>
> 4 is a distance of 4 units from 0. Therefore, $|4| = 4$.
> -4 is a distance of 4 units from 0. Therefore, $|-4| = 4$.

EXAMPLE 4

Evaluate each absolute value expression.

a) $|7|$ b) $|-3|$ c) $|0|$ d) $-|-9|$

Solution

a) To evaluate $|7|$, ask yourself, *"What is the distance between 0 and 7?"*

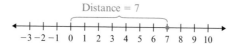

The distance between 0 and 7 is 7, so $|7| = 7$.

b) To evaluate $|-3|$, ask yourself, *"What is the distance between 0 and −3?"*

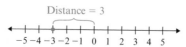

The distance between 0 and −3 is 3, so $|-3| = 3$.

c) $|0| = 0$ because 0 is *zero* units from 0.

d) When evaluating an expression like $-|-9|$, the absolute value symbol works like parentheses in the order of operations; evaluate the absolute value first.

$$-|-9| = -(9) = -9 \qquad \text{First evaluate } |-9|, \text{ then apply the negative sign}$$
$$\text{on the outside of the absolute value bars.}$$

> **W Hint**
>
> The absolute value of a number is never negative!

YOU TRY 4	Evaluate each absolute value expression.

a) |13| b) |−5| c) −|8| d) −|−14|

4 Find the Opposite of a Number

Earlier we saw that, on a number line, 4 and −4 are the same distance from 0 but they are on *opposite* sides of 0.

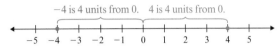

−4 is 4 units from 0.   4 is 4 units from 0.

We say that 4 and −4 are *opposites* of each other.

Definition

Two numbers are **opposites** of each other if they are the same distance from 0 on a number line but are on opposite sides of 0.

To find the opposite of a number, we write a negative sign in front of it.

Note

When we put a negative sign in front of a number to find its opposite, we will also put the original number in parentheses. This will help us avoid confusion in the future.

EXAMPLE 5

In-Class Example 5

Find the opposite of each number.

a) 3   b) $\dfrac{4}{9}$

c) 6.7   d) 0

Answer:

a) −3   b) −$\dfrac{4}{9}$

c) −6.7   d) 0

Find the opposite of each number.

a) 2   b) $\dfrac{5}{8}$ c) 7.3   d) 0

Solution

a) The opposite of 2 is $-(2) = -2$.

    Put a negative in
    front of the 2.

b) The opposite of $\dfrac{5}{8}$ is $-\left(\dfrac{5}{8}\right) = -\dfrac{5}{8}$.

c) The opposite of 7.3 is $-(7.3) = -7.3$.

d) The opposite of 0 is $-(0) = 0$. Remember, 0 is neither positive nor negative.

YOU TRY 5	Find the opposite of each number.

a) 19   b) $\dfrac{7}{10}$ c) 4.6   d) $5\dfrac{1}{6}$

Sometimes, a number will contain two negative signs. For example,

$$-(-5) \quad \text{means} \quad \text{the opposite of } -5.$$

The opposite of -5

Therefore, $-(-5) = 5$.

Note

The opposite of a negative number is a positive number.

Example: The opposite of -8 is $-(-8) = 8$.

This means "the opposite of."

Hint

Why does this make sense? Draw a number line to visualize it.

EXAMPLE 6

Find the opposite of each number.

a) -15 b) -0.8 c) $-\dfrac{3}{4}$ d) $-2\dfrac{1}{6}$

In-Class Example 6

Find the opposite of each number.
a) -17 b) -0.4
c) $-\dfrac{2}{3}$ d) $-5\dfrac{7}{8}$

Answer:

a) 17 b) 0.4 c) $\dfrac{2}{3}$ d) $5\dfrac{7}{8}$

Hint

Notice the use of parentheses!

Solution

Number	Opposite
a) -15	$-(-15) = 15$
b) -0.8	$-(-0.8) = 0.8$
c) $-\dfrac{3}{4}$	$-\left(-\dfrac{3}{4}\right) = \dfrac{3}{4}$
d) $-2\dfrac{1}{6}$	$-\left(-2\dfrac{1}{6}\right) = 2\dfrac{1}{6}$

[YOU TRY 6]

Find the opposite of each number.

a) -38 b) -8.1 c) $-\dfrac{11}{15}$ d) $-4\dfrac{5}{9}$

Hint

Check your answers manually first!

ANSWERS TO [YOU TRY] EXERCISES

1) a) 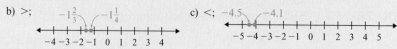 b)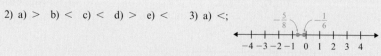

c) 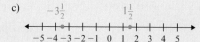 d)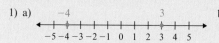

2) a) $>$ b) $<$ c) $<$ d) $>$ e) $<$ 3) a) $<$;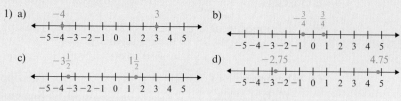

b) $>$; c) $<$;

4) a) 13 b) 5 c) -8 d) -14 5) a) -19 b) $-\dfrac{7}{10}$ c) -4.6 d) $-5\dfrac{1}{6}$

6) a) 38 b) 8.1 c) $\dfrac{11}{15}$ d) $4\dfrac{5}{9}$

E Evaluate 10.1 Exercises

Do the exercises, and check your work.

*Additional answers can be found in the Answers to Exercises appendix.

Objective 1: Understand Signed Numbers

1) What is a negative number?
   A negative number is a number that is less than zero.

2) Is zero a positive number, negative number, or neither? neither

Represent each statement with a signed number.

3) Justine owes $23. $-$23

4) Hector's checking account was overdrawn by $124.56. $-$124.56

5) Gary lost $3\frac{1}{2}$ lb this past week on a reduced-calorie diet. $-3\frac{1}{2}$ lb

6) The value of a stock decreased by $2.81/share.
   $-$2.81

7) Mount Whitney is the tallest mountain in the continental United States and rises 14,494 ft above sea level. (www.nps.gov/seki) 14,494 ft

8) The deepest part of Lake Erie is 210 ft below the surface of the water. (www.great-lakes.net) -210 ft

Graph each set of numbers on the number line.

$$-5\ -4\ -3\ -2\ -1\ \ 0\ \ 1\ \ 2\ \ 3\ \ 4\ \ 5$$

9) $0, 2, -1, -5, -3$

10) $-1, 0, -4, 4, -5$

11) $1\frac{1}{4}, -3, 4, -4\frac{1}{2}, -\frac{3}{4}$

12) $5, 2\frac{1}{4}, \frac{1}{2}, -2, -3\frac{3}{4}$

13) $\frac{4}{5}, 3, -\frac{2}{5}, -2\frac{3}{5}, -1\frac{3}{4}$

14) $4\frac{1}{4}, \frac{2}{5}, -1, -3\frac{3}{4}, -2\frac{1}{2}$

15) $2.5, -1.2, 3, -2.8, 0.5$

16) $-1.8, 3.4, 4, -2.8, -4$

17) $0.6, -1.6, -4, -3.5, 2.8$

18) $-2.5, 3.5, 0.8, -0.3, -4.9$

Objective 2: Compare Signed Numbers

Fill in the blank with *smaller* or *larger*.

19) As you move left on the number line, the numbers get _____. smaller

20) As you move right on the number line, the numbers get _____. larger

Fill in the blank with $<$ or $>$ to compare each pair of numbers.

21) -13 _____ 7 $<$

22) 11 _____ -11 $>$

23) -4 _____ -3 $<$

24) -11 _____ -12 $>$

25) -3 _____ 0 $<$

26) 0 _____ -12 $>$

27) $-\frac{1}{3}$ _____ $\frac{2}{5}$ $<$

28) $-\frac{3}{5}$ _____ $\frac{2}{3}$ $<$

29) $\frac{3}{8}$ _____ $\frac{2}{7}$ $>$

30) $\frac{3}{7}$ _____ $\frac{4}{9}$ $<$

31) $-\frac{2}{3}$ _____ $-\frac{5}{6}$ $>$

32) $-\frac{5}{8}$ _____ $-\frac{3}{5}$ $<$

33) $-2\frac{1}{2}$ _____ $-2\frac{5}{7}$ $>$

34) $-3\frac{4}{5}$ _____ $-3\frac{7}{9}$ $<$

35) -0.25 _____ -0.31 $>$

36) -0.3 _____ -0.299 $<$

37) -0.028 _____ -0.029 $>$

38) -1.055 _____ -1.054 $<$

Use the number line for Exercises 39–42. Fill in the blank with < or > to make the statement true.

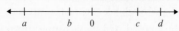

a b 0 c d

39) b _____ c <

40) 0 _____ a >

41) 2 _____ b >

42) -3 _____ c <

Objective 3: Evaluate Expressions Involving Absolute Value

43) Your friend asks you to explain to him the meaning of the absolute value of a number. What would you tell him?   It is the distance of the number from zero.

44) The absolute value of the number 3 is the same as the absolute value of what other number? -3

Evaluate each absolute value expression.

45) $|19|$ 19

46) $|87|$ 87

47) $|-17|$ 17

48) $|-13|$ 13

49) $|0|$ 0

50) $-|0|$ 0

51) $-|35|$ -35

52) $-|15|$ -15

53) $-|-24|$ -24

54) $-|-56|$ -56

55) $\left|-5\dfrac{8}{13}\right|$ $5\dfrac{8}{13}$

56) $\left|-\dfrac{19}{23}\right|$ $\dfrac{19}{23}$

57) $-|-11.6|$ -11.6

58) $-|-0.54|$ -0.54

Objective 4: Find the Opposite of a Number

59) How are 5 and the opposite of 5 related on the number line?
They are both a distance of 5 from zero on the number line.

60) What number is its own opposite?   0

Find the opposite of each number.

61) 1 -1

62) -8 8

63) 47 -47

64) 54 -54

65) -2.3 2.3

66) -8.7 8.7

67) -23 23

68) -16 16

69) $-\dfrac{3}{4}$ $\dfrac{3}{4}$

70) $-\dfrac{5}{6}$ $\dfrac{5}{6}$

71) $3\dfrac{5}{9}$ $-3\dfrac{5}{9}$

72) $5\dfrac{7}{11}$ $-5\dfrac{7}{11}$

73) -1.978 1.978

74) -0.013 0.013

For Exercises 75–82, answer *true* or *false*.

75) $|-7| < 0$ false

76) $|-18| < |-23|$ true

77) $-(-6) > 0$ true

78) $-10 > -(-10)$ false

79) $-|-8| > -|-12|$ true

80) $-|-0| < -(-1)$ true

81) $-(-13) < -|13|$ false

82) $-(-|-7|) < 7$ false

Use the number line for Exercises 83–88. Fill in the blank with < or > to make the statement true.

a b 0 c d

83) $-a$ _____ 0   >

84) $-d$ _____ c <

85) $-d$ _____ $-c$ <

86) $-(-a)$ _____ $-b$ <

87) $|a|$ _____ b >

88) $|b|$ _____ $-a$ <

R Rethink

R1) Explain how visualizing signed numbers on a number line helped you to understand absolute value and opposites.

R2) What would happen if you did NOT use parentheses when finding the opposite of a number?

10.2 Adding Signed Numbers

What are your objectives for Section 10.2?	How can you accomplish each objective?
1 Add Signed Numbers Using a Number Line	• Review Section 1.2 if you need more review on adding two positive numbers using a number line. • When adding a negative number, move left on the number line. • Complete the given example on your own. • Complete You Try 1.
2 Add Two Negative Numbers	• The sum of two negative numbers is always negative. • Write the procedure for **Adding Two Negative Numbers** in your own words. • Complete the given example on your own. • Complete You Try 2.
3 Add Numbers with Different Signs	• Write the procedure for **Adding Two Numbers with Different Signs** in your own words. • Complete the given examples on your own by following the procedure you wrote down. • Complete You Trys 3 and 4.

W Work   Read the explanations, follow the examples, take notes, and complete the You Trys.

1 Add Signed Numbers Using a Number Line

In Section 1.2, we first learned how to use a number line to add numbers. For example, to add two *positive* numbers, like $2 + 4$, we start at 0 and move 2 spaces to the *right* to reach 2. Then, we move 4 more spaces to the *right* to reach 6.

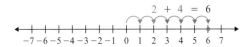

To add *negative* numbers, we move to the *left.*

EXAMPLE 1

In-Class Example 1

Add using a number line.
a) $6 + (-4)$ b) $-5 + 2$
c) $-3 + (-1)$

Answer:
a) 2;
$$6 + (-4) = 2$$

Add using a number line.

a) $5 + (-3)$ b) $-7 + 4$ c) $-4 + (-1)$

Solution

a) Start at 0 and move 5 spaces to the right to reach 5. Then, to add -3, move 3 spaces to the left. We finish at 2.

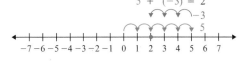

b) To add $-7 + 4$, move 7 spaces to the *left* to reach -7. Then, to add 4, move 4 spaces to the right. We finish at -3.

c) To add $-4 + (-1)$, first move 4 spaces to the left to reach -4. Then, move 1 more space to the left to add -1. The sum is -5.

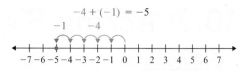

$$-4 + (-1) = -5$$

$\left[\begin{array}{c}\textbf{YOU TRY 1}\end{array}\right]$ Add using a number line.

a) $7 + (-9)$ b) $-3 + 8$ c) $-2 + (-4)$

b) -3;

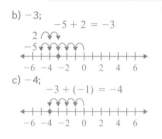

c) -4;
$-3 + (-1) = -4$

> ### Note
> When a negative number follows an operation symbol such as $+$, $-$, $\times$, or $\div$, we usually put the number in parentheses.
>
> Example: $-4 + (-1) = -5$
>
> This negative number is *after* the $+$, so put it in parentheses.

2 Add Two Negative Numbers

We know that when we add two positive numbers, the sum is positive. When we add two negative numbers, the sum is *always* negative.

> ### W Hint
> Look at Example 1c. Does the procedure make sense?

> ### Procedure Adding Two Negative Numbers
> **Step 1:** Find the absolute value of each number.
> **Step 2:** Add the absolute values.
> **Step 3:** Put a negative sign in front of the sum.

> ### Note
> The sum of two negative numbers is *always* negative.

EXAMPLE 2

In-Class Example 2

Add.
a) $-7 + (-11)$
b) $-68 + (-37)$
c) $-408.3 + (-251.8)$
d) $-\dfrac{4}{9} + \left(-\dfrac{2}{3}\right)$

Answer:
a) -18 b) -105
c) -660.1 d) $-\dfrac{10}{9}$ or $-1\dfrac{1}{9}$

Add.

a) $-6 + (-13)$ b) $-47 + (-29)$ c) $-351.6 + (-607.9)$

d) $-\dfrac{5}{8} + \left(-\dfrac{1}{2}\right)$

Solution

a) **Step 1:** Find the absolute value of each number: $|-6| = 6$, $|-13| = 13$

  Step 2: Add the absolute values: $6 + 13 = 19$

  Step 3: Put a negative sign in front of the sum: $-6 + (-13) = -19$

b) **Step 1:** Find the absolute value of each number: $|-47| = 47$, $|-29| = 29$

   Step 2: Add the absolute values: $47 + 29 = 76$

   Step 3: Put a negative sign in front of the sum: $-47 + (-29) = -76$

c) **Step 1:** Find the absolute value of each number:
  $|-351.6| = 351.6$, $|-607.9| = 607.9$

   Step 2: Add the absolute values: $351.6 + 607.9 = 959.5$

   Step 3: Put a negative sign in front of the sum: $-351.6 + (-607.9) = -959.5$

d) **Step 1:** Find the absolute value of each number: $\left|-\dfrac{5}{8}\right| = \dfrac{5}{8}$, $\left|-\dfrac{1}{2}\right| = \dfrac{1}{2}$

   Step 2: Add the absolute values: $\dfrac{5}{8} + \dfrac{1}{2} = \dfrac{5}{8} + \dfrac{4}{8} = \dfrac{9}{8}$ or $1\dfrac{1}{8}$

   Step 3: Put a negative sign in front of the sum: $-\dfrac{5}{8} + \left(-\dfrac{1}{2}\right) = -\dfrac{9}{8}$ or $-1\dfrac{1}{8}$

[YOU TRY 2] Add.

a) $-18 + (-9)$ b) $-52 + (-93)$ c) $-7123.2 + (-2519.4)$

d) $-\dfrac{1}{6} + \left(-\dfrac{3}{4}\right)$

---

3 Add Numbers with Different Signs

In-Class Example 3

Find each sum; then verify the answer using a number line.
a) $-4 + 7$ b) $2 + (-6)$

Answer:
a) 3;

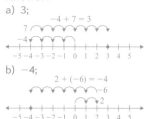

b) -4;

When we add a positive number and a negative number, sometimes the sum is positive (as in Example 1a) and sometimes the sum is negative (as in Example 1b).

> **Procedure** Adding Two Numbers with Different Signs
>
> **Step 1:** Find the absolute value of each number.
>
> **Step 2:** Subtract the smaller absolute value from the larger absolute value.
>
> **Step 3:** The sign of the *sum* will be the same as the sign of the number with the *greater* absolute value. Write the sum with this sign.

EXAMPLE 3   Find each sum; then verify the answer using a number line.

a) $-6 + 9$ b) $4 + (-10)$

Solution

a) **Step 1:** Find the absolute value of each number: $|-6| = 6$, $|9| = 9$

   Step 2: Subtract the smaller absolute value from the larger absolute value.

$$9 - 6 = 3$$

    Larger absolute   Smaller absolute
        value   value

Step 3: The sign of the *sum* will be the same as the sign of the number with the *greater* absolute value.

Positive 9 has a greater absolute value than *negative* 6, so **the sum will be positive.**

$$-6 + 9 = 3$$
↑
The sum is positive.

We can see why the answer makes sense on a number line.

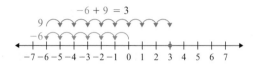

b) ***Step 1:*** Find the absolute value of each number: $|4| = 4, |-10| = 10$

Step 2: Subtract the smaller absolute value from the larger absolute value.

$$10 - 4 = 6$$
↗   ↖
Larger absolute   Smaller absolute
value   value

Step 3: The sign of the *sum* will be the same as the sign of the number with the greater absolute value.

Negative 10 has a greater absolute value than *positive* 4, so **the sum will be negative.**

$$4 + (-10) = -6$$
↑
The sum is negative.

Let's look at this on a number line.

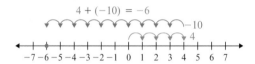

[**YOU TRY 3**] Find each sum; then verify each answer using a number line.

a) $-5 + 1$ b) $7 + (-3)$

EXAMPLE 4   Add.

In-Class Example 4

Add.
a) $42 + (-25)$
b) $-894 + 571$
c) $-0.53 + 0.8$
d) $-\dfrac{3}{10} + \dfrac{9}{10}$
e) $\dfrac{3}{5} + \left(-\dfrac{5}{8}\right)$

Answer:
a) 17   b) -323 c) 0.27
d) $\dfrac{3}{5}$ e) $-\dfrac{1}{40}$

a) $38 + (-21)$ b) $-562 + 301$ c) $-0.47 + 0.9$

d) $-\dfrac{4}{9} + \dfrac{7}{9}$ e) $\dfrac{3}{8} + \left(-\dfrac{5}{12}\right)$

Solution

a) ***Step 1:*** Find the absolute value of each number: $|38| = 38, |-21| = 21$

Step 2: Subtract the smaller absolute value from the larger absolute value.

$$38 - 21 = 17$$
↗   ↖
Larger absolute   Smaller absolute
value   value

Step 3: The sign of the sum will be *positive* because 38 has a greater absolute value than -21.

$$38 + (-21) = 17 \quad \text{The sum is positive.}$$

b) ***Step 1:*** Find the absolute value of each number: $|-562| = 562$, $|301| = 301$

Step 2: Subtract the smaller absolute value from the larger absolute value.

$$562 - 301 = 261$$

$$\text{Larger absolute} \qquad \text{Smaller absolute}$$
$$\text{value} \qquad\qquad \text{value}$$

Step 3: Will the answer be positive or negative? It will be *negative* because -562 has a larger absolute value than 301.

$$-562 + 301 = -261 \quad \text{The sum is negative.}$$

c) ***Step 1:*** Find the absolute value of each number: $|-0.47| = 0.47$, $|0.9| = 0.9$

Step 2: Subtract the smaller absolute value from the larger absolute value.

$$0.9 - 0.47 = 0.43$$

$$\text{Larger absolute} \qquad \text{Smaller absolute}$$
$$\text{value} \qquad\qquad \text{value}$$

Step 3: The sum will be *positive* because 0.9 has a larger absolute value than -0.47.

$$-0.47 + (0.9) = 0.43 \quad \text{The sum is positive.}$$

d) ***Step 1:*** Find the absolute value of each number: $\left|-\dfrac{4}{9}\right| = \dfrac{4}{9}$, $\left|\dfrac{7}{9}\right| = \dfrac{7}{9}$

Step 2: Subtract the smaller absolute value from the larger absolute value.

$$\frac{7}{9} - \frac{4}{9} = \frac{3}{9} = \frac{1}{3} \quad \text{Write in lowest terms.}$$

$$\text{Larger absolute} \qquad \text{Smaller absolute}$$
$$\text{value} \qquad\qquad \text{value}$$

Step 3: Will the answer be positive or negative? It will be *positive* because $\dfrac{7}{9}$ has a larger absolute value than $-\dfrac{4}{9}$.

$$-\frac{4}{9} + \frac{7}{9} = \frac{1}{3} \quad \text{The sum is positive.}$$

e) ***Step 1:*** Find the absolute value of each number: $\left|\dfrac{3}{8}\right| = \dfrac{3}{8}$, $\left|-\dfrac{5}{12}\right| = \dfrac{5}{12}$

Which of these absolute values is larger? We need to know which is larger in order to subtract. Therefore, **write each absolute value as a fraction with their least common denominator, 24.**

$$\frac{3}{8} = \frac{3}{8} \cdot \frac{3}{3} = \frac{9}{24} \qquad \frac{5}{12} \cdot \frac{2}{2} = \frac{10}{24}$$

$$\frac{5}{12} = \frac{10}{24} \text{ and } \frac{3}{8} = \frac{9}{24}. \text{ Therefore, } \frac{5}{12} \text{ is larger than } \frac{3}{8}.$$

Step 2: Subtract the smaller absolute value from the larger absolute value.

$$\frac{5}{12} - \frac{3}{8} = \frac{10}{24} - \frac{9}{24} = \frac{1}{24}$$

Larger absolute   Smaller absolute
value   value

Step 3: Will the answer be positive or negative? It will be *negative* because the absolute value of $-\frac{5}{12}$ is larger than the absolute value of $\frac{3}{8}$.

$$\frac{3}{8} + \left(-\frac{5}{12}\right) = -\frac{1}{24}$$ The answer is negative.

$\left[\text{YOU TRY 4}\right]$ Add.

     a) $-78 + 49$ b) $516 + (-497)$ c) $-0.6 + 0.39$

     d) $\frac{11}{16} + \left(-\frac{15}{16}\right)$ e) $-\frac{7}{9} + \frac{5}{6}$

BE CAREFUL   Adding signed fractions can be tricky. Get a common denominator to determine which absolute value is larger so that you can determine the correct sign of the answer.

ANSWERS TO $\left[\text{YOU TRY}\right]$ **EXERCISES**

1) a) -2;

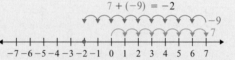

$7 + (-9) = -2$

   b) 5;

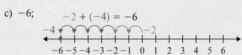

$-3 + 8 = 5$

   c) -6;

$-2 + (-4) = -6$

2) a) -27 b) -145 c) -9642.6 d) $-\frac{11}{12}$

3) a) -4;

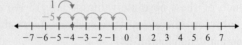

$-5 + 1 = -4$

   b) 4;

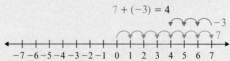

$7 + (-3) = 4$

4) a) -29 b) 19 c) -0.21 d) $-\frac{1}{4}$ e) $\frac{1}{18}$

E Evaluate 10.2 Exercises   Do the exercises, and check your work.

*Additional answers can be found in the Answers to Exercises appendix.

Objective 1: Add Signed Numbers Using a Number Line

Add using a number line.

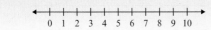

1) $8 + (-5)$ 2) $10 + (-3)$

3) $-6 + 9$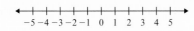

4) $-5 + 6$ 5) $5 + (-9)$

6) $2 + (-3)$ 7) $-3 + 1$

8) $-7 + 4$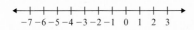

9) $-1 + (-2)$ 10) $-2 + (-5)$

11) $-1 + (-5)$ 12) $-3 + (-3)$

13) Explain, in your own words, how to add a positive number and a negative number on a number line. Answers may vary.

14) Explain, in your own words, how to add two negative numbers on a number line. Answers may vary.

Objective 2: Add Two Negative Numbers

15) Is the sum of two negative numbers *always, sometimes,* or *never* negative? always

16) Explain, in your own words, how to add two negative numbers. Answers may vary.

Add.

17) $-8 + (-3)$ -11 18) $-5 + (-7)$ -12

19) $-53 + (-45)$ -98 20) $-47 + (-32)$ -79

21) $-\dfrac{1}{2} + \left(-\dfrac{3}{4}\right)$ $-\dfrac{5}{4}$ or $-1\dfrac{1}{4}$ 22) $-\dfrac{7}{4} + \left(-\dfrac{5}{6}\right)$ $-\dfrac{31}{12}$ or $-2\dfrac{7}{12}$

23) $-\dfrac{7}{5} + \left(-\dfrac{3}{10}\right)$ $-\dfrac{17}{10}$ or $-1\dfrac{7}{10}$ 24) $-\dfrac{5}{2} + \left(-\dfrac{1}{8}\right)$ $-\dfrac{21}{8}$ or $-2\dfrac{5}{8}$

25) $-2.5 + (-5.9)$ -8.4 26) $-1.4 + (-3.5)$ -4.9

27) $-287.6 + (-108.3)$ 28) $-543.8 + (-211.6)$
-395.9 -755.4

29) $-4 + (-13) + (-15)$ -32

30) $-11 + (-10) + (-8)$ -29

31) $-22 + (-67) + (-36)$ -125

32) $-49 + (-33) + (-51)$ -133

Objective 3: Add Numbers with Different Signs

33) Explain, in your own words, how to add two numbers with different signs. Answers may vary.

34) Is the sum of a negative number and a positive number *always, sometimes,* or *never* negative?
sometimes

Add.

35) $-9 + 6$ -3 36) $-6 + 1$ -5

37) $-3 + 11$ 8 38) $-7 + 9$ 2

39) $10 + (-4)$ 6 40) $12 + (-8)$ 4

41) $2 + (-13)$ -11 42) $5 + (-18)$ -13

43) $-62 + 47$ -15 44) $-87 + 61$ -26

45) $-135 + 328$ 193 46) $-267 + 351$ 84

47) $546 + (-795)$ -249 48) $457 + (-603)$ -146

49) $24.6 + (-17.3)$ 7.3 50) $3.8 + (-31.2)$ -27.4

51) $16.7 + (-19.058)$ 52) $31.4 + (-24.027)$ 7.373
-2.358

53) $-\dfrac{3}{8} + \dfrac{1}{4}$ $-\dfrac{1}{8}$ 54) $-\dfrac{7}{3} + \dfrac{5}{12}$ $-\dfrac{23}{12}$

55) $\dfrac{15}{8} + \left(-\dfrac{7}{12}\right)$ $\dfrac{31}{24}$ or $1\dfrac{7}{24}$ 56) $\dfrac{3}{2} + \left(-\dfrac{3}{11}\right)$ $\dfrac{27}{22}$ or $1\dfrac{5}{22}$

57) $\dfrac{5}{6} + \left(-\dfrac{8}{9}\right)$ $-\dfrac{1}{18}$ 58) $\dfrac{1}{7} + \left(-\dfrac{9}{10}\right)$ $-\dfrac{53}{70}$

Represent each statement with an addition problem, and solve the problem.

59) Yesterday, LaShonte received her paycheck in the amount of $735.50, and today she spent $258.72 at the shopping mall. How much of her paycheck remains? $735.50 + (-$258.72); $476.78

60) Paulius received an email from the bank notifying him that his checking account was overdrawn by $132.36. He immediately went online and transferred $150 to his checking account from his savings account. Find the new balance of his checking account. $-$132.36 + $150; $17.64

61) A football team lost 12 yd on the first play and gained 9 yd on the second play. What is their net yardage after these two plays? -12 yd + 9 yd; -3 yd

62) While James had the flu, he lost 8 lb. After 1.5 weeks, he gained 5 lb back. What is his net weight gain?
-8 lb + 5 lb; -3 lb

Solve each problem.

63) Alma's 500-GB hard drive had 435 GB of data stored on it. After deleting 283 GB of data, Alma uploads 189 GB of family pictures and videos to the drive. How many gigabytes of storage are available on Alma's hard drive?   159 GB

64) Molika made a purchase at a department store in the amount of $135.56. Later that day, she received an email stating that her debit account was overdrawn by $17.56 and was charged an $18 overdraft fee. What is the balance in Molika's account if she deposits $125 into her account? $89.44

65) Alexandria deposited her $750 scholarship check into her debit account, which had a balance of $235.67. Later that week, Alexandria used her debit card to pay her $540 tuition fee and withdrew $300 cash to pay for books and school supplies. What is Alexandria's new debit account balance? $145.67

66) Kapila had $589.36 in his checking account when he deposited his paycheck in the amount of $1782.58. To pay his bills, he wrote checks for $278.25, $78.58, $156.50, and $750. After the checks clear, what is the balance in Kapila's checking account? $1108.61

Mixed Exercises
Add using a number line.

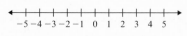

67) $-4 + 9$ 68) $-3 + 2$

Add.

69) $-\dfrac{7}{15} + \left(-\dfrac{1}{10}\right)$ $-\dfrac{17}{30}$ 70) $376 + (-508)$ -132

71) $-58 + 21$ -37 72) $-23.9 + 195.7$ 171.8

73) $105.3 + (-34.5)$ 70.8 74) $\dfrac{11}{20} + \left(-\dfrac{7}{15}\right)$ $\dfrac{1}{12}$

75) $-408 + (-521)$ -929 76) $-15 + 29$ 14

77) $-351 + 186$ -165 78) $-957 + (-604)$ -1561

Solve each problem.

79) A submarine dives to a depth of 675 ft and then rises 350 ft. Use a signed number to represent the depth of the submarine. -325 ft

80) On Monday morning, the temperature was $-12°$F. The next morning, the temperature was $17°$F higher. Use a signed number to represent Tuesday morning's temperature. $5°$F

R Rethink

R1) Can you think of another way to add signed numbers without using absolute value or a number line? Explain.

R2) Where have you encountered the addition of signed numbers this past week? Write a problem explaining the situation, and solve it.

10.3 Subtracting Signed Numbers

     O Organize

What are your objectives for Section 10.3?	How can you accomplish each objective?
1 Find the Additive Inverse of a Number	• Write the definition of *additive inverse* in your own words, and give an example. • Complete the given example on your own. • Complete You Try 1.
2 Subtract Signed Numbers	• Write the procedure for **Subtracting Signed Numbers** in your own words, and write an example. • Complete the given examples on your own. • Complete You Trys 2 and 3.
3 Combine Adding and Subtracting of Signed Numbers	• Use the order of operations to simplify expressions. • Complete the given examples on your own, and write a procedure for solving problems involving addition and subtraction. • Complete You Try 4.

 **W Work**   **Read the explanations, follow the examples, take notes, and complete the You Trys.**

1   Find the Additive Inverse of a Number

In Section 10.1, we learned that two numbers are opposites of each other if they are the same distance from 0 on a number line but are on opposite sides of 0.

For example, 3 and −3 are opposites.

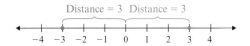

The opposite of a number is also called its **additive inverse.** So, the additive inverse of 3 is −3, and the additive inverse of −3 is 3.

What do we get if we add 3 + (−3)?

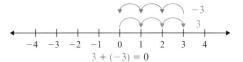

In fact, the sum of any number and its additive inverse is 0.

Definition

The opposite of a number is its **additive inverse.** The sum of a number and its additive inverse is 0.

> Example: 3 + (−3) = 0

EXAMPLE 1

Find the additive inverse of each number, then add the numbers.

In-Class Example 1

Find the additive inverse of each number, then add the numbers.

a) 8   b) −5   c) $-\dfrac{2}{3}$

d) 4.6   e) 0

Answer:

a) −8; 0   b) 5; 0

c) $\dfrac{2}{3}$; 0   d) −4.6; 0   e) 0; 0

a) 4   b) −7   c) $-\dfrac{3}{4}$ d) 1.2   e) 0

Solution

a)   The additive inverse of 4 is −4. $4 + (-4) = 0$

   └── Write a negative sign in front of the number to find its additive inverse.

b)   To find the additive inverse of −7, put a negative sign in front of the number and simplify: $-(-7) = 7$

   The additive inverse of −7 is 7. $-7 + 7 = 0$

c) $-\left(-\dfrac{3}{4}\right) = \dfrac{3}{4}$ The additive inverse of $-\dfrac{3}{4}$ is $\dfrac{3}{4}$, and $-\dfrac{3}{4} + \dfrac{3}{4} = 0$.

d)   The additive inverse of 1.2 is −1.2. $1.2 + (-1.2) = 0$

e)   The additive inverse of 0 is 0. $0 + 0 = 0$

[YOU TRY 1]   Find the additive inverse of each number, then add the numbers.

a) −16   b) 1   c) $\dfrac{3}{10}$ d) −7.4

We can subtract signed numbers using an additive inverse.

2 Subtract Signed Numbers

If we are working with positive numbers and the second number in a subtraction problem is smaller than the first number, we can subtract as we always have. Or, we can change the subtraction problem to an addition problem. Instead of subtracting the second number from the first, we *add the opposite,* or add the *additive inverse,* of the second number to the first number. We get the same answer.

$$8 - 2 = 6 \qquad 27 - 7 = 20$$
$$8 + (-2) = 6 \qquad 27 + (-7) = 20$$

Procedure Subtracting Signed Numbers

To subtract two numbers, $a - b$,

1)   Change subtraction to addition.
2)   Find the additive inverse of b.
3)   Add a and the additive inverse of b.

Notice that we keep the first number, a, the same.

Example: $9 - 4 = 5$ can be written as $9 + (-4) = 5$

   └─── Change subtraction to addition of the additive inverse.

We can also state the procedure using this formula:

$$\underset{\text{number}}{\text{First}} - \underset{\text{number}}{\text{Second}} = \underset{\text{number}}{\text{First}} + \underset{\text{of the second number}}{\text{Additive inverse}}$$

Again, notice that the first number stays the same.

EXAMPLE 2

Subtract.

a) $3 - 9$ b) $-14 - 11$ c) $-12 - (-25)$

d) $-10 - (-3)$ e) $2081 - (-1476)$

Solution

a) Use the formula $\underset{\text{number}}{\text{First}} - \underset{\text{number}}{\text{Second}} = \underset{\text{number}}{\text{First}} + \underset{\text{of the second number}}{\text{Additive inverse}}$

$$3 \quad - \quad 9 \quad = \quad 3 \quad + \quad (-9) \quad = -6$$

So, $3 - 9 = -6$.

b) $-14 - 11 = -14 + (-11) = -25$ c) $-12 - (-25) = -12 + (25) = 13$

Change subtraction to addition of the additive inverse of 11.   Change subtraction to addition of the additive inverse of −25.

d) $-10 - (-3) = -10 + (3) = -7$ e) Don't let larger numbers confuse you. We apply the rules the same way.

Change subtraction to addition of the additive inverse of −3.

$$2081 - (-1476) = 2081 + (1476) = 3557$$

Change subtraction to addition of the additive inverse of −1476.

[YOU TRY 2]   Subtract.

a) $5 - 9$ b) $-15 - 13$ c) $-10 - (-8)$

d) $-24 - (-47)$ e) $-4875 - (-2391)$

 BE CAREFUL   Make sure you can tell the difference between a subtraction sign and a negative sign.

$$18 - (-4)$$ Read this as "18 minus negative 4."

Subtraction sign   Negative sign

Use the same procedure when subtracting fractions and decimals.

| EXAMPLE 3 |
Subtract.

a) $\dfrac{3}{10} - \dfrac{1}{2}$ 　　 b) $-\dfrac{1}{3} - \left(-\dfrac{3}{4}\right)$ 　　 c) $-9.2 - 3.5$ 　　 d) $18.4 - (-7.1)$

Solution

a) $\dfrac{3}{10} - \dfrac{1}{2} = \dfrac{3}{10} + \left(-\dfrac{1}{2}\right)$ 　　 Change subtraction to addition of the additive inverse of $\dfrac{1}{2}$.

$\qquad\qquad = \dfrac{3}{10} + \left(-\dfrac{5}{10}\right)$ 　　 Rewrite $-\dfrac{1}{2}$ with a denominator of 10.

Step 1: Find the absolute values of $\dfrac{3}{10}$ and $-\dfrac{5}{10}$: $\left|\dfrac{3}{10}\right| = \dfrac{3}{10}, \ \left|-\dfrac{5}{10}\right| = \dfrac{5}{10}$

Step 2: Subtract the absolute values: $\dfrac{5}{10} - \dfrac{3}{10} = \dfrac{2}{10} = \dfrac{1}{5}$ 　　 Write in lowest terms.

　　　　　　　　　　　　 ↗ 　　　 ↖
　　　　　　 Larger absolute 　 Smaller absolute
　　　　　　　　 value 　　　　　　 value

Step 3: Will the final answer be *positive* $\dfrac{1}{5}$ or *negative* $\dfrac{1}{5}$? It will be *negative* because $-\dfrac{5}{10}$ has a larger absolute value than $\dfrac{3}{10}$.

The answer is $\dfrac{3}{10} - \dfrac{1}{2} = -\dfrac{1}{5}$.

b) $-\dfrac{1}{3} - \left(-\dfrac{3}{4}\right) = -\dfrac{1}{3} + \left(\dfrac{3}{4}\right)$ 　　 Change subtraction to addition of the additive inverse of $-\dfrac{3}{4}$.

$\qquad\qquad = -\dfrac{4}{12} + \dfrac{9}{12}$ 　　 Rewrite each fraction with a denominator of 12.

$\qquad\qquad = \dfrac{9}{12} - \dfrac{4}{12}$ 　　 Subtract the smaller absolute value from the larger absolute value.

$\qquad\qquad = \dfrac{5}{12}$ 　　 The final answer is positive because $\dfrac{9}{12}$ has a larger absolute value than $-\dfrac{4}{12}$.

c) $-9.2 - 3.5 = -9.2 + (-3.5)$ 　　 Change subtraction to addition of the additive inverse of 3.5.

$\qquad\qquad = -12.7$ 　　 Add.

d) $18.4 - (-7.1) = 18.4 + (7.1)$ 　　 Change subtraction to addition of the additive inverse of -7.1.

$\qquad\qquad = 25.5$ 　　 Add.

[YOU TRY 3] Subtract.

a) $\dfrac{2}{15} - \dfrac{4}{5}$ 　　 b) $-\dfrac{3}{4} - \left(-\dfrac{2}{9}\right)$ 　　 c) $-1.6 - 15.7$ 　　 d) $-8.3 - (-11.2)$

We can use a calculator to help us find the difference of large signed numbers.
To find the value of $-26 - 58 - (-173)$, we enter $\boxed{2}\,\boxed{6}\,\boxed{\pm}\,\boxed{-}\,\boxed{5}\,\boxed{8}\,\boxed{-}\,\boxed{1}\,\boxed{7}$ $\boxed{3}\,\boxed{\pm}\,\boxed{=}$ or $\boxed{(-)}\,\boxed{2}\,\boxed{6}\,\boxed{-}\,\boxed{5}\,\boxed{8}\,\boxed{-}\,\boxed{(-)}\,\boxed{1}\,\boxed{7}\,\boxed{3}\,\boxed{ENTER}$ into the calculator.
The display screen will show 89 as the result.

3 Combine Adding and Subtracting of Signed Numbers

Remember that the order of operations tells us that if a problem contains addition and subtraction, we perform the operations from left to right.

EXAMPLE 4

In-Class Example 4

Perform the operations.
a) $17 + (-11) - (-9) + 4$
b) $2.1 - (-8.8) - 5.3 + (-3.2)$
c) $-\dfrac{1}{6} - \dfrac{2}{3} + \left(-\dfrac{4}{9}\right)$

Answer:
a) 19 b) 2.4
c) $-\dfrac{23}{18}$ or $-1\dfrac{5}{18}$

Perform the operations.

a) $12 + (-8) - (-15) + 3$

b) $7.3 - (-9.4) - 10.2 + (-3.8)$

c) $-\dfrac{1}{5} - \dfrac{3}{4} + \left(-\dfrac{7}{10}\right)$

Solution

a) According to the order of operations, we perform the operations from left to right.

$$12 + (-8) - (-15) + 3$$
$$4 \quad\quad - (-15) + 3$$
$$4 \quad\quad + (15) + 3 \qquad \text{Change subtraction to addition of the additive inverse of } -15.$$
$$19 \quad + \quad 3$$
$$22$$

W Hint

Add or subtract two numbers at a time, moving from left to right until only one remains.

b) $7.3 - (-9.4) - 10.2 + (-3.8)$
$$7.3 + (9.4) - 10.2 + (-3.8) \qquad \text{Change subtraction to addition of the additive inverse of } -9.4.$$
$$16.7 \quad\quad - 10.2 + (-3.8)$$
$$6.5 \quad + \quad (-3.8)$$
$$2.7$$

c) $-\dfrac{1}{5} - \dfrac{3}{4} + \left(-\dfrac{7}{10}\right)$

$$-\dfrac{1}{5} + \left(-\dfrac{3}{4}\right) + \left(-\dfrac{7}{10}\right) \qquad \text{Change subtraction to addition of the additive inverse of } \dfrac{3}{4}.$$

$$-\dfrac{4}{20} + \left(-\dfrac{15}{20}\right) + \left(-\dfrac{7}{10}\right) \qquad \text{Rewrite the fractions with a common denominator.}$$

$$-\dfrac{19}{20} + \left(-\dfrac{7}{10}\right) \qquad \text{Add.}$$

$$-\dfrac{19}{20} + \left(-\dfrac{14}{20}\right) \qquad \text{Rewrite } -\dfrac{7}{10} \text{ with a denominator of } 20.$$

$$-\dfrac{33}{20} \text{ or } -1\dfrac{13}{20} \qquad \text{Add. Write the answer as an improper fraction or mixed number.}$$

$$\left[\text{YOU TRY 4} \right]$$ Perform the operations.

a) $-24 - (-3) + 7 - 45$ b) $6.2 - 11.5 + (-9.6) + 14.9$

c) $-\dfrac{5}{8} + \dfrac{5}{12} - \dfrac{1}{6} - \left(-\dfrac{2}{3}\right)$

ANSWERS TO $\boxed{\text{YOU TRY}}$ **EXERCISES**

1) a) 16; 0 b) -1; 0 c) $-\dfrac{3}{10}$; 0 d) 7.4; 0   2) a) -4 b) -28 c) 18 d) 23 e) -2484

3) a) $-\dfrac{2}{3}$ b) $-\dfrac{19}{36}$ c) -17.3 d) 2.9   4) a) -59 b) 0 c) $\dfrac{7}{24}$

Using Technology

Sometimes we have to make calculations with signed numbers following the order of operations. For example, to calculate $1.2 - (-8) + (-0.6) + 4$, we must work left to right.

To find the value of the expression, we enter $\boxed{1}\boxed{.}\boxed{2}\boxed{-}\boxed{8}\boxed{\pm}\boxed{+}\boxed{.}\boxed{6}$ $\boxed{\pm}\boxed{+}\boxed{4}\boxed{=}$ or $\boxed{1}\boxed{.}\boxed{2}\boxed{-}\boxed{(-)}\boxed{8}\boxed{+}\boxed{(-)}\boxed{.}\boxed{6}\boxed{+}\boxed{4}\boxed{\text{ENTER}}$ into the calculator. The display screen will show 12.6 as the result.

$\boxed{\text{E Evaluate}}$ **10.3** Exercises   Do the exercises, and check your work.

*Additional answers can be found in the Answers to Exercises appendix.

Objective 1: Find the Additive Inverse of a Number They are the same distance from 0 on the number line, but they are on opposite sides of 0; their sum is 0.

1) How are a number and its additive inverse related on a number line? What is their sum?

2) Is the additive inverse of a number *always, sometimes,* or *never* positive?   sometimes

Find the additive inverse of each number.

3) 6 -6

4) 11 -11

5) -23 23

6) -7 7

7) $\dfrac{3}{8}$ $-\dfrac{3}{8}$

8) $\dfrac{2}{5}$ $-\dfrac{2}{5}$

9) -5.3 5.3

10) -7.9 7.9

11) $-6\dfrac{3}{11}$ $6\dfrac{3}{11}$

12) $2\dfrac{4}{9}$ $-2\dfrac{4}{9}$

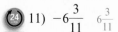

Objective 2: Subtract Signed Numbers

Rewrite the subtraction problem as an addition problem, then perform the operation using the number line.

```
+--+--+--+--+--+--+--+--+--+--+-->
0  1  2  3  4  5  6  7  8  9  10
```

13) $6 - 5$

14) $10 - 3$

```
+--+--+--+--+--+--+--+--+--+--+-->
-7 -6 -5 -4 -3 -2 -1  0  1  2  3
```

15) $3 - 7$

16) $2 - 5$

17) $-2 - 3$

18) $-1 - 4$

```
+--+--+--+--+--+--+--+--+--+--+-->
-5 -4 -3 -2 -1  0  1  2  3  4  5
```

19) $-3 - (-6)$

20) $-2 - (-2)$

21) Explain, in your own words, why $2 - (-3)$ is equivalent to $2 + 3$.   Answers may vary.

22) Explain, in your own words, how to tell a subtraction problem from a negative sign. *Answers may vary.*

Rewrite each subtraction problem as an addition. Then, simplify.

23) $15 - 6$
$15 + (-6) = 9$

24) $13 - 5$
$13 + (-5) = 8$

25) $5 - 14$
$5 + (-14) = -9$

26) $8 - 19$
$8 + (-19) = -11$

27) $125 - 183$
$125 + (-183) = -58$

28) $234 - 851$
$234 + (-851) = -617$

29) $-8 - 3$
$-8 + (-3) = -11$

30) $-7 - 5$
$-7 + (-5) = -12$

31) $-134 - 925$
$-134 + (-925) = -1059$

32) $-117 - 893$
$-117 + (-893) = -1010$

33) $-10 - (-18)$
$-10 + 18 = 8$

34) $-23 - (-27)$
$-23 + 27 = 4$

35) $-13 - (-2)$
$-13 + 2 = -11$

36) $-15 - (-7)$
$-15 + 7 = -8$

37) $-29 - (-15)$
$-29 + 15 = -14$

38) $-43 - (-12)$
$-43 + 12 = -31$

39) $-421 - (-91)$
$-421 + 91 = -330$

40) $-239 - (-58)$
$-239 + 58 = -181$

41) $-791 - 683$
$-791 + (-683) = -1474$

42) $-584 - 937$
$-584 + (-937) = -1521$

43) $3508 - (-2917)$
$3508 + 2917 = 6425$

44) $8106 - (-5876)$
$8106 + 5876 = 13,982$

45) $-54 - 54$
$-54 + (-54) = -108$

46) $-37 - 37$
$-37 + (-37) = -74$

47) $-21 - (-21)$
$-21 + 21 = 0$

48) $-49 - (-49)$
$-49 + 49 = 0$

49) $20.9 - 42.3$
$20.9 + (-42.3) = -21.4$

50) $31.2 - 45.7$
$31.2 + (-45.7) = -14.5$

51) $-1.7 - (-8.6)$
$-1.7 + 8.6 = 6.9$

52) $-2.9 - (-4.3)$
$-2.9 + 4.3 = 1.4$

53) $\dfrac{3}{2} - \dfrac{9}{4}$ $\dfrac{3}{2} + \left(-\dfrac{9}{4}\right) = -\dfrac{3}{4}$

54) $\dfrac{1}{5} - \dfrac{14}{15}$ $\dfrac{1}{5} + \left(-\dfrac{14}{15}\right) = -\dfrac{11}{15}$

55) $-\dfrac{1}{6} - \dfrac{2}{9}$ $-\dfrac{1}{6} + \left(-\dfrac{2}{9}\right) = -\dfrac{7}{18}$

56) $-\dfrac{3}{4} - \dfrac{1}{6}$ $-\dfrac{3}{4} + \left(-\dfrac{1}{6}\right) = -\dfrac{11}{12}$

57) $-\dfrac{1}{6} - \left(-\dfrac{1}{3}\right)$ $-\dfrac{1}{6} + \dfrac{1}{3} = \dfrac{1}{6}$

58) $-\dfrac{7}{10} - \left(-\dfrac{4}{5}\right)$ $-\dfrac{7}{10} + \dfrac{4}{5} = \dfrac{1}{10}$

The summit of Mount Everest is 29,035 ft (8850 m) above sea level and is the highest point on Earth. Mount McKinley is the highest mountain on the North American continent, and its summit is at 20,320 ft (6194 m) above sea level. The table at the top of the next column notes several of the lowest places on Earth.

Lowest Places on Earth
Dead Sea (Jordan/Israel) $-1,360$ feet (-414 m)
Lake Assal (Djibouti, Africa) -509 feet (-155 m)
Turpan Pendi (China) -505 feet (-154 m)
Qattara Depression (Egypt) -435 feet (-133 m)
Denakil (Ethiopia) -410 ft (-125 m)
Laguna del Carbón (Argentina) -344 ft (-105 m)
Death Valley (United States) -282 ft (-86 m)
Salton Sea (California) -227 ft (-69 m)
Salinas Chicas (Argentina) -131 ft (-40 m)
Caspian Sea (Central Asia) -92 ft (-28 m)

(www.nps.gov)

Use this information for Exercises 59–62 to find the difference in elevation between the given geographical locations.

59) Mount McKinley and the Salton Sea; give your answer in feet.   20,547 ft

60) Mount Everest and the Dead Sea; give your answer in feet.   30,395 ft

61) The Caspian Sea and Lake Assal; give your answer in meters.   127 m

62) Salinas Chicas and Laguna del Carbón; give your answer in meters.   65 m

Objective 3: Combine Adding and Subtracting of Signed Numbers
Perform the operations.

63) $-3 + (-14) - (-5)$ -12

64) $-7 - (-8) + (-9)$ -8

65) $3 - (-26) + (-7) - 14$ 8

66) $6 - (-19) + (-2) - 9$ 14

67) $34 - (-18) + (-26) + 11 - 15$ 22

68) $-59 - (-42) + (-10) + 23 - 7$ -11

69) $156 - 438 + (-257)$
-539

70) $106 - 357 + (-118)$
-369

71) $-9.4 - 6.7 + 3.5$
-12.6

72) $-7.3 + 4.1 - 9.2$ -12.4

73) $41.8 + (-80.6) - (-159.7) - 31.2$ 89.7

74) $62.2 - 97.4 + (-15.3) - (-129.1)$ 78.6

75) $\dfrac{5}{6} + \dfrac{1}{2} - \left(-\dfrac{4}{3}\right)$ $\dfrac{8}{3}$ or $2\dfrac{2}{3}$

76) $\dfrac{1}{18} + \dfrac{2}{9} - \left(-\dfrac{5}{3}\right)$ $\dfrac{35}{18}$ or $1\dfrac{17}{18}$

77) $\dfrac{4}{5} + \left(-\dfrac{1}{3}\right) - \dfrac{7}{15}$ 0

78) $\dfrac{1}{4} + \left(-\dfrac{5}{8}\right) - \dfrac{3}{2}$ $-\dfrac{15}{8}$ or $-1\dfrac{7}{8}$

79) $-\dfrac{1}{3} - \left(-\dfrac{8}{9}\right) - \dfrac{3}{2} + \dfrac{1}{6}$ $-\dfrac{7}{9}$

80) $-\dfrac{3}{4} + \dfrac{1}{3} - \dfrac{1}{2} - \left(-\dfrac{11}{12}\right)$ 0

81) $|-37| - 82 + |-14| + (-25)$ -56

82) $|-26| - 61 + |-11| + (-39)$ -63

83) $-1.2 - |7.3| + 9.6$ 1.1

84) $-1.8 - |3.9| + 7.2$ 1.5

(24) 85) $-\dfrac{3}{4} + \left|-\dfrac{3}{8}\right| + \dfrac{3}{16} + \left(-\dfrac{1}{2}\right)$ $-\dfrac{11}{16}$

86) $-\dfrac{5}{3} + \left|-\dfrac{5}{6}\right| + \dfrac{5}{12} - \left(-\dfrac{3}{4}\right)$ $\dfrac{1}{3}$

Evaluate each expression. Perform the operations in the parentheses first.

87) $|-8 + 3| + (-4) + 9$ 10

88) $-4 + (-13) + |-7 - 1|$ -9

89) $-571 - |-145 - 200| + (-87)$ -1003

90) $|-42 + 61| - 234 + 507$ 292

Determine the amount of money in the checking account after the following transactions have taken place.

(24) 91) Kalila's checking account is overdrawn by $23.17. She wrote checks for $72.04 and $86.89, then deposited a paycheck for $406.91. Finally, the bank charged an overdraw fee of $15.00. $209.81

92) Tantien's checking account is overdrawn by $59.32. He wrote checks for $31.69 and $92.03, then deposited a paycheck for $517.44. Finally, the bank charged an overdraw fee of $25.00. $309.40

93) Jim has $391.62 in his checking account. His bank took $50.00 out of his account for his safe-deposit box rental. He wrote checks for $374.63 and $122.07, then deposited a check for $600.00. $444.92

94) Pam has $501.08 in her checking account. Her bank took $30.00 out of her account for new checks. She wrote checks for $498.16 and $199.37, then deposited a check for $800.00. $573.55

Mixed Exercises: Objectives 1–3

Find the additive inverse of each number.

95) -5.31 5.31 96) $\dfrac{2}{7}$ $-\dfrac{2}{7}$

Perform the operations.

97) $\left|-\dfrac{1}{8}\right| + \dfrac{3}{5} - \dfrac{1}{4}$ $\dfrac{19}{40}$

98) $-9 + 7 + (-15) - (-6)$ -11

99) $154 - 273$ -119 100) $-\dfrac{1}{6} - \dfrac{5}{9}$ $-\dfrac{13}{18}$

101) $-4 - (-9) + 3 - 15$ -7

102) $|-97| + (-158) - (-112)$ 51

103) $102 + (-43) - 151 - (-62)$ -30

104) $-37.1 - 49.2$ -86.3

105) The highest temperature on record in North America was 134°F in Death Valley, California, in 1913. The coldest temperature on record in North America was -81.4°F in the Yukon Territory of Canada, in 1947. What is the difference in these two temperatures? (www.ncdc.noaa.gov)   215.4°F

106) Tiger Woods' highest 18-hole score in a professional tournament was $+10$, or 10 over par. His lowest score was -11, or 11 under par. What is the difference in these scores? (web.tigerwoods.com)   21

R Rethink

R1) Which exercises do you need help mastering?

R2) Think of three different scenarios that would involve addition and subtraction. Represent what that might look like on a number line.

10.4 Multiplying and Dividing Signed Numbers

P Prepare

O Organize

What are your objectives for Section 10.4?	How can you accomplish each objective?
1 Multiply Two Numbers with Different Signs	• Write the procedure for **Multiplying Two Numbers with Different Signs** in your own words. • Complete the given example on your own. • Complete You Try 1.
2 Multiply Two Numbers with the Same Sign	• Write the procedure for **Multiplying Two Numbers with the Same Sign** in your own words. • Complete the given example on your own. • Complete You Try 2.
3 Divide Signed Numbers	• Write the procedure for **Dividing Two Signed Numbers** in your own words. • Show what this would look like using a number line. Does it make sense? • Complete the given examples on your own. • Complete You Trys 3 and 4.
4 Write Equivalent Forms of a Negative Fraction	• Write a summary that describes the three different ways a negative fraction can be written. • Complete the given example on your own. • Complete You Try 5.

W Work   **Read the explanations, follow the examples, take notes, and complete the You Trys.**

1 Multiply Two Numbers with Different Signs

Recall that multiplication represents repeated addition. For example, we can write $3 + 3 + 3 + 3 + 3 = 15$ as $3 \times 5 = 15$. We can also write $-3 + (-3) + (-3) + (-3) + (-3) = -15$ or $-3 \times 5 = -15$. So, what is the rule for multiplying numbers with different signs? Let's make a table of some products.

As these numbers decrease by 1,

$3 \times 5 = 15$
$2 \times 5 = 10$
$1 \times 5 = 5$
$0 \times 5 = 0$
$-1 \times 5 = -5$
$-2 \times 5 = -10$
$-3 \times 5 = -15$

the products decrease by 5.

Procedure Multiplying Two Numbers with Different Signs

The product of a *positive number* and a *negative number* is *negative*.

EXAMPLE 1

Multiply

a) -2×9 b) $8 \cdot (-7)$ c) $0.3(-14)$

In-Class Example 1

Multiply.
a) -2×7
b) $4 \cdot (-9)$
c) $0.6(-13)$

Answer:
a) -14 b) -36 c) -7.8

Solution

a) $-2 \times 9 = -18$ The product of a negative and a positive number is negative.

b) $8 \cdot (-7) = -56$ The product of a positive and a negative number is negative.

c) $0.3(-14) = -4.2$ The product of a positive and a negative number is negative.

[YOU TRY 1] Multiply.

a) $9(-6)$ b) -5×10 c) $1.4 \cdot (-23)$

---

2 Multiply Two Numbers with the Same Sign

We know that when we multiply two positive numbers, the product is positive. For example, $3 \times 5 = 15$. What is the sign of the product of two negative numbers? Again, let's make a table.

As these numbers decrease by 1,

$$3 \times (-5) = -15$$
$$2 \times (-5) = -10$$
$$1 \times (-5) = -5$$
$$0 \times (-5) = 0$$
$$-1 \times (-5) = 5$$
$$-2 \times (-5) = 10$$
$$-3 \times (-5) = 15$$

the products increase by 5.

The table illustrates that the product of two negative numbers is a positive number.

Procedure Multiplying Two Numbers with the Same Sign

The product of two numbers with the *same sign* is *positive*.

EXAMPLE 2

Multiply.

a) $-6 \cdot (-3)$ b) $-10(-9)$ c) 4×12

In-Class Example 2

Multiply.
a) $-2 \cdot (-8)$
b) $-7(-6)$
c) 9×8

Answer:
a) 16   b) 42   c) 72

Solution

a) $-6 \cdot (-3) = 18$ The product of two negative numbers is positive.

b) $-10(-9) = 90$ The product of two negative numbers is positive.

c) $4 \times 12 = 48$ The product of two positive numbers is positive.

[YOU TRY 2] Multiply.

a) $-5(-10)$ b) $-4 \times (-3)$ c) $8 \cdot 7$

---

3 Divide Signed Numbers

The rules for dividing signed numbers are the same as the rules for multiplying signed numbers.

> **Procedure** Dividing Signed Numbers
>
> 1) The quotient of two numbers with *different signs* is *negative*.
> 2) The quotient of two numbers with the *same sign* is *positive*.

EXAMPLE 3

In-Class Example 3

Divide.
a) $-24 \div 6$
b) $-56 \div (-8)$
c) $\dfrac{30}{-5}$ d) $\dfrac{-99}{11}$
e) $\dfrac{-48}{-4}$ f) $\dfrac{0}{-3}$ g) $\dfrac{-2}{0}$

Answer:
a) -4 b) 7 c) -6
d) -9 e) 12 f) 0
g) undefined

Divide.

a) $-18 \div 3$ b) $-45 \div (-9)$ c) $\dfrac{28}{-7}$ d) $\dfrac{-72}{6}$

e) $\dfrac{-55}{-11}$ f) $\dfrac{0}{-2}$ g) $\dfrac{-4}{0}$

Solution

a) $-18 \div 3 = -6$ The quotient of two numbers with *different signs* is *negative*.

b) $-45 \div (-9) = 5$ The quotient of two numbers with the *same sign* is *positive*.

c) $\dfrac{28}{-7} = -4$ The quotient of two numbers with *different signs* is *negative*.

d) $\dfrac{-72}{6} = -12$ e) $\dfrac{-55}{-11} = 5$

f) $\dfrac{0}{-2} = 0$ 0 divided by a nonzero number is 0.

g) $\dfrac{-4}{0}$ is undefined.   Division by 0 is undefined.

[YOU TRY 3]

Divide.

a) $60 \div (-5)$ b) $-49 \div (-7)$ c) $\dfrac{-36}{-9}$ d) $\dfrac{8}{-1}$

e) $\dfrac{-54}{6}$ f) $\dfrac{-7}{0}$ g) $\dfrac{0}{-10}$

When working with fractions, we often write the negative sign in front of the fraction.

EXAMPLE 4

Divide.

a) $-\dfrac{5}{12} \div \dfrac{3}{4}$ b) $\dfrac{-\dfrac{7}{8}}{-\dfrac{5}{6}}$

Solution

a) $-\dfrac{5}{12} \div \dfrac{3}{4} = -\dfrac{5}{12} \cdot \dfrac{4}{3}$ Multiply by the reciprocal.

$\qquad = -\dfrac{5}{\underset{3}{12}} \cdot \dfrac{\overset{1}{4}}{3}$ Divide 12 and 4 by 4.

$\qquad = -\dfrac{5}{9}$ Multiply.

b) $\dfrac{-\dfrac{7}{8}}{-\dfrac{5}{6}}$ ← The fraction bar represents division.

$\dfrac{-\dfrac{7}{8}}{-\dfrac{5}{6}} = -\dfrac{7}{8} \div \left(-\dfrac{5}{6}\right)$ Write as a division problem.

$\qquad = -\dfrac{7}{8} \cdot \left(-\dfrac{6}{5}\right)$ Multiply by the reciprocal.

$\qquad = -\dfrac{7}{\underset{4}{8}} \cdot \left(-\dfrac{\overset{3}{6}}{5}\right)$ Divide 8 and 6 by 2.

$\qquad = \dfrac{21}{20}$ or $1\dfrac{1}{20}$ The product of two negative numbers is positive.

[YOU TRY 4]   Divide.

a) $-\dfrac{5}{18} \div \left(-\dfrac{15}{16}\right)$ b) $\dfrac{\dfrac{1}{6}}{-\dfrac{2}{3}}$

---

4 Write Equivalent Forms of a Negative Fraction

When a fraction is negative, the negative sign is usually written in front of the fraction. However, we can write other, equivalent forms if we know how to work with the negative sign.

EXAMPLE 5

In-Class Example 5

Write two equivalent forms of each fraction by moving its negative sign.

a) $-\dfrac{2}{7}$ b) $\dfrac{-1}{2}$

Answer:

a) $\dfrac{-2}{7}$ or $\dfrac{2}{-7}$ b) $-\dfrac{1}{2}$ or $\dfrac{1}{-2}$

Write two equivalent forms of each fraction by moving its negative sign.

a) $-\dfrac{4}{5}$ b) $\dfrac{-1}{2}$

Solution

a) Remember that the quotient of two numbers with *different signs* is *negative*. The negative sign can also be written in the numerator or in the denominator, but not in both at the same time. Therefore,

$-\dfrac{4}{5} = \dfrac{-4}{5}$ because negative number ÷ positive number = negative number,

W Hint

There are always three different ways to write a negative fraction.

and

$$-\frac{4}{5} = \frac{4}{-5}$$ because positive number ÷ negative number = negative number.

Therefore, $-\frac{4}{5}$ can also be written as $\frac{-4}{5}$ or $\frac{4}{-5}$.

b) If we divide $\frac{-1}{2}$, we get a *negative* quotient, -0.5. Therefore, we can also write $\frac{-1}{2}$ as $-\frac{1}{2}$. The negative sign in $\frac{-1}{2}$ can also be written in the denominator, $\frac{1}{-2}$, since this would also give a negative quotient.

$\frac{-1}{2}$ can also be written as $-\frac{1}{2}$ or $\frac{1}{-2}$.

[YOU TRY 5]

Write two equivalent forms of each fraction by moving its negative sign.

a) $-\frac{7}{10}$ b) $\frac{3}{-8}$

ANSWERS TO [YOU TRY] EXERCISES

1) a) -54 b) -50 c) -32.2 2) a) 50 b) 12 c) 56
3) a) -12 b) 7 c) 4 d) -8 e) -9 f) undefined g) 0
4) a) $\frac{8}{27}$ b) $-\frac{1}{4}$ 5) a) $\frac{-7}{10}$ or $\frac{7}{-10}$ b) $-\frac{3}{8}$ or $\frac{-3}{8}$

Using Technology

Sometimes we have to make calculations with signed numbers following the order of operations. For example, to calculate $-3.4 \cdot (-6) \div (-0.5)$, we must work left to right.

To find the value of the expression, we enter $\boxed{3}\,\boxed{.}\,\boxed{4}\,\boxed{\pm}\,\boxed{\times}\,\boxed{6}\,\boxed{\pm}\,\boxed{\div}\,\boxed{.}$ $\boxed{5}\,\boxed{\pm}\,\boxed{=}$ or $\boxed{(-)}\,\boxed{3}\,\boxed{.}\,\boxed{4}\,\boxed{\times}\,\boxed{(-)}\,\boxed{6}\,\boxed{\div}\,\boxed{(-)}\,\boxed{.}\,\boxed{5}\,\boxed{ENTER}$ into the calculator. The display screen will show -40.8 as the result.

E Evaluate **10.4** Exercises   Do the exercises, and check your work.

*Additional answers can be found in the Answers to Exercises appendix.

Objective 1: Multiply Two Numbers with Different Signs

1) The product of a negative number and a <u>positive</u> number is negative.

2) The product of a positive number and a negative number is <u>negative</u>.

Multiply.

3) $-5 \cdot 3$ $_{-15}$

4) $-10 \cdot 4$ $_{-40}$

5) $4 \times (-8)$ $_{-32}$

6) $6 \times (-3)$ $_{-18}$

7) $(0)(-17)$ $_0$

8) $(-30)(0)$ $_0$

9) $(-1)(38)$ $_{-38}$

10) $(-19)(1)$ $_{-19}$

11) $27(-34)$ $_{-918}$

12) $39(-56)$ $_{-2184}$

13) $-\frac{2}{3} \cdot 12$ $_{-8}$

14) $-\frac{5}{7} \cdot 21$ $_{-15}$

15) $\frac{8}{21}\left(-\frac{7}{6}\right)$ $_{-\frac{4}{9}}$

16) $-\frac{25}{12} \times \frac{4}{5}$ $_{-\frac{5}{3} \text{ or } -1\frac{2}{3}}$

17) $6.2 \times (-5)$ $_{-31}$

18) $5.5 \times (-4)$ $_{-22}$

19) $-2.7(5.3)$ $_{-14.31}$

20) $-3.4(9.7)$ $_{-32.98}$

Fill in the blank.

21) $7 \cdot \underline{\hspace{1cm}} = -63$ $\quad$ –9 $\quad$ 22) $-4 \times \underline{\hspace{1cm}} = -20$ $\quad$ 5

23) $\underline{\hspace{1cm}} \cdot -12 = -84$ $\quad$ 7 $\quad$ 24) $\underline{\hspace{1cm}} \cdot 5 = -15$ $\quad$ –3

Objective 2: Multiply Two Numbers with the Same Sign

25) The product of a negative number and a <u>negative</u> number is positive.

26) The product of a <u>positive</u> number and a positive number is positive.

Multiply.

27) $-3(-2)$ $\quad$ 6 $\qquad$ 28) $-7(-11)$ $\quad$ 77

29) $-5 \times (-9)$ $\quad$ 45 $\qquad$ 30) $-8 \times (-3)$ $\quad$ 24

31) $-123 \cdot (-8)$ $\quad$ 984 $\qquad$ 32) $-108 \cdot (-11)$ $\quad$ 1188

33) $-\dfrac{7}{39}\left(-\dfrac{13}{28}\right)$ $\quad \dfrac{1}{12}$ $\qquad$ 34) $-\dfrac{8}{45}\left(-\dfrac{15}{56}\right)$ $\quad \dfrac{1}{21}$

35) $-2\dfrac{2}{5} \times \left(-\dfrac{7}{8}\right)$ $\quad \dfrac{21}{10}$ or $2\dfrac{1}{10}$ 36) $-4\dfrac{1}{2} \times \left(-\dfrac{5}{6}\right)$ $\quad \dfrac{15}{4}$ or $3\dfrac{3}{4}$

37) $-0.5(-0.7)$ $\quad$ 0.35 $\qquad$ 38) $-0.9(-1.2)$ $\quad$ 1.08

39) $(-11.897)(-1)$ $\quad$ 11.897 $\quad$ 40) $(-1)(-5.513)$ $\quad$ 5.513

Fill in the blank.

41) $-10 \cdot \underline{\hspace{1cm}} = 80$ $\quad$ –8 $\quad$ 42) $\underline{\hspace{1cm}} \times (-6) = 54$ $\quad$ –9

Objective 3: Divide Signed Numbers

43) The quotient of a negative number and a <u>negative</u> number is positive.

44) The quotient of a positive number and a <u>positive</u> number is positive.

Divide.

45) $-16 \div (-2)$ $\quad$ 8 $\qquad$ 46) $-32 \div (-8)$ $\quad$ 4

47) $-35 \div 7$ $\quad$ –5 $\qquad$ 48) $-12 \div 3$ $\quad$ –4

49) $\dfrac{48}{-6}$ $\quad$ –8 $\qquad$ 50) $\dfrac{45}{-5}$ $\quad$ –9

51) $\dfrac{-72}{0}$ $\quad$ undefined $\qquad$ 52) $\dfrac{-50}{0}$ $\quad$ undefined

53) $63 \div (-1)$ $\quad$ –63 $\qquad$ 54) $27 \div (-1)$ $\quad$ –27

55) $\dfrac{-20}{-4}$ $\quad$ 5 $\qquad$ 56) $\dfrac{-18}{-6}$ $\quad$ 3

57) $0 \div (-5)$ $\quad$ 0 $\qquad$ 58) $0 \div (-9)$ $\quad$ 0

59) $\dfrac{-45}{-45}$ $\quad$ 1 $\qquad$ 60) $\dfrac{-36}{-36}$ $\quad$ 1

61) $\dfrac{-28}{28}$ $\quad$ –1 $\qquad$ 62) $\dfrac{-12}{12}$ $\quad$ –1

63) $-174 \div (-6)$ $\quad$ 29 $\qquad$ 64) $-848 \div (-8)$ $\quad$ 106

65) $-\dfrac{6}{5} \div \dfrac{22}{15}$ $\quad -\dfrac{9}{11}$ $\qquad$ 66) $-\dfrac{4}{25} \div \dfrac{8}{9}$ $\quad -\dfrac{9}{50}$

67) $-\dfrac{3}{4} \div (-6)$ $\quad \dfrac{1}{8}$ $\qquad$ 68) $-\dfrac{4}{5} \div (-8)$ $\quad \dfrac{1}{10}$

69) $7 \div \left(-\dfrac{14}{25}\right)$ $\qquad$ 70) $8 \div \left(-\dfrac{40}{21}\right)$ $\quad -\dfrac{21}{5}$ or $-4\dfrac{1}{5}$

$\quad -\dfrac{25}{2}$ or $-12\dfrac{1}{2}$

71) $\dfrac{\dfrac{6}{17}}{-\dfrac{1}{2}}$ $\quad -\dfrac{12}{17}$ $\qquad$ 72) $\dfrac{\dfrac{2}{7}}{-\dfrac{4}{49}}$ $\quad -\dfrac{7}{2}$

73) $\dfrac{-\dfrac{2}{7}}{-\dfrac{12}{35}}$ $\quad \dfrac{5}{6}$ $\qquad$ 74) $\dfrac{\dfrac{3}{5}}{\dfrac{18}{15}}$ $\quad \dfrac{1}{2}$

75) $-61.2 \div (-4)$ $\quad$ 15.3 $\quad$ 76) $-338.1 \div (-7)$ $\quad$ 48.3

77) $\dfrac{-6.45}{1.5}$ $\quad$ –4.3 $\qquad$ 78) $\dfrac{-26.64}{7.4}$ $\quad$ –3.6

Fill in the blank.

79) $-55 \div \underline{\hspace{1cm}} = 5$ $\quad$ –11 80) $36 \div \underline{\hspace{1cm}} = -3$ $\quad$ –12

81) $\underline{\hspace{1cm}} \div 6 = -7$ $\quad$ –42 82) $\underline{\hspace{1cm}} \div (-4) = 10$ $\quad$ –40

Objective 4: Write Equivalent Forms of a Negative Fraction

Write two equivalent forms of each fraction by moving its negative sign.

83) $-\dfrac{13}{25}$ $\quad \dfrac{-13}{25}$ or $\dfrac{13}{-25}$ $\quad$ 84) $-\dfrac{17}{20}$ $\quad \dfrac{-17}{20}$ or $\dfrac{17}{-20}$

85) $\dfrac{-5}{11}$ $\quad -\dfrac{5}{11}$ or $\dfrac{5}{-11}$ $\quad$ 86) $\dfrac{-3}{10}$ $\quad -\dfrac{3}{10}$ or $\dfrac{3}{-10}$

87) $\dfrac{16}{-17}$ $\quad -\dfrac{16}{17}$ or $\dfrac{-16}{17}$ $\quad$ 88) $\dfrac{1}{-14}$ $\quad -\dfrac{1}{14}$ or $\dfrac{-1}{14}$

Solve the application problem. Express your answer as a positive or negative number accordingly.

89) A college's enrollment decreased by 876 students over the past 6 years. What was the average change in enrollment each year? −146 students per year

90) A cable television company estimates it will lose 54 customers every week to a satellite television service. Find the change in the number of customers over a 1-year period. −2808 customers

91) The tuition at a community college is $112 per unit. How much will Nascha pay if she enrolls for 12 units? $1344

92) Tarun ate a package of 8 chocolate chip cookies having 26 calories per cookie. How many calories did he eat? 208 calories

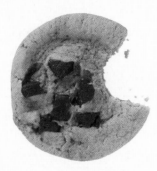

93) A deep-diving submersible can take up to 2 hours to dive to 6000 m. If it takes exactly 2 hours to dive 6000 m, what is the average change in depth every minute? (http://oceanexplorer.noaa.gov) −50 m

94) A department store finds that it loses $4380 of profit every year due to shoplifting. Find the average change in profit per month due to shop-lifting. −$365 per month

95) A high-protein diet promises that a person will lose 3 lb per week. If a husband and wife go on the diet together, find their combined total change in weight over a 4-week period. −24 lb

96) Karl is downloading a high-definition movie file to his computer at a rate of 4 megabits per second. If the file size is 12,240 megabits, how many minutes will it take for Karl to download the entire file? 51 min

Mixed Exercises: Objectives 1–4

Perform the indicated operations.

97) -2.8×7 −19.6

98) $\dfrac{-320}{-4}$ 80

99) $\left(-\dfrac{2}{7}\right) \div \left(-\dfrac{8}{21}\right)$ $\dfrac{3}{4}$

100) $-1.05(-2.84)$ 2.982

101) $\dfrac{3}{4}(-24)$ −18

102) $\dfrac{\frac{7}{6}}{-\frac{2}{15}}$ $-\dfrac{35}{4}$ or $-8\dfrac{3}{4}$

Simplify using the order of operations. That is, perform multiplication and division from left to right.

103) $-5 \cdot 3 \cdot (-2) \cdot (-1)$ −30

104) $(-12) \cdot \dfrac{1}{4} \cdot (-6)$ 18

105) $-24 \div (-3) \div (-2) \div (-2) \div (-1)$ −2

106) $-72 \div (-8) \cdot (-5) \div (-5) \div (-3)$ −3

107) $\dfrac{-3}{5} \div \dfrac{20}{7} \cdot \dfrac{5}{6}$ $-\dfrac{7}{40}$

108) $\dfrac{5}{6} \div \dfrac{7}{12} \cdot \left(\dfrac{-5}{8}\right)$ $-\dfrac{25}{28}$

109) $-7 \cdot |-8| \div |4| \cdot (-5)$ 70

110) $-5 \cdot |-9| \div |3| \cdot (-2)$ 30

R Rethink

R1) Demonstrate the equation $-3 \times 5 = -15$ on a number line.

R2) Why does this make sense?

R3) Write four statements that outline the procedure for **Multiplying and Dividing Signed Numbers** using the terms *multiplicand, multiplier,* and *product; dividend, divisor,* and *quotient.*

10.5 The Order of Operations

W Work   Read the explanations, follow the examples, take notes, and complete the You Trys.

1 Use Signed Numbers with Exponents

We have learned that an exponent can be used to represent repeated multiplication. For example,

$$2 \cdot 2 \cdot 2 = 2^3 \leftarrow \text{Exponent or power}$$

$$\uparrow$$

$$\text{Base}$$

where the *base* is 2 and the *exponent,* or *power,* is 3.

Note

If an exponent is used to represent repeated multiplication of a *negative number,* we *must* put the number in parentheses.

EXAMPLE 1

In-Class Example 1

Write each multiplication problem using an exponent.
a) $-8 \cdot (-8) \cdot (-8)$
b) $-3 \cdot (-3) \cdot (-3) \cdot (-3)$

Answer:
a) $(-8)^3$ b) $(-3)^4$

Write each multiplication problem using an exponent.

a) $-6 \cdot (-6) \cdot (-6)$ b) $-9 \cdot (-9) \cdot (-9) \cdot (-9)$

Solution

a) $\underbrace{-6 \cdot (-6) \cdot (-6)}_{\text{3 factors of } -6} = (-6)^3$ The factor of -6 is multiplied 3 times.

b) $\underbrace{-9 \cdot (-9) \cdot (-9) \cdot (-9)}_{\text{4 factors of } -9} = (-9)^4$ The factor of -9 is multiplied 4 times.

[YOU TRY 1]   Write each multiplication problem using an exponent.

a) $-7 \cdot (-7) \cdot (-7) \cdot (-7)$ b) $-2 \cdot (-2) \cdot (-2) \cdot (-2) \cdot (-2)$

EXAMPLE 2

Evaluate.

a) $(-5)^3$ b) $\left(-\dfrac{1}{2}\right)^4$ c) $(-3)^2$

Solution

a) $(-5)^3 = -5 \cdot (-5) \cdot (-5)$ Multiply -5 by itself *three* times.

$= 25 \cdot (-5)$

$= -125$

b) $\left(-\dfrac{1}{2}\right)^4 = -\dfrac{1}{2} \cdot \left(-\dfrac{1}{2}\right) \cdot \left(-\dfrac{1}{2}\right) \cdot \left(-\dfrac{1}{2}\right)$ Multiply $-\dfrac{1}{2}$ by itself *four* times.

$= \dfrac{1}{4} \cdot \left(-\dfrac{1}{2}\right) \cdot \left(-\dfrac{1}{2}\right)$

$= -\dfrac{1}{8} \cdot \left(-\dfrac{1}{2}\right)$

$= \dfrac{1}{16}$

c) $(-3)^2 = \underbrace{-3 \cdot (-3)}_{\text{2 factors of } -3} = 9$

W Hint

How can an objective from Section 2.6 help you to evaluate these problems more quickly?

[YOU TRY 2]

Evaluate.

a) $(-9)^2$ b) $\left(-\dfrac{1}{3}\right)^4$ c) $(-2)^3$

2 Use the Order of Operations with Signed Numbers

The order of operations applies to signed numbers. Let's use the order of operations to determine whether $(-3)^2$ and -3^2 mean the same thing.

W Hint

Write down the order of operations.

EXAMPLE 3

Evaluate $(-3)^2$ and -3^2.

Solution

In Example 2c, we saw that $(-3)^2 = \underbrace{-3 \cdot (-3)}_{\text{2 factors of } -3} = 9$ where the base is -3.

To evaluate -3^2, let's use the order of operations.
Because -3^2 does not contain parentheses, the base is 3, **not** -3.

$-3^2 = -1 \cdot 3^2$

$= -1 \cdot 9$ Evaluate exponents before multiplying.

$= -9$ Multiply.

Therefore, $(-3)^2 = 9$ but $-3^2 = -9$.

[YOU TRY 3] Evaluate $(-7)^2$ and -7^2.

> **BE CAREFUL**
>
> When simplifying an exponential expression containing a signed number, remember the difference between having parentheses in the expression and **not** having parentheses.
>
> Example: $(-3)^2 = \underbrace{-3 \cdot (-3)}_{\text{2 factors of } -3} = 9$ The base is -3. Multiply -3 by itself *two* times.
>
> $-3^2 = -1 \cdot 3^2 = -1 \cdot 9 = -9$ The base is 3. Evaluate the exponent before multiplying.

W Hint

Don't forget to review this box!

Let's evaluate other expressions using the order of operations.

EXAMPLE 4

In-Class Example 4

Simplify each expression using the order of operations.
a) $9 - 5 \cdot 6 + 4$
b) $-3\sqrt{100} - 2(7 - 13)$
c) $-8^2 \div (-4) - (-2)^3$

Answer:
a) -17 b) -18 c) 24

Simplify each expression using the order of operations.

a) $10 - 4 \cdot 7 + 3$ b) $-5\sqrt{64} - 2(6 - 15)$ c) $-6^2 \div (-9) - (-2)^3$

Solution

a) $10 - 4 \cdot 7 + 3 = 10 - 28 + 3$ Multiply before adding or subtracting.

$\qquad\qquad\qquad\quad = -18 + 3$ Perform operations from left to right.

$\qquad\qquad\qquad\quad = -15$ Add.

b) $-5\sqrt{64} - 2(6 - 15) = -5\sqrt{64} - 2(-9)$ Perform the operations in parentheses first.

$\qquad\qquad\qquad\qquad = -5(8) - 2(-9)$ Evaluate the square root.

$\qquad\qquad\qquad\qquad = -40 - (-18)$ Multiply.

$\qquad\qquad\qquad\qquad = -40 + (18)$ Change subtraction to addition of the additive inverse.

$\qquad\qquad\qquad\qquad = -22$ Add.

c) $-6^2 \div (9) - (-2)^3 = -36 \div 9 - (-8)$ Evaluate exponents first.
$-6^2 = -1 \cdot 6^2 = -1 \cdot 36 = -36$
$(-2)^3 = -2 \cdot (-2) \cdot (-2) = -8$

$\qquad\qquad\qquad\qquad = \quad -4 - (-8)$ Divide.

$\qquad\qquad\qquad\qquad = -4 + (8)$ Change subtraction to addition of the additive inverse.

$\qquad\qquad\qquad\qquad = 4$ Add.

[YOU TRY 4] Simplify each expression using the order of operations.

a) $13 - 8 \cdot 7 - 2$ b) $-7(5 - 9) + 9\sqrt{16}$ c) $-4^2 \div 2 - (-4)^3$

Next we will simplify some expressions involving fractions.

EXAMPLE 5

Simplify each expression.

a) $\left(\dfrac{1}{2} + \dfrac{1}{3}\right)^2 \cdot \left(-\dfrac{4}{5}\right)$ b) $\dfrac{-48 + 2(3 - 1)}{(-5)^2 - 6^2}$

Solution

a) $\left(\dfrac{1}{2} + \dfrac{1}{3}\right)^2 \cdot \left(-\dfrac{4}{5}\right) = \left(\dfrac{3}{6} + \dfrac{2}{6}\right)^2 \cdot \left(-\dfrac{4}{5}\right)$ Get a common denominator.

$= \left(\dfrac{5}{6}\right)^2 \cdot \left(-\dfrac{4}{5}\right)$ Add the fractions.

$= \dfrac{25}{36} \cdot \left(-\dfrac{4}{5}\right)$ Square $\dfrac{5}{6}$.

$= \dfrac{\overset{5}{25}}{\underset{9}{36}} \cdot \left(-\dfrac{4}{\underset{1}{5}}\right)$ Divide out common factors.

$= -\dfrac{5}{9}$ Multiply.

b) To simplify $\dfrac{-48 + 2(3 - 1)}{(-5)^2 - 6^2}$, first simplify the numerator and then simplify the denominator.

Numerator		**Denominator**	
$-48 + 2(3 - 1)$		$(-5)^2 - 6^2$	
$-48 + 2(2)$	Subtract.	$25 - 36$	Evaluate the exponents.
$-48 + 4$	Multiply.	$25 + (-36)$	Change subtraction to addition.
-44	Add.	-11	Add.
Numerator $= -44$		Denominator $= -11$	

Now, replace the values in the numerator and denominator and divide.

$$\dfrac{-48 + 2(3 - 1)}{(-5)^2 - 6^2} = \dfrac{-44}{-11} = 4$$

$\begin{bmatrix} \text{YOU TRY 5} \end{bmatrix}$ Simplify each expression.

a) $\left(\dfrac{1}{4} - \dfrac{5}{6}\right)^2 \div \left(\dfrac{3}{2}\right)$ b) $\dfrac{(-2)^4 - 9 \cdot 3 + 11}{5(4 - 7) - 8}$

ANSWERS TO $\begin{bmatrix} \text{YOU TRY} \end{bmatrix}$ EXERCISES

1) a) $(-7)^4$ b) $(-2)^5$ 2) a) 81 b) $\dfrac{1}{81}$ c) -8 3) $(-7)^2 = 49; -7^2 = -49$

4) a) -45 b) 64 c) 56   5) a) $\dfrac{49}{216}$ b) 0

Using Technology

We can use a calculator to help us evaluate expressions using the order of operations. For example, to find the value of $-7(8 - 13) \div (-0.4)^2$, we must use the parenthesis key to indicate the order of operations.

To find the value of the expression, we enter $\boxed{7}\,\boxed{\pm}\,\boxed{\times}\,\boxed{(}\,\boxed{(}\,\boxed{8}\,\boxed{-}\,\boxed{1}\,\boxed{3}\,\boxed{)}$ $\boxed{\div}\,\boxed{(}\,\boxed{(}\,\boxed{.}\,\boxed{4}\,\boxed{\pm}\,\boxed{y^x}\,\boxed{2}\,\boxed{)}\,\boxed{)}\,\boxed{=}$ or $\boxed{(\text{-})}\,\boxed{7}\,\boxed{(}\,\boxed{8}\,\boxed{-}\,\boxed{1}\,\boxed{3}\,\boxed{)}\,\boxed{\div}\,\boxed{(}\,\boxed{(}\,\boxed{(\text{-})}\,\boxed{.}\,\boxed{4}\,\boxed{)}$ $\boxed{x^2}\,\boxed{\text{ENTER}}$ into the calculator. The display screen will show 218.75 as the result.

It may be easier to work in steps by first evaluating the expression in the parentheses and performing the exponent operation. Doing this would give us the expression $-7(-5) \div 0.16$, making it easier for us to enter the expression into the calculator. Try it!

E Evaluate 10.5 Exercises

Do the exercises, and check your work.

*Additional answers can be found in the Answers to Exercises appendix.

Objective 1: Use Signed Numbers with Exponents

1) Whenever the exponent is even and the base is nonzero, the result will *always, sometimes,* or *never* be positive.   always

2) Whenever the exponent is odd and the base is nonzero, the result will *always, sometimes,* or *never* be positive.   sometimes

Write each multiplication problem using an exponent.

3) $-10 \cdot (-10) \cdot (-10)$ $(-10)^3$

4) $-4 \cdot (-4) \cdot (-4)$ $(-4)^3$

5) $-13 \cdot (-13)$ $(-13)^2$

6) $-18 \cdot (-18)$ $(-18)^2$

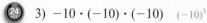 7) $-\dfrac{2}{3} \cdot \left(-\dfrac{2}{3}\right) \cdot \left(-\dfrac{2}{3}\right) \cdot \left(-\dfrac{2}{3}\right)$ $\left(-\dfrac{2}{3}\right)^4$

8) $-\dfrac{5}{8} \cdot \left(-\dfrac{5}{8}\right) \cdot \left(-\dfrac{5}{8}\right) \cdot \left(-\dfrac{5}{8}\right)$ $\left(-\dfrac{5}{8}\right)^4$

9) $-1.2 \cdot (-1.2) \cdot (-1.2) \cdot (-1.2) \cdot (-1.2) \cdot (-1.2)$ $(-1.2)^6$

10) $-0.3 \cdot (-0.3) \cdot (-0.3) \cdot (-0.3) \cdot (-0.3)$ $(-0.3)^5$

Evaluate.

11) $(-7)^2$ 49

12) $(-12)^2$ 144

13) $(-2)^6$ 64

14) $(-10)^4$ 10,000

15) $(-2)^5$ -32

16) $(-3)^5$ -243

17) $(-1)^4$ 1

18) $(-1)^6$ 1

19) $\left(-\dfrac{1}{8}\right)^2$ $\dfrac{1}{64}$

20) $\left(-\dfrac{1}{5}\right)^2$ $\dfrac{1}{25}$

21) $\left(-\dfrac{3}{5}\right)^3$ $-\dfrac{27}{125}$

22) $\left(-\dfrac{2}{3}\right)^3$ $-\dfrac{8}{27}$

23) $(-1.1)^2$ 1.21

24) $(-1.6)^2$ 2.56

Objective 2: Use the Order of Operations with Signed Numbers

25) Evaluate.

a) $(-9)^2$ 81

b) -9^2 -81

26) Evaluate.

a) $(-8)^2$ 64

b) -8^2 -64

27) Evaluate.

a) $(-5)^2$ 25

b) -5^2 -25

28) Evaluate.

a) $(-7)^2$ 49

b) -7^2 -49

29) Explain, in your own words, the difference between evaluating -10^2 and $(-10)^2$.   Answers may vary.

30) Identify the base of -7^2 and of $(-7)^2$, then evaluate each.   The base of -7^2 is 7, and $-7^2 = -49$. The base of $(-7)^2$ is -7, and $(-7)^2 = 49$.

Evaluate.

31) $(-2)^4$ 16

32) $(-3)^4$ 81

33) -2^4 -16

34) -3^4 -81

35) $(-10)^3$ -1000

36) $(-5)^3$ -125

37) $(-12)^2$ 144

38) $(-13)^2$ 169

39) -1^4 -1

40) -1^6 -1

41) $\left(-\dfrac{1}{3}\right)^3$ $-\dfrac{1}{27}$

42) $\left(-\dfrac{1}{2}\right)^3$ $-\dfrac{1}{8}$

43) $-\left(\dfrac{5}{8}\right)^2$ $-\dfrac{25}{64}$ 44) $-\left(\dfrac{3}{7}\right)^2$ $-\dfrac{9}{49}$

Simplify each expression using the order of operations.

45) $-3 + 16 + 4(-8)$ -19 46) $1 + (-6) + 3(-3)$ -14

47) $16 - 4 \cdot 9 - 5$ -25 48) $24 - 7 \cdot 6 - 10$ -28

 49) $-6(9 - 14) \div (-10)$ -3 50) $-9(5 - 17) \div (-6)$ -18

51) $4^2 + 7^2$ 65 52) $3^2 + 5^2$ 34

53) $8 - 8^2$ -56 54) $7 - 7^2$ -42

55) $5^2 + 6^2 - (-3)^2$ 52 56) $3^2 + 9^2 - (-4)^3$ 26

57) $4 - (-9) + 2^3$ 21 58) $5 - (-12) - 3^2$ 8

59) $(-2)^3 + (-4)^2 - 6$ 2 60) $(-3)^3 + (-6)^2 - 12$ -3

61) $6 + 8|2 - 9|$ 62 62) $7 + 5|1 - 3|$ 17

63) $-8 + 3(4 - 11)$ -29 64) $-9 + 2(5 - 13)$ -25

65) $52 \div (-2)^2 + (-7)$ 6 66) $32 \div (-2)^4 + 9$ 11

67) $7 - |7 - 11|(8 - 18)$ 47

68) $5 - |12 - 18|(3 - 12)$ 59

69) $-9(11 - 3) + 6\sqrt{144}$ 0

70) $-7(9 - 6) + 3\sqrt{49}$ 0

71) $42 \div (4 - 5^2) + (9)^2$ 79

72) $50 \div (6 - 4^2) + (-7)^2$ 44

73) $-\sqrt{16}\,|12 - 18| - 5\sqrt{4}$ -34

74) $-\sqrt{25}\,|16 - 25| - 3\sqrt{100}$ -75

75) $2 - (-7)(-4)^2$ 114 76) $3 - (-9)(-2)^3$ -69

77) $63 \div (-9) - 4(7 - 18)^2$ -491

78) $56 \div (-7) - 3(8 - 10)^2$ -20

79) $\left(-\dfrac{1}{2} + \dfrac{7}{8}\right)^2 \div \left(3 - \dfrac{1}{2}\right)$ $\dfrac{9}{160}$

80) $\left(-\dfrac{1}{3} + \dfrac{1}{5}\right)^2 \div \left(1 - \dfrac{1}{9}\right)$ $\dfrac{1}{50}$

81) $\dfrac{-3 + 4^2 + |5 - 7|}{-8 + 6 - 3}$ -3

82) $\dfrac{-7 + 5^2 + |15 - 19|}{-9 + 2 - 4}$ -2

83) $\dfrac{5 \cdot 3^2 - 7|11 - 16|}{2(13 - 17) \div (-4)}$ 5

84) $\dfrac{-3 \cdot 4^2 - 2|7 - 11|}{-7(9 - 14) \div (-5)}$ 8

Each problem is done incorrectly. Find the error and correct it.

85) $48 - 4 \cdot (-2)$

Work: $48 - 4 \cdot (-2) =$
$44 \cdot (-2) = -88$

86) $33 - 18 \div (-3)$

Work: $33 - 18 \div (-3) =$
$15 \div (-3) = -5$

87) $-10^2 \div |12 - 37|$

Work: $-10^2 \div |12 - 37| =$
$100 \div |12 - 37| =$
$100 \div \quad 25 \quad = 4$

88) $\sqrt{49} + (8 - 2)^2$

Work: $\sqrt{49} + (8 - 2)^2 =$
$7 + 64 - 4 =$
$71 - 4 = 67$

R Rethink

R1) Look at Example 5b) and notice that the denominator and numerator are simplified separately before simplifying the whole expression. Why is this?

R2) Use your explanation to the previous question to help explain the statement, "You can never divide out parts of sums."

Group Activity – Signed Numbers

Activity #1: True or False?

- Work with a partner to determine whether each statement below is *true* or *false*.
- If the statement is false, provide an example or contradiction to illustrate why it is false.
- Change ONE word of each false statement to make it a true statement.
  Note: There may be more than one way to do this.

1) If the numerator and denominator of a fraction are both negative, then the fraction itself is negative.

2) The sum of two negative numbers is a positive number.

3) The sum of a negative number and a positive number is always positive.

4) A number and its opposite have equal absolute values.

5) When two numbers are compared, the number with the greater absolute value is always the greater number.

Activity #2: Find the Missing Number

- Work with a partner to find the missing number in each statement below.
- Compare answers with another group when you are finished.

1) The difference between 5 and a number is -3. Find the missing number.

2) The product of -4.2 and a number is 4.2. Find the missing number.

3) The sum of -12 and a number is $-17\frac{1}{4}$. Find the missing number.

4) The difference between 12 and a number is 20. Find the missing number.

5) The quotient of $-\frac{1}{8}$ and a number is $-\frac{1}{6}$. Find the missing number.

Group Activity #1 Answers

1) False; examples will vary; If the numerator and denominator of a fraction are both negative, then the fraction itself is POSITIVE.
2) False; examples will vary; The sum of two negative numbers is a NEGATIVE number.
3) False; examples will vary; The sum of a negative number and positive number is SOMETIMES positive.
4) True
5) False; examples will vary; When two numbers are compared, the number with the greater absolute value is SOMETIMES the greater number.

Group Activity #2 Answers

1) 8   2) -1 3) $-5\frac{1}{4}$ 4) -8 5) $\frac{3}{4}$

em**POWER**me Discover Your Personal Financial Philosophy

In order to manage your financial life the way you want, it is important to understand just how much money matters to you. Complete the exercise below to learn about your personal financial philosophy. (The table continues on the next page.)

A. Attitudes Toward Money

	Strongly Disagree	Disagree	Neutral	Agree	Strongly Agree
1. Money is essential for happiness.					
2. Having money guarantees happiness.					
3. Money makes no difference to one's happiness.					
4. More money equals more happiness.					
5. Beyond having enough to live on modestly, money doesn't make much of a difference.					
6. I frequently worry about money.					
7. I frequently daydream about having a lot of money.					
8. If I suddenly had to live on very little money, I could adjust easily.					

	Strongly Disagree	Disagree	Neutral	Agree	Strongly Agree
9. If I suddenly won a lot of money, I would go on a spending spree.					
10. If I suddenly won a lot of money, I would share it with my relatives.					
11. If I suddenly won a lot of money, I would give a large percentage to charity.					
12. If I found a substantial amount of cash in a bag, I would try hard to find its rightful owner.					
13. If I could carry only a briefcase full of $100 bills out of a burning building or my pet dog, I would take the dog.					
14. I plan to make a lot of money in my career.					
15. I plan to make only enough money to live in reasonable comfort.					
16. It's great to have money.					
17. Money is a necessary evil.					
18. Money is the root of all evil.					

B. Sources of Satisfaction

1. Which activities that you engaged in over the last five years have given you the greatest satisfaction?

2. How much money did those activities cost?

3. How would you spend your time if you could do anything you chose?

4. How much money would this cost each year?

C. Personal Financial Philosophy

Consider your attitudes toward money and the sources of your satisfaction. Use this thinking to help shape your budget, as well as your long-term financial and career goals.

Chapter 10: **Summary**

Definition/Procedure	Example

10.1 Introduction to Signed Numbers

Signed Numbers

A **positive number** is a number that is greater than 0. On a number line, positive numbers are to the *right* of 0.

A **negative number** is a number that is less than 0. To indicate that a number is negative, we put a negative sign, $-$, in front of it. On a number line, negative numbers are to the *left* of 0.

Zero is neither positive nor negative. **(p. 717)**

Graph the numbers on a number line.

$$2, -4, 0, 3.8, -\frac{1}{2}$$

Solution

Comparing Signed Numbers

Remember that numbers get *smaller* as we move to the *left* on a number line, and numbers get *larger* as we move to the *right* on a number line.

We can use the $<$ and $>$ symbols to compare signed numbers. **(p. 718)**

Fill in the blank with $<$ or $>$ to compare the numbers.

a) $3 \underline{\hspace{1cm}} -2$ b) $-5 \underline{\hspace{1cm}} -1$

Solution

Let's look at a number line so that we can see how the numbers compare to each other.

a) $3 > -2$ because 3 is to the *right* of -2 on the number line.

b) $-5 < -1$ because -5 is to the *left* of -1 on the number line.

Absolute Value

The **absolute value** of a number is the distance of the number from 0.

Because distance is never negative, the absolute value of a number is never negative.

The absolute value of a number is denoted by two vertical bars, $|\ \ |$. **(p. 720)**

Evaluate $|4|$ and $|-4|$.

Solution

Read $|4|$ as "the absolute value of 4." $|4| = 4$
Read $|-4|$ as "the absolute value of -4." $|-4| = 4$

Distance $= 4$,   Distance $= 4$,
so $|-4| = 4$ so $|4| = 4$

The Opposite of a Number

Two numbers are **opposites** of each other if they are the same distance from 0 on a number line but are on opposite sides of 0.

To find the opposite of a number, we write a negative sign in front of it.

The opposite of a positive number is a negative number. The opposite of a negative number is a positive number. **(p. 721)**

Find the opposite of each number.

a) 8   b) -5.3 c) 0

Solution

a) The opposite of 8 is -8.

b) To find the opposite of -5.3, put a negative sign in front of the number: $-(-5.3)$. Now, evaluate: $-(-5.3) = 5.3$.

c) The opposite of 0 is $-0 = 0$.

Definition/Procedure	Example

10.2 Adding Signed Numbers

Adding Two Negative Numbers

Step 1: Find the absolute value of each number.

Step 2: Add the absolute values.

Step 3: Put a negative sign in front of the sum.

The sum of two negative numbers is *always* negative. **(p. 726)**

Add $-16 + (-12)$.

Solution

Step 1: Find the absolute value of each number.

$$|-16| = 16 \qquad |-12| = 12$$

Step 2: Add the absolute values: $16 + 12 = 28$

Step 3: Put a negative sign in front of the sum.

$$-16 + (-12) = -28$$

Adding Two Numbers with Different Signs

Step 1: Find the absolute value of each number.

Step 2: Subtract the smaller absolute value from the larger absolute value.

Step 3: The sign of the *sum* will be the same as the sign of the number with the *greater* absolute value. Write the sum with this sign. **(p. 727)**

Add.

a) $-37 + 15$ b) $295 + (-141)$

Solution

a) *Step 1:* Find the absolute value of each number:
$$|-37| = 37, |15| = 15$$

Step 2: Subtract the smaller absolute value from the larger absolute value.

$$37 - 15 = 22$$

Larger absolute value   Smaller absolute value

Step 3: The sign of the *sum* will be the same as the sign of the number with the greater absolute value.

Negative 37 has a greater absolute value than *positive* 15, so **the sum will be negative.**

$$-37 + 15 = -22$$

The sum is negative.

b) *Step 1:* Find the absolute value of each number:
$$|295| = 295, |-141| = 141$$

Step 2: Subtract the smaller absolute value from the larger absolute value.

$$295 - 141 = 154$$

Larger absolute value   Smaller absolute value

Step 3: The sign of the *sum* will be the same as the sign of the number with the greater absolute value.

Positive 295 has a greater absolute value than *negative* 141, so **the sum will be positive.**

$$295 + (-141) = 154$$

The sum is positive.

Definition/Procedure	Example

10.3 Subtracting Signed Numbers

Additive Inverse The opposite of a number is its **additive inverse.** The sum of a number and its additive inverse is 0. **(p. 733)**	Find the additive inverse of each number. a) 6 b) $-\dfrac{2}{3}$ **Solution** a) The additive inverse of 6 is -6. And, $6 + (-6) = 0$. b) The additive inverse of $-\dfrac{2}{3}$ is $\dfrac{2}{3}$. And, $-\dfrac{2}{3} + \dfrac{2}{3} = 0$.
Subtracting Signed Numbers To subtract two numbers, $a - b$, 1) Change subtraction to addition. 2) Find the additive inverse of b. 3) Add a and the additive inverse of b. Notice that we keep the first number, a, the same. **(p. 734)**	Subtract. a) $4 - 10$ b) $-9.8 - 1.3$ c) $\dfrac{1}{6} - \left(-\dfrac{2}{3}\right)$ **Solution** a) $4 - 10 = 4 + (-10) = -6$ Change subtraction to addition of the additive inverse of 10. b) $-9.8 - 1.3 = -9.8 + (-1.3) = -11.1$ Change subtraction to addition of the additive inverse of 1.3. c) $\dfrac{1}{6} - \left(-\dfrac{2}{3}\right) = \dfrac{1}{6} + \left(\dfrac{2}{3}\right) = \dfrac{1}{6} + \dfrac{4}{6} = \dfrac{5}{6}$ Change subtraction to addition of the additive inverse of $\dfrac{2}{3}$. Get a common denominator.

10.4 Multiplying and Dividing Signed Numbers

Multiplying Two Numbers with Different Signs The product of a *positive number* and a *negative number* is a *negative number*. **(p. 741)**	Multiply. a) -6×3 b) $0.8(-1.2)$ **Solution** a) $-6 \times 3 = -18$ b) $0.8(-1.2) = -0.96$ The product of two numbers with different signs is negative.
Multiplying Two Numbers with the Same Sign The product of two numbers with the *same sign* is *positive*. **(p. 742)**	Multiply. a) $5 \cdot 9$ b) $-11 \times (-7)$ **Solution** a) $5 \cdot 9 = 45$ b) $-11 \times (-7) = 77$ The product of two numbers with the same sign is positive.
Dividing Signed Numbers 1) The quotient of two numbers with *different signs* is *negative*. 2) The quotient of two numbers with the *same sign* is *positive*. **(p. 743)**	Divide. a) $-42 \div 6$ b) $\dfrac{-12}{-3}$ c) $\dfrac{40}{-8}$ **Solution** a) $-42 \div 6 = -7$ The quotient of two numbers with *different signs* is *negative*. b) $\dfrac{-12}{-3} = 4$ The quotient of two numbers with the *same sign* is *positive*. c) $\dfrac{40}{-5} = -8$ The quotient of two numbers with *different signs* is *negative*.

Definition/Procedure	Example

Negative Signs in Fractions

When a fraction is negative, the negative sign is usually written in front of the fraction. However, we can write other, equivalent forms of the fraction.

If a fraction has a negative sign in front of it, we can rewrite the fraction with the negative sign in the numerator or the denominator but not both. **(p. 744)**

Write two equivalent forms of $-\dfrac{5}{8}$ by moving its negative sign.

Solution

We can write $-\dfrac{5}{8} = \dfrac{-5}{8}$. We can also write $-\dfrac{5}{8} = \dfrac{5}{-8}$.

10.5 The Order of Operations

Using Exponents with Negative Numbers

We can use an exponent to represent repeated multiplication of a negative number. In this case, the negative number **must** be in parentheses. **(p. 748)**

Write $-8 \cdot (-8) \cdot (-8) \cdot (-8)$ using an exponent.

Solution

$$\underbrace{-8 \cdot (-8) \cdot (-8) \cdot (-8)}_{4 \text{ factors of } -8} = (-8)^4$$

Order of Operations

The order of operations applies to signed numbers.

Simplify expressions in the following order:

1) If **parentheses** or **other grouping symbols** appear in an expression, simplify what is in these grouping symbols first.

2) Simplify expressions with **exponents** or **square roots.**

3) **Multiply** or **divide,** moving from left to right.

4) **Add** or **subtract,** moving from left to right. **(p. 749)**

Simplify each expression.

a) $(-4)^2$ b) -4^2 c) $6 + 33 \div (-3) + (5 - 7)^3$

Solution

a) $(-4)^2 = -4 \cdot (-4) = 16$ The base is -4.

b) Notice that -4^2 does *not* contain parentheses. The order of operations tells us to evaluate exponents first.

$$-4^2 = -1 \cdot 4^2 = -1 \cdot 16 = -16$$

c) $6 + 33 \div (-3) + (5 - 7)^3$

$\quad 6 + 33 \div (-3) + (-2)^3$ Simplify inside parentheses first.

$\quad 6 + 33 \div (-3) + (-8)$ Evaluate the exponential expression.

$\quad 6 + (-11) + (-8)$ Divide.

$\quad\quad -5 + (-8)$ Add and subtract from left to right.

$\quad\quad\quad -13$ Add.

Chapter 10:   Review Exercises

*Additional answers can be found in the Answers to Exercises appendix.

(10.1) Represent the number in each statement as a signed number.

1) The British luxury passenger liner *Titanic* was found approximately 13,000 ft below the ocean's surface. (www.britannica.com/titanic) $-13,000$ ft

2) The Badwater area in Death Valley National Park is the lowest point in North America and is 282 ft below sea level. (www.nps.gov) -282 ft

Graph each group of numbers on the number line.

$$\overset{\longleftarrow\ \ |\ \ |\ \ |\ \ |\ \ |\ \ |\ \ |\ \ |\ \ |\ \ |\ \ |\ \ \longrightarrow}{-5\,-4\,-3\,-2\,-1\ \ 0\ \ 1\ \ 2\ \ 3\ \ 4\ \ 5}$$

3) $1, 5, -1, -3, -2$

4) $-4, 2, 5, -3, -2$

5) $-2\dfrac{1}{5}, 3, \dfrac{3}{4}, 1\dfrac{1}{2}, -\dfrac{5}{6}$

6) $2, -3\dfrac{1}{4}, \dfrac{7}{8}, -\dfrac{7}{8}, -4\dfrac{1}{2}$

7) $0.7, 5, -3.6, -0.9, -2$

8) $1.1, -1.1, 0, -4.5, -3.9$

Fill in the blank with < or > to compare each pair of numbers.

9) -45 _____ -44 $<$

10) $-\dfrac{4}{11}$ _____ $-\dfrac{5}{12}$ $>$

11) $-3\dfrac{2}{3}$ _____ $-3\dfrac{5}{6}$ $>$

12) -0.01 _____ -0.009 $<$

Use the number line below for Exercises 13–16. Fill in the blank with < or > to make the statement true.

$$\overset{\longleftarrow\quad\ |\quad\quad\ \ |\ \ |\quad\ |\ \ |\quad\ \longrightarrow}{a\quad\quad b\ \ 0\quad c\ \ d}$$

13) c _____ a $>$

14) b _____ 0 $<$

15) b _____ a $>$

16) 4 _____ a $>$

Evaluate each expression.

17) $|-6|$ 18) $-|-31|$ 19) $-\left|\dfrac{11}{15}\right|$ 20) $-|-2.57|$
6   -31 $-\dfrac{11}{15}$ -2.57

Find the opposite of each number.

21) -35 35

22) 27 -27

23) $2\dfrac{1}{4}$ $-2\dfrac{1}{4}$

24) $-\dfrac{7}{9}$ $\dfrac{7}{9}$

25) -0.8 0.8

26) 2.3 -2.3

Use the number line below for Exercises 27 and 28. Fill in the blank with $<$ or $>$ to make the statement true.

a   *b*   0   *c*   *d*

27) $-(d)$ _____ c $<$

28) $|b|$ _____ $-a$ $<$

(10.2)

29) In your own words, explain how to add two signed numbers.   Answers may vary.

30) The sum of a number and its opposite always equals what number?   0

Add.

31) $-31 + 19$ -11

32) $7 + (-23)$ -16

33) $-15 + 22$ 7

34) $54 + (-18)$ 36

35) $\dfrac{3}{8} + \left(-\dfrac{1}{4}\right)$ $\dfrac{1}{8}$

36) $-\dfrac{2}{3} + \dfrac{11}{12}$ $\dfrac{1}{4}$

37) $-205.9 + 237.8$ 31.9

38) $481.6 + (-420.2)$ 61.4

39) $-\dfrac{7}{5} + \left(-\dfrac{7}{10}\right)$ $-\dfrac{21}{10}$ or $-2\dfrac{1}{10}$

40) $-\dfrac{3}{2} + \left(-\dfrac{5}{8}\right)$ $-\dfrac{17}{8}$ or $-2\dfrac{1}{8}$

Represent each statement with an addition problem, and solve the problem.

41) On his first run, Marcus gained 16 yd. On his second run, he lost 7 yd. What was his net yardage after these two plays? $16 + (-7)$; 9 yd

42) Ellie's checking account was overdrawn by $57.62. She deposited $45.00 into the account. What is the balance of her account? $-\$57.62 + \$45$; $-\$12.62$

Solve each problem.

43) Svetlana deposited her $225.00 paycheck into her debit account, which had a balance of $37.50. Later that week, she used her debit card to purchase groceries costing $118.76 and withdrew $200 cash. What is Svetlana's new debit account balance? $-\$56.26$

44) Monte's 750-GB hard drive had 672 GB of data stored on it. After deleting 387 GB of data, Monte uploaded 157 GB of video and music files to the drive. How many gigabytes of storage are free on Monte's hard drive?   308 GB

(10.3)

45) What is the additive inverse of a number?   It is the opposite of the number.

46) What is the sum of a number and its additive inverse?   0

Find the additive inverse of each number.

47) 28 -28

48) -9.4 9.4

For Exercises 49 and 50, determine whether the statement is *always*, *sometimes*, or *never* true.

49) A negative number subtracted from a positive number equals a positive number.   always

50) A positive number subtracted from a positive number equals a positive number.   sometimes

Rewrite each subtraction problem as addition. Then, simplify.

51) $8 - 20$ $8 + (-20) = -12$

52) $11 - 19$ $11 + (-19) = -8$

53) $-52 - (-89)$ $-52 + 89 = 37$

54) $-43 - (-91)$ $-43 + 91 = 48$

55) $-18.6 - 13.5$ $-18.6 + (-13.5) = -32.1$

56) $-20.5 - 17.4$ $-20.5 + (-17.4) = -37.9$

57) $\dfrac{2}{3} - \dfrac{11}{6}$ $\dfrac{2}{3} + \left(-\dfrac{11}{6}\right) = -\dfrac{7}{6}$ or $-1\dfrac{1}{6}$

58) $\dfrac{7}{4} - \dfrac{3}{5}$ $\dfrac{7}{4} + \left(-\dfrac{3}{5}\right) = \dfrac{23}{20}$ or $1\dfrac{3}{20}$

Perform the operations.

59) $4 + (-19) - (-15)$ 0

60) $2 + (-17) - (-5)$ -10

61) $14.1 - |-5.2| - (-7.8)$ 16.7

62) $\left|-\dfrac{3}{5}\right| - \left(-\dfrac{1}{7}\right) - \dfrac{5}{2}$ $-\dfrac{123}{70}$ or $-1\dfrac{53}{70}$

(10.4) For Exercises 63–64, fill in the blank with *positive* or *negative*.

63) The product of a negative number and a positive number is __negative__.

64) The quotient of a negative number and a __negative__ number is positive.

Multiply.

65) $-12 \cdot 5$ -60

66) $-1 \times (-11)$ 11

67) $-5.6(-4)$ 22.4

68) $3.2(-9)$ -28.8

69) $-\dfrac{39}{18} \times \dfrac{6}{13}$ -1

70) $-8\left(-\dfrac{7}{10}\right)$ $\dfrac{28}{5}$ or $5\dfrac{3}{5}$

Divide.

71) $-44 \div (-11)$ 4

72) $\dfrac{54}{-6}$ -9

73) $\dfrac{-405}{9}$ -45

74) $\dfrac{-265}{5}$ -53

75) $\dfrac{12.72}{-5.3}$ -2.4

76) $\dfrac{11.18}{-8.6}$ -1.3

77) $-\dfrac{6}{7} \div (-10)$ $\dfrac{3}{35}$

78) $-\dfrac{7}{5} \div (-14)$ $\dfrac{1}{10}$

79) $\dfrac{-\dfrac{5}{6}}{\dfrac{7}{24}}$ $-\dfrac{20}{7}$ or $-2\dfrac{6}{7}$

80) $\dfrac{-\dfrac{3}{7}}{\dfrac{9}{22}}$ $-\dfrac{22}{21}$ or $-1\dfrac{1}{21}$

Write two equivalent forms of each fraction by moving its negative sign.

81) $\dfrac{-3}{11}$ $-\dfrac{3}{11}$ or $\dfrac{3}{-11}$

82) $-\dfrac{2}{9}$ $\dfrac{-2}{9}$ or $\dfrac{2}{-9}$

83) $-\dfrac{22}{23}$ $\dfrac{-22}{23}$ or $\dfrac{22}{-23}$

84) $\dfrac{15}{-19}$ $-\dfrac{15}{19}$ or $\dfrac{-15}{19}$

Fill in the blank.

85) $-77 \div \underline{\ \ \ }_{-7} = 11$

86) $42 \div \underline{\ \ \ } = 3$ 14

87) $\underline{\ \ \ }_{-27} \times (-4) = 108$

88) $\underline{\ \ \ } \times (-7) = -35$ 5

89) If an expression contains only multiplication and division, how do you simplify it? Perform the operations from left to right.

Simplify each expression.

90) $5 \cdot (-2) \cdot (-4)$ 40

91) $|-12| \div (-6) \cdot |8|$ -16

92) $\left(-\dfrac{1}{3}\right) \times \left(-\dfrac{3}{5}\right) \div \left(-\dfrac{7}{2}\right)$ $-\dfrac{2}{35}$

Solve the application problem. Express your answer as a positive or negative number accordingly.

93) A small plane descended 225 ft each minute for a 15-minute landing. What was the change in the plane's altitude during that time? -3375 ft

94) Krishna is downloading a large video file to his computer at a rate of 5 megabits per sec. If the file size is 6900 megabits, how many minutes will it take for Krishna to download the entire file?   23 min

(10.5) Write each multiplication problem using an exponent.

95) $-13 \cdot (-13) \cdot (-13) \cdot (-13)$ $(-13)^4$

96) $-\dfrac{4}{7} \cdot \left(-\dfrac{4}{7}\right) \cdot \left(-\dfrac{4}{7}\right)$ $\left(-\dfrac{4}{7}\right)^3$

Evaluate.

97) $(-7)^2$ 49

98) $(-10)^2$ 100

99) -7^2 -49

100) -10^2 -100

101) $(-2)^3$ -8

102) $(-4)^3$ -64

103) -2^3 -8

104) -4^3 -64

105) $-\left(-\dfrac{3}{4}\right)^2$ $-\dfrac{9}{16}$

106) $-\left(-\dfrac{1}{2}\right)^3$ $\dfrac{1}{8}$

Simplify each expression using the order of operations.

107) $3(8) - 7(5) + 4(6)$ 13

108) $-3^4 \div 9 - (-3)^2$ -18

109) $-15 - 3\sqrt{16} \div (18 - 6)$ -16

110) $-16 - 2\sqrt{81} \div (11 - 8)$ -22

111) $\left(\dfrac{1}{6} - \dfrac{2}{15}\right)^2 \div \left(\dfrac{7}{50}\right)$ $\dfrac{1}{126}$

112) $\left(\dfrac{5}{4} - \dfrac{1}{6}\right)^2 \div \left(\dfrac{13}{84}\right)$ $\dfrac{91}{12}$ or $7\dfrac{7}{12}$

113) $\dfrac{2^3(-4 - 3) + 4(-6)}{6 + 7(-3 \cdot 5) + (7 \cdot 14)}$ 80

114) $\dfrac{3^3(-8 + 7) + 9(-2)}{6 + 3(-4 \cdot 5) + (3 \cdot 19)}$ -15

Each problem is done incorrectly. Find the error and correct it.

115) $\sqrt{81} + (7 - 4)^2$

Work: $\sqrt{81} + (7 - 4)^2 =$

$9 + 49 + 16 =$

$58 + 16 = 74$

116) $32 - 24 \div (-4)$

Work: $32 - 24 \div (-4) =$

$8 \div (-4) = -2$

Mixed Exercises
Perform the indicated operations.

117) $-\dfrac{4}{15}\left(-\dfrac{3}{24}\right)$ $\dfrac{1}{30}$

118) $308 - 527$ -219

119) $-24\left(\dfrac{1}{3} - \dfrac{3}{4}\right)^2 + \dfrac{11}{6}$ $-\dfrac{7}{3}$ or $-2\dfrac{1}{3}$

120) $-6.12 \div (-6)$ 1.02

121) $-|125| - (-308) + (-649)$ -466

122) $\dfrac{-14 + 6 \cdot 2 + 38}{-5^2 - 7(1 - 4) + (-2)^4}$ 3

123) $33 - 3(-8) \div 2 - (-15)$ 60

124) $-|-2| + (-16)(3) \div (7 - 9)^3 - 10$ -6

Solve each problem.

125) Marika is on a mountain at an altitude of 9450 ft. At the same time, her friend is scuba diving at a depth of 68 ft. What is the difference between these two elevations?   9518 ft

126) An appliance store has seen its profits fall by $2100 per month for the last year. Use a signed number to determine the store's change in profit over the last year. $-\$25,200$

Chapter 10: Test

Fill in the blank with < or > to compare the numbers.

1) $-5\underline{\ \ \ }-2$ $<$

2) $4\underline{\ \ \ }-7$ $>$

3) $-\dfrac{5}{8}\underline{\ \ \ \ }-\dfrac{1}{2}$ $<$

4) $-5.7\underline{\ \ \ \ \ }-5.6$ $<$

5) Graph the numbers on the number line.

$4.5, -2, -\dfrac{3}{4}, 1\dfrac{2}{3}, -3.5$

$\xleftarrow{\ \ }\overset{\displaystyle|\ \ |\ \ |\ \ |\ \ |\ \ |\ \ |\ \ |\ \ |\ \ |\ \ |}{\underset{-5\ -4\ -3\ -2\ -1\ \ 0\ \ 1\ \ 2\ \ 3\ \ 4\ \ 5}{}}\xrightarrow{\ \ }$

6) Explain, in your own words, the definition of the absolute value of a number.   *Answers may vary. The absolute value of a number is its distance from zero.*

7) Evaluate each expression.

   a) $|-8|$ 8   b) $|32|$ 32

   c) $-|-7.9|$ -7.9 d) $|0|$ 0

8) Find the opposite of each number.

   a) $-\dfrac{1}{4}$ $\dfrac{1}{4}$ b) 6 -6

9) Find the additive inverse of 10. -10

Perform the indicated operation.

10) $-7 \cdot (-4)$ 28   11) $-11 - (-3)$ -8

12) $-26 + (-35)$ -61 13) $\dfrac{-24}{6}$ -4

14) $-\dfrac{9}{14} \div \left(-\dfrac{15}{7}\right)$ $\dfrac{3}{10}$ 15) $-5.35(6)$ -32.1

16) $28 - 52$ -24 17) $397.4 - (-128.9)$ 526.3

18) $\dfrac{-4}{0}$ undefined   19) $-\dfrac{7}{8} + \dfrac{2}{3}$ $-\dfrac{5}{24}$

20) $-49 - (-49)$ 0

Evaluate each expression.

21) $-2 \cdot 5 \cdot (-4) \cdot (-1)$ -40 22) $7 - 28 - (-19) + (-6)$ -8

23) $(-8)^2$ 64   24) -5^2 -25

25) $(-2)^3$ -8 26) $\left(-\dfrac{1}{3}\right)^4$ $\dfrac{1}{81}$

27) Write $-7 \cdot (-7) \cdot (-7) \cdot (-7) \cdot (-7) \cdot (-7)$ using an exponent. $(-7)^6$

Simplify each expression using the order of operations.

28) $12 - 10 \cdot 3 + 13$ -5

29) $-5(2 - 9) - 6^2 \div (-4)$ 44

30) $(-9)^2 - 2\sqrt{144} + 15 \cdot (-2) - (4 - 1)^3$ 0

31) $\left(\dfrac{3}{10} - \dfrac{3}{4}\right) \cdot \left(-\dfrac{4}{9}\right)$ $\dfrac{1}{5}$ 32) $\dfrac{7 - 2(-16 + 7) + (-6)(4)}{(-10)^2 - 7^2 + (-46)}$ $\dfrac{1}{5}$

Solve each problem.

33) A submarine that is cruising at a depth of 603 ft below sea level rises 149 ft. Use a signed number to represent the current depth of the submarine. -454 ft

34) Supatra has $314.78 in her checking account. To pay some bills, she writes checks in the amount of $98.76, $73.80, $182.66, and $124.32. Then, she deposits a check for $164.80. What is the balance of her checking account after these transactions? $0.04

35) The highest temperature on record is 136°F in El Azizia, Libya. The lowest temperature ever recorded is -128.5°F in Vostok, Antarctica. What is the difference between these two temperatures? (www.ncdc.noaa.gov)   264.5°F

36) The *plus-minus* is a hockey statistic that measures a player's goal differential. With the exception of penalty shots and power-play goals, a player gets a "+1" if he is on the ice  when his team scores a goal, but a player gets a "−1" if he is on the ice when his team allows a goal by the other team. If a player was on the ice when the other team scored 3 goals, and he was on the ice when his own team scored 2 goals, what is his *plus-minus* for the game? -1

Chapter 10:   Cumulative Review for Chapters 1–10

*Additional answers can be found in the Answers to Exercises appendix.

1) Identify the place value of each digit in 8.05739.

2) Find the missing side lengths; then find the perimeter of the figure.   8 cm; 2 cm; 43 cm

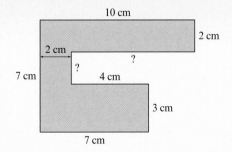

The pictograph shows the unit sales for food items at a community fair. Use the pictograph to answer Exercises 3 and 4.

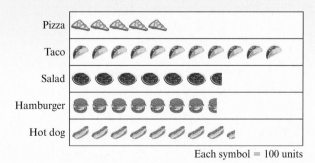

Each symbol = 100 units

3) How many salads were sold?   650; Answers may vary.

4) Approximately how many more tacos were sold than hamburgers?   325; Answers may vary.

Perform the operations.

5) $26\overline{)78{,}052}$ 3002

6) $\dfrac{5}{2} - \dfrac{2}{3} + \dfrac{3}{4}$ $\dfrac{31}{12}$ or $2\dfrac{7}{12}$

7) $0.00942 \times 10{,}000$ 94.2

8) $56 - 24 \div 8 + (7 - 2)^2$ 78

9) Write as a fraction in lowest terms. 64% $\dfrac{16}{25}$

10) Find the area of the shaded region. 488 cm²

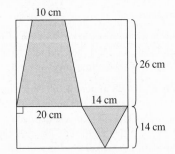

11) Find the volume of the right circular cylinder below. Give an exact value and an approximation using $\pi = 3.14$.
exact: 250π mm³; approximation: 785 mm³

12) Arrange the group of numbers in order from smallest to largest. $-2, -0.7, -\dfrac{2}{3}, -0.6, -\dfrac{59}{100}$

$$-\dfrac{2}{3}, -\dfrac{59}{100}, -2, -0.7, -0.6$$

13) Approximate the location of $-\dfrac{5}{8}$ on the number line.

$$\overset{\longleftarrow\;\;|\;\;|\;\;|\;\;|\;\;|\;\;|\;\;|\;\;\longrightarrow}{\quad-3\;-2\;-1\;\;\;0\;\;\;1\;\;\;2\;\;\;3\quad}$$

Fill in the blank with < or >.

14) $-19 \rule{1cm}{0.4pt} -|-15|$ <

15) $-\left(\dfrac{1}{4}\right)^2 \rule{1cm}{0.4pt} -\dfrac{1}{4}$ >

Simplify each expression using the order of operations.

16) $-7 + 3\sqrt{36} \div (-2) - (-3)^3$ 11

17) $\dfrac{-2^2(-4 - 3) + 4(-6)}{-5 + 3(-3 \cdot 5) + (5 \cdot 2)}$ $-\dfrac{1}{10}$

18) This problem is done incorrectly. Find the error and correct it.

$$-6^2 \div |13 - 17|$$

Work: $-6^2 \div |13 - 17| =$
$36 \div |13 - 17| =$
$36 \div 4 = 9$

Solve each problem.

19) Katherine has $\dfrac{7}{8}$ as many followers on Twitter as her best friend Cailen. If Cailen has 112 followers, how many followers does Katherine have? 98 followers

20) Jeanmarie's bill at a café is $5.33. She gives the cashier a $10 bill and eight pennies. How much change does she receive? $4.75

21) Here is Xiaopeng's grade report from last semester. Find his GPA. Let A = 4 points, B = 3 points, C = 2 points, D = 1 point, and F = 0 points. Round the answer to the nearest hundredth. 3.13

Course	Grade	Credits
Organic Chemistry	B	4
Calculus	A	5
English Literature	C	3
Speech	B	3

22) A nursing student observes an intravenous drip rate of 14 drops per 12 seconds. How many drops should be observed in 1 minute? 70 drops

23) Reza flies his kite using 25 m of kite string. How high above his hand is Reza's kite when he uses all 25 m of his kite string and he is standing 15 m away from directly below the kite? 20 m

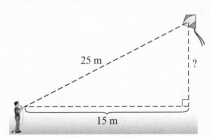

24) A health clinic found that approximately 4.5% of its patients are allergic to bee stings. If the clinic has 1800 patients, how many are allergic to bee stings? 81 patients

25) Tamara deposits $12,000 into an account for 6 years at 5% interest compounded annually. How much will be in her account after this time? How much interest will she earn? Use $A = P(1 + R)^T$.
total: $16,081.15; interest: $4081.15

Appendix

A.1 More on Bar Graphs and Line Graphs

Objectives

1. Use a Double-Bar Graph
2. Use a Comparison Line Graph

Data are facts or pieces of information. We can use *statistics* to organize and analyze data. **Statistics** is a branch of mathematics that includes the collection, analysis, and interpretation of data. We have used bar and line graphs throughout the textbook to organize data, and in this section, we will use graphs to compare *two* sets of data.

1 Use a Double-Bar Graph

A **double-bar graph** can be used to compare two sets of data. Use the double-bar graph to answer the questions in Example 1.

EXAMPLE 1

In-Class Example 1

Use the graph in Example 1.

a) Find the number of new subscribers in the fourth quarter of 2010.

b) Find the number of new subscribers in the fourth quarter of 2009.

c) How many more new subscribers did Netflix have in the fourth quarter of 2010 than during the same quarter of 2009?

d) Find the ratio of the number of new subscribers in the second quarter of 2009 to the number in the first quarter of 2009.

The double-bar graph shows the number of new Netflix subscribers during each quarter of 2009 and 2010. Use the graph to answer the questions. (files.shareholder.com/downloads/NFLX)

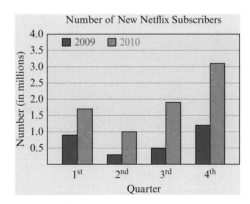

Number of New Netflix Subscribers

a) Find the number of new subscribers in the third quarter of 2009.

b) Find the number of new subscribers in the third quarter of 2010.

c) How many more new subscribers did Netflix have in the third quarter of 2010 than during the same quarter of 2009?

d) Find the ratio of the number of new subscribers in the fourth quarter of 2009 to the number of new subscribers in the first quarter of 2009.

Solution

a) First, notice that the graph tells us that the blue bars represent the numbers for 2009, and the red bars represent the numbers for 2010. Along the bottom of the graph, locate the 3rd quarter. The blue bar represents the number of new subscribers in the third quarter of 2009, and it reaches up to about 0.5 million. **In 2009, Netflix gained about 0.5 million new subscribers.**

b) The red bar above the 3rd quarter on the graph represents the number of new subscribers in the third quarter of 2010, and it reaches up to about 1.9 million. **In 2010, Netflix gained about 1.9 million new subscribers.**

c) To determine how many more new subscribers Netflix had in the third quarter of 2010 than in the third quarter of 2009, subtract the number found in part a) from the number found in part b).

$$1.9 \text{ million} - 0.5 \text{ million} = 1.4 \text{ million}$$

$$\uparrow \qquad\qquad \uparrow$$

Number   Number
in 2010   in 2009

In the third quarter of 2010, Netflix had 1.4 million more new subscribers than in the third quarter of 2009.

d) Locate the number of new subscribers in the fourth quarter of 2009. Go to the 4th quarter column. The blue bar reaches up to 1.2 million. Now, go to the 1st quarter column. The blue bar reaches up to approximately 0.9 million. Find the ratio.

$$\frac{\text{number in } 4^{th} \text{ quarter of 2009}}{\text{number in } 1^{st} \text{ quarter of 2009}} = \frac{1.2 \text{ million}}{0.9 \text{ million}} = \frac{1.2}{0.9} = \frac{1.2 \cdot 10}{0.9 \cdot 10} = \frac{12}{9} = \frac{4}{3}$$

The ratio of the number of new subscribers in the fourth quarter of 2009 to the number in the first quarter of 2009 is $\dfrac{4}{3}$. This means that for every 4 new subscribers in the fourth quarter of 2009, there were 3 new subscribers in the first quarter of 2009.

[YOU TRY 1] Use the graph in Example 1.

a) How many more new subscribers did Netflix have in the second quarter of 2010 than in the same quarter of 2009?

b) During which quarter were the 2009 numbers about half of the 2010 numbers?

c) Find the ratio of the number of new subscribers in the second quarter of 2009 to the number in the last quarter of 2009. Explain the meaning of the answer.

---

2 Use a Comparison Line Graph

We can also use a **comparison line graph** to compare two sets of data.

EXAMPLE 2

In-Class Example 2

Use Example 2.

The comparison line graph shows the corn crop yield (the amount of corn produced per acre), in bushels per acre, for Illinois and Minnesota from 2006 to 2010. Use the graph to answer the questions. (www.census.gov)

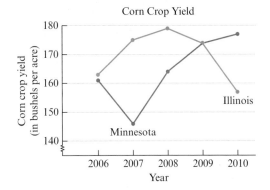

a) In which year did Minnesota have a greater yield than Illinois? What was Minnesota's yield during that year?

b) How many more bushels per acre did Illinois have in 2008 compared with Minnesota?

c) During which year were their yields the same? What was the yield?

Solution

a) First, notice that the blue line represents the crop yield for Illinois. The red line represents the crop yield for Minnesota. To determine when Minnesota had a greater corn crop yield than Illinois, locate the point where the red graph is above the blue graph. That year is 2010. **In 2010, Minnesota had a greater yield than Illinois.** Now, locate the height of the red point for 2010 by looking at the scale to the left. It matches up to about 177. **In 2010, the corn crop yield for Minnesota was 177 bushels per acre.**

b) Locate the year 2008 along the bottom of the graph. Move up to the red line to determine that Minnesota's yield was about 164 bushels per acre. Now, move up to the blue line. Illinois' crop yield was about 179 bushels per acre.

To determine the difference in their yields, subtract.

$$179 \text{ bushels per acre} - 164 \text{ bushels per acre} = 15 \text{ bushels per acre}$$

↑   ↑   ↑

Illinois' yield   Minnesota's yield   Difference in their yields

In 2008, Illinois' corn crop yield was 15 bushels per acre more than Minnesota's yield.

c) How do we know when their corn crop yields were the same? It is where their graphs *intersect*. (The place where two lines **intersect** is the place where they meet.) Locate this point. Read the year and yield. The year is 2009, and the yield is about 174 bushels per acre. **In 2009, the corn crop yield for both Illinois and Minnesota was 174 bushels per acre.**

[YOU TRY 2] Use the graph in Example 2.

a) In which year was Illinois' yield about 2 bushels per acre more than Minnesota's?

b) Which state had the higher yield in 2007? What was the difference?

c) Find the percent decrease in Illinois' yield from 2009 to 2010. Round the answer to the nearest tenth of a percent.

A.1 Exercises

Additional answers can be found in the Answers to Exercises appendix.

Objective 1: Use a Double-Bar Graph

1) How is a double-bar graph used?
   It is used to compare two sets of data.

2) What are *data*?   facts or pieces of information

Punkin chunkin is the sport of *chunking*, or hurling, a pumpkin using human power or a mechanical device. The World Championship Punkin Chunkin competition is held the first weekend after Halloween in Sussex County, Delaware. The double-bar graph shows the longest distance chunked by three teams in the 2010 and 2011 World Championship in the Adult Catapult division. Use the graph for Exercises 3–10. Answers may vary slightly.
(www.punkinchunkin.com)

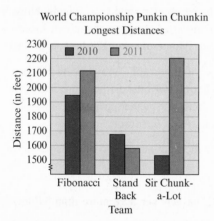

World Championship Punkin Chunkin Longest Distances

3) How far did team Fibonacci chunk a pumpkin in 2011?   2118 ft

4) How far did team Sir Chunk-a-Lot chunk a pumpkin in 2010?   1532 ft

5) How far did team Fibonacci chunk a pumpkin in 2010?   1947 ft

6) How far did team Sir Chunk-a-Lot chunk a pumpkin in 2011?   2206 ft

7) How much farther did Fibonacci chunk a pumpkin in 2011 than in 2010?   171 ft

8) How much farther did Sir Chunk-a-Lot chunk a pumpkin in 2011 than in 2010?   674 ft

9) Which team chunked the pumpkin farther in 2010 than in 2011?   Stand Back

10) See Exercise 9. Use a signed number to represent the change from 2010 to 2011.   −96 ft

The double-bar graph displays the 2009 and 2010 earnings of some of the music industry's top artists. Use the graph for Exercises 11–16. Answers may vary slightly. (www.billboard.com)

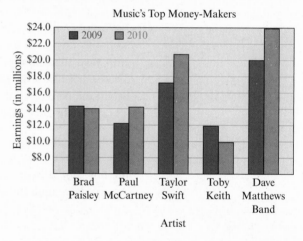

Music's Top Money-Makers

11) Which artists earned about the same amount of money in 2010? Approximately how much did each earn?   Brad Paisley and Paul McCartney; Paisley: $14.0 million, McCartney: $14.2 million

12) Which artists earned more in 2009 than in 2010?
    Brad Paisley and Toby Keith

13) How much more did Taylor Swift earn in 2010 than in 2009? $3.5 million

14) How much less did the Dave Matthews Band earn in 2009 than in 2010? $3.9 million

15) Find the ratio of the Dave Matthews Band's earnings in 2009 to Brad Paisley's earnings in 2010. Explain the meaning of this ratio.   ratio = $\frac{10}{7}$. For every $10 the Dave Matthews Band earned in 2009, Brad Paisley earned $7 in 2010.

16) Who earned the most and the least in 2010? What is the difference in their earnings?   most: Dave Matthews Band, least: Toby Keith. The difference in their earnings was $14.0 million.

Objective 2: Use a Comparison Line Graph

The comparison line graph displays the average number of viewers each night during a given week in 2011 for *The Daily Show* with Jon Stewart and *The Colbert Report* with Steven Colbert. Use the graph for Exercises 17–22. (tvbythenumbers.zap2it.com)

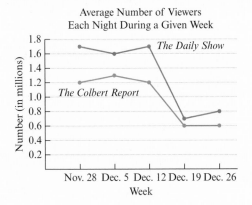

Average Number of Viewers Each Night During a Given Week

17) Which show had more viewers each week?
The Daily Show

18) How many more people watched *The Daily Show* each night during the week of Dec. 12? Write your answer in thousands.   500,000

19) How many fewer people watched *The Colbert Report* each night during the week of Dec. 26? Write your answer in thousands.   200,000

20) During which week did the two shows have the closest number of viewers? What was the difference in the numbers? Write your answer in thousands.
Dec. 19; 100,000

21) For *The Daily Show*, use a fraction to compare the average number of viewers each night during the week of Dec. 26 compared with the week of Dec. 5. Explain your comparison in a complete sentence.
The average number of viewers each night during the week of Dec. 26 was $\frac{1}{2}$ the number of average viewers during the week of Dec. 5.

22) For *The Colbert Report*, use a fraction to compare the average number of viewers each night during the week of Dec. 26 compared with the week of Nov. 28. Explain your comparison in a complete sentence.
The average number of viewers each night during the week of Dec. 26 was $\frac{1}{2}$ the average number of viewers during the week of Nov. 28.

The comparison line graph shows the scores for two cowboys in the Bareback Riding category at the Ram First Frontier Circuit Finals Rodeo in Harrisburg, Pennsylvania, January 12–14, 2012. Use the graph for Exercises 23–28.
(www.prorodeo.com)

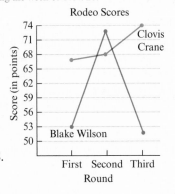

Rodeo Scores

23) Which cowboy improved with each round?
Clovis Crane

24) During which round did Blake Wilson score higher than Clovis Crane?   second round

25) How many more points did Crane score in the last round compared with Wilson?   22 points

26) How many fewer points did Wilson score in the first round compared with Crane?   14 points

27) Use a signed number to represent the change in Blake Wilson's score from the second to the third round.   −21 points

28) Between which two rounds did Clovis Crane's score increase by 6 points?   from the second to the third round

Mixed Exercises: Objectives 1 and 2

29) The table displays the approximate number of visitors to select cities in 2009 and 2010. Make a double-bar graph to display the information in the table. (www.visitorlando.com, www.lasvegassun.com, discoverlosangeles.com, newyork.cbslocal.com)

Number of Visitors to Select Cities (in millions)

	2009	2010
New York City	46	49
Las Vegas	36	37
Los Angeles	24	26
Orlando	47	52

30) The table displays the approximate total gross United States earnings of Brad Pitt movies and George Clooney movies during the years 2007–2011. Make a comparison line graph to display the information. (www.the-numbers.com)

Total Domestic Earnings of Movies (in millions)

	Brad Pitt	George Clooney
2007	$121	$166
2008	$188	$92
2009	$121	$137
2010	$148	$36
2011	$150	$88

A.2 Draw a Circle Graph

Objective

1. Make a Circle Graph

1 Make a Circle Graph

Circle graphs can be used to organize information about parts of a total amount. Throughout this book, we have analyzed data given in the form of a circle graph. Now, we will learn how to *make* a circle graph.

Recall that a circle has 360°. If we split a circle in half, each *sector* has 180°. (A **sector** of the circle is a pie-shaped portion of the circle.)

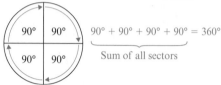

Each sector is $\frac{1}{2}$, or 50%, of the circle. And,

$$\underbrace{180° + 180°}_{\substack{\text{Sum of} \\ \text{both} \\ \text{sectors}}} = \underset{\substack{\uparrow \\ \text{Total number} \\ \text{of degrees in} \\ \text{a circle}}}{360°}$$

If we divide the circle in half again, how many degrees are in each sector? 90°

$$90° + 90° + 90° + 90° = 360°$$

Sum of all sectors

What *fraction* of the circle does each 90° sector represent?

$$\frac{\text{number of degrees in the sector}}{\text{total number of degrees in a circle}} = \frac{90°}{360°} = \frac{1}{4}$$

Each 90° sector is $\frac{1}{4}$ of the circle.

What *percent* of the circle does each 90° sector represent?

$$\frac{90°}{360°} = \frac{1}{4} = 0.25 = 25\%$$

Each 90° sector is 25% of the circle.

We use a tool called a **protractor** to draw a circle graph. A protractor measures the number of degrees in an angle, and it allows us to draw angles of certain degrees. To determine the size of each sector in a circle graph, we calculate the number of degrees in each sector using percents.

EXAMPLE 1

In-Class Example 1

Use Example 1.

Mrs. Szymanski's English Composition class has 20 students. The table gives us information about the number of hours worked each week by the students in her class. Make a circle graph to display this information.

Number of Hours Worked Each Week	Percent of the Students in the Class
Do not work at all	10%
Less than 20 hr	35%
20–40 hr	50%
More than 40 hr	5%
Total	100%

Each category for number of hours worked will be represented by a sector of the circle. We use the percentages to determine the size of each sector.

$$\begin{matrix} \text{Number of degrees} \\ \text{in a sector} \end{matrix} = \begin{matrix} \text{Percent of} \\ \text{students} \end{matrix} \cdot \begin{matrix} \text{Total degrees in} \\ \text{a circle} \end{matrix}$$

$$\begin{matrix} \text{Number of degrees} \\ \text{in a sector} \end{matrix} = \begin{matrix} \text{Percent of} \\ \text{students} \end{matrix} \cdot \quad 360°$$

Before we make the circle graph, let's figure out the number of degrees each sector will have.

Hours Worked	Percent	Number of Degrees in the Sector
None	10%	10% of 360° = 0.10 · 360° = 36°
Less than 20	35%	35% of 360° = 0.35 · 360° = 126°
20–40	50%	50% of 360° = 0.50 · 360° = 180°
More than 40	5%	5% of 360° = 0.05 · 360° = 18°
		Total number of degrees = 360°

Note

If the degrees in the table do not add up to 360°, then there is a mistake somewhere. Double-check your work.

Now let's draw the circle graph. We'll begin with the sector containing 36° and work our way down the table.

Draw a circle. Use a straightedge to draw a line from the center to the left edge of the circle. Place the protractor on the circle so that the hole in the protractor is over the center of the circle and so that the 0 on the left lines up with the line on the left. Read 36° from the left and make a mark at this point. Draw a line from the center of the circle to the mark at 36°. Label the sector.

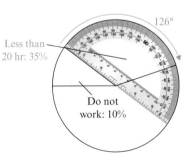

Next, let's make the sector that represents the percent of students who work less than 20 hr per week. According to the table, this sector will measure 126°.

Line up the protractor on the second line you drew, putting the hole in the protractor over the center of the circle. Starting at the left, move over 126°, and make a mark. Draw a line from the center of the circle to the mark. Label this sector.

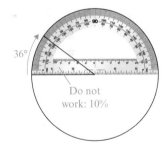

Number of Hours Students
Work, per Week

Now we will make the sector that represents the 50% of students who work 20–40 hr per week. Our calculations tell us that this sector will contain 180°. (To draw this sector, it may be helpful if you turn your paper so that you are not working upside down.)

Line up the protractor on the last line drawn with the hole in the protractor over the center of the circle. Make a mark at 180°, and label the sector.

The remaining, fourth sector represents the students who work more than 40 hr per week. (You can double-check that this sector has 18°.)

This is the circle graph that represents the data given in the table.

[YOU TRY 1] During the month of May, 340 people had their hair dyed at a certain salon. The table shows the percent of people who chose each color for dyeing their hair. Make a circle graph to display this information.

Hair Dyeing in May

Color	Percent of People Who Chose the Color
Blonde	50%
Brown	25%
Black	15%
Red	10%

We can use the circle graph to answer questions like we did in other sections of the book.

EXAMPLE 2

Use the circle graph in Example 1 to answer the questions.

a) How many students work 20–40 hr per week?
b) How many students do not work at all?

Solution

a) There are 20 students in the class, and the circle graph shows that 50% of the students work 20–40 hr per week. Therefore, the number of students who work 20–40 hr per week is 50% *of* 20.

$$50\% \text{ of } 20 = 0.50 \cdot 20 = 10$$

Ten students work 20–40 hr per week.

b) 10% of the students in the class do not work at all. Therefore, the number of students who do not work is 10% *of* 20.

$$10\% \text{ of } 20 = 0.10 \cdot 20 = 2$$

Two students do not work.

In-Class Example 2

Use the circle graph in Example 1 to answer the questions.

a) How many students work less than 20 hr per week? (Do not count those who do *not* work.)

b) How many students do not work at all?

Answer:

a) 7 students

b) 2 students

[YOU TRY 2] Use the circle graph in You Try 1 to answer the questions.

a) How many people dyed their hair blonde?
b) How many people dyed their hair red?
c) How many more people dyed their hair blonde compared with red?

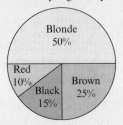
A.2 Exercises

*Additional answers can be found in the Answers to Exercises appendix.

Objective 1: Make a Circle Graph

1) How many degrees are in a circle?   360°

2) What is a sector of a circle?
It is a pie-shaped portion of a circle.

3) What is a protractor?   It is a tool that measures the number of degrees in an angle and that allows us to draw angles of certain degrees.

4) A table gives information in terms of the percent of the whole represented by each category. How do you determine the number of degrees in a sector of a circle graph that displays this information?
Multiply the percent in each category by 360°.

Each percent in Exercises 5–8 represents a share of the total in a table. If you are making a circle graph, determine the number of degrees in the sector.

5) 45%   162°   6) 65%   234°

7) 30%   108°   8) 50%   180°

9) After calculating the number of degrees in every sector of a circle graph, the degrees should add up to what number?   360°

10) In your own words, explain how to make a circle graph.   Answers may vary.

The table shows how Scott classifies his 320 Facebook friends.

Scott's Facebook Friends

Scott's Facebook Friends	Percent of the Total Number of Friends
Work-related	40%
Family	10%
Close friends	5%
Casual acquaintances	20%
Barely know them	25%

Follow the steps to make a circle graph. Then, answer the questions in Exercises 11–18.

11) a) Determine the number of degrees needed for each sector in the circle graph. work-related: 144°, family: 36°, close friends: 18°, casual acquaintances: 72°, barely know them: 90°
   b) Draw the circle graph.

12) How many of Scott's Facebook friends are family members?   32

13) How many of Scott's Facebook friends are close friends?   16

14) How many of Scott's Facebook friends does he know through work?   128

15) How many of Scott's Facebook friends does he barely know?   80

16) Find the ratio of family members to work-related friends. Explain what the ratio means.

17) Find the ratio of close friends to the people he barely knows. Explain what the ratio means.

18) How many more casual acquaintances does he have compared with those he calls close friends?
Scott has 48 more casual acquaintances.

Holly earns $2500 per month. The table displays how she spends her money each month.

Holly's Monthly Expenses

Expenses	Percent of Monthly Income
Rent	30%
Child care	20%
Food	15%
Utilities	10%
Other	25%

Follow the steps to make a circle graph. Then, answer the questions in Exercises 19–26.

19) a) Determine the number of degrees needed for each sector in the circle graph.
    rent: 108°, child care: 72°, food: 54°, utilities: 36°, other: 90°
    b) Draw the circle graph.

20) How much does Holly spend on rent? $750

21) How much does Holly pay for child care every month? $500

22) How much more does Holly spend on food than on utilities? $125 more

23) Find the ratio of the amount spent on rent to the amount spent on child care. Explain what the ratio means.   ratio = $\frac{3}{2}$. For every $3 Holly pays in rent, she pays $2 for child care.

24) Find the ratio of the amount spent on food to the amount spent on utilities. Explain what the ratio means.   ratio = $\frac{3}{2}$. For every $3 Holly spends on food, she spends $2 on utilities.

25) What are some expenses that might be included in the *Other* category?   Answers may vary.

26) After taking care of the first four expenses in the table, how much does Holly have left for *Other* expenses? $625

27) A total of 1200 students are taking Beginning Algebra at a community college. The course is offered in four different formats: in a *traditional classroom,* in a *math lab,* as a *hybrid* of lecture and online, and completely *online.* The table shows the number of students taking Beginning Algebra in each format.

Students Enrolled in Beginning Algebra

Format	Number of Students	Percent of Total	Degrees in the Sector
Traditional	540	45%	162°
Math lab	300	25%	90°
Hybrid	240	20%	72°
Online	120	10%	36°

a) Determine the percent of the total number of students taking Beginning Algebra in each format.

b) Determine the number of degrees needed to represent each category as a sector in a circle graph.

c) Make a circle graph to display the number of students taking Beginning Algebra in each format.

28) A total of 800 people were asked how many nights their family eats dinner together each week. The table displays the results of the survey.

Number of Nights Families Eat Dinner Together Each Week

Number of Nights Families Eat Dinner Together Each Week	Number of Families	Percent of Total	Degrees in the Sector
0	40	5%	18°
1–2	80	10%	36°
3–4	200	25%	90°
5–6	280	35%	126°
7	200	25%	90°

a) Determine the percent of the total for each category.

b) Determine the number of degrees needed to represent each category as a sector in a circle graph.

c) Make a circle graph to display the information labeled with the percent of the families who eat dinner together a given number of times each week.

A.3 Frequency Distributions and Histograms

Objectives

1. Make a Frequency Distribution Table
2. Make a Table Using Class Intervals
3. Use a Histogram

Frequency is defined as the number of times something occurs. If we have a lot of data, we can organize it in a *frequency distribution table*.

1 Make a Frequency Distribution Table

Joe is a construction worker. Here is a list of the number of hours he worked each week in 2012.

8	26	26	26	28	28	28	27	30	34	0	37	39
37	38	40	39	40	40	39	32	44	40	40	44	42
32	0	16	40	40	39	24	0	40	40	26	40	40
39	40	32	39	40	40	30	24	30	27	26	24	16

It seems that there is no organization in this table. Let's organize the data in a **frequency distribution table** so that they are easier to read.

EXAMPLE 1

In-Class Example 1

Make a frequency distribution table to organize the data on Joe's weekly hours worked given before Example 1.

a) How many times did Joe work 30 hr in a week?

b) Which number of hours did he work most often?

Answer:

a) 3 times b) 40 hr

Make a frequency distribution table to organize the data. Then, answer the questions.

a) How many times did Joe work 26 hr in a week?

b) The only time Joe did not work in a given week was when he took vacation time. How many times did this happen?

Solution

Begin by making a column listing the number of hours worked each week. Then, go through the list and put a tally mark, |, next to the number of hours worked each time that number appears. Finally, count the tally marks in each row and put that total in a third column labeled *Frequency*. This tells us the number of times that each number of hours appears in the list.

Number of Hours Worked	Tally	Frequency	Number of Hours Worked	Tally	Frequency
0	III	3	32	III	3
8	I	1	34	I	1
16	II	2	37	II	2
24	III	3	38	I	1
26	IIII	5	39	IIII I	6
27	II	2	40	IIII IIII IIII	14
28	III	3	42	I	1
30	III	3	44	II	2

(Notice that the sum of the numbers in the frequency column is 52, the total number of weeks in the first table.)

a) Now that we have organized the information in this table, it is easier for us to see that Joe worked 26 hr in a week 5 times.

b) Joe took vacation time 3 times during 2012.

[YOU TRY 1]

Use the table in Example 1.

a) How many times did Joe work 16 hr in one week?

b) Which number of hours did he work 5 times?

2 Make a Table Using Class Intervals

In Example 1, notice that there are 16 different categories for the number of hours worked. We can simplify the table by organizing the number of hours worked into *class intervals*. A **class interval** is a range of values into which data are organized.

EXAMPLE 2

In-Class Example 2

Make a table as in Example 2. Then, answer the questions.

a) How many times did Joe work between 0 and 9 hr per week?

b) Which range of hours did he work 16 times?

Answer:

a) 4 times

b) 30–39 hr

Make a new table from the data in Example 1 by organizing the data into class intervals. Then, answer the questions.

a) How many times did Joe work between 20 and 29 hr per week?

b) Which range of hours did he work the least?

Solution

Let's organize the number of hours worked into intervals 0–9, 10–19, 20–29, etc. (These are the class intervals.) Add the frequencies in those intervals in the table in Example 1 to get the numbers for the Class Frequency column in Example 2.

Number of Hours Worked (Class Intervals)	Class Frequency
0–9	4
10–19	2
20–29	13
30–39	16
40–49	17

a) Looking at the class interval 20–29, we see that the corresponding class frequency is 13. **Joe worked 20–29 hr in a week 13 times.**

b) Look for the smallest class frequency. That is 2. The corresponding class interval (number of hours worked) is 10–19. **The range of hours that Joe worked the least was 10–19 hr.**

Note

We can use any range of numbers in a class interval. Look at the numbers in the table to decide which range would make sense.

[YOU TRY 2] Use the table in Example 2.

How many times did Joe work 30–39 hr per week?

3 Use a Histogram

From the table containing the class intervals in Example 2, we can make a special type of bar graph called a *histogram*. In a **histogram,** the width of each bar represents the class intervals, and the height represents the class frequency. Also, the width of each bar, and therefore the size of each class interval, is the same in a histogram.

EXAMPLE 3

In-Class Example 3

Use Example 3.

The histogram displays the information in the table in Example 2. Use the histogram to answer the questions.

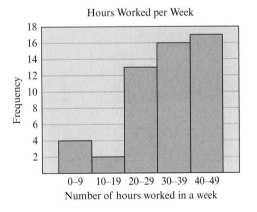

a) Which range of hours did Joe work most often?

b) How many weeks did Joe work less than 30 hr?

Solution

a) The highest bar is for the 40–49 hr class interval. Therefore, Joe worked 40–49 hours most often.

b) To determine the number of weeks he worked less than 30 hr, add the number of weeks in the categories 0–9 hr, 10–19 hr, and 20–29 hr.

$$4 \quad + \quad 2 \quad + \quad 13 \quad = \quad 19 \text{ weeks}$$

↑
number of
times worked
0–9 hr

↑
number of
times worked
10–19 hr

↑
number of
times worked
20–29 hr

[YOU TRY 3] Use the histogram in Example 3.

How many times did Joe work 30 hr per week or more?

ANSWERS TO [YOU TRY] EXERCISES

1) a) 2 times   b) 26 hr   2) 16 times   3) 33 times

A.3 Exercises

*Additional answers can be found in the Answers to Exercises appendix.

Objective 3: Use a Histogram

Seasonal snowfall is computed from July 1 of one year through June 30 of the next year. (For example, the 2010 seasonal snowfall amount is computed from July 1, 2010 through June 30, 2011.) The histogram shows the seasonal snowfall amounts in Syracuse, New York, from 1970 to 2011. Use the histogram for Exercises 1–8. (www.erh.noaa.gov)

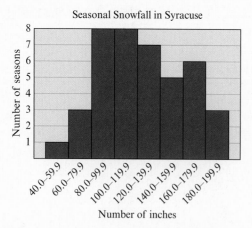

Seasonal Snowfall in Syracuse

1) During how many seasons did Syracuse have 140.0–159.9 in. of snow?   5

2) During how many seasons did Syracuse have 60.0–79.9 in. of snow?   3

3) Which snowfall amount occurred least often? How many seasons had this amount?   40.0–59.9 in.; 1

4) Which snowfall amount occurred most often? How many seasons had this amount?

Two amounts occurred 8 times each: 80.0–99.9 in. and 100.0–119.9 in.

5) Which snowfall amount occurred six times?
160.0–179.9 in.

6) Which snowfall amount occurred seven times?
120.0–139.9 in.

7) How many seasons did Syracuse have at least 120.0 in. of snow?   21 seasons

8) How many seasons did Syracuse have less than 100.0 in. of snow?   12 seasons

An active adult community has 800 residents, all of whom are aged 55 or older. The histogram shows the frequency of the residents' ages. Use the histogram for Exercises 9–18.

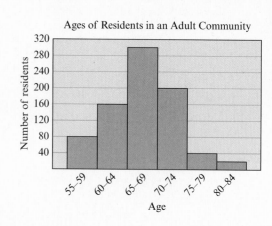

Ages of Residents in an Adult Community

9) How many residents are 60–64 yr old?   160

10) How many residents are 70–74 yr old?   200

11) Which age group has the most residents? How many residents are in this group?   65–69 yr; 300 residents

12) Which age group has the fewest residents? How many residents are in this group?   80–84 yr; 20 residents

13) What percent of the residents are 65–69 yr old? 37.5%

14) What percent of the residents are 80–84 yr old? 2.5%

15) Find the ratio of the number of oldest residents to the number of youngest residents. Explain the meaning of this ratio. ratio = $\frac{1}{4}$. For every resident who is 80–84 yr old, there are four residents who are 55–59 yr old.

16) Find the ratio of the number of 65–69 yr old residents to the number of oldest residents. Explain the meaning of this ratio. ratio = $\frac{15}{1}$. For every 15 residents who are 65–69 yr old, there is one resident who is 80–84 yr old.

17) How many residents are under 70? 540

18) How many residents are 70 or older? 260

A manufacturing company has 80 employees. The histogram shows the number of years its employees have worked at the company. Use the histogram for Exercises 19–30.

Number of Years Working at the Company

19) How many people have worked at the company for 10–14 yr? 15

20) How many people have worked at the company for 25–29 yr? 6

21) The greatest number of employees are in which range of years worked? 15–19 yr

22) The least number of employees are in which range of years worked? 35–39 yr

23) Find the ratio of the number of employees who have worked at the company 0–4 years to the number who have worked 40–44 yr. Explain the meaning of this ratio.

24) Find the ratio of the number of employees who have worked at the company 20–24 yr to the number who have worked 15–19 yr. Explain the meaning of this ratio.

25) How many people have worked at the company for at least 20 yr? 23

26) How many people have worked at the company less than 10 yr? 24

27) What percent of the employees have worked at the company for at least 20 yr? 28.75%

28) What percent of the employees have worked at the company less than 10 yr? 30%

29) What percent of the employees have been working the shortest time? 10%

30) What percent of the employees have been working the longest time? 2.5%

The histogram shows the heights, in inches, of members of a professional basketball team. Use the histogram for Exercises 31–40.

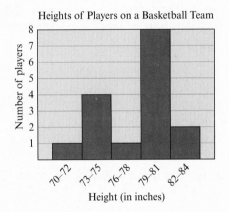

Heights of Players on a Basketball Team

31) The least number of players are in which height category? How many are in this category?

32) The greatest number of players are in which height category? How many are in this category? 79–81 in.; 8 players

33) a) How many team members are 82–84 in. tall? 2 players

b) We can also think of height in terms of feet and inches. For example, 63 in. = 5 ft 3 in. Rewrite the height range 82–84 in. as feet and inches. 6 ft 10 in.–7 ft

34) a) How many team members are 73–75 in. tall? 4 players

b) See Exercise 33 b). Rewrite the height range 73–75 in. as feet and inches. 6 ft 1 in.–6 ft 3 in.

35) How many players are less than 79 in. (6 ft 7 in.) tall? 6

36) How many players are 79 in. (6 ft 7 in.) or taller? 10

37) What percent of the team is less than 79 in. tall? 37.5%

38) What percent of the team is 79 in. or taller? 62.5%

39) How many more players are in the tallest group than in the shortest group? 1

40) How many fewer players are 79–81 in. tall compared with 76–78 in. tall?   7

Mixed Exercises: Objectives 1–3

41) Here are the test scores, in percent, for the 32 students in Mr. Garcia's Botany class.

73	82	51	94	76	71	68	73
85	90	72	63	76	83	79	73
81	59	66	77	91	60	70	46
75	54	78	43	88	73	80	74

a) Make a table like the one here to organize the information. Make a tally of the frequency of the scores in the class intervals, then count the tally marks and fill in the class frequency in the last column.

Test Scores (Class Intervals)	Tally	Number of Scores (Class Frequency)
40–49	II	2
50–59	III	3
60–69	IIII	4
70–79	IIII IIII IIII	14
80–89	IIII I	6
90–99	III	3

b) Make a histogram to display the information in the table.

c) Write three questions that could be asked about the data. Answer the questions.   Answers may vary.

42) At a wellness fair, 40 college employees had their LDL cholesterol levels checked. (This is the so-called *bad* cholesterol.) Here were their scores.

93	148	127	82	103	165	210	131	119	74
158	186	143	107	191	99	172	149	154	126
166	140	159	170	100	216	152	138	125	172
98	121	147	163	130	195	85	97	116	184

a) The medical community classifies the LDL scores as shown here. Make a table like this one to organize the information. Make a tally of the frequency of the scores in the class intervals, then count the tally marks and fill in the class frequency in the last column. (www.heart.org)

LDL Scores (Class Intervals)	Tally	Number of Scores (Class Frequency)
70–99 (Good)	IIII II	7
100–129 (Near optimal)	IIII IIII	9
130–159 (Borderline high)	IIII IIII II	12
160–189 (High)	IIII III	8
190–219 (Very high)	IIII	4

b) Make a histogram to display the information in the table.

c) Write three questions that could be asked about the data. Answer the questions.   Answers may vary.

A.4 Inductive and Deductive Reasoning

In this section, we will learn how to use inductive and deductive reasoning.

1 Use Inductive Reasoning

What is inductive reasoning? We are using **inductive reasoning** when we use specific observations to draw general conclusions. Scientists often draw general conclusions after performing experiments in which they get the same results every time. They are using inductive reasoning. We can use inductive reasoning to look at a sequence of numbers and figure out what the next number in the sequence will be.

EXAMPLE 1

Use inductive reasoning to find the next number in each sequence.

a) 1, 4, 7, 10, 13, ...   b) 3, 6, 12, 24, 48, ...

Solution

a) To use inductive reasoning, we want to find the *specific* pattern used to obtain the numbers in the sequence to come up with a *general* conclusion. Ask yourself, *"How do we get from one number in the sequence to the next?"* Add 3.

$$1 \quad\quad 4 \quad\quad 7 \quad\quad 10 \quad\quad 13$$
$$1+3=4 \quad 4+3=7 \quad 7+3=10 \quad 10+3=13$$

We get each number in the sequence by adding 3 to the previous number. Therefore, the next number is $13 + 3 = 16$.

b) Ask yourself, *"How do we get from one number in the sequence to the next?"* Multiply by 2.

$$3 \quad\quad 6 \quad\quad 12 \quad\quad 24 \quad\quad 48$$
$$3 \cdot 2 = 6 \quad 6 \cdot 2 = 12 \quad 12 \cdot 2 = 24 \quad 24 \cdot 2 = 48$$

We get each number in the sequence by multiplying the previous number by 2. Therefore, the next number is $48 \cdot 2 = 96$.

We could have looked for the pattern by dividing each number by the number before it: $\frac{6}{3} = 2$, $\frac{12}{6} = 2$, $\frac{24}{12} = 2$, $\frac{48}{24} = 2$. Since one number *divided by* the previous number is always 2, it follows that to get from one number to the next we *multiply* by 2.

In-Class Example 1

Use inductive reasoning to find the next number in each sequence.

a) 1, 7, 13, 19, 25, ...
b) 7, 14, 28, 56, 112, ...

Answer:
a) 31   b) 224

Use inductive reasoning to find the next number in each sequence.

a) 5, 9, 13, 17, 21, …   b) 320, 160, 80, 40, 20, …

Sometimes, more than one operation is used to get from one number to the next.

EXAMPLE 2

In-Class Example 2

Find the next number in the sequence 32, 16, 48, 24, 72, 36, …

Answer: 108

Find the next number in the sequence 10, 5, 30, 15, 90, 45, …

Solution

Write out how to get from one number to the next until you find a specific pattern.

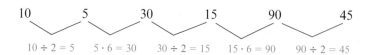

$10 \div 2 = 5$ $5 \cdot 6 = 30$ $30 \div 2 = 15$ $15 \cdot 6 = 90$ $90 \div 2 = 45$

To get the next number, multiply 45 by 6: $45 \cdot 6 = 270$. The next number is 270.

YOU TRY 2

Find the next number in the sequence 1, 10, 5, 14, 9, 18, …

EXAMPLE 3

In-Class Example 3

Use Example 3.

Find the next figure in the sequence.

Solution

The triangles follow the pattern of pointing up then pointing down.

So, the next triangle will point up. The number of dots increases by one, so the next figure will be

YOU TRY 3

Find the next figure in the sequence.

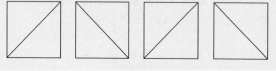

2 Use Deductive Reasoning

A statement that helps support a conclusion is called a **premise.** A set of premises together with a conclusion forms an **argument.** The mathematical symbol ∴ means **therefore.** In **deductive reasoning,** we start with *general* premises to come to a *specific* conclusion.

> **Note**
>
> Here is the difference between inductive and deductive reasoning: Inductive reasoning goes from specific observations to general conclusions while deductive reasoning goes from general premises to a specific conclusion.

EXAMPLE 4

In-Class Example 4

Identify the premises and the conclusion in this argument. Then, determine whether the conclusion follows from the premises.

All computers are machines. All laptops are computers. ∴ All laptops are machines.

Answer:

Premises: All computers are machines. All laptops are computers.

Conclusion: All laptops are machines.

The conclusion follows from the premises. Therefore, the conclusion is valid.

Identify the premises and the conclusion in this argument. Then, determine whether the conclusion follows from the premises.

All dogs are animals.   All poodles are dogs.   ∴ All poodles are animals.

Solution

Label each premise and the conclusion.

Premise: All dogs are animals.
Premise: All poodles are dogs.

Conclusion: All poodles are animals.

We can use Euler circles to analyze this argument. (**Euler circles** form a diagram in which statements are represented by circles.) Let's look at each premise.

All dogs are animals. The entire circle for Dogs is inside the Animals circle because the premise says that *all* dogs are animals.

All poodles are dogs. The entire circle for Poodles is inside the circle for Dogs because the premise says that *all* poodles are dogs.

Putting these circles together, we get this diagram to represent the premises taken together.

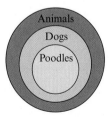

Because the circle representing the Poodles lies completely inside the Animals circle, it follows that all poodles are animals. Therefore, the conclusion *all poodles are animals* follows from the premises. We say that **the conclusion is valid.**

[YOU TRY 4] Identify the premises and the conclusion in this argument. Then, determine whether the conclusion follows from the premises.

All airplanes were built to fly.   All 747s are airplanes.   ∴ All 747s were built to fly.

EXAMPLE 5

In-Class Example 5

Identify the premises and the conclusion in this argument. Then, determine whether the conclusion follows from the premises.

All soccer balls are round. All basketballs are round. ∴ All basketballs are soccer balls.

Answer:

Premises: All soccer balls are round. All basketballs are round.

Conclusion: All basketballs are soccer balls.

The conclusion does *not* follow from the premises. Therefore, the conclusion is invalid.

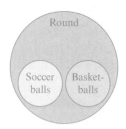

Identify the premises and the conclusion in this argument. Then, determine whether the conclusion follows from the premises.

All adults are tall.   All teenagers are tall.   ∴ All teenagers are adults.

Solution

Label each premise and the conclusion.

Premise: All adults are tall.
Premise: All teenagers are tall.

Conclusion: All teenagers are adults.

Use Euler circles to analyze this argument. Look at each premise.

All adults are tall. The entire circle for Adults is inside the Tall circle because the premise says that *all* adults are tall.

All teenagers are tall. The entire circle for Teenagers is inside the circle for Tall because the premise says that *all* teenagers are tall.

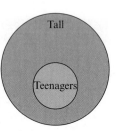

The Euler circles show that the premises do *not* relate teenagers and adults. The diagram at the right represents the premises taken together.

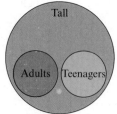

Therefore, the conclusion *all teenagers are adults* does **not** follow from the premises. We say that **the conclusion is invalid.**

[YOU TRY 5]

Identify the premises and the conclusion in this argument. Then, determine whether the conclusion follows from the premises.

All apples are fruit.   All strawberries are fruit.   ∴ All strawberries are apples.

---

3 Use Venn Diagrams to Solve Problems

A **Venn diagram** uses overlapping circles to show relationships between different sets of data.

EXAMPLE 6

Make a Venn diagram to solve the problem.

In a class of 32 students, 16 have iPhones, 23 have iPods, and 11 have both. How many students have neither an iPhone nor an iPod?

Make a Venn diagram to solve the problem.

In a high school class of 30 students, 19 of them take a foreign language, 15 take chemistry, and 12 take both. How many students take neither a foreign language nor chemistry?

Answer: 8

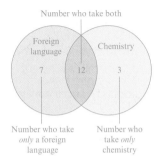

Solution

Draw one circle to represent the number of students who have an iPhone, another to represent the number who have iPods, and be sure they intersect. *The region where they intersect represents the number of students who own both.*

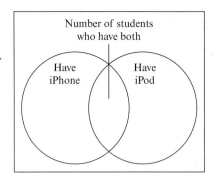

When you start writing the numbers in the circles, first write in the number of students who own both an iPhone and an iPod: 11.

Now, determine the number of students who own only an iPhone. If a total of 16 students have an iPhone and 11 have both, then 16 − 11 = 5 students have only an iPhone.

If a total of 23 students have an iPod and 11 have both, then 23 − 11 = 12 students have only an iPod.

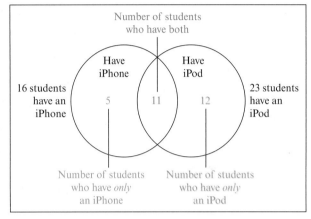

Add the numbers in the Venn diagram: 5 + 11 + 12 = 28. This tells us that 28 students own an iPhone, an iPod, or both. Because the total number of students is 32, the number of students who have neither an iPhone nor an iPod is 32 − 28 = 4 students.

[YOU TRY 6]

Make a Venn diagram to solve the problem.

Out of 78 participants at a flower show, 8 people have entered both the rose and the orchid competitions, 29 have entered the rose competition, and 24 have entered the orchid competition. How many participants are in a competition other than for roses or orchids?

ANSWERS TO [YOU TRY] EXERCISES

1) a) 25   b) 10   2) 13   3)

4) *Premises:* All airplanes were built to fly. All 747s are airplanes.
   Conclusion: All 747s were built to fly. The conclusion follows from the premises. Therefore, the conclusion is valid.
5) *Premises:* All apples are fruit. All strawberries are fruit.
   Conclusion: All strawberries are apples. The conclusion does *not* follow from the premises. Therefore, the conclusion is invalid.
6) 33 people

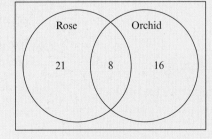

A.4 Exercises

*Additional answers can be found in the Answers to Exercises appendix.

Objective 1: Use Inductive Reasoning

Use inductive reasoning to find the next number in each sequence.

1) 4, 9, 14, 19, 24, … 29

2) 1, 8, 15, 22, 29, … 36

3) 2, 6, 18, 54, 162, … 486

4) 5, 10, 20, 40, 80, … 160

5) 91, 85, 79, 73, 67, … 61

6) 88, 77, 66, 55, 44, … 33

7) 9, 18, 10, 20, 12, 24, … 16

8) 4, 12, 7, 21, 16, 48, … 43

9) 1, 4, 9, 16, 25, 36, … 49

10) 1, 2, 4, 7, 11, 16, … 22

Find the next figure in each sequence.

11)
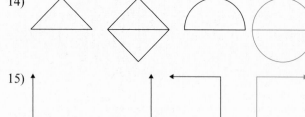

12)
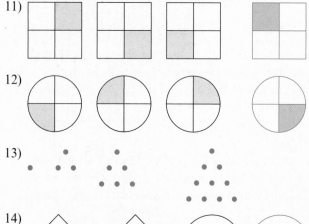

13)
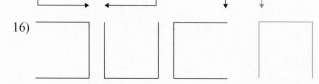

14)

15)

16)

Objective 2: Use Deductive Reasoning

17) What is the difference between inductive and deductive reasoning? Inductive reasoning goes from specific observations to general conclusions while deductive reasoning goes from general premises to a specific conclusion.

18) What does the mathematical symbol ∴ mean? therefore

Apply parts a)–c) to Exercises 19–26.

   a)   Identify the premises and conclusion in each argument.

   b)   Draw Euler circles to analyze each argument, then determine whether the conclusion follows from the premises.

   c)   Make a statement about whether the conclusion is valid or invalid.

19) All college graduates have diplomas. Ava is a college graduate. ∴ Ava has a diploma.

20) All four-sided, closed figures are quadrilaterals. A square is a four-sided, closed figure. ∴ A square is a quadrilateral.

21) All lakes contain water. Lake Michigan is a lake. ∴ Lake Michigan contains water.

22) All firefighters go through training. Hector is a firefighter. ∴ Hector goes through training.

23) All cats are animals. All rabbits are animals. ∴ All cats are rabbits.

24) San Antonio is in Texas. El Paso is in Texas. ∴ El Paso is in San Antonio.

25) Brett Favre was a football player. Joe Montana was a football player. ∴ Joe Montana was Brett Favre.

26) All bananas are yellow. All yield signs are yellow. ∴ All bananas are yield signs.

Objective 3: Use Venn Diagrams to Solve Problems

For Exercises 27–30, make a Venn diagram to solve each problem.

27) In a group of 50 people, 31 said they like chocolate ice cream, 20 said they like coffee ice cream, and 14 like both. How many people:

   a) like chocolate ice cream but not coffee ice cream? 17

   b) like coffee ice cream but not chocolate ice cream? 6

   c) do not like either flavor? 13

28) In a group of 83 people, 70 said they drink cow's milk, 16 said they drink soy milk, and 9 said they drink both. How many people:

 a) drink cow's milk but not soy milk? 61

 b) drink soy milk but not cow's milk? 7

 c) drink neither type of milk? 6

29) A country music recording company analyzed 100 of its songs. 68 songs contained lyrics about broken relationships, 43 contained lyrics about pickup trucks, and 29 contained lyrics about both. How many songs were about neither broken relationships nor pickup trucks?

30) Dobrila and her husband, Zoran, have season tickets to all 81 home baseball games. Last season, Dobrila attended 62 games, Zoran attended 65 games, and they attended 57 games together. How many games did neither of them attend?

Solve each problem.

31) Tanya, Sukhon, Charlie, and Daljeet are college friends who prefer different social networking sites: Facebook, Twitter, Google Plus, and Pinterest. Using the following information, match each person with his or her favorite social networking site. (Hint: Make a table to organize the information.)

 a) Daljeet, Charlie, and the Pinterest user went to the same high school.

 b) Tanya, Sukhon, and the Google Plus user are in the same college math class.

 c) The Pinterest user, the Twitter user, and Tanya eat lunch together every Friday.

 d) Charlie does not use Google Plus.

32) Cailen is an artist, and she lines up four watercolor pencils: red, green, yellow, and blue. Using the following information, determine the order of the pencils from left to right. (Hint: Let R represent the red pencil, G represent the green pencil, Y represent the yellow pencil, and B represent the blue pencil. Then, line up the letters according to the clues.)

 a) The blue pencil and the red pencil are next to each other.

 b) The green pencil is next to and to the left of the red pencil.

 c) The yellow pencil is not the last pencil. yellow, green, red, blue

A.5 Deriving the Area of a Parallelogram and the Area of a Triangle

Area of a Parallelogram

To find the formula for the area of a parallelogram, let's start with the parallelogram on the left. Cut out a triangle, and move it to the other end of the parallelogram. We get a rectangle with an area equal to the area of the parallelogram.

Area of parallelogram = Area of rectangle

Because the area of a rectangle = *base · height*, the area of a parallelogram = *base · height*.

Formula Area of a Parallelogram

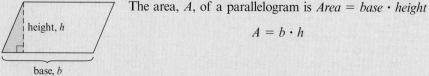

The area, A, of a parallelogram is *Area = base · height*   or

$$A = b \cdot h$$

where b = the length of the base and h = the height. Notice that the base is the side that forms a right angle with the height.

Area of a Triangle

We can derive the area of a triangle from the area of a parallelogram. Start with a parallelogram, and cut it diagonally to form two identical triangles as shown here.

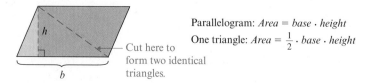

Parallelogram: *Area = base · height*

One triangle: *Area* = $\frac{1}{2}$ · *base · height*

Cut here to form two identical triangles.

Because each triangle is *half* of the parallelogram, the area of one of the triangles is *half* the area of the parallelogram.

Formula Area of a Triangle

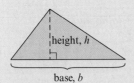

The **area,** A, of a triangle is $Area = \dfrac{1}{2} \cdot base \cdot height$ or

$$A = \frac{1}{2} \cdot b \cdot h \qquad \text{or} \qquad A = 0.5 \cdot b \cdot h$$

where b = the length of the base and h = the height.

The *base* of the triangle is always the side of the triangle that forms the right angle with the height. The height is not always labeled inside the triangle.

A.6 Table of Values for $(1 + R)^T$

Interest Compounded Annually
Value of $(1 + R)^T$

Years	3%	3.5%	4%	4.5%	5%	5.5%	6%	6.5%	7%	8%
1	1.0300	1.0350	1.0400	1.0450	1.0500	1.0550	1.0600	1.0650	1.0700	1.0800
2	1.0609	1.0712	1.0816	1.0920	1.1025	1.1130	1.1236	1.1342	1.1449	1.1664
3	1.0927	1.1087	1.1249	1.1412	1.1576	1.1742	1.1910	1.2080	1.2250	1.2597
4	1.1255	1.1475	1.1699	1.1925	1.2155	1.2388	1.2625	1.2865	1.3108	1.3605
5	1.1593	1.1877	1.2167	1.2462	1.2763	1.3070	1.3382	1.3701	1.4026	1.4693
6	1.1941	1.2293	1.2653	1.3023	1.3401	1.3788	1.4185	1.4591	1.5007	1.5869
7	1.2299	1.2723	1.3159	1.3609	1.4071	1.4547	1.5036	1.5540	1.6058	1.7138
8	1.2668	1.3168	1.3686	1.4221	1.4775	1.5347	1.5938	1.6550	1.7182	1.8509
9	1.3048	1.3629	1.4233	1.4861	1.5513	1.6191	1.6895	1.7626	1.8385	1.9990
10	1.3439	1.4106	1.4802	1.5530	1.6289	1.7081	1.7908	1.8771	1.9672	2.1589
11	1.3842	1.4600	1.5395	1.6229	1.7103	1.8021	1.8983	1.9992	2.1049	2.3316
12	1.4258	1.5111	1.6010	1.6959	1.7959	1.9012	2.0122	2.1291	2.2522	2.5182

Instructor Answer Exercises

Chapter 1

Section 1.2

3) 9;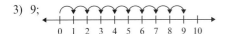

4) 9;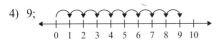

5) 10;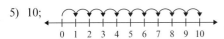

6) 8;

7) 9;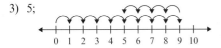

8) 8;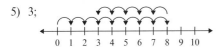

Section 1.4

3) 5;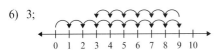

4) 4;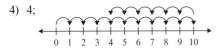

5) 3;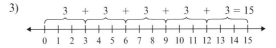

6) 3;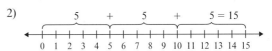

Putting It All Together Exercises

3) seven hundred twenty million, six hundred fifty-three thousand, eight; 2 ten-millions; 5 ten-thousands

Chapter 1: Review Exercises

5) four hundred ninety billion, six hundred seventeen million, five thousand, nine hundred fifteen

6) ninety-eight million, four hundred sixty-eight thousand, forty

7) 9;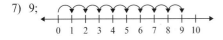

8) 8;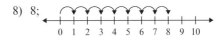

9) Answers may vary. It says that numbers can be added in any order and the sum will remain the same.

10) Answers may vary. It says that we can change the position of grouping symbols when adding numbers and the sum remains the same.

37) 6;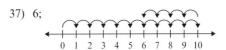

38) 5;

Chapter 2

Section 2.1

1)

a) $4 \times 3 = 12$

b) multiplicand: 4; multiplier: 3

c) factors: 4 and 3; product: 12

2)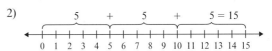

a) $5 \times 3 = 15$

b) multiplicand: 5; multiplier: 3

c) factors: 5 and 3; product: 15

3)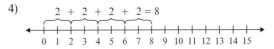

a) $3 \times 5 = 15$

b) multiplicand: 3; multiplier: 5

c) factors: 3 and 5; product: 15

4)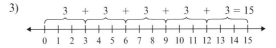

a) $2 \times 4 = 8$

b) multiplicand: 2; multiplier: 4

c) factors: 2 and 4; product: 8

3) $(3 \times 2) \times 4 = 6 \times 4 = 24; 3 \times (2 \times 4) = 3 \times 8 = 24$

4) $(6 \times 1) \times 9 = 6 \times 9 = 54; 6 \times (1 \times 9) = 6 \times 9 = 54$

5) $(9 \cdot 0) \cdot 7 = 0 \cdot 7 = 0; 9 \cdot (0 \cdot 7) = 9 \cdot 0 = 0$

6) $(2 \cdot 4) \cdot 0 = 8 \cdot 0 = 0; 2 \cdot (4 \cdot 0) = 2 \cdot 0 = 0$

Section 2.3

1) 3;

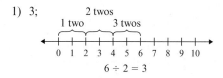

$6 \div 2 = 3$

a) dividend: 6; divisor: 2; quotient: 3

b) $\frac{6}{2} = 3, 2\overline{)6}^{\,3}$, or 6/2 = 3

2) 2;

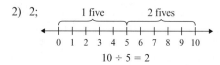

$10 \div 5 = 2$

a) dividend: 10; divisor: 5; quotient: 2

b) $\frac{10}{5} = 2, 5\overline{)10}^{\,2}$, or 10/5 = 2

3) 2;

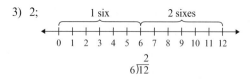

$6\overline{)12}^{\,2}$

a) dividend: 12; divisor: 6; quotient: 2

b) $\frac{12}{6} = 2, 12 \div 6 = 2$, or 12/6 = 2

4) 3;

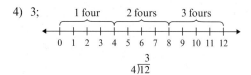

$4\overline{)12}^{\,3}$

a) dividend: 12; divisor: 4; quotient: 3

b) $\frac{12}{4} = 3, 12 \div 4 = 3$, or 12/4 = 3

5) 7;

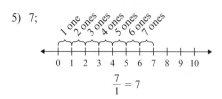

$\frac{7}{1} = 7$

a) dividend: 7; divisor: 1; quotient: 7

b) $7 \div 1 = 7, 1\overline{)7}^{\,7}$, or 7/1 = 7

6) 1;

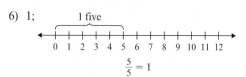

$\frac{5}{5} = 1$

a) dividend: 5; divisor: 5; quotient: 1

b) $5 \div 5 = 1, 5\overline{)5}^{\,1}$, or 5/5 = 1

Section 2.4

9) Multiply the divisor by the quotient, then add the remainder. The result should be the dividend.

37) Add the digits in the number. If that sum is divisible by 3, then the number is divisible by 3.

Section 2.6

34) This is the wrong answer. Laurel added before dividing, and this does not follow the order of operations. She should have divided before adding. The correct answer is 26.

Chapter 2: Review Exercises

1) a) $2 \times 5 = 10$;

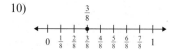

39) Multiply the divisor by the quotient, then add the remainder. The result should be the dividend.

44) Add the digits in the number. If that sum is divisible by 3, then the number is divisible by 3.

Chapter 3

Section 3.1

3)

4)

5)

6)

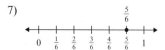

7)

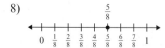

8)

9)

10)

11)
$$\overset{\hspace{5.5cm}1}{\vphantom{x}}$$
0 $\frac{1}{8}$ $\frac{2}{8}$ $\frac{3}{8}$ $\frac{4}{8}$ $\frac{5}{8}$ $\frac{6}{8}$ $\frac{7}{8}$ 1

12)
$$\overset{\hspace{5.5cm}1}{\vphantom{x}}$$
0 $\frac{1}{4}$ $\frac{2}{4}$ $\frac{3}{4}$ 1

13)
$$\frac{3}{6}$$
0 $\frac{1}{6}$ $\frac{2}{6}$ $\frac{3}{6}$ $\frac{4}{6}$ $\frac{5}{6}$ 1

14)
$$\frac{4}{8}$$
0 $\frac{1}{8}$ $\frac{2}{8}$ $\frac{3}{8}$ $\frac{4}{8}$ $\frac{5}{8}$ $\frac{6}{8}$ $\frac{7}{8}$ 1

15)
$$\frac{4}{5}$$
0 $\frac{1}{5}$ $\frac{2}{5}$ $\frac{3}{5}$ $\frac{4}{5}$ 1

16)
$$\frac{7}{8}$$
0 $\frac{1}{8}$ $\frac{2}{8}$ $\frac{3}{8}$ $\frac{4}{8}$ $\frac{5}{8}$ $\frac{6}{8}$ $\frac{7}{8}$ 1

17)
$$\frac{4}{5}$$
0 $\frac{1}{5}$ $\frac{2}{5}$ $\frac{3}{5}$ $\frac{4}{5}$ 1

18)
$$\frac{2}{5}$$
0 $\frac{1}{5}$ $\frac{2}{5}$ $\frac{3}{5}$ $\frac{4}{5}$ 1

19)
$$\frac{3}{6}$$
0 $\frac{1}{6}$ $\frac{2}{6}$ $\frac{3}{6}$ $\frac{4}{6}$ $\frac{5}{6}$ 1

20)
$$\frac{4}{8}$$
0 $\frac{1}{8}$ $\frac{2}{8}$ $\frac{3}{8}$ $\frac{4}{8}$ $\frac{5}{8}$ $\frac{6}{8}$ $\frac{7}{8}$ 1

21)
$$\frac{3}{8}$$
0 $\frac{1}{8}$ $\frac{2}{8}$ $\frac{3}{8}$ $\frac{4}{8}$ $\frac{5}{8}$ $\frac{6}{8}$ $\frac{7}{8}$ 1

22)
$$\frac{1}{5}$$
0 $\frac{1}{5}$ $\frac{2}{5}$ $\frac{3}{5}$ $\frac{4}{5}$ 1

23)
$$\frac{2}{6}$$
0 $\frac{1}{6}$ $\frac{2}{6}$ $\frac{3}{6}$ $\frac{4}{6}$ $\frac{5}{6}$ 1

24)
$$\frac{2}{5}$$
0 $\frac{1}{5}$ $\frac{2}{5}$ $\frac{3}{5}$ $\frac{4}{5}$ 1

25) $\dfrac{1}{2} = \dfrac{2}{4}$ 26) $\dfrac{2}{8} = \dfrac{1}{4}$

27) $\dfrac{1}{3} = \dfrac{2}{6}$ 28) $\dfrac{6}{8} = \dfrac{3}{4}$

29) $\dfrac{4}{6} = \dfrac{2}{3}$ 30) $\dfrac{8}{8} = \dfrac{3}{3}$

35) The numerator of an improper fraction is greater than or equal to the denominator. The numerator of a proper fraction is less than the denominator.

37)
$$\frac{7}{4}$$
0 $\frac{1}{4}$ $\frac{2}{4}$ $\frac{3}{4}$ 1 $\frac{5}{4}$ $\frac{6}{4}$ $\frac{7}{4}$ 2

38)
$$\frac{7}{5}$$
0 $\frac{1}{5}$ $\frac{2}{5}$ $\frac{3}{5}$ $\frac{4}{5}$ 1 $\frac{6}{5}$ $\frac{7}{5}$ $\frac{8}{5}$ $\frac{9}{5}$ 2

39)
$$\frac{7}{3}$$
0 $\frac{1}{3}$ $\frac{2}{3}$ 1 $\frac{4}{3}$ $\frac{5}{3}$ 2 $\frac{7}{3}$ $\frac{8}{3}$ 3

40)
$$\frac{10}{4}$$
0 $\frac{1}{4}$ $\frac{2}{4}$ $\frac{3}{4}$ 1 $\frac{5}{4}$ $\frac{6}{4}$ $\frac{7}{4}$ 2 $\frac{9}{4}$ $\frac{10}{4}$ $\frac{11}{4}$ 3

41)
$$\frac{3}{2}$$
0 $\frac{1}{2}$ 1 $\frac{3}{2}$ 2

42)
$$2$$
0 $\frac{1}{5}$ $\frac{2}{5}$ $\frac{3}{5}$ $\frac{4}{5}$ 1 $\frac{6}{5}$ $\frac{7}{5}$ $\frac{8}{5}$ $\frac{9}{5}$ 2

43)
$$\frac{8}{3}$$
0 $\frac{1}{3}$ $\frac{2}{3}$ 1 $\frac{4}{3}$ $\frac{5}{3}$ 2 $\frac{7}{3}$ $\frac{8}{3}$ 3

44)
$$\frac{8}{5}$$
0 $\frac{1}{5}$ $\frac{2}{5}$ $\frac{3}{5}$ $\frac{4}{5}$ 1 $\frac{6}{5}$ $\frac{7}{5}$ $\frac{8}{5}$ $\frac{9}{5}$ 2

45)

Answers may vary.

46)

Answers may vary.

47)

Answers may vary.

48)
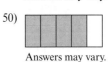
Answers may vary.

49)

Answers may vary.

50)
Answers may vary.

51)
Answers may vary.

52)
Answers may vary.

53)
$$\frac{2}{8}$$
0 $\frac{1}{8}$ $\frac{2}{8}$ $\frac{3}{8}$ $\frac{4}{8}$ $\frac{5}{8}$ $\frac{6}{8}$ $\frac{7}{8}$ 1

54)

$\frac{7}{8}$

$0 \quad \frac{1}{8} \quad \frac{2}{8} \quad \frac{3}{8} \quad \frac{4}{8} \quad \frac{5}{8} \quad \frac{6}{8} \quad \frac{7}{8} \quad 1$

55)

$\frac{2}{5}$

$0 \quad \frac{1}{5} \quad \frac{2}{5} \quad \frac{3}{5} \quad \frac{4}{5} \quad 1 \quad \frac{6}{5} \quad \frac{7}{5} \quad \frac{8}{5} \quad \frac{9}{5} \quad 2$

56)

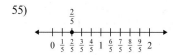

$\frac{6}{8}$

$0 \quad \frac{1}{8} \quad \frac{2}{8} \quad \frac{3}{8} \quad \frac{4}{8} \quad \frac{5}{8} \quad \frac{6}{8} \quad \frac{7}{8} \quad 1$

57)

$\frac{4}{6}$

$0 \quad \frac{1}{6} \quad \frac{2}{6} \quad \frac{3}{6} \quad \frac{4}{6} \quad \frac{5}{6} \quad 1$

58)

2

$0 \quad \frac{1}{3} \quad \frac{2}{3} \quad 1 \quad \frac{4}{3} \quad \frac{5}{3} \quad 2$

59)

$\frac{9}{4}$

$0 \quad \frac{1}{4} \quad \frac{2}{4} \quad \frac{3}{4} \quad 1 \quad \frac{5}{4} \quad \frac{6}{4} \quad \frac{7}{4} \quad 2 \quad \frac{9}{4} \quad \frac{10}{4} \quad \frac{11}{4} \quad 3$

60)

$\frac{4}{5}$

$0 \quad \frac{1}{5} \quad \frac{2}{5} \quad \frac{3}{5} \quad \frac{4}{5} \quad 1$

61)

3

$0 \quad \frac{1}{4} \quad \frac{2}{4} \quad \frac{3}{4} \quad 1 \quad \frac{5}{4} \quad \frac{6}{4} \quad \frac{7}{4} \quad 2 \quad \frac{9}{4} \quad \frac{10}{4} \quad \frac{11}{4} \quad 3$

62)

1

$0 \quad \frac{1}{5} \quad \frac{2}{5} \quad \frac{3}{5} \quad \frac{4}{5} \quad 1$

Section 3.2

1)

$1\frac{2}{5}$

$0 \quad \frac{1}{5} \quad \frac{2}{5} \quad \frac{3}{5} \quad \frac{4}{5} \quad 1 \quad 1\frac{1}{5} \quad 1\frac{2}{5} \quad 1\frac{3}{5} \quad 1\frac{4}{5} \quad 2$

2)

$1\frac{1}{4}$

$0 \quad \frac{1}{4} \quad \frac{2}{4} \quad \frac{3}{4} \quad 1 \quad 1\frac{1}{4} \quad 1\frac{2}{4} \quad 1\frac{3}{4} \quad 2$

3)

$2\frac{3}{4}$

$0 \quad \frac{1}{4} \quad \frac{2}{4} \quad \frac{3}{4} \quad 1 \quad 1\frac{1}{4} \quad 1\frac{2}{4} \quad 1\frac{3}{4} \quad 2 \quad 2\frac{1}{4} \quad 2\frac{2}{4} \quad 2\frac{3}{4} \quad 3$

4)

$2\frac{2}{3}$

$0 \quad \frac{1}{3} \quad \frac{2}{3} \quad 1 \quad 1\frac{1}{3} \quad 1\frac{2}{3} \quad 2 \quad 2\frac{1}{3} \quad 2\frac{2}{3} \quad 3$

5)

$1\frac{3}{5}$

$0 \quad \frac{1}{5} \quad \frac{2}{5} \quad \frac{3}{5} \quad \frac{4}{5} \quad 1 \quad 1\frac{1}{5} \quad 1\frac{2}{5} \quad 1\frac{3}{5} \quad 1\frac{4}{5} \quad 2$

6)

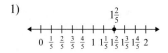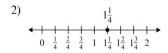

$1\frac{3}{4}$

$0 \quad \frac{1}{4} \quad \frac{2}{4} \quad \frac{3}{4} \quad 1 \quad 1\frac{1}{4} \quad 1\frac{2}{4} \quad 1\frac{3}{4} \quad 2$

7)

$1\frac{4}{5}$

$0 \quad \frac{1}{5} \quad \frac{2}{5} \quad \frac{3}{5} \quad \frac{4}{5} \quad 1 \quad 1\frac{1}{5} \quad 1\frac{2}{5} \quad 1\frac{3}{5} \quad 1\frac{4}{5} \quad 2$

8)

$1\frac{2}{3}$

$0 \quad \frac{1}{3} \quad \frac{2}{3} \quad 1 \quad 1\frac{1}{3} \quad 1\frac{2}{3} \quad 2$

9)

$2\frac{1}{4}$

$0 \quad \frac{1}{4} \quad \frac{2}{4} \quad \frac{3}{4} \quad 1 \quad 1\frac{1}{4} \quad 1\frac{2}{4} \quad 1\frac{3}{4} \quad 2 \quad 2\frac{1}{4} \quad 2\frac{2}{4} \quad 2\frac{3}{4} \quad 3$

10)

$2\frac{1}{2}$

$0 \quad \frac{1}{2} \quad 1 \quad 1\frac{1}{2} \quad 2 \quad 2\frac{1}{2} \quad 3$

11)

2

$0 \quad \frac{1}{5} \quad \frac{2}{5} \quad \frac{3}{5} \quad \frac{4}{5} \quad 1 \quad 1\frac{1}{5} \quad 1\frac{2}{5} \quad 1\frac{3}{5} \quad 1\frac{4}{5} \quad 2$

12)

3

$0 \quad \frac{1}{4} \quad \frac{2}{4} \quad \frac{3}{4} \quad 1 \quad 1\frac{1}{4} \quad 1\frac{2}{4} \quad 1\frac{3}{4} \quad 2 \quad 2\frac{1}{4} \quad 2\frac{2}{4} \quad 2\frac{3}{4} \quad 3$

Section 3.6

19) $\frac{1}{12}$ of dinner plates are vegan; 3 out of 36 dinner plates are vegan.

20) Women's group receives $\frac{3}{32}$ of Concetta's salary; amount is $216 out of her $2304 salary.

21) The customer pays $\frac{3}{10}$ of original sale price; sale price is $72.

Section 3.7

65) Each portion is $\frac{1}{8}$ of the entire circle.

Answers may vary.

66) Each portion is $\frac{1}{6}$ of the entire circle.

Answers may vary.

Putting It All Together Exercises

1) $1\frac{5}{8}$;

$1\frac{5}{8}$

$0 \qquad\qquad 1 \quad 1\frac{1}{8} \quad 1\frac{2}{8} \quad 1\frac{3}{8} \quad 1\frac{4}{8} \quad 1\frac{5}{8} \quad 1\frac{6}{8} \quad 1\frac{7}{8} \quad 2$

2) $\frac{1}{3}$;

$0 \quad \frac{1}{3} \quad \frac{2}{3} \quad 1$

Chapter 3: Review Exercises

1)

2)
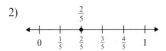

3)

4)

5)

6)
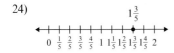

7)

8)

13)   14)

Answers may vary.   Answers may vary.

23)

24)
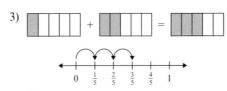

93) Each portion is $\frac{1}{4}$ of the entire circle.

Answers may vary.

94) Each portion is $\frac{1}{8}$ of the entire circle.

Answers may vary.

Chapter 3: Test

1) $\frac{3}{4}$;

$\left(\text{or } \frac{0}{4}\right)$ $\left(\text{or } \frac{4}{4}\right)$

2) $\frac{5}{8}$;
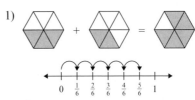
$\left(\text{or } \frac{0}{8}\right)$ $\left(\text{or } \frac{8}{8}\right)$

3) If the numerator of a fraction is less than the denominator, then it is a proper fraction. If the numerator of a fraction is greater than or equal to the denominator, then it is an improper fraction. Examples may vary.

4) $2\frac{1}{3}$;
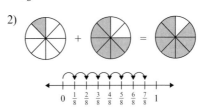

15) Yes. They are equivalent fractions because each of them can be written as $\frac{3}{4}$ in lowest terms.

Chapter 4

Section 4.1

1)
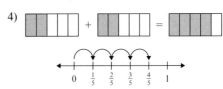
$\frac{5}{6}$; Shaded answer may vary.

2)

$\frac{7}{8}$; Shaded answer may vary.

3)

$\frac{3}{5}$; Shaded answer may vary.

4)

$\frac{4}{5}$; Shaded answer may vary.

5)

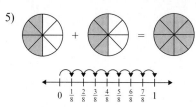

$\frac{8}{8}$ or 1; Shaded answer may vary.

6)

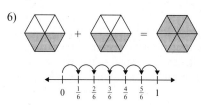

$\frac{6}{6}$ or 1; Shaded answer may vary.

7)

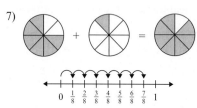

$\frac{7}{8}$; Shaded answer may vary.

8)

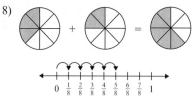

$\frac{5}{8}$; Shaded answer may vary.

Section 4.3

23) LCD = 14; $\frac{4}{7} = \frac{8}{14}$; $\frac{3}{14}$ already has the LCD

24) LCD = 12; $\frac{3}{4} = \frac{9}{12}$; $\frac{11}{12}$ already has the LCD

25) LCD = 15; $\frac{4}{5} = \frac{12}{15}$, $\frac{2}{15}$ already has the LCD

26) LCD = 21; $\frac{3}{7} = \frac{9}{21}$, $\frac{2}{21}$ already has the LCD

27) LCD = 24; $\frac{3}{8} = \frac{9}{24}$, $\frac{5}{12} = \frac{10}{24}$

28) LCD = 30; $\frac{5}{6} = \frac{25}{30}$, $\frac{3}{10} = \frac{9}{30}$

29) LCD = 24; $\frac{7}{8} = \frac{21}{24}$, $\frac{5}{6} = \frac{20}{24}$

30) LCD = 36; $\frac{4}{9} = \frac{16}{36}$, $\frac{3}{4} = \frac{27}{36}$

31) LCD = 54; $\frac{2}{9} = \frac{12}{54}$, $\frac{31}{54}$ already has the LCD

32) LCD = 48; $\frac{5}{12} = \frac{20}{48}$, $\frac{13}{48}$ already has the LCD

33) LCD = 60; $\frac{7}{12} = \frac{35}{60}$, $\frac{3}{20} = \frac{9}{60}$

34) LCD = 30; $\frac{3}{10} = \frac{9}{30}$, $\frac{4}{15} = \frac{8}{30}$

35) LCD = 38; $\frac{4}{19} = \frac{8}{38}$, $\frac{15}{38}$ already has the LCD

36) LCD = 22; $\frac{9}{11} = \frac{18}{22}$, $\frac{21}{22}$ already has the LCD

37) LCD = 36; $\frac{7}{12} = \frac{21}{36}$, $\frac{8}{9} = \frac{32}{36}$

38) LCD = 40; $\frac{9}{10} = \frac{36}{40}$, $\frac{1}{8} = \frac{5}{40}$

39) LCD = 42; $\frac{11}{6} = \frac{77}{42}$, $\frac{5}{7} = \frac{30}{42}$

40) LCD = 63; $\frac{10}{7} = \frac{90}{63}$, $\frac{4}{9} = \frac{28}{63}$

42) Even though 24 is a common denominator for 4 and 12, it is not the least common denominator. Tosh has used the *least* common denominator of 12.

43) LCD = 16; $\frac{1}{4} = \frac{4}{16}$, $\frac{3}{8} = \frac{6}{16}$, $\frac{1}{16}$ already has the LCD

44) LCD = 32; $\frac{3}{4} = \frac{24}{32}$, $\frac{11}{16} = \frac{22}{32}$, $\frac{1}{32}$ already has the LCD

45) LCD = 28; $\frac{5}{14} = \frac{10}{28}$, $\frac{1}{2} = \frac{14}{28}$, $\frac{9}{28}$ already has the LCD

46) LCD = 24; $\frac{5}{8} = \frac{15}{24}$, $\frac{1}{6} = \frac{4}{24}$, $\frac{13}{24}$ already has the LCD

47) LCD = 36; $\frac{5}{12} = \frac{15}{36}$, $\frac{5}{6} = \frac{30}{36}$, $\frac{4}{9} = \frac{16}{36}$

48) LCD = 40; $\frac{1}{20} = \frac{2}{40}$, $\frac{4}{5} = \frac{32}{40}$, $\frac{3}{8} = \frac{15}{40}$

49) LCD = 20; $\frac{7}{10} = \frac{14}{20}$, $\frac{3}{4} = \frac{15}{20}$, $\frac{1}{5} = \frac{4}{20}$

50) LCD = 72; $\frac{5}{8} = \frac{45}{72}$, $\frac{8}{9} = \frac{64}{72}$, $\frac{1}{6} = \frac{12}{72}$

51) LCD = 30; $\frac{4}{5} = \frac{24}{30}$, $\frac{1}{6} = \frac{5}{30}$, $\frac{2}{15} = \frac{4}{30}$

52) LCD = 30; $\frac{1}{2} = \frac{15}{30}$, $\frac{2}{3} = \frac{20}{30}$, $\frac{3}{10} = \frac{9}{30}$

53) LCD = 72; $\frac{2}{9} = \frac{16}{72}$, $\frac{7}{12} = \frac{42}{72}$, $\frac{9}{8} = \frac{81}{72}$

54) LCD = 84; $\frac{5}{12} = \frac{35}{84}$, $\frac{8}{21} = \frac{32}{84}$, $\frac{11}{7} = \frac{132}{84}$

55) LCD = 90; $\frac{5}{18} = \frac{25}{90}$, $\frac{7}{30} = \frac{21}{90}$

56) LCD = 80; $\dfrac{3}{16} = \dfrac{15}{80}, \dfrac{9}{40} = \dfrac{18}{80}$

57) LCD = 96; $\dfrac{5}{32} = \dfrac{15}{96}, \dfrac{11}{48} = \dfrac{22}{96}$

58) LCD = 84; $\dfrac{9}{12} = \dfrac{63}{84}, \dfrac{7}{28} = \dfrac{21}{84}$

59) LCD = 182; $\dfrac{5}{14} = \dfrac{65}{182}, \dfrac{3}{26} = \dfrac{21}{182}$

60) LCD = 112; $\dfrac{15}{16} = \dfrac{105}{112}, \dfrac{3}{28} = \dfrac{12}{112}$

61) LCD = 288; $\dfrac{5}{18} = \dfrac{80}{288}, \dfrac{3}{32} = \dfrac{27}{288}$

62) LCD = 252; $\dfrac{13}{28} = \dfrac{117}{252}, \dfrac{7}{36} = \dfrac{49}{252}$

63) LCD = 312; $\dfrac{13}{78} = \dfrac{52}{312}, \dfrac{31}{104} = \dfrac{93}{312}$

64) LCD = 228; $\dfrac{23}{57} = \dfrac{92}{228}, \dfrac{45}{76} = \dfrac{135}{228}$

Section 4.4

9) She added the numerators and added the denominators. She should have rewritten each fraction with the LCD of 20 then added the numerators while keeping the denominators the same.
$$\dfrac{1}{5} + \dfrac{3}{4} = \dfrac{4}{20} + \dfrac{15}{20} = \dfrac{19}{20}$$

79) Rowena needs $3\dfrac{1}{10}$ yd of decorative lemon-colored cloth to line the perimeter of the table.

81) The recipe requires a total of $1\dfrac{5}{8}$ teaspoons of ground nutmeg, almond extract, and rum-flavored extract.

82) The lifeguard applicants travel a total distance of $\dfrac{7}{10}$ mile.

Section 4.5

1) To add mixed numbers, add the whole-number parts and add the fractional parts. To subtract, subtract the whole-number parts and subtract the fractional parts. In both cases, write the final answer in lowest terms.

2) It is not in lowest terms because $\dfrac{10}{18}$ is not in lowest terms.
In lowest terms, $4\dfrac{10}{18} = 4\dfrac{5}{9}$.

Putting It All Together Exercises

4) False. The fractional part of a mixed number must be a proper fraction. In simplest form, $3\dfrac{11}{6} = 4\dfrac{5}{6}$.

5) False. $\dfrac{1}{2}$ is less than 1 whole, and $\dfrac{3}{2}$ is greater than 1 whole, so $\dfrac{1}{2}$ is less than $\dfrac{3}{2}$.

Chapter 4: Review Exercises

1)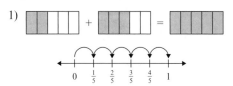

$\dfrac{5}{5}$ or 1; Shaded answer may vary.

2)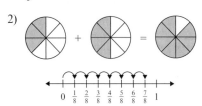

$\dfrac{7}{8}$; Shaded answer may vary.

3)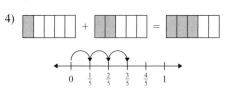

$\dfrac{3}{6}$; Shaded answer may vary.

4)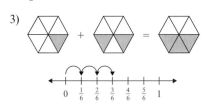

$\dfrac{3}{5}$; Shaded answer may vary.

23) LCD = 30; $\dfrac{5}{6} = \dfrac{25}{30}, \dfrac{3}{10} = \dfrac{9}{30}$

24) LCD = 24; $\dfrac{3}{8} = \dfrac{9}{24}, \dfrac{5}{12} = \dfrac{10}{24}$

25) LCD = 36; $\dfrac{1}{4} = \dfrac{9}{36}, \dfrac{2}{9} = \dfrac{8}{36}, \dfrac{7}{6} = \dfrac{42}{36}$

26) LCD = 40; $\dfrac{4}{5} = \dfrac{32}{40}, \dfrac{7}{8} = \dfrac{35}{40}, \dfrac{3}{20} = \dfrac{6}{40}$

27) LCD = 168; $\dfrac{5}{24} = \dfrac{35}{168}, \dfrac{9}{28} = \dfrac{54}{168}$

28) LCD = 252; $\dfrac{13}{28} = \dfrac{117}{252}, \dfrac{7}{36} = \dfrac{49}{252}$

29) The answer is wrong. You must get a common denominator before adding the fractions. This is the correct way to add the fractions: $\dfrac{5}{11} + \dfrac{4}{9} = \dfrac{45}{99} + \dfrac{44}{99} = \dfrac{89}{99}$.

51) 1) Add the whole-number parts and add the fractional parts. 2) Change each mixed number to an improper fraction, then add.

52) It is not in simplest form because the fractional part is improper. $5\dfrac{10}{7} = 6\dfrac{3}{7}$ in simplest form.

73) $\frac{19}{5}$

number line 0 1 2 3 4

74) $\frac{5}{3}$

number line 0 1 2 3 4

75) $3\frac{3}{4}$

number line 0 1 2 3 4

76) $2\frac{3}{8}$

number line 0 1 2 3 4

77) $\frac{7}{9}$

number line 0 1 2 3 4

78) $\frac{5}{7}$

number line 0 1 2 3 4

Chapter 4: Test

1) a) Answers may vary.

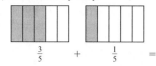

$\frac{3}{5}$ + $\frac{1}{5}$ = $\frac{4}{5}$

b)

$\frac{3}{5} + \frac{1}{5} = \frac{4}{5}$

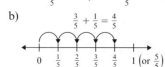

0 $\frac{1}{5}$ $\frac{2}{5}$ $\frac{3}{5}$ $\frac{4}{5}$ 1 $\left(\text{or } \frac{5}{5}\right)$

5) $\frac{3}{3} = 1$, so multiplying $\frac{8}{9}$ by 1 does not change the value of the fraction.

6) LCD = 18; $\frac{4}{9} = \frac{8}{18}$, $\frac{1}{6} = \frac{3}{18}$

Chapter 4: Cumulative Review for Chapters 1–4

10)

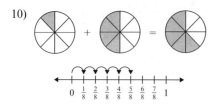

number line 0 $\frac{1}{8}$ $\frac{2}{8}$ $\frac{3}{8}$ $\frac{4}{8}$ $\frac{5}{8}$ $\frac{6}{8}$ $\frac{7}{8}$ 1

21) $2\frac{1}{5}$

number line 0 1 2 3 4

22) $\frac{9}{16}$

number line 0 1 2 3 4

Chapter 5

Section 5.1

3) $\frac{9}{10}$

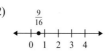
number line 0 0.1 0.2 0.3 0.4 0.5 0.6 0.7 0.8 0.9 1

4) $\frac{6}{10}$

number line 0 0.1 0.2 0.3 0.4 0.5 0.6 0.7 0.8 0.9 1

5) $\frac{5}{10}$

number line 0 0.1 0.2 0.3 0.4 0.5 0.6 0.7 0.8 0.9 1

6) $\frac{8}{10}$

number line 0 0.1 0.2 0.3 0.4 0.5 0.6 0.7 0.8 0.9 1

7) $\frac{3}{10}$

number line 0 0.1 0.2 0.3 0.4 0.5 0.6 0.7 0.8 0.9 1

8) $\frac{9}{10}$

number line 0 0.1 0.2 0.3 0.4 0.5 0.6 0.7 0.8 0.9 1

9) $\frac{4}{10}$

number line 0 0.1 0.2 0.3 0.4 0.5 0.6 0.7 0.8 0.9 1

10) $\frac{1}{10}$

number line 0 0.1 0.2 0.3 0.4 0.5 0.6 0.7 0.8 0.9 1

17) 0.58

number line 0 0.1 0.2 0.3 0.4 0.5 0.6 0.7 0.8 0.9 1

18) 0.63

number line 0 0.1 0.2 0.3 0.4 0.5 0.6 0.7 0.8 0.9 1

19) 0.06

number line 0 0.1 0.2 0.3 0.4 0.5 0.6 0.7 0.8 0.9 1

20) 0.89

number line 0 0.1 0.2 0.3 0.4 0.5 0.6 0.7 0.8 0.9 1

49) 0—ones, 3—tenths, 5—hundredths, 7—thousandths, 2—ten-thousandths

50) 0—ones, 1—tenths, 4—hundredths, 8—thousandths, 9—ten-thousandths

51) 4—tens, 0—ones, 1—tenths, 6—hundredths, 2—thousandths, 5—ten-thousandths, 9—hundred-thousandths

52) 9—tens, 0—ones, 5—tenths, 1—hundredths, 4—thousandths, 3—ten-thousandths, 7—hundred-thousandths

Section 5.2

1) 0.4

number line 0 0.1 0.2 0.3 0.4 0.5 0.6 0.7 0.8 0.9 1

2) 0.9

number line 0 0.1 0.2 0.3 0.4 0.5 0.6 0.7 0.8 0.9 1

3) 0.0

number line 0 0.1 0.2 0.3 0.4 0.5 0.6 0.7 0.8 0.9 1

4) 1.0

number line 0 0.1 0.2 0.3 0.4 0.5 0.6 0.7 0.8 0.9 1

5) 0.7

number line 0 0.1 0.2 0.3 0.4 0.5 0.6 0.7 0.8 0.9 1

6) 0.2

number line 0 0.1 0.2 0.3 0.4 0.5 0.6 0.7 0.8 0.9 1

Section 5.5

29) exact: 1.4333… or $1.4\overline{3}$; approximation: 1.433

30) exact: 2.5666… or $2.5\overline{6}$; approximation: 2.567

31) exact: 9.44666… or $9.44\overline{6}$; approximation: 9.447

32) exact: 5.69777... or 5.697̄; approximation: 5.698

33) exact: 0.4272727... or 0.42̄7̄; approximation: 0.427

34) exact: 0.7363636... or 0.73̄6̄; approximation: 0.736

Putting It All Together Exercises

10) Answers may vary. Write the numbers vertically, lining up the decimal points. Add like you would add whole numbers. Put the decimal point in the answer directly below the decimal in the problem.

Section 5.6

13)

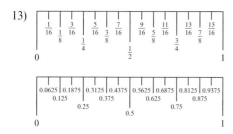

19) exact: 0.3̄; approximation: 0.333

20) exact: 0.1̄; approximation: 0.111

21) exact: 0.7̄; approximation: 0.778

22) exact: 0.8̄; approximation: 0.889

23) exact: 0.83̄; approximation: 0.833

24) exact: 0.16̄; approximation: 0.167

25) exact: 0.96̄; approximation: 0.967

26) exact: 0.09̄; approximation: 0.091

75) $4\frac{1}{5}$, 4.259, 4.26, $4\frac{3}{10}$ 76) 5.45, $5\frac{1}{2}$, 5.503, $5\frac{7}{10}$

77) $2\frac{1}{16}$, $2\frac{1}{8}$, 2.7, 2.75   78) $3\frac{1}{15}$, $3\frac{1}{9}$, 3.6, 3.68

79) 0.3, $\frac{5}{16}$, $\frac{7}{8}$, 0.97   80) $\frac{3}{8}$, 0.38, 0.8, $\frac{15}{16}$

Chapter 5: Review Exercises

1) $\frac{3}{10}$ = 0.3;

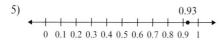

2) $\frac{8}{10}$ = 0.8;

5) 0.93

6) 0.17

11) 5—tens, 2—ones, 4—tenths, 0—hundredths,
6—thousandths, 7—ten-thousandths,
9—hundred-thousandths, 8—millionths

12) 3—ones, 0—tenths, 1—hundredths, 5—thousandths,
8—ten-thousandths, 4—hundred-thousandths

27) Write the numbers vertically so that the decimal points are lined up. If any numbers are missing digits to the right of the decimal point, insert zeros. Then, add the same way we add whole numbers. Place the decimal point in the answer *directly below* where the decimal point appears in the problem.

111) c) Vernon: $13.50, Jane: $7.20, Aliyah: $6.30,
Domingo: $14.40, Nayana: $12.60, Steve: $7.20

Chapter 5: Test

1) 0.6;

3) a) four and nine hundredths

b) six hundred fourteen ten-thousandths

9) Answers may vary. You do not need to line up the decimals when you multiply decimals. Write the problem vertically, line up the numbers on the right side, and multiply as if they were whole numbers. The number of decimal places in the answer equals the *total* number of decimal places in the factors.

29) mean: 33.9 customers per hour; median: 30 customers per hour; mode: 26 customers per hour

Chapter 5: Cumulative Review for Chapters 1–5

10)

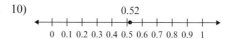

Chapter 6
Section 6.2

1) A rate compares quantities with different units, and a ratio compares quantities with the same units.

2) It is a rate because it compares quantities with different units.

Section 6.3

47) No. To determine whether a proportion is true, you find the cross products or write each fraction in lowest terms. To multiply fractions, you multiply the numerators and multiply the denominators.

Section 6.4

29) First, find the cross products. Then, set the cross products equal to each other, and solve the equation. Finally, check the solution by substituting it into the original proportion and finding the cross products.

30) No, it is not the solution because the cross products of $\frac{4}{7} = \frac{8}{21}$ are not equal: 4 · 21 = 84 but 7 · 8 = 56.

Chapter 6: Review Exercises

19) A ratio compares two quantities with the same units, and a rate compares quantities with different units.

Chapter 6: Test

15) Elsa did not multiply correctly. Cross products are used to determine whether a proportion is true or false. We do not use cross products to multiply fractions. Correct:

$$\frac{3}{10} \cdot \frac{4}{9} = \frac{\overset{1}{\cancel{3}}}{\underset{5}{\cancel{10}}} \cdot \frac{\overset{2}{\cancel{4}}}{\underset{3}{\cancel{9}}} = \frac{2}{15}$$

Chapter 7

Section 7.1

33) Step 1: Identify the units given and the units we want to get. Write down the relationship between those units. Step 2: Multiply the given measurement by the unit fraction relating the unit given and the unit we want to get so that the given unit will divide out and leave us with the unit we want.

34) b) Set up the problem this way so that the units of minutes divide out and we are left with seconds:

$$4.2 \text{ min} \cdot \frac{60 \text{ sec}}{1 \text{ min}} = \frac{4.2 \ \cancel{\text{min}}}{1} \cdot \frac{60 \text{ sec}}{1 \ \cancel{\text{min}}}$$

Chapter 7: Cumulative Review for Chapters 1–7

1) A digit is a single character in a numbering system, but a number is what you get when you write digits together in a certain order.

18) A ratio compares two quantities with the same units, but a rate compares quantities with different units.

Chapter 8

Section 8.1

1) 23% means 23 out of 100, so the statement means that 23 out of 100 students who consume media approximately 3 hours per day earn mostly C grades or lower.

2) 30% means 30 out of 100, so the statement means as of 2009, 30 out of 100 American women aged 25 and older obtained a bachelor's degree or more.

3) 52% means 52 out of 100, so the statement means 52 out of 100 Americans have listened to online radio.

4) 48% means 48 out of 100, so the statement means 48 out of 100 Americans have a profile on one or more social networking websites.

5) 44% means 44 out of 100, so the statement means that approximately 44 out of 100 online videos are being viewed in the workplace.

6) 67% means 67 out of 100, so the statement means that 67 out of 100 U.S. middle school students spend less than 1 hour each day on math homework.

7) In 2007–2008, approximately 18% of public school principals reported that their school required students to wear a uniform.

8) In 2007–2008, 76% of public school teachers were female.

9) In 2009, 26% of veterans were aged 25 and older with at least a bachelor's degree.

10) In 2008, 9% of New Orleans residents aged 5 and older spoke a language other than English at home.

11) As of September 2008, 14% of all members of the armed forces were women.

12) 26% of all Americans read news on mobile devices.

53) Move the decimal point two places to the right, and put the percent symbol at the end of the number.

Section 8.2

87) 1) Write the fraction with a denominator of 100. 2) Use long division to change the fraction to a decimal, then change the decimal to a percent. 3) Use a proportion.

89) $\frac{21}{25}$; 0.84; 84%   90) $\frac{3}{5}$; 0.60; 60%

91) $\frac{9}{50}$; 0.18; 18%   92) $\frac{9}{16}$; 0.5625; 56.25%

Section 8.8

1) c) If interest is compounded annually, Romero will earn $2.50 more than if it is computed as simple interest.

2) c) If interest is compounded annually, Alnira will earn $21.60 more than if it is computed as simple interest.

4) c) If interest is compounded annually, Grace will earn $14.59 more than if it is computed as simple interest.

5) c) If interest is compounded annually, Athena will earn $1.80 more than if it is computed as simple interest.

6) c) If interest is compounded annually, Tyrone will earn $6.40 more than if it is computed as simple interest.

Chapter 8: Review Exercises

3) In 2009, 92% of veterans were 25 years and older with at least a high school diploma.

Chapter 8: Test

12) a) The decimal point in the number 40 is after the zero. To find 10% of 40, move the decimal point one place to the left. 10% of 40 = 4.

Chapter 9

Section 9.1

17) ∠1: ∠TZU or ∠UZT
    ∠2: ∠UZN or ∠NZU
    ∠3: ∠NZP or ∠PZN
    ∠4: ∠PZT or ∠TZP

18) ∠1: ∠TYQ or ∠QYT
    ∠2: ∠TYR or ∠RYT
    ∠3: ∠RYD or ∠DYR
    ∠4: ∠DYQ or ∠QYD

19) ∠1: ∠DTW or ∠WTD
    ∠2: ∠WTP or ∠PTW
    ∠3: ∠PTV or ∠VTP
    ∠4: ∠VTD or ∠DTV

20) ∠1: ∠RHB or ∠BHR
    ∠2: ∠RHK or ∠KHR
    ∠3: ∠AHK or ∠KHA
    ∠4: ∠BHA or ∠AHB

21) ∠1: ∠EBA or ∠ABE
    ∠2: ∠ABC or ∠CBA
    ∠3: ∠CBD or ∠DBC
    ∠4: ∠DBE or ∠EBD

22) ∠1: ∠BGS or ∠SGB
    ∠2: ∠BGR or ∠RGB
    ∠3: ∠RGN or ∠NGR
    ∠4: ∠SGN or ∠NGS

Section 9.2

53) ∠K and ∠M are vertical angles; therefore, ∠K ≅ ∠M.
    ∠N and ∠L are vertical angles; therefore, ∠N ≅ ∠L.

54) ∠L and ∠H are vertical angles; therefore, ∠L ≅ ∠H.
    ∠M and ∠G are vertical angles; therefore, ∠M ≅ ∠G.

Section 9.4

1) $A = \frac{1}{2} \cdot$ base $\cdot$ height or $A = \frac{1}{2} \cdot b \cdot h$ or $A = 0.5 \cdot b \cdot h$

Section 9.5

1)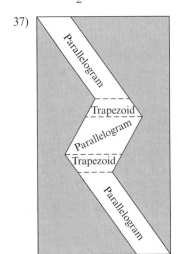

15) Area $= \frac{1}{2} \cdot$ height $\cdot$ (short base + long base)

    or $A = \frac{1}{2} \cdot h \cdot (b + B)$ or $A = 0.5 \cdot h \cdot (b + B)$

37)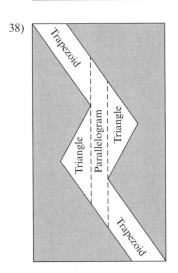

38)

Section 9.6

1) The radius is the distance from the center to a point on the circle; the diameter is the distance across the circle passing through the center.

18) π is the ratio of the circumference of a circle to its diameter. $\pi \approx 3.14$ and $\pi \approx \frac{22}{7}$

34) exact: 10π cm; approximation: $\frac{220}{7}$ cm or $31\frac{3}{7}$ cm or 31.43 cm

35) exact: $1\frac{5}{9}\pi$ in.; approximation: $4\frac{8}{9}$ in.

36) exact: $\frac{1}{4}\pi$ mi; approximation: $\frac{11}{14}$ mi

37) exact: $\frac{14}{15}\pi$ cm; approximation: $2\frac{14}{15}$ cm

38) exact: $1\frac{2}{5}\pi$ mm; approximation: $4\frac{2}{5}$ mm or 4.4 mm

44) exact: 16π ft²; approximation: 50.24 ft²

46) exact: 2.56π km²; approximation: 8.0384 km²

48) exact: 2.25π yd²; approximation: 7.065 yd²

50) exact: 1.21π dm²; approximation: 3.7994 dm²

52) exact: 18π ft²; approximation: 56.52 ft²

54) exact: 40.5π cm²; approximation: 127.17 cm²

56) exact: 450π cm²; approximation: 1413 cm²

69) Using $\pi \approx \frac{22}{7}$: 3850 mi²; using $\pi \approx 3.14$: 3846.5 mi²

    The answers are different because both values for π are approximations, *not* exact values.

Section 9.7

13) exact: $\frac{4}{375}\pi$ mm³; approximation: $\frac{88}{2625}$ mm³ ≈ 0.03 mm³

14) exact: $\frac{4}{81}\pi$ mi³; approximation: $\frac{88}{567}$ mi³ ≈ 0.16 mi³

15) exact: $\frac{9}{16}\pi$ m³; approximation: 1.77 m³

16) exact: $\frac{32}{3}\pi$ yd³; approximation: $\frac{704}{21}$ yd³ ≈ 33.52 yd³

17) exact: $\frac{2}{3}\pi$ ft³; approximation: $\frac{44}{21}$ ≈ 2.10 ft³

20) exact: $\frac{16}{3}\pi$ in³; approximation: $\frac{352}{21}$ in³ ≈ 16.76 in³

24) exact: 24π in³; approximation: 75.36 in³

42) exact: $\frac{25}{2}\pi$ ft³ or $12\frac{1}{2}\pi$ ft³ or 12.5π ft³; approximation: 39.25 ft³

43) exact: $\dfrac{1331}{12}\pi$ m^3 or $110\dfrac{11}{12}\pi$ m^3;

approximation: 348.28 m^3

44) $\dfrac{15}{4}$ yd^3 or $3\dfrac{3}{4}$ yd^3 or 3.75 yd^3

46) exact: $\dfrac{9}{2}\pi$ in^3 or $4\dfrac{1}{2}\pi$ in^3 or 4.5π in^3;

approximation: 14.13 in^3

Section 9.9

1) Similar triangles have the same shape, the measures of their corresponding angles are the same, and the lengths of their corresponding sides are proportional.

5) corresponding angles:
$\angle A$ and $\angle F$, $\angle C$ and $\angle D$, $\angle B$ and $\angle E$;
corresponding sides:
$\overline{AC}$ and $\overline{FD}$, $\overline{CB}$ and $\overline{DE}$, $\overline{BA}$ and $\overline{EF}$

6) corresponding angles:
$\angle R$ and $\angle Y$, $\angle Q$ and $\angle Z$, $\angle P$ and $\angle X$;
corresponding sides:
$\overline{RQ}$ and $\overline{YZ}$, $\overline{QP}$ and $\overline{ZX}$, $\overline{PR}$ and $\overline{XY}$

7) corresponding angles:
$\angle K$ and $\angle H$, $\angle L$ and $\angle F$, $\angle M$ and $\angle G$;
corresponding sides:
$\overline{KL}$ and $\overline{HF}$, $\overline{LM}$ and $\overline{FG}$, $\overline{MK}$ and $\overline{GH}$

8) corresponding angles:
$\angle B$ and $\angle M$, $\angle D$ and $\angle L$, $\angle C$ and $\angle N$;
corresponding sides:
$\overline{BD}$ and $\overline{ML}$, $\overline{DC}$ and $\overline{LN}$, $\overline{CB}$ and $\overline{NM}$

9) corresponding angles:
$\angle M$ and $\angle B$, $\angle N$ and $\angle A$, $\angle P$ and $\angle C$;
corresponding sides:
$\overline{MN}$ and $\overline{BA}$, $\overline{NP}$ and $\overline{AC}$, $\overline{PM}$ and $\overline{CB}$

10) corresponding angles:
$\angle T$ and $\angle Z$, $\angle U$ and $\angle X$, $\angle V$ and $\angle Y$;
corresponding sides:
$\overline{TU}$ and $\overline{ZX}$, $\overline{UV}$ and $\overline{XY}$, $\overline{VT}$ and $\overline{YZ}$

Chapter 9: Test

9) a) rectangle   b) $\dfrac{253}{6}$ ft^2 or $42\dfrac{1}{6}$ ft^2 c) $26\dfrac{1}{3}$ ft

16) a) exact: 100π in^2; approximation: 314 in^2

b) exact: 20π in.; approximation: 62.8 in.

17) a) exact: $\dfrac{81}{2}\pi$ cm^2 or $40\dfrac{1}{2}\pi$ cm^2 or 40.5π cm^2;

approximation: 127.17 cm^2

b) exact: 9π cm; approximation: 28.26 cm

19) a) sphere   b) exact: 36π ft^3; approximation: 113.04 ft^3

Chapter 9: Cumulative Review for Chapters 1–9

10)

Chapter 10

Section 10.1

9)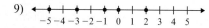

10)

11)

12)

13)

14)

15)

16)

17)

18)

Section 10.2

1) 3;

2) 7;

3) 3;

4) 1;

5) −4;

6) −1;

7) −2;

8) -3;

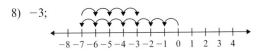

$$\begin{array}{cccccccccccc} -8 & -7 & -6 & -5 & -4 & -3 & -2 & -1 & 0 & 1 & 2 & 3 & 4 \end{array}$$

9) -3;

$$\begin{array}{ccccccccccc} -7 & -6 & -5 & -4 & -3 & -2 & -1 & 0 & 1 & 2 & 3 \end{array}$$

10) -7;

$$\begin{array}{ccccccccccc} -7 & -6 & -5 & -4 & -3 & -2 & -1 & 0 & 1 & 2 & 3 \end{array}$$

11) -6;

$$\begin{array}{ccccccccccc} -7 & -6 & -5 & -4 & -3 & -2 & -1 & 0 & 1 & 2 & 3 \end{array}$$

12) -6;

$$\begin{array}{ccccccccccc} -7 & -6 & -5 & -4 & -3 & -2 & -1 & 0 & 1 & 2 & 3 \end{array}$$

67) 5;

$$\begin{array}{ccccccccccc} -5 & -4 & -3 & -2 & -1 & 0 & 1 & 2 & 3 & 4 & 5 \end{array}$$

68) -1;

$$\begin{array}{ccccccccccc} -5 & -4 & -3 & -2 & -1 & 0 & 1 & 2 & 3 & 4 & 5 \end{array}$$

Section 10.3

13) $6 + (-5)$; 1;

$$\begin{array}{ccccccccccc} 0 & 1 & 2 & 3 & 4 & 5 & 6 & 7 & 8 & 9 & 10 \end{array}$$

14) $10 + (-3)$; 7;

$$\begin{array}{ccccccccccc} 0 & 1 & 2 & 3 & 4 & 5 & 6 & 7 & 8 & 9 & 10 \end{array}$$

15) $3 + (-7)$; -4;

$$\begin{array}{ccccccccccc} -7 & -6 & -5 & -4 & -3 & -2 & -1 & 0 & 1 & 2 & 3 \end{array}$$

16) $2 + (-5)$; -3;

$$\begin{array}{ccccccccccc} -7 & -6 & -5 & -4 & -3 & -2 & -1 & 0 & 1 & 2 & 3 \end{array}$$

17) $-2 + (-3)$; -5;

$$\begin{array}{ccccccccccc} -7 & -6 & -5 & -4 & -3 & -2 & -1 & 0 & 1 & 2 & 3 \end{array}$$

18) $-1 + (-4)$; -5;

$$\begin{array}{ccccccccccc} -7 & -6 & -5 & -4 & -3 & -2 & -1 & 0 & 1 & 2 & 3 \end{array}$$

19) $-3 + 6$; 3;

$$\begin{array}{ccccccccccc} -5 & -4 & -3 & -2 & -1 & 0 & 1 & 2 & 3 & 4 & 5 \end{array}$$

20) $-2 + 2$; 0;

$$\begin{array}{ccccccccccc} -5 & -4 & -3 & -2 & -1 & 0 & 1 & 2 & 3 & 4 & 5 \end{array}$$

Section 10.5

85) It is incorrect to do the subtraction first. Multiplication should be done before subtraction.

$$48 - 4 \cdot (-2) = 48 - (-8) = 48 + 8 = 56$$

86) It is incorrect to do the subtraction first. Division should be done before subtraction.

$$33 - 18 \div (-3) = 33 - (-6) = 33 + 6 = 39$$

87) The error is in evaluating -10^2.

$-10^2 = -100$, not 100.

$$\begin{aligned} -10^2 \div |12 - 37| &= -100 \div |12 - 37| \\ &= -100 \div |-25| \\ &= -100 \div 25 \\ &= -4 \end{aligned}$$

88) The expression $(8 - 2)^2$ was evaluated incorrectly. First, subtract inside the parentheses, then square the value.

$$\begin{aligned} \sqrt{49} + (8 - 2)^2 &= 7 + (6)^2 \\ &= 7 + 36 \\ &= 43 \end{aligned}$$

Chapter 10: Review Exercises

3)
$$\begin{array}{ccccccccccc} -5 & -4 & -3 & -2 & -1 & 0 & 1 & 2 & 3 & 4 & 5 \end{array}$$

4)
$$\begin{array}{ccccccccccc} -5 & -4 & -3 & -2 & -1 & 0 & 1 & 2 & 3 & 4 & 5 \end{array}$$

5) $\quad -2\frac{1}{5} \quad -\frac{5}{6} \quad \frac{3}{4} \quad 1\frac{1}{2}$
$$\begin{array}{ccccccccccc} -5 & -4 & -3 & -2 & -1 & 0 & 1 & 2 & 3 & 4 & 5 \end{array}$$

6) $\quad -4\frac{1}{2} \ -3\frac{1}{4} \quad -\frac{7}{8} \quad \frac{7}{8}$
$$\begin{array}{ccccccccccc} -5 & -4 & -3 & -2 & -1 & 0 & 1 & 2 & 3 & 4 & 5 \end{array}$$

7) $\quad -3.6 \quad -0.9 \ 0.7$
$$\begin{array}{ccccccccccc} -5 & -4 & -3 & -2 & -1 & 0 & 1 & 2 & 3 & 4 & 5 \end{array}$$

8) $-4.5 \ -3.9 \quad -1.1 \quad 1.1$
$$\begin{array}{ccccccccccc} -5 & -4 & -3 & -2 & -1 & 0 & 1 & 2 & 3 & 4 & 5 \end{array}$$

115) The expression $(7 - 4)^2$ was evaluated incorrectly. First, subtract inside the parentheses, then square the value.

$$\begin{aligned} \sqrt{81} + (7 - 4)^2 &= 9 + (3)^2 \\ &= 9 + 9 \\ &= 18 \end{aligned}$$

116) It is incorrect to do the subtraction first. Division should be done before subtraction.

$$32 - 24 \div (-4) = 32 - (-6) = 32 + 6 = 38$$

Chapter 10: Test

5) $\quad -3.5 \ -2 \ -\frac{3}{4} \qquad 1\frac{2}{3} \qquad 4.5$
$$\begin{array}{ccccccccccc} -5 & -4 & -3 & -2 & -1 & 0 & 1 & 2 & 3 & 4 & 5 \end{array}$$

Chapter 10: Cumulative Review for Chapters 1–10

1) 8 – ones
0 – tenths
5 – hundredths
7 – thousandths
3 – ten-thousandths
9 – hundred-thousandths

13) $\qquad\qquad -\frac{5}{8}$
$$\begin{array}{cccccc} -3 & -2 & -1 & 0 & 1 \end{array}$$

18) The error is in evaluating -6^2. $-6^2 = -36$, not 36. The correct way to evaluate the expression is

$$\begin{aligned} -6^2 \div |13 - 17| &= -36 \div |13 - 17| \\ &= -36 \div |-6| \\ &= -36 \div 6 \\ &= -9 \end{aligned}$$

Appendix

Section A.1

29)

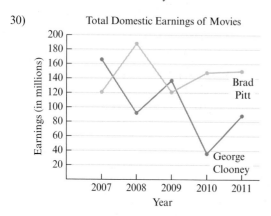

Number of Visitors

30)

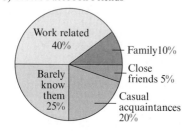

Total Domestic Earnings of Movies

Section A.2

11) b) Scott's Facebook Friends

16) ratio = $\frac{1}{4}$. For every Facebook friend who is a family

member, he has four Facebook friends he knows through work.

17) ratio = $\frac{1}{5}$. For every Facebook friend who is a close friend,

he has five Facebook friends he barely knows.

19) b) Holly's Monthly Expenses

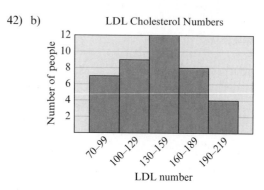

27) c) Number of Students Enrolled in Beginning Algebra

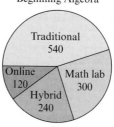

28) c) Number of Nights Families Eat Dinner Together Each Week

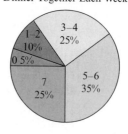

Section A.3

23) ratio = $\frac{4}{1}$. For every four employees who have been at the

company 0–4 yr, there is one employee who has been at the company 40–44 yr.

24) ratio = $\frac{2}{3}$. For every two employees who have been at the

company 20–24 yr, there are three employees who have been at the company 15–19 yr.

31) Two height ranges tie for having the least number of players: 70–72 in. and 76–78 in. There is one player in each of these categories.

41) b)

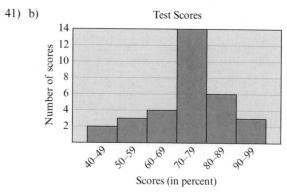

Test Scores

42) b)

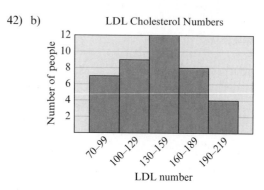

LDL Cholesterol Numbers

19) a) *Premises:* All college graduates have diplomas. Ava is a college graduate. *Conclusion:* Ava has a diploma.

   b) The conclusion *Ava has a diploma* follows from the premises.

   c) The conclusion is valid.

20) a) *Premises:* All four-sided, closed figures are quadrilaterals. A square is a four-sided, closed figure. *Conclusion:* A square is a quadrilateral.

   b) The conclusion *A square is a quadrilateral* follows from the premises.

   c) The conclusion is valid.

21) a) *Premises:* All lakes contain water. Lake Michigan is a lake. *Conclusion:* Lake Michigan contains water.

   b) The conclusion *Lake Michigan contains water* follows from the premises.

   c) The conclusion is valid.

22) a) *Premises:* All firefighters go through training. Hector is a firefighter. *Conclusion:* Hector goes through training.

   b) The conclusion *Hector goes through training* follows from the premises.

   c) The conclusion is valid.

23) a) *Premises:* All cats are animals. All rabbits are animals. *Conclusion:* All cats are rabbits.

   b) The conclusion *All cats are rabbits* does not follow from the premises.

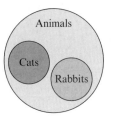

   c) The conclusion is invalid.

24) a) *Premises:* San Antonio is in Texas. El Paso is in Texas. *Conclusion:* El Paso is in San Antonio.

   b) The conclusion *El Paso is in San Antonio* does not follow from the premises.

   c) The conclusion is invalid.

25) a) *Premises:* Brett Favre was a football player. Joe Montana was a football player. *Conclusion:* Joe Montana was Brett Favre.

   b) The conclusion *Joe Montana was Brett Favre* does not follow from the premises.

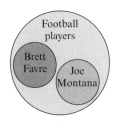

   c) The conclusion is invalid.

26) a) *Premises:* All bananas are yellow. All yield signs are yellow. *Conclusion:* All bananas are yield signs.

   b) The conclusion *All bananas are yield signs* does not follow from the premises.

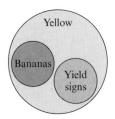

   c) The conclusion is invalid.

27)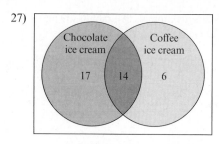

28)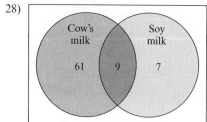

29) 18;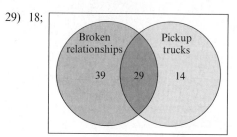

30) 11;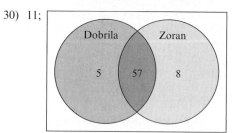

31) Tanya prefers Facebook, Sukhon prefers Pinterest,
Charlie prefers Twitter, and Daljeet prefers Google Plus.

Photo Credits

Page 1: © Thinkstock Images/Getty RF; p. 2: © Veer RF; p. 37(top): Design Pics/Kelly Redinger RF; p. 37(bottom): © Photodisc/PunchStock RF; p. 48(top): © Steve Allen/Brand X Pictures RF; p. 48(bottom): © Design Pics/Kelly Redinger RF; p. 61: © Gabriela Medina/Blend Images RF; p. 62: Ingram Publishing RF; p. 65: © Kablonk/SuperStock RF; p. 66: © Andersen Ross/Blend Images RF; p. 80(top): © Somos Photography/Veer RF; p. 80(bottom): © Image Source/Getty RF; p. 91: © John Lund/Sam Diephuis/Blend Images RF; p. 93(top): © Rob Melnychuk/Photodisc/Getty RF; p. 93(bottom): © 2009 Jupiterimages Corporation; p. 99: © Iain Crockart/Getty RF; p. 100(top right): © Ariel Skelley/Blend Images RF; p. 100(middle left): © Royalty-Free/Corbis; p. 100(bottom right): © Royalty-Free/Corbis; p. 113: © Royalty-Free/Corbis; p. 114: © Andersen Ross/Getty RF; p. 117(top left): © VStock LLC/age fotostock RF; p. 117(bottom right): © Royalty-Free/Corbis; p. 118: © moodboard/Alamy RF; p. 124: © Image Source/SuperStock RF; p. 125: © Ingram Publishing/Alamy RF; p. 126: © Royalty-Free/Corbis; p. 127: © Ingram Publishing RF; p. 129: © Hans Neleman/Getty RF; p. 130: © John Lund/Sam Diephuis RF; p. 172(top): © Design Pics/Don Hammond RF; p. 172(bottom): © Design Pics/Natural Selection Craig Tuttle RF; p. 173: © Ariel Skelley/Getty RF; p. 178: © Ingram Publishing RF; p. 184: © Brand X Pictures/PunchStock RF; p. 185: © PNC/Getty RF; p. 187(left): © Stockbyte/PunchStock RF; p. 187(right): © Ingram Publishing RF; p. 192: U.S. Census Bureau, Public Information Office (PIO); p. 194: © Jose Luis Pelaez Inc./Blend Images/age fotostock RF; p. 198: © Uppercut/Getty RF; p. 199: © Photographer's Choice/Getty RF; p. 202(left): © Royalty-Free/Corbis; p. 202(right): © Digital Vision/Alamy RF; p. 215(top left): © Ingram Publishing/SuperStock RF; p. 215(bottom left): © John A. Rizzo/Getty RF; p. 215(bottom right): © Beverley Lu Latter/Alamy RF;

p. 216(top right): © The McGraw-Hill Companies Inc./Ken Cavanagh Photographer; p. 216(bottom right): © Royalty-Free/Corbis; p. 219: © Jon Feingersh/Blend Images/age fotostock RF; p. 220: © BananaStock/PictureQuest RF; p. 255(bottom left): © SuperStock Inc RF; p. 255(top right): © Dynamic Graphics Group/PunchStock RF; p. 256: © Nancy Honey/Getty RF; p. 266: © Comstock Images/Jupiterimages RF; p. 270(left): © Dana Hoff/Getty RF; p. 270(right): © Hola Images/Getty RF; p. 286: © Mychal M. Richardson/Blend Images/Corbis RF; p. 289: © Paul King/Alamy RF; p. 291: Ryan McVay/Getty RF; p. 292: Noel Hendrickson/Getty RF; p. 310: © Rachel Slepekis/Getty RF; p. 314(top): © The McGraw-Hill Companies, Inc./Andrew Resek, photographer; p. 314(bottom): PhotoLink/Getty RF; p. 322(top): © Lars A. Niki; p. 322(bottom): Erica Simone Leeds; p. 330(top): © Stockdisc/PunchStock RF; p. 330(bottom): © ColorBlind Images/Blend Images RF; p. 331: © Jupiterimages RF; p. 340: © DreamPictures/Blend Images RF; p. 345: Ingram Publishing RF; p. 354: © Asia Images Group Pte Ltd/Alamy RF; p. 358: Thomas Northcut/Getty RF; p. 360: © Comstock Images/Jupiterimages RF; p. 362: © Adam Crowley/Getty RF; p. 363(top): © Ingram Publishing RF; p. 363(bottom left): © Jupiterimages RF; p. 363(bottom right): © Royalty Free/Corbis; p. 374(top): © John Lund/Drew Kelly/Blend Images RF; p. 374(bottom): © Jupiterimages RF; p. 375: © Royalty Free/Corbis; p. 377: © Ingram Publishing RF; p. 378: © Ingram Publishing RF; p. 379: Keith Brofsky/Getty RF; p. 380: Fuse/Getty RF; p. 384: © liquidlibrary/PictureQuest RF; p. 388: © Jonelle Weaver/Getty RF; p. 390(top): © Sonntag/beyond fotomedia/Getty RF; p. 390(bottom left): © John Lund/Sam Diephuis/Blend Images RF; p. 390(bottom right): © Apis Abramis/Alamy RF; p. 394: © Creatas/PunchStock RF; p. 396(left): © Ingram Publishing RF; p. 396(right): © Ingram Publishing/SuperStock RF; p. 397(top):

© Blend Images/Getty RF; p. 397(bottom): © Philip & Karen Smith/Getty RF; p. 403: © Radius Images/Corbis; p. 414(left): © Ingram Publishing RF; p. 414(right): © George Brits/Gallo/Getty RF; p. 424: © Pixland/Corbis RF; p. 425: © Kate Mitchell/Corbis RF; p. 426: © Mikael Karlsson/Alamy RF; p. 429: © Comstock/Getty RF; p. 430: © Rubberball/PunchStock RF; p. 440: © Jetta Productions/Walter Hodges/Getty RF; p. 443: © Nature Picture Library/Alamy RF; p. 444: © BananaStock/PunchStock RF; p. 454(left): © Jack Hollingsworth/Getty RF; p. 454(right): Glowimages/Getty RF; p. 463: © Glowimages/Getty RF; p. 464: © Imagestate Media (John Foxx)/Imagestate RF; p. 465: © Aaron Roeth Photography RF; p. 467: © Getty/Digital Vision RF; p. 470(left): © Janis Christie/Getty RF; p. 470(top right): © PhotoAlto/Michele Constantini/Getty RF; p. 470(bottom right): © Getty/Jon Feingersh Photography Inc. RF; p. 471: © Stockbyte/Getty RF; p. 473: © Tstock/Jupiterimages RF; p. 475(top): © Glowimages RF; p. 475(bottom): USDA, Be Safe Food Campaign; p. 478: © Photo 24/Getty RF; p. 479(left): © Photodisc/Getty RF; p. 479(right): © Lars A. Niki; p. 480: © Frank Lukasseck/Getty RF; p. 488: © Comstock/PunchStock RF; p. 489(top): Glowimages/Getty RF; p. 489(bottom): © Dynamic Graphics/Jupiterimages RF; p. 490(top): © Comstock/Jupiterimages RF; p. 490(bottom): © Ingram Publishing RF; p. 491(top): © Author's Image/PunchStock RF; p. 491(middle): © Comstock Images RF; p. 491(bottom): © Jose Luis Pelaez, Inc./Getty RF; p. 493: © Paul Bradbury/Getty RF; p. 494: © Purestock/Getty RF; p. 497: © Ryan McVay/Photodisc/Getty RF; p. 501(left): © Ingram Publishing RF; p. 501(right): U.S. Air Force photo by Staff Sgt. Bryan Bouchard; p. 511: © Digital Vision/PunchStock RF; p. 518: © Don Mason/Blend Images RF; p. 521: © Ingram Publishing RF; p. 522(left): © Denise McCullough; p. 522(right): The

Index

Calculator—(*continued*)
    temperature conversion on, 478
    unit conversion on, 442
    unknown length of right triangle on, 680
    volume of sphere on, 671
Calendar, master, 130
Capacity, units of
    metric, 455–457, 484–485
    relationship between system, 472
    U.S. customary, 433
Carrying. *See* Borrowing
Celsius scale, 475–477, 487
Centimeter, 446
Charts, solving problems with, 171
Circle
    area of, 654–657, 700
    circumference of, 651–654, 700
    definition of, 649, 699
    diameter of, 650–651, 699
    radius of, 650–651, 699
Circumference
    of circle, 700
    definition of, 651
    finding, 652–654
    formula for, 652
Commission, 550–551, 587
Common factors
    dividing out
        in dividing fractions, 182
            before multiplying fractions, 164–167
    fractions in lowest terms using, 156–158
    in lowest terms, 155
Commutative property of addition, 12–13, 57
Commutative property of multiplication, 70–71, 101, 121
Complementary angles, 607–609, 696
Complex fractions, 183, 192
Composite numbers
    definition of, 148, 207
    factors of, 148
    identifying, 148–149
Compound interest
    annual compounding, 567, 588
        with calculator, 572
        with tables, 569–571
    definition of, 567, 588
    formula for, 573, 588
Cone, volume of, 669–670, 702
Congruent angles, 610–611, 696
Corresponding angles, 684, 703
Corresponding sides, 684, 703
Cross products, of proportions
    in determining whether true or false, 400–401, 421
    solving proportions with, 406–407
Cube, volume of, 664, 701
Cylinder
    definition of, 667, 702
    volume of, 668, 702

D

Daily to-do list, 130
Decimal(s)
    addition of, 316–317, 343, 369
    applied problems with, 320, 328–329
    comparing, 349
    definition of, 295, 367
    division of, 343

        by decimals, 336–338, 370
        remainder from, 333–335
        by whole numbers, 332–336, 370
    on figures, 295
    as fractions, 302–303, 342, 367
    fractions as, 298–299, 341
        using division, 346–348, 370
        using equivalent fractions, 348–349, 371
    fractions compared to, 349–351
    as mixed numbers, 302–303, 342, 367
    mixed numbers as, 299
    multiplication of, 324–326, 343, 369
        by powers of ten, 326–328, 369
    on number line, 295
    order of operations with, 338–339, 343–344, 370
    as percents, 498–499, 541–542, 579
    percents as, 499–500, 541, 579
    percents with, as fractions, 504–506, 579–580
    place value in, 297–300, 341, 367
    proportions with, solving, 407–409
    ratios comparing, 384–387
    reading, 301, 367
    repeating, 334–335
    rounding, 306–310, 342, 368
    subtraction of, 316, 318–320, 343, 369
    understanding, 295–297
    in words, 300–302, 342
Decimal point, 295, 316, 324
Decimal system, 5, 57
Decision-making, 596
Degrees, of angles, 601, 695
Degree symbol, 475
Denominator
    decimals and, 295
    in fractions, 133, 206
    with same numerator, 135
    zero as, 133, 206
Diameter, of circle, 650–651, 699
Difference
    definition of, 26, 58
    estimating, 45–47, 59
Digits
    definition of, 5, 57
    identifying, 5–6
    writing whole numbers in, 8
Dividend, definition of, 81, 121
Divisibility
    definition of, 88, 103
    rules of, 88–90, 122
Division
    applied problems with
        of fractions, 184–186, 192–193, 211
        of whole numbers, 91–92, 98–99, 112
    of decimals, 343
        by decimals, 336–338, 370
        remainder from, 333–335
        by whole numbers, 332–336, 370
    of fractions, 191–192, 210, 267–268
        applied problems with, 184–186, 192–193, 211
        decimals from, 346–348, 370
        on number line, 179–180
        in order of operations, 274–276, 285
    fractions as, 133
    of metric units, 466
    of mixed numbers, 196–198, 212
    multiplication and, 81–82

        by one, 82
    in order of operations, 108, 123
        with fractions, 274–276, 285
    of signed numbers, 743–744, 759
    unit conversion with, 434–435, 483
    of whole numbers
        applied problems with, 91–92, 98–99, 112
        checking with multiplication, 87, 122
        even, 86, 122
        long, 94–97, 102, 122
        of nonzero number by zero, 83–84
        of number by same number, 83
        of number ending in zero, 97–98, 103, 122
        remainder in, 86–87, 122
        review of, 101–104
        short, 90–91, 101, 122
        understanding, 81–83
        writing, 81–82
    by zero, 83
Division property of equality, 404–406, 422
Divisor, 81, 121
Dot, multiplication written with, 69

E

Eight, divisibility by, 88
Equality, division property of, 404–406, 422
Equals, key words for, 112
Equation(s)
    definition of, 404, 422
    percent from, 524–527, 544–545, 582–583
        applied problems with, 532–535, 584
    solutions to, definition of, 404, 422
    solving
        definition of, 404, 422
        with division property of equality, 405–406, 422
Equilateral triangle, 634, 698
Equivalent fractions
    definition of, 154, 208
    determining, 160–161, 208
    negative, 744–745
    understanding, 154–156
    in writing fractions as decimals, 348–349, 371
Estimating, with rounding, 45–47, 59
Even numbers, divisibility of, 88, 89, 122
Exponent(s)
    definition of, 106, 122
    fractions with, 274, 285
    in order of operations, 108, 123
        with fractions, 274–276, 285
        with signed numbers, 749–751
    signed numbers with, 748–749, 760
    table of, 107
    using, 106–107
Exponential expressions, evaluating, 106–107
Expressions
    definition of, 404, 422
    evaluating, 404

F

Factors. *See also* Greatest common factor
    of composite numbers, 148
    definition of, 147, 207
    in multiplication, 69, 121
    from prime factorization, 149–152
    of prime numbers, 148

One
  composite numbers and, 148
  division by, 82
  prime numbers and, 148, 207
Opposites, 721–722, 757
Order of operations
  with decimals, 338–339, 343–344, 370
  with fractions, 274–276, 285
  procedure for, 108, 123
  with signed numbers, 749–751, 760
  using, 108–110

P

Parallel lines, 603–604, 696
Parallelogram
  area of, 640–641, 699
  definition of, 639
  perimeter of, 640
Parentheses
  in associative property of addition, 14–15
  multiplication written with, 69
  in order of operations, 108, 123
    with fractions, 274–276, 285
Partial product, 76
Percent
  applied problems with, 518–520, 581–582,
    586–587
    commission, 550–551, 587
    percent decrease, 553–555
    percent increase, 553–555
    proportion in finding, 535–537,
      585–586
    sale price, 552–553
    sales tax, 547–549, 586
  computing mentally, 512–518,
    543–544, 581
    5%, 515–517, 581
    10%, 512–513
    multiples of 100%, 517–518, 581
    multiples of five, 581
    multiples of ten, 514–515, 581
  as decimal, 498–499, 541, 579
  with decimals, as fractions, 504–506,
    579–580
  decimals as, 499–500, 541–542, 579
  definition of, 497, 579
  from equation, 524–527, 544–545,
    582–583
  finding
    from equation, 524–529, 583
    from multiplication, 523–524
  as fraction, 498, 503–504, 579
  with fractions, as fractions, 504–506,
    579–580
  fractions as, 498, 506–509, 542–543, 580
  understanding, 497–498
Percent decrease, 553–555
Percent increase, 553–555
Perfect square, definition of, 107, 702
Perfect square roots, 676, 702
Perimeter, 21, 58
  of irregular figure, 623
  of parallelogram, 640
  of rectangle, 618–619, 697
  of square, 622–623, 697
  of trapezoid, 642–645
  of triangle, 629, 698
Periods, 5

Perpendicular lines, 603–604, 696
Pi (π)
  approximations for, 652
  definition of, 652, 700
Pictographs, 49–50, 59
Place value
  in decimals, 297–300, 341, 367
  identifying, 5–6, 42, 57
Place-value (character), 367
Place-value chart, 297
Plane, 599, 695
Please **E**xcuse **M**y **D**ear **A**unt **S**ally, 108, 123
Point, 599, 695
Positive number. *See also* Signed numbers
  definition of, 717, 757
  opposite of, 721–722, 757
Power. *See* Exponent(s)
Powers of ten, decimals multiplied by,
  326–328, 369
Prime factorization
  definition of, 149, 207
  finding, 149–152
  fractions in lowest terms from, 190–191
  least common denominators from, 238–239
  least common multiples for, 232–233, 281
Prime numbers
  definition of, 148, 207
  factors of, 148
  identifying, 148–149
  least common multiple of, 231
  from prime factorization, 149–152
Principal
  definition of, 560, 587
  plus interest, 563–564
Problem-solving skills, 694
Procrastination quotient, 205
Product
  definition of, 69, 121
  partial, 76
Proper fractions
  definition of, 135, 189, 206
  identifying, 136–137
Properties of equality, division property,
  404–406, 422
Proportions
  applied problems with, 411–414, 423
  cross products of, 400–401, 421
  definition of, 398, 421
  determining whether true or false,
    399–401, 421
  fractions as, 398
  fraction to percent conversion with,
    507–509, 542–543
  percents from, 535–537, 585–586
  solving, 406–407, 422
    with decimals, 407–409
    with mixed numbers, 407–409
  writing, 398–399
Public speaking, 494
Pyramid, volume of, 670–671, 702
Pythagorean theorem, 678, 680, 703

Q

Quotient, 81, 121, 207

R

Radians, 602
Radius, of circle, 650–651, 699

Rate(s)
  definition of, 392, 420
  as fractions, 392
Ratio(s), 383–384
  of decimals, 384–387
  definition of, 383–384, 420
  as fractions, 383–384
  of fractions, 384–387
  of mixed numbers, 384–387
  after unit conversion, 387–388, 420
  writing, 383–384, 420
Ray, 599, 695
Reading attention span, 120
Reciprocals
  definition of, 180, 210
  in division of fractions, 181
  finding, 180–181, 210
  of zero, 181
Rectangle
  area of, 175–176, 619–621, 697
  definition of, 617, 697
  length of, 617
  perimeter of, 618–619, 697
  width of, 617
Rectangular pyramid, volume of,
  670–671, 702
Rectangular solid, volume of, 663–664, 701
Regrouping
  addition with
    and improper fractions, 263
    of mixed numbers, 259–260
    of whole numbers, 19–21, 57
  multiplication with, 75, 121
  subtraction with
    of decimals, 318
    and improper fractions, 263
    of mixed numbers, 260–262
    of whole numbers, 32–34, 58
Remainder
  from decimal division, 333–335
  in mixed number, 207
  understanding, 86–87, 122, 189
Repeating decimals, 334–335
Right angles, 601, 602, 695
Right triangle, 633, 698, 702
  unknown length in, 678–679, 703
Rounding
  of decimals, 306–310, 342, 368
  definition of, 42, 59
  estimating with, 45–47, 59
  of money, 310–313, 368
  of whole numbers, 42–45

S

Sale price, 552–553
Sales tax, 547, 586
Scalene triangle, 634, 698
Semicircle, area of, 656–657
Short division, 90–91, 101, 122
Short-term goals, 2
Signed numbers. *See also* Negative number;
  Positive number
  addition of
    combined with subtraction, 737–738
    with different signs, 727–730, 758
    negative numbers, 726–727, 758
    on number line, 725–726
  comparing, 718–719, 757
  division of, 743–744, 759